MAKING LIFE CHOICES:
Health Skills and Concepts
Wraparound Edition

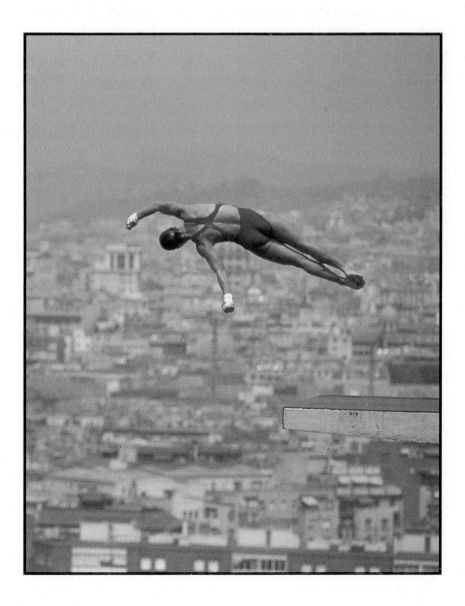

WRAPAROUND EDITION

The fifteen teachers listed below wrote all of the activities suggested
in this Teacher Wraparound Edition:

Kimberly Dawn Ballard
Walter Williams
High School
Burlington, NC

Robin GrayBallard
Suva Intermediate School
Montebello Unified
School District
Montebello, CA

Deneise J. Crace
Meridian High School
Meridian, ID

Donna J. Ketchum
Frontier Central
High School
Hamburg, NY

Susan E. Kurtin
Bleyl Junior High School
Cypress/Fairbanks I.S.D.
Houston, TX

Roxanna L. Laycox
West Carrollton
High School
West Carrollton, OH

Carol A. Martin
Pekin Community
High School
Pekin, IL

Betzy L. Nelson
Orange Park
High School
Orange Park, FL

Donna S. Paris
Haywood County
Schools
Waynesville, NC

Candace O. Purdy
Maine South
High School
Park Ridge, IL

Kathleen M. Schaefer
Gates Chili High School
Rochester, NY

Linda Troolin
East High School
Duluth, MN

Todd V. Urbanek
Boswell High School
Fort Worth, TX

Kathleen Zammett Walter
Great Neck North
High School
Great Neck, NY

Constance P. Wood
Orange Park
High School
Orange Park, FL

MAKING LIFE CHOICES:
Health Skills and Concepts
Wraparound Edition

Frances Sienkiewicz Sizer

Eleanor Noss Whitney

Linda Kelly DeBruyne

with
Caroline Ann Sizer

CONTRIBUTING AUTHORS

The Section Review and Chapter Review exercises were
written by high school teachers:

Patricia Kosiba
P.D. Schreiber High School
Port Washington, New York

Rhonda Helgerson
Del Rio High School
Del Rio, Texas

West Publishing Company
Minneapolis/St. Paul   New York   Los Angeles   San Francisco

Copyedit: Mary Berry
Proofreading: Suzie Defrazio
Interior Art: Randy Miyake, Miyake Illustration; Rolin Graphics;
    Todd Smith, J/B Woolsey Associates; and Judy Waller
Cartoons: Gary Carroll
Photomicrographs: Michael Davidson, Florida State University
Index: Linda Cupp
Dummy Artist: Gary Hespenheide, Hespenheide Design
Composition: American Composition & Graphics, Inc.
Cover Image: Richard Mackson/Sports Illustrated

A full list of photo and art credits found in this text follows the index.

WEST'S COMMITMENT TO THE ENVIRONMENT

In 1906, West Publishing Company began recycling materials left over from the production of books. This began a tradition of efficient and responsible use of resources. Today, up to 95 percent of our legal books and 70 percent of our college texts are printed on recycled, acid-free stock. West also recycles nearly 22 million pounds of scrap paper annually—the equivalent of 181,717 trees. Since the 1960's, West has devised ways to capture and recycle waste inks, solvents, oils, and vapors created in the printing process. We also recycle plastics of all kinds, wood, glass, corrugated cardboard, and batteries, and have eliminated the use of styrofoam book packaging. We at West are proud of the longevity and the scope of our commitment to our environment.

A Word about Photomicrographs

The photomicrographs in the textbook were made of recrystallized vitamins using a variety of different techniques. Many vitamins can be imaged using the melt-recrystallization process where a few milligrams of the chemical are sandwiched between a microscope coverslip and slide, then heated until melted and allowed to slowly recrystallize. Alternately, for vitamin-salts that will not melt, the chemical is dissolved in a suitable solvent (water or alcohol) and a few microliters of solution are allowed to slowly evaporate between a microscope slide and coverslip. Upon recrystallization, the vitamins are viewed in a microscope using cross-polarized illumination where the crystallites diffract light depending both on the molecular orientation within the crystal and the crystal thickness. The colorful patterns illustrated in this text are a manifestation of both molecular orientation and crystal thickness.

OVERVIEW OF THE MAKING LIFE CHOICES
TEXTBOOK PROGRAM

The *Making Life Choices* textbook program consists of the following components:

- *Making Life Choices*, Student Text
- *Making Life Choices*, Student Text, Expanded Edition
- *Making Life Choices*, Teacher Wraparound Edition
- *Sexual Behavior and Pregnancy Prevention*, Human Sexuality Supplement
- *Making Life Choices*, Teacher Supplement Package (reproducible handouts, tests, worksheets, etc. Also includes color transparencies, lesson plans, and answers)
- *Making Life Choices*, Video Bonus Package (free videos accompanying text)
- *Making Life Choices*, Video Library (up-to-date videos offered at reduced prices)
- *Making Life Choices*, Nutrition Videodisc (live action, still photos, and text on videodisc)
- *Making Life Choices*, *Diet Analysis* (user-friendly software for analyzing diets)
- *Making Life Choices*, *Health Update* (bi-annual newsletter)
- *Making Life Choices*, WESTEST (computerized testing)

Each component listed above is described in the following pages. Making yourself familiar with the components and their relationships to each other will help you obtain maximum benefit from the individual components and from the program as a whole.

MAKING LIFE CHOICES, STUDENT TEXTBOOK

Making Life Choices is a new textbook, written for high school, comprehensive health courses. The text covers a broad range of topics, including areas of mental, physical, and social health. The text is divided into the following eight units:

    I. Introduction to Health
   II. Your Emotional and Mental Health
  III. Your Physical Health
  IV. Drug Use and Abuse
   V. Disease Prevention
  VI. The Life Cycle
 VII. First Aid and Safety
VIII. Global Issues

Perhaps the full scope and intent of *Making Life Choices* is best stated in its opening sentence: "*This book is about enjoying life.*" Ten years ago, or even five years ago, to many people this sentence would have seemed completely inappropriate as a description of the content covered in a high school health course. Today, it says exactly what it should say, for the essence of contemporary health education is teaching self-responsibility and skills to promote a long and happy life for everyone.

How does *Making Life Choices* help teenagers learn to enjoy life? To begin, as the title indicates, it focuses on the development of student decision-making skills. Two primary goals of the text are to give students the information they need to understand the different aspects of health and wellness, and to provide instruction and strategies to help students evaluate information so that they can make wise lifestyle choices—choices that will promote total wellness and inhibit the development of lifestyle diseases.

Another major goal of the text is to build all students' self-esteem. In almost every chapter of the text, students learn of the connection between self-esteem and the topic being discussed in that particular chapter. A full section is devoted to self-esteem in Chapter 3. Throughout the text, students read that it's okay to be different, to look the way they look, and to feel what they're feeling. It would be impossible for students to read through the text without developing a greater sense of their self-worth and a realization that they can achieve their goals.

Another theme woven throughout the text is that of abstinence—abstinence from sexual intercourse and the use of the drugs of abuse, alcohol, and tobacco. Students learn about the dangers and drawbacks involved with these choices and are provided with information about the various kinds of pressure to participate in sexual behaviors and to abuse substances such as drugs, alcohol, and tobacco. Students also learn strategies for resisting these pressures.

In addition to its emphasis on the goals and themes mentioned above, *Making Life Choices* is different from the other high school health textbooks in several ways. Following is a brief mention of these differences.

Accuracy

You can count on each and every fact in *Making Life Choices* to be scientifically accurate and current. The authors receive over 30 professional journals and publications each month and file the information in a computer retrieval system. Each fact is thoroughly checked and rechecked and the information is updated constantly. You will not find a more accurate, up-to-date text than *Making Life Choices*.

More Thorough Coverage

If a topic is introduced in *Making Life Choices*, it is thoroughly explained. Topics are not treated superficially. For most, if not all of the major topics included in the standard health course, *Making Life Choices* contains more information than do the other available texts. On topics such as stress, mental and emotional problems, nutrition, weight control, drugs of abuse, alcohol, tobacco, and human sexuality—the topics *health teachers around the country say are the most important*—*Making Life Choices* contains several more pages of in-depth information than do the other texts.

You will also find that each page of *Making Life Choices* contains more information than a page from another text. The traditional double-column textbook format used in *Making Life Choices* means more words and illustrations, and less white (empty) space on each page. Rather than just a brief mention and sketchy definition of a new topic, students are provided with complete explanations that tell why, when, and how—explanations that will result in greater student interest and understanding.

Increased Reading Comprehension

Several aspects of *Making Life Choices* will help students increase their reading comprehension. As was previously mentioned, the topics covered in *Making Life Choices* are explained fully and completely. Students are not left with vague impressions and unanswered questions.

If you have an opportunity to show the different texts you are considering for your health course to your students, notice that they will stop and read what they see in *Making Life Choices* much more so than they will with any other text. This happens because *Making Life Choices* passes the test that so many of today's textbooks fail—it's interesting. The author's writing style is concerned, personal, and relevant to today's teenagers.

Making Life Choices was printed with larger type and shorter line lengths than are found in other texts. Readability studies have proven that this de-sign makes the text easier to read for students and thereby helps increase their comprehension. Additional features to help increase comprehension include "Mini Glossaries" in the lower right-hand corner of every two-page spread, which provide students easy access to definitions that they are often reluctant to search for, and "Key Points" at the end of each heading, which will help students summarize what they have just read. You will find none of these reading enhancements in any of the other high school health textbooks.

High Student Appeal

It is doubtful that you will find another high school text that will appeal to high school students as much as *Making Life Choices*. All of the texts are, of course, bright and colorful, with lots of photos and art. In addition, however, *Making Life Choices* has several text features that should capture students' attention and spark their curiosity and enthusiasm. Features such as the "Fact or Fiction" questions at the beginning of the chapters, the colorful cartoons that teach with humor, the "Straight Talks" that present a variety of topics in a conversational format that students will enjoy, the "Life Choice Inventories" that require students to deal with their favorite topic—themselves—and finally, the "Teen Views" features that give your students opinions about the key health topics straight from the mouths of their peers all across the country. All of these features are unique to *Making Life Choices*. The last one mentioned, "Teen Views," should be of special interest to your students.

Illustrations

In research prior to the development of the text, many teachers said that the illustrations in a health book were of critical importance. Therefore, a special attempt was made to produce large, colorful, easy to understand drawings, charts, and tables. Quickly scanning the text should make it evident that *Making Life Choices* contains many interesting and informative illustrations not found in any other text.

Cross References

Few high school textbook authors are as concerned with helping students make the best use possible of the text as are the authors of *Making Life Choices*. Therefore, throughout the text, students will find references to related information and special features located in other parts of the text. This gives students every opportunity to follow their interests and pursue further information at the appropriate times. Once again, you will not find this kind of careful construction and concern for the students in any other text.

To sum up, *Making Life Choices* is a carefully designed, carefully crafted, thoroughly researched and written text that your students will enjoy reading. It deals with the issues that concern today's teens, and it gives them strategies to help them lead a productive, enjoyable life.

MAKING LIFE CHOICES, EXPANDED EDITION

The *Making Life Choices* expanded edition is essentially the same text as described above. The sole difference is the insertion of a 48-page special unit entitled "Sexual Behavior and Pregnancy Prevention" within the Life Cycle unit of the text. This means that for the first time you have an opportunity to buy a hardbound health text that includes all the sexuality and contraception material that you have previously had to teach from a separate book.

The special unit is divided into two parts: Part A, Sexual Behavior, and Part B, Pregnancy Prevention. The three major sections of Part A deal with sexual activity, sexual myths, and sexual orientation. Part B deals with the major contraceptive methods, sterilization, and contraceptive failure.

Please note that this special unit is included in your Teacher Wraparound Edition (described later) so that you can have all of the information that you teach in your course, and all of the related teacher annotations, in one text. Regardless of whether you choose the regular student edition or this expanded edition, you should also be aware of the fact that the pages of the special sexuality unit are numbered in such a way that all of the other pages of the text are the same in the expanded edition and the regular edition. This means that you could even use both texts in the same class and make assignments without any confusion. This might be desirable if you have students whose parents have prohibited them from taking the sexuality unit.

SEXUAL BEHAVIOR AND PREGNANCY PREVENTION

The 48-page special unit described above for the expanded edition of the student text is also available in a separate 48-page softcover text. This softcover text will appeal to you if you want to keep the sexuality information separate from the other information in the text. If you want to keep this information inside the classroom, if your school district will not permit the inclusion of this information in the main text, or if, for a variety of other reasons, you want to teach this special unit but do not want the information in the main text, you may purchase it in the separate softcover text, which is the way that other publishers have made this information available in the past. As stated previously, an advantage to West's *Making Life Choices* program that is not available from other publishers is that all of the information in the special unit, whether you desire it in the student text or in a separate softcover text, is contained in one teacher's edition so you have all the information you need in one place.

TEACHER WRAPAROUND EDITION

The *Making Life Choices* Teacher Wraparound Edition was designed to help you make the most effective use possible of the student text, whether it be the standard edition, the expanded edition, or the separate "Sexuality and Pregnancy Prevention" supplement. This wraparound edition is similar to many others that you have seen. The pages from the student text have been reduced to 85% of their actual size, which allows space for the teacher notes that appear along both sides of the text and across the top.

While this Teacher Wraparound Edition is similar in many ways to others you have seen, it is also unique in several ways. The most obvious difference is found in the activities suggested across the top of the wraparound edition. All of these activities were written by teachers who are currently teaching health in classrooms across the country. Compare these activities to those you will see in other texts. The differences are obvious. In the directions for conducting the activities in the *Making Life Choices* wraparound edition, the teachers tell you such things as how much time to allow for a particular aspect of an activity, likely reactions from students to a certain question or instruction, specific directions for dividing students into groups and assigning different responsibilities to different group members, which props are needed to conduct an activity, and on and on. In short, you will find the kind of information you would expect from a teacher who has conducted that activity several times in a classroom much like your own. Although you might expect to find this sort of assistance in any teacher edition, it is unique to *Making Life Choices*.

Another unique aspect of the activities in the *Making Life Choices* wraparound is the attention given to students of different ability levels and learning styles. Whereas most of the activities in other wraparound editions are paper/pencil and discussion types of activities, here you will find many activities involving props and games. Students are constantly making things such as posters, bulletin boards, and audio visual aids for oral presentations, and playing games such as bingo and jeopardy. In short, they are doing the types of activities that most high school teachers must do to keep their students interested and motivated.

A third significant difference between the *Making Life Choices* wraparound and other wraparounds is the keying of teacher notes to specific words, sentences, and passages in the student text. You will find brackets with circled numbers in the margin between the columns of the student pages. These numbers match up with the numbered notes at the side of the student pages. This feature will make it much easier for you to use the teacher notes provided during your classroom presentation of a lesson. You will also find that these notes are more closely tied to the text, and therefore, more immediately usable than are the teacher notes in other wraparound editions.

Following is a brief review of the many additional features of this wraparound teacher edition that will help you teach your course with *Making Life Choices*.

CHAPTER PLANNER PAGES

Each chapter opens with a special two-page, chapter planner spread. The two student pages on this spread have been reduced to 50% of their actual size to allow more space for information you can use in planning how you will teach that particular chapter. Each of these chapter planner spreads contains seven different features:

- **Overview**—short summing up of the key points and themes of the chapter to enable you to get a quick feel for what's included in the chapter.
- *Making Life Choices* **Resources**—reminder of the many materials included in the supplementary material, with a list of some of the unique handouts, overheads, and teacher information sheets contained in the supplementary material for that particular chapter.
- **Chapter Project**—typically, a suggestion or two for more long-term activities that can be done over the length of time devoted to that chapter. Research and interviews outside of class are often suggested.
- **Activity to Introduce the Chapter**—one or two suggestions for activities to get students

interested in the main points of the chapter before you make the first reading assignment.

- **Answers to "Fact or Fiction"**—answers to the true/false "Fact or Fiction" exercise that appears on the first student page. On some planner pages there was not enough space for these answers, in which case, a page reference directs you to the answers on a page toward the end of the student chapter.
- **Suggested Resources**—includes suggested books for students and teachers, videos, and software to supplement your lessons.
- **Not Enough Time**—Because research indicated teachers all across the country were having a difficult time including all of the information they wanted to include in their one-semester courses, suggestions have been made as to how you might want to teach each chapter of this text if you only have one day or two days to teach it. Obviously, all of the health texts available have much more information and activity suggestions than could possibly be incorporated into a one-semester course. The Not Enough Time feature tries to help you make sure that you include the most important information and do the most effective activities. You will also notice beneath the Not Enough Time box a reference to the detailed 18-week daily lesson plan that's found in the supplementary material.

TOP NOTES

Across the top of your wraparound you will find objectives and activities for each section of the student text. The teaching suggestions for each section are divided into five parts: **Focus, Teach, Evaluate, Close, and Reteach/Bonus.**

Focus:

Under the Focus heading are the main learning objectives for that particular section and one or two activities to focus the students' attention on the topics covered in that section.

Teach:

Under the Teach heading, you will find a variety of activity suggestions, including both Guided and Independent Practice, for teaching that section. Depending on the length of the section, there could be as few as one activity or as many as twenty activities. It is not expected that you will complete all of these activities. You should pick and choose those that you think will work best for you and your students.

Many of the activities have been designated as to type. These types of the activities are:

- Reteach, Reinforce
- Extend, Enrich
- Special Needs
- Advanced
- Cooperative Learning
- Interdisciplinary
- Multicultural
- Critical Thinking

Not all of the activities fall into one of these categories, and therefore, some activities are not designated as being of any particular type. It's also the case that many of the activities can be designated as more than one type. To keep the designations from becoming cumbersome, decisions were made to list the one or two designations that seemed most obvious and important for that particular activity.

You will also notice that most activities have a suggested time frame. These suggestions are, of course, arbitrary. As you know from experience, a discussion that you plan to last ten minutes can sometimes evolve into a two-day discussion, while other activities that you would expect to take a full period are finished in ten minutes. For this reason, the classroom teachers who wrote these activities were in some cases reluctant to provide the suggested times. A decision was made, however, to provide them as guidelines. If nothing else, they will give you a better idea as to the relative lengths of the activities.

Evaluate:

For each section, following the Teach heading, you will find an activity or two to help you evaluate the students' comprehension of the material contained in that section. In many cases, this activity is a pop quiz. These quizzes were designed for you to use orally, with little or no preparation. Most are true/false, but many are also fill-in-the-blank, short answer, and matching. In some cases, such as with the matching, you may need to write one side of the matching exercise on the board and then read aloud the other side so the students can match the two columns. For the most part, however, these pop quizzes will require no preparation time on your part. For variety, and in many cases for applicability reasons, some of the evaluations are subjective rather than objective. These include essays, role plays, and oral presentations.

Close:

Under the Close heading, you will find one or two activities to sum up that section's lesson for the students. In many cases, the activity calls for the students to cite key points. In many other cases the activity is a different version of one of the Teach activities.

Reteach/Bonus:

At the end of the chapter you will find a Reteach/ Bonus heading. Following this heading are activities that go along with the Straight Talk feature in the student text. Also included are some additional activities from which you may want to choose as alternatives to those given earlier. These activities may belong with a particular section or they may involve concepts from a combination of several sections.

SIDE NOTES

The side notes contain information different from the activities across the top of the pages. Following is a brief description of the different kinds of notes that you will find in these side columns:

Teacher Support Notes:

Most of the space in the side columns is devoted to the Teacher Support Notes. These are the notes that are keyed directly to words, sentences, and paragraphs of the student text. The bracket and number in the margin between the columns of the student text relate to the note at the side designated by the same number. These support notes are of various types:

- **Enrichment**—notes that give you information in addition to what's included in the text. You can give this information to students in your lectures if you have time and you think it's appropriate and interesting for your students.
- **Discussion Questions**—suggestions for promoting classroom discussion of the designated passage.
- **Supplementary Materials**—reminders to you that your supplementary package contains material related to the bracketed text passage. This material could be a full-color overhead, a student activity handout, or background information for you.
- **Comprehension Checks**—questions (with answers) to check that students have read a particular passage and identified the key points in that passage.
- **Activities**—suggestions for teaching a particular passage or feature in the text. These activities differ from those at the top in that they are much more specific and more closely tied to a particular term or concept in the student book.
- **Cross References**—where helpful, references are given to other passages and chapters throughout

the text related to the particular passage being discussed.

Answers to Section Reviews:

Each section in the student text ends with a review that includes vocabulary exercises, questions, and activities. Answers to any objective questions are provided in the side column.

Fast Facts:

Research indicated that health teachers like having bits of information they can give to students that may not be terribly significant points to remember but are interesting and, therefore, help catch and keep student interest. These facts are included in the teacher edition rather than in the student text for a couple of reasons: (1) There is limited space in the student book for all the important information that needs to be included. Including these facts in the student text would have meant deleting other information deemed to be more important. (2) Including the facts in the teacher edition gives you the opportunity to pick and choose the ones that you want students to have. (3) Many of the facts are statistics which, over time, become outdated. As new information becomes available, you may want to change or replace some of the facts.

You can use these facts in a couple of different ways. If you read and frequently discuss passages aloud in class, you could simply interject the facts as you come to the relevant passages. Another way to use the facts would be to write them on the board the day that the lessons to which they apply are being taught. You could either discuss them as a lead-in to the lesson or simply leave them on the board for students to see and notice without further discussion, unless students initiate discussion.

Thoughts on Health:

The Thoughts on Health boxes contain quotes that relate to passages in the student text. Most of the quotes are from well-known writers, philosophers, teachers, and scientists whose names the students will recognize from other courses; others are proverbs or anonymous quotes. You will find a listing of the people who have been quoted with a very brief description of those people on page T24.

Like the Fast Facts, the Thoughts on Health could be used in different ways. You may want to casually work them into classroom discussion as you see fit and as they seem to apply. Another tactic would be to write the quotes on the board prior to class. You could ask students to explain the mean-

ing of the quote or ask other questions about the ideas contained in it as a way of beginning the lesson, or you could put the quote up somewhere in the classroom without calling attention to it. A third possibility would be to make a display on the bulletin board with a sampling of the quotes and/or Fast Facts for a given chapter.

Where to Write:

The Where to Write boxes contain addresses for various agencies and organizations that could supply you and your students with additional information about the topic at hand. In addition to locating these addresses at relevant points throughout the text, they have been placed in one comprehensive list on page T17–T23 of this teacher edition.

Where to Call:

Similar to the Where to Write boxes, the Where to Call features give you 800 numbers of agencies and organizations supplying additional information and resources in a particular health area. You may want to call the numbers or give them to students to call. As with the Where to Writes, these numbers are included in the comprehensive list in this teacher edition.

Chapter Review Answers:

The chapter review answers are all the answers to the objective questions and exercises at the end of the chapter. You should note that the answers to the recall questions are divided into the sections to which they apply, whereas the student text simply has one listing of questions. This will help you assign questions for a particular section should you be teaching one section in a chapter but not another.

TEACHER SUPPLEMENT PACKAGE

Accompanying the *Making Life Choices* student text and teacher edition is an extensive package of already prepared, reproducible classroom material for you and your students. Here is a brief listing of what you will find in the supplementary material:

- **Detailed Daily Lesson Plans**—These lesson plans provide a complete semester's teaching plan for using *Making Life Choices* and its accompanying material. While this is only one of many ways to teach the course, it may provide a helpful starting point, especially if you are new to the course or you are using *Making Life Choices* for the first time.
- **Study Material**—For each chapter of the text you will find the following worksheets to help you teach the vocabulary and to reteach concepts

OVERVIEW (CONTINUED)

that prove difficult for some students:

a) *Vocabulary Games*—includes crossword puzzles, word searches, word scrambles, etc. for the key terms from the text.

b) *Reteaching Sheets*—for each section or two, a sheet that gives students an opportunity to relearn the most important concepts of that section, or sections.

c) *Study Outlines*—a sheet that lists the main heads of the text with space for students to write in either your lecture notes or the key points from the chapter.

d) *Reading Clozes*—reading comprehension exercises that call for students to fill in the blanks of a chapter summary. These exercises have been shown to increase student retention of the material studied and to improve students' overall reading comprehension skills.

- **Activities**—includes a variety of activity handouts, such as enrichment activities, self-assessment activities (including worksheets of the Life Choice Inventories contained in the student text), fully developed cooperative learning activities, multicultural activities, and an abundance of activity handouts related to specific concepts in the chapters.

- **Overheads**—96 full-color transparency acetates are included in the supplementary material. These are referenced in your wraparound edition to help you know when and where to use them.

- **Spanish Language Exercises**— Several activities have been translated into Spanish to help Spanish-speaking students learn the vocabulary and key concepts in *Making Life Choices*.

- **Chapter Tests**—For each chapter of the student text, you will find two chapter tests. Version A is a lower-level test consisting only of objective-type questions. Version B is an average to higher-level test including some objective questions, at least four or five short-answer questions, and a couple of essay questions.

- **Teacher Information Sheets**—Also referenced in the wraparound edition are Teacher Information Sheets that give you background information on various topics to help you teach those topics.

- **Special AIDS Unit**—As an addition to Chapter 17, you will find in your supplementary material an AIDS unit that includes lesson plans,

handouts, blackline masters, and teaching suggestions—all organized into a ready-to-teach unit on AIDS.

VIDEOS

The *Making Life Choices* program includes videos on various topics. The video library makes a variety of titles available at greatly reduced prices. These titles will change as new topics and new videos become available.

NUTRITION LASERDISC

The Nutrition laserdisc accompanying *Making Life Choices* contains a wealth of material related to the nutrition and weight control chapters. Included on this disc are live action videos from CNN.

DIET ANALYSIS SOFTWARE

The Diet Analysis software is available for IBM PCs and the Macintosh computers. The software is free to adopters of the text, and you are free to copy it. Students use this software program to analyze their diets. After filling out a food recall form, students go through the step-by-step program to analyze their intakes of major nutrients. Results are printed out and the students can analyze the nutritional content of up to three days intake of as many as 30 foods for each day. Percentages of RDA, calories, fats, proteins, carbohydrates, vitamins and minerals for the individual are provided. There is also an exercise option that allows students to enter type and duration of exercise so that the program can alter the personal RDA recommendations accordingly.

MAKING LIFE CHOICES NEWSLETTER

Twice a year adopters of the text will receive a newsletter with summaries of recent research relating to the various topics in the text.

WESTEST

This computerized testing software is available for the IBM PC, compatibles, and Macintosh, and includes all of the questions contained on the printed chapter tests in the supplementary material. The program allows you to create, edit, store, and print your own individual tests.

MULTICULTURAL CONSIDERATIONS IN TEACHING HEALTH

. . . Among the Wodaabe of Niger, mothers are not allowed to speak directly to their first or second born children, and except for nursing, they aren't allowed to touch them. The grandmothers and aunts take care of these children. The Wodaabe feel that this child-rearing practice emphasizes loyalties throughout the entire clan.

. . . In years past, Chinese parents often adopted an infant girl to marry their son. They raised the girl, training her themselves so she would be more agreeable to them and more compatible with other members of the family. This custom is still practiced today in Taiwan.

. . . It is fairly common in the Middle East for a man to marry one of his father's brother's daughters.

The first sentence in Section 1 of *Making Life Choices* says that "You make hundreds of choices every day—what to eat, whom to be with, how active to be, when to sleep, and more." This sentence introduces the major theme of the text—that each person is responsible for his or her own health and wellness and that each individual makes lifestyle choices that will determine to a great extent that person's level of health and wellness throughout life.

How your students make their choices will be deeply affected by their cultures, which may have been influenced by those as diverse as the ones described at the beginning of this essay. Even if two students were the same in every way—age, maturity level, personality, intelligence, etc.—and even if these two students read *Making Life Choices* and tried to implement its strategies with equal enthusiasm and commitment, these two students would make very different choices in their lives if they came from different cultural backgrounds. Their most fundamental choices—the foods they eat, their friends, their social activities, their mates, and their values—would differ considerably because of their different cultures.

The fact that culture exerts a powerful influence on an individual's thoughts, motives, feelings, and behaviors is obviously something of which you are well aware. The problem that may not be as immediately obvious is how this awareness can and should affect the ways in which you teach your

health course. The answer to this question will depend on many factors, including the cultural backgrounds of your students, your own personal beliefs as to the importance of broadening the cultural awareness of all your students, the resources you have available, and the amount of time that you can devote to multicultural issues.

For the most part, the content of *Making Life Choices* is acultural—the information presented is scientific in nature and the strategies presented may be used by people of all cultures and races. Information about the drugs of abuse, alcohol, and tobacco, for example, and recommendations for the use or non-use of these substances is accurate and useful for all people, regardless of their culture. Certain topics, however, such as the emotional health issues discussed in Chapter 2 and the social behaviors discussed in Chapter 20, "Pairing, Commitment, and Marriage" could be treated differently if approached from different cultural perspectives. Unfortunately, the wide range of topics covered in today's typical health course make it impossible for the authors of any high school health textbook to deal with the different cultural aspects of the individual topics in the depth required to make the discussions meaningful and useful for students.

Of course you need to be aware of the fact the students may respond differently to different activities as a result of their cultural background. For example, suppose you were to try an exercise such as the following as you taught sections on self-knowledge and self-awareness in Chapter 2. Let's say that you asked the students to write 20 different statements in response to the question, "Who am I?" If, after students finished, you had them count the number of entries that related to a social identity, such as family ("I am a son/daughter"), religion ("I am a Roman Catholic"), or a group to which they belong ("I am a member of the basketball team"); and then you had them count the number of entries that related to individual characteristics ("I am intelligent" or "I am bashful"); the exercise would tend to evoke different patterns of response based on the respondent's dominant culture. People from individualistic cultures such as the United States and Canada would be more likely to define their self-identities primarily in terms of individual traits rather than in terms of social groups. In contrast, students who had grown up in collectivist societies such as in Japan and China, would be more likely to define their self-identities in terms of the social entities to which they belong.

An example such as the one above makes it clear how important it is for today's teachers, especially those in areas serving students from a variety of cultures, to learn more about the cultures of the students they teach. The following reading list is by no means a comprehensive list of multicultural readings, but it does provide you with beginning sources in your attempt to become more knowledgeable about different cultures and how they might be dealt with in the classroom. It also provides some resources for materials that you could use in implementing multicultural education in your classroom.

Although the amount of material that must be covered in a one-semester health course does not allow time for examination of different cultural perspectives on health in the main body of content, the *Making Life Choices* Teacher Edition, does provide you with suggestions for supporting the student text in terms of multicultural issues. The Teacher Support Note on page 86 is one example, the activity suggestions on pages 41 and 201 are two more examples. You will also find in your supplementary package several enrichment lessons, the purpose of which is to give all students a sampling of the health attitudes and practices from many different cultures. Part of one such lesson is reprinted on pg. T16 as an example. As time permits, distribution of these enrichment lessons will allow you to broaden your students' understanding of other cultures and thereby hopefully increase their tolerance of peoples of different colors and cultures so that tomorrow's world will be a more peaceful, harmonious world for all people.

READINGS AND RESOURCES FOR MULTICULTURAL EDUCATION

Acuña, Rodolpho. *Occupied America: A History of Chicanos.* Glenview, IL: Harper Collins Publishers.

Allen, P. G. (1986). *The Sacred Hoop: Recovering the Feminine in American Indian Traditions.* Beacon Press.

American Ethnological Society, 1703 New Hampshire Ave. N.W., Washington, D.C. 20009.

Aptheker, H. (1973). *The Education of Black People: Ten Critiques, 1906–1960* by W. E. B. DuBois. New York: Monthly Review Press.

Asante, Molefi Kete. *The Afrocentric Idea.*

Asante, Molefi Kete. *Kemet Afrocentricity, and Knowledge.*

Banks, J. A. (1989). *Multicultural Education: Issues and Perspectives.* Boston, Mass.: Allyn and Bacon.

Banks, J. A. (1988). *Multiethnic Education: Theory and Practice.* 2nd ed. Newton, Mass.: Allyn and Bacon, Inc.

Banks, J. A. (1991). *Teaching Strategies for Ethnic Studies,* 5th ed. Boston: Allyn and Bacon.

Baringer, F. (February 4, 1990). "Africa's Claim to Egypt's History Grows More Insistent," *New York Times*, p. 6E.

Barzun, J. (1965). *Race: A Study in Superstition.* New York: Harper.

Beard, M. R. (1972). *Women as Force in History.* New York: Collier Books.

Belenky, M., B. Clinchy, B. Goldberger, and N. Tarule. (1986) *Women's Ways of Knowing.* New York: Basic Books.

Benedict, R. (1959). *Race: Science and Politics.* New York: Viking.

Bernal, M. (1987). *The Afroasiatic Roots of Classical Civilization*, Vol. 1: *The Fabrication of Ancient Greece 1785–1985.* London: Free Association Books.

Biddis, M. D. (1970). *Father of Racist Ideology: The Social and Political Thought of Count Gobineau.* New York: Weinright and Talley.

Brock-Utne, B. (1985). *Educating for Peace: A Feminist Perspective.* New York and Oxford: Pergamon Press.

Carlson, L. H. and Colburn, G. A. (1972). *In Their Place: White America Defines Her Minorities, 1850–1950.* New York: John Wiley and Sons.

Chase, A. (1977). *The Legacy of Malthus: The Social Costs of the New Scientific Racism.* New York: Alfred A. Knopf.

Clarke, J. H. (1990). "African People on My Mind." In *Infusion of African and African American Content in the School Curriculum: Proceedings of the First National Conference*, edited by A. G. Hilliard III, L. Payton-Stewart, and L. O. Williams, Morristown, N.J.: Aaron Press.

The Commission on Minority Participation in Education and American Life. (May 1988). *One-Third of a Nation.* Washington, D.C.: The American Council on Education.

Common Bonds: Anti-Bias Teaching in a Diverse Society. Wheaton: MD. Association for Childhood Educational International.

Cultural Survival, 11 Divinity Ave., Cambridge, Mass. 02138.

DeMott, Benjamin. (1990). *The Imperial Middle: Why Americans Can't Think Straight about Class.*

MULTICULTURAL CONSIDERATIONS (CONTINUED)

DePalma, A. (May 19, 1991). "Ethnic Diversity Brings Separate Worlds." *Montgomery Advertiser* (quotes Ernest L. Boyer).

D'Souza, D. (1991). *Illiberal Education: The Politics of Race and Sex on Campus.* New York: The Free Press.

Donald Duk. Minneapolis: Coffee House Press. A novel for young adults that explores Chinese culture from viewpoint of Chinese-American.

Downing, T. E., and G. Kusher, eds. (1988). *Human Rights and Anthropology.* Cambridge, Mass.: Cultural Survival, pp. 21–26.

Drake, St. C. (1987). *Black Folk Here and There.* Vol. 1. Los Angeles: Center for Afro-American Studies, University of California.

DuBois, W. E. B. (1969). *The Souls of Black Folk.* New York: Signet. (First published 1903).

Edelman, M. (1992). *The Measure of Our Success.* Boston: Beacon Press.

Elshtain, J. B. (1987). *Women and War.* New York: Basic Books.

"Everyone's Kids Books Newsletter" (71 Elliot St., Brattleboro, VT, 05301).

Gossett, T. F. (1973). *Race: The History of an Idea in America.* New York: Schoken.

Gould, S. J. (1981). *The Mismeasure of Man.* New York: W. W. Norton.

Grant, M. (1924). *The Passing of the Great Race: Or, The Racial Basis of European History.* New York: Charles Scribner's Sons.

Gray, P. (July 8, 1991). "Whose America?" *Time* 138: 13–17.

Greene, M. (1988). *The Dialectic of Freedom.* New York: Teachers College Press.

Grumet, M. R. (1988). *Bitter Milk.* Amherst: University of Massachusetts Press.

Hall, E. T. (1981). *Beyond Culture.* Garden City, N.Y.: Anchor Press/Doubleday.

Henry, J. (1965). *Culture Against Man.* N.Y.: Random House.

Hilliard, A. (1976). "Alternatives to IQ Testing: An Approach to the Identification of Gifted Minority Children." *Final Report to the California State Department of Education.*

Hilliard, A., and C. Leonard. (eds). (1990). *African American Baseline Essays.* Portland, Or.: Portland Public Schools, revised 1990.

Hilliard, A. G. III, L. Patyon-Stewart, and L. Obadele. (1990). *The Infusion of African and African American Content in the School Curriculum.* Morristown, N.J.: Aaron Press.

Hirsch, E. D. (1987). *Cultural Literacy: What Every American Needs to Know.* Boston: Houghton Mifflin.

Howe, I. (February 18, 1991). "The Value of the Canon." *The New Republic:* 40–44.

Jones, S. M. (1972). "The Schlesingers on Black History," *PHYLON: The Atlanta University Review of Race and Culture* 33, 2:104–111.

Kamin, K. (1974). *The Science and Politics of I.Q.* Potomac, Md.: Lawrence Erlbaum Associates.

Keita, S. (1990). "Studies in Ancient African Crania." In *American Journal of Physical Anthopology* 83: 35–48, 1990.

Kinnear, M. (1982). *Daughters of Time: Women in the Western Tradition.* Ann Arbor: University of Michigan Press.

Kohn, A. (1986). *No Contest: The Case Against Competition.* Boston: Houghton Mifflin.

Lee, C. C. "Cultural Dynamics." In *Multicultural Issues in Counseling.* Alexandria, VA: American Association of Counseling and Development.

Marriott, M. (August 11, 1991). "As a Discipline Advances, Questions Arise on Scholarship." *The New York Times.*

Martel, E. (Spring 1991). "Teacher's Corner: Ancient Africa and the Portland Curriculum Resource." *Anthro Notes: National Museum of Natural History* (Smithsonian) Bulletin for Teachers 13, 2.

Martin, J. R. (1984). "Bringing Women into Educational Thought." *Educational Theory* 4, 34: 341–354.

Minority Rights Group, 29 Craven St., London VC2N 5N5, England.

Montague, A. (1968). *The Concept of the Primitive.* New York: Collier-Macmillan.

"Multicultural Books for Children" (newsletter), The Boston Globe. P.O. Box 2378, Boston, MA 02107-2378.

Murray, N. (January/February 1991). "Is the Playing Field Really Level?" *Rethinking Schools:* 7.

National Afrocentric Institute, Temple University, Philadelphia, PA 19122

The National SEED Project Center for Research on Women, Wellesley College, Wellesley, MA 02181

Nelson, L., and S. Kagan. (September 1972). "Competition—The Star Spangled Scramble." *Psychology Today* 53, 6:90–91.

Noddings, N. (1984). *Caring: A Feminine Approach to Ethics and Moral Education.* Berkeley: University of California Press.

Our Family, Our Friends, Our World: An Annotated Guide to Significant Multicultural Books for Children and Teenagers. New Providence, NJ: R. R. Bowker Co.

Pallas, A. M., G. Natriello, E. L. McDill. (June–July 1989). "The Changing Nature of the Disadvantaged Population: Current Dimensions and Future Trends." *Educational Researcher* 18, 2: 2.

Parekh, B. (1986). "The Concept of Multi-Cultural Education." *In Multicultural Education: The Interminable Debate,* edited by S. Modgil, G. K. Verma, K. Mallick, and C. Modgil. Philadelphia: The Falmer Press, pp. 19–31.

Pardo, W., B. S. Adams, and N. Schniedewind. (1988). "A Systemwide Program In Human Rights Education." *Educational Leadership* 45, 8: 48–50.

Parker, W. P. (1991). "Multicultural Education in Democratic Societies." Paper presented at the annual meeting of the American Educational Research Association, Chicago.

Rossiter, M. W. (1982). *Women Scientists in America: Struggles and Strategies to 1940.* Baltimore and London: Johns Hopkins University Press.

Ruddick, S. (1989). *Maternal Thinking: Towards a Politics of Peace.* Boston: Beacon Press.

Schniedewind, N., and E. Davidson. (1983). *Open Minds To Equality: A Sourcebook of Learning Activities To Promote Race, Sex, Class, and Age Equity.* Englewood Cliffs, N.J.: Prentice Hall.

Schniedewind, N., and E. Davidson. (1987). *Cooperative Learning, Cooperative Lives: A Sourcebook of Learning Activities for Building a Peaceful World.* Dubuque, Iowa: W. C. Brown.

Schwartz, B. N. and R. Disch. (1970). *White Racism: Its History, Pathology, Practice.* New York: Dell.

Serfontein, J. H. P. (1978). *Brotherhood of Power: An Expose of the Secret Afrikaner Broederbond.* Bloomington, Indiana: Indiana University Press.

Sertima, I. V., ed. (1984). (Ed.) *Black Women in Antiquity.* New Brunswick, N.J.: Transaction Books.

Service, Elman. *Profiles in Ethnology.* Harper & Row, 1978.

Sherritt, C. (1990). "What Not to do in the Name of Multiculturalism." *Contemporary Education* 61, 4: 215–216.

Sirkin, G. (January 18, 1990). "The Multiculturalists Strike Again." *The Wall Street Journal*, p. A14.

Sleeter, C. (1991). *Empowerment Through Multicultural Education.* Albany: S.U.N.Y. Press.

Sleeter, C. E. (September 1990). "Staff Development for Desegregated Schooling." *Kappan*: 33–40.

Smith, P. (1970). *Daughters of the Promised Land.* Boston and Toronto: Little, Brown.

Stanton, W. (1960). *The Leopard's Spots: Scientific Attitudes Toward Race in America 1915–1959.* Chicago: University of Chicago Press.

Steele, S. (February 1989). "The Recoloring of Campus Life." *Harpers Magazine*: 47–55.

Stoddard, L. (1971). *The Rising Tide of Color Against White World Supremacy.* Westport, Conn.: Negro University Press. (First Published 1920).

Stotsky, S., P. Anderson, with D. Beierl. (Fall 1990). "Variety and Individualism in the English Class: Teacher-Recommended Lists of Reading for Grades 7–12." Pull-out section in *The Leaflet* 89, 3: 1–11.

Sue, D., and Sue, D. W. *Counseling the Culturally Different: Theory and Practice.* New York: Wiley.

Takaki, Ronald. Strangers from a Different Shore: A History of Asian-Americans. New York: Penguin USA.

Teaching Tolerance, 400 Washington Ave., Montgomery, Alabama 36104, 1-205-264-0286. Publish a free semi-annual magazine that provides educators with ideas, resources, and techniques for teaching tolerance in a diverse society.

Teacher's Resource Guide: North American Indians. Anthropology Outreach & Public Information. National Museum of Natural History, Smithsonian Institution, Washington D.C. 20560.

Tetreault, M. K. (1986). "The Journey from Male-Defined to Gender-Balanced Education." *Theory Into Practice* 25: 227–234.

UNESCO. (1981). *General History of Africa.* Berkeley: University of California Press.

Van Sertima, I. (1976). *They Came Before Columbus.* New York: Random House.

Weatherford, J. (1988). *Indian Givers: How the Indians of the Americas Transformed the World.* New York: Fawcett Columbine.

Wilson, W. J. (1987). *The Truly Disadvantaged: The Inner City, the Underclass, and Public Policy.* Chicago: the University of Chicago Press.

Woodson, C. G. (1933). *The Miseducation of the Negro.* Washington, D.C.: Associated Publishers.

Yurco, F. (March 1991). "An Evaluation the Portland Social Studies Baseline Essay." *Network News and Views* 10, 25.

Yurco, F. (Sept.–Oct. 1989). "Were the Ancient Egyptians Black or White?" *Biblical Archaeological Reveiw* 15, 5: 24.

LIST OF RESOURCES

WHERE TO WRITE/WHERE TO CALL

Chapter 1

University of California Berkeley Wellness Letter
P.O. Box 4201248
Palm Coast, FL 32142

*Harvard Health Letter, Harvard Heart Letter,
Harvard Mental Health Letter*
164 Longwood Avenue
Boston, MA 02115

Wellness and Health Activation Networks
P.O. Box 923
Vienna, VA 22180

The Johns Hopkins Medical Letter Health After 50
550 North Broadway, Suite 1100
Baltimore, MD 21205

Mayo Clinic Health Letter
200 First Street NW
Chester, MN 55905

U.S. Department of Health and Human Services
5600 Fishers Lane
Rockville, MD 20857

Chapter 2

Mental Health Association
1021 Prince Street
Alexandria, VA 22314

National Clearinghouse for Mental Health Information
Public Inquiries Section
5600 Fishers Lane, Rm. 15C-17
Rockville, MD 20857

Emotions Anonymous
P.O. Box 4245
St. Paul, MN 55104

Human Relations Media
175 Tompkins Avenue
Pleasantville, NY 10570

Mental Health Foundation, Inc.
2 East 86th Street
New York, NY 10028

Mental Health Materials Center
30 E. 29th Street
New York, NY 10016

National Mental Health Association
1800 N. Kent Street
Rosslyn, VA 22209

The Catalog of Volunteer Opportunities
P.O. Box 117
New York, NY 10009

Chapter 3

Stepfamily Association of America
215 Centennial Mall South
Suite 212
Lincoln, NE 68508
1-800-735-0329

Health Education Services
10000 Culver Blvd., Dept. H2
Culver City, CA 90223

Chapter 4

American Institute of Stress
124 Park Avenue
Yonkers, NY 10703

Chapter 5

American Anorexia and Bulimia Association, Inc.
418 E. Seventy-sixth St.
New York, NY 10021
1-212-734-1114

American Association for Partial Hospitalization, Inc.
1411 K St. NW, Suite 1000
Washington, DC 20005
1-202-347-1649

American Association of Suicidology
2459 S. Ash
Denver, CO 80222
1-303-692-0985

American Mental Health Counselors Association
5999 Stevenson Ave.
Alexandria, VA 22304
1-800-354-2008

American Psychiatric Association
1400 D St. NW
Washington, DC 20005
1-202-682-6000

American Psychological Association
1200 Seventeenth St. NW
Washington, DC 20036
1-202-955-7600

Anorexia Nervosa and Related Eating Disorders (ANRED)
P.O. Box 5102
Eugene, OR 97405
1-503-344-1144

The Compassionate Friends
P.O. Box 3696
Oak Brook, IL 60522-3696
1-708-990-0010

International Association of Psychosocial
Rehabilitation Services
P.O. Box 278
McLean, VA 22101
1-703-237-9385

National Alliance for the Mentally Ill
1234 Massachusetts Ave. NW
Washington, DC 20005

National Alliance of Mental Patients
P.O. Box 618
Sioux Falls, SD 57101
1-605-344-4067

National Association of Private Psychiatric Hospitals
1319 F St. NE, Suite 1000
Washington, DC 20004
1-202-393-6700

National Association of Social Workers
7981 Eastern Ave.
Silver Spring, MD 20910
1-301-565-0333

National Association of State Mental Health Program Directors
1101 King St., Suite 160
Alexandria, VA 22314
1-703-739-9333

National Council of Community Mental Health Centers
12300 Twinbrook Pkwy., Suite 320
Rockville, MD 20852
1-301-984-6200

National Institute of Mental Health
Public Inquiries Office, Room 15C-05
5600 Fishers Lane
Rockville, MD 20857
1-301-443-4513

National Mental Health Association
1021 Prince Street
Alexandria, VA 22314
1-800-969-6642

National Association of Anorexia Nervosa
and Associated Disorders
Box 7
Highland, IL 60035
1-708-831-3438

National Depressive and Manic Depressive Association
Merchandise Mart
P.O. Box 3395
Chicago, IL 60654

National Foundation for Depressive Illness, Inc.
20 Charles Street
New York, NY 10014
1-800-248-4344

Recovery, Inc.
802 N. Dearborn St.
Chicago, IL 60610
1-312-337-5661

Self-Help Clearinghouse
St. Claires-Riverside Medical Center
Denville, NJ 07834
1-201-625-7101

American Mental Health Fund
1-800-433-5959

Childhelp USA Hotline
1-800-4-A-CHILD

Coalition Against Domestic Violence
1-800-288-3854

Chapter 6

American Medical Association
Department of Health Education
535 N. Dearborn Street
Chicago, IL 60610

American School Health Association
P.O. Box 708
Kent, OH 44240

Association for the Advancement of Health Education
1900 Association Drive
Reston, VA 22091

Managing Back Pain
Room 176 B
Baylor College of Medicine
Houston, TX 77030

The San Francisco Spine Institute
San Francisco, CA
1-800-523-BACK

Chapter 7

American Dietetic Association
216 W. Jackson Blvd.
Chicago, IL 60606-6995
1-800-877-1600

American Home Economics Association
2110 Massachusetts Avenue
Washington, DC 20036

American Meat Institute
59 East Van Buren Street
Chicago, IL 60605

Beech-Nut Nutrition Hotline
1-800-523-6633

Consumer Nutrition Hotline
1-800-366-1655

Department of Agriculture
Food and Consumer Services Division
Washington, DC 20250

Food and Drug Administration
Consumer Inquiry Department
5600 Fishers Lane
Rockville, MD 20852

Food, Food Safety and Nutrition,
Alliance for Food and Fiber Food Safety Hotline
1-800-266-0200

Gerber Products Company
1-800-443-7237

Tufts University Diet and Nutrition Letter
80 Bolyston Street
Boston, MA 02116

U.S. Department of Agriculture
Food and Nutrition Information Center
Washington, DC 20250

U.S. Department of Agriculture
Meat and Poultry Hotline
1-800-535-4555

Chapter 8

Community Nutrition Institute
2001 S. St. NW, Suite 530
Washington, DC 20009
1-202-462-4700

Consumer Nutrition Hotline
1-800-366-1655

Food and Agriculture Organization
of the United Nations (FAO)
Liaison Office for North America
1001 Twenty-second St. NW
Washington, DC 20437
1-202-654-2400

National Dairy Council
6300 North River Road
Rosemont, IL 60018

Nutrition Foundation, Inc.
99 Park Avenue
New York, NY 10016

U.S. Department of Agriculture
Human Nutrition Information Service
6505 Belcrest Rd.
Federal Bldg. #1, Room 325-A
Hyattsville, MD 20782
1-202-720-8732

World Health Organization
1501 New Hampshire, NW
Washington, DC 20006

Chapter 9

American Dietetic Association
1-800-366-1655

The Facts about Weight Loss Products and Programs,
Weight Loss, Federal Trade Commission
Washington, DC 20580

Glenbeigh Food Addictions Hotline
1-800-4A-BINGE

Overeaters Anonymous
World Service Office
2190 190th Street
Torrance, CA 90504
1-800-743-8703

Chapter 10

American College of Sports Medicine
P.O. Box 1440
Indianapolis, IN 46204
1-317-637-9200

American Running and Fitness Association
P.O. Box 4704
N. Hollywood, CA 91607
1-800-776-2732

The Ballroom Dance Information Bureau
1-800-330-FADS

Collage Video 1-800-433-6769 and
Fitness Wholesale 1-800-537-5512
for large selection of exercise videos

National Recreation Association
8 W. 8th Street
New York, NY 10011

President's Council on Physical Fitness
400 6th St. SW
Washington, DC 20201

U.S. Bicycle Polo Association
1-212-369-3599

Chapter 11

The American Medical Hair Replacement Directory
1-800-456-8090

National Headache Foundation
1-800-843-2256

National Organization of Mall Walkers
P.O. Box 191
Hermann, MO 65041

Chapter 12

Food and Drug Administration (FDA)
HFE 881, Room 16-63
5600 Fishers Lane
Rockville, MD 20857
1-301-443-3170

Chapter 13

Just Say No International
1-800-258-2766

National Association of Drug Abuse Problems
355 Lexington Avenue
New York, NY 10017

National Clearinghouse for Alcohol and Drug
Information
P.O. Box 2345
Rockville, MD 20847-2345
1-800-729-6686

National Cocaine Hotline
1-800-COC-AINE

National Institute of Drug Abuse Hotline
Bethesda, MD 20205
1-800-662-HELP

Chapter 14

Al-Anon/Alateen Family Group
Headquarters, Inc. (Materials & Publications)
P.O. Box 862
Midtown Station
New York, NY 10018-0862
1-800-356-9996

Alateen Meeting Information
1-800-344-2666

Alcohol and Drug Helpline
1-800-821-4357

Alcohol, Drug Abuse, and Mental Health Service
Office of Public Affairs
5600 Fishers Lane
Rockville, MD 20857

Alcoholics Anonymous
Box 459, Grand Central Station
New York, NY 10163
1-212-870-3400

Covenant House "9-Line"
1-800-999-9999

National Council on Alcoholism and Drug
Dependence
12 W. Twenty-first Street
New York, NY 10010
1-800-NCA-CALL

National Institute on Alcohol Abuse and Alcoholism
Bethesda, MD 20205

Chapter 15

American Lung Association
1740 Broadway
New York, NY 10019

Americans for Nonsmokers' Rights
2054 University Ave., Suite 500-H
Berkeley, CA 94704
1-510-841-3032

Department of Health and Human Services
Office on Smoking and Health
Park Building, Rm. 1-16
Rockville, MD 20857

Office on Smoking and Health
Technical Information Center
5600 Fishers Lane
Park Building Room 116
Rockville, MD 20857
1-301-443-5287

Centers for Disease Control
1600 Clifton Rd. NE
Atlanta, GA 30333
1-404-639-3311

Tobacco Institute
1845 I Street, Suite 841
Washington, DC 20006

Chapter 16

American Medical Association
515 N. State Street
Chicago, IL 60610
1-312-464-5000

Center for Disease Control Information Hotline
1-404-332-4555

National Foundation for Infectious Diseases
4733 Bethesda Ave. #750
Bethesda, MD 20814

The National Institute of Allergy and Infectious Diseases
1-800-TRIALS-A

The National Kidney Foundation
1-800-622-9010

U.S. Public Health Service
Public Affairs Office
Hubert H. Humphrey Bldg., Rm. 725-H
200 Independence Ave. SW
Washington, DC 20201
1-202-245-6867

Chapter 17

AIDS Action Council
729 8th Street SE, Suite 200
Washington, DC 20003

AIDS Information
U.S. Public Health Services
Office of Public Affairs, Rm. 721-H
200 Independence Avenue SW
Washington, DC 20201

AIDS Information Exchange
U.S. Conference of Mayors
1620 I Street NW
Washington, DC 20006

The AIDS Institute
New York State Health Department
Empire State Plaza
Corning Tower, Room 1931
Albany, NY 12237

AIDS Referral
1620 I Street NW
Washington, DC 20006

AIDS-Related Discrimination Unit
Civil Liberties Union
123 West 43rd Street
New York, NY 10036

AIDS Task Force
Centers for Disease Control
1600 Clifton Road NE
Atlanta, GA 30333

American Association of Marriage and Family Therapy
1-202-429-1825

WHERE TO WRITE/WHERE TO CALL (CONTINUED)

American Association of Physicians for Human Rights
(AAPHR)
2940 16th Street, Room 309
San Francisco, CA 94103
1-415-558-9353

American Foundation for AIDS Research (AmFAR)
40 West 57th Street, Suite 406
New York, NY 10019
and
5900 Wilshire Blvd., 2nd Floor —East Satellite
Los Angeles, CA 90036

American Red Cross AIDS Education Office
1730 D Street NW
Washington, DC 20006

American Social Health Association
260 Sheridan Avenue
Palo Alto, CA 94306

Lambda Legal Defense and Education Fund
132 West 43rd Street
New York, NY 10036

Mothers of AIDS Patients (MAP)
P.O. Box 3132
San Diego, CA 92103

National AIDS Network (NAN)
1012 14th Street NW, Suite 601
Washington, DC 20005

National Association of People with AIDS
2025 I Street NW, Suite 415
Washington, DC 20006

National Child Abuse Hotline
1-800-422-4553 (24 hr.)

National Council of Churches AIDS Task Force
475 Riverside Dr., Room 572
New York, NY 10115

National Hemophilia Foundation
110 Greene Street, Room 406
New York, NY 10012
1-212-219-8180

National Institute on Drug Abuse
1-800-662-HELP

National Leadership Coalition on AIDS
1150 17th Street NW, Suite 202
Washington, DC 20036

Pan American Health Organization
(W.H.O. U.S. Chapter)
1-202-861-3200

San Francisco AIDS Foundation
333 Valencia Street, 4th Floor
San Francisco, CA 94103

Chapter 18

American Diabetes Association
1660 Duke Street
Alexandria, VA 22314
1-703-549-1500
1-800-232-3472

American Heart Association
Box BHG, National Center
7320 Greenville Avenue
Dallas, TX 75231
1-800-242-8721

National High Blood Pressure Education Program
7200 Wisconsin Ave., Suite 200
Bethesda, MD 20814
1-301-951-3260

The National Stroke Association Resource Center
1-800-367-1990

Stroke Information Center
1-800-787-6537

Chapter 19

American Cancer Society
1701 Rickenbacker Dr. B-5
Sun City Center, FL 33573-5361
1-800-227-2345

American Cancer Society
Tower Place
3340 Peachtree Rd. NE
Atlanta, GA 30026

Cancer Information Center
American Cancer Society
3709 W. Jetton Avenue
Tampa, FL 33629
1-800-ACS-2345

The Komen Alliance
1-800-IM-AWARE

National Alliance for Breast Cancer Organizations
(NABCO)
1180 Ave. of the Americas, 2nd Floor
New York, NY 10036

National Cancer Institute
Office of Cancer Communications
Building 31, Room 10824
Bethesda, MD 20892
1-800-4-CANCER

National Cancer Institute
1-800-638-6694

Chapter 20

American Association for Marriage and Family Therapy
1717 K Street NW
Washington, DC 20006
1-202-429-1825

National Council on Family Relations
1910 W. County Road B
St. Paul, MN 55113

Chapter 21

Beech-Nut Nutrition Hotline
1-800-523-6633

Child Care Information Service
National Association for the Education of Young Children
1-800-424-2460

Gerber Products Company
1-800-443-7237

National Center for Education in Maternal and Child Health
1-202-842-7617

National Health Information Clearinghouse
Maternal and Child Health
38th and R Streets NW
Washington, DC 20057

National Institute of Child Health and Human Development
Bethesda, MD 20205

Chapter 22

Alzheimer's Disease Information and Referral Service
919 N. Michigan Ave.
Chicago, IL 60611
1-800-272-3900

American Association of Retired Persons
1225 Connecticut Ave. NW
Washington, DC 20036

National Council on Aging
1828 L Street NW., Suite 504
Washington, DC 20036

National Hospice Organization
1901 N. Moore St.
Arlington, VA 22209
1-703-243-5900

National Institute of Aging
Bethesda, MD 20205

National Osteoporosis Foundation
2100 M St. NW, Suite 602
Washington, DC 20037

WHERE TO WRITE/WHERE TO CALL (CONTINUED)

Chapter 23

American Association of Poison Control Centers
3800 Reservoir Rd. NW
Washington, DC 20007

National Safety Council
251 Salina Meadows Parkway
Syracuse, NY 13212
1-800-432-5251

Chapter 24

The Alliance for Food and Fiber
1-800-266-0200

American Red Cross
17th and D St. NW
Washington, DC 20006

Chapter 25

Consumer Information Center
Dept. 572Y
Pueblo, CO 81009

EarthShare
1-800-488-8887

Environmental Protection Agency
401 M. Street SW
Washington, DC 20460

Freedom from Hunger
P.O. Box 2000
1644 DaVinci Ct.
Davis, CA 95617
1-916-758-6200

Habitat for Humanity International
121 Habitat St.
Americus, GA 31709
1-912-924-6935

Kids for a Cleaner Environment
Kids F.A.C.E.
P.O Box 158524
Nashville, TN 37215
1-800-952-3223

National Pesticide Telecommunications
Network Hotline
1-800-858-PEST

U.S. Environmental Protection Agency Safe
Drinking Water Hotline
1-800-426-4791

Chapter 26

CARE
660 First Avenue
New York, NY 10016

Consumer Information Center
Dept. 572Y
Pueblo, CO 81009

The Consumer Product Safety Commission
1-800-638-CPSC

Consumer Reports Health Letter
P.O. Box 52148
Boulder, CO 80322

Consumer's Union
101 Truman Ave.
Yonkers, NY 10703-1057
1-914-378-2000

Office of the Secretary
Federal Trade Commission (FTC)
1-202-523-3598

National Council Against Health Fraud, Inc.
P.O. Box 1276
Loma Linda, CA 92354

Office of Health Maintenance Organizations
Department of Health and Human Services
1-800-638-6686

"THOUGHTS ON HEALTH" AUTHORS

Listed below are the names of the people who have been quoted in the "Thoughts on Health" enrichment boxes found throughout this wraparound edition. Brief biographical information is provided here should students inquire about the source of the quotation.

Allen, Fred (1894–1956) American humorist
Asher, Richard (information not available)
Blake, William (1757–1827) English artist, poet, and mystic
Browning, Robert (1812–1889) English poet
Chesterfield, Philip (1694–1773) English statesman and author
Chu, Hsi (1130–1200) Chinese philosopher
Churchill, Winston (1874–1965) English statesman; Prime Minister
Cicero (106–43 B.C.) Roman statesman, orator, and author
Colette, Sidonie-Gabrielle (1873–1954) French author
Connolly, Cyril (1903–1974) English author and editor
Conrad, Joseph (1857–1924) English novelist
Cosby, Bill (1937–   ) American actor
Crisp, Quentin (1908–   ) English writer, critic
Darrow, Clarence (1857–1938) American lawyer and author
de La Mettrie, Julien (1709–1751) French materialist
de Saint-Exupery, Antoine (1900–1944) French novelist, essayist, and aviator
de Vries, Peter (1910–   ) Journalist
Diderot, Denis (1713–1784) French encyclopedist
Ebner von Eschenbach, Marie (1830–1910) Austrian poet and novelist
Emerson, Ralph Waldo (1803–1882) American essayist and poet
Fischer, Martin (1879–1962) American scientist
Ford, Henry (1863–1947) American automobile manufacturer
Franklin, Benjamin (1706–1790) American statesman and philosopher
Gide, Andre (1869–1951) French novelist, critic, and essayist
Goethe, Johann (1749–1832) German poet and dramatist
Greer, Germaine (1939–   ) Author
Harris, Sydney (1917–1986) American journalist and editor
Hazlitt, William (1778–1830) English essayist
Hippocrates (ca 460–ca 377 B.C.) Greek physician
Hoffer, Eric (1902–1983) American author
Holmes, Oliver Wendell (1841–1935) American jurist
Hoppe, Art (1925–   ) Author
Horace (65–8 B.C.) Roman poet and satirist
Hugo, Victor (1802–1885) French poet, novelist, and dramatist
Hunt, Leigh (1784–1859) English writer
Hutchins, Robert Maynard (1899–1977) American educator
Huxley, Aldous (1894–1963) English novelist and critic
Huxley, Julian (1887–1975) English biologist
Ingersoll, Robert (1833–1899) American orator
Jerome, Jerome (1859–1927) English humorist
Johnson, Samuel (1709–1784) English lexicographer and author
Jung, Carl (1875–1961) Swiss psychologist
Juvenal (AD 55 to 60–ca 127) Roman poet and satirist
Kant, Immanuel (1724–1804) German philosopher
Kennedy, John F. (1917–1963) American politician; 35th President of the United States

Kerr, Jean (1923–   ) American writer
King James I of England (1566–1625)
Koop, C. Everett (1916–   ) Former U.S. Surgeon General
La Rochefoucauld, Francois de (1613–1680) French writer and moralist
Lamb, Charles (1775–1834) English essayist and critic
Lebowitz, Fran (1950–   ) Writer
Lerner, Max (1902–1992) American writer
Levenson, Sam (1911–1980) Humorist
Lewis, Joey (information not available)
Lubbock, Sir John (1834–1913) English financier and author
Lynd, Robert (1892–1970) American sociologist
Marx, Groucho (1890–1977) Comedian
Milligan, Spike (1918–   ) English actor and author
Montaigne, Michel (1533–1592) French essayist
Napoleon (1769–1821) French emperor
Osler, William (1849–1919) Canadian physician
Ott, Maris S. (information not available)
Pasteur, Louis (1822–1895) French chemist
Plutarch (ca A.D. 46–after 119) Greek biographer and moralist
Pollock, Channing (1880–1946) American critic, playwright, novelist, and essayist
Rabelais, Francois (1483–1553) French humorist and satirist
Reagan, Ronald (1911–   ) American actor and politician; 40th President of the United States
Richter, Jean Paul (1763–1825) German writer
Roosevelt, Eleanor (1884–1962) American humanitarian and writer
Rousseau, Jean-Jacques (1712–1778) French philosopher and writer
Santayana, George (1863–1952) American poet and philosopher
Schopenhauer, Arthur (1788–1860) German philosopher
Selden, John (1584–1654) English jurist and antiquarian
Selye, Hans (1907–1982) Endocrinologist
Shakespeare, William (1564–1616) English dramatist and poet
Shaw, George Bernard (1856–1950) Irish or British author
Socrates (ca 470–399 B.C.) Greek philosopher
Sophocles (ca 496–406 B.C.) Greek dramatist
Stanley, Edward, Earl of Derby (1799–1869) English statesman
Swift, Jonathan (1667–1745) English satirist
Syras, Publius (1st Century) Roman slave
Thoreau, Henry David (1817–1862) American writer
Thurber, James (1894–1961) American writer
Toynbee, Arnold (1889–1975) English historian
Twain, Mark (1835–1910) American writer
Vauvenargues (1715–1747) French moralist
Voltaire (1694–1778) French writer
Wallace, William (1819–1881) American poet and lawyer
Wilde, Oscar (1854–1900) Irish writer

MAKING LIFE CHOICES:

Health Skills and Concepts
Expanded Edition

Frances Sienkiewicz Sizer

Eleanor Noss Whitney

Linda Kelly DeBruyne

with
Caroline Ann Sizer

CONTRIBUTING AUTHORS

The Section Review and Chapter Review exercises were
written by high school teachers:

Patricia Kosiba
P.D. Schreiber High School
Port Washington, New York

Rhonda Helgerson
Del Rio High School
Del Rio, Texas

West Publishing Company
Minneapolis/St. Paul   New York   Los Angeles   San Francisco

Copyedit: Mary Berry
Interior Art: Randy Miyake, Miyake Illustration; Rolin Graphics;
    Todd Smith, J/B Woolsey Associates; and Judy Waller
Cartoons: Gary Carroll
Photomicrographs: Michael Davidson, Florida State University
Index: Linda Cupp
Proofreading: Jennifer Miller
Dummy Artist: Gary Hespenheide, Hespenheide Design
Composition: American Composition & Graphics, Inc.
Cover Image: Richard Mackson/Sports Illustrated

A full list of photo and art credits found in this text follows the index.

WEST'S COMMITMENT TO THE ENVIRONMENT
In 1906, West Publishing Company began recycling materials left over from the production of books. This began a tradition of efficient and responsible use of resources. Today, up to 95 percent of our legal books and 70 percent of our college texts are printed on recycled, acid-free stock. West also recycles nearly 22 million pounds of scrap paper annually—the equivalent of 181,717 trees. Since the 1960's, West has devised ways to capture and recycle waste inks, solvents, oils, and vapors created in the printing process. We also recycle plastics of all kinds, wood, glass, corrugated cardboard, and batteries, and have eliminated the use of styrofoam book packaging. We at West are proud of the longevity and the scope of our commitment to our environment.

A Word about Photomicrographs

The photomicrographs in the textbook were made of recrystallized vitamins using a variety of different techniques. Many vitamins can be imaged using the melt-recrystallization process where a few milligrams of the chemical are sandwiched between a microscope coverslip and slide, then heated until melted and allowed to slowly recrystallize. Alternately, for vitamin-salts that will not melt, the chemical is dissolved in a suitable solvent (water or alcohol) and a few microliters of solution are allowed to slowly evaporate between a microscope slide and coverslip. Upon recrystallization, the vitamins are viewed in a microscope using cross-polarized illumination where the crystallites diffract light depending both on the molecular orientation within the crystal and the crystal thickness. The colorful patterns illustrated in this text are a manifestation of both molecular orientation and crystal thickness.

COPYRIGHT © 1994   By WEST PUBLISHING COMPANY
                    610 Opperman Drive
                    P.O. Box 64526
                    St. Paul, MN 55164-0526
All rights reserved
Printed in the United States of America
01 00 99 98 97 96 95 94   8 7 6 5 4 3 2 1 0
Library of Congress Cataloging-in-Publication Data
Sizer, Frances Sienkiewicz.
    Making life choices : health skills and concepts / Frances Sienkiewicz Sizer, Eleanor Noss Whitney.
    p. cm.
    Includes index.
    ISBN 0-314-01686-4 (student ed. : acid-free paper).—ISBN 0-314-01158-7 (expanded ed. : acid-free paper)
    1. Health. I. Whitney, Eleanor Noss. II. Title.
RA776.S6424 1994
613—dc20
                                                            92-39251
                                                            CIP

ABOUT THE AUTHORS

Frances Sienkiewicz Sizer, MS, RD, attended Florida State University's College of Human Sciences where, in 1980, she received her BS, and in 1982, her MS in nutrition. She has counseled clients in the University's stress-reduction clinic and served as nutrition consultant to schools and alcoholism programs in Florida. She coauthors the textbooks *Nutrition: Concepts and Controversies,* now entering its sixth edition; *Life Choices: Health Concepts and Strategies,* now in its second edition; *Essential Life Choices;* and *The Fitness Triad: Motivation, Training, and Nutrition.* She has published in *Shape* magazine, in the health newsletter *Healthline,* and in the *Journal of Chemical Senses.* She is vice-president and a founding member of Nutrition and Health Associates, an information resource center in Tallahassee, Florida, where she devotes full time to studying and writing in the areas of health and nutrition.

Eleanor Noss Whitney, Ph.D. received her bachelor's degree in biology from Harvard University in 1960 and her doctoral degree in biology from Washington University in 1970. She has taught biology and nutrition at Washington University, Florida A & M University, and Florida State University; has taught community classes and workshops in weight control, stress-reduction, and addiction recovery; and has served as counselor for people recovering from alcoholism. She now devotes full time to research, writing, and consulting in nutrition, health, and environmental health. She is the president of Nutrition and Health Associates, where she authors and coauthors numerous textbooks on nutrition, health, and environmental topics. She is the founder of an environmental education foundation, and writes a weekly column for the *Tallahassee Democrat* on environmentally sensitive lifestyles. She is a member of and contributor to many environmental organizations including the Union of Concerned Scientists, the National Resources Defense Council, the Nature Conservancy, the Worldwatch Institute, and Zero Population Growth.

Linda Kelly DeBruyne, MS, RD, received her BS in 1980 and her MS in 1982 in nutrition and food science at the Florida State University. She serves on the board of directors of Nutrition and Health Associates, an information resource center in Tallahassee, Florida, where her specialty areas are fitness and life-cycle nutrition. Her other textbooks are *Life Span Nutrition: Conception through Life; The Fitness Triad: Motivation, Training, and Nutrition;* and *Nutrition and Diet Therapy.* She also serves as consultant to a group of Tallahassee pediatricians for whom she teaches infant nutrition classes to parents. She is a member of the American Dietetic Association and the American Alliance for Health, Physical Education, Recreation and Dance.

CONTRIBUTING AUTHORS

Patricia A. Kosiba received her B.S. in health and physical education from West Chester University in Pennsylvania and her M.A. in health education from Adelphi University in New York. She is presently a health educator for the Port Washington Public Schools in Port Washington, New York. She has developed both junior and senior high school health curriculums for the school district and serves as an advisor for the Students Against Driving Drunk program. In 1991 she was selected Nassau County SAAD Faculty Advisor of the Year.

Rhonda Helgerson received her degree from the University of Wisconsin at La Crosse with a double major in health and physical education and a coaching concentration. Since 1985 she has been teaching health at Del Rio High School in Del Rio, Texas. In addition to teaching health, she is the assistant varsity coach for both basketball and volleyball. She is affiliated with the American Alliance for Health, Physical Education, Recreation and Dance; Texas Girl's Coaches Association, and the Women's Sports Foundation.

DEDICATION

To my children, Casy and David, whose encouragement, help, and love have made this book and every other worthwhile thing possible.

Fran

To my beloved husband Jack Yeager with gratitude for all his love and support—and to his grandson Will Brookes, whose future we strive to protect.

Ellie Whitney

To my Mom, Dorothy Kelly, and to my husband, Tom, and our boys, Zachary and Tyler—your goodness, wisdom, and love enrich my life and give me so much happiness—Thanks.

Linda

ACKNOWLEDGMENTS

To Caroline Ann Sizer, many thanks for applying her excellent writing skills and insightful perspective to many of this book's features from its inception to its publication. To Lori Turner, our associate and a faculty member at Tallahassee Community College's Health Education department, our gratitude, especially for her knowledge and work concerning dysfunctional family life. To our partner Sharon Rolfes, thanks for her support and ready ear. To our families, our deepest gratitude for their support throughout this project. To Bill Wood, our appreciation for generously lending us his skill in instructional design and for his many other good ideas. To Paramedic Bill Brookes, our thanks for his expert advice on first aid and accident prevention. We appreciate the artwork of Gary Carroll, John Woolsey and his Associates, Judy Waller, Randy Miyake, and Rolin Graphics that grace the pages of this book. We thank our editors, Bob Cassell, Mario Rodriguez, Lynda Kessler, Glenda Samples and all of their associates. Our appreciation to Vivienne Glidewell for her expert word-processing help. We are grateful to the teenagers who inspired us with their questioning minds. We also appreciate the efforts of our reviewers.

REVIEWERS

Patricia Kosiba
P.D. Schreiber High School
Port Washington, New York

Cheryl Bower
Newberg High School
Newberg, Oregon

William K. Brookes
(Technical Review), Florida

Deneise Crace
Meridian High School
Meridian, Idaho

Paul Dean
Pine Bluff High School
Pine Bluff, Arkansas

Thomas Dolde
Connellsville Area High School
Connellsville, Pennsylvania

Rick Ford
Carter High School
Strawberry Plains, Tennessee

Ira Gibel
Oceanside High School
Oceanside, New York

Rhonda Helgerson
Del Rio High School
Del Rio, Texas

Nancy Kidd
Oshkosh North High School
Oshkosh, Wisconsin

Roxanna Laycox
West Carrollton High School
West Carrollton, Ohio

Charles Lee Libby
East Central High School
San Antonio, Texas

John Markham
Northbrook High School
Houston, Texas

Carol Martin
Pekin Community High School
Pekin, Illinois

Sandy Mayon
Robert E. Lee High School
Baytown, Texas

Ron Meurer
West Mesa High School
Albuquerque, New Mexico

Bruce Miller
Heritage High School
Broadlands, Illinois

Betzy Nelson
Orange Park High School
Orange Park, Florida

Peter Olson
South Carroll High School
Sykesville, Maryland

Don Rogers
Richmond High School
Richmond, Indiana

Michael Smith
Wilson High School
Long Beach, California

Marlene Snyder
Sharon High School
Sharon, Pennsylvania

Steven Sykes
Harrison Central High School
Gulfport, Mississippi

Ron Topolinski
California

Linda Troolin
East High School
Duluth, Minnesota

Todd Urbanek
Boswell High School
Fort Worth, Texas

Laura Van Dellen
Bell High School
Los Angeles, California

Glenda Warner
Ferncreek High School
Louisville, Kentucky

Dennis Weisz
Sioux City West High School
Sioux City, Iowa

TEEN VIEWS

We would also like to take this opportunity to thank the teachers and principals at the high schools listed below who helped us obtain responses from the students who participated in the development of the Teen Views feature. Thanks also to the parents of all the teens whose responses appear in these features for giving us their consent to print their child's response. Finally, our sincere thanks to all the students who sent us their thoughtful, mature, and honest replies to the questions we posed. We regret that we didn't have space to print all the responses. We received literally thousands of comments and found it quite difficult to choose from so many great replies. We hope that all the teens benefitted from this unique experience. We feel confident that these teens are representative of their peers around the country.

Carter High School, Strawberry Plains, Tennessee
Connellsville High School, Connellsville, Pennsylvania
East High School, Duluth, Minnesota
Farrington High School, Honolulu, Hawaii
Ferncreek High School, Louisville, Kentucky
Frontier Central High School, Hamburg, New York
Great Falls High School, Great Falls, Montana
Hilltop High School, Chula Vista, California
Robert E. Lee High School, Baytown, Texas
Newberg High School, Newberg, Oregon
Newman High School, Newman, Georgia
Orange Park High School, Orange Park, Florida

Oshkosh North High School, Oshkosh, Wisconsin
Pine Bluff High School, Pine Bluff, Arkansas
Poughkeepsie High School, Poughkeepsie, New York
Sharon High School, Sharon, Pennsylvania
Sioux City West High School, Sioux City, Iowa
Somerville High School, Somerville, Massachusetts
South Carroll High School, Sykesville, Maryland
South High School, Fargo, North Dakota
Thousand Oaks High School, Thousand Oaks, California
Westside High School, Omaha, Nebraska
Woodrow Wilson High School, Long Beach, California

CONTENTS IN BRIEF

CONTENTS

HEALTH STRATEGIES

LIFE CHOICE
INVENTORY

STRAIGHT
TALK

Consumer Awareness

Teen Views

STUDYING HEALTH

Have you ever spent a half hour or hour reading one of your homework assignments, only to realize that you couldn't remember anything you had just read? If this has happened to you, you are not alone. All students—even those who get straight A's—occasionally fail to make effective use of their study time.

There is a study technique, however, that can help you become a more efficient reader and studier. You can use this method in your health class, as well as most of your other courses. This method, known as the *SQ3R Method*, is one of the most effective ways to improve your reading comprehension and your grades.

The symbols S-Q-R-R-R stand for *Survey, Question, Read, Recite and Review.* The following descriptions tell how you can use the SQ3R method to learn more in less time, in almost any course. You will also find here specific directions for using SQ3R with your health text, *Making Life Choices.*

S = Survey. The first step in studying a chapter is to get a broad picture of it—to prepare your mind for what you are about to learn. Don't just open your book and begin reading. Leaf through the chapter before you begin. Read the headings, the illustration captions, and the bold type. Also look at the drawings and photos. As you skim through the chapter, think about what you will be learning.

Making Life Choices has three components that will be of special help to you in the survey process: "Outcomes," "Contents," and "Fact or Fiction." All three of these features are on the second page of the chapter. Just by skimming the Outcomes and Contents, answering the Fact or Fiction questions, and looking at the photo on the opposite page, you will get a pretty good idea of the most important topics covered in the chapter.

Q = Question. You understand and remember more of what you read if you are concentrating on your reading material. How do you keep your mind from wandering? One of the most effective ways is to ask and answer questions about the reading as you go. One common questioning technique is to turn headings into questions. For example, in Chapter 1, the first heading is "Wellness and Your Choices." Before you read the material under that heading, turn the heading into a question, or two questions. In this case you might ask yourself, "What is wellness?" and "How do my choices affect wellness?"

R(1) = Read. The first R in SQ3R refers to *read.* You are now ready to actually read the material. As you read, try to answer the questions that you formed from the headings. *Making Life Choices* was printed in fairly large type and on short line lengths to make your reading easier. The textbook also lists complete definitions of all the terms you might not know in the "Mini Glossaries" at the bottom of the right-hand pages.

R(2) = Recite. The second R stands for *recite.* It does you no good to read a long passage and then simply go on to another. You need to state in your own words what it is that you just read so that you will be sure to understand and remember the most important points. The "Key Points" at the end of each heading in *Making Life Choices* will help you do this. Answering the "Section Review" questions is another way of "reciting" what you've read.

R(3) = Review. The third R stands for *review.* After you have finished reading a chapter, you will need to check yourself to see that you remember all that you learned earlier. *Making Life Choices* has an abundant supply of questions and exercises in the "Chapter Review" to help you review the chapter.

As stated earlier, studies have shown that SQ3R improves both reading comprehension and grades. The special study features of *Making Life Choices* will help you make the most effective use possible of the SQ3R method.

INTRODUCTION

This book was written for you, the high school health student, to meet your needs for knowledge about health. A new day has dawned in health education, because science has revealed that personal choices exert powerful influences on health and illness, and even on life and death. You are a member of the first generation in history to face so many choices of such lasting impact on your health. You are also among the first to be privileged with access to sound health information with which to make those choices.

The first part of this book's title, *Making Life Choices*, tells you that our mission is to help you in making the choices that so deeply affect your life both today and in the future. The second part of the title, *Health Skills and Concepts*, identifies the two tools you will need to make wise choices. Learning the facts about health (learning the concepts) is of first importance, but this alone is not enough. To truly benefit from your studies, you must develop ways of applying facts, (develop skills) and use them in your daily life.

A note about our style: We present health concepts in a comfortable, informal style of writing, which makes concepts more simple to understand. As scientists, we place a high value on accuracy, and we check and recheck our facts so that you can rely on them. Stay aware that facts change with time, and issues sometimes develop in unexpected ways.

We hold a positive attitude. Our emphasis is on what *to* do, not on what *not* to do, to gain the best quality of life. The chapters tell how to *prevent* disease, not how to cure it; how to eat well, not how to diet; how to give up destructive habits; and how to cultivate healthful habits in their place.

Some notes about the book's features: Here are the major features you can expect to find in the chapters:

- *Fact or Fiction* is the name of a for-fun quiz at each chapter's start that identifies and corrects common misconceptions about the topics in the chapter.

- *Mini Glossaries* are little glossaries that appear in the bottom corners of most right-hand pages to give you easy access to the definitions of key terms when you need them.
- *Key Points* follow the smaller sections within the chapters. They quickly review and reinforce the important concepts.
- *Life Choice Inventories* let you explore where you stand today with regard to health issues. These self-assessment questionnaires have been tested for validity in many classrooms across the nation.
- *Health Strategies* boxes present skills and actions to help you apply the chapter material to daily life.
- *Consumer Awareness* boxes can guide you in judging health information you may read or hear about, and in purchasing health products.
- *Teen Views* present the thoughts and opinions of teenagers in health classes across the country, written by them especially for you.
- *Straight Talk* sections ask and answer some interesting questions that may be on your mind about concepts related to the chapter topics.

America has seen a healthy trend toward eating right, exercising more, and making other lifestyle choices that support a better quality of life. These trends were not easily or quickly established, but resulted from the efforts of health educators, medical professionals, political figures, and consumers who demanded more health education and more health-supporting products. People's choices make trends, and it is up to you and all teens today to decide where we go from here—forward toward healthier lives, or backwards to greater risks.

We hope you enjoy learning from our book as we have enjoyed producing it. We will consider our book successful if it provides you with the knowledge you need to face today's world and to choose wisely in the years that lie ahead.

Frances S. Sizer
Eleanor N. Whitney
Linda K. DeBruyne
—January, 1993

CHAPTER 1 PLANNER

OVERVIEW

Chapter 1 is 22 pages long and divided into the three sections listed to the right. Major learning outcomes of the chapter also are listed to the right. Briefly, this chapter introduces students to the concept of wellness and the different areas of health. It stresses the importance of the individual's daily choices in determining that person's level of wellness. It also gives students some key concepts and skills for changing their health behaviors for the better.

MAKING LIFE CHOICES SUPPLEMENTARY MATERIAL

A variety of activities, handouts, quizzes, and tests to accompany this chapter are available in the *Making Life Choices* supplementary material. You may pick and choose from those materials as appropriate for your amount of class time and the ability levels of your students. Some of the resources you might want to consider using are:

Overheads
• Lifestyle Choices Affect Health
• Invest in Learning

Handout
• Steps to Goal Setting

SUGGESTED RESOURCES

Student Readings
1. Bennett, Walt. *Your Good Health.* Cambridge, MA: Harvard University Press, 1987.
2. Smith, Robert. *The Good Health Kit.* NY: Holt and Co., 1987.

Teacher Readings
1. Belloc, N.B. "Relationship of Physical Health Status and Health Practices." *Preventive Medicine* 1 (1972): 409–421.
2. Gotchman, D. S. *Health Behavior.* NY:

Plenum Publishing, 1988. pp. 43–63.

Videos
1. *Taking Control* (about healthy lifestyle, reducing cancer risk). NY: American Cancer Society, 1986.
2. *Body Watch: Will to Be Well.* Dearfield, IL: Coronet Films, 1986.

Software
1. Ellis, L.B. *Health Awareness Games.* Pleasantville, NY: HRM Software, 1985, Apple, IBM.

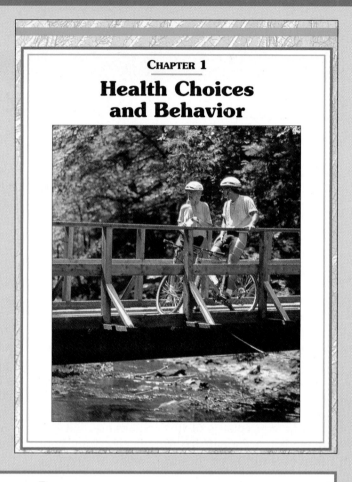

CHAPTER 1
Health Choices and Behavior

CHAPTER PROJECT

Have students survey adults in their communities. For each adult, have them obtain the age, weight, and general feelings of overall health. Also, have them note whether they think each person appears to be older or younger than their chronological age. Compile the results in class.

Activity To Introduce Chapter

Since this is probably the beginning of the semester, you should have at least two goals as you begin Chapter 1: **1.** to develop a comfortable, safe atmosphere for discussions of health issues, and **2.** to begin the content of the course. This activity will serve to introduce the chapter as well as allow the students to begin to get to know each other.
1. Count how many students are in the room.
2. Find a series of numbers by which that number can be divided evenly. (Example: 28 students; series of numbers—2, 4, 7, 14.) If the number can't be divided evenly (e.g., 27), divide the class into six groups of four and one group of three, etc.
3. Explain to the students that you will call out a number. The students must quickly get into a group that contains that number of members. (Example, you call 4—the students will get

OUTCOMES

After reading and studying this chapter, you will be able to:

✓ **Explain the relationship between health and wellness.**

✓ **Describe how most of the lifestyle diseases of today are related to lifestyle choices.**

✓ **List the lifestyle habits that you can adopt to maximize your wellness.**

✓ **Describe how your social, mental, spiritual, and physical health are associated with wellness.**

✓ **Explain how you can use motivation to change your health behaviors.**

✓ **Define the steps in goal setting.**

CONTENTS

FACT OR FICTION

What do you think? Are the following statements true or false? If you think they are false, then say what is true.

1. People make hundreds of choices every day that affect their health.
2. The way adults contract most diseases is by catching them from somebody else.
3. You can make yourself physically younger or older by the ways you choose to live.
4. Accidents are among the major causes of death for teenagers.
5. To give up a harmful health habit, all you need is the motivation to do so.

(Answers on page 17)

■ **Reminder:** Knowing how to study can increase your knowledge, improve your grades, *and* cut down on your study time. See the *Studying Health* section at the front of your text for some suggestions to help you study this chapter.

Answers to "Fact or Fiction"

1. True. **2.** False. Today, most of the leading causes of death are primarily related to lifestyle. **3.** True. **4.** True. **5.** False. To give up on a harmful health habit, you also need commitment. It also helps to have support from others, as well as high self-esteem.

NOT ENOUGH TIME?*

You could easily spend four or five days teaching this chapter if students read the entire chapter, do a fair number of the suggested activities in the teacher's edition, and review a sampling of the handouts from the resource material accompanying this text. It is likely, however, that you will have only one or two days to devote to this chapter. Following are some suggestions to help you make sure that you cover the key topics if you have limited time.

TIME	SUGGESTIONS
1 Day	Assign Section I and II prior to class. Also, assign the "Life Choice Inventory" and the "Fact or Fiction." During class have students do Activity 1.1 in Section I and Activity 2.2 in Section II. Conclude the class with the combination of the pop quizzes given under the Evaluate for Sections I and II. You may want to assign reteaching activities from the supplementary material for those students doing poorly on the quiz.
2 Days	On the second day assign Section III, including the "Consumer Awareness" and the "Straight Talk" at the end of the chapter. During class do Activities 3.3, 3.4, and 3.6 for Section III.

Please refer to the 18-week daily lesson plans in the supplementary material for additional suggestions.

---

into seven groups of four).

4. Once they're in their groups, tell them what to discuss in the given time allotment. Allow enough time for everyone to speak.

5. Here is a suggested list of numbers and topics to be discussed:

a. Two students—Give your name and your favorite junk food.

b. Four students—Give your name and explain how often you eat breakfast and include what you eat for breakfast.

c. Seven students—Give your name and state how long you'd like to live (until what age?).

d. Fourteen students—Give your name and state on a scale of 1 to 10 how healthy you think you are and why.

6. You should either participate in their groups or move from group to group. Have students change groups after they've all talked. Students should be told *not* to stay with the same students—they *must* switch partners to make new groups. **(10–12 min.)**

In this section students will learn the:
1. Correlation between wellness, life choices, and longevity.
2. Benefits of positive lifestyle choices.

Activity 1.1

Defining Wellness. Please place two posters on the wall, one with the word "Wellness" placed in the middle of a circle and one with the word "Health" in the middle of a circle. Ask the students to write their definitions of the two words on the poster but *outside* the circle. Once all students who want to contribute have done so, read their definitions aloud to the class. Focus on the definitions that will be used in class. Then, with a bright marker, write a brief definition of each word *under* the word *in* the circle—Example: "Wellness is maximum well-being." This allows students both to invest in the concepts and to start with the same definition. **(10 min.)**

Activity 1.2

Lifestyle Choices. Number 1 through 5 on the board. Quickly ask for a raise of hands on the following questions and record the answers on the board next

---

Teacher Support Notes

① **Enjoying Life:** The first sentence of the text, *"This book is about enjoying life,"* gives students the reason for studying and working through this health course. Ask students to list the courses they've taken in the past two years and the real-life applications for those courses. Have them do the same for health. After discussing all their reasons, direct their attention to this first sentence. Did anyone think that the personal advantages to studying health would be as broad as "enjoying life?"

② **Improve or Harm?** Have students reread "Today's choices will either improve you or harm you." Then have them list the choices they make in a typical day and write "improved me" or "harmed me" next to each choice. Discuss their lists.

2

---

2   UNIT 1 Introduction

This book is about enjoying life. It challenges you to increase your knowledge, strengths, and skills in many areas—in self-awareness, emotional health, stress management, nutrition, fitness, friendships and love relationships, disease prevention, health consumerism, and many others. It aims to help you move forward in all these areas with confidence. ①

This is an ambitious goal, especially since everyone already has at least some experience in, and knowledge about, these subject areas. Most schoolwork ensures that people learn the basics of language and mathematics. However, people also need to learn **life management skills**, the skills people use to meet their own needs every day. If you apply yourself as you read and study this book, you can fill in important gaps in your own knowledge. You can also grow more successful at taking care of yourself.

SECTION 1

Wellness and Your Choices

You make hundreds of choices every day—what to eat, whom to be with, how active to be, when to sleep, and more. In making these daily choices, you change your **health**, whether you mean to or not. Today's choices will either improve you or harm you. Furthermore, their effects will multiply over time. Today's choices, repeated for a week, will have seven times the impact. Repeated every day for a year, they will have 365 times the effect on your health. Over years, the effects accumulate still further. ②

Today's choices affect not only your physical health, but also your **wellness**—all the

All the characteristics that make you strong, happy, and able to function well with friends add up to your wellness.

characteristics that make you strong, happy, and able to function well with friends and family and in school. Consider, first, your physical health.

Physical Health Yesterday and Today

If you use the information presented in this book, you can make choices today that will improve your chances of living a long life. In the past, many children and teenagers, as well as older people, died helplessly of **infectious diseases,** such as malaria and smallpox, that raged out of control. Today, however, that rarely happens. The only infectious disease threatening great numbers of young people in our society today is acquired immune deficiency syndrome (AIDS). Its cause is known, though, and efforts to find new treatments for it are under way. A later chapter shows how to prevent infectious diseases.

Most infectious diseases are well controlled, today. As a result, people who are young today can expect to live longer lives than ever before. What do you want to be like when you are in your 80s? You can plan for those years now, and strive to make them a healthy, happy time of your life.

You can also ruin those years. The longer your life, the greater the influence of the choices you make today—choices that affect

1. How many of you skipped breakfast today?

2. How many of you eat or drink junk food every day (soda pop, candy, chips, french fries, etc.)?

3. How many of you smoke cigarettes?

4. How many of you will admit you've driven over the speed limit *and* you *enjoyed* doing so? (Of course, use of this question will depend on the age of your students.)

5. How many of you have ever ridden in a car with the driver being under the influence of alcohol? (optional)

6. How many of you have ever "hung out" in an area that was not considered a safe neighborhood?

Point out that the resulting numbers on the board indicate lifestyle choices and that these choices can affect our health—especially if the choices become patterns. Ask for volunteers to give examples of

how each of the choices in the questions can affect a person's life, especially if the choice is repeated and becomes a pattern. **(10–15 min.)**

TEACH
SECTION 1
(Guided and Independent Practice)

Activity 1.3
Diseases Past and Present. With

(continued on next page)

---

your body, mind, and spirit. The daily choices that have the power to affect your health are called **lifestyle choices**. They are your choices of how to treat your body and your mind.

Because people today are living longer than ever before, they are able to maintain better health far longer than in the past. By the same token, they are also able to harm their health more. People who consistently make poor lifestyle choices, on a daily basis, can expect to suffer from a set of diseases known as **lifestyle diseases**. These diseases include heart and lung diseases, cancer, diabetes, and liver disease. Figure 1–1 below contrasts the major causes of death 100 years ago with those today. It shows that while people used to "catch" many diseases from disease agents ("germs"), they now are more likely to "contract" diseases because of the ways they choose to live.

When people neglect their own bodies, they become likely to suffer from lifestyle diseases. The choice to smoke, for example, is a major cause of lung disease. The choice to abuse alcohol is a major cause of liver disease. Poor choices in nutrition and physical activity can make heart disease and diabetes likely. Figure 1–2 on the next page shows that the vast majority of people affect their own health by the choices they make.

This is not to say that people who contract lung disease, liver disease, heart disease, or cancer are always solely responsible. Two causes, besides people's own choices, can bring on these diseases. One is heredity. Some people simply tend to develop certain diseases, while others do not. The other cause is factors in the environment—not only infectious disease

MINI GLOSSARY

life management skills: the skills that help a person to realize his or her potential to be well and enjoy life. This book's Health Strategies sections give examples.

health: a range of states with physical, mental, emotional, spiritual, and social components. At a minimum, *health* means freedom from physical disease, poor physical condition, social maladjustment, and other negative states. At a maximum, *health* means *"wellness."*

wellness: maximum well-being; the top of the range of health states; the goal of the person who strives toward realizing his or her full potential physically, mentally, emotionally, spiritually, and socially.

infectious diseases: diseases that are caused by infecting organisms and that can be passed from person to person. You'll learn more about these diseases in Chapters 16 and 17.

lifestyle choices: choices, made daily, of how to treat the body and mind. Examples are what to eat, when to exercise, and whether to use alcohol or other drugs.

lifestyle diseases: diseases that are made likely by neglect of the body. They cannot be passed from person to person. Examples are heart disease, cancer, and diabetes. Lifestyle choices that promote health can help prevent lifestyle diseases.

1890s   **1990s**

Figure 1–1 The Leading Causes of Death. For teenagers today, accidents are one leading cause of death. Violence, including self-inflicted injury, is another leading cause of death.

Teacher Support Notes

① **Lifestyle and Infectious Diseases:** Ask students if they can name a major difference between lifestyle diseases and infectious diseases. (Infectious diseases can be passed from person to person; lifestyle diseases can't.)

② **Understanding Contract:** *Contract* is a word used frequently throughout the text. Some students may confuse the meaning here with the more common use of the word as a legal agreement. Discuss the different meanings and ask students to write several sentences of their own for both meanings.

their textbooks closed, students should name the diseases that were the major causes of death in *past history*. List their answers on the board. Then ask them what diseases are the major causes of death today. List those on the board. Ask them to compare the two lists and to

explain the differences. (Tuberculosis, scarlet fever, digestive diseases, and kidney disease do *not* appear in the 1990s list; heart disease, cancer, accidents, suicide, diabetes, and liver disease do *not* appear in the 1890s list.) Be sure the point is made that in the past diseases were "infectious" in nature and today the diseases are often "contracted" from lifestyle choices. Discuss the terms "catch" and "contract." **(10–12 min., Critical Thinking)**

Activity 1.4
Lifestyle Choices and Diseases.
Ask the students to look at the definitions of lifestyle choices and lifestyle diseases on page 3. Then, with books closed, ask students to link specific lifestyle choices with specific lifestyle diseases. Record these on newsprint or on the board. Possible list results: smoking cigarettes—heart disease, lung cancer, emphysema; drinking alcohol—alcoholism, cirrhosis of liver; poor

Teacher Support Notes

① **Overhead—Choosing Health:** Use the overhead of this illustration to make sure students understand it. Ask them which of the three groups they think they fall into. (Except for very special circumstances, *all* students should say the middle group—those whose lifestyle choices affect their health.)

② **Research Heredity:** Ask students if they are aware of any diseases that "run" in the family. Ask students who don't raise their hands if this means there are no diseases, or they don't know. Ask those who don't know to do some research and report back to class. Compile a class list. How does the list compare with the diseases listed in Figure 1–1?

📖 Fast Facts

The current overall life expectancy in Japan is 79 years, which is four years longer than the overall life expectancy in the United States.

4 UNIT 1 Introduction

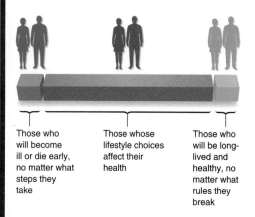

Those who will become ill or die early, no matter what steps they take

Those whose lifestyle choices affect their health

Those who will be long-lived and healthy, no matter what rules they break

Figure 1–2 Lifestyle Choices Made Today Affect Health in Later Life. The vast majority of people affect their health by the choices they make. Only a few people with excellent health habits have their lives cut short by disease. Only a few people who ignore all health warnings have long lives and remain healthy. ①

agents but also pollution of air, water, and food.

Although you cannot avoid harmful hereditary and environmental factors, you can control them to some extent. Knowledge of your heredity can help you learn what steps to take to lessen your chances of developing diseases that run in your family. Knowing what effects your environment can have on your health can help you decide where to live, what laws to vote for, and what causes to support. ②

The more you learn, the more control you can gain. Figure 1–3 shows that your wellness can exist anywhere along a line, from maximum wellness on the one end to total failure to function (death) on the other. Where would you like to be on this line? If you read the figure, you'll see that it also shows how your choices affect your position on the wellness line.

When people understand that they have some control over their health, they real-

ize that the responsibility for their health is also theirs. People are not helpless victims of chance. They have power to change things. And that power lies within themselves: *you* change your health. Taking responsibility lays the foundation for lifelong health. It is central to wellness, as Figure 1–4 on page 6 demonstrates.

Key Points *Deaths from diseases of the past were caused mainly by infections. Today's deaths from diseases, in contrast, are closely linked to lifestyle choices. It is possible to benefit your state of health by gathering information about positive choices and applying that information throughout life.*

Age: A Matter of Definition

As fine, strong, and young as you may be, you already carry within you the older person you will become. Will that person, at 30, 60, or 90 years of age, be fine, strong, and young, too? You can choose the answer to that question. You can aim your body now, like an arrow, toward the goal you set for yourself.

Of course, chance may change your plans. Accidents or diseases may come along over which you have no control. Barring bad luck, though, you can choose your later health. In other words, you can tilt the odds in your favor, even in terms of *how old* you will be.

"Wait a minute," you may say. "When I've lived 60 years, I'll be 60 years old. No one can change *that*." That's true, but only on the calendar. Your **chronological age** after 60 years will be 60, but what about your **physiological age**?

Two scientists have proved that people can dramatically alter the age they seem to be. These scientists studied nearly 7,000 adults in California and noted that some people seemed younger, and others older, than their years.

eating habits—high blood pressure, atherosclerosis, heart disease; intravenous drug abuse—hepatitis, AIDS; sexual activity—AIDS, gonorrhea, other STDs. Now, ask the students to give examples of people they know who have had any of these diseases as a result of lifestyle choices. Be sure students know they can "pass" on the question, and they should *not* give names—only the relationship (a neighbor, grandfather, etc.), except for famous

people. Once three or four examples have been given, ask the students if they think any of these could happen to them. Point out that one of our major problems is *denial*. People who make poor lifestyle choices really don't believe anything bad is going to happen to them. Smokers don't smoke cigarettes hoping to contract cancer. Heavy alcohol drinkers don't hope to die early from cirrhosis of the liver. They *know* the facts but *deny* the

possibility. **(15 min.; Reteach, Reinforce, Extend, Enrich)**

Activity 1.5
Physiological vs. Psychological Age. Decide which day you will discuss the differences between physiological and psychological age. Two or three days prior to that day, ask the students to interview five people of varying ages over 30.

(continued on next page)

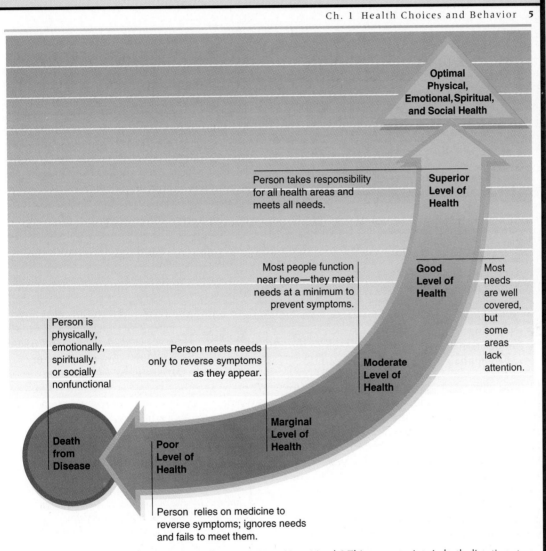

Figure 1–3 The Wellness Line—How Well Do You Meet Your Needs? This arrow points in both directions to form a continuum. This means that no matter how well you maintain your health today, you may still be able to improve tomorrow. Likewise, a person who is well today can slip down the scale in the future by failing to maintain health-promoting habits. ①

To find out what made the difference, the scientists focused on the lifestyle habits of the people they were studying. Six practices seemed to have the most impact on the condition of these people's body systems—that is, on their physiological age. The six factors were:

> **❝ Thoughts on Health ❞**
>
> *May you live all the days of your life.*
> *– Jonathan Swift*

Teacher Support Notes

① Understanding Continuum: The word *continuum* will be new to many students. Tell them that a continuum is something that changes gradually from one end to another. For example, the range of temperatures of their tap water is a continuum, especially if they have one handle that swivels from hot to cold and vice versa. The main point for them to understand is that you cannot divide a continuum into two halves (hot and cold, good and bad, etc.). Health is shown on a continuum because you can't separate people into two groups and say the people on one side have good health and the people on the other side have bad health. Health and wellness are matters of degree.

 MINI GLOSSARY

chronological age: age as measured in years from date of birth.
physiological age: age as estimated from the body's health and probable life expectancy.

They are to record answers to these questions:
1. How old are you?
2. How old do you feel
   a. physically?
   b. mentally?
3. How would you rate your lifestyle on a scale of 1 to 10 with 1 being excellent health habits? (Questions could be expanded to include what they regret, what they are thankful for, etc.) Then, before you collect this assignment, discuss with the students what they found out. After the discussion, ask the students to write down any conclusions they can draw from their "mini survey." **(15 to 20 min.; Extend, Enrich)**

Activity 1.6
   Making Posters. List on the board or poster board the six practices listed below that seem to have the most impact on the condition of people's physiological age. Ask the students if they agree with them and why. Then ask them how many *they* follow. Get some responses. (It's doubtful they follow all six.) Restress the denial—we assume we will always feel young and healthy no matter what we do to our-

Teacher Support Notes

① Chronological and Physiological Age:
Make sure students understand the difference between *chronological* and *physiological* age. Have them close their books, then for each of the following, ask them to say which type of age is being discussed: **a.** "Her birthday was yesterday—she was 37" (chronological); **b.** "He looks old, doesn't he?" (physiological); **c.** "She had a party to celebrate turning 40" (chronological); **d.** "He is young for his years" (physiological); **e.** "Although she was 60, her blood pressure and body weight were the same as when she was 40." (physiological)

Section I Review

Answers
1. **a.** chronological age **b.** centenarians **c.** physiological age **d.** wellness
2. improve you or harm you
3. false
4. smallpox and malaria; AIDS
5. Answers will vary; could include: heart and lung diseases, cancer, diabetes, and liver disease.
6. Answers will vary.

6 UNIT 1 Introduction

Figure 1–4 Personal Responsibility is Central to Wellness.

- Sleeping regularly and adequately.
- Eating regular meals, including breakfast.
- Engaging in regular physical activity.
- Not smoking.
- Not using alcohol, or using it in moderation.
- Keeping their weight under control.

The effects of these practices tended to add together. The more of them that a person habitually chose, the younger the person seemed to be. Those who followed all six positive practices were in the best health, even if older in calendar years than some of the other people. In fact, the physical health of those who reported all six health practices was about the same as that of people *30 years younger* who followed few or none. Such findings demonstrate that although you cannot alter the year of your birth, you can, in effect, make yourself younger or older by the way you choose to live.

These effects are only beginning to be visible in people in their teen years, but are very noticeable in adults. Think about people your parents' age. Have you noticed that the healthiest ones appear much younger than their agemates? Have you noticed that those who appear healthiest are often the most attractive ones?

Lifelong health habits also affect the length of life. Proof comes from the study of **centenarians**—people who are 100 years old or older. Scientists naturally are curious to know how these people's lifestyles differ from those of people who died earlier. Often, the same factors turn up. Centenarians are usually well nourished, but not overweight. They usually are nonsmokers and don't abuse alcohol or other drugs. They maintain regular patterns of eating and sleeping. Above all, they are usually physically active. Try answering the questions in this chapter's Life Choice Inventory to see the effects of your lifestyle choices on the probable length of your own life.

> **Key Points** *Lifestyle choices affect the condition of body systems, health in later life, and even length of life. Lifestyle choices also affect the apparent ages of people in their adult years.*

①

_____ **S**ECTION I _____ **R**EVIEW _____

Answer the following questions on a sheet of paper.
Learning the Vocabulary
The vocabulary terms in this section are *life management skills, health, wellness, infectious diseases, lifestyle choices, lifestyle diseases, chronological age, physiological age,* and *centenarians*.
1. Match the following phrases with the appropriate terms:
   a. age as measured in years from date of birth
   b. people 100 years old or older
   c. age as estimated from the body's health and probable life expectancy
   d. maximum well-being

Learning the Facts
2. Each choice you make today will do one of two things to your health. What are the two possibilities?
3. In general, infectious diseases do more harm today than they did 100 years ago—True or False?

selves. **(10 min., Reteach, Reinforce)**

EVALUATE
> SECTION I

Activity 1.7
Pop Quiz. One option for use of this true–false pop quiz would be as bonus points toward the chapter test.
1. Heredity and environment play a major part in our potential to develop lifestyle illnesses. (T)
2. Chronological age is the same thing as physical age. (F)
3. Wellness is a person's maximum state of well-being. (T)
4. The major causes of death are the same today as they were 50 years ago. (F)
5. A person has no control over his or her life expectancy. (F) **(10 min.)**

CLOSE
> SECTION I

Activity 1.8
Contract for Change. Have the students make out a contract for change to improve or maintain a specific lifestyle pattern. Let the students know these contracts will be used for self-evaluation

(continued on next page)

LIFE CHOICE INVENTORY

How Long Will You Live? ①

No one can answer the "How long will you live?" question for sure, of course. But you can add to or shorten the probable length of your life by a good many years, depending on what choices you make. Your chances of dying younger or older are affected by how you live.

The Longevity Game illustrates this principle. To play the game, answer the ten questions that follow. For each question, add or subtract years as instructed. Start with age 74 (the average life expectancy for adults in the United States today) on the top line of the scoring section on the next page. If a question doesn't apply, go on to the next one. If you are not sure what to add or subtract, make a guess.

1. *Physical activity.* If your routine activities require regular, vigorous activity or you work out each day, add 3 years. If you don't get much exercise at home, work, school, or play, subtract 3 years.
2. *Relaxation.* If you have a relaxed approach to life (you roll with the punches), add 3 years. If you're aggressive, ambitious, or nervous (you have sleepless nights, you bite your nails), subtract 3 years. If you consider yourself unhappy, subtract another year.
3. *Driving.* Drivers under 30 who have had traffic tickets in the last year or who

have been involved in an accident, subtract 4 years. Other violations, minus 1. If you always wear seatbelts, add 1.
4. *Blood pressure.* High blood pressure is a major cause of the most common killers—heart attacks and strokes. However, most victims don't know they have it. If you know you have it, you are likely to do something about it. If you *know* your blood pressure, add 1 year.
5. *Family history.* If any grandparent has reached age 85, add 2; if all grandparents have reached age 80, add 6. If a parent died of a stroke or heart attack before age 50, minus 4. If a parent, brother, or sister has (or had) diabetes since childhood, minus 3.
6. *Smoking.* Smoking seriously damages health. Cigarette smokers who finish more than two packs a day, minus 8; one or two packs a day, minus 6; and one-half to one pack, minus 3.

(Continued on next page)

4. Give two examples of uncontrollable infectious diseases of the past and name one infectious disease threatening young people today.
5. People who neglect their own bodies are likely to suffer from lifestyle diseases. List three examples described in this section.

Making Life Choices:
6. Let's say that right now you are happy with your state of wellness, and want to be

healthy in the future, too. What daily choices can you make now that will enhance your future wellness? What choices should you *not* make?

MINI GLOSSARY

centenarians: people who have reached the age of 100 years or older.

66 Thoughts on Health 99

Idleness is the holiday of fools.
– Philip Chesterfield

Teacher Support Notes

① **Secrets to a Long Life:** Before you assign the inventory, ask students to talk about relatives or acquaintances who lived to be 100 or almost 100. What characteristics come to mind when they think of these people? Why do these people think they have lived longer than most?

✉ Where to Write

Harvard Health, Heart, and Mental Health Letters
164 Longwood Ave.
Boston, MA 02115
You may want to subscribe to these newsletters.

throughout the semester. If students are comfortable enough, they can volunteer to share some of the changes they are making. You should also make a contract and volunteer your choice. **(10–15 min.)**

FOCUS
SECTION II

In this section, the students will learn:
1. Three general areas of a person's life.
2. The qualities necessary to achieve optimum health in each of these areas.

Activity 2.1
   Qualities for Wellness. Do this activity before you assign Section II.

Divide the class into three subgroups in the following manner: If there are 30 students in the class, put the word *Physical Health* on ten 3 × 5 cards; the words *Social Health* on ten cards; and the words *Mental Health* (mental, emotional, spiritual) on ten cards. Shuffle the cards and have each student choose one. Students are then to find the other students with the same type of card and form the three groups. Direct them to brainstorm all the

Teacher Support Notes

① **Defining *Abstain*:** *Abstain* is the one term in this inventory that some students may not know. Of course they'll be encountering it often throughout the text. For now, you may want to tell them that it means to "not do something."

② **Young at Heart:** As you conclude Section I, here's just one example of many you could give students to show them how their personal choices will affect their health in their later years. Dr. Paul Spangler of Santa Barbara, California ran in and completed the New York City Marathon, a distance of 26.2 miles at the *chronological* age of 93. He works out six days a week—a 7-mile run and 1/2-mile swim Tuesday, Thursday, and Saturday and a 45-minute workout at a Nautilus Center the other three days. His goal? To complete the marathon when he's 100+ and to improve upon his last marathon time of almost nine hours!

> 66 **Thoughts on Health** 99
>
> *Your prayer must be for a sound mind in a sound body.*
> – *Juvenal*

How Long Will You Live? (continued)

7. *Drinking.* The best plan is to abstain from drinking alcohol. Adults who drink two drinks a day on average, subtract 1 year. Those who drink more lose 1 more year for each additional drink in a day. ① ⌐

8. *Gender.* Women live longer than men. Females add 3 years; males subtract 3 years.

9. *Eating.* If you avoid eating fatty foods and don't add salt to your meals, your heart will be healthier. You're entitled to add 2 years.

10. *Weight.* Now, weigh in. If your doctor says you are overweight by 50 pounds or more, minus 8; 30 to 40 pounds, minus 4; or 10 to 29 pounds, minus 2.

attention to those areas where you lose years. They could point to choices you might want to change.

Start with:	74 years
1. Physical activity	_____
2. Relaxation	_____
3. Driving	_____
4. Blood pressure	_____
5. Family history	_____
6. Smoking	_____
7. Drinking	_____
8. Gender	_____
9. Eating	_____
10. Weight	_____
Your probable length of life	_____ years

SCORING

Add up the column of numbers, beginning with 74, to obtain the total number of years you can expect to live. Don't take the score too seriously. However, do pay

Source: Adapted for young people from "The Longevity Game" by Northwestern Mutual Life Insurance Company, copyright 1992 with permission. For older people, points are also given for age (already having lived a while) and for being 65 and working (that is, for being active at retirement age).

②

SECTION II

Portrait of a Well Person

Wellness expresses itself in all parts of your life: not only physical, but also mental, emotional, spiritual, and social health. To show you what high goals you can aim for in your own life, these next sections describe a superbly well person. The descriptions are roughly in the order of the chapters to come.

Mental, Emotional, and Spiritual Health

A well person works on developing many mental, emotional, and spiritual strengths. Among other things, the person:

- Maintains a strong sense of self.
- Is willing to accept new ideas and try new behaviors.
- Handles setbacks without loss of self-esteem.
- Is aware of emotions, and manages and expresses them appropriately.
- Recognizes emotional problems in self or others, and seeks help when needed.

qualities necessary to maintain optimum wellness in the area indicated on their cards. Each group should have one marker and one sheet of newsprint and should record all answers on the newsprint. Tack up the three sheets. Be sure that each one is labeled. **(5–7 min.)**

A spokesperson for each group can review the list for the class. You then state that these lists will remain on display and will be compared with the lists in the book. This activity allows students to begin focusing on the specifics of wellness. **(15 min.)**

TEACH

SECTION II
(Guided and Independent Practice)

Activity 2.2
Equilateral Triangle. Draw an equilateral triangle on the board. Label each side with one of the components of wellness (physical, social, mental). Ask students if they agree that optimum health needs equal amounts of the three components—that there needs to be balance between the three. Then, ask how weaknesses on one side would influence the others. (Examples: How would low self-esteem influence a person's social side? How would constant colds and flu affect a person's mental health?) The point

(continued on next page)

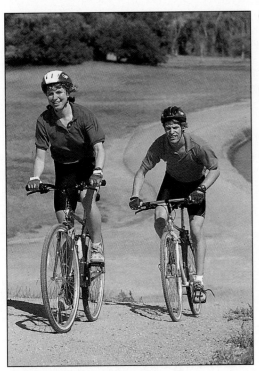

Well people enjoy outdoor play.

- Feels that life has meaning.
- Lives by cherished values.
- Manages stress with skill and enjoyment, not letting it become overwhelming.

You might wonder if *spiritual health* means belonging to any particular religious organization. It could, but it doesn't have to. It does mean having a feeling of purpose and a sense of values in life.

> **Key Points** *Mental, emotional, and spiritual health are a part of wellness.*

Physical Health and Preventive Care

A well person also values physical health and works to maintain it. Among other things, the person:

① • Sleeps enough to function well.
② • Enjoys food and uses it to meet nutritional needs.
- Maintains appropriate weight.
- Works to achieve and maintain physical fitness; enjoys outdoor play.
- Uses over-the-counter drugs with respect; uses prescription drugs with care.
- Does not abuse any drugs, including alcohol and tobacco.

Since life's events are at times outside an individual's control, a well person is also alert to the chances of accidents and diseases. Thus a well person:

- Is aware that accidents are a real possibility and takes preventive measures.
- Is aware that infectious diseases (especially sexually transmitted diseases, including AIDS) are a real possibility and takes measures to prevent them.
- Knows what his or her disease risks are and takes whatever measures can help prevent them.
- Views health information and products realistically and is on the lookout for misinformation and fraud.
- When necessary, can use the health care system wisely.

> **Key Points** *A well person attends to physical health and uses the health care system appropriately.*

Social Health

A well person realizes that other people and groups are an important part of life. Although the person doesn't forget to take care of his or her own wellness needs, the person also:

- Develops supportive friendships.
- Socializes well with others without the influence of alcohol or other drugs.
- Develops and maintains psychological intimacy with others.

Fast Facts

70% of all New Year's resolutions are health related.

Teacher Support Notes

① **Enough Sleep?:** Students might ask how much sleep is enough. There is no one, easy answer to this question. Children need more than eight hours a night. Some adults, about 8%, are short sleepers, averaging five hours a night, and some are long sleepers, sleeping up to ten or 11 hours a night. Most, however, fall into the six–eight hour range. People over the age of 50 do tend to sleep less—only six hours a night on the average.

② **Healthful Eating:** Ask students if they think these two items contradict each other. In other words, does maintaining an appropriate weight mean that you can't really enjoy food, and vice versa?

should be made that unless all three sides are in a healthy balance, a person cannot be considered well or healthy.**(10 min.; Reteach, Reinforce)**

EVALUATE
SECTION II

Teacher Support Notes

① **Social Health:** You might have the students make two columns on a sheet of paper entitled "Understood Completely" and "Need to Know More." Have them write each of the factors listed under "Social Health" in the appropriate column. Discuss their lists in class. Point out that they will be learning about each topic in chapters to come. Of course, if you are not teaching a sexuality unit as part of your health course, and, therefore, students are not using the expanded edition of this text, you will need to point out to students that they will not be covering the second and third bulleted items in this list.

Section II Review
Answers

1. physical, mental, emotional, spiritual, social
2. Answers will vary;
a. could include any of the ways listed under the heading "Mental, Emotional, and Spiritual Health" on pages 8 and 9. **b.** could include any of the ways listed under "Physical Health and Preventive Care" on page 9. **c.** could include any of the ways listed under "Social Health" on page 9 and on this page.
3. Answers will vary.

Activity 2.3
Pop Quiz.
1. What are the three general areas of a person's life? (physical, mental, social)
2. Which general area is most important? Why? (They are all equally important.)
3. Give two examples of a healthy behavior in each of these three general areas. (Answers will vary.)
(15 min.)

- Can form a successful long-term partnership.
- Understands and accepts his or her sexuality.
- Understands the principles of contraception; talks about them; and when appropriate, applies the principles.
- Continues growing, learning, and facing new challenges throughout life.
- Knows what is involved in facing death (one's own or someone else's) and expects grief in all of its stages.
- Relates to the larger environment (home, community, world) and takes a share of the responsibility for it.

Key Points *Social health is a part of wellness.* ①

Figure 1–5 sums up all that has been said so far. Outside factors affect health, but daily decisions do, too. The descriptions given here not only define wellness but imply actions to achieve it. The Health Strategies sections throughout this book are about taking action—they tell what to do. The first of them appears in the next section.

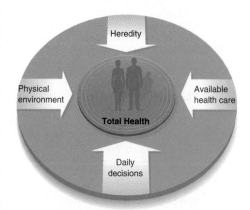

Figure 1–5 The Factors That Affect Health. The figure shows that heredity, environment, and available health care affect your health. Daily choices do, too.

CLOSE
SECTION II

Activity 2.4
Rate Yourself. Ask the students to rate themselves on a scale from 1 to 10 in each of the three general areas of their lives. Then, ask them to put next to each rating the ideal rating they'd like to have in one month. Finally, have them write

___ SECTION II ___ REVIEW

Answer the following questions on a sheet of paper.
Learning the Facts
1. Wellness expresses itself in five parts of your life. Name these five parts.
2. List at least three ways to describe:
   a. mental, emotional, and spiritual health.
   b. physical health.
   c. social health.

Making Life Choices
3. Social health has many parts. One part is the ability to socialize with others without being influenced to do unhealthy things. Recall how you have been tempted or influenced by others to do things that are not healthy. How would those things affect your wellness?

SECTION III

Making Behavior Changes

Health knowledge is of little value if people only use it to make "A"s on their health tests. It is valuable only when people use it to guide their behavior. If you are not making good health decisions, you may need to change your behavior. To do that, you need **motivation**.

Motivation to Change Health Behaviors

Motivation is the force that moves people to act. It may come naturally, or it may be learned. Whichever type it is, powerful motivation makes action almost a certainty.

The motivation that comes naturally is from instincts, or human **drives**—deep, physical urges such as hunger, thirst, fear, and tiredness. Drives are strong motivators that make you take the actions necessary to meet your needs for food, water, safety,

FOCUS
SECTION III

In this section, the students will learn:
1. The factors that influence the motiva-

tion to improve one's health.
2. The steps to goal setting.
3. The factors needed to make the goal achievement successful.

Activity 3.1

Motivation. Put four dollar signs ($) on the board. Number each one. Tell the students they are going to choose one of the "prizes." Then explain each one:
1. $ = If you work every weekend for a

full year with no exceptions, you will be guaranteed two free years of college (tuition, room, and board).
2. $ = If you work one full month every day after school and weekends, you will receive a $1,000 bonus in addition to your paycheck.
3. $ = If you pay $5 a week for four weeks, you will receive $100 at the end of that one month.

(continued on next page)

---

and sleep. Drives may also urge you to act in situations involving other people. The sex drive, the need to protect family members, and aggression are examples.

The other kind of motivation, learned motivation, may also be powerful. Consider how some people are driven by the desire for possessions, recognition, or achievement. Others desire to shed their possessions and lead a simple life. Still others are driven to work extremely hard for things they believe in. These types of motivation are learned.

You can understand motivation from the example of a black box with a reward inside. Suppose you were told, "If you put a dollar in the slot, you can take $1,000 out." Most people would not hesitate for a moment. They would drop their dollar in. Suppose you were told, however, "If you put a dollar in the slot today, you can take $1,000 out 20 years from now." Now you might think a minute. Today's dollar may mean more to you than many more dollars years away. Still, you might decide to drop your dollar in. Now suppose you were told "If you put a dollar in, you may take $1,000 out, but when you touch the box, you'll get an electric shock." Most people want to know, "How much will it hurt?" Now suppose you were told, "If you put a dollar in, there's a one in ten *chance* you can take $1,000 out."

People are motivated to act at times like these only if they think that the rewards or benefits are worth waiting for, outweigh the costs, and are pretty likely. That is, motivation is shaped by four factors:

- **The value of the reward.** (How big is the reward?)
- **Its timing.** (How soon will the reward come, or how soon will the price have to be paid?)
- **The costs.** (What will be the risks or consequences of seeking the reward?)

- **Its probability.** (How likely is the reward, and how certain the price?)

Now think about someone's health behavior—not your own, because it's easier to see someone else's behavior clearly. Pick a person who smokes a lot, or eats too much, or drinks a lot, or has some other negative health habit. Probably, the person knows that the bad habit harms health, yet the person goes ahead and does it anyway. Why?

If people find it hard to get motivated to seek health, the reason is often because of the timing and probability factors. They have to wait too long to receive the reward, or they aren't sure they'll ever receive it.

Here's an example:

- If you enjoy ice cream now (immediate reward), you won't notice your weight gain (consequences) until next month (pay later).
- If you go without ice cream now, you can't expect to see any weight loss until next week (no immediate reward).

Here is another example:

- If you smoke a cigarette now (immediate reward), you won't contract lung disease (consequences) until the far future (pay later).
- If you give up smoking now, you can't expect to start enjoying better health until next month (no immediate reward).

MINI GLOSSARY

motivation: the force that moves people to act. Motivation may be either instinctive (drives) or learned.

drives: motivations that are inborn, not learned, such as hunger, thirst, fear, and needs for sleep and sex. Also known as *instincts*.

Teacher Support Notes

① **Motivation:** Ask students to explain in their own words the kinds of motivation. Ask them to give a personal example of each type.

② **Rewards of Motivation:** A few types of learned motivation were given in the above text. These could be described as *possessions*, *recognition*, and *achievement*. Ask students to name rewards (sources of motivation). Can they name at least one reward that would be personally desirable for each of these three categories?

③ **Patience vs. Immediate Gratification:** After reading the two examples, students should begin to see that patience is an important quality for people wanting to change a behavior. Ask students to describe instances in their lives where they have chosen patience over immediate gratification.

4. $ = If you work ten hours a week for one year, you *might* win a four-year scholarship.

Ask for a show of hands as to which one they would choose. Record the votes for each one. Then ask for volunteers to explain the reasons for their choices.

Write abbreviated answers on the board. Then, after several responses, write these four words on the board: *value, timing, costs, probability*. Explain that students were probably motivated by one of these four factors. Substantiate this using answers listed on the board to correlate with these factors. Then discuss the problems in motivation when it comes to improving health practices. **(15 min.)**

Activity 3.2
Rewards. Put the number $50,000 on the board. Ask students what they'd do to get that $50,000. Give examples such as work, sacrifice, and gambling. Then put the phrase "Perfect Health Until Age 85" on the board. Ask them what they'd do to be assured of that outcome. You may also ask for their reactions to the Montaigne quote. (Tell them *arduous* means difficult, hard.) Stress the difficulty

Teacher Support Notes

① **Teen Views—Follow-Up Questions:** Following are some questions you can use to encourage discussion of the ideas expressed in the Teen Views feature:
a. Do students agree with Alisa Dichter that adults treat children "as if they were aliens?" Can they give examples?
b. Do students think that adults, especially parents, are role models for teens, or do teens tend to create their own sets of values and behaviors?
c. Do the sexual practices of adults concern students? Why?
d. How serious a problem is drinking among adults? What percentage of adults have drinking problems?
e. Can adult laziness promote laziness among teens? Are adults as a group lazy? Is this a health behavior?
f. How many students believe their parents must routinely deal with too much stress?
g. How many adults do students know who smoke? Is this still a serious problem in our society or have most adults quit?
② **Special Note:** Tammy's dad died of lung cancer just a few weeks after she wrote her response to this question.

TEEN ① VIEWS
What health behaviors of adults concern you most?

Laziness. The adults today seem to be very lazy. As a result, they usually become overweight and begin having health problems. These people are around children—so those children learn these health behaviors. **Alison Inman, 14, Westside High School, NE**

Actions of adults, especially parents, influence the actions of younger children who look up to them for guidance. If an adult does drugs or tends to curse around their children, the chances are more likely that their children will do drugs and curse. The same goes for adults who drink and smoke. Children need good role models to teach them the difference between right and wrong. **Brandon Buell, 17, Robert E. Lee High School, TX**

The indiscriminate sex practices of reckless individuals. The rise of sexually transmitted diseases has begun to gain people's attention. Most people have the attitude, "It'll never happen to

me." Even after the news of Magic Johnson contracting the HIV virus, people continue to have unprotected sex. It is more and more dangerous to have sex. Even if I don't contract the disease, I will have to pay with my tax dollars for the mistakes others have made. **Gabriel Lawson, 17, Orange Park High School, FL**

Drinking. The majority of adults know when to stop, but there are those who don't. At football games you can see many people who get drunk and get into fights. They may become an even greater risk to the public, because they may try to drive themselves home. The last thing I will want to worry about is an irresponsible, drunk driver. **Michael Bastedo, 15, Frontier Central High School, NY**

Adults treat many children as if they are aliens. Maybe, if they treated kids as if they were important and took what they have to say to heart, the relationship between kids and adults would be better. **Alisa Dichter, 14, Thousand Oaks High School, CA**

High stress. My father is an example of a stress victim. He wears himself out working to keep a family of six together with food in our mouths and clothes on our back. He rarely sleeps. When he does have extra time, he works on the maintenance of our house. If you were to ask him if all the working and stress are worth it, his answer would be positive. **Jason Chervenak, 16, Orange Park High School, FL**

What bothers me is when adults know the facts about how bad both smoking and drinking are for them and continue to use them anyway. If for nothing else, I wish they would quit for their families' sake. **Charity Rupp, 16, East High School, MN**

Smoking. My dad has lung cancer and he waited too long to get checked. If he had quit or controlled his smoking, he might not have cancer now. There's nothing I can do to save him and it really scares me. **Tammy Oldham, 17, Connellsville High School, PA**

②

in motivating ourselves in health matters because of the lack of immediate rewards. Many poor health choices give immediate rewards; consequences come later. **(10–15 min.)**

T EACH

S ECTION III

(Guided and Independent Practice)

Activity 3.3

Changing Behavior. Use this as an introductory discussion to "From Awareness to Action." Ask the students to quickly list five things that they'd like to change about themselves. (The changes must be possible.) Then ask them to put a "+" next to each one that they know how to change. Tell them to put another "+" next to those they *really, really* want to change. Then another "+" next to the ones they definitely will change, and finally a "+" next to those that they are already changing. **(10–15 min.)**

Activity 3.4

Steps to Changing Behavior. Place the capital letters A T E D A on the board, one underneath the other. Begin a discussion/information session on the steps listed in "From Awareness to Action." Ask for examples of each step. (Ex. A = "I could change my weight." T =

(continued on next page)

No wonder people sometimes fail to change their poor health habits! You have to know, and really believe, that you will benefit before you'll be willing to change your behavior. That's why health education is so important.

Since you are about to read a whole book on your personal choices and your health, you are probably going to learn facts that will make you want to improve your health behavior. If you want to change, will you do it? The next section describes how awareness leads to action.

> **Key Points** *Motivation is the force that moves people to act. It is affected by the weights people give to the rewards and the consequences that will follow the action.*

From Awareness to Action

How does a person go about changing a health behavior? The question is important, because even people who are motivated, and who know how to improve their health, still fail to do those things. The steps that lead to behavior change seem to be these:

- *Awareness*: "I could choose to change."
- *Thinking*: "I know how to change."
- *Emotion*: "I want to change (motivation)."
- *Decision*: "I will change."
- *Action*: "I am changing."

The elements of behavior change.

These steps don't always appear in the same order. However, they always seem to appear.

Do you think about your own behavior and possible changes? If so, you should realize that it is important to know when you are ready for change. A lot of thinking goes into changing behavior. No one can see this thinking but you. Others may push you to alter your behavior, but only you can actually do it. People outside you may think that nothing is happening if they don't see action. However, when you are thinking, something very important is happening. You are moving toward the decision point.

Much needless energy is wasted struggling with other people's saying "you should; you ought to; you must." Worse, you may waste energy with shame and guilt over "I can't; I failed again." You will make needed changes in your own time. People can push you, and this may help or it may not. In any case, only *you* can act.

① An important part of changing behavior permanently is the knowledge that success may require many practice runs. You should expect to stumble along the way. You don't have to succeed totally the first time. Be gentle with yourself.

> **Key Points** *People who change their behaviors go from awareness to action. Setbacks are normal and expected.*

Action: Setting Goals

② To succeed in big ways, it's best to start small. Undertake manageable changes, one at a time. Suppose a person decides to give up smoking and drinking, and take up exercising, and get a job, and write more letters, and go to religious services every day, and spend at least two added hours each day on homework, and. . . . That person is in for a rude surprise. All these changes are possible, but not all at once. After only a

Teacher Support Notes

① **Anticipating Failures:** Ask students why it helps to know that success may require several attempts. (The person who is unprepared for failure may give up completely, thinking that he or she is incapable of achieving the goal.)

② **Eating Elephants:** You might help students remember and understand this concept by asking them "How do you eat an elephant?" (one bite at a time)

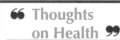
"I could do this by decreasing my sweets intake." etc.) **(20 min.; Extend, Enrich)**

Activity 3.5
Goal Setting. Your supplementary material contains a goal-setting worksheet. Make copies of this worksheet for each student. As homework, after you have discussed the steps in class, students are to fill out the worksheets based on their own personal goals. Be sure they know the homework will be discussed in class. Then, on the day the homework is due, have two large empty versions of the worksheet ready on newsprint. Tape these to the board. Ask the students to review the steps and check their homework to be sure it is complete. Then ask two volunteers to fill out their worksheets on the newsprint (or you write while they recite their steps to you). Once both are done, ask the class to evaluate the possibilities of both goals. Are they "doable?" Would you make any suggestions or additions to make them stronger? Now, have the students get into groups of four. Once in groups, the students take turns sharing their goals and steps. The others in the group make suggestions and give

---

Well begun is half done.
– *Horace*

Teacher Support Notes

① **Successful Change:** This is an important sentence to discuss with your students: *"A major part of ensuring successful change is setting reasonable goals."* A common mistake among young people trying to change a behavior is to attempt more than is possible.

② **Long-Term vs. Short-Term:** You might want to introduce students to the concept of short-term goals, versus long-term goals. The short-term goals are more specific, more easily obtained goals. They should have dates assigned to some. For example, if most of your students are freshmen and sophomores, they could have a long-term goal of choosing and applying for admission to a college or university. Short-term goals would include discussing their career interests with a counselor this semester, writing for information next semester, taking an aptitude test the following semester, and so on.

---

14 UNIT 1 Introduction

few days, such a person will be exhausted and will give it all up. We congratulate the person on having identified many worthy goals, but we suggest the person plan realistically to achieve them. New behaviors require energy. They need to be taken up a few at a time—in fact, probably one by one. A major part of ensuring successful change is setting reasonable goals. ①

Experts suggest that a way to begin goal setting is to write down some areas you would like to work on. Then pick a goal to work on first. Perhaps you'd like to choose the goal that you know you can accomplish most quickly. Perhaps you'd choose the one that would bring you the most benefits. Maybe you'd start with a goal that just "feels right." If you can't think of any goal to work on right now, that's OK, too. You'll know when you are ready. The Health Strategies feature to the right, "Steps to Goal Setting," will start you on your way. Figure 1–6 gives examples of how to make your goals specific. ②

HEALTH STRATEGIES

Steps to Goal Setting

1. Identify something you'd like to work on—your goal. Write it down in general terms.

2. State three or more specific behaviors that will help you achieve your goal. Write them down.

3. Identify steps you'll have to take to get ready.

4. Commit to a specific time to get your plan underway.

5. Set up a chart on which you can measure your progress in units.

6. Plan rewards for yourself that fit the goal you've chosen.

FIGURE 1-6

How to Set Specific Goals

Don't Say:	Do Say:
"I will get better at dancing."	"I will attend all my dance classes and practice as instructed."
"I will lose weight this week."	"I will write down everything I eat every day."
"I will prepare better for exercising."	"Each Saturday morning, I will wash, dry, and fold my exercise clothes for the week."
"I will do well on the test (in the game) Thursday."	"I will study (practice) for the test (game) in the library (gym) every evening from seven to eight o'clock."
"I will exercise with friends so that I'll enjoy it more."	"Each Sunday evening I'll call and make dates for at least three workouts the next week."
"I will make progress at my chosen activity."	"I will keep a daily log of my improvement."

affirmations. They all sign each other's goals, indicating support for one another. These can then be collected for grading. You may want to put them up on a bulletin board for one week after you've graded them. At the end of the week, ask how people are doing—possibly tune in to a few specifics. **(25 min.; Cooperative Learning, Extend, Enrich)**

Activity 3.6
Imagining a Life. As a possible concluding activity for the chapter, you may want to have students think of an adult who is either very healthy or very unhealthy. If they can't think of an adult for either category, tell them to create an imaginary character for the activity. If they are using a real person, they should give that person a fictional name so that no one will know who the person really is.

They are then to write a one- or two-page story describing the person's lifestyle. In the story they should be sure to describe the person's sleeping habits, eating habits for each meal, physical activity during a typical day, and any habits that the person might have that could affect the person's health either positively or negatively.

In the final paragraph or two, students should predict their character's ending

(continued on next page)

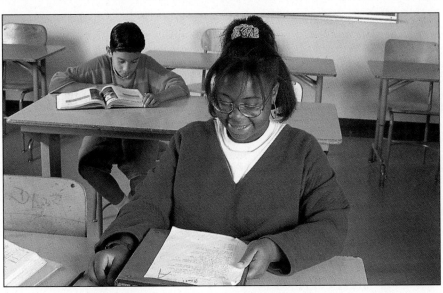

Once you have started meeting your goals, congratulate yourself.

Following is an example of how to apply ① the Health Strategies steps.

1. My goal: I'd like to get in shape.
2. Three behaviors that will help me achieve my goal:
   a. I'll save $3 a week so that I can buy some hand weights.
   b. I'll read a good book on fitness.
   c. I'll join a walking club.
3. Preparation:
   a. I'll keep the money in my top drawer.
   b. I'll borrow the book from the library.
   c. I'll clean up my walking shoes.
4. My time commitment: I'll start on Tuesday, and I'll continue saving and walking for a month.
5. How I'll measure my progress:
   a. I'll record how far I walk each day.
   b. I'll graph my distances over a month.
6. My first reward: When I've collected $12 and walked for a month, I'll buy my hand weights.

Meaningful, specific plans like these can carry you through the rough spots in a behavior change program. Therefore, it's worth putting some effort into thinking them through. A vague desire to improve is not enough. You must translate that desire into specific actions that you can achieve. It's OK to state a goal in general terms. However, be sure to translate it into specific, doable action behaviors.

Key Points *In taking action to change behavior, it helps to set goals. Try one at a time. Make it realistic, give yourself a time limit, measure your progress, and reward yourself.*

Commitment

To change a behavior, a person has to make a **commitment**—a decision not just

MINI GLOSSARY

commitment: a decision adhered to for the long term; a promise kept.

years. They should tell how long their character will live and whether or not the character will be happy and healthy during those last years, or if the character would be ill and unhealthy during those years. Have the students read their papers in class, then discuss the common

elements of both the healthy and the unhealthy choices. **(Extend, Enrich, Interdisciplinary)**

EVALUATE
SECTION III

Activity 3.7
Goals Chart. Put the students back into the same groups as in Activity 3.5. Give each group *one* totally blank goals

worksheet, with lines where the steps should be. When you say "Go," the groups are to quickly fill in the steps. The first "team" with the worksheet filled in correctly gets extra credit. **(10–12 min.; Reteach, Reinforce, Cooperative Learning)**

Activity 3.8
Essay. Give the students the following essay assignment: Using the following

---

❝ Thoughts on Health ❞

People do not lack strength, they lack will.
– *Victor Hugo*

Teacher Support Notes

① **Understanding *Will*:** Tell students that a person's will is the person's determination to do something; it determines whether or not a person will begin and carry through with an action. Some common expressions students may know are "*will* power," "where there's a *will* there's a way," "it's the *will* of the people," and "iron *will*."

② **Answers to Critical Thinking:**
1. Diets are short term. To improve health one needs to adopt a long-term eating behavior.
2. Commitment
3. They are easier than working toward improved wellness.

✍ Fast Facts

The average American teenager spends about 38 hours a week in class or studying; the average Japanese teenager spends 59 hours.

---

for today, but for the long term. Commitment is a step in which the **will** is involved. ①

Sometimes, even after what seems to be a firm commitment to changed behavior, a person slips back. Why? Once you have made a change, you will maintain it only if you continue to feel rewarded by the change.

At the time of committing to a change, a "rule of three" seems to help people get through the early stages. This means trying a new behavior at least three times, or for at least three days, without rejecting it. This goes for every little piece of behavior change.

Take the decision to eat better, for example. One small change might be to drink milk every day, but suppose you don't much like milk. You could apply the rule of three as follows. Try milk once and you may not like it. Try it a second time and you may say to yourself, "This isn't as good as cola, but I can drink it." Try it a third time and you may say, "This is OK—I like it." At that point, the new choice has become easier. It may even become the preferred choice. The Consumer Awareness section on this page shows how valuable such habit changes can be.

CONSUMER **A**WARENESS   **The Miracle of Hard Work**

In reading about the way a person might try switching from cola to milk, notice the committed attitude you can take. You aren't just impulsively trying a new behavior, only to abandon it later. You are making the effort to install and maintain a behavior change for life.

Notice, too, that you are willing to put in the necessary effort and practice for a permanent change. Now compare yourself with your friend Amy, who wants to go on a crash diet to get thin, but *not* to change any of her habits permanently. Amy has bought some diet pills to cut her appetite long enough to lose 10 pounds. She has no plans to change any of her eating habits, so she's going to regain the 10 pounds, plus some. You should have no trouble predicting which person will gain health and fitness: you will. Amy will be a yo-yo dieter.

Promises of instant health gains without effort are more inviting to consumers than plans suggesting that people have to work to get what they want. That's why diet pills and other quick fixes are advertised so often on TV. But diet pills are precisely that—quick fixes, not permanent solutions. Permanent behavior changes, like switching from cola to milk, take work, not miracles.

② **C**RITICAL **T**HINKING

1. *At any one time, millions of people are "on a diet." Why is it that "dieting" will not truly improve a person's health?*
2. *What is required to make a permanent change in behavior?*
3. *Why are people so attracted to promises of quick fixes?*

---

terms, develop a 200-word (minimum) essay on "Achieving Short- and Long-Term Goals." Terms: *Support System*; *Self-Esteem*; *Commitment*; *Will Power*; *Rewards*; *"Rule of Thumb;"* *Time*; *Steps to Success.* **(Homework or 30 min.; Reteach, Reinforce, Interdisciplinary)**

CLOSE
SECTION III

Activity 3.9
Self-Evaluation. Hand out envelopes to each student. Then hand back their goals homework assignment (Activity 3.5, and possibly all other writings they did for this chapter). On the back of the assignment, the students are to write a short note to themselves explaining how far they expect to be on this goal three months from now. They are then to put these in their envelope

and address the envelope to themselves. Explain to the students that these will be mailed to them in three months for their own self-evaluation. **(20 min.)**

RETEACH/BONUS

Here are some additional activities for the various sections of this chapter. You

(continued on next page)

A factor that can help you maintain changed behavior is the approval of supportive family members or friends. Ask them to pat you on the back, or to join you.

A final factor that people changing their behavior have to realize is that the way they think of themselves must change as well. Sometimes a behavior slips back because a person's view of self is slow to change. People have to do some psychological work along with their physical work in order to change through and through. A person who gives up smoking has to imagine, and really see, herself as a confirmed ex-smoker. A person who takes up swimming every day has to adopt a new identity: "I am a swimmer." In short, the person needs:

• A changed self-image.

One additional factor helps immensely if behavior change is to succeed. This factor may be more important than any others named in this chapter:

• High self-esteem.

People who prize themselves enough to invest energy and effort in their own wellness are most likely to maintain healthy behavior changes. The person who begins to succeed in changing behavior gains improved self-esteem from the effort and so wins an advantage for the efforts ahead.

Key Points *Commitment to a behavior depends on continued rewards from it. To maintain a positive new behavior, a person must receive support from other people, develop a new self-image, and cultivate high self-esteem.*

SECTION III REVIEW

Answer the following questions on a sheet of paper.
Learning the Vocabulary
The vocabulary terms in this section are: *motivation, drives, commitment,* and *will.*

Fill in the blank with the correct answer. ①
1. _____ are strong motivators that make you take the actions necessary to meet your needs.
2. A firm decision to do something, not just for today, but for a long time, is a _____.

Learning the Facts
3. What are the two basic types of motivation?
4. Motivation is shaped by four factors. What are they?
5. List the five steps that lead to behavior change.
6. In changing your health behavior, it's best to make several big changes at once rather than one at a time—True or False?
7. Explain the "rule of three." Tell why it is useful.

Making Life Choices
8. List a behavior that you would like to change in your life. How would you go about changing this behavior—what steps would you follow and why?

Answers to Fact or Fiction

Here are the answers to the questions at the start of the chapter.

1. True. **2.** False. Today, most of the leading causes of death are primarily related to lifestyle. **3.** True **4.** True. **5.** False. To give up a harmful health habit, you also need commitment. It also helps to have support from others, as well as high self-esteem.

MINI GLOSSARY

will: a person's intent, which leads to action.

Teacher Support Notes

① **Family Support:** Ask students which family members would be most supportive if they tried a major behavioral change. Would they be embarrassed to ask for support?

Section III Review
Answers
1. Drives
2. commitment
3. natural (drives, instincts) and learned
4. value of the reward, its timing, the costs, its probability
5. awareness, thinking, emotion, decision, action
6. false
7. It is trying a new behavior at least three times, or for at least three days, without rejecting it. It's useful because it causes a person to make real effort to install a behavior change and causes a person to realize that behavior changes take work, not miracles.
8. Answers will vary.

may want to use these activities to reteach certain concepts, or you may choose them as alternatives to earlier activities.

Checklist of Healthy Behavior.
Use the eight points listed under "Mental, Emotional, and Spiritual Health" on pages

8 and 9 as a checklist for the students. Hand out a copy of the checklist to each student. Ask them to put a "+" (plus sign) next to each item they do well and a "–" (negative sign) next to each item they need to work on. Let them know those items with the minuses are the ones they need to work on throughout the course. Give examples of how each one can be achieved. **(10 min.)**

Physical and Social Health Checklists. Use the same format described in the preceding activity for the "Physical Health and Preventive Care" and "Social Health" checklists on pages 9 and 10. At the end of the three checklists, explain that these three "evaluations" represent the strengths and weaknesses we have. They can help us develop our goals to strive toward optimum health or wellness. **(5–7 min.)**

❝ Thoughts on Health ❞

There's nothing wrong with teenagers that reasoning with them won't aggravate.
– Anonymous

Teacher Support Notes

① **Teenagers and Adults:** Both of the quotes on this page offer thoughts on the relationships between teenagers and adults. Write the quotes on the board and ask students to pick one and explain how the quote relates to the passage in the text. Do their own thoughts most closely match the hypothetical student speaking in the text, "Anonymous," or Mark Twain?

❝ Thoughts on Health ❞

When I was a boy of fourteen, my father was so ignorant I could hardly stand to have the old man around. But when I got to be twenty-one, I was astonished at how much the old man had learned in seven years.
– Mark Twain

S**TRAIGHT**

T**ALK**

Suit Yourself

With all that people have to deal with during their teen years, does it make sense to make health a subject of study? Educators seem to think so. But how do teens themselves feel about it? These Straight Talk sections, which appear at the ends of all the chapters in this book, explore questions teens might honestly ask about subjects of interest to them. In this Straight Talk, the person asking the questions is a health educator. The person answering them is a teenager.

A lot of states require that all students must take a health course during high school. Do you agree that this is a good idea?

Of course it is. But I have to say that I don't expect to find it interesting. I take care of myself pretty well anyway, most ways, and the ways I don't take care of myself are my choices. I'll change my behavior when I choose to, and not when some parent or teacher tells me I should.

Fair enough. Your health is absolutely your own, no one else's. No one can force you to change your health behavior.

I wish they wouldn't even try. I have enough to deal with, without some adult telling me to brush my teeth, or eat right, or not take drugs. What bothers me the most is that I already do the right things, pretty much, and I'm in good shape. Why is it that with all the things my friends

and I do right, some people need to pick out the one thing we do wrong and focus on that?

When someone tells you how to take care of yourself, does it ever make you feel like doing exactly the opposite?

It sure does. I hate phrases like "It's for your own good, dear." If it were for my own good, I'd do it, believe me. But I'm doing something that's more important to me right now. And I hate it when my father says, "You don't want to do that." What makes him think he knows what I want to do? Or when someone says, "That's bad for you." If it were bad for me, would I do it? With all the pressures I'm under, don't they see I don't need them telling me what to do?

Besides, they weren't perfect at my age, either. My uncle smoked until he was 40. Then he quit—and he didn't get cancer. Now he

tells me not to start smoking. And my parents tell me not to marry until I'm over 21. Well, they were married at 18 and had me when they were 19. Why do I have to be perfect, when they weren't?

Surely you know one reason. They might choose to do differently, if they had it to do over again. They might be trying to spare you some grief they couldn't avoid for themselves.

OK, I know that's true. I know they care about me. ① But I still don't like them telling me what to do when they are not models of sterling behavior, themselves. Why don't they control their own actions, and let me control mine?

OK, but suppose they just want you to know the facts about health? If they didn't make any

(Continued on next page)

Listing Strengths. On a bulletin board, list separately the three parts of a person's life—physical, mental, and social. Give each student three 3 × 5 cards and a thin marker. Without putting their names on the cards, have them choose one item they do well from each checklist completed in the preceding activities and write examples on each card. (For example: Item says, "Is willing to accept new ideas and try new behav- iors." Student's example: "I love trying new things that are fun, such as wind surfing or new restaurants.") Tack the cards on the bulletin board around the appropriate part of a person's wellness and then read the cards aloud. **(15 min.)**

judgments, but just laid out the facts for you to look at, would this be acceptable to you?

That sounds OK, but I think I pretty much know the facts. I know smoking and drugs are bad for you, and exercise is good for you. I know to brush my teeth every day.

Do you know how to get what you want without getting into an argument?

No, actually, I don't. But what does that have to do with health?

Health is defined broadly in this book. It includes emotional health and social health—the ways you get along with important people in your life, and with groups. Health is defined as "life management skills," which means how you manage your life in every area.

Some of those skills are important to me, I admit. You know what I'd like? I'd like a book or a course that answers my questions, not the questions of some adult who has forgotten what it's like to be a teenager. I'd like to talk about the things that really matter. Like how to deal with peer pressure. How to feel good about yourself without seeming conceited. How to get it across to your parents that you can be trusted. How to balance sports and schoolwork and dating and

Only you can choose health for yourself.

home responsibilities. How to not go crazy when people criticize you, how to please everybody else and still do some of what you want to do for yourself. How to figure out who you are and who you want to become.

Those are the important questions, and there are more. I'd like to get those questions answered.

That's what this book is intended to do. Of course, it won't succeed totally (nobody's perfect). If you'll help, though, it may succeed in part. Ask the questions that are important to you. Get your classmates and teachers talking about them. The more you express your own interests and concerns, the better the chance that you'll get them met.

I don't want to be told how to behave, though. With that understanding, I'll participate in discussions.

OK, let's keep it that way. The facts are here, and you can apply the ones that seem important to you. Your body is your own. So are your mind and your relationships. So *you* choose. Pick the rewards you want. Go after them. And best wishes.

✉ **Where to Write**

University of California Berkeley Wellness Letter
P.O. Box 420148
Palm Coast, FL 32142

❝ **Thoughts on Health** ❞

Without health life is not life; it is unlivable.
– Francois Rabelais

❝ **Thoughts on Health** ❞

The most decisive actions of our life—I mean those that are most likely to decide the whole course of our future—are, more often than not, unconsidered.
– Andre Gide

Answers

Vocabulary

1. a. Chronological age is measured in years from date of birth, while physiological age is estimated from the body's health and probable life expectancy.
2. Drives come naturally and are inborn. The need for food is an example of a drive. Learned motivation is driven by the desire for possessions, recognition, or achievement. Working hard for things you believe in is an example of learned motivation.
3. a. will **b.** lifestyle choices **c.** infectious diseases **d.** lifestyle diseases
4. a. motivation **b.** health **c.** wellness
5. a. life management skills **b.** centenarians **c.** commitment

Recall

Section I
1. enjoying life; increasing knowledge, strength and skills in self-awareness; emotional health; stress management; nutrition; fitness; friendships and love relationships; disease prevention; health consumerism
2. 1890—tuberculosis, digestive diseases, pneu-monia, bronchitis, scarlet fever
1990—accidents, suicide, bronchitis, cancer, pneumonia
See Figure 1-1 on page 3 for additional answers.
3. heredity, environment
4. Answers will vary; could include: where to live, what laws to vote for, and what causes to support.
5. sleeping regularly and ade-quately; eating regular meals, including breakfast; engaging in regular physical activity; not smoking; not using alcohol, or using it in moderation; keeping weight under control
6. The more good lifestyle choices (good sleep, eating, exercise, weight, etc.) you make, the younger you will be physiologically, while bad choices (smoking, excessive alcohol) will age you physiologically.

Section II
7. Answers will vary; could include: maintains a strong sense of self; willing to accept new ideas and try new behaviors; handles setbacks without loss of self-esteem; aware of emotions, and manages and

---

CHAPTER REVIEW

Learning the Vocabulary

life management skills	lifestyle diseases	motivation
health	chronological age	drives
wellness	physiological age	commitment
infectious diseases	centenarians	will
lifestyle choices		

Answer the following questions on a separate sheet of paper.

1. Explain the difference between chronological age and physiological age.
2. Explain the difference between learned motivation and drives, and give an example of each one.
3. *Matching*—Match each of the following phrases with the appropriate vocabulary term from the list above:
   a. a person's intent, which leads to action
   b. decisions made daily that have to do with how a person treats his or her body and mind
   c. diseases that can be passed from person to person
   d. diseases made likely by neglect of the body, not passed from person to person

4. *Word Scramble*—Use the clues from the phrases below to help you unscramble the terms:
   a. **ooaiittmnv** _____ the force that moves people to act
   b. **ealhht** _____ a range of states with physical, mental, emotional, spiritual, and social components
   c. **eenllssw** _____ maximum well-being
5. a. The skills that help a person realize his or her potential to be well and enjoy life are called _____.
   b. People who are 100 years old or older are called _____.
   c. A _____ is a decision adhered to for the long term; a promise kept.

Recalling Important Facts and Ideas

1. This book, which you are just beginning to study, is about what, according to the first page of the chapter?
2. What were five of the leading causes of death in 1890? in 1990?
3. Name the two causes, besides people's own choices, that bring on lifestyle diseases.
4. Knowing what effects your environment can have on your health, what decisions can you make about your environment to maintain or improve your health?
5. List the six lifestyle practices that greatly affect the difference between chronological and physiological age.
6. State how the lifestyle factors can affect a person's physiological age.
7. Name five of the eight characteristics of mental, emotional, and spiritual health.
8. Briefly describe five ways a person can be alert to the chances of accidents and diseases.
9. List five ways a person can be socially healthy.
10. Give two examples of learned behavior.
11. What are the six steps in goal setting?
12. How does high self-esteem enhance behavior changes?
13. What must a person continue to feel in order to maintain a change in his or her behavior?
14. What are two factors, in addition to the rule of three, that can help a person maintain a changed behavior?

expresses them appropriately; recognizes emotional problems in self or others, and seeks help with them when needed; feels that life has meaning; lives by cherished values; manages stress with skill and enjoyment.

8. aware that accidents are a real possibility and takes preventive measures; aware that infectious diseases (especially sexually transmitted diseases, including AIDS) are a real possibility and takes measures to prevent them; knows what his or her disease risks are and takes whatever measures can help prevent them; views health information and products realistically and is on the lookout for misinformation and fraud; uses the health care system wisely, when necessary

9. Answers will vary; could include: develops supportive friendships; socializes well without the influence of drugs/alcohol; develops and maintains psychological intimacy with others; forms successful long-term partnerships; understands and accepts his or her sexuality; understands the principles of contraception, is able to talk about them and applies the principles; continues growing, learning, and facing new challenges; knows what is involved in facing death (one's own or another's) and expects grief in all stages; relates to the larger environment (home, community, world) and shares responsibility for it.

Section III

10. desire for possessions, recognition, or achievement

11. identify what you want to achieve, state three or more specific behaviors that will help attain the goal, identify steps you will have to take to get prepared, commit to a specific time to start your plan, set a chart on which you can measure progress, plan rewards that fit the goal chosen

12. When a person feels worthwhile, he or she will invest energy in themselves to maintain wellness and a healthy behavior.

13. improved self-image

14. Answers will vary; could include: support from others, a new self-image, high self-esteem.

CRITICAL THINKING

1. After completing the Life Choice Inventory, are you satisfied with your results? What can you do to change the negative areas into positive ones? If all your areas are positive, what will you do to keep them positive?

2. Explain what the health and wellness line (continuum) is. Where do you think you are on that line right now? List five things you could do to move toward the positive end, and five things you could avoid doing to stay away from the negative end, of health.

3. Many Americans are concerned with the treatment of diseases, but they neglect disease prevention. Discuss some of the barriers people might face in disease prevention. How can we promote prevention instead of waiting until treatment is needed? How would or could you do this in your school?

ACTIVITIES

1. Keep a daily activity log of what you do. After a week write down changes you can make to improve your wellness. What do you need to do more? What should you do less?

2. Imagine a Mr. and Mrs. Wellness. What characteristics do you think Mr. and Mrs. Wellness have? Brainstorm with your classmates to develop a complete picture of the perfect Mr. and Mrs. Wellness.

3. You are asked to speak at a local elementary school about the importance of wellness. List some of the main points you would stress to the students. How would you help the students understand the importance of maintaining wellness throughout their lives? Since these students are younger than you, you may need to devise interesting and unique approaches to get their attention and get your points across.

4. Explain why it is important to balance your physical, mental, emotional, spiritual, and social health. Can you achieve wellness in only one area? Explain your answers.

5. Examine the impact that heredity might have on your wellness. Make a list of as many relatives as you can. Next to each name list any important facts you can discover about that person's wellness. After completing your list, write a paragraph about any family tendencies toward ill health that you need to be aware of. What are you going to do to offset those conditions?

6. Study your local environment. Is pollution a problem? Do you have adequate health care professionals and facilities in your area? Summarize the negative environmental factors in your area and state what you can do to offset these factors.

7. Find advertisements in magazines or newspapers for devices that claim to increase your physical health. Write an editorial for the class newspaper discussing the claims these articles make and contradictions involved with each.

8. Make a video to promote health and wellness for the class. Include at least one aspect of each part of health: physical, social, spiritual, and mental.

9. List a goal you have for the future. Below your goal list specific steps that will help you reach your goal.

MAKING DECISIONS ABOUT HEALTH

1. Imagine that a friend of yours has told you that she has developed some friendships that she is now afraid will lead to trouble. The new friends are engaging in some risky behaviors. Your friend says that she sees trouble ahead, but at the same time, she is enjoying the thrill of these new and somewhat dangerous activities. She wants advice on how to change her behavior before it's too late. Remembering what you have learned in this chapter, what can you tell your friend?

CHAPTER 2 PLANNER

OVERVIEW

Chapter 2 is 26 pages long and is divided into the seven sections listed to the right. Major learning outcomes are also listed to the right. This chapter introduces the concept of self-understanding and how it relates to emotional and mental health.

A person's self-concept is reflected in the person's relationships and the way the person fits into his or her environment. Healthy persons accept who they are and strive to adjust or change those factors that inhibit their successful progress in society. How one feels about oneself and others, and how one interacts with people, influence health in many ways.

This chapter helps students discover who they are, while examining the behaviors that will help them fit into society more successfully. This chapter will also help them learn a six-step decision-making strategy.

MAKING LIFE CHOICES SUPPLEMENTARY RESOURCES

A variety of activities, handouts, quizzes, and tests to accompany this chapter are available in the *Making Life Choices* supplementary material. You may pick and choose from those materials as appropriate for your amount of class time and the ability levels of your students. Some of the resources you might want to consider using are:

Overheads
• Negative Self-Talk
• Positive Self-Talk

Handout
• Describing Yourself

SUGGESTED RESOURCES

Student Readings
1. Plutchik, R. *Emotion.* New York: Harper and Row, 1980.

Teacher Readings
1. Matarazzo, Joseph D., et al. *Behavioral Health: A Handbook of Health Enhancement and Disease Prevention.* New York: John Wiley

and Sons, 1984.

Videos
1. *Self-Esteem.* Cambridge Educational. 800-468-4227.

Software
Help-Esteem. The user's self-image is assessed. National Wellness Institute. 715-346-2172.

CHAPTER 2
Emotional Health

Answers to "Fact or Fiction"

See page 42 for answers to the Fact or Fiction questions.

Activity To Introduce Chapter

"About Me" Poem. Write the following poem format on the board. Have the students write a poem about themselves using this format as a guide.

line 1—(first name only)
line 2—(four traits that characterize you)
line 3—(sister, brother), of (sister's or brother's first name only)
line 4—who loves (three things)
line 5—who fears (three things)
line 6—who feels (three things)
line 7—who would like to see (three things),
line 8—resident of (town, state, country, etc.)
line 9—(last name only)

Collect the poems, save them, and read them aloud at the end of the chapter or unit.

OUTCOMES

After reading and studying this chapter, you will be able to:

✓ Discuss the importance of self-acceptance, positive thinking, and values clarification to emotional health.
✓ Recognize the acceptance and appropriate expression of feelings as important to emotional health.
✓ Discuss the advantages of assertive behavior and identify assertive behavior strategies.
✓ Describe the role that fear of rejection plays in forming new relationships and discuss ways to overcome this fear.
✓ Outline the steps for making a decision.
✓ Discuss the need for developing a workable relationship with society.

CONTENTS

I. Self-Knowledge
II. Thoughts
III. Values
IV. Emotions
V. Relating to Others
VI. Making Decisions and Solving Problems
VII. Finding a Place in Society

      Straight Talk: Sleep and Dreams

FACT OR FICTION

What do you think? *Are the following statements true or false? If you think they are false, then say what is true.*

1. Emotional health is not related to physical health.
2. The most important relationship in your life is the relationship with your closest friend.
3. Once a person adopts values, they remain firmly fixed for a lifetime.
4. It is best to reject illogical or unpleasant feelings.
5. The most emotionally healthy people do not need the help of others—they stand alone on their own two feet.
6. The primary problem people have in making new relationships is the fear of being rejected.
7. The best way to solve a problem is to think up a solution and to concentrate on making it work.

(Answers on page 42)

■ **Reminder:** Knowing how to study can increase your knowledge, improve your grades, *and* cut down on your study time. See the *Studying Health* section at the front of your text for some suggestions to help you study this chapter.

CHAPTER PROJECT

Here are three ideas that you could use while studying Chapter 2 to help tie the different sections together:
1. Have students make a personal collage or scrapbook of photos, drawings, or pictures to go along with each of the sections.
2. Read the book or watch the movie, "Jonathan Livingston Seagull," by Richard Bach. Then have students write an essay about how the story relates to their lives.
3. Assign students to interview mental health workers in the school and/or community to learn more about local resources for: **a.** helping people learn more about themselves; **b.** where to get help for addiction, depression, eating disorders, etc.; **c.** costs for various mental health services; **d.** support groups; **e.** treatment facilities; **f.** other topics as appropriate to the size of the community and availability of information. Have students share this information on posters and/or in oral presentations at the end of the chapter.

NOT ENOUGH TIME?*

You could easily spend seven or eight days teaching this chapter if students read the entire chapter, do a fair number of the suggested activities in the teacher's edition, and review a sampling of the handouts from the resource material accompanying this text. It is likely, however, that you will have only three or four days to devote to this chapter. Following are some suggestions to help you make sure that you cover the key topics if you have limited time.

TIME	SUGGESTIONS
1 Day	Begin with the Activity to Introduce the Chapter ("About Me" Poem). During class have students do Activity 2.1, followed by Activity 4.1. Then do Activity 3.1. If you have extra time at this point you may wish to include Activities 5.3 and 5.8. Conclude with a review of the steps in decision making and use Activity 6.3. Assign students to read Chapter 2 for the next day if you have more time for this chapter. Even if you don't have more time, you may want to assign the chapter for extra credit because of the personal benefit of reading the material.
2 Days	On day 2, begin with Activity 5.1 (set up ahead of time with a student) or 5.3. Review SOFTEN technique (p. 38) and have students do Activity 5.6. Review decision-making steps (p. 39) and have students do Activity 6.2.
3 Days	On day 3, begin with Activity 2.2 and Activity 3.2. Conclude with Activity 4.2 or do Chapter Review on pages 46–47.
4 Days	On day 4, conclude with the Life Choice Inventory, "Do You Cultivate Emotional Well-Being?" (p. 26). Discuss. Follow with the Project Reports if previously assigned or do Chapter Review (p. 46–47) and/or chapter test.

*Please refer to the 18-week daily lesson plans in the supplementary material for additional suggestions.

In this section students will learn that:
1. Self-knowledge is important for good mental health.
2. The way others see us can influence the way we see ourselves.
3. The way we see ourselves is projected in the way we present ourselves to others.

Activity 1.1
Whitney Houston Song. Play the music, or read the words from Whitney Houston's song, "The Greatest Love." Ask students, "Is self-love important to have good self-esteem? Must we love ourselves before we can love others? Must we accept ourselves for who we are, or change so we can love ourselves?" Agree—disagree? Discuss. **(10 min.)**

Activity 1.2
Circulate Positive Papers.
Arrange the desks in one large circle around the room. Have each student put his or her name at the top of a blank piece of plain paper (best if paper has no lines). Pass the papers one person to the

Teacher Support Notes

① **Receiving Support:** Make sure students know what it means to receive support from a relationship. Ask for examples.

② **Relationship with Yourself:** Students need to remember this sentence: *"The most important relationship in your life is the relationship you have with yourself."* Most students probably have not thought of their self-concept as a relationship. To reinforce this idea, you might have them discuss or write about times when they are home alone, but to write about these times as though they were with someone—themselves. What do they "talk" about? What do they like to do? Do they enjoy their own company?

③ **Handout—Describe Yourself:** At this point, you might have students complete the handout "Describing Yourself."

④ **Self-Confidence vs. Conceit:** Ask students if they believe that conceited people are really insecure. Have them think about, but not name, people they think of as conceited. What actions indicate that the person is really insecure?

If you possess **emotional health**, you seek, value, and maintain good relationships with yourself, with others, and with society. These relationships are a key part of total wellness. Emotionally healthy people like themselves. Therefore, they take care of themselves physically—they eat well, exercise, and get enough rest. Emotionally healthy people successfully develop personal relationships. They receive support from these relationships, which helps them feel secure. Emotionally healthy people have also found ways to fit in, or get along, with the larger society to which they belong. Thus emotional health benefits overall wellness and all areas of life.

In contrast, many people who are emotionally unhealthy are self-destructive. Emotionally unhealthy people often abuse alcohol, nicotine, or other drugs. They often overeat or undereat, overwork or work too little. They may take dangerous risks such as driving while intoxicated or participating in other illegal activities. These self-destructive behaviors can lead to drug addictions, cancer, obesity, heart disease, accidents and injuries, and other ills.

How can you know if you are emotionally healthy? How can you become *more* emotionally healthy? This chapter attempts to help you answer these questions. To see what the parts of emotional health are, take the Life Choice Inventory on page 26.

SECTION I

Self-Knowledge

The most important relationship in your life is the relationship you have with yourself. Your relationship with yourself must support you throughout your lifetime. Besides, it supports your relationships with others and with society.

To develop a good relationship with yourself, you first need to think about yourself. Get to know yourself as you are right now. The point is to develop a relationship with yourself that pleases you. Then when asked, you can honestly reply, "This is the way I am, and I feel OK about it."

This doesn't mean you should stop changing. You may want to improve yourself in a lot of ways; most people do. But you can still say, "This is the way I am—I am a person with faults and virtues, I am learning and growing, and I like myself."

Self-confidence is attractive. It's attractive to friends, to dating partners, to teachers, to everyone. The emotional warmth, energy, and enthusiasm that seem to radiate from a confident person set up a sort of chain reaction. Before long the people around that person start to feel good, too. Who wouldn't like someone who made them feel that way?

Being self-confident is not the same as being conceited. A person who is conceited is proud of how he or she seems to others. Such a person constantly puts on a show of being smart, or tough, or physically attractive, or rich. Other people's opinions are overly important to such a person, because the person doesn't have a secure sense of self. When you are with conceited people, you can almost sense that they feel empty and insecure inside.

left or right every 20–30 seconds (you say "pass") until everyone has written something *positive* about each person, on that person's paper. DO NOT SIGN NAMES. After all the papers have made their way around the circle, take time for students to silently read what the others have written about them. This lets students know how others perceive them in a positive way. (Comments can include physical attributes, values, personality characteristics, academic ability, etc.) **(20–30 min.; Extend, Enrich)**

EVALUATE

Activity 1.3
Pop Quiz.
1. You are the most important person in your life with whom you must have a good relationship to be emotionally healthy. (T)

2. To develop a good relationship with yourself, you first need to think about who you are. (T)
3. Being self-confident is the same as being conceited. (F)
4. People who are conceited often feel empty and insecure inside. (T)
5. If you are imperfect, you can never accept yourself. (F)

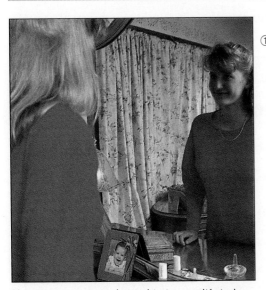

The most important relationship in your life is the relationship you have with yourself.

In contrast, a person who is confident may be smart, or tough, or attractive, or rich, or may not be. In any case the confident person feels OK and doesn't need to show off. When you are with confident people, you feel that they are comfortable with themselves.

Sometimes your values pull you one way, and your feelings another.

① Self-confidence starts with self-knowledge, which is not given at birth. Human beings normally are conscious of only a small part of themselves. To discover more takes learning and practice that, ideally, continue for a lifetime.

Self-knowledge begins when you ask yourself, "Who am I?" You may answer this question by just saying your name: "I am Leslie Owens." You may add that you are a young man or woman, an important aspect of yourself. You may go on to describe other outward traits, such as your height, weight, age, occupation, and race. Beneath these surface traits, though, who are you, really?

To become acquainted with yourself, you must learn about and manage three parts of your private, internal world—your thoughts, values, and emotions (feelings). Once you've discovered how you function in these areas, you can judge which parts serve you well and which you wish to change, now or later.

② Thoughts, values, and emotions also play roles in the decisions you make. We all know what it's like to face a decision in which feelings pull us one way and values another. The process of making a decision involves weighing and evaluating what you think is true, what you believe is right, and how you feel about it. The best decisions from an emotional health point of view are those that are in line with all three aspects of the self.

Key Points *A first step toward emotional health is getting to know yourself. You can accept yourself as you are (imperfect, like everyone else), even though you may wish to change some things.*

MINI GLOSSARY

emotional health: health in relationship to self, others, and society.

Teacher Support Notes

① **Self-Knowledge:** Ask students if they have discussed self-knowledge in classes prior to this health class. What do they think it means to know yourself? Do they feel that they know everything there is to know?

② **Values vs. Emotions:** Refer students to the cartoon and then ask them if they can think of situations in which they were torn in this way. Does the cartoon accurately represent the way they felt? Which side won?

❝ Thoughts on Health ❞
"We are so vain that we even care for the opinion of those we don't care for.
– Marie Ebner von Eschenbach

CLOSE
SECTION I

Activity 1.4
Self-Assessment. Have students write a positive statement about themselves. They should look at this statement daily for one week. Have them reevaluate how they feel about themselves after one week of reading something positive

everyday. Have their feelings about themselves changed? If so, how?

FOCUS
SECTION II

In this section students will learn that:
1. Replacing negative thoughts with positive ones can help improve a person's health.

Activity 2.1
Thumbs Up (or Down)? Ask students, "How are you feeling right now? Put your thumb up for positive or down for negative." Get a general feel for the class. Ask some of the students to volunteer to tell why they are feeling/thinking this way. **(1–5 min.)**

 Where to Write

Emotions Anonymous
P.O. Box 4245
St. Paul, MN 55104

Teacher Support Notes

① **Understanding Stress:** *Stress*, which is discussed at length in Chapter 4, is mentioned in questions 4 and 10. You might want to ask students before they do the inventory if they know what stress is. (the physical and psychological demands on a person)

② **The Results Are:** Students shouldn't take the results of the inventory too seriously. They should remember, however, the emphasis on *work* in Chapter 1. Whatever the emotional state, it could probably be better, but they must work at it. If their scores are low, they might want to get to work on their emotions.

66 Thoughts on Health 99

Sixty minutes of thinking of any kind is bound to lead to confusion and unhappiness.
– James Thurber

LIFE CHOICE
INVENTORY

Do You Cultivate Emotional Well-Being?

Do you cultivate emotional well-being? Try answering these questions to get an idea. Don't take your score too seriously. This is just for fun.

1. I spend time doing work that I enjoy.
   (a) Almost always. (b) Sometimes.
   (c) Almost never.
2. I find it easy to relax.
   (a) Almost always. (b) Sometimes.
   (c) Almost never.
3. In my spare time, I participate in activities that I enjoy.
   (a) Almost always. (b) Sometimes.
   (c) Almost never.
4. When I am about to be in a stressful situation, I realize it ahead of time, and I prepare for it.
   (a) Almost always. (b) Sometimes.
   (c) Almost never. ①
5. I handle anger: (a) By expressing it in ways that hurt neither myself nor other people. (b) By bottling it up so that no one knows I'm angry. (c) I am never angry, or I express anger aggressively.
6. I participate in group activities at school, in sports, in a religious organization, or in my community. (a) Quite often.
   (b) Very seldom. (c) Never.

7. I find it easy to express my feelings.
   (a) Almost always. (b) Sometimes.
   (c) Almost never.
8. I can talk to close friends, relatives, or others about personal matters.
   (a) Almost always. (b) Sometimes.
   (c) Almost never.
9. When I need help with personal matters, I seek it out.
   (a) Almost always. (b) Sometimes.
   (c) Almost never.
10. When I am under stress, I make extra sure to exercise regularly, to work off my tension.
    (a) Almost always. (b) Sometimes.
    (c) Almost never.

② ## SCORING

For each *a* answer, give yourself 2 points. For each *b* answer, give yourself 1 point. For each *c* answer, give yourself 0 points. Find where you are now on the emotional health line (continuum).

Where Are You on the Emotional Health Line (Continuum)?

Below 13 needs improvement	14 or 15 good but could be better	16–17 very good	18–20 excellent

Lowest level of emotional health   Highest level of emotional health

---

TEACH
SECTION II
(Guided and Independent Practice)

Activity 2.2
Restate Put-Downs. List some examples of put-downs on the board. Have students think of ways to restate the comments in a more positive way, then share these with the class. This makes both people feel better because it creates

positive thinking for both. (Example: Instead of "What are you trying to prove getting a 100% on that history test?" say "You must have really studied hard to do so well on that history test." **(15–20 min., Critical Thinking)**

EVALUATE
SECTION II

Activity 2.3

Reword Negative Statements. Have students restate or rewrite negative comments into positive ones. Do individually or in pairs. Discuss. **(10–20 min.)**

CLOSE
SECTION II

Activity 2.4
Replace Negative Thoughts. Ask

(continued on next page)

SECTION I — REVIEW

Answer the following questions on a sheet of paper.

Learning the Vocabulary
The vocabulary term in this section is *emotional health.*
1. Write a one-sentence description of *emotional health.*

Learning the Facts
2. List two characteristics of an emotionally healthy person and two characteristics of an emotionally unhealthy person.
3. What is the difference between being conceited and being confident?
4. What are the three parts of a person's private internal world?

Making Life Choices
5. To gain self-knowledge, you need to be aware of your strengths and weaknesses. Knowing your strengths builds your self-esteem. Knowing your weaknesses helps you form a realistic self-concept. Take a personal inventory by making two lists—one that includes at least ten strengths and one that includes at least ten weaknesses. List ways you can improve your weaknesses and build on your strengths.

SECTION II

Thoughts

Your **thoughts** take place in the outermost layer of your brain—the brain's **cortex.** Your thoughts are conscious; you are always aware of them. They help you to gather information about yourself and your world, and to make sense of it.

Your thoughts shape your actions. If you think destructive, negative thoughts, you will act in destructive, negative ways. If you think constructive, positive thoughts, you will act in constructive, positive ways. In general, negative thoughts breed more negative thoughts, and can lead a person to

---

HEALTH STRATEGIES

Thinking Positively

To change negative thoughts into positive ones:

1. Recognize your negative thoughts.
2. Stop them.
3. Replace them with positive thoughts.

---

think badly of everything. On the other hand, a person can acquire peace of mind, reduced stress, and improved health through simply learning to think positively.

The idea is simple, but training your mind to think positively is not easy. It requires effort, discipline, and practice. The rewards, however, are well worth the work. The Health Strategies feature above, "Thinking Positively," shows how to change negative thoughts into positive ones.

For example, suppose you frequently think to yourself, "I'm so dumb," or "I'm ugly," or "I'm low-class." Notice that, and quickly tell yourself, "Stop!" Then say to yourself, "I'm learning," "I'm becoming fit," "I'm street-wise," or the like.

Sometimes it helps to hold an image in your mind whenever a negative thought takes over. The image could be a check mark or a "positive" (plus) sign. It gives your mind the time it needs to switch tracks to a positive point of view.

MINI GLOSSARY

thoughts: those mental processes of which a person is always conscious.
cortex: the outer layer of an organ; in the brain, the outer, thinking portion—the gray matter.

Thoughts on Health

Life consists of what a man is thinking of all day.

– Ralph Waldo Emerson

Section I Review
Answers
1. Answers will vary.
2. *healthy*—seek, value, and maintain good relationships; eat well; exercise; feel secure; get along and fit in; *unhealthy*—self-destructive; often abuse drugs; take dangerous risks
3. Self-confident people are comfortable with who they are, while conceited people try to present themselves as better than they are to others.
4. thoughts, values, emotions (feelings)
5. Answers will vary.

CLOSE
(Continued)

students to think of a negative thought they've replaced today—or identify one during the day. Remind students to practice replacing negative thoughts with positive ones whenever they occur. **(5 min.)**

FOCUS
SECTION III

In this section students will learn that:
1. Values guide our behavior.
2. The family's values have the greatest influence on the values of its children.

Activity 3.1
Value Symbols. Have students

bring two to five items (trophy, photo of someone special, souvenir, etc.) from home to share with the class that illustrate personal values. Ask students to show their items to the class and explain what values they depict. **(Extend, Enrich)**

TEACH

SECTION III
(Guided and Independent Practice)

Activity 3.2

✉ Where to Write

Mental Health Association
1021 Prince St.
Alexandria, VA 22314

Section II Review
Answers
1. thoughts, cortex
2. negative thoughts may turn to negative actions
3. recognize negative thoughts, stop them, replace them with positive or neutral thoughts
4. Answers will vary.

Teacher Support Notes
① **Know Your Values:** Ask students how they can benefit from knowing their values. (prevents emotional distress that results from being unable to decide what to do)
② **Identifying Values:** Help students identify their values by listing *fame, helping others, leadership, friendship, honesty, wealth,* etc. on the board.

❝ Thoughts on Health ❞

A truth that is told with bad intent beats all the lies you can invent.
– William Blake

28

---

28   UNIT 2 Your Emotional and Social Health

Key Points ▶ *Thoughts help you gather information about yourself and the world. Positive thoughts are believed to set the stage for positive life experiences.*

SECTION II REVIEW

Answer the following questions on a sheet of paper.

Learning the Vocabulary
The vocabulary terms in this section are *thoughts* and *cortex.*
Fill in the blank with the correct answer.
1. Your _____ take place in the _____ of your brain.

Learning the Facts
2. What is the danger of negative thinking?
3. List three strategies for positive thinking.

Making Life Choices
4. Think back to what kind of day you had yesterday. Try to recall the course of events and the emotions you felt during the day. List all the positive thoughts and all the negative thoughts you had. Which type of thoughts dominated the day? What effect did these thoughts have on your overall emotional health yesterday? If you could replay the day, what changes would you make and why?

SECTION III
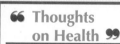

Values

Your **values** are your rules for behavior— ②
or more simply, what you view as right and wrong. Values have been called *life's steering wheel,* because they guide the direction your life takes. You learn your first values from your family. You learn such statements as "We work hard," "We believe in education," or "We stick together."

A person's values change from time to time. Working them out remains a lifelong task. The teen years are a time when most

people struggle to balance the values of their parents with those they observe in peers. Some teens reject their parents' values for a while. However, most return to them as proven rules for living.

Your values guide you in assigning positive and negative weights to behaviors. For example, you may value sports and reading highly, but shopping and housework negatively (or the reverse). The weights that you assign then guide your thinking and actions.

Values are both conscious and unconscious. Sometimes you can state them in words, but many times they guide your behavior without your awareness.

People who know themselves well are keenly aware of their values. That awareness helps them to choose their behaviors without confusion. For example, a student who values honesty and is conscious of this value will choose without hesitation not to cheat on exams. Another student may have the same values but may not be aware of them. This student may suffer emotional distress in trying to decide whether or not to cheat. ①

Some sellers of products have learned that subconscious values can direct purchasing decisions. They may try to "give" you some values concerning products they sell, as the Consumer Awareness feature on page 30 points out.

You can discover your own values by stating your beliefs. For example, you might say, "I believe it is best to be honest." This means you value honesty. Then, to discover how strong your values are, you can ask some questions about them. For each value that you state, ask the following questions:

- Would I be willing to state this value to others?
- How faithfully will I stand by this value when it is challenged, or when acting

Values Collages. Have students make collages from pictures depicting various values. They should label groups of pictures by the value depicted: beauty, health, cleanliness, exercise, family, wealth, etc. Put the collages up on the walls for everyone to see. Ask some students to tell about their collages. This activity could be done individually or in small groups. **(20 min.; Reteach, Reinforce)**

EVALUATE

SECTION III

Activity 3.3
Pop Quiz.
1. Define values. (See Mini Glossary.)
2. Do a person's values always remain the same? Why or why not? (No, family, peers, etc., cause changes.)

CLOSE
SECTION III

Activity 3.4
Essay. Have students write a paragraph about their values.

FOCUS
SECTION IV

(continued on next page)

---

according to the value brings negative consequences?
• Do I act consistently and repeatedly in line with this value?

If the value you place on honesty is very strong, you will be honest even when it's hard to be honest, or tempting to lie.

Values often arouse strong feelings within a person, especially when they conflict with one another. This makes action difficult. At such points you may struggle to decide: Should I go have fun or study? Should I keep my promise or break it? Such decisions become easier as you learn more about which values you really care about.

Values keep on changing. One of the skills to develop in moving through life is to learn when to change to new values and when to stick by old ones.

Key Points *Knowing your values is a key part of self-knowledge. Learning to manage and live by your values is an important part of emotional health.*

SECTION III   REVIEW

Answer the following questions on a sheet of paper.
Learning the Vocabulary
The vocabulary term in this section is *values.*
1. Write a sentence using the vocabulary term.

Learning the Facts
2. Where do you learn your first values?
3. Why is it important to be aware of your own personal values?

Making Life Choices
4. List all the different influences you can think of that have affected the development of your value system. Describe a situation in which a value guided your behavior. Where do you believe that particular value came from?
5. List ten values that you have. Is it possible to be friends with someone whose values are very different from yours? Explain.

SECTION IV

Emotions

An **emotion** is a feeling of being attracted to or repelled by something. Some emotions are present in people from birth, such as affection, anger, and fear. Others, such as envy and prejudice, are learned. The terms *emotions* and *feelings* are often used to mean the same thing.

The emotions you feel in response to an event often depend on earlier experiences of the same kind. The experience of hearing the front door open, for example, may bring on the emotion of fear or happiness or interest, depending on what you are expecting. Failing to reach a goal may arouse a mixture of emotions, including impatience, anger, and irritation. Losing a loved one (the experience of grief) brings a series of emotions, including both anger and sorrow.

Sometimes a person has a feeling and cannot pinpoint its cause. When this happens, the person may try to ignore the feeling because it doesn't make sense. Even when feelings seem unreasonable, though, they are not "wrong." They are as natural as the wind. Feelings are acceptable and healthy—all of them.

The cartoon at the bottom of page 31 shows a shouting person who is angry but won't admit it. Anger is not accepted in many social settings, so people often deny

MINI GLOSSARY

values a person's set of rules for behavior; what the person thinks of as right and wrong, or sees as important.
emotion: a feeling of being attracted to or repelled by something. Examples are love, anger, and fear.

Thoughts on Health

Great thoughts come from the heart.
– Vauvenergues

Section III Review
Answers
1. Answers will vary.
2. parents
3. to be able to choose behaviors without confusion
4. Answers will vary.
5. Answers will vary.

Thoughts on Health

Man is the only animal that laughs and weeps, for he is the only animal that is struck with the difference between what things are and what they ought to be.
– William Hazlitt

In this section students will learn that:
1. Everyone has feelings.
2. Emotions are OK, but it may not be acceptable to act on all feelings.
3. People who express their feelings appropriately are generally more mentally healthy than those who don't.
4. There are different levels of emotions.

Activity 4.1
List Emotions. Write on the board or say, "Think about all the emotions you have felt today. List them on a piece of paper. Put a '+' by those you think are 'good' emotions and a '–' (minus) by those you think are 'bad'." Give students a few minutes to make their lists and then say, "Think about why you marked each emotion with a plus or minus." Discuss reasons for their choices. Values will

influence their choices. **(5–10 min.)**

TEACH
SECTION IV
(Guided and Independent Practice)

Activity 4.2
Relate Emotions to Experiences. Give students examples of situations that evoke different emotions. The situations can be either mental or physical. (move to a new house, enter a contest, get straight

---

Teacher Support Notes

① **Added Value:** Ask students to explain how value has two meanings in this feature. (*value* as an important rule for behavior; *value* as something having worth or benefit)

② **Legitimate Value:** Explain the difference between the real value of a product (shoes protect your feet) and the false value (you will be popular because you wear shoes endorsed by a star player). Ask students to list products in addition to those mentioned in the text and give both a real and a false value for each.

③ **Answers to Critical Thinking: 1.** Some examples are autos, beer, athletic shoes, jeans, perfume, and makeup. **2.** An example is groups of attractive people socializing, having fun as they drink a certain beer. **3.** One reason is to gain acceptance and approval from peers.

CONSUMER AWARENESS

"Added-Value" Advertising

Did you ever know someone who always "had to have" the latest gadget or fashion item on the market? Advertisers wish everyone felt this way. They use all sorts of gimmicks to convince you that you need what they are selling. One gimmick is to imply that your self-worth depends on your owning their product. Cars, sneakers, jeans, sports equipment, and many other products are sold by way of the concept of "added value."

Advertisers convey the idea that the products themselves are worthwhile. Cars deliver you where you need to go, sneakers cover and protect your feet, jeans clothe you, and sports equipment may help you become more fit.

Beyond these functions, advertisers suggest that their brand names also have an added value. You must have a *certain* basketball shoe or jacket to prove to others that you are worthwhile. Some people may even begin to feel unworthy if they do not possess the "in" brands, even if the brand they own is just as high in quality as the popular brand. Such images are carefully developed by advertisers to sell products, and they do promote business success. Some people, though, are led to define their own emotional health by

their ownership of products.

What happens to such people when a brand's image wears off or the jacket goes out of fashion? They scramble to replace them with the latest added-value items, because without them they feel diminished in **status**. Only people who value themselves for their own internal worth are protected from this effect. Such people will not suffer loss of status as defined by ownership of added-value items. Their sense of worth is based on substance, not on symbols.

Beware of the sellers of products who imply that you can gain added value or status by buying their products. Spend your efforts not on collecting things that will age and tarnish, but on building internal strengths that will last a lifetime.

CRITICAL THINKING

1. *What sorts of products can you think of that sellers try to tie to people's values?*
2. *What sorts of visual images are used in television and magazine ads to make the connection between a product and a certain status?*
3. *Why do some people spend money on products that are promoted in this way?*

---

it. Other emotions people often deny are hurt and loneliness—feelings that reveal weakness and vulnerability.

It is acceptable to feel anything. It may not be acceptable to act on all feelings, but you must deal with them somehow.

Sometimes you must hold back an emotion for a moment (for example, if fear would prevent action needed to help a loved one in danger, you would hold back your fear and take action). It is fine to do so, and sometimes necessary for survival.

Bs on report card, eat a steak dinner, fix the lawn mower, borrow the family car, etc.) Say to students, "Identify what emotions you would feel and how you would deal with these emotions if they happened to you." Do in pairs or small groups. See if different people would react differently. Why? **(10–30 min., Critical Thinking)**

Activity 4.3
Emotion Charades. Divide students into two teams. Have them pantomime various emotions. Have the other team try to guess the correct emotion. Give team points for correct guesses. **(10–30 min.)**

Activity 4.4
Media Representations of Emotion. Ask students to bring in newspaper or magazine stories that illustrate emotions and the ways that people have dealt with the emotions. Discuss whether the story depicts a positive or negative way of responding to the emotion. Ask students to think of ways that people could have responded to the situation differently. **(Critical Thinking)**

EVALUATE

Activity 4.5

(continued on next page)

However, it is usually best to face the feeling as soon as possible. Emotions can build up, making it difficult for a person to function. Generally, people who are aware of their feelings and who express them appropriately are more emotionally healthy than people who ignore them.

People may fear some feelings because the feelings could lead to unacceptable behaviors. It helps to keep in mind the difference between feelings and actions. Some actions are not acceptable, of course, but impulses toward them are OK.

As an example, a young mother, listening to her baby crying, may have a sudden urge to hit the baby. That is natural. Many mothers have such feelings. It is not OK to actually hit the baby, though. Instead, the mother should take a deep breath, pace around, or sit down and relax a minute.

As another example, a teen rejected by a steady date, in a flood of self-pity, may feel like committing suicide. That feeling, too, is natural. An appropriate action, though, would be to cry, to go for a walk, to release anger through physical activity, or to ask a friend for sympathy.

In each example above, the impulse to do something destructive is OK, but the action would not be. The main point, though, is that the emotion *is* OK.

Expressing your anger physically may help you relax. Once you are relaxed, you can consider the situation rationally.

When you can do the following, you have grown toward emotional health:

- Recognize all kinds of feelings in yourself.
- Admit that you have all sorts of feelings.
- Express all kinds of feelings in acceptable ways.

① Expressing feelings is best done physically. That means doing something: speaking, writing, crying, shouting, laughing, or otherwise acting out emotions. Calmly saying "I'm angry" may not fully express the feeling of anger. It releases more of the emotion to speak angrily, or to pound the table, or to beat on a punching bag.

It is not acceptable to knock down another person with a blow to the jaw just to express your anger. However, doing nothing at all can be harmful to you. Once you

People deny anger because, in our society, it seems unacceptable or inappropriate.

MINI GLOSSARY

status: a person's standing or rank in relation to others, many times falsely based on wealth, power, or influence. While desirable to many, these characteristics do not define human worth.

Physiologists estimate that the face is capable of producing about 20,000 different expressions.

Teacher Support Notes

① **Physical Reactions:** Here are some added facts about the physical aspects of emotion:
a. Physical reactions in the body accompany most emotions. Examples are a pounding heart, sweaty palms, "butterflies" in the stomach, dry throat and mouth, and trembling.
b. These reactions are *involuntary*, not under the individual's control. They are caused by the autonomic nervous system (ANS).
c) The lie detector (polygraph) is an example of a device that monitors the physical changes in the body associated with emotions. The machine records general emotional arousal; not truth or falsehood.

Pop Quiz.

1. Emotions and feelings are terms used to describe the same thing. (T)
2. Past experience helps determine emotions. (T)
3. All emotions are learned rather than inherited. (F)
4. People can always pinpoint the cause

of their feelings. (F)
5. It is a normal reaction in some situations, if a baby is crying, for the mother to want to hit it. (T)
6. Suicidal feelings are common when someone has been rejected—as when someone breaks up with his or her steady girlfriend/boyfriend. (T)
7. All feelings are healthy. (T)
8. There is usually only one correct way to deal with an emotion. (F)

9. A good way to express anger is to kick the dog. (F)
10. Punching a pillow is a good way to get rid of angry feelings. (T)

CLOSE
◀ Sᴇᴄᴛɪᴏɴ ɪᴠ

Activity 4.6
Advice Column. Ask students to

📣 **Fast Facts**

People who are hostile are inclined to have more coronary artery blockage.

Teacher Support Notes

① **Coping with Feelings:** *Cope* is an important word students will learn more about in Chapter 4. For now, tell your students that it means to deal with problems; to try to overcome difficulties.

② **Expressing Anger:** Ask students if they ever become angry with their parents. How do they express their anger? Do they hold it inside sometimes? Has the anger they feel toward their parents ever affected their behavior toward other people? Could they benefit from using the strategies for dealing with emotions described on the next page?

✉ **Where to Write**

National Clearinghouse for Mental Health Information Public Inquiries Section
5600 Fishers Lane
Room 15C-17
Rockville, MD 20857

Happiness   Sadness

Anger   Affection
Emotions are expressed physically.

have let off steam by yelling, crying, running, dancing, or whatever, you can relax again. Then you can calmly think about the event that triggered the emotion in the first place.

Sometimes you may find that expressing the feeling is all you need to do to cope with it. But other times negative emotions return over and over again. If they do, they are a signal that you need to think about the situation. You may need to change something.

Take Tom, for example. Tom was furious at his parents. He recognized the anger, ac-

cepted it, and verbalized it. Tom also expressed it physically in a socially acceptable way every day after school—by digging a hole in the back yard. After a year the hole was big enough for a swimming pool, and Tom was a superb physical specimen—but still an angry person. He had to change the situation. It was time for a confrontation. After Tom presented his parents with the reasons for his anger, the problem proved solvable. The Health Strategies feature on the next page, "Dealing with an Emotion," outlines steps you can take to live comfortably with your feelings.

think of situations that make it difficult to decide how to act (i.e., someone says something that hurts their feelings). Pretend someone has written a letter to an "advice" column in the school newspaper about one of these situations. You write the letter yourself. Have students write a "Dear (student name)" response to the person with the problem, advising the person how to respond. Collect the responses and read some of them to the class. This could be done anonymously. **(10–20 min.; Critical Thinking, Interdisciplinary)**

FOCUS
SECTION V

In this section students will learn that:
1. There are differences between passive, aggressive, and assertive behavior.
2. Support groups can be crucial to a person's sense of belonging and well-being.
3. Overcoming shyness may take practice.
4. Making your wishes known through assertive behavior gets better results than passive or aggressive behavior.

Activity 5.1
Role-Play Behaviors. Ahead of time, set up a scenario in which a student

(continued on next page)

HEALTH STRATEGIES

Dealing with an Emotion

To deal with an emotion, you must:

1. **Recognize it.** What am I feeling?
2. **Own it.** Accept that you feel it.
3. **Verbalize it.** Express it in words to yourself or someone else:

I'm angry.	I'm frustrated.
I'm upset.	I'm afraid.
I'm hurt.	I'm thrilled.
I'm sad.	I'm stressed.
I'm excited.	I'm uneasy.
I'm resentful.	I'm touched.
I'm envious.	I'm nervous.
I'm anxious.	I'm lonely.

4. **Express it physically.** Take physical action to express emotions:

Pat yourself on the back.	Hug someone.
Sing a song.	Laugh.
Punch a pillow.	Dance.
Jump in the air.	Cry.

5. If a negative emotion persists or returns, **think about the situation**. A confrontation may be necessary.

Key Points ▶ *Recognizing, accepting, and expressing feelings are important to emotional health. Feelings sometimes need physical expression and sometimes indicate other needs for action.*

SECTION IV REVIEW

Answer the following questions on a sheet of paper.
Learning the Vocabulary
The vocabulary terms in this section are *emotion* and *status*.
1. Write a sentence using each vocabulary term.

Learning the Facts
2. What are the three emotions that are present in people from birth?
3. What happens when emotions build up and are not dealt with?
4. List two healthy strategies to deal with emotions.

Making Life Choices
5. Look over the Health Strategies feature, "Dealing With an Emotion," on this page. Which recommendations on the list are you skilled in and which ones listed do you need to improve upon? Give a few suggestions on how you could go about making the necessary improvements. What do you have to gain by making these improvements? What other recommendations for dealing with emotions could you add to the list?

SECTION V

Relating to Others

Recall that the emotionally healthy person functions well in three areas—in relation to self, to others, and to society. So far, this chapter has been devoted to the most important relationship in anyone's life—the relationship with self. Now, what about relationships with others?

① People who value themselves, because they are confident and happy, attract other people into friendships. A person's friends situation? **(1–5 min.)**

Activity 5.2
Mentor Stories. Write on the board, "Think of a person (mentor) who has really helped you in your life. Think about what this person did that was so special." (listened, acted interested, shared feelings, total acceptance, good advice, etc.) Ask students to volunteer to tell about their special people. **(1–10 min.)**

TEACH
SECTION V
(Guided and Independent Practice)

Activity 5.3
Discuss Cultural Responses. Discuss how people from different cultures and ethnic backgrounds might respond to or handle various situations because of tradition. Situations might include the death of a family member, a

will act a certain way when coming to class and you will respond passively and/or aggressively—then assertively. Have the student respond appropriately for each method used. Have the other students respond to what they saw. What were they thinking and feeling about the

---

Teacher Support Notes

① **Teen Views—Follow-Up Questions:** Following are some questions you may want to use to encourage discussion of the ideas expressed by the students in the Teen Views feature:
a. Do students agree with Victoria Hopkins that the first five minutes are the toughest?
b. Do students think they can trust most people, or not? What experiences support their views?
c. Can you "buy" friendships? If so, how?
d. Do real friends try to make you more like themselves?
e. Do you have to work at friendships, as Jenny Callan suggests, or do real friendships just happen naturally, without special effort?

✍ Fast Facts

The frequency of touching varies among cultures. In one study, researchers found that American friends touch two times in an hour while having coffee; English friends, 0; French, 110; Puerto Rican, 180.

---

34 UNIT 2 Your Emotional and Social Health

TEEN VIEWS

What is hardest about making and keeping friends? ①

The first five minutes you ever spend with them. If you can make it through that you are off to a real good start. I have a real hard time trying to keep my mind from trying to guess what the other person is thinking. I've learned to keep my friends by being up front with my feelings and worries and my friendships seem to last forever. **Victoria Hopkins, 17, Orange Park High School, FL**

Trust. Nowadays it's hard to be able to trust. Everyone seems to be out for themselves. It doesn't matter who they hurt as long as they get what they want. It's a *me* society rather than a *we* society. **Rebecca Herbert, 17, Connellsville High School, PA**

Trying to make them notice you. You may try to buy friendship by having a party or something to persuade them to become your friend. You may try to become somebody you really aren't just to make them happy.

Latonya Epperson, 15, Pine Bluff High School, AR

Opening up and getting to know that person and getting them to do the same. **James Lain, 15, Pine Bluff High School, AR**

The hardest thing is, when you have friends, they try to change you so that you fit their qualifications. They want you to do things that you have never done before. Sometimes they want you to do something like drink or smoke with them and you don't want to. They put a lot of pressure on you. Who needs friends like that! **Alicia Hansen, 17, Poughkeepsie High School, NY**

As much as you think you know that friend or group, you never really know what they will do or how they will react to tough situations. Keeping friends isn't that hard because a real friend knows that to have friends you must be one. **Alia Whitlock, 14, Oshkosh North High School, WI**

You have to be flexible. You must be able to enjoy doing the things that your friend

enjoys, regardless of your personal interest. Every friendship is a "give and take" relationship. Some people will only be your friend because of all the giving that you will do. This is not a strong, lasting friendship. **Eric Amrozowicz, 17, Frontier Central High School, NY**

I believe that the hardest thing is getting up the nerve to even introduce yourself and be confident enough about yourself to start a conversation and initiate a new friendship. Once you have a friend you learn to "read" their moods and know their likes and dislikes. A lot of work goes into a strong friendship, from both sides. You have to be willing to give. **Jenny Callan, 16, Orange Park High School, FL**

When you know that the way you are acting is not your real personality and you're faking it just to have friends. You're scared that they'll find out that it's just an act. **Madeline Gemmati, 16, Poughkeepsie High School, NY**

Activity 5.4
   Practicing Emotion Strategies.
1. Name the five steps in dealing with an emotion. (1—Recognize it; 2—Own it; 3—Verbalize it; 4—Express it physically; 5—If a negative emotion persists or returns, think about the situation and confront if necessary.)
2. Repeat aloud (choral response) the

words for the letters SOFTEN (page 38), to help students remember what to do during conversations with new people. (S = smile; O = open posture; F = forward lean; T = touch; E = eye contact; N = nod)
3. Have two students demonstrate initiating and conducting a conversation with a new person, using the suggestions on pages 37 and 38 about listening, talking about feelings, and using the SOFTEN method.

Activity 5.5
   Guest Speakers—Support Groups. Invite students or community members who are in support groups to come into the class as guest speakers to discuss the value of the groups, how someone gets into a group, the purpose of the group, etc. These groups are often listed in the phone book under headings like "Self-Help" or "Support Groups." They

(continued on next page)

Family members can be an important part of your support system.

can form a strong **support system**, which can be a great help in time of need. The members of your support system may be family members, neighbors, school friends, members of a sports team, people in a religious organization, a **mentor** or adviser, or a therapy or self-help group. Of course, the person participating in such friendships and social groups stands ready to give, as well as to receive, and so does not need to be embarrassed about asking for support sometimes. You will learn some basic skills for getting along with others in this chapter. You'll learn more about peer groups in the next chapter.

Preventing and Resolving Conflicts

There is always a gap between what you want or need and what you are receiving. Sometimes the gap is large; sometimes it is small. The gap occurs in every setting—school, job, home, friendships, dealings with storekeepers, and more. To help close the gap, you must express your wants and needs. At the same time, you need to stay aware of other people's feelings and not wound them unnecessarily.

To express yourself successfully to others, you have to perform a sort of balancing act between getting what you want and meeting the needs of others. The happy center between the extremes of mousiness and assault is **assertive** behavior, rather than **passive** or **aggressive** behavior.

To be assertive is to say what you mean—not to tiptoe around and drop hints, at the one extreme, and not to attack the other person, at the other. Assertiveness does not come naturally to many people. They may not even value it. They may think it's selfish. But once a person understands the value of assertiveness, the person can learn and practice assertive behaviors, and can work out problems better than before.

In Figure 2–1 on the next page, three situations are described in which people are behaving passively or aggressively. They are not succeeding in getting what they want. See if you can decide how they could get what they wanted by being assertive.

In the first example, Sarah is passive. She simply does not speak up for herself. In the

MINI GLOSSARY

support system: a network of individuals or groups with which one identifies and exchanges emotional support.
mentor: a wise person who gives advice and assistance.
assertive: possessing the characteristic of appropriately expressing feelings, wants, and needs. Assertiveness is the key to obtaining cooperation.
passive: possessing the characteristic of not expressing feelings appropriately, of remaining silent.
aggressive: possessing the characteristic of being insulting to others or otherwise invading their territory; an inappropriate expression of feelings.

❝ Thoughts on Health ❞

Strong and bitter words indicate a weak cause.
   – Victor Hugo

Teacher Support Notes

① **Time of Need:** Ask students, what do they think the author means by "a time of need?" What's a time of need for a teenager? For an adult it's when you lose your job and you have a family to support, or when you realize that you and your spouse can't get along. Can students give examples of time-of-need situations? How did friends help?

② **Assertiveness:** Ask students to think of examples where they've "dropped hints" rather than being straightforward with a request. Why did they do this? Were they trying to protect their own feelings or those of the other person?

are also listed weekly in some newspapers. **(Extend, Enrich)**

EVALUATE
SECTION V

Activity 5.6

SOFTEN. Have students practice SOFTEN in pairs. Then change partners and try again, and again. Do this as many times as you think necessary to have it feel natural. Have students discuss anything they feel comfortable with (the game last night, the activity they are now doing, etc.). Discuss whether it gets easier each time it is practiced. **(5–10 min.; Reteach, Reinforce)**

CLOSE
SECTION V

Activity 5.7
Role-Play Assertiveness. Say, "Assertive behavior is not passive or aggressive, but lets the person know what you want and does not attack the person personally." Have students practice ways to say things in an assertive

---

Teacher Support Notes

① **Resentment:** *Resentment* is a word some students may not know. It means to feel anger or dislike toward someone, usually over a period of time, and often as a result of a specific incident involving a wrong, an injury, or an insult. Have students fill in the blank to complete the following sentence, using fictitious names: "I resented it when _____." Discuss their sentences in class.

② **Action vs. Person:** Ask students to explain in their own words the difference between speaking "of the action" and "of the person." It's important that they see this distinction.

> **66 Thoughts on Health 99**
>
> *Most remarks that are worth making are commonplace remarks. The thing that makes them worth saying is that we really mean them.*
>
> **– Robert Lynd**

FIGURE 2-1

Nonassertive versus Assertive Responses

Situation	Nonassertive Responses	Assertive Responses
1. A person steps in front of Sarah, who has been standing in line for an hour.	*Sarah:* "Well, excuse *me!*" or *Sarah:* Says nothing aloud; mutters "Some people . . ."	*Sarah:* "Excuse me. I was here first. The end of the line is back there."
2. James comes home, pours some juice, sits down, and flips on MTV.	*James's mom (from kitchen):* "I sure wish I could rest like that at the end of the day. But no, I have to cook dinner, bathe the baby, wash up. . . . I'm tired, too."	*James's mom:* "Would you please cook dinner while I bathe the baby?"
3. Ken notices that his little sister hasn't cleaned up her room even though he told her to do so earlier.	*Ken:* "Sis, I told you to clean up your room. What's the matter with you? You're the laziest child I ever saw."	*Ken:* "I told you to clean up your room. Now do it." (And he sees that she does.)

second, Mom makes it clear to James that she feels overworked, tired, and grumpy. However, she doesn't say what she wants him to do about it. In the third example, Ken tells his little sister what to do, which is assertive. However, he then goes on to insult her, which is aggressive and hurtful.

James's mom and Ken share a problem common to people who have trouble being assertive. They have let their resentments build up for so long that when they do speak, they express not a simple wish of the moment but an age-old gripe. James's mom does it slow-burn style. Ken does it by way of a loud explosion. Both are painful to express and painful to witness.

By contrast, notice how the appropriate responses differ in tone and content. They each express a single, specific, concrete re-

quest of the moment. Assertive statements are like that: "Please wash the dishes." "Please pay me the five dollars you owe me." Also, they speak of the action they want, not of the person. The responder knows exactly what to do and does not have to feel attacked.

Sometimes, situations repeat themselves many times. Over and over again, someone fails to honor your wants or needs. Then a **confrontation** is necessary. To insist that someone change a behavior that has been bothering you for a long time, apply the Health Strategies on the next page.

Assertiveness is the key to getting cooperation. It makes it easier, not harder, for people to get along with you. It is worth practicing for people who want to enjoy harmony in their relationships with others.

manner. Have volunteers role-play some ways to say things assertively. **(10 min.)**

Activity 5.8
Support Group Presentation. Review the importance of support systems. List and explain the systems in your school and community, e.g., school support groups; aftercare for substance abuse; Alcoholics Anonymous; and special groups for depression, pregnant and

parenting teens, children of dysfunctional families, eating disorders, chronic illness, children of alcoholics, grief, or others in your school. Counselors can provide this information for you or may come in to explain the student support services available in your school district. Community support systems can be located through the mental health association, school counselors, treatment facilities, newspapers, or phone books. **(Extend, Enrich)**

FOCUS
SECTION VI

In this section students will learn:
1. A six-step strategy for making decisions.

Activity 6.1
Problem to Solve. Write a "problem"

(continued on next page)

Key Points ▶ *Conflicts are normal in relationships. Assertive behaviors can resolve them.*

HEALTH STRATEGIES

Making Your Wishes Known

To confront someone, express yourself assertively but not aggressively:

1. To decide whether to mention something that bothers you, ask yourself, "Does this bother me every time it happens, or is it an isolated incident?" If it happens often, mention it. If not, handle it yourself by walking it off or waiting it out.
2. Make feeling statements about yourself ("It hurts my feelings when you . . ."), not judgment statements about the other person ("You are insensitive").
3. Pair a resentment with an appreciation: "I appreciate (this), but resent (that)." It's easiest for the other person to deal with a problem behavior if you indicate that the person's other behaviors are OK.
4. Focus on the one incident that bothers you. Don't discuss everything else that has made you mad for months.
5. Be specific. Identify the *behavior* you want. Don't just complain.
6. If the problem is major, don't just burst forth with it. Pick a time to express it. If the other person is in a hurry to go somewhere, or is having strong feelings about something, too, the person may not be able to respond appropriately.

Forming New Relationships

Sometimes people need to make new friendships. Many people fear trying to make new friends at first. *Why Am I Afraid to Tell You Who I Am?* is the title of a book written by John Joseph Powell to help people overcome their fears about relationships. The title reveals the primary problems people have: the fear of making fools of themselves and the fear of being laughed at or rejected. ①

Reaching out to other people usually does not lead to rejection. To get started, though, you have to be willing to risk rejection and to handle it if it occurs. It helps to keep two things in mind. First, "If I'm rejected, I won't be any worse off than I am now." Second, "If it doesn't work out, it's no reflection on me, because I tried. The other person had other needs." ②

What more often happens when you reach out is that the other person is pleased to be approached. At least you have the benefit of some contact. At best, a rewarding relationship has a chance to form.

Many people who know this can't act on it, though, because they don't know how. A few suggestions can help. Each can be practiced, as suggested in the Health Strategies, "Tips for Overcoming Shyness," on the next page. One expert suggests thinking of the word *soften* to remind you of what to do during actual conversations with new people:

MINI GLOSSARY

confrontation: a showdown; an interaction in which one person expresses feelings to another. Managed aggressively, a confrontation may be a destructive fight. Managed assertively, a confrontation may be a constructive conversation in which one person makes his or her wishes known to another.

Teacher Support Notes

① **Developing Assertiveness:** This is an excellent list of specific suggestions for developing assertiveness skills. Have students role-play situations in which they practice these skills. They should do some ad-libbing. Also have them prepare scripts and recreate these scripts.

② **Assertive vs. Aggressive:** Ask students to give examples of the difference between assertive and aggressive behavior, which they should know at this point. Give them the following situations and then ask them to tell you how an aggressive person and an assertive person would react: 1. a fellow worker is not doing his fair share of the work; 2. a classmate is disrupting class, making it hard for others to concentrate; and 3. a brother or sister is spending too much time listening to your radio in your room.

on the board for students to think about. It might be something that is currently in the national or local news, a school issue, etc. Ask, "What do you think should be done about this problem?" After getting several ideas, ask how they came up with their "solutions." Discuss ways that

people decide how to solve problems. (5–10 min.)

TEACH
SECTION VI
(Guided and Independent Practice)
Activity 6.2
Group Problem Solving. Ask students to brainstorm typical problems that teenagers encounter (no money and want to go to the prom, boyfriend/girlfriend

seems to be jealous all the time, parents are overly protective, friend is talking about shoplifting last weekend, people have been spreading untrue rumors about someone, etc.). Then divide the class into small groups and give each group one of the problems. Have them use the decision-making process to arrive at possible solutions. Then have them rank-order the proposed solutions. Share the results with the class and discuss the

---

❝ Thoughts on Health ❞

Remember that as a teenager you are in the last stage of your life when you will be happy to hear that the phone is for you.
– Fran Lebowitz

Section V Review
Answers

1. assertive is being able to make your wishes known, but aggressive attacks a person as this is being done
2. support system
3. mentor
4. passive
5. family members, neighbors, members of a sports team, people in a religious organization, adviser
6. by expressing your needs and wants
7. Answers will vary. Refer to the Health Strategies on page 37 for possible answers.
8. tell of your own feelings, ask about the other person's feelings, listen closely
9. Answers will vary.

HEALTH
STRATEGIES

Tips for Overcoming Shyness

For many people, shyness takes the fun out of life. Psychologists who treat shyness say to:

- Rehearse what you have to say. Write down what you'd like to say. Read it out loud—first by yourself, then in front of a mirror, then with a friend, and finally in the setting you've been rehearsing for.
- Build your self-esteem by focusing on your strong points and praising yourself for good deeds or a good performance. Turn stumbling blocks into stepping stones.
- Talk into a tape recorder to improve your speaking voice.
- Observe and copy the behaviors of people you admire.
- Learn to laugh at yourself when things go wrong. Don't put yourself down.
- Remember that you are not alone. At least two out of every five people are as uncomfortable as you are.
- Do not try to hide your "true self." Accept who you are, with all your traits.
- Focus your attention on others and what they are saying. Do not focus on your own words, actions, and appearance.
- Before you enter a social setting, imagine yourself succeeding in it.
- Avoid using alcohol or other drugs to relax. They are not shortcuts to the social skills you desire. Also, using them can increase the chance that you will make a fool of yourself.

S Smile.
O Open posture.
F Forward lean.
T Touch.
E Eye contact.
N Nod.

Here are some other helpful hints:
- Tell of your own feelings (people always find feelings interesting).
- Ask about the other person's feelings (people like you to be interested in them).
- Listen closely (people love to be listened to).

Key Points → *People need other people to form a support network. Rejection is a risk in forming new friendships, but the risk is worth taking. The "SOFTEN" steps can help bridge the gap to others.*

___ **S**ECTION V ___ **R**EVIEW ___

Answer the following questions on a sheet of paper.
Learning the Vocabulary
The vocabulary terms in this section are *support system, mentor, assertive, passive, aggressive,* and *confrontation.*
1. What is the difference between being assertive and being aggressive?
2. A _____ is a network of people that lends emotional support.
3. A wise person who gives advice is known as a _____.
4. A _____ person fails to speak up.

Learning the Facts
5. In addition to friends, what other people can be part of a support system?
6. How can you attempt to close the gap between what you want and what you get?
7. List four strategies to become more assertive.
8. Give three helpful hints that could assist you when meeting someone for the first time.

Making Life Choices
9. Look over the Health Strategies feature, "Making Your Wishes Known," on page 37. Which strategies listed are you skilled in using? Which strategies listed do you need to improve on? How could you go about making each improvement?

process that was used. Each group can write their solutions on construction or butcher paper to hold up when explaining to the class. Post these ideas in the room later. Discuss the problems of making joint decisions when different people have different values. **(30–50 min.; Cooperative Learning, Critical Thinking)**

EVALUATE
SECTION VI

Activity 6.3
Pop Quiz. Without using the book, have students name the six steps in the decision-making process. (see Health Strategies, page 39)

CLOSE
SECTION VI

Activity 6.4
Develop a Plan. Have students identify a current problem in their lives and make a plan to solve it using the decision-making steps.

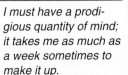

SECTION VI

Making Decisions and Solving Problems ①

Some decisions—What shall I wear today?—are easy to make. Others are more weighty, such as "How can I tell my parents I don't want to be the person they want me to be?" In tackling tough decisions, it helps to follow a plan. One such plan is presented in the Health Strategies feature on this page, "A Method for Making Decisions." The discussion that follows offers help with the steps.

The first step, *naming the problem*, may be simple, but it may not be. Pinpointing the problem of what to wear usually is simple enough. Some problems, though, are so complex that they require years to figure out ("How can I straighten out my relationship with my parents?"). Whatever the problem is, the first step is to put it into words. Then you can begin seeking a solution.

Breaking a problem up into parts will make it more manageable. Say, for example, that you feel you don't fit in with your peers. Stated that way, the problem seems impossible to solve. But stated in its smallest units, it may look like this:

- I like to discuss world events. The group likes gossip.
- The group spends more money than I can afford to spend.

When you think about these smaller components, you can deal with them one by one. If they arouse emotions such as resentment, anger, or embarrassment, this may be a sign that the group's values are not in line with your own. This realization may help you to think up solutions that will meet your needs.

The brainstorming step involves thinking

HEALTH STRATEGIES

A Method for Making Decisions

When you find yourself saying, "What should I do?" try this:

1. **Name the problem.** Be sure it's the *real* problem.
2. **Describe it specifically.** Name its parts.
3. **Brainstorm.** Name all the solutions you can think of, no matter how crazy they may seem.
4. **Think about each solution:**
   - How does it square with your values?
   - Does it honor the values of your parents and others whom you respect?
   - Would it solve the problem?
   - Would it affect others for better or worse?
5. **Choose a solution, and act on it.**
6. **Evaluate the outcome:**
   - Is the problem solved?
   - What else happened?
   - Would another solution work better?

---

up many different solutions to the problem. During this step, don't try to solve the problem. Instead, exercise your imagination, and tap your creativity. This can be fun—and funny.

Brainstorming for the problem just described can bring out possibilities such as seeking other friendships, joining a club for people with more common interests, taking a class dealing in world events, and so on. Some ideas may be impractical. Some may be pure fantasy: move to another state;

Teacher Support Notes

① **Decision Making:**
Present students with the following list of strategies people use to make decisions. Ask them which method most people use, which one they personally use, and which one they think would be the most effective.
a. The first idea you get is usually the best.
b. It's best to follow someone else's plan.
c. It "feels" right. Follow your instincts.
d. Looking at all the possibilities is overwhelming. I'll cross that bridge later.
e. Things will work out. Leave it up to fate.
f. I'll develop a plan so I'll be sure to end up satisfied.

39

In this section students will learn that:
1. All societies have expectations for their members, but that not all societies are the same.
2. People who differ from the majority of society may be ostracized.
3. Volunteer work is a good way to learn about different careers.

Activity 7.1
Career Options. Write on the board, "List as many jobs/careers as you can think of in two minutes." Ask students how many they listed. Discuss why some had more than others. (have done more reading/research, know more people who have a variety of jobs, etc.) Have each student name a career on his or her list.

Go around the room two or three times, trying not to duplicate any that have already been said. Conclude that there are many career options available if we become aware of them. **(5–10 min.)**

TEACH
SECTION VII
(Guided and Independent Practice)

Activity 7.2
Guest Speaker—Employer

Teacher Support Notes

① **Analyzing Solutions:** Divide students into groups so that they can practice the decision-making process with the following situations:
a. Baby-sit or hang out with friends at the mall.
b. Go out for the soccer team, which means after-school practice four nights a week; or take music lessons, which require two nights a week after school.
c. Buy a new pair of tennis shoes, or buy a new sweater for the same price.
d. Ride your bike to school, or take the bus.

Section VI Review

Answers

1. name the problem, describe it specifically, brainstorm, think about each solution, choose a solution and act on it, evaluate the outcome
2. It begins the process of finding a solution.
3. Often a combination of solutions is the best.
4. Did the solution produce the results you expected; How did the solution fit with your feelings and values; Did the solution fail to meet your needs in any significant way?
5. Answers will vary.

Talk over decisions with friends to develop the best ideas.

don't leave the house for a year; call the president of the United States. Writing down even impractical solutions is valuable, though. It could just be that a combination of answers is best. It helps to view them all.

In thinking about each solution, judge it based on your own values and feelings. Imagine and list the probable outcomes, both positive and negative. Compare the ideas. Then rank them in order from best to worst.

Consider the practicality of each solution. For example, a person who wanted to socialize with a group of friends but who had money problems might consider helping the group plan some affordable but enjoyable activities, such as a potluck dinner or a hike. By helping plan, the person could as-

sist the group without spending needed money. Then the person could participate because the activities would be low in cost.

Once you have thought all possible solutions through, you can pick one that fits ① your values and your personal circumstances. Try it out. Then answer the following questions to evaluate the solution:

- Did the solution produce the results you expected?
- How did the solution fit with your feelings and values?
- Did the solution fail to meet your needs in any significant way?

If the solution seems satisfactory, the decision was a good one. If the solution seems less than ideal, you can usually adjust it or discard it in favor of another. In that case, you begin the process of deciding all over again.

> **Key Points** *Problems can be solved by making decisions and taking action. A method that helps is to go through these steps: name the problem, describe it, brainstorm about it, and evaluate all possible solutions in view of your values. Then choose a solution, act on it, and evaluate the results.*

SECTION VI REVIEW

Answer the following questions on a sheet of paper.

Learning the Facts
1. List the six steps for making decisions.
2. Why is the first step in the process so important?
3. Why should you be sure to brainstorm all the possible solutions to a problem?
4. What are three questions you can use in the evaluating process?

Making Life Choices
5. List a problem you are facing right now and work it through using the Health Strategies feature, "A Method for Making Decisions," presented on page 39.

Expectations. Invite a guest speaker (employer, state Job Service representative, etc.) to discuss what is expected of employees and job applicants. Discuss growing occupations, educational requirements, applications, résumés, work ethics, etc. (up to one full period; Extend, Enrich)

Activity 7.3
Career Interest Inventory. Have students take a career interest inventory if they haven't already done so. There are many types available. Check with your school counselors or Job Service for ideas. (up to one period)

Activity 7.4
Research/Report. Have students research and report on societal values and expectations in other cultures/countries with regard to careers. (Extend, Enrich, Multicultural)

Activity 7.5
Discuss Homeless Situations. Discuss the problems with and for homeless people. (You may have students in your class/school who are homeless.) Ask, "How did they become homeless?" "What challenges do they face?" "How can society help them fit back into the main-

(continued on next page)

SECTION VII

Finding a Place in Society

You and the other people with whom you have relationships fit into a larger circle—your society. Your society may consist of the community you live in, your school, and your ethnic or religious group. It may also include other circles. Societies have sets of values and expectations of their own that they impose on their members. Sometimes the fit is easy, sometimes not.

Our society has traditionally been steered by the middle class. The middle class tends to put off enjoying today so that tomorrow there will be money or prestige or time to have fun. It also values doers—those devoted to action and achievement. In another culture, a mother may enjoy her child because he is sitting in her lap and laughing in her face. In our culture, a mother is more likely to be thinking of how well the child is preparing for tomorrow.

Not all societies uphold the same values for their members. No law says people must live by the values of their own society. However, if they don't go along, they lose approval and support. People whose values differ from society's may experience **alienation** and **ostracism**. A person who doesn't fit in is a **nonconformist**. ①

In any case, each person has to work out some relationship with the larger world. One person may choose to live totally in keeping with personal goals and values. Another may choose to live with a subgroup in society whose values differ from the majority's values.

Society is really a mosaic of many small societies, each a group of like-minded people. The important thing is to find a place ②

SELF
OTHERS
SOCIETY

that provides comfort and rewards and that respects your individuality. Be careful, though, not to get caught in a subgroup such as a gang, whose values and practices destroy your hopes for your future. Chapter 3 talks more about gangs.

For most people, an important part of finding a place in society is to discover a fitting job or career. A book written for people trying to find their place in the world of work is *What Color Is Your Parachute?* by R. N. Bolles. The title implies that the leap into a job is somewhat like jumping from an airplane. You have no guarantee of success. All you have is what you came with—yourself. The better you know yourself, the better you can choose, and succeed at, a job or career.

Some experts believe that rewarding work is the single most important aspect of adult life relating to well-being. Many people who

MINI GLOSSARY

alienation: withdrawing from others because of differences that cannot be resolved.
ostracism: rejection and exclusion from society.
nonconformist: a person who does not share society's values and therefore behaves in unconventional ways.

Teacher Support Notes

① **Nonconformist Lifestyle:** Ask students if they know of adults or older teens who have pursued a nonconformist lifestyle. Is that person happy with his or her choice of a different lifestyle? What difficulties has the person encountered as a result of the choice? Do the students think they could make such a choice?

② **Mosaic of Society:** Ask students what a *mosaic* is. For those who don't know, it's something in which many different pieces have been combined in random and different ways to form a whole. Ask them if they can identify different pieces of their local society's mosaic.

stream society better?" "Are they really different from everyone else?" **(10–20 min.; Extend, Enrich)**

EVALUATE
SECTION VII

Activity 7.6
   Essay. Assign students an essay in which they describe ways in which they know they are accepted by a group or society. (don't put you down; accept you for who you are; feel comfortable with the group; have similar ideas, values, interests; feel you "fit in")

CLOSE
SECTION VII

Activity 7.7
   Discuss Nonconformists. Ask students to discuss ways to get people who are nonconformists to conform to society's expectations, or ways that society can better accept their differences. (tolerance for differences, don't put others

---

 Fast Facts

According to a professor at Bowling Green State University, people who regularly volunteer their time get what's called a *helper's high*, which is similar to a runner's high. It's theorized that the good feeling is triggered by an increase in endorphins, the body's natural opiates.

Section VII Review
Answers

1. Alienation
2. Ostracism
3. nonconformist
4. Among others are the community you live in, your school, your ethnic or religious group.
5. loss of approval and support, alienation, ostracism
6. volunteer in different occupational fields
7. Answers will vary.

✉ **Where to Write**

The Catalog of Volunteer Opportunities
P.O. Box 117
New York, NY 10009
This $7.95 book lists organizations looking for volunteers.

---

are unhappy at work wish they had explored more options, through courses and summer jobs, before specializing in one field. Such people may decide to change careers later in life. They may find it worth all the effort to finally be in the right career.

If you are uncertain about a career for yourself, you might try some volunteer work with a variety of industries. For example, some veterinarians may appreciate your help in their offices a few hours a week. A local theater might need people to usher the attending crowds. A hospital, nursing home, or other health care facility might welcome some afterschool help.

The best experience for glimpsing careers comes not from the typical paying jobs that teens take to earn spending money. Instead, the best experience comes from volunteer positions that allow teens a behind-the-scenes look at what life in those positions is really like. Take volunteering seriously. The experience and relationships with mentors are more valuable than the money you might earn elsewhere.

> **Key Points** *Each person must work out a relationship with society that is rewarding. Finding suitable work is a major task that supports emotional health. Efforts to discover your own interests and talents are well spent.*

SECTION VII   REVIEW

Answer the following questions on a sheet of paper.
Learning the Vocabulary
The vocabulary terms in this section are *alienation, ostracism,* and *nonconformist.*
Fill in the blank with the correct answer.
1. _____ is self-chosen withdrawal from society.
2. _____ is rejection by society.
3. A person who is a _____ does not share society's values and therefore behaves in unconventional ways.

Learning the Facts
4. What elements make up society?
5. What are the disadvantages of having values that differ from society's?
6. Give some suggestions to a teenager who is unsure about a future career.

Making Life Choices
7. At this point in your life much of your time is spent in school, a type of self-contained society. The school staff has a set of values and expectations they impose on you. Which values and expectations do you accept? Are there any you reject? Give an example of a values confrontation you have experienced in school and how you handled it.

Answers to Fact or Fiction

   Here are the answers to the questions at the start of the chapter.

1. False. Emotional health is closely tied to physical health. **2.** False. The relationship with self is the most important. **3.** False. Once a person adopts values, that person continues to test those values and can change them when necessary. **4.** False. It is best to face and deal with all feelings as promptly as possible, even those that seem illogical or unpleasant. **5.** False. Emotionally healthy people do need others for friendship and support. This helps them stand on their own two feet. **6.** True. **7.** False. The best way to solve a problem is to think up many possible solutions, select from among them, try out solutions, evaluate results, and move on to try other solutions if the problem remains unsolved.

down for being different, try to find out what they do and think that is *like* society in general—not different)

RETEACH/BONUS

Here are some additional activities for the various sections of this chapter. You may want to use these activities to reteach certain concepts, or you may

choose them as alternatives to earlier activities. Some could also be used in conjunction with the Straight Talk feature below.

Write Positive Qualities. Have students list at least ten positive qualities about themselves under the heading "I am . . . ." Then have them share their lists in pairs, small groups, or with the entire class. Ask for conclusions: What did they

learn from this process? Students should see that it is often very difficult to say positive things about ourselves because we feel as though we are bragging, which we've been taught is wrong. It is easier to think of negative things. **(5–20 min.)**

Essay. Have students write a half-page description of who they are. They should include information from the chap-

(continued on next page)

STRAIGHT TALK

Sleep and Dreams

During sleep, people recover from physical and emotional stresses and injuries. They also dream. Chapter 1 said that people who had regular, adequate sleep were physically younger for their years than people who did not. This Straight Talk explores the importance of sleep and dreams and tells what is known about their effects on health.

I've always wondered what goes on during sleep. What exactly does sleep do for me?

This question is difficult to answer. Even though people spend a third of their lives sleeping, no one seems to know for sure what goes on during all that time. However, we know some of the things that happen physically: the blood pressure falls, breathing and heartbeat slow down, the muscles relax, and the body temperature falls. Perhaps most important, **growth hormone** is released at almost no time other than during sleep. Growth hormone provides for growth and renewal of body cells. It is probably growth hormone that brings about the physical recovery that sleep brings.

What happens if a person doesn't get enough sleep?

All body systems work less and less well. People become irritable, can't concentrate, think slowly, and lose

coordination. If deprived of sleep long enough, people may start feeling confused, begin seeing imaginary things, or even feel that they are going insane. Irregular sleep or chronic lack of sleep over years can shorten life. Other problems with too little sleep include fatigue, reduced ability to work, and increased risks of heart disease and digestive disorders. A few reports suggest that going ① without sleep for many months may even prove fatal, although such reports are extremely rare.

People who do not sleep enough at night tend to nod off during the day. This can be dangerous if they are driving. Drivers who fall asleep at the wheel cause 6,000 auto-related deaths a year.

Does everybody need eight hours of sleep a night?

People's sleep needs vary. About 2 percent of adults

Many people have difficulty sleeping.

habitually sleep ten hours a night, and some even more. Children need more than eight hours a night. Babies sleep 16 hours or even more; most adults, about six to seven hours. These differences seem to reflect the rate of cell growth, which is fastest in the young and which slows throughout life. Amazingly, though, by the age of 60, you will have slept for about 20 years of your life.

(Continued on next page)

Teacher Support Notes

① **Awake or Asleep:** For enrichment, tell students that people appear to be somewhat alert even while asleep. Studies have shown that people are more likely to wake up if their own names are spoken; sleeping mothers seem to be more responsive to soft noises from their children than other loud noises; and some subjects in studies have even learned to touch a switch to avoid electric shocks, while still asleep.

Fast Facts

The world record for going without sleep is 268 hours (11 days). Randy Gardner was 17 when he established this record.

ter, activities, and/or personal evaluation. Tell them that if there are any areas they want to learn more about or change, to indicate what they are and how they plan to approach the task. **(15 min.; Extend, Enrich)**

Evaluate Personal Solutions. Ask students to think of a recent problem they have had and what they did about it. Have them evaluate the effectiveness of their solutions using the three questions on page 40. Have them discuss what their plans are now, depending on how it turned out. Will they do anything differently in the future if this type of problem comes up? **(20 min.)**

Personal Qualities Store. Tell the students that they have just entered a special store where they can buy any personal qualities that they want. These qualities are all designed to make them feel good about themselves. Examples might be: a clear complexion, straight teeth, nice hair, self-confidence, and popularity. Have students list the qualities they would like to purchase. After they have made their selections, tell them that

---

✍ Fast Facts

Percentage of men who snore—53%; percentage of women who snore—23%.

Teacher Support Notes

① **Insomnia:** You may want to expand upon this discussion of insomnia. Tell students drugs create a dependence, as well as interfere with normal sleep patterns. This combination can leave a person exhausted and hooked. Better than taking drugs is to find the cause of the insomnia, with a health care provider if necessary. The most common cause is pain or discomfort. Other causes are anxiety, change of surroundings, change in schedule, caffeine, alcohol, and nicotine. Possible cures are changing bedding, relaxation exercises, "white" noise (air conditioner, fan, etc.), maintaining a regular daily schedule, exercise, and bedtime rituals (snacks, boring books, counting, etc.).

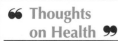

66 Thoughts on Health 99

Dreams are the touchstone of our character.
– Henry David Thoreau

Is there such a thing as beauty sleep? I've heard that an hour of sleep before midnight is worth two afterward.

There's nothing special about the hour of midnight. It is true, however that early hours of sleep are "deeper" than others, and therefore more restful. You go through several stages during sleep. First, after you start to sleep, your body temperature falls, and your brain slows its activity. At this point, you may suddenly jerk half awake—the sign of a sudden burst of brain activity that signals the start of the first stage of sleep. During the first stage of sleep, your muscles relax, and your heartbeat slows down.

Minutes later, you enter the second stage of sleep. The brain activity slows still more. Your eyes roll from side to side, but if they were to open, they would not see. This lasts for about half an hour.

The third and fourth stages of sleep bring very slow brain activity, relaxed muscles, and even breathing. This is the deepest sleep of all. It occurs mostly in the early hours of a night's sleep.

It is during the deepest stage that **REM sleep** occurs. (REM stands for "rapid eye movements.") The rapid eye movements seem to reflect dreaming, as if the person's eyes were following the actions of the dreams. You cycle several times a night through REM, into other stages of sleep, and back into REM.

That's amazing. I had no idea so much was going on while I was asleep. What do you suppose it's all for?

We don't know. But we do know that REM sleep seems to be essential to a person's well-being. People deprived of REM sleep become hostile, irritable, and anxious. When sound sleep is again possible, people who have been deprived of REM sleep will experience longer periods of REM to "make up" for what they've missed. This is one reason why sleeping pills may actually harm people. Many of them interfere with this important phase of sleep.

People who drink alcohol, consume caffeine, or smoke cigarettes may also be interrupting their normal sleep patterns without knowing it. Even a single alcoholic drink before bedtime has caused abnormal stoppage of breathing in sleep experiments. Caffeine and nicotine, the drug of tobacco, are both stimulants and can change the brain's activity to prevent normal sleep.

When I remember my dreams, they seem interesting. Do dreams have any functions?

There have been many theories about what purpose dreaming may serve. The emerging view seems to be that dreams are tied to the workings of the unconscious mind. Some researchers who earlier dismissed dreaming as meaningless or random now believe that dreams may have some significance.

Should I try to remember my dreams?

Even without conscious remembering, dreams may be useful. It is thought that dreaming helps the brain to make sense of events that occur in awake life. The theory holds that the subconscious mind "learns" the day's events during REM sleep. Even if people don't ① become aware of their dreams, says the theory, dreaming still affects their minds. Still, some people do try to remember their dreams and even write them down. They say this provides insights into their awake lives.

I'd like to know what my dreams mean. Is there a way I can interpret them?

Dreams can be random images, without any particular "message." However, they can also bring to your conscious attention some important concerns of your unconscious mind. Many psychologists believe that the images and events of dreams may be symbols for things or events in life. For example, if you feel threatened by a financial problem, you may dream of as they leave the store, they are required to throw away one old quality for each one purchased (i.e., bought self-confidence, throw away shyness). Have students decide which new quality will make the biggest difference in their lives and why. Discuss what influence the new qualities will have on their self-concepts. **(15 min., Critical Thinking)**

some physical threat, such as a dangerous animal. This makes logical sense. You cannot bring an image to mind that looks like "a threatening financial problem," but you can easily visualize other threats. Just for fun, Figure 2–2 provides some common dream symbols and one way of interpreting them.

① Probably the best way to respond to dreams that seem important to you is to take a few minutes to think about them. Ask yourself about issues you are dealing with in your life and how your dreams might reflect them. You might be able to think of some new ways of coping with the real problems of your awake life.

Mini Glossary

growth hormone: a hormone that promotes growth of body tissues.

REM (rapid eye movement pronounced as the syllable *rem* **) sleep:** the periods of sleep in which a person is dreaming.

Teacher Support Notes

① **Creative Solutions:** Tell students that many artists and scientists developed ideas for their art or their experiments while dreaming. For example, Nobel Prize winner, Dr. Otto Loewi, after studying the chemical transmission of nerve impulses for three years, dreamed of the same experiment three nights in a row. He did the experiment, which proved to be an important breakthrough.

✍ **Fast Facts**

By the age of 70, the average person has spent over 200,000 hours sleeping.

Images in dreams may be symbols for real-life events. The following dream symbols can be interpreted in many ways, and most experts rely on the dreamer's interpretation.

accident: something that has shocked or hurt the dreamer.

actor: a desire for public attention.

alien: some aspect of the dreamer's personality that seems out of character and foreign.

alligator: being gripped by fears, ideas, or urges that arise from inside.

baby: the dreamer as an infant, who needs care from others in order to survive.

basement: unknown feelings, hidden motives, or memories of the past.

beach: the line between the conscious and unconscious mind, and deep ideas and feelings.

blindness: a refusal to admit or understand something.

bomb: explosive emotions of the dreamer that may harm others.

burial: fear of death, or fear of disturbing memories.

butterfly: a change, emotional or physical, from something undesirable to something desirable.

cat: understanding and knowledge.

chicken: fear of abuse by others.

clothes: the dreamer's body image or a preferred image shown to others.

fish: the inner, unconscious self.

flying: mastery of a new skill.

frog: unconscious knowledge, and the power to change.

ghost: an old lingering fear.

legs: support systems, such as parents, friends, and religion.

lightning: release of tension or revenge.

mermaid: love of which the dreamer is not aware.

olive: peace, love, and kindness.

rainbow: harmony.

sand: passing of time.

shampoo: trying to forget or come to terms with something negative.

test: fear of failure.

Figure 2–2 Some Common Symbols in Dreams.

Vocabulary
1. **a.** alienation
b. growth hormone
c. REM **d.** thoughts
e. ostracism **f.** cortex
2. **a.** support system
b. status **c.** nonconformist **d.** emotional health
3. Answers will vary.
4. **a.** assertive, passive
b. emotion **c.** Values **d.** confrontation

Recall
Section I
1. relationship with one's self
2. The emotional warmth, energy, and enthusiasm of a self-confident person make other people feel good.
Section II
3. peace of mind, reduced stress, and improved health
4. Answers will vary; could include: recognize your negative thoughts, stop them, or replace them with positive thoughts.

Section III
5. It makes choosing behavior less confusing.
6. Would I state this value to others; Will I stand by this value when challenged; Do I act consistently and repeatedly in line with this value?
Section IV
7. They are natural.
8. anger, hurt, loneliness

CHAPTER REVIEW

LEARNING THE VOCABULARY

emotional health	support system	alienation
thoughts	mentor	ostracism
cortex	assertive	nonconformist
values	passive	growth hormone
emotion	aggressive	REM (rapid eye movement) sleep
status	confrontation	

Answer the following questions on a separate sheet of paper.

1. *Matching*—Match each of the following phrases with the appropriate vocabulary term from the list above:
   a. withdrawing from others because of differences that cannot be resolved
   b. a hormone that promotes growth of body tissues
   c. dream sleep
   d. conscious mental processes
   e. rejection by society
   f. the gray matter of the brain
2. *Word Scramble*—Use the clues from the phrases below to help you unscramble the terms:
   a. **popurts myests** A _____ _____ offers emotional help.
   b. **tautss** A person's standing in relation to others is called _____.
   c. **ocnitnfrsonom** A _____ has values that are different from society's and behaves unconventionally.
   d. **oamtineol tehhal** _____ _____ involves self, others and society.
3. Create a story using ten vocabulary terms from the list above. Underline all the vocabulary terms in the story.
4. a. An _____ person expresses feelings appropriately, while a _____ person remains quiet.
   b. Fear is an example of an _____.
   c. _____ are what a person views as important.
   d. An interaction in which one person expresses feelings to another is called _____.

RECALLING IMPORTANT FACTS AND IDEAS

1. What is considered to be the most important relationship in a person's life?
2. Why is self-confidence so attractive?
3. List three benefits of positive thinking.
4. Describe how to change a negative thought into a positive one.
5. What is the advantage of being aware of your values?
6. What three questions can you ask yourself about how strong your values are?
7. Why are all feelings considered acceptable?
8. Name three emotions people often deny.
9. What are some of the physical ways of expressing feelings?
10. Why is it helpful to express emotions physically?
11. What are the problems with passive and aggressive behaviors?
12. Why does assertive behavior improve your relationships with people?
13. What is the most common fear people have when meeting someone new?
14. What is the "SOFTEN" technique?
15. What are the six steps you should follow when faced with making a decision?
16. What does the middle class tend to put off?
17. What are the advantages of having a career you enjoy?

9. speaking, writing, crying, shouting
10. Not expressing emotions at all would be harmful. Physical expression allows you to think about what triggered the emotion initially.
Section V
11. With passive behavior a person's wishes are never expressed, and with aggressive behavior a person's feelings are expressed but at the expense of the feelings of another person.
12. It makes it easier, not harder, to get along with others, because you make your wishes and needs known to them. It is the key to cooperation.
13. fear of rejection
14. smile, open posture, forward lean, touch, eye contact, nod
Section VI
15. name the problem, describe it specifically, brainstorm, think about each solution, choose a solution and act on it, evaluate the outcome
Section VII
16. enjoying today so that there will be money or prestige for tomorrow
17. Rewarding work is the single most important aspect of adult life relating to well-being.

CRITICAL THINKING

1. Take the Life Choice Inventory on page 26. Then answer the following questions. Are you satisfied with your score? Why or why not? Why is it necessary to continually work towards improving your score? What do you have to gain by putting your efforts into improving your emotional health?
2. Think back over your recent experiences and identify a situation in which you did not act assertively.
   a. Write a description of the experience. Include the reason for the conflict as you perceive it, the verbal interchange that occurred, and the outcome of the situation.
   b. Analyze your behavior. According to the definitions provided in Section V, were your responses passive or aggressive?
   c. Write a revised version of the incident in which you act assertively. Describe the feelings you would probably experience after such an exchange.
3. Maintaining emotional health is easier for a person with a strong, well-developed support system than for someone who remains isolated from others. Examine how extensive your support system is by making a list of all your supports. Be sure to include people you have relationships with in all areas of your life. Which people on your list would you consider to be the most valuable supports? Are you satisfied with the support system you have developed for yourself? Describe any changes or improvements you would like to make.

ACTIVITIES

1. Create a collage of magazine illustrations of different emotions.
2. Make a list of activities in your school and community that enhance emotional health. Suggest other activities the school could offer.
3. Interview a person that you believe has excellent emotional health. Include the following questions in your interview. Hand in a tape or short transcript of the interview.
   a. Why do you feel comfortable with yourself?
   b. Do you have a strong support system?
   c. Why do you feel you have been able to develop healthy relationships?
   d. What are some of the methods you use to handle the demands placed on you?
4. Devise a list of community resources for people seeking help for emotional problems. Provide the name, address, and phone number of each agency.
5. Write a short report on how school has affected your emotional health in the past year.
6. Keep an emotion diary for two days. List the emotions you felt, the situations that prompted them, and the outlets you used to deal with them.
7. Select a popular song that depicts a particular emotion. Discuss the music and lyrics that portray emotion.

MAKING DECISIONS ABOUT HEALTH

1. You have just been treated unfairly and are uptight and tense. You return to your room where you pace around, shaking your head, many unsaid remarks still tumbling in your thoughts. Several times you start to pick up the phone, but there's no one you want to bother with your problems. Several times you start towards the door, but there's no place you want to go, feeling so uptight. Finally, you settle down, still angry, and try to do some homework, but you end the day with a knot in your stomach. Describe how you could have handled this situation to reduce your distress.

CHAPTER 3 PLANNER

OVERVIEW

Chapter 3 is 26 pages long and divided into the four sections listed to the right. Major learning outcomes are also listed to the right. Briefly, this chapter introduces students to the concepts of human needs, personality development, self-esteem, peer groups, peer pressure, and deviant peer groups. It stresses the importance of having our needs met, but doing so in a constructive rather than destructive way. Special emphasis is given to peer pressure and selection of peer groups during the teen years. The chapter has a theme: all that we are and all that we become depend on the development of self-esteem and the choices we make in our attempts to satisfy our needs.

MAKING LIFE CHOICES RESOURCES

A variety of activities, handouts, quizzes, and tests are available in *Making Life Choices* supplementary material. You may pick and choose from those materials as appropriate for your amount of class time and the ability levels of your students. One of the resources you might want to consider using is:
Overhead
• Maslow's Hierarchy of Needs

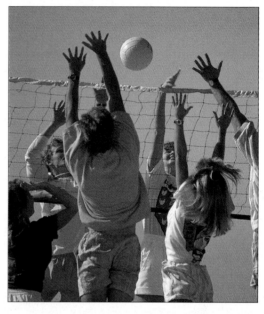

CHAPTER 3
Your Changing Personality

SUGGESTED RESOURCES

Student Readings
1. Elkind, D. *All Grown Up and No Place to Go.* Reading, MA: Addison-Wesley, 1984.
Teacher Readings
1. Brown, Lynn Mikel and Gilligan, Carol. *Meeting at the Crosswords.* Harvard University Press, 1992.
2. Feirfstein, Bruce. *Real Men Don't Eat Quiche.* New York: Pocket Books, 1982. A humorous look at male gender roles.
3. Marcia, J.E. "Identity in Adolescence." In J. Adelson (Ed.), *Handbook of Adolescent Psychology.* New York: Wiley, 1980.
Videos
1. *Who Am I?* Cambridge Educational. 800-468-4227.
Software
Multidimensional Personality Evaluation. This program helps students better understand themselves through personality evaluation. Opportunities for Learning, Inc. 800-243-7116.

CHAPTER PROJECT

Have the class go to the library and research destructive cults, cliques, or gangs. In groups of four or five, have students pick one cult or group to study by reading articles and books, and viewing videotapes if available. Have each group member

Activity To Introduce Chapter

A. Put this quote (or another of your choice from this chapter) on the board or on an overhead and leave it up throughout the chapter: "To be nobody but yourself, in a world which is doing its best, night and day, to make you everybody else, means to fight the hardest battle which any human being can fight, and never stop fighting." —e. e. cummings
B. Write these words on the board or an overhead: **1.** friendly, **2.** helpful, **3.** honest, **4.** funny, **5.** responsible, **6.** grateful, **7.** patient, **8.** good listener, **9.** empathic, **10.** inventive, **11.** generous, **12.** sensitive, **13.** loyal, **14.** kind.

OUTCOMES

After reading and studying this chapter, you will be able to:

✓ Describe the eight stages of life according to Erik Erikson.

✓ Discuss the importance of developing an identity during the teen years.

✓ Summarize Maslow's Hierarchy of Needs.

✓ Describe how sexual maturation and gender identity affect personality.

✓ Discuss how positive self-talk, positive body image, and self-acceptance help in the development of high self-esteem.

✓ Identify the value of positive peer groups. Identify the dangers of deviant peer groups.

CONTENTS

I. Life's Stages and Human Needs
II. Gender and Personality
III. Developing Self-Esteem
IV. The Importance of Peer Groups

Straight Talk: Dealing with Peer Pressure

FACT OR FICTION

What do you think? Are the following statements true or false? If you think they are false, then say what is true.

1. One of the most important tasks of the teen years is to work out an individual identity.
2. Human beings need the respect of others even more than they need shelter.
3. People with high self-esteem see only the good parts of themselves and ignore the bad parts.
4. People who imagine themselves as greater or more successful than they are need to get a grip on reality and stop dreaming.
5. A peer group is usually a negative and destructive force that changes good kids into bad kids.

(Answers on page 68)

■ **Reminder:** Knowing how to study can increase your knowledge, improve your grades, *and* cut down on your study time. See the *Studying Health* section at the front of your text for some suggestions to help you study this chapter.

---

write a one-page report on the kinds of destructive effects these groups have had on individuals, as well as our society. Have students share reports at the end of the chapter.

Now have the students remember a time when they displayed each of these qualities. On a piece of paper have them jot down their examples for each one. Don't let them give up until they have an example for each one. Give them ten points for each example. Then say, "If you have 140 points, you have a pretty good start on developing self-esteem. You are a fine human being. If you have less than 140 points you are still a fine human being, but your memory is shot!!" This activity will show the students that everyone has good qualities, but using them requires daily practice.

NOT ENOUGH TIME?*

You could easily spend five–ten days teaching this chapter if students read the entire chapter, do a fair number of the suggested activities in the teacher's edition, and complete a sampling of the handouts from the resource material accompanying this text. You may, of course, have less time to spend on this chapter, although you should keep in mind that this is a very important chapter because so many of our social problems and so many personal problems, including teen suicide, are associated with low self-esteem, lack of support groups, and poor choices in peer group selection. If you find you have only two or three days to devote to this chapter, the following are some suggestions to help you make sure you cover the key topics.

TIME	SUGGESTIONS
1 Day	Assign Sections I and II prior to class. Also assign Activity 1.3 from Section I. In class have the students do Activities 2.2 and 2.3 from Section II. Conclude the class with a combination of pop quizzes given under the Evaluate Sections I and II. You may want to assign reteaching activities from the resource materials for those students doing poorly on the quiz.
2 Days	On day 2 assign Sections III and IV, including the introductory activity at the beginning of the chapter. During the class do Activities 3.1 and 3.4 in Section III, and 4.2 in Section IV.
3 Days	On day 3 assign Activity 4.5 prior to class. Have a class discussion on 4.5. In addition do Activities 3.2, 4.3, and 4.4 in class as time allows. Use quizzes in the Evaluate Sections III and IV to review material.

*Please refer to the 18-week daily lesson plans in the supplementary material for additional suggestions.

Answers to "Fact or Fiction"

For answers to "Fact or Fiction" questions, see page 68.

In this section students will learn the:
1. Two popular theories of personality, one developed by Eric Erikson, the other by Abraham Maslow.
2. Ways Erikson's developmental stages combine with Maslow's hierarchy of needs to help people understand how personality develops.

Activity 1.1

List of Needs. Have students list the needs they feel they must have satisfied to live a happy and productive life. Have them look up the word "need" in the dictionary. Help them out by starting them thinking about when they were first born. Ask the question, "When you were first born, what were your needs?" Then tell them to progress chronologically to where they are now, listing any needs they feel they had or have now, including fulfilled and unfulfilled needs. Have a class discussion of the needs listed and why they feel those needs are so important to them. Collect, or have them keep the lists in their notebooks to be used later in the chapter.

Teacher Support Notes

① **Picking Personality Traits:** Have the students list traits that they feel best describe their own personalities. Give them two or three minutes and then put up an overhead transparency with the following traits listed: aggressive, caring, impulsive, confident, outgoing, cooperative, sincere, creative, curious, careless, blunt, courteous, tactful, narrow-minded, pessimistic, intelligent, realistic, selfish, humble, nervous, optimistic, sensitive, mature, proud, honest, humorous, and serious. Give them an additional two minutes to add to their lists. Then, after each trait they have listed, have them write a (P) if they think that trait is a positive one and an (N) if they think that trait is a negative one. Have students put their papers in their notebooks to be used later in the chapter.

> ❝ **Thoughts on Health** ❞
>
> *We have no more right to consume happiness without producing it than to consume wealth without producing it.*
> – **George Bernard Shaw**

50

You may overhear someone say, "Leticia is so great to be around" or "I think Mr. Wood is awful." In each case, the speaker is reacting to Leticia's or Mr. Wood's personalities. Your **personality** is how people see the total "you," on the outside. There is much more to you than what's seen from the outside, but at first your personality is all that shows.

Personalities are not fixed for life. Each person has certain tendencies, and these are inborn. Personalities can keep changing through life, however. A baby may be born shy or outgoing, but the future child, teen, or adult can become more outgoing or more quiet. You are continually molding your personality to fit the picture you have of who you really are, your **self-image.**

This chapter explains some influences that affect personality. It also guides you in developing a healthy sense of self.

SECTION 1

Life's Stages and Human Needs

Certain patterns of change take place during people's lives and affect their personalities. When people see the patterns of their lives, they can make conscious choices that would not be possible otherwise. In this section you will learn about two personality theories that may help you better understand your own development and behavior.

Erikson's Eight Stages of Life

A famous thinker, Erik Erikson, has described how people become who they are. Erikson's widely accepted theory says that people move through eight stages in the course of their lives. In each stage they learn important things about themselves and about the world.

Each stage ideally consists of positive development, and each builds on the one before it. The one-year-old learns basic trust as an infant, for example, and then can progress toward becoming independent in the next year. Each stage also has, however, a negative side. The less well one task is achieved, the less successful will be the next. The eight stages are shown in Figure 3–1 on page 52.

Erikson's theory can be destructive if it is applied too heavy-handedly. It is not meant to be a grading scale. You are not "better" if you are higher on the scale or "worse" if you are lower. No one has had a perfect childhood—not your parents, your teachers, nor the authors of this book. No one moves perfectly through life's tasks.

The positive path of development, according to Erikson, might go like this. If, as an infant, toddler, and preschooler, you received mostly approval from the adults in your life, you progressed confidently from one stage to the next. By the time you started school, you were sure of your ability to master new tasks. As a result, you worked confidently and persistently through the school years, even in the face of frustrations. You became industrious.

A person who starts out strong like this develops a strong, positive self-image. By the end of the teen years, the successful person has achieved a positive sense of identity. From there, it is natural to move to the first stage of adulthood—the stage of building a mature, intimate relationship with another person. Intimacy and dating are later topics of this book.

Suppose, however, that a person's life story is primarily negative. Suppose the baby is neglected, frightened, beaten, or abused. The baby is already mistrustful and fearful of the environment. If faced with ridicule and punishment, the child will become unruly or afraid to try new things.

Activity 1.2

The *Trust* Game. Play the "trust" game. Have each student choose a partner—someone they "trust." Decide who will trust in the other person and which partner will assume that trust. Have the partner who is putting his or her trust in the other stretch his or her arms straight out to the side and on the count of three, keeping the body rigid, fall back into the arms of the partner who will catch him or her. Then reverse the procedure. Set ground rules:

1. Do not make students do this if they do not wish to participate.

2. Do not let students do this activity if you feel there is some physical reason that they would not be able to "catch" their partners. (example: mismatch in size, cast on an arm or leg, poor vision, etc.)

3. You may want to take your class to a gym to do this game. More room and mats would make the game safer.

4. If you choose to do the game in the classroom, have maintenance bring a lightweight, folding tumbling mat to your classroom. Place the mat at the front of the room and have one or two sets of

(continued on next page)

The child develops guilt and a negative self-image ("I'm not OK"). This person may have trouble rising to challenges in school, sticking with demanding tasks, and forming a strong identity as a teenager. Such a person is unlikely to be ready to form a successful relationship with another person and may become an inadequate parent, later on.

If you see yourself at all in the negative description just given, you are not alone. Many people who cross your path in a day feel they are "not OK" to some extent, falling short of the standard they think has been set for them. It's normal to feel "not OK," but you can grow out of it.

Key Points *Erikson's theory divides the human life span into eight stages. Each stage presents different developmental tasks. One must successfully complete earlier tasks before moving on to later ones.*

The Tasks of the Teen Years

The teen years present a demanding task to the developing person—that of working out an individual identity. To develop an identity means to partially move away from what is known and to explore the unknown. Teens try out new ideas, develop new words, and give new meanings to old phrases. "Cool," "awesome," or "radical" have had special meanings when spoken by some teens. Clothes, music, and art are other areas in which teens use their imagination to explore and search for their identity.

At the same time that teens are searching for an individual identity, they may tightly associate with a group identity, especially in the early teen years. This may seem to work against the struggle for individuality. However, it is really a step toward independence, because joining a group is a way of joining the larger society outside the family.

Teens are also developing a new way of thinking. Children think only in concrete

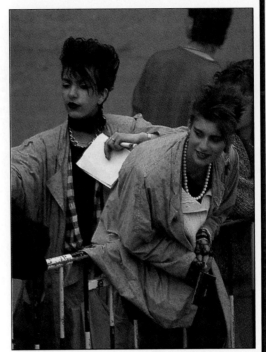

To find their identity, teens have to experiment with different styles.

terms, relying on past experiences to predict the future. They experience things as they come. Teenagers, though, begin to think in more abstract terms. They can imagine what might happen "if this" or "should that" be the case.

① Teenagers can consider **variables** and use logic to make predictions of what might

M̲I̲N̲I̲ G̲LOSSARY

personality: the characteristics of a person that are apparent to others.
② **self-image:** the characteristics that a person sees in himself or herself.
variables: changeable factors that affect outcomes.

Teacher Support Notes

① **Personal Identities:** Ask students which of their behaviors indicate their personal identities. Do they believe they have identities?

② **Forming Your Identity:** Ask students if they agree that a person can be forming his or her own individual identity by joining a group. Do they think belonging to a group hinders the person's ability to develop a personal identity?

✉ Where to Write

Health Education Services
10,000 Culver Blvd.
Department H2
Culver City, CA 90223

partners do it at once, depending on the space you have available.

Activity 1.3
Listing Positive/Negative Comments. Tell students that the negative words we say to each other can be as destructive and damaging as a physical attack and the effects are often more long lasting. Words hurt. Words help form our personalities. There are positive words or phrases that make us feel good about ourselves and there are negative words or phrases that make us feel bad about ourselves. *The way* someone says something can affect us in a positive or negative way. Have the students, during the next 24 hours, jot down every positive comment they hear either about themselves or someone else. Also have them jot down every negative comment they hear. The next day in class count the number of positive comments and the number of negative comments.

Have a class discussion on the observations they made while writing the comments. Stimulate discussion by asking: Where were most negative comments made—directly to the person or behind

Teacher Support Notes

① **Personalizing Erikson:** Have students summarize in their own words the positive and negative sides of each of Erikson's stages. Then ask them to rate their own development in each of the first four or five stages, depending upon their ages, on a scale from one to ten, with ten being the highest development. Ask for volunteers to give their summaries and to discuss their ratings.

② **Teacher Background:** Erikson said that each of the eight stages is characterized by a primary crisis or dilemma, which he called a *development task.* An individual's failure to resolve or succeed at these tasks throws off the individual's balanced development and makes life harder. Erikson considered answering the question "Who am I?" to be the most important task of the teen years.

❝ Thoughts on Health ❞

The confidence which we have in ourselves gives birth to much of that which we have in others.
— **Francois La Rochefoucauld**

1 Infancy (0 to 1) To learn trust. The infant learns that needs will be met. (If neglected or abused, the person learns distrust that can last a lifetime.)

2 Toddler stage (1 to 2) To learn independence. The toddler learns self-will. (If thwarted in this development, the adult may remain dependent and feel inadequate.)

3 Preschool age (3 to 5) To learn initiative (the ability to think and act without being told to do so). The child explores with curiosity and imagination. (If discouraged in this development, the adult may avoid leadership and risks.)

4 School age (6 to 12) To develop industriousness (earnest, steady effort). The child has confidence to pursue self-chosen goals. (If this development fails, the adult will lack social confidence and will perform poorly.)

5 Adolescence (13 to 20) To develop an identity. The teenager develops a strong sense of self, goals, and timing; and becomes busy learning how to fit into the social circle—as leader, follower, female, male. The adolescent picks out role models and grows with confidence. (The failure of this development produces a confused person without a secure sense of direction.)

6 Young adulthood (21 to 40) To develop intimacy (close, personal relationships). The young adult can commit to love, to work, and to a social group. (Failure leads to avoidance of intimacy, misuse of sexuality, isolation, and destructiveness.)

7 Adulthood (41 to 60) To develop generativity (giving yourself and your talents to others.) The mature adult moves through life with confidence, taking pride in accomplishments. (The negative side of this is stagnation, self-involvement, and failure to encourage others.)

8 Older adulthood (61 and older) To retain ego integrity (satisfaction with life.) The person feels fulfilled and faces death with serenity. (The adult who has not moved positively through earlier stages experiences isolation, despair, and fears of death.)

Figure 3–1 Eight Stages of Life According to Erikson. The numbered paragraphs describe the tasks a healthy person will master at each stage. ②

that person's back? Why do we handle negative things the way we do? Do you believe you received more positive or negative comments from adults when you were a child? How do you think that affected you? **(Extend, Enrich)**

Activity 1.4
Guest Speaker. Have a foreign exchange student or a guest speaker from another country come into your

classroom and discuss identity and differences in culture, race, social norms, etc. Also have that person explain how he or she feels about learning about other cultures or races and how this knowledge can bring about a unity among all people. **(Multicultural)**

EVALUATE
SECTION I

Activity 1.5
Pop Quiz.
1. Eric Erikson said that each of his eight stages of development builds on the one before it. (T)
2. Your personality is the picture you have of who you really are. (F)
3. Your personality is how you see yourself on the inside. (F)
4. Personalities are fixed for life. (F)

(continued on next page)

---

happen. They can plan to achieve desired outcomes, and they spend hours with one another exploring "what ifs." (One caution: people develop on their own timetables. Although many people develop these high-level reasoning abilities in their teens, many others are still developing along these lines after entering college.)

The hours teenagers spend in each other's company permit them to practice reasoning, a skill that gives them a great advantage in working out relationships with others. Thinking develops considerably during adolescence.

Many teens feel emotions in extremes:

- Loving parents and then hating them.
- Feeling like total successes and then like total failures. ②
- Wanting freedom and needing safety.
- Being thrilled with new experiences and seeking comfort in familiarity.

Teens imitate others, yet search for a unique identity. They may be generous and unselfish one day, self-centered and greedy the next.

These extremes are all normal, and experimenting with them leads to the development of an identity. Teens need to keep their options open. At times almost anything they try may seem a possible way to pattern their lives.

Although it may sound as if the teen years are "out of control," they are not. The teen is in the driver's seat, steering a course to the future self. Wrong turns are everywhere, and mistakes are common. Luckily, few teens permanently damage themselves by their wrong turns. If they are harmed, it is usually by allowing their mistakes and false starts to damage their internal sense of self-worth, their self-esteem.

A person who emerges from the teen years feeling "OK" can move on to adult tasks without difficulty. The less fortunate teen who internalizes a sense of self-doubt ①

and failure may have difficulty in performing the tasks of adulthood. Happily, much is known about enhancing even a sagging sense of self-esteem, as you will see in a later section.

Key Points ➤ *People develop their identities and their ability to reason during the teen years. This prepares them to accomplish the tasks of adulthood.*

Human Needs According to Maslow

Erikson saw life's tasks as associated with age groups. The theorist Abraham Maslow, in contrast, described a **hierarchy,** or a sort of ladder, of human **needs** that people of all ages experience. He linked these needs to life's accomplishments. Some people don't even know they have needs, but everyone does.

According to Maslow, people will struggle to meet their basic needs before they can begin to think about "higher" needs. Hunger is a basic need. People who are hungry may not be able to think about their need for love. Once the basic need for food is met, however, other needs naturally arise. In other words, needs build on one another. When you have met the most basic ones, you become aware of, and can strive to meet, the "higher" ones (see Figure 3–2 on the next page).

Most basic are needs related to survival—needs for food, clothing, and shelter (physiological needs). Next are the needs to feel physically safe and secure (safety needs). If safe and secure, people are free to notice

MINI GLOSSARY

---

hierarchy: a ranking system in which each thing is placed above or below others.
needs: urgent wants for necessary things. ①

❝ Thoughts on Health ❞

It is better to know some of the questions than all of the answers.
– James Thurber

Teacher Support Notes

① **Understanding**
Internalize: Internalize is a term that's becoming more commonplace—students should know and understand it. It means to make something such as a value, belief, or idea part of a person's permanent personality or mental makeup. The belief or idea that is internalized becomes part of the person's guiding principles. It may be a conscious or unconscious decision to internalize the idea.

② **Erikson vs. Maslow:** Ask students to explain a basic difference between Erikson and Maslow (Erikson's theory says tasks progress primarily by age; Maslow's says they develop by needs).

5. The major task of the teen years is to work out an individual identity. (T)
6. Teenagers often use variables to make predictions of what might happen. (T)
7. Teenagers and children think basically the same way. (F)

8. Abraham Maslow believes that people will struggle to meet their basic needs before they begin to think about higher needs. (T)
9. All people have a common need to be respected and have the esteem of others. (T)
10. If you get a negative start in life during the early formative years, your chances of living a productive, happy life are doomed. (F)

Activity 1.6
Making Maslow Pyramids. On 8 1/2 × 11-inch paper, have the students draw a pyramid and divide it into five horizontal parts. In the bottom part have them write physical needs; next—safety needs; next—love needs; next—esteem needs;

---

66 Thoughts on Health 99

He who is not satisfied with himself will grow.
– Chinese Proverb

Teacher Support Notes

① **Overhead— Maslow's Hierarchy of Needs:** Your supplementary material contains an overhead of this illustration, which might be useful at this point.

② **More on Maslow:** If you want to extend the lesson on Maslow, tell students that Maslow believed that a person whose basic needs were met, but who failed to fulfill higher needs, became sad, apathetic, and alienated. Maslow identified what he called *meta-needs*, which were his ideas as to the ways in which people could express their self-actualization. These needs are wholeness, perfection, completion, justice, richness, simplicity, awareness, beauty, goodness, uniqueness, playfulness, truth, autonomy, and meaningfulness. Ask students if they know anyone who has these needs. As the text states, few people reach this level of needs.

54 UNIT 2 Your Emotional and Social Health

Figure 3–2 Maslow's Hierarchy of Needs ┐①

their needs to be loved and to feel emotionally secure (love needs). If those needs are met, people can try to get in touch with their needs for respect and esteem. Given that, they can seek to achieve the ultimate: **self-actualization.** This is the realization of their full potential: becoming "all that they can be." Only a few people, perhaps 1 to 2 percent, ever develop that far.

Like all people, teens share the common need for respect and the esteem of others. Many people say that some of their best experiences as teenagers involved some sort of service to others. To be helpful, especially to those who really need help, fills a

Once basic needs are met, a person can aspire to meet higher needs.

need to feel important and to be appreciated by others. Being helpful enhances self-esteem.

Performing needed service to others helps also in the development of identity. Teens who work together during disasters to assist other people may "find themselves" (develop part of their identities) in the process. Other teens who join service clubs that volunteer help in the community may find that this experience adds to self-understanding and identity.

No one ever arrives at the point of being completely finished with any level of needs. Needs at all levels surface every day. Still, at a given time in life, needs on one or two levels take center stage in importance.

Needs never end. As soon as one is met, another takes its place. It can be said that life is a series of needs to be satisfied or problems to be solved, but this is not a complaint. It gives us something to work on, ② which is itself a need we all seem to have.

Key Points *Personality develops throughout life, according to Erikson. The development is propelled by the needs in Maslow's hierarchy.*

SECTION I   REVIEW

Answer the following questions on a sheet of paper.
Learning the Vocabulary
The vocabulary terms in this section are *personality, self-image, variables, hierarchy, needs,* and *self-actualization.*
1. What is the difference between personality and self-image?
2. _____ is the highest attainable state in Maslow's _____ of Needs.
3. Write a sentence using each vocabulary term.

Learning the Facts
4. According to Erik Erikson, how many stages do people move through in their lives?
5. How does the thinking of teenagers differ from children's thinking?
6. What are some of the extremes in emotions that teens may feel?

and next—self-actualization needs. Have them read the section of the text *Human Needs According To Maslow* on pages 53 and 54. Now hand back or have the students take out of their notebooks Activity 1.1. Have them copy those needs below the pyramid they drew. Now have the students look at each need and decide if it is a physical need (PN), a safety need (SN), a love need (LN), an esteem need (EN), or a self-actualization need (SA). Have

them write the corresponding letters by each need. Now, by each need, have them write either *daily* (if that need has to be met everyday) or *not daily* (if that need is not an every day need). Finally, have a class discussion on needs—how we satisfy them, their importance, etc. Here you may want to bring up the issues of cults and gangs. What need do these organizations try to fill? You could also talk about the homeless and their needs.

(30 min.; Extend, Enrich, Critical Thinking)

FOCUS
SECTION II

In this section students will learn about the:
1. Two parts of human development that

(continued on next page)

---

7. What are some of the most basic human needs according to Maslow?
8. What percentage of people are able to reach self-actualization?

Making Life Choices

9. List in order Maslow's Hierarchy of Needs (refer to Figure 3–2 on page 54 if you need help). Identify what your specific needs are in each of Maslow's major categories. Try to come up with at least six items for each of the five areas. Make a list of some steps you could take that you believe would help to bring you closer to self-actualization.

SECTION II

Gender and Personality

Two parts of human development change rapidly during the teen years. One is the development of physical gender characteristics. Another, which goes along with the physical events, is the development of gender identity—a personality with maleness or femaleness.

Physical Maturation

Children grow and mature physically from birth to adulthood. However, not until some time around the early teen years do they enter the period of sexual maturation called **adolescence** or **puberty**. During these years, nature seems in a hurry to complete the final details needed for full adulthood. The adolescent growth spurt is a time of rapid growth and change (see Figure 3–3 on the next page). It includes the development of an identity that lasts a lifetime.

During adolescence, individual growth rates vary tremendously. Generally, girls begin an intensive growth spurt by age 10

or 11, while boys hit this time of rapid growth at 12 or 13. Two healthy, normal adolescents of the same age may vary in height by a foot. At this time in life, external standards such as growth charts and weight tables are all but useless. To take them too seriously is a mistake—a mistake that could lead to a damaged self-image.

As they grow toward adulthood, girls naturally develop more body fat than do boys. This normal fat is needed for breast formation and other normal development. Sadly, most normal-weight high school girls fear this fat and, when asked, report that they are overweight. Especially damaging are comparisons of their normal, living bodies with the super-skinny models seen in advertisements. The models are not for real.

In contrast to girls, boys naturally develop more muscle tissue. As is true in girls, this tissue grows in response to hormones.

The hormonal changes of adolescence greatly affect every organ, including the brain. Hormones also bring mood changes and sexual feelings. (You will learn more about the development of sexual feelings and the reproductive system in later chapters.)

As the body improves in coordination, movements requiring control and skill become possible. Athletics, acting, dancing, and playing musical instruments all may now be in reach.

MINI GLOSSARY

self-actualization: the reaching of one's full potential; the highest attainable state in Maslow's hierarchy of needs.
adolescence: the period of growth from the beginning of puberty to full maturity. Timing of adolescence varies from person to person.
puberty (PYOO-ber-tee): the period of life in which a person becomes physically capable of reproduction.

Section I Review
Answers
1. Personality is how others see you; self-image is how you see yourself.
2. Self-actualization, Hierarchy
3. Answers will vary.
4. eight
5. Children think in concrete terms, teenagers in more abstract terms.
6. Answers will vary; could include: complete success vs. complete failure, loving parents then hating them, wanting freedom and needing safety, and new experiences vs. comfort in familiarity.
7. hunger; survival, including clothing and shelter
8. 1 to 2 percent
9. Answers will vary.

Fast Facts

34% of women say they control their household's TV remote control; 56% of men make this claim.

---

occur rapidly during the teen years—physical maturation and the development of gender identity.

2. Ways stereotypes can stifle individual development of your potential as a person.

Activity 2.1

Gender Differences. Show a picture of three babies—one dressed in blue; one in pink; and one in green (or color other than pink or blue). Answer no questions about the pictures. Tell the students you are turning them loose in a toy store and they must pick out five toys for each baby. Then discuss the results. How did the toys selected for the baby in green differ from those cho-sen for the babies dressed in pink or blue? Ask them why they chose those toys. **(15 min., Critical Thinking)**

TEACH
SECTION II
(Guided and Independent Practice)

Activity 2.2

Listing Gender Traits. Tell students that within the human species we have male and female gender roles.

🖎 Fast Facts

In 1880 the average male didn't reach full height until sometime between the ages of 23 and 25 and the average female not until the ages of 19 or 20. Today, males reach their full height from 18 to 20 and females from 16 to 17.

Teacher Support Notes

① **Additional Facts on Muscle Development:**
Tell students:
a. Girls increase their strength by about 45% during puberty; boys by 65%.
b. Boys develop greater amounts of oxygen-carrying hemoglobin. This fact, along with the male's larger heart and lungs, give him greater endurance.
c. Boys are only slightly stronger than girls before puberty. After puberty, the average male can bench press about 1.7 times as much weight as the average female.
d. Boys secrete about 30 to 200 micrograms of testosterone each day, following puberty. Girls secrete from 5 to 20 micrograms. Because testosterone stimulates muscle growth, this difference means that girls do not develop as much muscle tissue as do boys in response to exercise.

56 UNIT 2 Your Emotional and Social Health

Females:

Growth
Rapid gains peak around age 12, then growth slows to a stop at maturity.

Hair
Hair grows on underarm and genital area, and other body hair may grow coarser and longer.

Skin
Acne may develop.

Body shape and composition
Hips widen, fat deposits collect, and breasts develop.

Hormonal changes
Ovaries produce more estrogens and progesterone.

Reproductive organs
Uterus and ovaries enlarge; genitals enlarge; ovum ripening begins; and monthly menstruation begins.

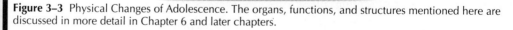

Males:

Growth
Rapid gains peak around age 14, then growth slows to a stop at maturity.

Hair
Hairline of forehead begins to move upward (recede). Hair grows on face, in underarms, and around genitals. Other body hair grows coarser and longer.

Skin
Acne may develop.

Body shape and composition
Muscle tissue develops.

Hormonal changes
Testicles produce more testosterone.

Reproductive organs
Penis and testicles enlarge; sperm production begins.

Figure 3–3 Physical Changes of Adolescence. The organs, functions, and structures mentioned here are discussed in more detail in Chapter 6 and later chapters. ①

For some, the changes occur faster than the individuals can adjust to them. For others, the changes come so slowly that they fear being left behind. Most important is to accept and welcome your emerging identity. The teen years soon pass; you then join society's adults as an equal.

As boys and girls become young men and women, their social relationships must also change. They must develop new ways of dealing with their peers and work out new rules to govern their relationships. Physical maturity does not mean the end of growth and change—far from it. Mental, emotional,

Using one- or two-word answers, have
students list the personality traits they
feel are considered feminine by our society. In a separate column they are to list
the personality traits they feel are associated with masculinity. Have a class discussion. Students should identify any
traits that could be either masculine or
feminine. **(15 min., Critical Thinking)**

Activity 2.3

Gender Roles. Have the students
number a paper from 1 to 20. Read the
following job titles and have the students
write an F if they think it is a "female" job
description, an M if they think it is a
"male" job description, or a B if they think
"both," either male or female, could fit into
that job description.
1. welder; **2.** nurse; **3.** doctor;
4. lawyer; **5.** construction worker;
6. telephone operator; **7.** TV news

anchor; **8.** telephone lineperson;
9. president of a large company;
10. U.S. senator; **11.** collegiate volleyball player; **12.** data processor;
13. circuit judge; **14.** officer in the
armed forces; **15.** principal of a high
school; **16.** elementary school teacher;
17. high school teacher; **18.** chef
(cook); **19.** plumber; **20.** ballet dancer
Have a class discussion about why

(continued on next page)

and spiritual growth and change can continue for a lifetime. But the changes that have taken place during adolescence do tend to become a permanent part of a person's identity. ①

> **Key Points** *Adolescence is a time of rapid physical and mental change that makes possible the development of sexual and other forms of maturity.*

Gender Identity

Your personality is affected by your **gender.** You are male or female, and this helps mold your behaviors and your self-image.

The male or female roles people play, known as their **gender roles,** depend on the expectations of society. From birth on, each society trains individuals to act as it expects male or female people to act. Not everyone adopts all of society's gender roles. In fact, if enough people find them a bad fit, the roles themselves may change. The parts of the male or female role that a person accepts and lives by become that person's **gender identity.**

Society responds even to its newest members according to its gender roles. People can be overheard to say, when observing a newborn boy, "My, how big and strong he is!" If the baby is a girl, they might say, "She's so tiny and delicate!" Actually, newborns differ in size, strength, and activity not according to gender but according to their individual hereditary makeups.

Toddlers begin to learn gender roles before they can even talk, and two-year-olds show real understanding of these roles. By age 11, the patterns are deeply ingrained; they are virtually cast in concrete in adults. Young teens, with their newly maturing sexual bodies, often exaggerate these roles to make sure that those around them are aware of their **femininity** or **masculinity.**

Today, if you are male, you have probably grown up under pressure to "succeed"; to be

**Society imposes gender roles
on its members.**

strong, brave, and independent; and to hide emotions. You may have been encouraged to play rough games, to defeat others, and not to get too close emotionally.

If you are female, you probably grew up with demands to be beautiful or attractive and sensitive to others' feelings. Perhaps you were urged to be artistic, to avoid aggression, and to take care of others. ②

Complete acceptance of society's gender roles is not always easy or desirable. People are individuals. Roles that may fit one person perfectly may be unsuitable for another. If everyone accepted roles without question, societies would never change. And strict roles—**stereotypes**—may stifle individual development. No one is treated fairly when allowed only a limited space in which to grow toward personhood.

MINI GLOSSARY

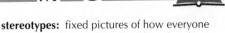

stereotypes: fixed pictures of how everyone in a group is thought to be; ideas that do not recognize anyone's individuality.

gender: the classification of being male or female.

gender roles: roles assigned by society to people of each gender.

gender identity: that part of a person's self-image that is determined by the person's gender.

femininity: traits, including biological and social traits, associated with being female.

masculinity: traits, including biological and social traits, associated with being male.

Teacher Support Notes

① **Continuing Change:** Ask students which of the following continue to change after adolescence, and which do not: thoughts, emotions, spiritual beliefs, and physical growth? (All but physical growth change.)

② **Roles vs. Identity:** Ask students to explain the difference between *gender roles* and *gender identity.* (Gender roles are behaviors society expects; gender identity refers to each person's behavior. The roles are broader; identity is specific to each person—no two are identical.)

they classified each occupation as they did. Make the point that these jobs *reflect traditional gender roles* but that not everyone accepts gender roles. Some people find them a bad fit, and they change their roles. A woman who doesn't feel comfortable in a traditional role may become a truck driver and be very good at that trade. A male may succeed in a profession, such as nursing, that has in the past been seen by society as a predominately female gender role. **(15 min.; Extend, Enrich, Critical Thinking)**

EVALUATE
SECTION II

Activity 2.4
Pop Quiz.
1. A person's gender is the classification of being male or female. (T)
2. If everyone accepted gender roles without question our society would never change. (T)
3. Within a society different cultures and religions may have somewhat different expectations for boys and girls. (T)
4. Gender identity is a part of your

---

66 Thoughts on Health **99**

Treat people as if they were what they ought to be and you help them become what they are capable of being.
– Johann Goethe

Teacher Support Notes

① **Cultural Gender Roles:** Margaret Mead found that among the Arapish of New Guinea, men were passive, cooperative, peaceful, and nurturing—the father was said to "bear children!" Eighty miles away, the Mandugumor women were expected to be violent, competitive, sexually aggressive, and eager to solve disputes by fighting.

Section II Review

Answers

1. gender **2.** Masculinity
3. Puberty **4.** Gender roles are assigned by society, while gender identity includes traits that are determined by a person's gender. **5.** 10 or 11
6. Answers will vary. Refer to Figure 3–3 on page 56. **7.** Refer to bulleted list on this page.
8. Answers will vary.
9. Answers will vary.

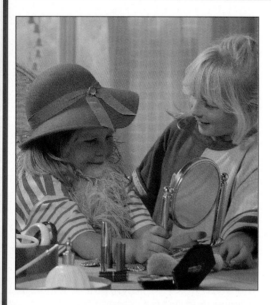

Before the teen years, children's gender roles are shaped by society.

It takes generations to replace old gender stereotypes completely. Some that you may see changing during your lifetime are these: ①

• Men are active and independent; women are passive and dependent.
• Men hide their emotions; women show their emotions.
• Men discipline their children; women nurture them.
• A man's success is seen in his earnings or status; a woman's success is measured by the man she marries.

Evidence that these confining roles are breaking down can be seen in the armed forces' acceptance of women in their ranks, in the nursing profession's welcoming men into the field, and in once-exclusive clubs' opening their doors to both genders.

One of the happiest outcomes of these recent changes in our society's gender roles is that men today can enjoy some of the roles formerly reserved for women only.

Just as women can now work in politics, become corporate executives, or build bridges, so men can enjoy cooking, nurturing children, and performing other peaceful tasks in the home.

Your gender identity is important, but it is only a part of your personality. More important still is the full realization of your potential as a person. The next section explains one of the key requirements for developing a healthy personality, and in fact for all emotional health—self-esteem.

Key Points *In developing an identity, each person adopts characteristics that go with that person's gender. Gender roles are useful as long as they allow freedom for individual differences.*

SECTION II   REVIEW

Answer the following questions on a sheet of paper.
Learning the Vocabulary
The vocabulary terms in this section are *adolescence, puberty, gender, gender roles, gender identity, femininity, masculinity,* and *stereotypes.*
1. The classification of being male or female is called your _____.
2. _____ consists of the traits associated with being male.
3. _____ is the period of life in which a person becomes capable of reproduction.
4. What is the difference between a person's gender identity and gender role?

Learning the Facts
5. At approximately what age do girls begin a growth spurt?
6. List some changes that occur due to increased levels of hormones during puberty.
7. Name some common gender stereotypes.

Making Life Choices
8. The changes that take place during adolescence tend to become a permanent part of a person's identity. What do you think are some of the most common things boys and girls your age worry about most as their bodies show physical changes? Overall, do you think boys or girls go through the

personality. (T)

5. Young teens, with their sexually maturing bodies, often exaggerate their gender roles for the benefit of those around them. (T)

CLOSE
SECTION II

Activity 2.5
Breaking Stereotypes. Have the

class list any people they know—famous or not—who have broken stereotyped roles and have become very individualistic people. Some examples are: Robyn Smith—female jockey; Shirley MulDowney—female drag racer; Greta Garbo, Katharine Hepburn, Margaret Thatcher, Madonna, and Rosanne Barr. Now have them write a short paragraph on why it is important for each human being to become an individual, whether it

fits into a stereotype or not, and what these differences add on the positive side to our society. Discuss. **(20 min.; Critical Thinking, Interdisciplinary)**

FOCUS
SECTION III

In this section students will learn :

(continued on next page)

---

most changes during puberty? Who seems to have the most difficult time? Why?

9. Besides puberty, what are some other things that influence a person's identity?

SECTION III

Developing Self-Esteem

How many people do you know who really believe in and respect themselves? Do you? People who know and like themselves are emotionally healthy: they have high **self-esteem.** People with high self-esteem ① do not think they are perfect. In fact, they know they are not, but they like themselves anyway. They not only cherish the positive sides of themselves, they have learned to accept the negative, even though they may be trying to improve. In contrast, a person who *claims* to be perfect probably has low self-esteem. Such a person cannot admit imperfections without feeling threatened by them, and so the person denies having any faults.

Self-esteem is crucial for emotional health. Poor self-esteem is closely linked with a wide range of problems: drug and alcohol abuse, addictions of all kinds, crime and violence, child and family abuse, teenage runaways, teenage pregnancy, prostitution, gang membership, and failure of children to learn. Poor self-esteem, therefore, diminishes not only individuals, but also society. Society spends billions of dollars in medical expenses, law enforcement, and education every year because of the problems caused by poor self-esteem. At the same time, a shortage of productive workers means that smaller revenues must stretch to meet all of society's needs.

People with high self-esteem, on the other hand, contribute to society's well-

being. In return, they reap benefits from society in terms of emotional and financial support. They feel worthwhile, and so they do not hesitate to assert themselves to get what they want.

This chapter's Life Choice Inventory, beginning on the next page, provides a way to measure your self-esteem. One way to improve self-esteem is by developing a positive view of your inner self, as described next.

Positive Self-Talk

A technique for viewing your inner self positively is to practice making positive statements about yourself. These statements, called **positive self-talk,** can be ones you think are true now or statements you plan to make true by means of practice. Positive self-talk gives you power—that is, it makes you feel effective. You give yourself the power to become the person you want to become and to do the things you want to do. Positive ideas replace self-defeating messages. The Health Strategies section on page 62, "Improving Self-Esteem," lists some positive actions for developing a more successful you.

To practice positive self-talk, repeat to yourself an idea that you wish to become a reality. For example, a person who wishes ② to feel less anxious might think or say aloud, "I can relax when under stress." A person who wishes to feel less lonely might think, "I can be alone without being lonely" or "I like people, and they like me."

MINI GLOSSARY

self-esteem: the value a person attaches to his or her self-image. Self-esteem is high in those who value themselves. It is a vitally important part of emotional health.

positive self-talk: the practice of making affirming statements about oneself to oneself, helpful in building self-esteem.

Teacher Support Notes

① **Understanding Esteem:** Ask students what *esteem* is. (to hold in high regard; to think of with respect; to prize) Esteem comes from a Latin word meaning "to estimate." Can they see the connection?

② **Discussing Problems:** Ask students to think of a person they know who has one of these problems. Do they think that person has or had low self-esteem? If not, what do they think was the cause of the person's problem?

Focus
(Continued)

1. The definition of self-esteem.
2. How important self-esteem is in developing emotional health.
3. Ways to evaluate self-esteem and raise their own personal self-esteem.

Activity 3.1
Understanding *Self-Esteem*.

Write "self-image" on the board. Ask the students for a definition. (the characteristics a person sees in himself or herself) Now write "self-esteem" on the board. Ask for a definition. (the value a person attaches to his or her self-image) Write "value" on the board. Ask for a definition. (relative worth, importance, degree of excellence) Discuss the value each of us places on the different parts of our self-image, and how these values relate to our self-esteem.

TEACH
SECTION III
(Guided and Independent Practice)

Activity 3.2
On the "Hot Seat." You will need one piece of 24 × 36-inch paper for each student; masking tape; one broad-tip marker for each group. Divide the class into groups of six to eight students.

Teacher Support Notes

① **Desired Behavior:**
Students learned about the differences between passive, assertive, and aggressive behaviors in the last chapter. For review, ask students which is the desired behavior. (assertive) Ask them why it's important to learn this behavior. (get what they want without hurting anyone else)

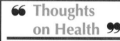
Thoughts on Health

Every man is his own worst enemy.
— *Proverb*

LIFE CHOICE INVENTORY

How Well Do You Speak Up for Yourself?

If you have high self-esteem, you will find it easy to be assertive, rather than aggressive or passive, in speaking up for yourself. These questions offer a way to measure your assertiveness, and indirectly they measure your self-esteem. (Some items may not apply to you. Try to imagine that they do.) ①

1. Your mother has said that she wants you with the family at six o'clock today. At five o'clock, a friend invites you to a get-together you can't refuse. You:
   a. Go with your friend, stay through six, and explain to your mother later.
   b. Call your mother and explain that you must go with your friend.
   c. Complain to your mother that she is too demanding, but stay home.
   d. Tell your friend you can't go, and say nothing to your mother.

2. You studied with several of your friends for a test. They all got good grades. You wrote the same kind of answers but got a low grade. You think your work was just as good as theirs. You:
   a. Write an anonymous note to the principal saying that the test grades are obviously unfair.
   b. Take your test to the teacher, and ask why your grade was low.
   c. Complain to all your friends, and say nothing to the instructor.
   d. Keep your mouth shut so that the teacher won't be even more unfair to you the next time.

3. You have just cleaned the kitchen. Then someone puts a greasy pan on the countertop and starts to leave. You:
   a. Wait until you are alone, then put the greasy pan between the person's bedsheets.
   b. Tell the person, "Please wash your frying pan before you leave."
   c. Make a general remark about how inconsiderate people leave dirty dishes for others to clean up.
   d. Say nothing; wash it yourself later.

4. You are on your first date with someone you have admired from a distance for a long time. At the end of the evening, the other person gets much more physical than you want to be. You:
   a. Back off, and leave as quickly as you can without saying anything.
   b. Tell the other person that things are going too far for you.
   c. Keep pulling away, and let the other person guess the message.
   d. Say nothing and go along, because you want to date the person again.

5. You get home with a new cassette tape of your favorite music, only to find that the tape you just bought is already ruined in the package. You:
   a. Storm into the store and make a scene so that all the customers will know you were sold a messed-up tape.
   b. Go back to the store, ask to see the manager, and explain that the tape you just bought is ruined.
   c. Never shop in that store again.
   d. Do nothing.

6. You are in your room, studying for a big exam. Your sister is playing the stereo loudly. You:
   a. Knock on your sister's door, walk in, and switch off the stereo.

(Continued on next page)

Choose one person in each group to be the recorder. Have each group sit in a semicircle facing a wall. Place a chair against the wall and tape a sheet of paper to the wall next to the chair. One student sits on the chair. Go around the circle and have each student tell one positive trait that he or she knows or has observed about the person on the chair. After all the comments are written down, the recorder then reads the list and asks the student on the chair if he or she agrees or disagrees with the traits observed. Give the paper to the student and put up a clean sheet for the next student. Students can "pass" going to the chair if they choose. After all groups have finished, have a discussion about what was learned. Include these points in the discussion: **1.** body language of the person in the chair and the person telling the trait; **2.** the way others see us—it's not always the way we see ourselves; **3.** self-image and self-esteem; **4.** the good traits others see in us; and **5.** value. **(30 min.; Cooperative Learning, Extend, Enrich)**

EVALUATE
SECTION III

**Activity 3.3
Pop Quiz.**

(continued on next page)

Ch. 3 Your Changing Personality **61**

How Well Do You Speak Up for Yourself? *(continued)*

b. Ask your sister to turn down the volume, and explain why.
c. Go someplace else to study; refuse to speak to your sister for the week.
d. Give up trying to study.

7. Your friends like horror movies, but you don't enjoy them at all. Your friends are making plans to see the latest horror movie this Saturday night. You:
   a. Tell them you think horror movies are for mental midgets and you're not going.
   b. Tell them you don't enjoy horror movies, and ask if they'd consider another movie.
   c. Go to the movie, then make humorous negative remarks about it, hoping they will get the message.
   d. Stay home Saturday night.

8. You occasionally babysit for Mrs. Harper's three children. Lately she has been making excuses when it comes time to pay you. You:
   a. Tell her that you're fed up and that you won't babysit for her anymore.
   b. Tell her that it's inconvenient for you to be paid late.
   c. Decide you won't work for her again.
   d. Say nothing.

9. You and your friend are in a pet store together, and you see your friend slip a rubber dog bone into a coat pocket. You:
   a. Grab the dog bone, put it back on the shelf, and threaten to turn your friend in.
   b. Tell your friend how you feel about shoplifting, and recommend replacing the dog bone.
   c. Say nothing, but resolve never to go shopping with your friend again.
   d. Act as if nothing has happened.

10. Your parents have given you some money to spend on clothes. They have told you exactly what they want you to buy. You need clothes, but you disagree with the style they are urging you to buy. You:
    a. Buy what you want, and tell them they are way out of touch with today's styles.
    b. Tell them how you'd rather spend the money and why it's important to you.
    c. Buy what they want you to have, and try to trade it for something else later.
    d. Buy what they want you to have, wear it, and thank them for it.

① SCORING

Give yourself 10 points for each *a* answer, 8 for each *b*, 6 for each *c*, and 4 for each *d*. Add them up.

If you scored:

85 to 100—You have no trouble asserting yourself, but your behavior borders on aggressiveness. You know what you want, but you have to give more thought to how you go about getting it.

75 to 84—You are assertive to the right degree. You have a good sense of what you want, and you speak your mind. People are not offended by your frankness, and they accommodate you when they can.

50 to 74—You need to practice voicing your opinions and speaking up for your rights. Get in touch with your needs, and speak up.

Below 50—You almost never voice an opinion. You are building up some resentments. Work on raising your self-esteem; start practicing assertiveness—be honest with yourself and others.

Source: Adapted from S. Schlatner, Get smart, *Coed*, March 1981, p. 36b.

❝ **Thoughts on Health** ❞

The young always have the same problem—how to rebel and conform at the same time. They have now solved this by defying their parents and copying one another.
– Quentin Crisp

Teacher Support Notes

① **The "Right" Answers:** This Life Choice Inventory contains a wealth of material for class discussion. Many students will be inclined to argue that the best or most idealistic answers are *a* or *c*, rather than *b*. Try to get students who've answered *b* to explain the advantages to that choice. The more aggressive students should see the potential advantages of not alienating people, while the passive students should see the advantages for their emotional well-being in not harboring grudges, anger, and self-pity.

61

1. Poor self-esteem is linked to a wide range of social problems. (T)
2. People with high self-esteem think they are perfect. (F)
3. Positive self-talk has the power to make you feel you can become the person you want to be. (T)
4. A kind of positive imaging called *visualizing* has helped people fight diseases like cancer. (T)
5. The theory of "fake it till you make it" rarely works in improving personal growth. (F)
6. Our society stresses individualism for males and group behavior in females. (T)
7. A part of self-esteem is a positive body image. (T)
8. A negative body image and intense pressure from society for a sexier appearance make many people easy prey for advertisers who take advantage of us. (T)
9. Striving for a body image similar to those of extremely thin models in advertisements can lead to eating disorders. (T)
10. Part of developing self-esteem is to value just what you do—not who you are. (F)

CLOSE
SECTION III

---

66 Thoughts on Health 99

No man can make you feel inferior without your consent.
– Eleanor Roosevelt

Teacher Support Notes

① **Accepting Negatives:** Tell students you are confused. In the first paragraph on page 59 the text says that it's important for people to accept their negatives, yet here it says you should "refuse to think negatively about yourself." Don't these statements contradict each other? Class discussion should help students see this potentially confusing point—that even if you admit weaknesses, you are not really thinking negatively if mentally you know that you are a good person and that everyone has weaknesses.

② **Positive Thinking:** One possibility for an ongoing project would be to have students write a positive statement about themselves each Monday. They would then focus on their statements for a week, repeating them to themselves frequently each day for a week. You could set aside a minute of each class for them to reinforce the statements by practicing self-talk.

62

HEALTH
STRATEGIES

Improving Self-Esteem

These actions can improve your self-esteem:

1. Write out positive statements about yourself.
2. Find activities that are related to your goals, and join in.
3. Be grateful; remember to take count of and appreciate what you have.
4. Practice positive self-talk and positive self-imaging.
5. Seek out books and movies with positive themes.
6. Surround yourself with friends who believe in you.
7. Support others—believing in, supporting, and speaking positively about others helps you become more positive and stronger.
8. Refuse to think negatively about yourself or others. Accept that everyone is growing emotionally at their own pace.
9. Celebrate your successes.
10. Give and receive affection—hugs, for example.

Other statements that can start one changing for the better are "I deserve success" and "I accept myself as I am."

You can also help yourself to succeed at whatever task you choose or to develop whatever quality you desire by mentally seeing yourself already there. This technique is called **positive imaging** in psychology. Visualizing success helps people battle diseases, win athletic contests, and overcome emotional problems.

Another suggestion for making desires become reality is "acting as if" you already have the quality you are seeking. This is often called "fake it 'til you make it." This technique is not only useful for personal growth. It is also used to teach salespeople how to sell products successfully, athletes to win sports competitions, and others to succeed in many other areas of life.

Key Points ▶ *To develop self-esteem, use positive self-talk and positive imaging to turn ideas about what you'd like to be like into realities. Act as if qualities you wish for were already yours.*

Positive Body Image

Another part of self-esteem is a positive **body image.** Negative body image is a common problem in our society. Each year, millions of people try to change the way they look. Forty million go on diets; half a million undergo cosmetic surgery; and multitudes try contact lenses, facials, and new cosmetics in hopes of becoming more attractive. People feel that they must be sexually attractive, and our society defines sexual attractiveness very narrowly.

A factor in the body image of teens is how early or how late an individual develops an adult-looking body. It might seem that the earlier developers would have an advantage in this regard, and this is so—but only for boys. Early-maturing boys report feeling positive about their bodies. Many early maturing girls, though, report the opposite. They feel threatened by becoming different from their peers and may even try to hide their maturity under baggy clothing.

These gender differences in self-acceptance may be the result of a society that stresses individualism for males, but that values group behavior in females. The important thing is that each person is maturing normally on his or her own timetable, and each deserves respect and acceptance.

Some are early to mature, some are later, but all eventually arrive.

As you might guess, a negative body image and the intense pressure from society for a sexier appearance make many people easy prey for advertisers who want to take advantage of us.

Improving your body's appearance by means of good nutrition and physical activity benefits your physical health. Chapters 7 through 10 offer many tips on how to develop nutritional health and fitness. Once you've attained a healthy body, though, let that be enough. Don't compare your body with the unrealistic, overly thin or overly developed standards for sexual attractiveness you see in advertisements or on television. Fitness is beautiful, but both thinness and bulkiness can be taken to extremes.

Key Points ▶ *A positive body image is part of self-esteem, but the bodies seen in advertisements and on television are unrealistic. Learn to see through insulting sales pitches. Aim for fitness, not for thinness or bulkiness.*

Self-Acceptance

Another way to acquire a positive view of your inner self is to appreciate your own uniqueness. Many unhappy people compare themselves to others and rate themselves poorly by comparison. Learn to see yourself as special and unique—as a person who is worthwhile and valuable.

Instead of making comparisons between yourself and others, celebrate the strengths you see in others and also those you know you possess. This is possible even in the "faking it" stage. Believe in yourself.

Part of developing self-esteem is to value who you *are*, and not just what you *do*. Society often focuses on achievements such as how much money people make, how many awards they win, the grades they earn, and the like. While these all are worthy goals,

stay aware that they do not define the worth of a person. People who link their inner selves too tightly with outer accomplishments easily fall into the trap of defining themselves by their deeds. Then, when they fail or make mistakes, they think of themselves as failures and mistakes. They don't realize that the mistake is what they *did*, not what they *are*.

Know that you are unique and worthwhile aside from your achievements and accomplishments, and in spite of your failures and mistakes. Once you've developed high self-esteem, achievements and accomplishments follow naturally.

Key Points ▶ *Enjoy your accomplishments and admit to your failures, but don't let them define you.*

SECTION III REVIEW

Answer the following questions on a sheet of paper.

Learning the Vocabulary

The vocabulary terms in this section are *self-esteem, positive self-talk, positive imaging,* and *body image.*

1. What is the difference between positive self-talk and positive imaging?
2. _____ is the value a person attaches to himself or herself.
3. _____ is the way a person views his or her body.

Learning the Facts

4. Name two qualities of a person who has high self-esteem and two qualities of a person who has low self-esteem.

(Continued on next page)

MINI GLOSSARY

positive imaging: a technique of mentally viewing an image of one's self as successful.
body image: the way a person thinks his or her body looks, which may or may not be the way it actually does look.

great it is that everyone is one of a kind, a unique individual, and that these differences should bring us together and make us strong—rather than divide us. **(20 min., Critical Thinking)**

FOCUS
SECTION IV

In this section students will learn the:
1. Definition of peer groups and their value in normal development.
2. Ways deviant peer groups can cause negative peer pressure and lead to rejection and punishment from society.
3. Ways peer groups help bridge the gap between the dependent state of childhood and the independent state of adulthood.

Activity 4.1

Understanding *Peer Groups*. Tell students that individual positive development is very important. However, a normal part of development, starting in the teen years, is an association with peer groups. Have a class discussion. Ask for a definition of "peer group." Ask them for the names of some peer groups they have been associated with since starting to school. Examples they might mention are students, girls, boys, minorites, Boy

Section III Review

Answers

5. It gives you the power to become the person you want and to do the things you want to do.
6. acting as if you already have the quality you are seeking
7. People try to change the way they look. They feel they must be sexually attractive.
8. Answers will vary.

Teacher Support Notes

① **Defining *Peer*:** Tell students *peer* comes from the Latin word meaning "equal."
② **Tight Groups:** A key word here is *tight*. Ask students if a group can be too tight, or do they think the tighter the better? Do they think that belonging to these groups helps or hinders someone in developing his or her personal identity? How?

> **❝ Thoughts on Health ❞**
>
> *When a dove begins to associate with crows, its feathers remain white, but its heart grows black.*
> *– German Proverb*

64 UNIT 2 Your Emotional and Social Health

5. What is to be gained by using positive self-talk?
6. How does the "fake it 'til you make it" technique work?
7. Why is a negative body image so common in our society?

Making Life Choices

8. List four features of your body that you are proud of (don't be modest). Now list four features of your body that you would like to change to some degree. Discuss how you can go about making each one of these changes. Why do you think making the most of your physical appearance can be beneficial to your emotional health?

Peer groups can be a major, positive influence on development.

SECTION IV

The Importance of Peer Groups

So far, this chapter has emphasized the individual. However, an important part of normal development in the teen years is an association with **peer groups.** A peer group is simply a group of friends similar to yourself in age and stage of life. For many adolescents, peer groups are a positive influence on development. Peer groups help to bridge the gap between the dependent state of childhood and the independent state of full adulthood.

You also hear about peer groups in a negative way when they apply **peer pressure,** or when they become **cliques, gangs,** or **cults.** Kids sometimes ignore their own values and do things just to fit in with the crowd.

Peer groups operate as many other organizations do. Each has a set of rules and expects certain behaviors from its members. For example, if the crowd expects sophisticated, "cool," or snobbish behavior, stu-

dents who act otherwise may be treated with hostility, to force them "back into line" with the group's rules. Sometimes, the pressure can be fierce, because individuals so strongly need to belong. Still, individuals are free to move naturally from group to group as their interests change or as certain groups prove not to fit them.

The Value of Peer Groups

Children have friends, but they still receive their initial sets of values and identities from their parents. Then, for most people in their early teens, peers become as important as parents in providing clues to each individual's identity. By observing the reactions of their peers, young teens learn valuable lessons about their own tendencies and how they interact with others.

You can often observe groups of young teens who talk alike, dress alike, and do everything together. These tight groups help young people who are breaking into larger society find their places—their identities. By the late teen years, associations with peers usually loosen to become less demanding.

Scouts, Girl Scouts, church groups, clubs, bands, speech teams, sports teams, etc. Discuss in class the reasons they enjoyed these peer groups and stress that sometimes we outgrow certain peer groups and go on to others.

TEACH

SECTION IV
(Guided and Independent Practice)

Activity 4.2

Constructive vs. Destructive Outcomes. On the left side of the board or on an overhead transparency, write "Constructive Outcomes." On the right, write the words "Destructive Outcomes." Now have the students tell you all the constructive or good outcomes that can be experienced from being connected to peer groups. List their answers under Constructive Outcomes. Now do the same thing for Destructive Outcomes, list-

ing all the negative outcomes that can be experienced from being connected to peer groups. Have a class discussion of your lists. Are there any trends that can be seen? In the overall scheme of an 80-year life span, which outcomes would be the most desirable in allowing individuals to reach their full potential? **(15 min.; Extend, Enrich)**

(continued on next page)

They still remain important, however, and evolve into more mature friendships that may last throughout life.

An important function of peer groups is to help lessen teenagers' natural fears. Young people often feel an exaggerated sense of uniqueness—"I'm the only one who feels this way!" or "Everyone is looking at me, and I must look awful!" These extreme feelings are natural, but of course, they are not based on reality. Most people feel the same emotions from time to time. As for the judging stares from the crowd—they're all thinking about themselves and probably believing that everyone is staring at *them*.

Peer groups provide a shelter from these extremes. As part of the group that talks alike and looks alike, young teens have positive proof that others feel as they do. Numbers also provide safety and a degree of anonymity in which each person can try out a new, tender identity.

Peer groups may form when individuals with similar backgrounds or interests get together. They naturally develop rules that govern the behavior of the members. Sometimes they go to extremes and become cliques that exclude most outsiders and demand total loyalty. Cliques exclude and ridicule those who fail to conform. Most peer groups, though, provide their members with benefits. A circle of friends offers a place to share ideas and opinions in addition to providing support and strength in a sometimes threatening world. It's easier to be confident when you know others are on your side.

Some teens hesitate to try getting into new groups. They have trouble "breaking the ice" with new people—they are shy. Shyness is really a fear that if other people knew the person within, rejection would follow. Shy people can get over these fears by arranging positive meetings with others and

by realizing that many other people feel the same way. Tips for shy people were offered in a Health Strategy feature in Chapter 2.

Although parents may fear that peer group values will replace parents' values, research shows otherwise. Along with a search for independence, most teens maintain strong relationships with their parents and permanently adopt many parental values. Teenagers are not simply blank pages awaiting scripts written by their peers. Teens are already close to maturity and are simply fine-tuning the lessons they've learned in life up to that point.

In general, teens adopt their parents' values on issues that matter—family, religion, work, morals, standards, and the like. Teens most often adopt peer values concerning style and taste—dress, music, clothes, cars, and so forth. Teens also may turn to peers for attitudes on issues their parents may hesitate to discuss—sexuality, drugs, birth control, and dating. In this way, teens tend to blend family values with new values they've worked out for themselves. However, they usually end up with sets of values very like those of their parents.

Some peer groups serve other needs, too. A jogging club, for example, provides companionship and exercise. School bands, sports teams, service clubs, and other

MINI GLOSSARY

peer groups: groups of people who are similar in age and stage of life.

peer pressure: the internal pressure one feels to behave as a peer group does, to gain its members' approval.

cliques: peer groups that reject newcomers and that judge their members harshly.

gangs: peer groups that exist largely to express aggression against other groups.

cults: groups of people who share intense admiration or adoration of a particular person or principle.

> **66 Thoughts on Health 99**
>
> *Who speaks ill of others to you will speak ill of you to others.*
> — *German Proverb*

Teacher Support Notes

① **Understanding Uniqueness:** Ask students to explain the word *unique.* (one of a kind) Then ask them to explain "exaggerated sense of uniqueness." Can they see that it's unhealthy (although quite natural for teens) to imagine oneself to be more unique than one really is? Ask them to list their "unique" behaviors that only they possess. How much duplication is there when lists are compared?

② **Conforming:** Ask students what it means to *conform.* (to go along with agreed-upon rules or customs) What word in the last chapter had an opposite meaning? (nonconformist)

Activity 4.3

Identifying Negative Terms. Ask for a definition of the words *deviant*, *cliques*, *gangs*, and *cults*. After a class discussion of the definitions, stress the following definitions:
Cliques—peer groups who *reject* new-comers and *judge* their members *harshly*. Gangs—peer groups that exist largely to express *aggression against other people*. Cults—groups of people who share *intense admiration* of or give *adoration* to a particular *person* or *principle*.

In these definitions, have the class pick out the negative words within the defini-tion. (words in italics) Ask them what the use of negative words within a definition tell them about each type of peer group.

(15 min., Critical Thinking)

Activity 4.4

My Perfect Friend(s). Have stu-dents list the ten qualities that they look for in a perfect friend. They are to make their answers short. Example: listens, sense of humor, accepts me, etc. Now have them number their papers from 1 to 10 and put the most important quality in the number 1 spot; the second most

---

Teacher Support Notes

① **Teen Views—Follow-Up Questions:**
Following are some ques-tions to help you promote discussion of the student views concerning peer pressure:

a. Do students feel that they encounter a lot of peer pressure? How often?

b. Do they agree with Jordan Hedges that peer pressure is anything that causes them to "stray from your uniqueness?"

c. What sorts of physical dares like the one described by Andy Vartmann have students received?

d. Is feeling foolish a fre-quent result of *not* giving in to peer pressure? What's the solution to this problem?

e. Are there times when it's right to fight, or is fight-ing always a poor choice?

f. We usually think of peer pressure as being nega-tive. Can students cite positive examples, such as the one given by Sean Niles?

66 Thoughts on Health **99**

I wouldn't want to join a club that would have me as a member.
– Groucho Marx

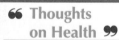

---

66 UNIT 2 Your Emotional and Social Health

T**EEN** V**IEWS**

What experiences have you had with peer pressure? ①

It would be impossible to list and explain every encounter I have had with peer pres-sure. Experiences involving peer pressure occur every day. It deals with more than just drugs and alcohol. Peer pressure is anything that tries to make you stray from your uniqueness. In order to fall victim to it, all you have to do is adopt the ideas of an-other that do not coincide or are hypocritical to your own ideas. **Jordan Hedges, 17, Orange Park High School, FL**

One day my friends and I went down to this bridge. You are supposed to jump off the bridge and land in the water. I told them that I wouldn't jump. I was scared and I didn't want to get hurt. They started to call me names, so I just left. I wasn't going to do something I didn't want to do. **Andy Vartmann, 15, East High School, MN**

People are pressuring people to be on the same side of an issue as themselves. They have made me feel like a fool be-cause I wouldn't take a side or I disagreed with them. **Carrie Zimmerman, 16, Newberg High School, OR**

I witnessed a fight that hap-pened because of peer pres-sure. The two people who were fighting did it because people told them to fight. These two people fought over a silly thing because they thought they would be cool. In the end, they both got into trouble. **Julie Zakara, 14, Westside High School, NE**

My experiences with peer pressure have been limited due to the type of people with whom I associate. They are the studious type and are inclined to be overachievers. When I want to go out and have fun, they usually pres-sure me back into studying. This type of peer pressure is not bad, but it also does not allow me to do some of the things I enjoy. **Sean Niles, 17, Orange Park High School, FL**

I have had a lot of incidences dealing with alcohol and drugs. My friends were tak-ing pills to make them hyper for a game coming up. They asked me if I wanted some. I kind of rejected them. They said they were only hyper pills made of caffeine. I al-most gave in to the pressure, but I didn't. I wanted to see how they would react to the pill. Before the game they were shaking really bad and their hearts were beating hard and very fast. They thought it was neat, but I got scared. **Matt Stephenson, 15, South Carroll High School, MD**

---

groups also meet other needs. The impor-tant thing is to find people you can be comfortable with. Some experts think that belonging to a wide variety of groups may best serve the needs of older teenagers. Those who learn to get along with many kinds of people in their teen years are probably best prepared to meet the rela-tionship demands of adult life.

Peer groups can help teens through tough times. It's natural to share feelings with others. For example, a student whose parents were divorcing was constantly upset. She talked about her feelings to important quality goes into the number 2 spot, and so on. Compare the lists in a class discussion. **(15 min.)**

Activity 4.5
Developing a "Safety Net." Students should understand the need for positive safety nets. When we are "down" or when we fall, we each need a "human support net" to break the fall and reassure us of our self-worth. The more friends and family we have supporting us, the safer we are and the fewer chances we have of "breaking through" the support net and hitting the bottom. Have the students make a list of their safety nets—the names of people they can count on in both good and bad times. After they complete their lists, have them write a sentence or two on whether or not their nets are strong enough and whether or not they should add more support. Have a class discussion on numbers and ways to make friends and develop trust. **(15–20 min.; Extend, Enrich)**

EVALUATE
SECTION IV

Activity 4.6
Pop Quiz.

(continued on next page)

A peer group that values achievement can help motivate its members to stay in school.

some friends and was surprised to learn how many had gone through similar experiences. As she listened to their stories, she came to realize that although her pain was significant, it was not permanent. She also found that talking with others made her feel better. It helped to know that she wasn't alone.

Key Points *Peer groups offer support and security to changing, growing teens. Such groups assist people in defining their identities.*

Deviant Peer Groups— Gangs and Cults

The need to belong to a social group is strong—so strong, in fact, that it can lead a person to join up with a group that is not beneficial to the person. Such **deviant** groups may meet the person's need to belong, but they do so at a high price. A positive-minded peer group may help a student stay in school. A deviant group, however, may influence the person to drop out.

Gangs make up their own rules and values. They establish an organization of authority outside of the larger society. People who belong to them may learn to "obey the rules," but the rules are those of the gang and are often in opposition to society's rules. The gang's rules may require committing serious crimes, taking or selling illegal drugs, or taking part in other harmful activities mostly related to obtaining money in illegal ways for the benefit of high-ranking gang members.

Cults are related to gangs in that they are often money-making groups, with the top organization leaders profiting most. According to one group that monitors "mind control" cults, about 200 such organizations are active today. Some of them have enormous scope and power.

MINI GLOSSARY

deviant: outside the normal system.

1. Deviant peer groups exert positive influences on the people who join them. (F)
2. The rules of gangs are often in opposition to the rules of society. (T)
3. For many teens, peer groups are a positive influence on development. (T)

4. Sometimes kids ignore their own values just to fit in with the crowd. (T)
5. Peer groups do not help bridge the gap between childhood and adulthood, they widen it. (F)

C LOSE
SECTION IV

Activity 4.7
Positive Peer Groups? Have the

students evaluate the peer groups they are in now. On a piece of paper, for their eyes only, have them list the peer groups in which they have chosen to become involved. Have the students then label each a positive or negative peer group based on its rules, its controls, its punishments, and its outcomes. Then have the students evaluate their dependency on the group. If that peer group has made them a more independent person (able to

---

Section IV Review
Answers

1. Peer pressure
2. Cults
3. cliques
4. Peer groups for early teens become as important as their parents. By observing their peers, young teens learn valuable lessons and how to interact with others. By late teens, associations loosen to become less demanding. More mature friendships evolve that may last for a lifetime.
5. They help lessen teenagers' natural fears. They provide proof that others feel as they do. They provide teens with a circle of friends to share ideas as well as for support.
6. Being able to get along with many different groups helps prepare teens to meet the relationships and demands of adult life.
7. a. Answers will vary.
b. Answers will vary.
c. Answers will vary.

---

66 Thoughts on Health 99

We forfeit three-fourths of ourselves to be like other people.

– Arthur Schopenhauer

Cults may masquerade as religious groups, healing centers, addiction treatment centers, or even financial advisers. In reality, though, they may exist for the sole purpose of amassing hundreds of millions of dollars for themselves. People who are drawn into cults are often convinced—through guilt, brainwashing, threats, or even legal actions—to hand over their worldly goods, and to work for the profit of the cult while living in poverty. Beware of religious organizations that require that you pay large sums for the promise of "spiritual cleansing" or "clearing out internal evils." The only thing they'll clear out is your wallet.

When people join groups that step outside of the rules of the larger society, they bring on themselves rejection and punishment from the majority. The people most drawn to such groups seem to be those who fail to fit in successfully with peer groups during young life, and for whom the larger society has little to offer as adults.

Peers are important. Make sure you choose them with care. If the ones you find yourself with are losers, pick others. Run with the winners. The Straight Talk section that follows offers tips on how to stand up to unwanted peer pressure.

Key Points *Deviant peer groups such as gangs exert negative influences on the people who join them. The rules of gangs are often in opposition to the rules of society. Cults often exist for the sole purpose of obtaining large sums of money from those who join them.*

SECTION IV REVIEW

Answer the following questions on a sheet of paper.
Learning the Vocabulary
The vocabulary terms introduced in the section are *peer groups, peer pressure, cliques, gangs, cults,* and *deviant.*
Fill in the blank with the correct answer.
1. _____ is the internal pressure a person feels to behave as a group does.

2. _____ are often interested primarily in making money.
3. Peer groups that reject newcomers and judge their members harshly are called _____.

Learning the Facts
4. What changes occur in peer groups from early teens to late teens?
5. What is the function of peer groups?
6. What is the advantage of being able to get along with many types of people?

Making Life Choices
7. Peer groups can pressure teens toward positive or negative behaviors.
   a. Relate a positive personal experience with peer pressure. What did you gain?
   b. Describe a negative personal experience with peer pressure. If you had this situation to live over again, how would you do it?
   c. Has it become easier or harder to resist peer pressure as you have gotten older? Why?

Answers to Fact or Fiction

Here are the answers to the questions at the start of the chapter.

1. True. **2.** False. Human beings first need the essentials for survival—food, clothing, and shelter—then they become free to notice other needs. **3.** False. People with high self-esteem cherish their good parts, but also acknowledge and work on the areas that need improvement. **4.** False. People who imagine themselves as greater or more successful than they are may be taking an important first step toward a more successful future. **5.** False. Peer groups are usually positive forces that can help teens develop a sense of identity.

grow and change within the group) have them write "more" beside that group's name. If that peer group has made them a more dependent person (everyone is the same and only the group's set of values are allowed) have them write "less" beside that group. Then have students ask themselves this question: "Based on Shelley's quote 'Iron bars do not a prison make . . .' have the peer groups I have selected imprisoned me or set me free to

be myself?" Discussion is optional. **(15–20 min., Critical Thinking)**

RETEACH/BONUS

Here are some additional activities for the various sections of this chapter. You may want to use these activities to reteach certain concepts, or you may choose them as alternatives to earlier activities. Some

could also be used in conjunction with the Straight Talk feature.

Positive Self-Talk Essay. Put this positive self-talk statement on the board: "What you do with your problem is far more important than what your problem does to you."—Robert Schuller. Another way of saying this is "You do life—life doesn't do you." Ask the students to write

(continued on next page)

STRAIGHT TALK

Dealing with Peer Pressure

Each day presents teenagers with new choices to weigh against personal values. Which choices are right? Which are wrong? While many productive and positive experiences are possible, other paths lead to destructive lifestyles that can set a negative course that lasts a lifetime. Teenagers don't make these choices alone. They are influenced by the behaviors of their peer groups.

When people talk about peer pressure, they usually say that your friends are pushing you to do things you don't want to do—and that you can "say no." Are peers usually a bad influence? ①

No, they are not. In fact, a positive peer group can encourage individuals to achieve things they never thought possible. Group values can give individuals the strength to say no to temptations. A peer group can be a major influence in a student's decision to stay in school.

Groups that offer the most positive influences may be service clubs, special interest clubs, scouting, religious groups, and the like. However, all groups offer some benefits. Even a gang may be the only family a young person has, for a while. That person may learn skills of communication, cooperation, compromise, and leadership from the gang.

Some groups are mostly negative, though. The inborn human need to belong is so strong that teens who lack strong self-esteem will do almost anything to fit in with some group. They seek approval from others, even at enormous personal cost. At the extreme, some teens may even risk their lives performing high-risk stunts required by some gangs for admission. Also, they may take up drinking alcohol or begin using other drugs to prove to a group that they can do as the members do. This may be even more destructive, because it may set up lifelong patterns of behavior.

How can kids fight against the urge to do self-destructive things in order to fit in?

Most important is to first decide for yourself, away from the group, what you will or will not do. In other words, the first person to say no to is yourself. Then, be prepared to

say no to others. If people whom you normally admire start behaving in ways that are against your values or against the law, try to wait ② out their experimentation. However, sometimes abandoning them is the only way to preserve your self-esteem and personal safety.

Frankly, I don't have that many friends, and I'd be afraid to abandon them. Are you saying I'd have to live life without friends?

Not at all. Just that it sometimes becomes necessary to gradually change your affiliations. You need not drop your old group like a hot potato. You can still accept the parts of it that you find beneficial. Still, you are free to make new friends.

You may not know it, but most people can fit in with many different groups. Everyone has unique abilities of some sort. Your special

(Continued on next page)

Teacher Support Notes

① **Good or Bad Influences:** Refer students back to Sean Niles's comment about peer pressure in the Teen Views feature on page 66. You might ask students which type of peer pressure is more common for them—the positive type that Sean describes, or the more negative types, such as described by the other students in the feature.

② **Belonging vs. Being Alone:** Discuss with students their need to belong to groups—to be with others. You might want to use the Gide quote on this page together with this text page to help them see both sides of the issue.

a paragraph on what the Schuller quote means to them. What is the author trying to say? How could they apply this statement to themselves and problems they have had in their lives? **(Critical Thinking)**

Maslow and Gangs. On the board, make a list of reasons people join gangs. Ask the class what needs, according to Maslow, aren't being met. Conclude with a class discussion. **(15 min.; Reteach, Reinforce, Critical Thinking)**

Discussing Gangs. Ask the following questions: Why do you feel violence is such a big part of gang activity? What unresolved emotion is often at work in gangs? Would you say a gang member has high or low self-esteem? Is there any difference between the answer you just gave and what gang members show to others on the outside? **(Critical Thinking)**

Write an Epitaph. Have the students write their own epitaphs. (five-line limit) Use these questions to get them started: If they were to die today, how would they want to be remembered? How would they define themselves? In a nut-

---

Friendship is almost always the union of a part of one mind with a part of another; people are friends in spots.
– George Santayana

Teacher Support Notes

① **Varied Interests:** Ask students to list differences they have with their best friends. Also ask them to think of people with whom they share one interest, but that they are different from in every other way. Can they see that no two people are totally alike? What does this imply with regard to friendships and peer groups? You may want to give them the Santayana quote and ask if they can see how his thought relates to this discussion. Can they think of quotes of their own that express this idea? You could also ask if anyone disagrees with this idea.

Thoughts on Health

I don't know the key to success, but the key to failure is trying to please everybody.
– Bill Cosby

STRAIGHT TALK   *(Continued)*

traits can make you valuable to many groups. For example, your grades may not be as high as those of kids in a "brainy" group, but you may have some writing talents to offer to the school newspaper. You may excel at games of logic, so that you can offer challenges that would interest "the brains." Or you may be a skilled negotiator, and be able to make their social lives go more smoothly.

The point is that if you let yourself get stuck or limited to a particular group, you ① aren't exploring all of your options. Here are just a few ways to find new interests and friends who share them:

- Take a photography class.
- Learn to work in pottery.
- Try out for a school play.
- Sign up for a nature course.
- Learn a sport; join a team.
- Enroll in a fitness program.
- Volunteer your time.
- Work in a youth group.
- Work at a job.
- Call someone you admire but don't know well.
- Organize a group to attend concerts.
- Join the Reserve Officer's Training Corps (ROTC).

These are only a few possibilities. There are many, many more. Brainstorm about others for yourself.

When I was younger, my friends were being mean to a new kid. I thought the kid was OK. I didn't want to be mean, but I went along with my friends. Is this what you mean by peer pressure?

It's certainly part of it. You had no great need to harm the new kid, but you went along with your group for fear of losing favor with them. The first thing to realize is that an immature "us against them" mentality leads young adolescents to behave this way. Now that you're older, no doubt your "us" world has expanded to include many other people. Now you probably have the self-confidence you need to accept newcomers.

Does peer pressure disappear as people mature?

People encounter the most peer pressure during early adolescence but even adults, experience some peer pressure. The phrase *keeping up with the Joneses* applies to adults who still feel a need to live as others do. Unfortunately, some people get stuck in the "us against them" mentality of early adolescence. It expresses itself in many forms of prejudice and bigotry, including racism, sexism, ageism, and others.

I want to make new friends. What should I do?

A way to begin is to work on the three areas that are most essential to any effective human interaction: communication, cooperation, and compromise.

Communication is a two-way street. Individuals who communicate well have the ability to listen—really listen—as well as the ability to take their turn speaking.

Cooperation is teamwork—working together for the good of all. Working as a team builds strong relationships. To be a good team player, you need to have an open mind and a willingness to carry a part of the load.

Compromise is the result of each person's giving up something in order to reach a solution that can be accepted by all. This is also known as "give and take." This does not mean to let people take advantage of you, or to give up strong moral beliefs, or to give in to others when the results are harmful. It means expressing your views, hearing others' views, and reaching a decision that is somewhere in between.

What about the impression I make on people. Does that matter?

(Continued on next page)

shell, what is unique about them? What have they accomplished?

Listing Personal Values. Have each student list two of their personal values. (examples: I believe stealing is wrong; I believe abortion is wrong.) Now have them think about and then write a description of a situation in which they *would go against* their value systems. Conclude this activity with a discussion.

Peer Pressure vs. Values. Have the students describe an actual situation in which they went against their own values because of pressure from peers. Have them write answers to these questions: Why did you go against your value system even though you knew it was wrong for you? How big a part did "peer pressure" play in helping you "forget" your values?

Defining *Human*: Have students write down their definition of "human." What does it mean to be a "human being" as opposed to an animal? Now have them list ten things that a human can do that an animal cannot do. Have them answer the question, "Why can't animals do what we do?" **(20 min., Advanced)**

STRAIGHT TALK — *(Continued)*

It certainly does. People who do not know you may judge you on the surface only—just by your manners. Like it or not, first impressions are lasting in people's minds. Manners do make a difference.

Imagine this: You are invited to share a meal with someone's family. You want to impress them, but you arrive sloppily dressed, chew with your mouth open, make a mess at the table, and belch loudly as you finish your meal.

Do you mean that to have friends, I have to memorize a bunch of stupid rules about which fork to use? My family eats in front of the TV on paper plates.

Nothing is wrong with eating off of paper plates in front of the TV if your family chooses it. However, in the situation described above, you desire acceptance by people who have other customs. When you want to belong to a social group, you need to observe how they do things. Manners alone can open doors, sometimes—even the door to someone's positive impression of you. Remember the old saying "When in Rome, do as the Romans do."

What else do I need to know about the right way to resist peer pressure?

There is no one right way. A starting point, however, is to work on keeping your self-esteem high. Self-esteem is like a protective armor that can deflect the arrows of rejection shot your way by weaker individuals. Associate yourself with the most mature members of a group, the ones who value individual differences. ①

A way to respond to the less mature members is to prepare an answer in advance. A simple "No thanks" is often enough. The following all work for a while: "I don't like the taste of beer"; "I have sports practice tomorrow and can't do that"; "That stuff slows down my thoughts, and I need to study." Eventually, you may feel the need to confront the person: "I want to remain friends, so please don't ask me to do that."

It's important not to allow your emotions to make you act aggressive or apologetic. Simple, assertive statements of fact, held to firmly, work best.

No one should feel that they must march in step with a group that is heading in the wrong direction. A person with self-esteem can gracefully exit and enter another, more productive group. A way to do

this is to take a look at the new group you want to join and see what its interests are. Make friends with one of its members. Soon, others will grow accustomed to your being with that person—and with them. Be persistent, and don't let one person's negative reaction throw you. It's natural to fear that one negative opinion is the *group's* opinion. In reality that person may be the only one with negative thoughts and feelings. Ignore that person, and make your special traits known to the others.

It takes a commitment to yourself to risk rejection by speaking and acting according to your values. Many of the exercises and strategies suggested earlier provide the tools you need to do so:

- Deal effectively with your emotions.
- Know your values.
- Make decisions in line with your emotions and values.
- Deliver assertive messages.
- Develop a positive attitude.
- Enhance your self-esteem.

Keep in mind that the most important person in your life is you. Taking care of that person will ease the way to desired friendships.

Teacher Support Notes

① **Choosing Friends:** Give students the two quotes above and ask them to choose one and then write a short paragraph explaining how that quote relates to this sentence from the text about choosing friends. Discuss their responses, then ask them to compare the strategies they've just discussed with the strategies they've been using for choosing friends.

Chapter Review
Answers
Vocabulary
1. **a.** adolescence **b.** Femininity **c.** Peer groups **d.** gender roles
2. **a.** Needs **b.** positive imaging **c.** Stereotypes **d.** hierarchy
3. **a.** deviant **b.** personality **c.** positive self-talk **d.** gender **e.** self-esteem
4. **a.** Self-image is the characteristic that a person sees in him or herself while body image is how a person thinks his or her body looks. **b.** Gangs usually tend to express aggression against laws and society. Members must obey the rules which often include crimes, selling drugs, or other harmful activities. Cults are related to gangs, but are usually disguised as religious groups, healing centers, and addiction treatment centers. People are drawn in through guilt, brainwashing, or legal action.

Recall
Section I
1. School age (6–12)
2. physiological, safety, love, esteem, and self-actualization
3. They feel a need to be important and appreciated. It also helps in the development of identity.
Section II
4. age 12 or 13
5. Girls develop more body fat, while boys develop more muscle tissue.
6. Answers will vary; could include: acceptance of women in the ranks of the armed forces, men in the nursing profession, exclusive clubs opening to both genders, women becoming corporate executives, women building bridges, men enjoying cooking and other tasks in the home.
Section III
7. They don't think they are perfect. They believe in and respect themselves and are emotionally healthy.
8. Answers will vary; could include: Low self-esteem is linked to drug and alcohol abuse, crime, prostitution,

---

CHAPTER REVIEW

LEARNING THE VOCABULARY

personality	gender	positive imaging
self-image	gender roles	body image
variables	gender identity	peer groups
hierarchy	femininity	peer pressure
needs	masculinity	cliques
self-actualization	stereotypes	gangs
adolescence	self-esteem	cults
puberty	positive self-talk	deviant

Answer the following questions on a separate sheet of paper.

1. **Word Scramble**—*Use the clues from the phrases below to help you unscramble the terms:*
   a. **deccnlaosee** The period of growth from the beginning of puberty to full maturity is called _____.
   b. **minfitiyen** _____ refers to biological, social, and physical traits associated with being female.
   c. **reep srougp** _____ _____ are groups of people who are similar in age and stage of life.
   d. **negder lores** Roles assigned by society to people of each gender are called _____ _____.

2. a. _____ are urgent wants for necessary things.
   b. A technique called _____ involves mentally viewing an image of one's self as successful.
   c. _____ are fixed pictures.
   d. A _____ is a ranking system in which each thing is placed above or below others.

3. **Matching**—*Match each of the following phrases with the appropriate vocabulary term from the list above:*
   a. outside the normal system
   b. the characteristics of a person that are apparent to others
   c. the practice of making affirmative statements about oneself to oneself
   d. classification of being male or female
   e. the value a person attaches to himself or herself

4. a. What is the difference between self-image and body image?
   b. What is the difference between a gang and a cult?

RECALLING IMPORTANT FACTS AND IDEAS

1. According to Erikson, during what age span should a person develop industriousness?
2. Summarize Maslow's Hierarchy of Needs.
3. Why is it especially beneficial for teens to provide service to others?
4. When do boys begin a growth spurt?
5. What is the main difference between girls' and boys' body composition?
6. List three changes that have occurred in gender roles over the years.
7. What are some qualities of a person with high self-esteem?
8. List five problems linked with poor self-esteem.
9. List four strategies for improving self-esteem.
10. What type of pressures are advertisers using to their advantage?
11. What is the danger in always comparing yourself to others?
12. Give three examples of negative peer groups.

gangs, teenage runaways, child and family abuse, and violence.

9. Answers will vary; could include: write out positive statements, find activities related to goals, be grateful, practice positive self-talk, seek out books and movies with positive themes, support others, don't think negatively, celebrate your successes, give and receive affection.

10. A negative body image and intense pressure from society for a sexier appearance make teenagers easy prey for advertisers.

11. If you're an unhappy person, you rate yourself poorly. You should learn to see yourself as special and unique. Celebrate the strengths you see in others and those you know you possess. Believe in yourself.

Section IV

12. cliques, gangs, cults

13. By observing their peers, young teens learn valuable lessons and how to interact with others. Peer groups help bridge the gap between the dependent state of childhood and the independent state of adulthood. They see they are not alone in their problems.

14. Answers will vary; could include: family, religion, work, morals, standards.

15. They require people to pay large sums of money for "spiritual cleansing" or "clearing out internal evils;" use guilt, brainwashing, threats, and legal actions to take over.

16. They face rejection and punishment from the majority.

17. Answers will vary; could include: take a photography class, learn to work with pottery, try out for a school play, sign up for a nature course, learn a sport, enroll in a fitness class, volunteer, join a youth group, call someone you admire, attend a concert, join the ROTC.

---

13. What are some benefits peer groups provide?
14. What are some common parental values that teens are likely to adopt?
15. What common techniques do cults use to pressure people into doing what they want?
16. What tends to happen when people join groups that do not follow society's rules?
17. Give some suggestions for positive ways to find new interests and friends.

CRITICAL THINKING

1. Think of some labels that were frequently used to describe you as a young child. List two that you feel are positive and two that you find negative.
2. Think of some labels that others might use to describe you as a teenager. List two positive and two negative labels.
3. Analyze how each past and present label has influenced your self-esteem.
4. Many times people do not like the way others see them. Fortunately, you have the ability to change your personality and self-esteem if you so choose. List four labels you would like to have attached to you and describe how you could best achieve them.

ACTIVITIES

1. Write a description of the person you think you will be ten years from now. What are you like? What is your lifestyle like?
2. Analyze an advertisement from a magazine in relation to the gender stereotypes that are used to sell that particular product. Write a brief report and include a copy of the advertisement.
3. Give yourself a boost! Write a letter to yourself convincing you of your worth as a person. Tell why you are special and include all your good points, talents, and skills.
4. Transfer your interpretation of Maslow's Hierarchy of Needs onto a poster by using pictures from magazines or your own original illustrations to portray each need.
5. Make a list of ten events that took place in one particular day. Evaluate each in relation to how it affected your self-esteem. Clearly state if the event raised, lowered, or had no effect on your esteem.
6. Identify a product being advertised in a magazine which you know to be a product that takes advantage of people's low self-esteem. Write a letter to the editor expressing your anger for running false advertising. Submit a copy of the advertisement and letter before you mail it.
7. Look through some family photographs and find some pictures that represent different developing phases of your life. Coordinate these pictures with Erikson's theory. Create an album and label each photograph. Give your album a title and write a short script to tell the story of your life.
8. Watch television for two hours. List the commercials that appeal to gender identity and contain stereotypical gender roles. Write a one-sentence description of how each commercial used this theme.

MAKING DECISIONS ABOUT HEALTH

1. You have been hanging out with a gang for quite a while, and you are beginning to feel a bit uneasy about it. They seem to be pressuring you into doing things that make you uncomfortable. You really would like to get out, but several questions keep running through your mind. Will my friends be angry with me if I quit? I don't really have any friends outside the gang—if I leave who will be my friends? How much longer can I keep my gang membership a secret from my parents? You are becoming more and more confused each time you think about making a decision. How can this situation best be remedied?

CHAPTER 4 PLANNER

OVERVIEW

Chapter 4 is 28 pages long and divided into the five sections listed to the right. Major learning outcomes of the chapter are also listed to the right. Briefly, this chapter introduces students to the concept of stress, its effects on the body, and ways to reduce the stress. The chapter emphasizes the importance of the individual's need to deal with stress effectively to reduce harmful effects on the body systems. It also gives students some positive ideas for identifying stressors, developing time management skills, and using relaxation techniques to cope with everyday living.

MAKING LIFE CHOICES RESOURCES

A variety of activities, handouts, quizzes, and tests to accompany this chapter are available in the *Making Life Choices* supplementary material. You may pick and choose from those materials as appropriate for your amount of class time and the ability levels of your students. Some of the resources you might want to consider using are:

Overhead
• Stress Ending in Recovery or Exhaustion

Handouts
• Medical Signs of Stress
• Interventions to Manage Stress
• Stress Reducing Strategies

CHAPTER PROJECT

As a class, develop ten questions that students can ask of someone in their community who they feel has a positive stress management technique. Have each student use the ten questions to interview a person in their community. Compile the results. Compare what the people interviewed have in common. Look at their reasons for using the stress management technique. Discover the benefits of stress management these people have achieved by using this skill.

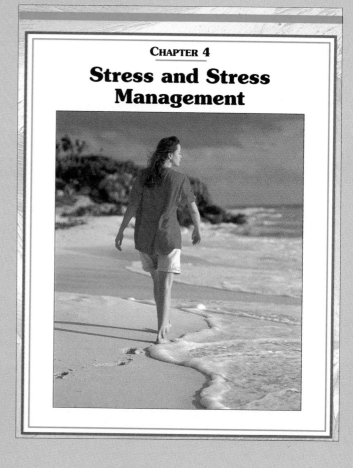

CHAPTER 4

Stress and Stress Management

Answers to "Fact or Fiction"

Here are the answers to the questions at the start of the chapter. **1.** True. **2.** True. **3.** False. People today experience the fight-or-flight reaction just as our ancestors did. **4.** True. **5.** False. You can change the way you perceive a stressor so that it will benefit you. **6.** True.

Activity To Introduce Chapter

Have the students think of a time of day that is very stressful for them. Is it morning, a certain class at school, homework time, etc.? Have the students write all that they can about that stressful time. Who is involved? Why do they feel stressed? What are their feelings? Tell the students to decide what they could do to change the stress. List some changes that they would be willing to make to reduce the stress. List both the factors that they can and cannot control. Ask the students to describe how they feel when the stressful moment has ended.

OUTCOMES

After reading and studying this chapter, you will be able to:

✓ Identify common stressors experienced by high school students.
✓ Describe how the nervous system, hormonal system, and immune system respond to stress.
✓ Describe the three phases of the stress response.
✓ Identify signs of stress, coping devices, and defense mechanisms.
✓ Explain how to prevent and manage stress.

CONTENTS

I. Stressors and Stress
II. Stress and the Body's Systems
III. Stress and Too Much Stress
IV. Dealing with Stress
V. Willed Relaxation

    Straight Talk: *Healing and the Placebo Effect*

FACT OR FICTION

What do you think? Are the following statements true or false? If you think they are false, then say what is true.

1. Buying a new car and taking a final exam are more similar than different, as far as your body is concerned.
2. Prolonged stress can make a person likely to suffer diseases.
3. The fight-or-flight reaction only occurred in the days of our ancestors; people today do not experience it.
4. Whether an event is stressful depends more on the person experiencing it than on the event itself.
5. You cannot change the way you react to stress.
6. Machines can help you learn to relax.

(Answers on page 96)

Reminder: Knowing how to study can increase your knowledge, improve your grades, *and* cut down on your study time. See the *Studying Health* section at the front of your text for some suggestions to help you study this chapter.

SUGGESTED RESOURCES

Student Readings
1. Gillespie, Peggy Roggenbuck and Bechtel, Lynn. *Less Stress in 30 Days: An Integrated Program for Relaxation.* New York: New American Library, 1986.

Teacher Readings
1. Curtis, John D. and Detert, Richard A. *How to Relax: A Holistic Approach to Stress Management.* Palo Alto, CA: Mayfield Publishing Company, 1981.
2. Friedman, Meyer and Roserman, Ray H. *Type A Behavior and Your Heart.* New York: Knopf, 1983.

Software
1. *Stress Management.*

Stress and its causes are defined and students can test their own stress levels. Opportunities for Learning, Inc. 800-243-7116.

Videos
1. *Teenagers, Stress, and How to Cope,* 35 min., Sunburst Communications, 39 Washington Ave., Pleasantville, NY 10570, 1-800-431-1934. This video dramatizes the stories of three stressed-out teenagers as they learn coping techniques. This program helps students understand what stress is and what they can learn about it.

NOT ENOUGH TIME?*

You could easily spend five or six days teaching this chapter if students read the entire chapter, do a fair number of the suggested activities in the teacher's edition and complete a sampling from the resource material accompanying this text. Perhaps you have only two or three days to devote to this chapter. Following are some suggestions to help you make sure that you cover the key topics if you have limited time.

TIME	SUGGESTIONS
2 Days	Have students read Sections I, II, and III ahead of time. Also, have the students do "Psychological Stressors for High School Students" on page 77. During class have students do Activity 1.2 in Section I, Activity 2.2 in Section II, and Activity 3.4 in Section III. Conclude the class with a combination of quizzes given under Evaluate for Sections I, II, and III.
	Have the students read Sections IV and V ahead of time. Also, have students read Straight Talk "Healing and the Placebo Effect" on page 97. During class have students do Activities 4.7 and 4.9 in Section IV and Activity 5.2 in Section V. Conclude the class with a combination of quizzes given under Evaluate for Sections IV and V. You may want to assign reteaching activities from the resource material for those students doing poorly on the quizzes.
3 Days	On day 3, do Activity 5.3 in Section V.

*Please refer to the 18-week daily lesson plans in the supplementary material for additional suggestions.

FOCUS
SECTION 1

In this section students will learn:
1. What a stressor is.
2. How to differentiate between physical and psychological stressors.
3. To recognize some common stressors among teenagers during their high school years.

4. To identify some stressors that exist in their own lives.

Activity 1.1
Common Stressors. Write the word *stressor* on the board and define the word for students. Have students list stressors that exist in their lives. Compare how commonly the stressors given exist among teenagers. Now have students divide the stressors listed on the board into physical or psychological stressors. Discuss ways in which teenagers deal with these stressors. Have students list some more effective ways of dealing with the situations if their methods seem ineffective. **(15 min., Cooperative Learning)**

TEACH
SECTION 1
(Guided and Independent Practice)

Activity 1.2

Teacher Support Notes

① **Beneficial Stress:** Write "Stress = Inspiration" on the board. Ask students to discuss this equation. Can they think of specific examples that would prove the equation true? Many writers and other artists have said, for example, that the pressure (stress) of deadlines was the motivation (inspiration) for some of their greatest works. Many athletes perform best under stress.

② **Hurry-up Lifestyle:** Do students think most people "overload" themselves? Have them make a list of ten adults and ten teenagers they know. Have them put a check next to the name of each person they think is living a "hurry-up" lifestyle. Discuss the percentage of people who have this problem, if indeed it is a problem.

③ **Acute Stress:** *Acute* means sharp, sudden, intense. This is in direct contrast to chronic, which is not so intense and lasts much longer.

④ **Types of Stress:** If you want students to learn the terms *eustress* and *distress*, point out that the word *stress* is included in both terms. What they need to remember is that eu = "good," dis = "bad."

---

76   UNIT 2 Your Emotional and Social Health

The word **stress** is widely used today. When a person says, "I am under stress," he may mean that he is ill, that his love life has gone off course, that he is under financial pressure, or any of a hundred other things.

In contrast, another person who says she is under stress may mean that things are going great—that she is thriving. Stress can be a threat to health, or it can be the fuel for progress and achievement. For some, it almost borders on inspiration. This kind of stress produces beneficial energy and alertness.]①

Stress tends to get out of hand in some people's lives. Life in today's urban world can be so demanding that people respond by constantly overloading themselves. They study on the way to school and eat on the run between classes. They drive cars and talk on their phones at the same time. Even when on vacation, people who are supposed to be at leisure sign up for tours that visit 15 countries in two weeks. For them, "hurry up" becomes a way of life.

Never-ending, **chronic stress** is the kind that can damage body systems in a number of ways. The heart and blood vessels are especially responsive to stress and often suffer the brunt of its impact on the body. Tragically, some people have not learned how to deal with stress. Many seek relief in self-destructive habits such as using alcohol or other drugs. These substances cause stress themselves, and their effect is to worsen the toll being taken.

You may have noticed some effects of another kind of stress, the short-term kind that arises when a problem suddenly demands to be solved—**acute stress.** This sort of stress may bring you new energy. You may be amazed at all you can accomplish. If the stress continues, though, it becomes chronic, energy gives way to exhaustion, and you may become sick. Students often]③

push hard to study for tests and to complete assignments toward the end of the grading period, only to find that when they relax in the break that follows, they become ill.

The high school years are stressful, for they represent a period of change that requires teenagers to adapt. This chapter describes the physical effects of stress on your body. It also shows you ways of dealing with the stress in your own life.

SECTION 1

Stressors and Stress

A **stressor** is anything that requires you to cope with, or **adapt** to, a situation. Physical stressors include all physical conditions, such as air temperature, intensity of lighting, bacteria, injuries, or radiation. Psychological stressors include life-changing events, both desirable and undesirable (see Figure 4–1 on the next page).]②

The high school years are believed by

MINI GLOSSARY

stress: the effect of physical and psychological demands (stressors) on a person. Stress that provides a welcome challenge is *eustress* ("good" stress, pronounced YOU-stress); stress that is perceived as negative is *distress* ("bad" stress).]④

chronic stress: unrelieved stress that continues to tax a person's resources to the point of exhaustion; stress that is damaging to health.

acute stress: a temporary bout of stress that calls forth alertness or alarm to prompt the person to deal with an event.

stressor: a demand placed on the body to adapt.

adapt: change or adjust to accommodate new conditions.

Determining Stressors. Tell the students to list on a sheet of paper the stressors listed in Figure 4–1 that apply to them. Have the students put an "X" next to all the psychological stressors that they listed over which they have control. Put a "*" next to the stressors over which they do not have control. What does this tell them about the stress in their lives? Ask them if they are surprised with the results. **(15 min.; Extend, Enrich)**

EVALUATE
SECTION 1

Activity 1.3
Pop Quiz.
1. A stressor is a demand that requires you to adapt to a situation. (T)
2. Physical stressors include temperature, drugs, work conditions, and injury. (T)
3. Adapting to stress means to remain rigid in a situation. (F)

4. Psychological stressors include desirable and undesirable changes in life. (T)
5. School grades can be affected by stress. (T)
6. Job choices can affect the stress levels in your life. (T)
7. The high school years are among the least stressful periods of a person's life. (F)
8. Stress can be positive as well as negative. (T)

(continued on next page)

FIGURE 4-1

① Psychological Stressors for High School Students

People ranked these events according to how stressful they perceived them to be, on a scale from 1 to 100. Note that some "happy" events are included here. Individual people may score these events higher or lower than they are here and may be stressed by events not named here.

Life Event	Stress Points
Death of parent	100
Divorce of parents	73
Breakup with boyfriend/girlfriend	65
Something bad happening to friend or family member	63
Death of close family member (except parent)	63
Major personal injury or illness	53
Marriage	50
Failing grades at school	47
Expulsion from school	47
Dating	45
Major illness of family member or close friend	44
Pregnancy	40
Peer difficulties	39
Gain of new family member	39
Money troubles	38
Death of close friend	37
Loss or death of loved pet	37
Change in number of arguments with peers	35
Change in responsibilities at school or home	29
Getting a job	29
Brother or sister leaving home	29
Trouble with parent	29
Outstanding personal achievement	28
Parent beginning or stopping work	26
School beginning or ending	26
Change in personal appearance	24
Trouble with teachers/principal	23
Moving away	20
Change in schools	20
Change in recreation	19
Change in church activities	19
Change in social activities (joining new group)	18
Change in sleeping habits	16
Change in number of get-togethers	15
Change in eating habits	13
Vacation	13
Christmas	12
Traffic tickets or other minor violations of the law	11

Check the list, and identify the events that have happened to you in the past year or that you expect within the next year. Use the number system to determine how many stress points you are experiencing in this period of your life. Then score yourself as follows:
Over 200: Urgent need of intelligent stress management.   100–149: Stressful life; keep tabs on your mental health.
150–199: Careful stress management indicated.   Under 100: No present cause for concern about stress.

Teacher Support Notes

① **More about Psychological Stressors:** This rating scale was adapted from the Social Readjustment Rating Scale (SRRS) developed by Dr. Thomas Holmes. What are simplified here for high school students as stress points, Dr. Holmes calls his *life change units (LCUs)*. The SRRS is not a foolproof way to rate stress, and it's necessary to remember that people differ greatly in their reactions to the same event. This means that the SRRS is, at best, a rough index for stress. Still, a high score should be taken seriously.

Other psychologists have examined the effect of minor, but more frequent, stressors. Psychologist Richard Lazarus refers to such daily frustrations as "hassles" or "microstressors." According to one of his studies, frequent and severe hassles turned out to be better predictors of day-to-day emotional and physical health than major life events.

9. Stressors can be physical or psychological in nature. (T)
10. Sometimes the relationships we choose can create stress in our daily lives. (T)
(10 min.)

CLOSE
SECTION 1

Activity 1.4
Reducing Classroom Stress.
Have the students observe their classroom environment and describe as many physical and psychological stressors as possible within the room. List them on the board. Ask the students to agree or dis-

agree as a group that the items listed are stressors. Make some suggestions to reduce or eliminate the stressors within the classroom if at all possible. Are the suggestions feasible in the classroom environment? If they are, as a class try to reduce or eliminate the stressors for one week. At the end of the week, decide if the environment in the classroom has improved. **(15 min., Special Needs)**

---

many to be among the most stressful periods in life. Figure 4–2 illustrates stressors in the lives of students.

Each person under stress responds to stressors in an individual way. Some researchers studied the effects of life changes on high school students and found that when students faced more than one change at a time, their grade point averages dropped. So did their scores on a test of self-esteem.

Those students who handled changes one at a time were least affected by stress. If you are experiencing many changes or stressors, try focusing on them one at a time to reduce your level of stress and to protect your self-esteem.

Key Points ▶ *A stressor is anything that requires you to cope with, or adapt to, a situation. High school students face many stressors.*

---

66 Thoughts on Health 99

To be totally without stress is to be dead.
– Hans Selye

Teacher Support Notes

① **Illustrating Stressors:** Have students do an illustration similar to the one on this page for their own personal stressors. They can select the stressors included in this illustration that apply and omit those that do not. They may want to add additional stressors as well.

② **Dealing with Stress:** Ask students what strategy for handling stress is presented on this page. (deal with one stressor at a time) Ask students if they are currently feeling stressed from more than one source. If so, ask them to list those sources. Now, ask students if they are trying to deal with more than one of these stressors at once. Which one would they pick if they had to focus on just one stressor?

66 Thoughts on Health 99

Laughter is the best medicine.
– Proverb

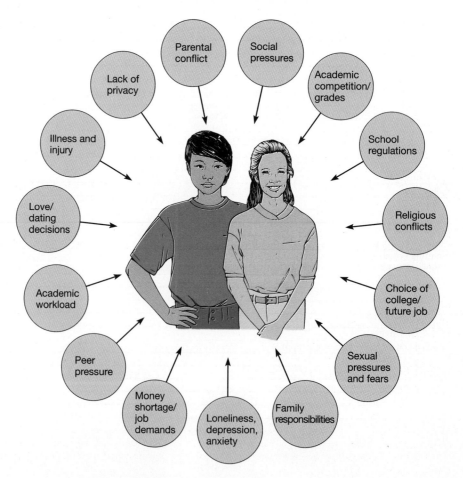

Figure 4–2 Stressors in the Lives of Students

FOCUS
SECTION II

In this section students will learn:
1. That stress affects each of the body's systems.
2. How the various glands and the hormones they secrete react within the body during times of stress.
3. About effects that occur to the immune system as a result of prolonged stress.

Activity 2.1
Creating Stress. Create some major stressful situations within the classroom—use both positive and negative stressors. For example, bang on a desk, turn lights on and off, change the temperature of the room, have someone come into the room saying pizza is on the way for everyone, raise your voice, and end by announcing a pop quiz. Have students note what happened to their bodies physically and how they felt psychologically. Ask students to share and compare their responses. **(15 min.; Cooperative Learning, Critical Thinking)**

TEACH
SECTION II

(Guided and Independent Practice)

(continued on next page)

SECTION I REVIEW

Answer the following questions on a sheet of paper.

Learning the Vocabulary
The vocabulary terms in this section are *stress, chronic stress, acute stress, stressor,* and *adapt.*
1. _____ is the effect of a physical or psychological demand on a person.
2. A _____ is anything that requires you to cope with, or _____ to, a situation.
3. What is the difference between chronic stress and acute stress?

Learning the Facts
4. What can happen when acute stress becomes chronic stress?
5. When you are dealing with many stressors at one time, what is the best way to handle things?

Making Life Choices
6. Add up your stress points as instructed in Figure 4–1 on page 77. What stressors are you currently facing that are not on the list? What stressors do you anticipate dealing with in the near future that are not on the list? Develop your own personal stress scale and list what you believe to be your top ten stressors in order of most to least stressful.

SECTION II

Stress and the Body's Systems

Exercising, taking an exam, or buying a new car all affect your body in about the same way. Physically, your heart beats faster. You breathe faster than normal, signaling that your body is getting ready to act. All external changes stimulate you this way to some degree. They require you to change in some physical way—that is, to adapt. All environmental changes—changes in the temperature, the noise level around you, what is touching you, and countless others—require your body to adapt. So do all psychological events, both desirable and undesirable.

All of the body's systems, and especially the **nervous system,** the **hormonal system,** and the **immune system,** are affected by stress. Chapter 6 provides more information about the anatomy and workings of these three systems.

The Nervous System

① A stressful event may be a mental challenge (such as an exam) or a physical challenge (such as cold weather). Whatever the challenge, the responses of the nervous system are always similar. That is, they always produce a set of reactions to restore normal conditions inside the body. As an example, let's look at the body's responses to cold weather.

When you go outside in cold weather, nerves in your skin act as a thermometer, sending "cold" messages to the spinal cord and brain. The central nervous system reacts to these messages and signals the

MINI GLOSSARY

nervous system: the system of nerves—organized into the brain, spinal cord, and nerves—that send and receive messages and integrate the body's activities.
hormonal system: the system of glands—organs that send and receive blood-borne chemical messages—that control body functions in cooperation with the nervous system.
immune system: the cells, tissues, and organs that protect the body from disease. The immune system is composed of the white blood cells, bone marrow, thymus gland, spleen, and other parts.

Section I Review
Answers
1. Stress
2. stressor, adapt
3. Acute stress is a short-term stress, sometimes producing new energy; while chronic stress is unrelieved stress that can damage body systems.
4. Energy gives way to exhaustion and one may become sick.
5. It is best to focus on one change or stressor at a time.
6. Answers will vary.

Teacher Support Notes

① **Nervous System Responses to Stress:** Have students explain the difference between the way the nervous system responds to a psychological stressor as compared to a physiological stressor. (There is no basic difference.) As a follow-up question ask, "What does the body always do in response to stress?" (It restores normal conditions inside the body.)

Teach
(Continued)

Activity 2.2
Stress and the Common Cold. Discuss how stress can strengthen or weaken the immune system. Ask the students to examine the past year of their lives and think about how many colds they have had and the amount of stress that they have experienced. Does there appear to be a connection? **(20 min.; Extend, Enrich)**

EVALUATE
SECTION II

Activity 2.3
Pop Quiz. Write the following numbered terms on the board. Have students number 1–9. They should then write the letter of the correct phrase next to the right number as you read the phrases.
1. nervous system (f); **2.** immune system (d); **3.** hormonal system (i); **4.** target organ (h); **5.** gland (a); **6.** hormone (g); **7.** white blood cells (b); **8.** immunity (e); **9.** epinephrine/norepinephrine (c)
a. organ that secretes hormones **b.** made in bone marrow **c.** stress hormones **d.** offers protection against a disease **e.** body's ability to destroy disease-causing agents **f.** contains

---

Teacher Support Notes

① **Goose Bumps:** Ask students what causes goose bumps. (muscle contractions) What is the by-product of goose bumps? (heat)

② **Real Life Comparisons:** Ask students to compare the nervous system to systems in their homes. If they can't, tell them that the nervous system is a type of communication system. Ask if they can think of communication systems in their homes that are similar to the nervous system. One possibility would be a stereo system. They might have a CD player, a tape player, turntable, etc., all hooked up to an amplifier. The amplifier is like the brain. The wires connecting the components are similar to the spinal cord. Other possibilities would be computer and heating systems. See how many different comparisons students can create. You might want to divide them into groups to do this activity.

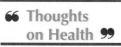

66 Thoughts on Health 99

There is nothing either good or bad, but thinking makes it so.
– William Shakespeare

---

smallest blood vessels, closest to the skin's surface, to shut down. This action forces your blood to circulate deeper in your tissues, where its heat will be conserved. The system also signals the muscles just under the skin surface to contract, forming goose bumps. All muscle contractions, even goose bumps, produce heat as a by-product. If these measures do not raise your body temperature enough, the nerves signal your large muscle groups to shiver. The shivering (contractions) of these large muscles produces still more heat. All of this activity adds up to a set of adjustments that maintain a constant body temperature under conditions of an external extreme (in this case, cold). ①

Now let's say you come in and sit by a fire and drink hot cocoa. You are warm, and you no longer need the body's heat-producing activity. At this point, the nervous system signals the skin surface capillaries to open up again, the goose bumps to subside, and the muscles to relax. These responses show that the nervous system is helping to keep you from getting too warm. Your body has maintained its temperature throughout the cold time and the warm time.

This example described only the nervous system's role in managing a brief period of one type of stress. The nervous system plays many other roles, too, depending on the type and degree of stress.

Key Points *The nervous system responds to challenges by producing reactions that restore normal body conditions.*

The Hormonal System

The hormonal system works together with the nervous system to maintain communication between body organs. The two systems complement each other in helping the body adapt to changes in the environment.

A **hormone** is a chemical messenger released by a **gland.** Glands receive information about body conditions. They then release hormones into the bloodstream to control those conditions. A hormone flows everywhere in the body. However, only the hormone's target organs respond to it, because only they possess the equipment to do so. ①

Like the nervous system, the hormonal system is busy during times of stress. It sends messages from one body part to another to maintain order. The hormones that control the stress response are called the **stress hormones.** Among the stress hormones, **epinephrine** and **norepinephrine** are well known. They regulate the body's activities during emergencies and between times.

Key Points *The hormonal system consists of glands that produce chemical messages that communicate body conditions to target organs. Release of the stress hormones brings on the stress response.*

The Immune System

Many tissues perform jobs in the immune system. The main cells of **immunity** are the white blood cells. These are made in the bone marrow and travel to other glands, where they mature. White blood cells make antibodies, the body's main ammunition against infections. All the body's tissues work together to provide immunity. All the body's fluids connect the parts of the system so that they act as a unit—one system. ②

The activity of the immune system is lower than normal during the stress response. However, between times it recovers quickly. Short periods of stress, followed by periods of relief from stress, can strengthen the immune system. Long periods of unrelieved stress, however, can weaken immunity and make a person likely to suffer diseases.

brain, spinal cord, nerves **g.** chemical messengers **h.** organs that respond to hormones **i.** system of glands

C LOSE
SECTION **II**

Activity 2.4
Stress and Careers. Discuss some career choices that your students have in mind for their futures. Analyze the stress

level of their career choices. Discuss the importance of the amount of stress involved in a job in their decision-making process for choosing a career. **(10 min., Interdisciplinary)**

F OCUS
SECTION **III**

In this section students will learn the:
1. Three phases of the stress response.

2. Body's responses during the fight-or-flight reaction.
3. Benefits and harmful effects of stress on the body.

Activity 3.1
Indicators of Stress. Ask students to bring in magazine photos that depict people experiencing stress. Display the photos, then have students identify

(continued on next page)

The immune system, after all, is the main system of defense against germs that cause colds, flu, measles, tuberculosis, pneumonia, and hundreds of other diseases (see Chapter 16). The immune system also helps defend against cancer. Cancer cells grow from a person's own body tissues, but the immune system can often recognize these abnormal cells and destroy them. Anything that harms the immune system (such as the AIDS virus, which you'll read about in Chapter 17) threatens life. Anything that strengthens the system supports health.

 The immune system is the body's main defense against disease. Unrelieved stress can weaken the immune system.

S ECTION II   R EVIEW

Answer the following questions on a sheet of paper.
Learning the Vocabulary
The vocabulary terms in this section are *nervous system, hormonal system, immune system, hormone, gland, stress hormones, epinephrine, norepinephrine, immunity.*
Fill in the blank with the correct answer.
1. A _____ is a chemical messenger released by a _____.
2. The brain, spinal cord, and nerves make up the _____.
3. Two stress hormones are _____ and _____.

Learning the Facts
4. What are the three body systems most affected by stress?
5. How does the hormonal system react to stress?
6. What happens to the immune system when it is exposed to long periods of unrelieved stress?

Making Life Choices
7. List three things that upset you and cause you stress. Identify each stressful situation as acute or chronic. Have you or anyone you

know ever experienced a chronic stress that in turn affected health in a negative way? Describe the situation and the outcome.

S ECTION III

Stress and Too Much Stress

A little stress can be beneficial. But too much stress, unrelieved, can be exhausting and harmful. Consider what stress, both physical and psychological, does to you.

Whatever the stressor that triggers it, the **stress response** has three phases. The first phase is always **alarm**.

Alarm occurs when you think that you are facing a challenge. The body releases the stress hormones, which activate the nerves and all systems.

M INI G LOSSARY

hormone: a chemical that serves as a messenger. Each hormone is secreted by a gland and travels to one or more target organs, where it brings about responses.
gland: an organ of the body that secretes one or more hormones.
stress hormones: epinephrine and norepinephrine, secreted as part of the reaction of the nervous system to stress.
epinephrine (EP-uh-NEFF-rin),
norepinephrine: two of the stress hormones; also called *adrenaline* and *noradrenaline*.
immunity: the body's capacity for identifying, destroying, and disposing of disease-causing agents.
stress response: the response to a demand or stressor. The stress response has three phases—*alarm*, *resistance*, and *recovery* or *exhaustion*.
alarm: the first phase of the stress response, in which the person faces a challenge and starts paying attention to it.

Section II Review
Answers
1. hormone, gland
2. nervous system
3. epinephrine, norepinephrine
4. nervous, hormonal, and immune systems
5. It sends messages from one body part to another to maintain order.
6. Long periods of stress weaken immunity and make a person more likely to suffer disease.
7. Answers will vary.

Fast Facts

Since 1980 there has been an increase in occupational disease claims attributed to stress.

indicators in the photos that make them think the person is stressed. Then have the students draw pictures of themselves in stick-figure form, drawing all the indicators that *they* display during stress. Have friends of students add any other indicators that they notice their friends display

during stressful periods. **(30 min., Cooperative Learning)**

TEACH
SECTION III
(Guided and Independent Practice)

Activity 3.2
Fight or Flight. Bring in a photo of boxing gloves and a photo of a bird in flight. Under each of the photos have students list some examples of stressful situ-

ations that students tend to deal with immediately (fight response) and some examples that they tend to deal with later or not at all (flight response). Discuss different views with students. **(15 min., Critical Thinking)**

Activity 3.3
Phases of Stress Response.
Describe a stressful scene to the class. (examples—car accident, failing a test,

---

Teacher Support Notes

① **Overhead—The Stress Response:** The overhead *Stress Ending in Recovery or Exhaustion* will help you expand your discussion of the stress response. To help students understand the illustration, ask them what the alarm represents. (first awareness of stress) What are they resisting? (the stress) Tell them that the straight line represents the normal level of resistance—it shows the body's behavior when no new stressors are encountered. Then, give them a sample situation such as a teacher asking a student to stay after class. This is alarm. Suppose that the teacher confronts the student with a failing grade. What sorts of resistance occur? Point out that if this happens only occasionally, the student recovers, goes on to the next class, and soon everything is back to normal. If it occurs regularly, the student will eventually become exhausted and could develop a serious health problem. Ask students to draw their own illustrations, identifying specific stressors and responses. Have them show recovery or exhaustion depending upon whether or not the type of stress is chronic.

The second phase of the stress response is always **resistance**. Resistance is a state of speeded-up functioning. The stress hormones continue to flow, causing muscles to contract and other body functions to shut down. (We'll describe this *unbalanced state* in more detail shortly.)

During the resistance phase, your resources are mobilized just as an army mobilizes its equipment and supplies to fight a battle. In the case of your body, the resources are your attention, strength, and fuels. You can use your resources until they run out or wear out. Then you need to replace or repair them.

The third phase of the stress response may be either of two opposite states—**recovery** or **exhaustion**. Figure 4–3, below, shows both. Recovery occurs when stress ceases to affect the body. It is hoped that before your resources run out, you deal with the source of stress or it goes away,

and you recover. Then your stress hormone levels drop to normal, your body systems slow down, your muscles relax, blood flows to all body parts, needed repairs take place, fuel stores are refilled, and you become ready for the next round of excitement. It is because of the need for recovery between times of stress that the military provides "R and R" (Rest and Recreation) times for its personnel.

Stress can make you stronger. Each time you go through a period of stress and recover, you are better able to meet the next round of stress. Just as your muscles grow stronger with repeated use, so does your stress resistance—but you must have rest between times to build that strength.

If stress continues to affect you without a break and your body stays in overdrive for too long, your resistance finally breaks down. Then recovery is delayed or becomes impossible. This is exhaustion.

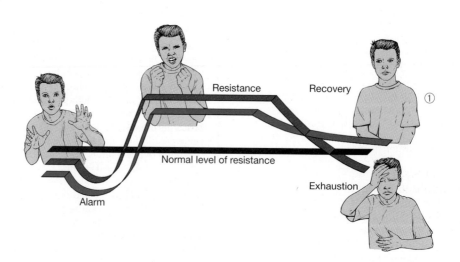

Figure 4–3 Stress Ending in Recovery or Exhaustion. Alarm briefly lowers resistance but is followed by a high level of resistance. Recovery restores the normal level. If resistance is required for too long, exhaustion sets in, and resistance temporarily falls below the level normally maintained.

breaking up with a boyfriend/girlfriend) Have the students write answers to these questions: What would be the alarm reaction? What would be the resistance? What would be necessary to get to recovery? What would cause exhaustion? Upon completion of the activity, compare answers as a class. **(15 min.; Reteach, Reinforce)**

Activity 3.4

Webbing of Stress. Have the students create a webbing of stress in their lives on a blank sheet of paper or construction paper. At the center of the web write the word *stress.* Divide the web into the following areas—home, school, social life, and work. Have students give four examples of stressors in each area. Once the students have completed their webs on paper, ask for volunteers to put their webs on the board.

EVALUATE
SECTION III

Activity 3.5
Pop Quiz.
1. Recovery occurs when the stress no longer affects the body. (T)
2. The state of stress resistance is a balanced state. (F)

(continued on next page)

Although stress itself arises in the mind, the body's response is physical in nature. The stress response developed long ago to permit our Stone Age ancestors to react quickly to *physical* danger. But while our ancestors had to cope with fierce tigers and spear-wielding foes, they were never faced with class speeches or final exams. Today, people facing class speeches or final exams feel fear, just as their ancestors did when facing tigers. Today's human body responds to the fear caused by these stressors in the same way as human bodies did long ago. The body still prepares to act physically. Unfortunately, while the stress response is perfectly suited to times when physical action is needed, today's crises rarely call for physical action.

The stress response is often called the **fight-or-flight reaction,** because when someone is faced with a physical threat, the two possible actions are to fight or run away. Every organ responds to the alarm:

- Heart rate speeds up.
- Pupils of the eyes widen (enhancing vision).
- Muscles tense (ready to jump, run, or struggle).
- Fuels, such as fat, are released from storage (for use by the muscles).
- Blood flow to skin is reduced (to protect against blood loss in case of injury).

The threats to your ancestors were physical, and the reaction was to fight or flee.

The threats you face today are seldom physical but your reaction is still the same.

①
- Blood flow to digestive organs is reduced (these can wait).
- Blood flow to muscles and brain increases (these need extra supplies right now).
- Immune system temporarily shuts down (to free up energy).

② Earlier, we called the state of stress resistance an *unbalanced state.* Here's why. It is a state that favors muscular activity while it shuts down other necessary body functions, such as digestion and immune defenses. This unbalanced state is beneficial at times—it helps the body deal with an emergency. Later, when the danger has

MINI GLOSSARY

resistance: the second phase of the stress response, in which the body mobilizes its resources to withstand the effects of the stress.

recovery: a healthy third phase of the stress response, in which the body returns to normal.

exhaustion: a harmful third phase of the stress response, in which stress exceeds the body's ability to recover; breakdown follows.

fight-or-flight reaction: the body's response to immediate physical danger; the stress response. Energy is mobilized, either to mount an aggressive response against the danger, or to run away.

Teacher Support Notes

① **Physical Response to Stress:** Students should agree that today's stress situations rarely call for physical action. Have them brainstorm a list of stressors, then divide the list into those that do and do not call for physical action.

② **Organ Responses to Stress:** This is a good list for students to remember. To add some interest to the process of memorizing the list, you might ask students to create imaginary stress situations in which they're the main characters as lead-ins to this list. After each lead-in, they would then copy the eight organ responses. For example, "If you wake up and your house is on fire, your. . . ." (list eight responses) Or, "This enormous, scary-looking guy walks toward us and he has a knife, my. . . ." (list eight responses)

3. If a stress reaction ends in recovery, it can benefit the body. (T)
4. If a stress reaction ends in exhaustion, it can harm the body. (T)
5. Not having any stress in life is what everyone should strive for. (F)

CLOSE
SECTION III

Activity 3.6
Stories about Stress. For extra credit have the students tell stories that would follow along with Figure 4–3. The stories can be made up or something that really happened. The stories can be written or done orally for the class.

(Interdisciplinary)

FOCUS
SECTION IV

In this section students will learn:
1. The importance of managing stress while using physical strength, psychological strength, and knowledge.
2. The importance of time management in reducing stress.

✍ Fast Facts

Men who earn less than $10,000 per year suffer migraine headaches 60% more often than men who earn more than $30,000.

Section III Review

Answers

1. Recovery, exhaustion
2. fight-or-flight reaction
3. Alarm
4. alarm, resistance, and recovery or exhaustion
5. There is a state of speeded-up functioning. Stress hormones continue to flow, causing muscles to contract and other body functions to shut down.
6. Every organ responds. The heart rate speeds up; the pupils of the eyes widen; the muscles tense; fat is released into the body; circulation to the skin, digestive system, and internal organs is reduced, and circulation to the muscles and brain is increased. The immune system temporarily shuts down.
7. diseases of the heart and arteries
8. Answers will vary.

---

passed, the body functions become balanced once again—recovery. Digestive system activity and immune defenses can resume. Both states are important—normal functioning to keep you running smoothly during peaceful times, and stress resistance to get you through emergencies.

Prolonged stress can make diseases of the heart and arteries likely. The fat released into the bloodstream to serve as fuel for the muscles may not be used up if no physical action occurs. When this fat is left in the bloodstream, it tends to collect along artery walls, damaging them. You'll learn more about heart disease in Chapter 18. For now, you should realize that psychological stress is believed to contribute to the development of heart disease.

If a round of stress leads to recovery and to a greater ability to respond to the next round, then it has benefited you. On the other hand, if it leaves you drained and *less* able to respond the next time, it has harmed you. How can you make sure that your stressful experiences benefit you and do not harm you? The next section provides some insight.

Key Points *The stress response (fight-or-flight reaction) is a physical response, even if the stressor is psychological. The phases are alarm, resistance, and recovery; or alarm, resistance, and exhaustion. If the reaction ends in recovery, it can benefit you. If it ends in exhaustion, it may harm you.*

SECTION III REVIEW

Answer the following questions on a sheet of paper.
Learning the Vocabulary
The vocabulary terms in this section are *stress response, alarm, resistance, recovery, exhaustion,* and *fight-or-flight reaction.*
Fill in the blank with the correct answer.
1. _____ is the healthy third phase of the stress response, while _____ is the harmful third phase.
2. The stress response is often called the

_____.
3. _____ is the first phase of the stress response, in which a person faces a challenge and begins paying attention to it.

Learning the Facts
4. What are the three phases of the stress response?
5. What occurs in the resistance phase of the stress response?
6. What parts of the body experience changes during the fight-or-flight reaction?
7. What diseases are associated with prolonged exposure to stress?

Making Life Choices
8. A little stress can be beneficial, but once it exceeds your limit, it can be both exhausting and harmful. Consider what stress, both physical and psychological, does to you. Describe a situation in which you experienced a stress response that followed the pattern of alarm, resistance, and recovery. Describe a situation in which the stress was chronic and resulted in a stress response of alarm, resistance, and exhaustion. Looking back on the situation now, how might you have achieved a faster recovery?

SECTION IV

Dealing with Stress

People who use stress management strategies are better able to cope with periods of stress than those who do not. Also, people who maintain strong programs of personal wellness during ordinary life are best able to withstand crises when they arrive.

At the heart of such programs is a strong sense of self-esteem. In addition to enhancing your physical wellness in general, high self-esteem can improve your ability to manage crises when they arise. People with high self-esteem learn to view challenges as positive, rather than negative, situations.

3. Some coping devices that help people through difficult situations.

Activity 4.1

Resisting Stress. Have students do the Life Choice Inventory, "How Well Do You Resist Stress?" Discuss the ways in which the various scores indicate how well a person handles a stressful situation. Discuss students' scores with them. Have students decide whether or not they are happy with their scores. Now divide the class into groups of four and have the students share their answers within the groups. What did they discover that they had in common with their groups? What conclusion can the class make about how teenagers handle stress and what they all do to resist stress? **(30 min.; Cooperative Learning, Critical Thinking)**

Activity 4.2

Time Chart. Not having enough time to do all they want to do is often a major complaint among teenagers, as well as adults. Ask the students to give some well-known statements or phrases using the word "time." Some examples are: "Gee, how time flies when you are having fun!", "Time passes, will you?", "Time's up!", "Be on time." Write the examples on the board. If time permits (another,

(continued on next page)

Therefore, they react with less fear and experience less stress than people with low self-esteem. For example, a person with low self-esteem might fear meeting new people. This person would feel stress during these meetings, whereas a person with high self-esteem would feel at ease. This illustrates that whether an event is stressful or not depends more on the person experiencing it than on the event itself.

TEEN VIEWS ①

What causes the most stress in your life?

My home environment causes the most stress in my life. This involves my siblings, parents, and after school activities. It seems the days get shorter and shorter. I never seem to have enough time to do everything. There is much pressure to be mature and responsible at home. When you're with your friends you can relax and be yourself but at home there is a specific format you feel you must follow. Also, when you're home you have more time to think about your current problems, and they all come together at once. **Diane Lewis, 17, Connellsville High School, PA**

When I have to go to school and after school I have to go straight to work and I don't have enough time to spend the money I make. Also, parents in the 90s have a hard time staying together and when they get divorced the kids go through a lot, trying to decide where to live. If one parent moves away, the kid might have a sister or brother that might have to go with one parent and that spreads the family apart. **Dustin Bennett, 15, Great Falls High School, MT**

I think that school causes the most stress in my life. Starting high school was very stressful and it still is. There are so many rules and so many things to worry about. You have to worry about your clothes, your hair, and fitting in; your grades, your future, and getting into college. **Karie Baker, 14, Fargo South High School, ND**

School causes the most stress in my life. There are many things in and out of the classroom to worry about. If I don't receive high grades in high school, I won't have a future. I have to do excellent on every test. Another stress in my life is my peers. Sometimes my peers try to persuade me to do things that I don't want to be involved in. **Darlene Filighera, 15, Frontier Central High School, NY**

High school gives students the most stress. Today there are more and more AP and honor classes offered. Test grades play the biggest part in the stress problem. I personally have gone through four AP and honor classes. I tell myself I'm just human and doing the best I possibly can. I would recommend all high school students take one psychology course. Understanding psychology will solve many stress-related problems for students and I am proof. **Andy Le, 18, Woodrow Wilson High School, CA**

I would have to pick violence. My family was raised under violence. We lived in and around the projects. There were drug sellers, drunks, fights, and shootings every week. I would worry where I was and who I was with. **Kenyana Greene, 14, Somerville High School, MA**

---

unintended phrase for the board) make some signs that can be placed around the classroom with the various statements or phrases. Have the students discuss what role time plays in their lives. What does the rigid school bell schedule do to their feelings about being ruled by time? What other specific parts of their lives are ruled by time? Ask students to develop a chart to help them decide what can be done to reduce the amount of time required in their daily schedules. In the first column of the chart, have them list school, home, work, and social life. In the second column they should show how much time is spent in each of these four areas by listing specific activities and the amount of time spent on each. In column three they should write what they can do to reduce the amount of time spent on these activities. In the fourth column, have students include what they would do with the amount of free time that they would have if any time was reduced from their required daily activities. **(45 min.)**

T**EACH**
S**ECTION** IV
(Guided and Independent Practice)

Teacher Support Notes

① **Multicultural Stress:** For enrichment, you may want to tell students that more and more people in our society are being forced to adapt to dramatic changes in language, dress, values, and social customs as they grow up in cultures other than their native cultures. The difficulty that people encounter in these situations is sometimes referred to as **acculturative stress,** which is marked by confusion, anxiety, hostility, depression, alienation, and physical illness. Four common methods of adapting to this stress are: **a.** integration—maintain old cultural identity, but participate in a new culture; **b.** separation—maintain old identity and avoid contact with new culture; **c.** assimilation—adapt the new culture as your own, and have contact with its members; **d.** marginalization—reject old culture, but also suffer rejection by members of new culture.

Ask students if they can guess which type of adaptation leads to the most stress. (Marginalization and separation cause high stress.)

86   UNIT 2 Your Emotional and Social Health

L**IFE** C**HOICE**
I**NVENTORY**

How Well Do You Resist Stress?

To determine how likely you are to be affected by stress, answer the following questions. Beside each question, fill in the number corresponding to how much of the time each statement applies to you.

4: Always.   3: Almost always.   2: Most of the time.   1: Some of the time.   0: Never.

During most of my life I: Score

1. Eat at least two full, balanced meals a day.   _____
2. Get seven to eight hours' sleep.   _____
3. Give and receive affection regularly.   _____
4. Have at least one relative on whom I can rely.   _____
5. Exercise to the point of perspiration at least twice a week.   _____
6. Do not smoke, or smoke less than half a pack of cigarettes a day.   _____
7. Do not drink alcohol or abuse drugs.   _____
8. Am at an appropriate weight

for my height.   _____
9. Feel that my basic needs are being met.   _____
10. Get strength from my values and beliefs.   _____
11. Regularly attend club or social activities.   _____
12. Have a network of friends and acquaintances.   _____
13. Have one or more friends to talk to about personal matters.   _____
14. Am in good physical health (including eyesight, hearing, and teeth).   _____
15. Am able to speak openly about my feelings when angry or worried.   _____

In addition to maintaining high self-esteem, the strategies of eating well, sleeping well, and being physically active can help equip you to withstand stress. Just as important are seeking out daily joy and laughter and acting in harmony with your values. These steps can help you move serenely through most of life.

To determine how well you protect yourself from stress during ordinary life, complete the first 20 questions of this chapter's Life Choice Inventory. Answer the last five questions to see how well you manage the stressful times.

The sections that follow present some key components of stress control. As you'll see, managing stress well takes all your capacities—physical strength, psychological strength, and knowledge. "Stress vitamins" do not help, though, as the Consumer Awareness in this chapter explains.

Exercise

Physical activity is always important. It keeps your body strong and strengthens your immune system between times of stress. Then, during stress, physical activity plays a special role. Consider what happens

Activity 4.3
 Signs of Stress. Have the students call out some recognizable signs of stress that they have noticed among their peers/classmates. Now have each student think of a stressful time that occurred to them recently. Tell the students to recall the early warning signs that were present when this situation occurred. What did they do? Impress upon the students how important it is to be able to rec-ognize their own personal signs of stress to be better able to deal with the situation. Depending upon the makeup of your class, you might also wish to have other students tell their classmates some signs that they have recognized in each other. Sometimes we may not recognize different behaviors that others may see in us. **(20 min.; Critical Thinking, Cooperative Learning)**

Activity 4.4
 Weekend Time Chart. Use the chart developed in Activity 4.2 as a guide for students to develop a chart showing how their weekend time is spent. Compare the two charts. What happens to their time restraints on the weekends? If the weekends are as regulated as the weekday during the school year, what does this say about the students' amount

(continued on next page)

How Well Do You Resist Stress (continued)

16. Have regular conversations with the people I live with about domestic issues (such as chores or money). _____
17. Have some fun each day. _____
18. Organize my time effectively. _____
19. Drink two or fewer cups of caffeinated beverages (coffee, tea, or cola drinks) a day. _____
20. Take quiet time for myself each day. _____

During stressful times I:

21. Organize my responsibilities and meet the most important ones first. _____
22. Refuse to take on too many responsibilities. _____

23. Express my feelings at intervals. _____
24. Use willed relaxation methods. _____
25. Seek outside help as needed. _____

Score _____

SCORING

81–100: Congratulations! Your defenses against daily stresses are strong.
61–80: You are well defended against stress, but you could still improve your defenses.
41–60: You are too vulnerable to stress. Try to improve.
0–40: You urgently need strategies for handling stress.

if you experience alarm (anxiety, fear), but you *don't* fight or flee—that is, your body takes no physical action. The body gets *ready* to exercise, but it doesn't act.

Now your muscles are tense and can't relax. Your blood is rich with fuels that are building up and can damage your heart. You are in a state of high alert with no relief in sight. This state drains your reserves, exhausts you mentally, and lowers your resistance to diseases of all kinds. It's time to work out.

Physical activity works your muscles so they can relax again. It burns the fuels in your blood and prevents them from building up. It relieves your anxiety and brings temporary relief. When you've had a good workout, it helps you relax.

Key Points ▶ *Between times of stress, physical activity strengthens stress resistance.*

During times of stress, physical activity can work off muscle tension, use up ready fuels, and help the body recover.

Attitude Control

While physical activity works well to combat stress that has already set in, you can also change the way you react to events so that the events aren't so stressful. An example is performing on stage: the stress response can help you get "up for it." Some excitement ahead of the event will give you the physical energy to turn out a spectacular performance. You are most attractive when you are aroused and alert. Too much nervous energy, however, will hinder you. If you allow yourself to think about what a disaster it will be if you do less than a perfect job, you will be trem-

Fast Facts

In a study by a researcher at Stanford University, five male medical students watched tapes of Gallagher, a comedian, while five colleagues rested in a room without entertainment. The students who saw the comedy showed lower levels of cortisol, dopac, and epinephrine, all stress-related hormones.

Teacher Support Notes

① **Physical Response to Stress:** Students should see that they don't have to engage in a lot of physical activity to become tired.

② **High Alert—No Activity:** This probably happens to students frequently without their being aware of it. Ask them to think of three or four situations in which they were very tired, without knowing why. Can they think of stressful situations that might have preceded their periods of exhaustion?

Focus on Texas

Essential Elements: **1A, 1C**
TAAS Objectives: **Mathematics—6**

of stress? What can be done to free up the time restraints during the weekend? Discuss answers to these questions with the class. **(45 min.; Critical Thinking, Extend, Enrich)**

Activity 4.5

Planning Ahead. As a preclass activity, have students plan one full week-day of their time from midnight to mid-night. Have them include all the things they *have* to do for the day. Have them write in all the things they would *like* to do for the day. Account for every half-hour of the day. Discuss if time management helps to reduce stress. In what ways does time management help to reduce stress? Ask students to explore time manage-

ment and whether it would work for them. If students think it would be effective, the activity can be increased to plan out a whole week to a whole month at a time. Give extra credit to students who plan a week or a month at a time. **(15 min.; Interdisciplinary, Critical Thinking, Reteach, Reinforce)**

Activity 4.6
Reducing Stress. Tell students to

Stress caused already clogged arteries to narrow an additional 24% according to researchers at Harvard Medical School. Healthy patients (no clogged arteries), however, actually experienced a slight opening of arteries when exposed to stress.

Teacher Support Notes

① **Critical Thinking Answers: 1.** Stress uses up protein from muscle and other lean tissue, cal-cium from the skeleton, and vitamins and minerals from every cell of the body. Stress vitamins seem to be a quick and easy way to provide the body with the vitamins it's lacking.
2. They can't provide all of the nutrients and sub-stances that the body needs. They can't take the place of nourishing food. There are no quick fixes.
3. Eat well-balanced meals all the time so that your body is prepared when the crisis hits.

❝ Thoughts on Health ❞

Man needs difficulties; they are necessary for health.
— *Carl Jung*

---

bling visibly, your teeth will be chattering, and your knees will be knocking together. In such a state, you can hardly reach your audience at all, and you will suffer from exhaustion afterward. It is to your advan-tage to learn to react to the event as if it were not-so-stressful and to relax before and after it.

The stage performance example illus-trates another strategy: use the stress re-sponse to your advantage. Direct and control the energy it gives you. It is a mag-nificent response to challenges, after all. It's only when the energy is scattered and wasted that it drains you without giving

you anything in return. (In other words, it's OK to have butterflies in your stomach as long as they're all flying in formation.)

Key Points ▷ *The energy of the stress response can be harnessed and used to a person's benefit. To do so, view events positively instead of negatively.*

Time Management

Efficient time management can also help you to minimize stress. Time is similar to a regular income: you receive certain amounts of it at regular intervals. In the

---

CONSUMER **A**WARENESS   **Stress Vitamin Claims**

People often wonder if any particular diet protects against the ill effects of stress. Stress does drain the body of its nutrients. It uses up protein from muscle and other lean tissue, calcium from the skeleton, and vitamins and minerals from every cell of the body. Yet most people cannot eat during crises or cannot digest their food, because the stress response shuts down di-gestive activity in favor of muscular activity. Going without food and nutrients further stresses the body.

To store the needed nutrients ahead of time, you need to eat foods that contain ① them. Proper nutrition, as described in Chapters 7, 8, and 9 of this book, can build up your defenses.

As for the pills that advertise themselves as "stress vitamins," they are not the best choice. They simply cannot provide all of the nutrients and other substances that

the body needs. If you cannot eat for a long time, you probably do need vitamins, but you need minerals as well. It may help a little to take a vitamin-mineral preparation that supplies a balanced as-sortment of nutrients, not in "megadoses" but in the amounts needed daily (see Chapter 8). But even the best pills can't take the place of nourishing food, so it's still important to eat as well as possible. There are no quick-fix pills that will make you strong in a crises.

CRITICAL **T**HINKING

1. In what ways can stress drain the body of its nutrients? Why are stress vitamins popular?
2. Why are they not the best choice for supplying the needs of the body under stress?
3. How should a person prepare nutritionally for times of stress?

think of a very stressful time they have every day. (math class, getting home from school, etc.) What is it that creates the stress? Why do they feel stressed out during this time? What can they do to prepare for this stressful time? Are they willing to do the preparation necessary to help reduce the stress? Have students answer these questions on paper and turn it in as a written assignment. **(20 min., Critical Thinking)**

Activity 4.7

The Best Medicine. Allow the students to have a good belly laugh. (You may have to think of a stimulus for this.) Talk about how they feel now that they have finished laughing. Discuss the idea that a good laugh helps to maintain balance with all body systems. Ask them to decide whether they think a good cry would do the same thing as a good laugh. Discuss why or why not. Discuss the notion that "laughter is the best medicine." Discuss what people mean when they say to "let it all out" when you are crying. **(10 min.)**

Activity 4.8

Coping Devices. On the board, list several positive ideas that teenagers use to relieve stress. Have the students give examples of using coping devices appro-

(continued on next page)

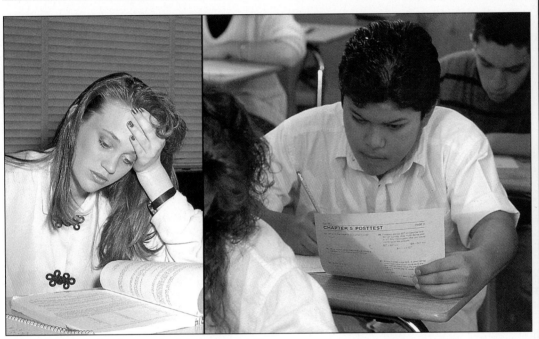

A benefit of stress: the alertness that brings clear thinking.

case of time, you receive 24 hours of it each day. Time is like money, too, in that you have three ways in which to spend it:

- You can save ahead (do tasks now so you won't have to do them later).
- You can spend as you go.
- You can borrow from the future (have fun now and hope you will find the time later to do things you have to do). ①

The goal for managing time wisely is to ensure security for the future while enjoying the present. It takes skill to treat yourself to enough fun so that you enjoy your present life, and still save enough so that you will have time available when you need it. When your friends call on a Sunday to invite you out, you don't want to be caught with no money on hand, no clean clothes, and no studying done for the big exam on Monday. That is an avoidable stress. Planning ahead can prevent it.

Make a time budget. If this sounds boring, remember that you have to do it only once. Besides, an hour of time spent organizing buys many hours of time doing what you choose. One way is to make two records—one, a list of things to do, and the other, a weekly time schedule (see Figure 4–4 on the next page). To make the time schedule, set up a grid that lists the days of the week across the top, and lists blocks of time (such as each hour from waking to bedtime) down the left-hand side. Fill in your set appointments such as class meetings first. Then add study time, waking and travel time, and mealtimes. Allot a space each day to exercise. In the time left, decide when to take care of your regular weekly chores, such as laundry, yard work, or room cleaning. Then make time for your need to play and relax.

Teacher Support Notes

① **Discuss Procrastination:** Many psychologists believe that procrastination is a problem ultimately related to a lack of self-esteem. High levels of procrastination have been associated with lower grades. Even when it doesn't lead to failure, it can cause much suffering. By putting off work until the last moment, procrastinators increase the amount of pressure and stress. By procrastinating, students can blame poor work on their late start, rather than their lack of ability. An opposite feeling, *perfectionism*, can cause the same problem. It can cause students to put off starting an assignment because they expect unrealistic accomplishments. If they don't know how to do the task better than anyone else, they delay starting. Present these two causes of procrastination to students and ask them to write a short piece about whether or not they procrastinate, and if so, why.

priately. Next to these coping devices list some negative examples that teenagers use. Discuss how negative coping devices can create more stress. **(15 min.; Extend, Enrich)**

Activity 4.9

Methods of Stress Relief. Put the following statements on the board:
1. Work off stress. **2.** Talk out your worries. **3.** Learn to accept what you cannot change. **4.** Avoid self-medication. **5.** Get enough sleep and rest. **6.** Balance work and recreation. **7.** Do something for others. **8.** Take one thing at a time. **9.** Give in once in awhile. **10.** Don't worry, be happy. **11.** Go off by yourself for awhile. **12.** Write it down.

13. Do something for yourself.
Ask the students which of these examples of dealing with stress fits them the best. Can they think of any more examples of ways to deal with stress effectively? Have the students share their answers with the class. **(10 min.; Reteach, Reinforce)**

Activity 4.10
Stressful Miscommunication.

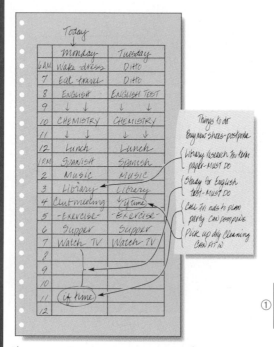

Figure 4–4 Time Management (example)

Now make a list of special things you have to do. Place tasks from this list in the empty spaces in your days. Decide how urgent each one is ("This I can do next week; this I have to do today"). Enter the most urgent items into today's schedule, carry it with you, and check off each item when you have completed it. Move uncompleted tasks to the next day's schedule.

To schedule a long-term assignment, such as a big report, first identify every task you must do to complete the project. Then, working backward from the due date, schedule the tasks. For example, if it will take you six hours to type the report, schedule those six hours on a grid that you have started for the due-date week. Back up and schedule time before that to write the final draft, and schedule time still earlier for the first drafts and the reading. If you have been realistic

about the time each step will take, you will not be caught short at the end.

A part of wise time management is knowing your limits so you don't take on more tasks than you can handle. Spreading yourself too thin is a source of stress. After identifying your limits, learn to say no when others ask you to do more than you feel comfortable doing. (Assertiveness helps here, as was explained in Chapter 2.)

Key Points *Wise time management helps control stress in life.*

Coping Devices and Defense Mechanisms

When major stressors strike, you may not be able to deal with them all at once. The human mind has some temporary measures it can use to get through the hardest times: **coping devices.** These are useful only for a while. They do nothing to solve problems permanently.

One coping device is **displacement,** the transferring of energy to a familiar, even pointless, activity for a while. Ignoring the pain caused by extreme stress, a person will clean house, or rebuild a bicycle, or manicure fingernails, or mow lawns as if life depended on nothing else. Healthy people use displacement behaviors to handle tough times. It takes time to heal. While the healing is taking place, it makes sense to do whatever works for you—as long as what you choose to do harms or endangers neither you nor anyone else.

A form of displacement is **sublimation,** becoming absorbed in high-level work such as church work, studying, or playing music. This is a beneficial coping device because it produces rewards, but even this can be overused. Sooner or later it is necessary to deal directly with problems, even painful ones.

Another way of coping is **ventilation.** To ventilate is to let off steam, by expressing feelings to another person. This helps to re-

---

Fast Facts

One study found that 15% of a group of 25-year-old doctors and lawyers who scored high on a hostility test were dead by age 50.

Teacher Support Notes

① **Symptoms vs. Cause:** Ask students if they know the difference between treating the symptoms of an illness and the cause of an illness. Taking aspirin to give relief to chronic headaches would be an example of treating symptoms. Of course, this is a distinction they should know since it applies to many different areas of health.

Fast Facts

It is estimated that at least half of all patients who see a doctor have a psychosomatic disorder or an illness that is complicated by a psychosomatic symptom.

❝ Thoughts on Health ❞

To avoid sickness, eat less; to prolong life, worry less.
– Chu Hui Weng

Much stress comes from miscommunication. Use some statements that teenagers commonly misinterpret and discuss what the person making the statement means and how the person hearing the statement interprets it. Some examples are: parent to child, "Clean up your room"; teacher to student, "Study for your test," "Be quiet," "Write neatly"; boyfriend to girlfriend, "I love you." Have the students write down what they think each of the two people involved thinks the statement means. Now have the students read aloud what they wrote. How many different answers are there to each statement? Are the students surprised? Why or why not? **(25 min.; Extend, Enrich)**

Activity 4.11
Student Portraits. Obtain some butcher paper that is 3 feet wide. Ask the students to have someone draw their outlines, from the waist up, onto the paper. Have them draw any significant items on their drawings that help to identify them. Now on their heads, have them write five things they are good at doing; on their hearts, five hopes or goals that they want to achieve in their lifetimes; on their shoulders, five things they are not good at doing; on their arms, five coping skills that they use to handle stress; on

(continued on next page)

lieve pain. After ventilating, a person can often go on to work directly on solving a stressful problem.

Some coping devices have negative effects and are useful only because they prevent a worse thing from happening: complete breakdown. These are sometimes known as **defense mechanisms:**

- Denial—the refusal to admit that something unpleasant or painful has occurred: "No, I don't believe it." Also called *repression.*
- Fantasy—imagining, in the face of a painful or unpleasant situation, that something positive has happened instead: "He hasn't really left me. He's gone to buy me a present."
- Projection—the belief, in the face of an unpleasant or painful situation you have caused, that it is the other person's fault: "The teacher asked the wrong questions on the exam."
- Rationalization—the justification of an unreasonable action or attitude by manufacturing reasons for it: "I couldn't prevent the accident, because I had to pay attention to something else."
- Regression—using inappropriate childish ways of dealing with painful realities: chronic crying or whining.

**Defense mechanisms:
Forms of mental avoidance.**

- Selective forgetting—memory lapse concerning an experience or piece of news too painful to bear: not remembering it.
- Withdrawal—drawing away from people and activities to avoid pain: living in fantasy (daydreaming), refusing to talk with anyone, or sleeping excessively.

① Coping devices and defense mechanisms help people survive bad periods of stress. They are especially useful when the stress is unexpected and severe, like the sudden death of a loved one. Often, though, you can see stress coming. You don't have to wait until it has become severe. You can take early steps to relieve it, as the next section shows.

Key Points *Coping devices can help you deal with severe stress temporarily. Defense mechanisms are self-destructive, though, and are best used only for short periods, if at all.*

Preventing and Managing Stress

A smart stress prevention strategy is to listen to your body sensitively. Too many

 MINI GLOSSARY

coping devices: nonharmful ways of dealing with stress, such as displacement, sublimation, or ventilation.
displacement: channeling the energy of suffering into something else, for example, using the emotional energy churned up by problems for tasks or recreation.
sublimation: channeling the energy of suffering into creative, productive work.
ventilation: the act of verbally venting one's feelings; letting off steam by talking, crying, swearing, or laughing.
② **defense mechanisms:** self-destructive ways of dealing with stress; automatic subconscious reactions to emotional injury, such as denial, fantasy, projection, rationalization, regression, selective forgetting, or withdrawal.

Teacher Support Notes

① **Coping vs. Defense:** Ask students to explain the main difference between coping devices and defense mechanisms. (Coping is nonharmful, defense mechanisms are self-destructive.) Then, ask students to write a short paper describing which coping devices and defense mechanisms they use. Have them try to describe specific instances in which they've used these devices and mechanisms. Generate a class list. If students are uncomfortable talking about these, have them hand the papers in and then pull the best examples together into a handout that you can distribute to students for discussion.

② **Discuss Subconscious:** *Conscious* was used and discussed in earlier chapters. Tell students that *subconscious* refers to thoughts that are not immediately available to a person's consciousness. It refers to mental activities just below the threshold of consciousness.

 Focus on Texas

Essential Elements: **1B, 1C**
TAAS Objectives: **Reading Comprehension—1**

their bellybuttons, five things that make them mad; in their stomachs, five things that worry or upset them. **(45 min., Critical Thinking)**

EVALUATE
SECTION IV

Activity 4.12
Pop Quiz. (Answers will vary.)
1. Give three positive examples of ways in which teenagers can reduce their daily stress.
2. Name three signs of physical stress and three signs of psychological stress.
3. What is time management and how does it help to reduce stress?
4. What are coping skills? Name three coping skills that teenagers use.

5. Name five signs of stress that you show when you are upset.

CLOSE
SECTION IV

Activity 4.13
Review Questions. As a minimum, before going on to the next lesson, students should be able to answer these questions.

Teacher Support Notes

① **Anxiety:** Most students will have a general understanding of what anxiety is. You may want to elaborate somewhat, however, since it is such a key term. In context, anxiety is an emotional state in which a person feels tense, uneasy, apprehensive, worried, and vulnerable. Anxiety often leads to the defense mechanisms discussed in this section. You may want to refer students to page 110 in Chapter 5 for more on anxiety.

② **Handout—Stress Reducing Strategies:** You may want to distribute the handout *Stress Reducing Strategies*, which summarizes several of the additional strategies explained in this chapter.

③ **Physical Activity:** After the general strategy of maintaining overall wellness, physical activity is the first item on the list. It is extremely important to question those students who feel a great deal of stress as to whether or not they are getting enough physical activity. You may want to refer students at this point to Chapter 10, which deals with physical fitness.

92 UNIT 2 Your Emotional and Social Health

It only slows you down to worry about things you have to do.

people think that they have to wait for stress to cause real trouble before they can relieve it. That's not true. At each step along the way, you can monitor your body for the early warning signals of too much stress. That way, you can take action before exhaustion sets in and does damage. Cold hands and feet are among the first signs. Figure 4–5 on the next page lists others. When you see these signs, seek relief. Don't let the situation get worse. (One relief strategy is willed relaxation, discussed later.)

Sometimes stress becomes really severe, in spite of all your efforts. Then even small details become overwhelming. Example: a student who is moving to a different state, breaking up with his girlfriend, and changing schools all at the same time is trying to get his belongings packed. He picks up a guitar pick and can't decide what packing box to put it in. He starts to sob; he can't handle the situation.

There's nothing wrong with crying at such a time; it is a form of release, and it will help to change anxiety to relaxation, the reverse of the stress response. Once relaxed, though, our student still has a problem to solve. He needs to ask himself what parts of the problem he can control, and pay strict attention to those parts. The

move, the breakup, and the change of schools are beyond his control right now. The packing is not. He can go on with it, or stop. He may need to take a break—for food, sleep, or exercise. He may need to tap a friendship—to get help packing boxes or just to talk to someone. If his friend can help him laugh, so much the better. Laughter works as crying does, to relieve tension.

The Health Strategies section on this page, "Managing Stress," gives you some

---

HEALTH
STRATEGIES

Managing Stress

To manage stress:

1. During ordinary times, maintain a program of strong personal wellness.
2. Be sure to include regular physical activity.
3. Cultivate high self-esteem.
4. Maintain a positive attitude toward stressors—view them as opportunities for growth.
5. Manage time wisely.
6. Take on tasks only within your limits.
7. Practice assertiveness to maintain your limits.
8. Monitor your body for the early warning signs of too much stress.
9. Release tension by crying, laughing, talking with friends, or willing yourself to relax.
10. When stress becomes intense, identify which stressors you can control. Put the others out of your mind. Take action by focusing on the immediate task.
11. If stress becomes unmanageable, seek outside help.

1. What are some signs of stress and what are some ways to reduce stress?
2. What is the importance of time management when dealing with everyday stressors?
3. What are some coping devices commonly used by teenagers to get them through a difficult situation?
    Discuss the answers with the class.

Activity 4.14

Positive Attitude. Tell the students to stand up and go to three people in the room they do not know very well. Have them introduce themselves to that person showing confidence, physical strength and stature, positive psychological attributes, and knowledge. Have the students say one complimentary thing to the other person. After everyone is finished and sitting down, discuss how acting positively helps one to be positive in dealing with stressful situations. **(15 min.)**

FOCUS
SECTION V

In this section students will learn the:
1. Normal state of the body.
2. Ways in which the relaxation response and other techniques help return the

(continued on next page)

FIGURE 4-5

Signs of Stress ①

Physical Signs

Pounding of the heart ②

Rapid, shallow breathing

Dryness of the throat and mouth

Raised body temperature

Feelings of weakness, light-headedness, dizziness, or faintness

Trembling; nervous tics; twitches; shaking hands and fingers

Tendency to be easily startled (by small sounds and the like)

High-pitched, nervous laughter

Stuttering and other speech difficulties

Insomnia—that is, difficulty in getting to sleep, or a tendency to wake up during the night

Grinding of the teeth during sleep

Restlessness, an inability to keep still

Sweating (not necessarily noticeably); clammy hands; cold hands and feet; cold chills

Blushing; hot face

The need to urinate frequently

Diarrhea; indigestion; upset stomach, nausea

Headaches; frequent earaches or toothaches

Premenstrual tension or missed menstrual periods

More body aches and pains than usual, such as pain in the neck or lower back; any localized muscle tension

Loss of appetite; unintended weight loss; excessive appetite; sudden weight gain

Increased use of substances (tobacco, legally prescribed drugs such as tranquilizers or amphetamines, alcohol, other drugs)

Accident proneness

Frequent illnesses

Psychological Signs

Irritability, tension, or depression

Impulsive behavior and emotional instability; the overpowering urge to cry or to run and hide

Lowered self-esteem; thoughts related to failure

Excessive worry; insecurity; concern about other people's opinions; self-deprecation in conversation

Reduced ability to communicate with others

Increased awkwardness in social situations

Excessive boredom; unexplained dissatisfaction with job or other normal conditions

Feelings of isolation

Avoidance of activities

Irrational fears (phobias) about specific things

Irrational thoughts; forgetting things more often than usual; mental "blocks"; missing of planned events

Guilt about neglecting family or friends; inner confusion about duties and roles

Excessive work; omission of play

Inability to organize oneself; tendency to get distraught over minor matters

Inability to reach decisions; erratic, unpredictable decisions

Decreased ability to perform tasks

Inability to concentrate

General ("floating") anxiety; feelings of unreality

A tendency to become fatigued; loss of energy; loss of spontaneous joy

Nightmares

Feelings of powerlessness; mistrust of others

Teacher Support Notes

① **Handouts—More on Stress:** The handouts *Medical Signs of Stress* and *Interventions to Manage Stress* will help you expand your discussion of stress.

② **Combating Depression:** For enrichment, tell students that implementing a daily schedule is an effective method for combating depression. Students might check off each daily activity as they complete it. The advantage to this is that they begin to break the self-defeating cycle of feeling helpless and falling further behind. Some experts also say that depression is supported by self-critical or negative thoughts. They recommend writing down such thoughts as they occur. Students should then write a sound, logical answer to each of those thoughts. Another strategy is not to minimize or ignore positive results. When good things happen, take credit for them, note them, and use them as a sign that things will continue to get better.

FOCUS (Continued)

body to a normal state.

Activity 5.1

Lessen Stress. Have the students close their eyes and recall a time in their lives when they felt good about themselves. Tell them to remember what they were doing, and the sights and sounds of the time. Have them put themselves in that situation again and repeat to themselves three times, "I like myself no matter what!" Talk about how this exercise made them feel. Inform students that this activity can be done on a daily basis to return their bodies to a normal state when stress has them unbalanced. **(5 min.; Extend, Enrich)**

TEACH

SECTION V
(Guided and Independent Practice)

Activity 5.2

Relaxation Breathing. Tell the students to close their eyes and focus only on breathing in through their noses and out through their mouths. Tell them to try and clear their heads of all thoughts but the process of breathing. Follow the

---

Teacher Support Notes

① **Deep Muscle Relaxation:** Tell students to tense the muscles in the right arm until they tremble. They should hold the muscles tight for about five seconds and then allow the hand and arm to go limp. Repeat the procedure until the arm muscles are relaxed. Continue this process with different parts of your body. As a last step, curl the toes and tense your feet, then release. Students can practice this until they can do it quickly.

Section IV Review

Answers

1. Sublimation
2. Ventilation
3. defense mechanisms
4. Having high self-esteem improves one's ability to manage crises when they arise, and to view challenges as positive situations.
5. Physical activity can help you relax. It relieves anxiety and brings temporary relief.
6. Answer will vary. Refer to the Health Strategies on page 92 for possible answers.
7. Answers will vary. Refer to Figure 4–5 on page 93 for possible answers.
8. **a and b.** Answers will vary.

---

suggestions for handling stress in your life. If you find, however, that most of the time you have trouble functioning because stress is so overwhelming, it may be time to seek outside help.

> **Key Points** — *Listen carefully to your body. Try to deal with stressful events promptly. If stress overwhelms you, don't be afraid to show your emotions, to seek help from friends, or to seek outside help.*

SECTION IV REVIEW

Answer the following questions on a sheet of paper.

Learning the Vocabulary

The vocabulary terms in this section are *coping devices, displacement, sublimation, ventilation,* and *defense mechanisms.*

Fill in the blank with the correct answer.

1. _____ involves channeling the energy of suffering into creative, productive work.
2. _____ means venting one's feelings verbally.
3. Self-destructive stress outlets are _____.

Learning the Facts

4. How does a person's self-esteem affect the person's ability to manage stress?
5. How can the energy of stress be controlled and used to a person's benefit?
6. Give three suggestions for managing stress.
7. Name four physical and four psychological signs of stress.

Making Life Choices

8. a. Describe an incident in which stress affected your judgment and caused you to behave in an unsafe way. If you could replay this situation, how would you behave differently?
   b. Describe a situation in which stress worked to your advantage, enabling you to achieve more than you thought possible.

SECTION V

Willed Relaxation

The exact opposite of the stress response is the **relaxation response.** This response reduces blood pressure, slows the pulse, quiets anxiety, and releases tension. Relaxation permits your body to recover from the effects of stress. You can will it to happen, even in the middle of a stressful situation. You can relax anywhere, at any time.

Willed relaxation always has these components:

- A comfortable position.
- A quiet, calm environment.
- A passive attitude toward mental thoughts.

The following paragraphs describe various methods of achieving this response.

"Relax!" When someone tells you this, can you do it? How do you know when you've succeeded? Many clinics use a **biofeedback** technique to teach people how to monitor their own physical condition. A machine (the electromyograph, or EMG) measures muscle tension and sounds a tone that changes in pitch as muscles tighten or relax. Harmless sensors are fastened to the forehead, neck, jaw, or anywhere muscles may be tense. The pitch drops lower and lower as the person relaxes. By listening and working to lower the tone, the person learns how to relax.

① A way to relax without machines is **progressive muscle relaxation.** The technique involves lying flat and then locating and relaxing muscles all over the body, beginning at either the head or the feet. People who have never tried this are surprised to discover the tightness they may have in the muscles of the belly, the upper back and neck, and the face. Fifteen different sets of muscles in the face alone can be-directions in Steps to Relaxation on page 96.

Explain to your students that this technique can be used at any time under any circumstances. This method has been used by many people to reduce stress in their daily lives. **(10 min.; Extend, Enrich)**

Activity 5.3
Desk Exercises. Contact your local hospital's wellness center. Ask them if they have an exercise specialist who could demonstrate exercises students can do to relax their necks, shoulders, arms, legs, and stomachs while still sitting at their desks. These exercises are easy to do and can be done by the students at any time to help ease stress. Spend class time over a period of a week doing these exercises for five minutes at the beginning of class. **(5 min.; Extend, Enrich)**

EVALUATE
SECTION V

Activity 5.4
Pop Quiz.
1. The relaxation response is the exact opposite of the stress response. (T)
2. Progressive muscle relaxation works by relaxing one muscle group at a time. (T)

(continued on next page)

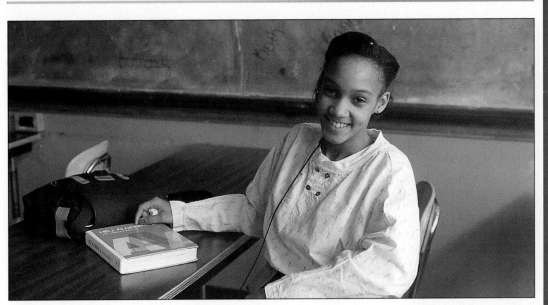

With practice, you can learn to relax whenever you need to.

come tense. Some people learn that the only thing preventing them from relaxing is ① that their shoulders are hunched up. Others find that they clench their jaws; others, that they are squinting or frowning without knowing it.

With practice, you can learn to relax your muscles whenever you think of it—not only when you have time to keep still for 30 minutes. Professional mountain climbers train themselves to do it while climbing—the so-called mountain rest step. Any time you take a step, you have to tense one leg—but why tense the other one? At each step, relax the unused leg. That way, you're resting throughout the climb, and you won't be exhausted when you get to the top. Students may not often have physical mountains to climb, but they do have mental ones. If your shoulders (for example) are tense while you are reading, what good does that do you? Relax them.

The benefits of relaxation are so great that many cultures promote it. One way is

through **meditation**. Meditation usually involves sitting straight, closing the eyes, breathing deeply, and relaxing the muscles. The Health Strategies section on the next page, "Steps to Relaxation," presents a summary of one method that might be used. Many variations are possible, and a complete

MINI GLOSSARY

relaxation response: the opposite of the stress response; the normal state of the body.
biofeedback: a clinical technique used to help a person learn to relax by reflecting back muscle tension, heart rate, brain wave activity, or other body activities.
progressive muscle relaxation: a technique of learning to relax by focusing on relaxing each of the body's muscle groups in turn.
meditation: a method of relaxing that involves closing the eyes, breathing deeply, and relaxing the muscles.

Teacher Support Notes

① **Meditation:** For enrichment, tell students there are two basic forms of meditation. *Concentrative meditation* focuses attention on a single focal point, such as an object, a thought, or one's own breathing. *Receptive meditation* does not focus on one point. It is wider and more difficult to attain. Many religions and groups use a mantra in their meditation. A mantra is a word or a group of words that is easily repeated. It helps to block out unwanted thoughts during the meditation. Some believe that it matters what mantra a person chooses, but others have found that the physical benefits of meditation are the same no matter what word is used. These experts believe that meditation produces a relaxation response which opposes the fight-or-flight mechanism.

EVALUATE
(Continued)

3. Relaxation can occur anywhere despite the surroundings and the circumstances. (T)
4. Not everyone can learn to relax his or her body. (F)
5. Relaxation techniques have no place in the daily routine of a teenager. (F)

CLOSE
SECTION V

Activity 5.5
Choose Relaxation Technique.
Have the students choose which method of willed relaxation they feel would work best for them. Ask them to answer the following questions about the technique:
1. Would you be willing to try the tech-

nique each day for one week? Why or why not? **2.** If so, what benefits would you hope to achieve?

For extra credit, have the students try a technique and report on their results. Students should keep a diary to record the results and make notes of both physical and psychological benefits that the willed relaxation techniques have on the body.

Section V Review
Answers

1. Biofeedback helps people to relax by reflecting back muscle tension, heart rate, brain-wave activity, or other body activities. Meditation helps people to relax through closing the eyes, breathing deeply, and relaxing the muscles.
2. Progressive muscle relaxation
3. relaxation response
4. This response reduces blood pressure, slows the pulse, quiets anxiety, and releases tension.
5. It measures muscle tension and sounds a tone that changes in pitch as muscles tighten or relax.
6. progressive muscle relaxation or meditation
7. Answers will vary.

✍ Fast Facts

During the meditation–relaxation response, breathing decreases from the usual 16–20 breaths per minute to 11 per minute. Each breath takes in about 5% less oxygen. Each exhale contains less carbon dioxide. Your skin resistance is some 300 times higher than normal, a sign that anxiety is at an absolute minimum. Blood flow to the brain increases by 25%.

96

---

96 UNIT 2 Your Emotional and Social Health

HEALTH STRATEGIES

Steps to Relaxation

To relax at will:

1. Assume a comfortable sitting position.
2. When you are ready, close your eyes.
3. Become aware of your breathing. Breathe in deeply, hold it, then breathe out. Each time you breathe out, say the word *one* silently to yourself.
4. Allow each of your muscles to relax deeply, one after another. Imagine that you are floating, drifting, or gliding.
5. Maintain a passive attitude. Permit relaxation to occur at its own pace. Thoughts will pass through your mind. Allow them to come and go without resistance.
6. Continue for 20 minutes. You may open your eyes to check the time, but do not use an alarm. When you finish, sit quietly for several minutes, and open your eyes when you are ready.

set of instructions would provide many more details. If you practice meditations as described here once or twice daily, then the relaxation response will come with little effort after a while.

To practice relaxation is to take control of the body's responses, and to enjoy a benefit beyond the simple pleasure it brings. Just as stress leads to disease, stress management helps prevent it.

> **Key Points** *People who learn to relax at will can enjoy the benefits of the relaxation response regardless of their circumstances and surroundings.*

SECTION V REVIEW

Answer the following questions on a sheet of paper.
Learning the Vocabulary
The vocabulary terms in this section are *relaxation response, biofeedback, progressive muscle relaxation,* and *meditation.*
1. What is the difference between biofeedback and meditation?
2. _____ is a technique of learning to relax by relaxing specific muscle groups.
3. The opposite of the stress response is the _____.

Learning the Facts
4. What occurs in the body during the relaxation response?
5. What does a machine that is used to teach biofeedback do?
6. What two relaxation methods can be practiced without the use of machines?

Making Life Choices
7. Refer to the Health Strategies section on this page entitled "Steps to Relaxation." Take some time to try to relax at will and then answer the following questions. How did you feel before, during, and after the exercise? Did you find this an effective stress reduction activity? Why or why not? Describe any variations in the activity you might incorporate.

Answers to Fact or Fiction

Here are the answers to the questions at the start of the chapter.

1. True. **2.** True. **3.** False. People today experience the fight-or-flight reaction just as our ancestors did. **4.** True.
5. False. You can change the way you perceive a stressor so that it will benefit you. **6.** True.

RETEACH/BONUS

Here are some additional activities for the various sections of this chapter. You may want to use these activities to reteach certain concepts, or you may choose them as alternatives to earlier activities.

Stress-Caused Problems. Initiate a discussion concerning the idea that all changes in life (good or bad) produce stress. Help students realize that all events that occur in life produce change. Stress is not necessarily good or bad but how people deal with stress is effective or not effective. Ask for volunteers to describe a very happy time in their lives. As a group, discuss the stressors that existed even though the event was positive. Then ask for a volunteer to describe a negative situation that occurred in his or her life. As a group, discuss the stressors that existed. Draw conclusions about what happens to the body whether or not the event that causes the stress is good or bad. **(15 min., Critical Thinking)**

Essay on Stress Response. Have the students write a paper that includes the following: **a.** Describe a stressful

(continued on next page)

STRAIGHT TALK

Healing and the Placebo Effect

An unusual story about surviving intense stress is that of Norman Cousins's bout with a crippling illness. Cousins, the editor of the famous Saturday Review *magazine, took a stressful trip overseas and returned home exhausted. A week later, he found himself hardly able to stand up, and he had to go to the hospital. His story is one of an unexpected recovery.*

What happened to Mr. Cousins?

At first, Cousins was told that the diagnosis was an ever-worsening disease of the connective tissue of the spine, almost always fatal. His physicians predicted that his spine would weaken until he was paralyzed. Stress and exhaustion had led to disease. The disease was expected to be totally disabling, the expectation caused further stress, and the end would be tragic.

Lying in his hospital bed, Cousins considered what he already knew about stress, diseases, and cures. It occurred to him that if negative emotional experiences could harm the body, then positive emotional experiences might restore health. To his way of thinking, the most positive emotional experiences would be "hope, faith, laughter, confidence, and the will to live."

Finding the hospital an unpleasant environment, Cousins checked out and moved, with his physician's approval, into a hotel room. There he could be equally well taken care of without being surrounded by illness. Each day, he watched comedy films and had funny stories read to him. He had spent weeks with hardly any sleep and was in severe pain, but now he made a wonderful discovery. After a hearty laugh, he could relax and sleep soundly for an hour or two at a time.*

The laughter, relaxation, and sleep brought about a healing that no amount of medical attention could have achieved. The long of the story is in Cousins's article "Anatomy of an Illness," which was published in the *Saturday Review* and the *New England Journal of Medicine* as a landmark in medical history. The short of it is that Cousins recovered completely. After some weeks he was able to walk on the beach, to use all of his limbs, to return to work, and to lead a normal life.

Well, how do you suppose he did it? What accounts for his recovery?

There has been much talk about that. Most people (including Cousins himself) agree that it was certainly due, at least in part, to the **placebo effect.** A placebo is an **inert,** or dummy, substance labeled "medicine" and used for its psychological effect. The placebo effect is the healing that occurs in people given such medication.

How common is the placebo effect?

(Continued on next page)

*Cousins also believed in the power of vitamin C to cure diseases of connective tissue and so took large doses as part of his plan. Vitamin C has since proved useless for treating any diseases except those caused by too little Vitamin C.

Teacher Support Notes

① **Thinking Healthy:** Ask students if they agree with Cousins's reasoning. They read earlier in the chapter that stress (negative emotional experiences) can contribute to the development of disease. If so, why not believe that positive experiences could contribute to better health?

✎ Fast Facts

In a study done at the University of Arizona College of Medicine in Tucson, surgery patients who heard tapes of get-well tips while under anesthesia seemed to recover faster than those who did not have the tapes played for them. In another study, patients who heard specific pain-relief suggestions recovered more easily than those who heard vague suggestions such as "think of being well."

situation that occurred sometime in your life. **b.** What was your immediate response to the stressor? **c.** What were the physical and psychological changes that occurred during your response? **d.** Describe how you progressed through the three phases of the stress response. **e.**

Did you feel comfortable with how you handled the situation? **f.** What could you have done differently in the stressful situation that you described? **(30 min.; Reteach, Reinforce, Critical Thinking)**

Role-Playing Emotions. Pick five students in the class to role-play the following emotions/situations: happy/very excited, scared, mad, surprised, lonely. Ask students to describe their initial reac-

tions to each of the "actors." Ask students to decide what emotions are being displayed. Discuss what can happen to the body if these emotions are not dealt with effectively. **(20 min.; Extend, Enrich)**

Biofeedback. Obtain a biofeedback machine. Follow the directions that go with the machine you have obtained. Have the students try to get their breathing and pulse rates down even with vari-

---

Thoughts on Health

The art of medicine consists of amusing the patient while Nature cures the disease.

– Voltaire

Teacher Support Notes

① **A Disease by Any Other Name:** Read students the Kant quote below or write it on the board. Ask students to compare the text's point of view with Kant's regarding the value of a doctor's diagnosis. With which point of view do students agree?

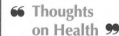

Thoughts on Health

Physicians think they do a lot for a patient when they give his disease a name.

– Immanuel Kant

Where to Write

American Institute of Stress
124 Park Ave.
Yonkers, NY 10703

STRAIGHT TALK   *(Continued)*

It is not unusual for experiments using placebos to record a benefit in 30 to 60 percent of subjects. That is, people given only distilled water or sugar pills will recover about half the time, as completely as if they had received a powerful medication.

Placebos, given with encouragement ("This will make you better"), are sometimes so effective that physicians have on occasion prescribed them when they didn't know what else to prescribe. The curious thing is that people will recover, given placebos, when they would not recover without them. In other words, the placebo effect is valuable. It is an important weapon against illness.

Are you telling me that my physician may give me fake medicine?

No, that would be against medical **ethics**. But the point is that your response, even to the real drug, may be aided by your faith in the treatment, whether you or your physician know it or not.

We want to warn you, though: **quacks** will sell you placebos every chance they get. Since 30 to 60 percent of people given anything will recover, there will be plenty of people around to praise

the virtues of the quack's miracle cures.

Are you saying I don't need to see a doctor when I get sick?

No, not at all. You *do* need to see a doctor. Pick the most competent, well-qualified physician that you can, so that your faith in him or her will help you get well.

How does the placebo effect work?

No one knows for sure. Part of the effect may come from the relaxation that brings relief from anxiety. The patient wonders what is wrong, feels helpless, and worries so much that symptoms become worse. Then the patient goes to a trusted expert. The expert names the disease, and the patient feels reassured: the expert has the answer. The expert then prescribes a treatment, and the patient relaxes. Both stress and the symptoms begin to disappear. ①

The placebo effect can be measured. Blood pressure falls, pulse rate slows, and the patient proceeds to get well, whatever treatment has been prescribed.

So you think the placebo effect works through the relaxation response?

That certainly must be part of it. Research has often illustrated the effect. For example, it had been thought, at various times, that ulcers were caused by poor circulation to the stomach or intestine, by hot foods, by cold foods, by coarse foods, by spices such as pepper, by alcohol, and by caffeine. Patients were warned to avoid all these things. One physician, however, attempted to treat ulcers simply by giving shots of distilled water with the guarantee that they would heal the ulcers. The patients recovered. We now know that a common thread in all such ulcers is anxiety. In such cases, the placebo effect works through relaxation. Faith heals.

I see what you mean. I suppose witch doctors and other healers work their cures the same way.

Probably so. Don't forget that the body will often heal itself, given time. Frequently, all that healers have to do is to wait out the course of the illness. If they can offer reassurance and confidence, they will be providing support as important as any chemical or physical procedure might be. In fact, health care providers in training are taught not only to manage

(Continued on next page)

---

ous distractions going on. For extra credit, ask students to find out if there is a biofeedback clinic in their community and what services they offer to their clients. **(5 min. per student, Special Needs)**

Relaxing at Will. On the board, list some benefits of being able to relax at will. Discuss why people do not use these relaxation techniques more often. After being shown various ways to relax, are

the students willing to try them? For extra credit, have students keep a diary of when they used the technique(s) and what effects the technique(s) had on their bodies. **(10 min.; Reteach, Reinforce)**

Relaxation Tapes. Obtain a relaxation tape from any music store. Follow the directions on the tape. Create a classroom environment that will allow relaxation—warm, quiet, dark. Discuss how

students felt while responding to the tape. Use these questions to develop an evaluation sheet for the students to fill out at the end of the tape. Did it work? Was it beneficial? Why or why not? **(30 min.)**

STRAIGHT TALK   *(Continued)*

Love heals.

their clients' medical care but also to dole out liberal doses of TLC, Tender Loving Care. Children given TLC recover faster than those deprived of it. They even grow better.

Does the placebo effect work for pain?

Yes. People in pain, given placebos, often experience relief of their pain. It is thought that placebo treatments stimulate the brain to produce natural chemicals that relieve pain even more powerfully than the drug morphine. People in pain who are given placebos with a drug that blocks the brain's production of these natural painkillers experience no relief at all. This shows that placebos relieve pain by triggering the brain's production of painkillers.

How powerful can the placebo effect be in relieving pain?

The brain produces painkillers more powerful than morphine, which has been used for centuries to relieve severe pain. The natural chemicals don't necessarily produce a cure—you still need a surgeon to operate on a medical problem. But mobilizing the body's natural resources speeds healing.

Some fascinating stories are told about healing in the hospital. Just physically touching people has been shown as hastening healing. Researchers now know it works. They are experimenting to find out how and why.

So faith really heals. But I'm skeptical—to say the least—about those faith-healing scenes we sometimes see on television.

Rightly so. Anything as dramatic as faith healing is bound to attract quacks in multitudes. Fraud is most successful when it imitates amazing true events. A viewer should always watch such scenes skeptically and judge each one on its own merits. Just remember, though: the fact that a quack can try to rip off the public by faking "miracle cures" does not mean that the placebo effect is fake. It is real. Faith does heal—or at least it

helps enormously—in any situation where stress has contributed to illness.

I see what you mean. I think you've partially explained the healing effect of love, too.

You might be right. Anything that makes people feel cared for helps them to produce their own internal tranquilizers and strengthens their bodies. As Dr. Francis Weld Peabody of Harvard University put it, "The secret of the care of the patient is in caring for the patient."

Mini Glossary

placebo effect: the healing effect that faith in medicine, even inert medicine, often has.
inert: not active.
ethics: moral principles or values.
quacks: people pretending to have medical skills, and usually having products for sale.

Teacher Support Notes

① **Miraculous Healing:** Ask students if they have heard any stories of amazing cures that have taken place. If so, ask them to describe what happened.

✍ **Fast Facts**

In one study an injection of a saline solution was found to be 70% as effective as morphine in reducing pain.

Vocabulary

1. a. The stress response is the response to a demand of a stressor, and is the opposite of the relaxation response, which is the normal state of the body. **b.** They are similar because both are the third phase of the stress response. They are different because the recovery phase goes into effect when the source of stress is dealt with. There must be rest between times to build up strength. Exhaustion occurs when the stress continues to affect you without a break and your resistance finally breaks down. The body does not return to normal as quickly as it needs to during exhaustion.
2. a. immunity **b.** stress **c.** gland **d.** chronic stress **e.** inert **f.** hormone **g.** ethics
3. a. hormonal system **b.** norepinephrine, stress hormone **c.** displacement, coping devices **d.** resistance **e.** Quacks
4. a. immune system **b.** defense mechanisms **c.** Biofeedback

Recall
Section I
1. Answers will vary; could include: physical—air temperature, intensity of lights, bacteria, injuries, or radiation. Psychological—refer to Figure 4–1 on page 77 for possible answers.
2. grade point averages and scores on a test of self-esteem drop
Section II
3. epinephrine, norepinephrine
4. It makes the immune system stronger.

CHAPTER REVIEW

LEARNING THE VOCABULARY

stress	epinephrine	sublimation
chronic stress	norepinephrine	ventilation
acute stress	immunity	defense mechanisms
stressor	stress response	relaxation response
adapt	alarm	biofeedback
nervous system	resistance	progressive muscle relaxation
hormonal system	recovery	meditation
immune system	exhaustion	placebo effect
hormone	fight-or-flight reaction	inert
gland	coping devices	ethics
stress hormones	displacement	quacks

Answer the following questions on a separate sheet of paper.

1. a. Explain the differences between the stress response and the relaxation response.
   b. How are the recovery and exhaustion phases of the stress response similar? How are they different?
2. *Matching—Match each of the following phrases with the appropriate vocabulary term from the list above:*
   a. the body's capacity for identifying, destroying, and disposing of disease-causing agents
   b. the effect of stressors on a person
   c. an organ of the body that secretes one or more hormones
   d. prolonged, unrelieved, damaging stress
   e. not active
   f. a chemical messenger that travels to target organs
   g. moral principles or values
3. a. The _____ is made up of glands that control body functions in cooperation with the nervous system.
   b. Epinephrine and _____ are each a _____ secreted as part of a reaction of the nervous system to stress.
   c. Sublimation, ventilation, and _____ are non-harmful ways to deal with stress called _____.
   d. The second phase of the stress response is called _____.
   e. _____ are people pretending to have medical skills.
4. *Word Scramble—Use the clues from the phrases below to help you unscramble the terms:*
   a. **mumnie metssy** The cells, tissues, and organs that protect the body from disease are called the _____ _____.
   b. **fesened misnashcem** Fantasy, denial, and regression are all examples of _____ _____.
   c. **odaikecbfbe** _____ is a clinical technique that focuses on the brain waves and heart rate to teach relaxation.

RECALLING IMPORTANT FACTS AND IDEAS

1. Identify three physical and three psychological stressors.
2. How do multiple stressors affect a high school student's self-esteem?
3. Name two hormones that react to stressors.
4. How do short periods of stress followed by relief affect the immune system?
5. How can stress make you stronger?
6. What causes the body to go into exhaustion rather than recovery?

Section III

5. When a person goes through a period of stress and recovers, they are better able to meet the next round of stress. Just as muscles grow stronger with repeated use, so does stress resistance, but there must be rest between times of stress to build strength.

6. When stress continues to affect you without a break and your body stays in overdrive for too long, your resistance breaks down.

7. Circulation to the brain and muscles is increased, while circulation to the skin and digestive system is reduced.

8. It is a state that favors muscular activity while it shuts down other necessary body functions, such as digestion and immune defenses.

Section IV

9. Physical activity works your muscles so they can relax again. It burns the fuels in your blood and prevents them from building up. It relieves anxiety and brings temporary relief.

10. Learn to react to an event as if it were not so stressful and to relax before and after it. Also learn to direct and control the energy from a stressful situation.

11. save ahead (do now so you won't have to do later), spend as you go, and borrow from the future (have fun now and hope to find time later)

12. projection

13. seek outside help

Section V

14. a comfortable position; a quiet, calm environment; a passive attitude toward mental thoughts

---

7. What parts of the body experience reduced circulation and what parts experience increased circulation during a fight-or-flight reaction?

8. Why is the phase of stress resistance called an unbalanced state?

9. Why is physical activity considered an excellent stress management technique?

10. How can you change the way you react to stress so that events are less stressful?

11. Give three suggestions for managing time efficiently.

12. What defense mechanism are you using when you blame someone else for your own problems?

13. What should you do if stress becomes so overwhelming that it affects your ability to function?

14. What are the three essential components of willed relaxation?

CRITICAL THINKING

1. What type of stressors did people living one hundred years ago have to deal with? Do you think life was more stressful then or now? Why? Would you want a life totally without stress? Why or why not?

2. What aspects of school do you think are the most stressful? Why? What aspects of family life do you find most stressful? Why? Make a list of the changes you would like to make in each environment in order to reduce the amount of stress you feel.

3. Develop a personal plan for improved stress management. List three negative coping strategies that you tend to use. Describe how you can benefit from using a positive coping strategy in each situation.

ACTIVITIES

1. Keep a diary for three consecutive days in which you record stressful situations you encounter. Each time you make an entry, include the following information:
   a. Describe the situation.
   b. Identify the stressor.
   c. Tell how you felt.
   d. Explain what you did to reduce the stress.
   e. Identify your coping strategy as beneficial or harmful.
   After you complete your diary, go over all your entries and describe any patterns that emerged.

2. Create some original cartoon illustrations which portray two defense mechanisms and two coping devices.

3. Make a chart in which you keep track of the way you manage your time, hour by hour, for two full days. Do you think you managed your time well? How could you change the way you spend your time in order to reduce stress?

4. Interview a child, adult, and elderly person to find out what aspects of their lives they consider most stressful and why. Find out how each person copes with stress. Write a report on your findings.

5. Create a collage on poster board. Divide the poster in half. On one side place pictures that depict teenage stressors and on the other side place pictures of positive stress outlets.

6. Develop a pictorial essay portraying the three phases of the stress response. You may use photographs, magazine pictures, or your own original illustrations.

MAKING DECISIONS ABOUT HEALTH

1. Last year you found you experienced a tremendous amount of stress during final exam time. You don't want to find yourself in the same position this year. Final exams are one month away and already you are beginning to worry. Design a plan of effective stress management that you can follow to help you reduce your stress.

CHAPTER 5 PLANNER

OVERVIEW

Chapter 5 is 30 pages long and divided into the four sections listed to the right. The major learning outcomes for the chapter are also listed to the right. This chapter identifies and describes several types of common emotional problems in a clear, straightforward manner and then identifies possible solutions.

MAKING LIFE CHOICES RESOURCES

A variety of activities, handouts, quizzes, and tests to accompany this chapter are available in the *Making Life Choices* supplementary material. You may pick and choose from those materials as appropriate for your amount of class time and the ability levels of your students. Some of the resources you might want to consider using are:

Handouts
• Performance During the Past Year as Indicator of Severity of Mental Disorders
• Negative Rules and Messages Commonly Heard in Alcoholic and Other Troubled Families
• Family Roles in Dysfunctional Families
• Developing Emotional Health Through Recovery

SUGGESTED RESOURCES

Student Readings
1. Cohen, Susan. *Teenage Competition: A Survival Guide.* New York: Evans & Co., 1986.
2. Leder, Jane Mersky. *Dead Serious: A Book for Teenagers About Teenage Suicide.* New York: Atheneum, 1987.
Teacher Readings
1. Aguilera, Donna and Messick, Janice. *Crisis Intervention: Theory and Methodology.* St. Louis:

C.V. Mosby, 1986.
2. Smith, Judie. *Suicide Prevention: A Crisis Intervention Curriculum for Teenagers and Young Adults.* Learning Publications, Inc., 1989.
Video
1. *ABC Notebook: Teen Suicide.* Produced by ABC. Coronet/MTI Teleprogram, 100 Wilmot Road, Deerfield, IL 60015. 800-777-2400.

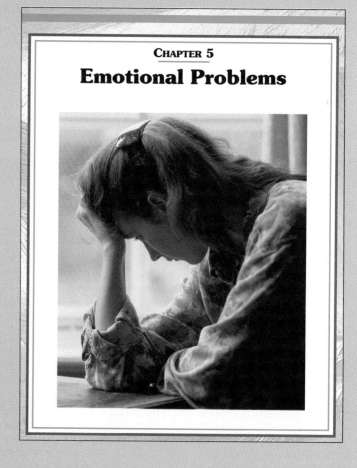

CHAPTER 5
Emotional Problems

CHAPTER PROJECT

Invite to class a series of mental health speakers. Allow the students to interview the speakers and compile a booklet of information regarding mental health. Possible speakers may include: an Alateen volunteer, a school counselor, a marriage and family counselor, a psychologist, and a suicide hot line volunteer.

An alternate project could be to allow students to do research on the mental health facilities available in and near their community. All the resources can be included in a pamphlet or poster to be made available to the entire student body.

OUTCOMES

After reading and studying this chapter, you will be able to:

✓ Describe the causes of emotional problems.
✓ Identify common emotional problems.
✓ List the characteristics of a functional family and a dysfunctional family.
✓ Identify professionals who can offer help for emotional problems and explain how to find competent psychological services.
✓ Discuss how to go about helping another person who has an emotional problem.

✓ Discuss the issue of teen suicide.

CONTENTS

I. The Causes of Emotional Problems
II. Common Emotional Problems
III. Families with Problems
IV. Emotional Healing

   Straight Talk: *Young People's Suicide*

FACT OR FICTION

What do you think? Are the following statements true or false? If you think they are false, then say what is true.

1. People who are emotionally healthy handle life's problems without the help of counseling.
2. The people who most need professional help for emotional problems are often least likely to seek it.
3. People who engage in regular physical activity experience less

depression and anxiety than people who do not.
4. Anxiety can be beneficial.
5. To express resentment only provokes conflict; it is best to deal with resentment in private.
6. To deal with an emotional problem, you first need to discover who is at fault.

(Answers on page 127)

■ **Reminder:** Knowing how to study can increase your knowledge, improve your grades, *and* cut down on your study time. See the *Studying Health* section at the front of your text for some suggestions to help you study this chapter.

Answers to "Fact or Fiction"

Here are the answers to the questions at the start of the chapter.
1. False. Emotionally healthy people often benefit from such help, and it is well worth seeking. **2.** True. **3.** True. **4.** True. **5.** False. To express resentment helps resolve conflict. To keep it private can harm a relationship. **6.** False. Assigning blame is not useful; it is destructive.

Activity To Introduce Chapter

Have the class, or small groups, brainstorm a list of words or phrases they think of when they hear the word *psychiatrist.* Write this list on the board and follow up with the six questions listed under "Fact or Fiction." It's a good idea to bring the students' prejudices and ignorance out in the open, as well as to identify students with positive attitudes toward the mental health field before you begin the chapter.

NOT ENOUGH TIME?*

Because it is likely that many of your students will have experienced some of the problems described in this chapter, it is important that you give the chapter as much time as possible. Students who identify with the problems in the chapter will be feeling many confusing emotions and may wish to discuss them if sufficient time is allowed.

TIME	SUGGESTIONS
1 Day	Assign Section I prior to class. Use the Activity to Introduce Chapter. Do Activity 1.1. Discuss Section I and have students do the review. Do Activity 1.2. Assign Section II and the review work as homework.
2 Days	Correct the Section II review orally. During class do Activities 2.1 and 2.6. Assign Activity 2.2 as homework.
3 Days	Open class with a discussion of the homework. Do Activity 2.13. Upon completion do Activity 3.1 and assign Section III as homework.
4 Days	Discuss homework. Do Activity 3.9 and 3.10 at the same time with half the class working on 3.9 and the other half working on 3.10. Close class by sharing results. Assign Section IV for homework.
5 Days	Open class with Activity 4.1. Follow this with Activity 4.8. Use class time for Activity 4.10. The quiz can be given the next day or at the end of class. Have class work on the chapter review.

Please refer to the 18-week daily lesson plans in the supplementary material for additional suggestions.

In this section students will learn:
1. The causes of emotional problems.
2. Traits of emotionally healthy and unhealthy people.

Activity 1.1
Television Character Analysis.

Have each student choose five traits from the list for emotionally healthy people and five traits from the list for emotionally unhealthy people on page 106. Have students identify television or movie characters who display traits from their group of ten. This may be done in class using their recall or as a homework assignment for a next-day discussion. Sample: "Married With Children" character Peg Bundy is irresponsible to an extreme, acts on

TEACH
▶ SECTION 1
(Guided and Independent Practice)

impulse, and manipulates others. Doogie Howser considers consequences before acting, can have close relationships, and strives to be honest. **(30 min.)**

Activity 1.2
Trait Cards. Write the traits for emotionally healthy and unhealthy people

---

Teacher Support Notes

① **Emotional Problems:** The students' major question as they begin this chapter will probably be "What is an emotional problem?" Focus their attention on the definition given here—*"patterns of thinking or behavior that cause a person significant emotional pain or prevent normal functioning."* The key words are *significant* and *prevent normal functioning.* Students need to be able to distinguish between the temporary, fleeting moments of emotional pain and the pains that don't go away. Have them make a list of things that have caused them emotional pain. Next to each item have them list the amount of time they think they spent concerned about that situation. Would this be considered significant? Discuss the list in class.

104 UNIT 2 Your Emotional and Social Health

Emotional problems are a normal part of everyone's life. Healthy people keep working to solve them much of the time, but sometimes problems become overwhelming. They can then interfere with daily life. When that happens to someone, the person may feel alone and ashamed, but comfort can come easily. People can overcome problems or learn to deal with them with the support of self-help groups, counselors, and others. In other words, emotional problems are treatable.

People are more aware of, and better informed about, emotional problems than they used to be. They also value psychological help from counseling and support groups more than in the past. Most people now realize that counseling is helpful for everyone, not just for people who are mentally ill.

Anyone who could use some help in coping with life's events should seek counseling. There's no point in wondering, "What will people think?" or "Why can't I solve this problem on my own?" The only useful question to ask is, "How can I best recover?" The hardest part of dealing with an emotional problem is facing it. From there on, things get easier.

The choice of exactly when to seek professional help is different for each person. Many people seek help right away, before minor events become major problems. Others wait until problems begin to cause them distress and seem beyond their own control. Some people *never* obtain outside help, even for serious emotional problems that cripple their ability to function throughout life. Some therapists claim that the people who most need professional help often are least likely to seek it.

This chapter uses the term **emotional problems** to describe patterns of thinking or behavior that cause a person significant emotional pain or prevent normal functioning. Any of three important areas can be

For a person who feels lonely or depressed, comfort may be just around the corner.

affected by emotional problems:

1. Social or family relations.
2. Performance of tasks (including school-work).
3. Leisure time activities.

Emotional problems range from common, mild, temporary depression or anxiety to severe long-term problems, such as a loss of the sense of reality. Some traits that are considered to be emotionally healthy are compared with those considered to be unhealthy in Figure 5–1 on page 106.

This chapter is devoted to the most common emotional problems. The emphasis is practical: how to recognize them, understand them, and deal with them. First, though, how do they develop?

① **Key Points** *Even emotionally healthy people need help with emotional problems from time to time, especially when the problems interfere with social, occupational, or leisure activities.*

(Figure 5–1) on individual index cards. Have each student select six cards, unseen. Tell the students to write a description of themselves if all the cards accurately reflected their own emotional states. Allow volunteers to read their descriptions aloud while other students try to identify the traits being described. **(15 min., Critical Thinking)**

Activity 1.3

Trait Bingo. Make up bingo boards using the various traits for emotionally healthy and unhealthy people in each space on the board. Use descriptive phrases as clues. Students win the game in typical bingo fashion. For example, if the healthy trait "can have close relationships" is on a student's bingo board, he or she can mark that space when the teacher says, "enjoys spending time with grandparents." **(30 min.; Reteach, Reinforce)**

Activity 1.4
Personal Traits. Have students list the positive inborn traits with which they arrived in the world. Help them make this list if they have trouble. Remember, the sometimes annoying class clown has the ability to find humor and bring laughter to many situations. The inattentive doodler may be very artistic. **(15 min., Critical Thinking)**

(continued on next page)

SECTION I

The Causes of Emotional Problems

No one but an expert can pinpoint the exact cause of an emotional problem. Sometimes even the experts can't do it. Many different causes can produce symptoms that, on the surface, may appear quite similar.

A student who feels too tired and unmotivated to study for a test may think the cause is psychological, but the tiredness could have a physical cause. The fumes given off by fresh paint, for example, could make a person feel sick. Alternatively, the cause might be a poor diet. Nutrient deficiencies can cause a long list of symptoms that resemble those of emotional problems. Lack of exercise can bring mental discomfort, as can lack of sleep.

For the reasons above, it is important to seek a professional diagnosis for an emotional problem. People should no more attempt to diagnose their own or their friends' emotional problems than they would their physical illnesses.

Some emotional problems run in families. These problems may be inherited, learned, or both. Other severe emotional problems are caused by brain damage from drugs; injuries; and diseases, such as syphilis and senility. Some emotional problems result from unbalanced body chemistry and can be worsened by stress. Regardless of cause, though, the vast majority of emotional problems can be treated successfully.

An example of a serious mental illness that tends to run in families is **schizophrenia.** A person with schizophrenia gradually loses the ability to distinguish fantasy from reality, and becomes less and less able to function. If one identical twin develops ① schizophrenia, then the other twin is likely to develop it, too. Some think that this proves that schizophrenia is hereditary. However, many people with schizophrenia grew up in families with serious problems, including violence or sexual abuse. Possibly, an unsupportive upbringing also plays a role.

Child abuse does not always leave people emotionally crippled, though. Why some people who were abused as children grow up to be normal is a mystery. Perhaps some ② people inherit a tendency to be emotionally healthy and so they develop normally despite problems. Others may start life with a tendency toward developing problems and do so even if they receive excellent parenting.

Whatever the role of heredity, some environmental factors clearly aggravate emotional problems. Among these factors are pressures from society. Each child arrives in this world with certain inborn traits: some children are physically strong, some artistic, some sensitive, and so forth. Yet parents and society seem to want children to develop in specific ways. A parent who desperately wants a child to play sports is a familiar example. The child may not possess talent or interest in sports. Placed in a tug-of-war between the need to please the parent and the need to follow inner guidance, the child can develop emotional problems in a hurry.

MINI GLOSSARY

emotional problems: patterns of behavior or thinking that cause a person to feel significant emotional pain or to be unable to ① function in one of three important areas— social or family relations, occupation (including school performance), or use of leisure time.

schizophrenia (SKITZ-oh-FREN-ee-uh): a mental illness, a condition of losing touch with reality accompanied by reduced ability to function.

Teacher Support Notes

① **Schizophrenia:** Break this word up to help students remember its meaning. The Greek word, *schizein*, means to split. The Greek word, *phren*, means mind. Thus, the mind is split between reality and fantasy. Students should not confuse this term with dual personalities. The schizophrenic does not have a multiple personality.

② **Heredity vs. Environment:** These two sentences suggest that heredity may be the most important factor in determining whether or not people will have emotional problems. Ask students if they agree. Do they have any personal experiences to support their beliefs?

Teach
(Continued)

Activity 1.5
Applause Please. Using your roll sheet as a guide to ensure that everyone has a turn, have one or two students stand each day (independently) while the rest of the class praises, cheers, and applauds them. Students will soon be reminding you of this activity and requesting it. Be sure to praise the student yourself. Mention emotionally healthy traits whenever possible. **(5 min.)**

Activity 1.6
Inner Values. Have students write a working set of inner values for themselves. Have them write a working set of values for their future children. Compare the two sets. Encourage a discussion of why we often want more for, and expect more from, our children. **(20 min.; Extend, Enrich)**

EVALUATE
SECTION 1

Activity 1.7
Trait Posters. Have students make a set of miniposters illustrating the emotionally healthy and unhealthy traits. Groups

---

Teacher Support Notes

① **Comparing Traits:** This figure contains 24 pairs of traits. To get students involved in comparing these pairs of traits, have them create a grading scale on a sheet of paper. Healthy traits would be listed at the far left, unhealthy traits at the far right. Between each pair of traits students would then number from 1–10 across the page, with 10 being at the far left, 1 at the far right. After creating this scale they can rate themselves by circling the number that represents their places on each scale. A total of 240 points would represent maximum emotional wellness; 0 points would represent someone with serious emotional problems. This is by no means a scientific assessment but it could be an effective way of getting students to read about, compare, and better understand the traits that indicate emotional health or lack of emotional health. You may want to have students hand in their scales and then talk to any student who had a low score about whether or not the student should talk to a school counselor or other person about any emotional problems he or she might be having.

FIGURE 5-1

Comparing Emotionally Healthy and Emotionally Unhealthy Traits ①

Emotionally Healthy People:	Emotionally Unhealthy People:
Have high self-esteem.	Have low self-esteem.
Are confident that their behavior is normal.	Guess at what normal behavior is.
Strive to be honest.	Often lie when it would be just as easy to tell the truth.
Accept themselves.	Judge themselves without mercy.
Can have fun.	Have difficulty having fun.
Don't take themselves too seriously.	Can never laugh at themselves.
Enjoy other people but do not make others the sole source of their happiness.	Are certain their happiness hinges on others.
Can have close relationships.	Find close relationships unusually difficult.
Accept the things they cannot control.	Try to change and control everything.
Find approval within themselves.	Constantly seek approval from others.
Are assertive and ask directly for what they want or need.	Manipulate others and try to get their way by underhanded means.
Usually feel they are similar to other people.	Usually feel they are different from other people.
Take responsibility appropriately, but do not take too much responsibility for others.	Are responsible or irresponsible to an extreme.
Give loyalty when it is appropriate and deserved.	Are extremely loyal (even when loyalty is undeserved) or are disloyal to those who have proved themselves worthy.
Consider consequences before acting.	Act on impulse.
Are not driven by compulsions.	Are prone to addictions and compulsions.
Continue to mature emotionally throughout their lives.	Tend to remain immature.
Live with balance, not extremes.	Live lives that swing between extremes.
Accept and trust their observations, feelings, and reactions.	Deny and reject their observations, feelings, and reactions.
Attend to their physical and psychological needs.	Neglect their own needs.
Disclose family problems when appropriate.	Hide family or other secrets.
Refuse to tolerate inappropriate behavior.	Tend to tolerate inappropriate behavior.
Feel emotional pain; are able to grieve when they suffer losses.	Deny emotional pain; are unable to grieve losses.
Are not prone to stress-related illnesses.	Are prone to stress-related illnesses.

of students may work together on an assigned set of traits. Creativity should be encouraged in the drawings. Students can have animals as the characters in the posters demonstrating the traits. A sample: Two little bears find out that the concert they wished to attend is sold out, so they decide to go to the movies instead. (accept the things they cannot control) **(30 min.; Interdisciplinary, Cooperative Learning)**

CLOSE
SECTION I

Activity 1.8
Rudolph's Peer Pressures. Play or sing the song, "Rudolph the Red-Nosed Reindeer," as a sample of how emotional problems can be increased by peer and family pressures and decreased or eliminated by the realization of one's own value. Brainstorm ways people can come to realize their own worth. Be sure that seeking help from a qualified professional is on the list. **(15 min.; Interdisciplinary, Reteach, Reinforce, Critical Thinking)**

Activity 1.9
Self-Esteem Songs. Give students extra credit for identifying song lyrics that promote self-esteem.

Society's ideals don't always fit the individual.

Struggles such as the one just described may continue through life. People of all ages may try to please others at the cost of their own emotional growth. This damages self-esteem. If a chronic pattern develops, it can chip away at emotional health.

A young person who strives to meet, and falls short of, performance standards set by others may seek relief from the resulting stress by using alcohol or other drugs, and may develop an **addiction.** Another young person striving for an unreasonable ideal of slimness may develop an **eating disorder** (discussed in the Straight Talk in Chapter 9). These addictions and disorders require treatment, but they are not necessarily flaws within the person.

Part of the problems mentioned above may be caused by the society that puts such pressures on people. This is one reason why it is so important to develop a working set of inner values to live by. With strong values, a person can act according to internal standards and not invite such harsh external judgment.

Key Points | *Emotional problems may be inherited or learned. Some people have tendencies toward emotional health, some toward emotional problems. Pressures from society can worsen problems.*

SECTION I   REVIEW

Answer the following questions on a sheet of paper.
Learning the Vocabulary
The vocabulary terms in this section are *emotional problems, schizophrenia, addiction,* and *eating disorder.*
Fill in the blank with the correct answer.
1. An _____ is characterized by an abnormal intake of food stemming from emotional causes.
2. In _____ a person loses touch with reality.
3. A dependence on a substance, habit, or behavior is called an _____.
4. Patterns of thinking that cause severe emotional pain are known as _____.

Learning the Facts
5. Why is it important to seek professional help for an emotional problem?
6. List four possible causes of emotional problems.
7. Name three emotionally healthy traits and three emotionally unhealthy traits.

Making Life Choices
8. Brainstorm a list of terms people use to describe people who suffer from emotional problems or mental illness. Circle all the terms that have a negative connotation. Why do you think mental illness still continues to carry such a stigma? Suggest some ways that might help people to better understand it.

MINI GLOSSARY

addiction: dependence on a substance, habit, or behavior.
eating disorder: abnormal food intake stemming from emotional causes and related to addiction. In *anorexia nervosa,* young people starve themselves to lose weight. In *bulimia,* they binge on food, then starve or vomit. (See the Straight Talk at the end of Chapter 9 for details.)

Teacher Support Notes

① **Pleasing Others:** Many people believe in "Doing unto others as you would have others do unto you." Ask students if they agree with this idea. If so, how do they balance that belief with this sentence? Does it seem to say that people should put themselves ahead of others?

Section I Review
Answers
1. eating disorder
2. schizophrenia
3. addiction
4. emotional problems
5. People should no more attempt to diagnose their own or their friends' emotional problems than they would their physical illnesses.
6. Answers will vary; could include: brain damage from drugs; injuries; syphilis and senility; and unbalanced body chemistry.
7. Answers will vary. Refer to Figure 5–1 on page 106 for possible answers.
8. Answers will vary.

In this section students will learn:
1. Common emotional problems.
2. Strategies for coping with emotional problems.
3. Effective communication of anger.

Activity 2.1

Common Feelings. Have students write descriptions of situations in which they have experienced each of the common negative feelings: anxiety, depression, guilt, shame, and resentment. Share your own experiences with these feelings to help students see how truly common these feelings are. Discuss how students have gotten over these feelings and how they can help others get over such feelings. **(20 min.; Extend, Enrich)**

Activity 2.2
A Day of Laughter. Assign the following homework. Each student must come to class the next day prepared with a joke. Spend the next day sharing jokes and laughing. Discuss laughter's relationship to lifting depression. Be sure to set guidelines for joke telling. These guidelines should include: no sexual references, no racial heritage or gender slurs, no racial references, no inappropriate lan-

Teacher Support Notes

① **Outside Help:** Ask students when a person needs outside help according to the text. (when intense feelings overwhelm a person's ability and desire to solve problems)

② **Physical Activity:** Make sure students reread this important sentence: *"Physically active people feel less depressed and anxious than inactive people."* Remind students of a key strategy for combating stress—engage in regular physical activity.

③ **Psychotherapy:** Students may not be familiar with the term *psychotherapy.* Tell students that it's a term that sounds and looks harder than it really is. In very simple terms, it can be described as two people talking about one person's problems. It most commonly refers to therapy provided by professional therapists.

📖 Fast Facts

According to the National Institute of Mental Health, at any one time, 6 to 10 percent of the population is clinically depressed.

108

SECTION II

Common Emotional Problems

Whether or not they grew up with family problems, all people, from time to time, have negative feelings that require attention. Most common among those feelings are depression, anxiety, guilt, shame, and resentment. Usually people can deal with, and get over, these feelings when they arise. Sometimes, though, intense feelings can overwhelm the ability and desire to solve a problem. The person may then need outside help to completely get over the negative feelings.

Problems vary in degree. Each can be mild or extreme, short-lived or long-lasting. The more severe the disorder, the more critical the need for professional help. Guilt, shame, and resentment, while not strictly classified as emotional disorders themselves, are strong contributing factors to other emotional problems, worsening and compounding them.

Depression

If you have never felt "down," you are a most unusual person. Ten million U.S. citizens suffer from **depression** each year, and 5 of every 100 teenagers suffer its most severe form. Depression drives more people to seek counseling than does any other emotional problem.

Most likely, you know exactly what depression feels like. You have been there: taking no joy in life, looking forward to nothing, wanting to withdraw from people and activities. Being extremely tired can make you feel this way. In the case of depression, though, it doesn't go away, even after a night's sleep.

Depression can be difficult to diagnose because it disguises itself as other illnesses—flu, chronic fatigue syndrome, or **insomnia.** A person in a long-term depression (more than two weeks) needs a skilled diagnosis. Learn to recognize the signs of serious depression listed in this chapter's Life Choice Inventory.

Seek a diagnosis if any of these symptoms lasts for more than a week or two. The Life Choice Inventory is a self-test that helps people to detect depression's associated feelings and behaviors.

Sometimes a depression is the warning sign of a disease. Depressed mood is one of the early symptoms of certain kinds of cancer, for example. A major depression, at least sometimes, can be due to imbalances in the body's chemistry. The brain is extremely sensitive to chemical changes. Too much or too little of the normally present substances can greatly affect mood. It is important, therefore, to have a physical checkup if a depression sets in and refuses to go away. Blood tests can reveal imbalances that can be reversed by proper medication.

A mild depression may go away by itself. Often, though, you can hurry it on its way. Over a lifetime, most people learn what kinds of things depress them. Some people tend to become depressed at certain times of the day, month, or year. A loss of any kind, even of a cherished toy or a pet, may bring depression as one of the stages of grief. People can learn how to recognize the early signs of depression and how best to prevent or relieve it. The Health Strategies section on the next page, "Coping with Mild Depression," reviews ways of dealing with these common feelings.

Physically active people feel less depressed and anxious than inactive people. Running has been shown to be useful— even as useful as psychotherapy—to treat mild depression. Physical activity alters the body's chemistry; lifts mood and attitude;

TEACH

SECTION II
(Guided and Independent Practice)

Activity 2.3

Trait Auction. Have an auction of emotionally healthy and unhealthy traits. Tell students they must buy at least two unhealthy traits. Give each student $2,000. Sell healthy traits for $300–$500 each and unhealthy traits for $50 each. After all the traits have been sold, allow students to tear up the unhealthy traits and throw them away. Encourage students to see that it is often easier (cheaper) to behave in an unhealthy manner. Point out that healthy traits often "cost" more in risks and time, but the results are worth it. **(20 min.; Extend, Enrich)**

Activity 2.4

Ending Mild Depression. On index cards, list a wide variety of causes of mild depression. Distribute the cards to small groups of students. (three to five) Have the groups develop a plan to end the mild depression listed on the card by choosing activities (one or more) from the Health Strategies box below. The causes of depression might include: death of a pet, poor sports performance, failed test, no

(continued on next page)

---

and provides a benefit to those with heart disease, diabetes, alcoholism, and other conditions. It makes people feel good, physically and emotionally.

HEALTH STRATEGIES

Coping with Mild Depression

To ease the passing of a mild depression:

1. Identify the cause.
2. Take action. Make a change in your life; change the terms of a negative relationship; stop wishing for something or someone you can't have; renew self-care activities you have been neglecting (bathe, exercise).
3. Force yourself to do something different, something fun (the first move in this direction is the hardest).
4. Do something physically active.
5. Eat a pick-me-up snack.
6. If possible, avoid difficult or unpleasant tasks for a while.
7. Do not put pressure on yourself to achieve too much too soon (don't set the stage for failure).
8. Break large tasks into manageable parts. Set small, attainable goals.
9. Seek out other people.
10. Reject negative thinking. Replace it with positive thinking (see Chapter 2 for tips).
11. Find reasons to laugh. Time off from self-pity may end a depression.
12. Go outdoors. The green color of living plants in the sun has a known beneficial effect on the viewer.
13. If you feel stuck, get help.

Lasting serious depression, whatever the cause, can be terrifying. Some people who have experienced it say that they would rather endure any kind of physical pain than the mental torture of total hopelessness and helplessness. Serious depression affects not just the individual, but that person's family, co-workers, and others.

To the depressed person, it seems that all is lost, that help is unattainable, that only despair awaits in the future. Depressed people, by their very behavior, repel others as if they were saying, "Leave me alone." Too often, they get what they seem to be asking for.

What the depressed person needs, however, is understanding, patience, and encouragement. Depressed people need others to help them out of their negative patterns. They also need an accurate diagnosis, and they may need medication and therapy.

No one should continue to suffer from depression, because help is available for the asking. When help finally comes, depression can lift. Life can be restored to normal.

Key Points *Depression can be mild and short-lived or severe and long-lasting. Everyone should learn to recognize the signs of depression. People can often pull themselves out of mild depressions by changing their routines. Severe depression, however, requires competent diagnosis and treatment for its reversal.*

MINI GLOSSARY

depression: the condition of feeling apathetic, hopeless, and withdrawn from others. A *major depression* is an emotionally crippling depressed state linked to physical causes; it may be, at the extreme, a suicidal state.

insomnia (in-SOM-nee-uh): sleep abnormalities including difficulty in falling asleep and wakefulness through the night.

Teacher Support Notes

① **Coping with Depression:** Students may wonder why they need to study these strategies. Even if depression is a problem they say they will never have, they could develop it someday. It will help them now to try to understand that there are strategies available. Also, they may have a friend or relative who is suffering from depression. Perhaps they can pass along some of these strategies to those people.

Fast Facts

Depression affects women twice as often as men according to research at Stanford University.

partner for a dance, family fight, cancelled plans, activity ruined by weather, break up with boyfriend or girlfriend, awkward injury. **(30 min., Cooperative Learning)**

Activity 2.5
Role-Play. An expansion to the pre-ceding activity is to add a role-play ele-ment. The same small groups act out the strategies they developed for coping with mild depression. Encourage all students in the group to come to the front of the room for the role-play while allowing shier students to have a nonverbal role. **(40 min., Cooperative Learning)**

Activity 2.6
Coping Strategies. Use the symp-toms of depression in the Life Choice Inventory below. Have students, working alone or in small groups, classify the vari-ous symptoms in terms of how they may best be coped with. The coping strategies may be ones they develop themselves and/or strategies from the book. Additional strategies may include: talk with a friend, write out pros and cons, dress up, read a good book, spend time with a younger child, get help from a professional, etc.

Teacher Support Notes

① **Anxiety:** Some stu-dents may not be that familiar with *anxiety*. After pointing out the definition in the Mini Glossary, add that anxiety is similar to fear, except that anxiety is the response to an unclear or uncertain threat; where-as, when a person is afraid, the person knows what he or she is afraid of. Compared to anxiety, fear is more focused and intense.

② **Too Much Anxiety?** Ask students how, if it's common for people to feel anxiety, do people know if their feelings of anxiety are excessive and of concern. Psychologists talk of gen-eralized anxiety disorders as being at least six months of unrealistic or excessive anxiety. They sometimes describe the disorder as *free floating anxiety* because the anxi-ety is so general and related to so many different worries.

✍ Fast Facts

On any given day, roughly 7% of the adult population could be diagnosed as hav-ing an anxiety disorder.

LIFE **C**HOICE **I**NVENTORY

Do You Experience Symptoms of Depression?

The first step in reversing depression lies in identifying it. If you never feel the symptoms listed here, answer the quiz with someone else in mind. Answer yes if, for most of the past two weeks, you have felt:

Emotional:

- Sad or down most of the time.
- A depressed, down-hearted mood.
- The need to cry often.
- An unfillable "emptiness."
- That the future holds no hope.
- Worse in the mornings, better as the day progresses.
- Useless, like a fifth wheel, unimportant.
- Unable to decide which option to take.
- Unable to think clearly or to concentrate.
- Difficulty making decisions.
- Unable to remember things you should.
- No joy from things you once enjoyed (reading magazines, talking on the phone).
- Irritable, easily aggravated.
- Thoughts of death come to mind.
- Thoughts of suicide come to mind.

Social:

- Loss of affection or feelings for others.
- Problems in school and at home.
- A need to be alone.
- A desire to stay away from classes, hobbies, or activities.

Physical:

- Slowed down; always tired, with no drive.
- Restless, unable to sit still.
- Unable to fall asleep, stay asleep, or get up.
- Uninterested in food, without appetite.
- Always tired, unexplainable fatigue.
- A racing heartbeat.
- Uninterested in dating.
- Aches and pains (headache, backache).
- Unable to care about your appearance (don't bathe, care for clothing, fix your hair).
- Digestive upsets (constipation, stom-achache).
- A desire to drink alcohol or take drugs.

SCORING

If several of these items apply to you or to someone you know, it may help to talk to your parents, a teacher, the family physician, a school guidance counselor, or other trusted adults.

Source: Adapted from the pamphlet *Depression: Define it. Defeat it.* Available from D/ART, National Institute of Mental Health, Public Inquiries, Room 15C-05, 5600 Fishers Lane, Rockville, MD 20857.

Anxiety

Like depression, **anxiety** is familiar to everyone. And like depression, anxiety is a normal state, some of the time. However, while depression is a low-energy state, anx-iety is one of high energy and therefore can be beneficial in short spurts. A small dose of anxiety can spur a student to take a test with intense concentration. Too much test anxiety, though, can freeze the test taker's mind. Too much anxiety is disabling.

Anxiety can unexpectedly hit people who have been through stressful experiences such as bombings, wars, rape, floods, torture, kidnapping, or hurricanes. After such an experience, a person may have disturbed sleep and memory loss (especially of the stressful time). The individual is said to have a **post-traumatic stress disorder.** The person may repeatedly relive the experience and may be unable to focus on present tasks. Sometimes the person acts unresponsive to other people. At other times the person overreacts to minor disturbances.

Post-traumatic stress disorders may arise long after the stressful periods have ended. Many of the veterans who fought in Vietnam during the 1960s, for example, still had symptoms 15 to 20 years later. Not until the 1980s and 1990s did they begin to come to terms with their war experiences. Also, many women, after being raped or abused as children, show signs of distress months or years after the actual incident.

An **anxiety attack** is a sudden, extreme, and disabling attack of panic that comes on for no apparent reason. You may have experienced an anxiety attack at some time in your life. You felt suddenly panicky and extremely stressed. Your heart started hammering, you felt dizzy, and you broke out in a sweat. It lasts only a few minutes, but an anxiety attack renders you helpless to cope with anything for as long as it is going on.

An occasional attack of anxiety can hit anyone. In fact, an overdose of caffeine (six to eight cola beverages in as many hours) can bring one on. The body's reaction to anxiety is the stress response. It includes rapid heartbeat and breathing, extreme alertness, and the other aspects of readiness to fight or flee, as discussed in Chapter 4. The Health Strategies section on this page, "Dealing with Anxiety," gives you some suggestions for dealing with ordinary anxiety.

For people who have severe anxiety attacks, self-help may not be enough. Some

HEALTH STRATEGIES

Dealing with Anxiety

If you find yourself in an anxious state, it is wise to:

① 1. Identify the cause. What do you fear? State it in words.
2. Deal with it. Can you change it? How? Do it.
3. If you can't change it, let it go. Worry is not helpful, and it wastes energy. Replace it with concentration, relaxation, or positive imaging.
4. Imagine a positive outcome. If you can, start working to bring it about. Live in the solution, not in the problem.
5. Use any extra energy in some physical way: be active.
6. Practice relaxation techniques.

people have such attacks frequently and never know when to expect them. This makes them constantly fearful and handicaps them throughout life. These people can obtain outside help if they seek it. Qualified counselors have special skills in

MINI GLOSSARY

anxiety: an emotional state of high energy, with the stress response as the body's reaction to it.
post-traumatic stress disorder: a reaction to stress such as wartime suffering or rape, arising after the event is over.
anxiety attack: a sudden, unexpected episode of severe anxiety with symptoms such as rapid heartbeat, sweating, dizziness, and nausea.

(15 min.; Cooperative Learning, Critical Thinking)

Activity 2.7
Individuality. As a follow-up to the preceding activity, help students see that everyone has different coping skills. Encourage students to appreciate the uniqueness of the individual as well as understand that one's own problems are always important to oneself.

Tell students that an old fable says if our problems were clothes and we hung them out on the line to dry, once we saw other people's problems we would be glad to take ours back. Do they agree with the idea expressed in this fable? **(10 min.; Extend, Enrich)**

Activity 2.8
Coping With Phobias. Use the Health Strategies, "Dealing with Anxiety" below and the list of phobias on the next page. Have the students work in small groups. Assign each group two or more phobias. Have the groups write out a plan using the Health Strategies and their own ideas to try to cope with the different phobias.

On a regular basis, remind students that emotional problems are not a person's fault; a person with emotional

(continued on next page)

Teacher Support Notes

① **Coping With Test Anxiety:** Since test taking is a common cause of anxiety among students, you may want to give them some general tips on how to deal with the stress they feel prior to an important test. Here are some tips:
1. *preparation*—Hard work and preparation for the test is by far the most effective way to combat test anxiety;
2. *relaxation*—Learning self-relaxation techniques can help. Studying with a friend with whom you can share anxiety also helps you relax;
3. *rehearsal*—Imagine running out of time, feeling panic at not knowing an answer, or drawing a blank. Try to simulate the test situation;
4. *restructuring thoughts*—Thinking before the test that you will fail can become a self-fulfilling prophecy. Changing these negative thoughts to practical, positive thoughts will improve the performance.

problems is a victim as is any ill person. **(30 min., Cooperative Learning)**

Activity 2.9
Beneficial Anxiety. Have students brainstorm times when anxiety can be beneficial in short spurts. Ideas generated

may include: sports, tests, amusement park rides, performing, school dance. **(15 min., Critical Thinking)**

Activity 2.10
Brainstorm Ailments. Have students brainstorm a short list of physical ailments. (flu, cancer, measles) Ask students who is at fault for these illnesses. Encourage a discussion that points out that disease is no one's fault and no one

is to blame. (Lifestyle choices are important factors but many people who make all healthy choices still contract lifestyle diseases.) Lead a discussion about the concept that all persons deserve compassion and understanding, not anger or guilt.

Introduce emotional problems as deserving compassion and understanding. Encourage students to realize that emotional problems are not the fault of

---

✍ **Fast Facts**

The National Institute of Mental Health says that the average age at which an American develops a phobia is 13-1/2 years.

Teacher Support Notes

① **Phobias:** For enrichment, tell students that people suffering from phobias realize that their fears are unreasonable, irrational, and excessive, but they can't help it. Also tell students that a person is not suffering from a phobia unless the fear is strong enough to disrupt the person's daily life. Lots of people are afraid of spiders, but unless that fear is causing a problem every day, it would not be a phobia. One of the most destructive phobias is *agoraphobia*, which often begins after a stressful event. This leads to the fear of leaving the familiar settings of home.

② **Appropriate Guilt:** Make sure that students read this sentence carefully. Many think that all guilt is bad. Some guilt is appropriate and good. Get students to list situations in which they felt guilty and discuss whether or not feeling guilty was appropriate and beneficial in those cases.

112

---

112   UNIT 2 Your Emotional and Social Health

teaching people how to deal with anxiety attacks.

A special form of anxiety, a **phobia,** is a fear of some particular object or situation. People can develop phobias linked to all sorts of things: ①

- Acrophobia—fear of being in high places.
- Aerophobia—fear of flying.
- Agoraphobia—fear of being in large, open spaces, or of leaving home.
- Anthropophobia—fear of people.
- Aquaphobia—fear of water.
- Arachnophobia—fear of spiders.
- Astraphobia—fear of lightning.
- Brontophobia—fear of thunder.
- Claustrophobia—fear of being in small, closed spaces, such as elevators.
- Gephyrophobia—fear of bridges.
- Murophobia—fear of mice.
- Nyctophobia—fear of darkness.
- Thanatophobia—fear of death.
- Triskaidekaphobia—fear of the number 13.
- Xenophobia—fear of strangers.

Long-term or intense anxiety out of line with any real danger or threat is a signal that the situation may be getting out of

A little anxiety heightens performance, but too much anxiety can be debilitating.

control. Signs of extreme anxiety are the same as those of extreme stress (listed in Figure 4–5 in Chapter 4). If these symptoms persist, it is time to get help.

> **Key Points** ▶ *Small doses of anxiety can energize a person to meet challenges, but too much anxiety is disabling. The emotionally healthy person uses slight anxiety to advantage and copes with extreme anxiety by finding relief for it.*

Guilt and Shame

Ordinary **guilt,** like ordinary anxiety, is desirable up to a point. A guilty feeling means that you have crossed a line your values say you should not cross. The guilty feeling is a reminder from your conscience to act according to your values. Appropriate guilt can be useful to keep your values straight and your conscience functioning. ②

The extreme version of guilt is **shame.** While guilt begins within the self, shame originally comes from outside the self as a form of control. Shame is communicated with a look, with a tone of voice, or with words such as "Shame on you!" Shame is often used by well-meaning parents and other authorities to control behavior. In contrast to guilt, shame handicaps a person's functioning and destroys self-esteem.

While normal guilt separates the behavior from the person, shame bonds the behavior with the person. Guilt says, "What you did was bad, but you are OK, and you can decide not to do it again." Shame says, "What you did was bad, you are bad, and nothing you do will change that."

To show the difference between guilt and shame, compare these two responses to a child who hits another:

Parent #1: *"Stop that, child. I don't ever want to see you hitting again. It's not right to hit."*

Parent #2: *"Stop that, child. Only bad boys hit. You are a bad, bad boy."*

the victim nor are these problems a cause for shame by the victim or family members. Be sensitive to the possibility that some students may have a family member with emotional problems. **(20 min., Critical Thinking)**

Activity 2.11
Emotional Benefits of Physical Exercise. Discuss with the class the emotional health benefits of physical

exercise. Have students develop written exercise programs that fit their lifestyles. Encourage them to have a program that includes 20 minutes of aerobic exercise at least three days a week. Invite your physical education teacher as a guest speaker to address this issue. **(30 min., Interdisciplinary)**

EVALUATE
SECTION II

Activity 2.12
Role-Playing Anger. Provide students with some role-play situations to allow students to practice effective communication of anger. Students will be able to find some clues for communicating their

(continued on next page)

In the first case, the child learns appropriate guilt but knows he is still loved. In the second, the child learns that something about him (he hits) makes him bad. This chips away at his self-esteem.

Many adults have to work to reverse the effects of shame instilled in them from childhood. To regain self-esteem, they must reject shame, get in tune with appropriate guilt, and listen to its messages about their values. Someone who has lied to a friend, for example, may feel ashamed of doing so and take on the label of "liar." A more productive way of dealing with the situation is to allow the appropriate guilt ("I feel bad that I lied") to modify future behavior ("I'll tell the truth next time").

Key Points *The emotionally healthy person tunes in to appropriate guilt to stay in touch with values. At the same time, the person rejects shame as destructive to self-esteem.*

Resentment

A person who feels anger and is afraid or unable to express it holds it inside and builds **resentment** instead. Resentment is anger turned inward. It is healthier to admit and to express anger in appropriate and assertive ways than to be consumed inwardly by resentment.

Suppose someone who lives with you plays loud music when you would prefer quiet. When you ask assertively for the person to turn the volume down, the person tells you to go someplace else. You have only two alternatives at that point—to express anger, or to **suppress** it and feel resentful. The Health Strategies section on this page, "Effective Communication of Anger," gives some hints about how to express anger constructively.

Suppose that, to avoid conflict, you suppress your anger and "burn" inwardly. You pay a price when you swallow your feel-

HEALTH STRATEGIES

Effective Communication of Anger

When you get mad:

• Don't blame. Don't accuse. Use "I" statements: "I'm angry because this music annoys me, and you have ignored my requests for less noise."

• Think in terms of a solution, not in terms of a "war" to be "won." "Which hours of the day can you plan to leave the radio off?" "Would you use earphones some of the time?"

• Don't stray from the incident. Don't complain about dirty dishes and an unpaid debt while trying to solve the present problem of loud music.

• Take extra care not to call names or attack the person. Say, "I'm furious that the music continues to be so loud." Don't say, "You're an inconsiderate jerk."

ings: it makes you tense and upset. Also, your relationship with the person will be

---

MINI GLOSSARY

phobia (FOH-bee-uh): an extreme, irrational fear of an object or situation.

guilt: the normal feeling that arises from the conscience when a person acts against internal values ("I did a bad thing").

shame: the extreme feeling of guilt that arises when a person internalizes mistakes ("I am a bad person because I did it").

resentment: anger that has built up due to failure to express it.

suppress: to hold back or restrain.

Teacher Support Notes

① **Suppressing Anger:** Ask students if they ever keep anger inside when they would like to express it. Why do they do this? Do they feel that it's wrong to be angry? Do they feel that people who can suppress anger are superior in some way, more in control of themselves and their lives? Do those who express their anger wish they were better able to suppress it?

② **Internalize:** You may need to remind students of the meaning of *internalize*. It means to make a feeling or idea part of your values, beliefs, personality, etc. To internalize is to make that thought or idea a permanent part of your conscious or subconscious mind.

66 Thoughts on Health 99

We boil at different degrees.
 – **Ralph Waldo Emerson**

---

anger in the Health Strategies box on the preceding page. Role-plays may include:

Parent and child: early curfew, too many chores, strict dating rules, strict dress code.

Friend and friend: date competition, pressure to drink, broken trust/promise,

exclusive activity. **(30 min., Cooperative Learning)**

CLOSE
SECTION II

Activity 2.13
Emotion Analysis. Have students decide which emotion—depression, anxiety, guilt and shame, or resentment—will be most likely to arise from the following

situations: death of a pet, upcoming test, lying to a friend, disagreement over party plans, loss at a sporting event, divorce of parents, shoplifting at a store, offer to try drugs, championship game, teammate who takes charge. Discuss student responses. **(30 min.; Reteach, Reinforce)**

FOCUS
SECTION III

Teacher Support Notes

① **Dysfunctional:** You may want to break up this difficult term. Tell students that *dys* means not and *function* means to be able to do something. *Dysfunctional*, then, means not able to perform; thus, a dysfunctional family is one that is not performing right, or isn't working correctly.

Section II Review
Answers

1. Guilt arises from your conscience while shame is the extreme version of guilt that arises when a person internalizes mistakes. Shame destroys self-esteem.
2. depression
3. Anxiety
4. Ten million U.S. citizens suffer from depression and 5 of every 100 teenagers.
5. Answers will vary. Refer to the Health Strategies on page 111 for possible answers.
6. keeps your values straight and your conscience functioning
7. Answers will vary.

114

---

weakened until you express your resentment and both of you resolve the problem. Until you do, even simple requests from that person can make you irritable.

To handle situations like this without hurting yourself or others, it is important to remember that even unkind feelings are acceptable. A person feeling anger must find assertive ways of expressing it to stay healthy and to keep healthy relationships with others.

If, after you have expressed your anger appropriately, the other person still refuses to consider your rights, this is an indication of a breakdown in the relationship between you. The situation may require the help of an objective third party, such as a counselor.

> **Key Points** *Resentment is anger turned inward and is expressed as irritability. To avoid resentment, express anger assertively (not aggressively) and resolve the problem. Outside help may be required.*

SECTION II REVIEW

Answer the following questions on a sheet of paper.
Learning the Vocabulary
The vocabulary terms in this section are *depression, insomnia, anxiety, post-traumatic stress disorder, anxiety attack, phobia, guilt, shame, resentment,* and *suppress.*
1. What is the difference between guilt and shame?
2. The condition of feeling discouraged and hopeless is known as _____.
3. _____ is an emotional state of high energy with the stress response as the body's reaction to it.

Learning the Facts
4. How common is depression?
5. Give three recommendations for dealing with anxiety.
6. How can guilt be a useful emotion?

Making Life Choices
7. Why do you think depression is so common among teenagers? List some things that make you depressed.

SECTION III

Families with Problems

Emotionally healthy adults in a family provide the solid support that children need to grow up emotionally healthy. On the other hand, a family of adults with problems—a **dysfunctional family**—weakens its children by failing to support them. This type of family has abnormal ways of dealing with problems and damages the self-esteem and emotional health of its members. Family environments are an important part of emotional health, and some family situations can cause emotional problems. Figure 5–2 lists two of the many services available.

Dysfunctional Families

All families face problems sometimes. Families are neither perfectly healthy nor totally unhealthy. Healthy families may behave in unhealthy ways during hard times. However, healthy families do not remain upset. They return to a normal, healthy state. Dysfunctional families tend to grow worse. The unhealthy ways of coping grow more frequent and more severe.

Dysfunctional families often have members who:

Teenage children, friends, and relatives of people with addictions can find help and support for themselves through

Alateen and the National Coalition Against Domestic Violence

Figure 5–2 Family Crisis Resources

In this section students will learn:
1. How the family is linked to emotional problems.
2. The distinctions between functional and dysfunctional families.
3. The causes and effects of codependency.
4. How certain events, such as divorce, can contribute to emotional problems.

Activity 3.1

Castaway Characters. Help students discover the roles they play in their families in a nonthreatening manner. Do this by using a television situation comedy, such as "Gilligan's Island." Ask the students to decide which character they would be if they were on the island. Tell them to pick the character they are most similar to (as opposed to their favorite characters).
Captain—hero

Gilligan—scapegoat
Mrs. Howell—lost child
Mr. Howell—passive abuser—not helping
Ginger—codependent
Mary Ann—mascot/caregiver
Professor—problem solver

Encourage students to identify the role played by each castaway. If your students are not familiar with Gilligan's Island, work with them to identify a familiar show

(continued on next page)

Shelters provide a safe haven for victims of abuse.

- Have alcoholism or other drug additions, or long-term mental or physical illnesses.
- Depend on people who have such conditions (**codependency**).
- Engage in **active abuse**—physical or sexual child abuse, spouse abuse, or elder abuse.
- Engage in **passive abuse**—withholding affection or physical necessities from children, spouse, or elders.

Handicapped by these influences, families cannot meet their children's emotional needs. Addictions especially consume parental energy and focus, leaving children to fend for themselves. This has lasting effects that may stretch into future generations (see Figure 5–3 on the next page). Addictions and their effects are the focus of several later chapters of this book.

The ways parents in a dysfunctional family behave may be unpredictable. Sometimes parents may be loving, warm, caring, interested, and involved. At other times, though, they may be unloving, cold, harsh,

and distant. The more severe the family problem, the greater the emotional damage to the children.

How can you tell if a family is dysfunctional? Such a family usually has rigid rules, such as those listed here:

MINI GLOSSARY

dysfunctional family: a family with abnormal or impaired ways of coping that injures the self-esteem and emotional health of family members.
codependency: a pattern of helping others in unhealthy ways; a group of behaviors, beliefs, and feelings that direct all energies toward people and things outside the self, along with neglect of one's own needs.
active abuse: abuse involving one person's aggression against another, such as hitting or sexually abusing the victim.
passive abuse: abuse involving not taking needed actions, such as neglecting to provide food or shelter to a dependent victim.

① **Passive Abuse:** You may want to discuss *passive abuse* with students since the word *abuse* is so much more commonly associated with physical abuse. The idea that *not doing* something or withholding something is abuse may be difficult for some students to comprehend. Have students make a list of both physical and psychological things that are so essential that withholding them could be considered abuse. Discuss these in class.

📖 Fast Facts

The best estimate is that roughly 30% of all parents who were abused as children will mistreat their own children. Studies also indicate that the tendency to abuse children shows up almost immediately.

115

that will serve the purposes of this activity. **(20 min., Critical Thinking)**

Activity 3.2
   Role Limitations. Place the students in groups based on the previous activity. Try to have at least one of each character in each group. Give each castaway group a situation to deal with. Remind the students that in participating in the role-play, they must stay within their roles. Follow up with a discussion of the limitations roles can place on individuals. Also discuss how difficult it is to change one's role.

   Sample situations: planning a party, setting up general rules, choosing a vacation site, naming a pet, buying a new car, renting a movie. **(20 min., Cooperative Learning)**

TEACH
   SECTION **III**
   (Guided and Independent Practice)

Activity 3.3
   Problem Charts. Divide the class into groups of four or five. Give each group a large sheet of paper. Have students divide the paper into three columns

---

Teacher Support Notes

① **Dependency/Co-dependency:** Codependency was defined on the preceding page and will be discussed later in this chapter. Dependency on drugs and alcohol will be discussed in later chapters. Many of these types of dependency could be causing the problems shown in this illustration. Students should realize that dependency means excessive, absolute, uncontrollable reliance on something or someone outside the self.
② **Unmet Needs:** Ask students to brainstorm lists of needs that the mother in the illustration may be failing to meet for her child.
③ **Developmental Tasks:** Ask students to list developmental tasks that might not be accomplished. Students should be able to recall some of the tasks discussed in Chapter 3. Refer them back to the discussions of Erikson and Maslow in Chapter 3.
④ **Functional vs. Dysfunctional:** To have students compare the traits of functional and dysfunctional families, reproduce the traits in Figure 5–4 on a sheet of paper, cut them out, scramble them, and have students arrange them in the proper pairs.

116

---

116   UNIT 2 Your Emotional and Social Health

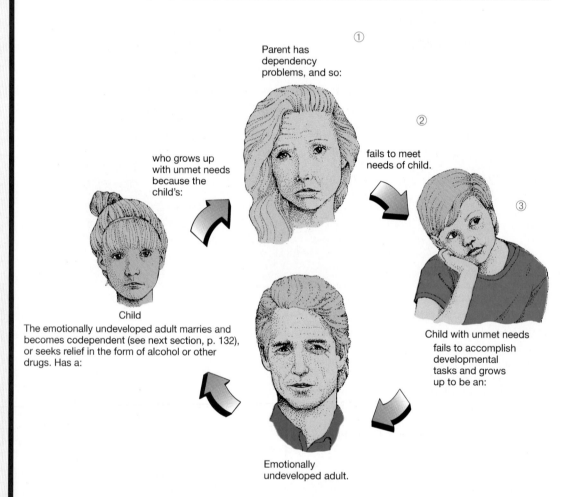

① Parent has dependency problems, and so:

② fails to meet needs of child.

③ Child with unmet needs fails to accomplish developmental tasks and grows up to be an:

Emotionally undeveloped adult.

The emotionally undeveloped adult marries and becomes codependent (see next section, p. 132), or seeks relief in the form of alcohol or other drugs. Has a:

who grows up with unmet needs because the child's:

Child

Figure 5–3 How a Dysfunctional Family Can Affect Future Generations

- Don't feel—do not admit to unpleasant feelings, such as sadness and anger.
- Don't talk—do not discuss problems or unpleasant feelings.
- Don't trust—because you cannot trust those who care for you.

   A dysfunctional family also may have family secrets such as alcoholism or physical abuse; may have no sense of humor; may value appearances more than individuals; and may lack togetherness or unity. In contrast, the functional family shares and accepts feelings. It strives for a sense of caring, support, and trust. Functional and dysfunctional families are compared further in Figure 5–4 on the next page.

④   Children in a dysfunctional family often develop somewhat exaggerated traits in an attempt to supply for themselves forms of support that normal parents would supply. One child may become a sort of "hero," and label them "Problem," "Creates," and "Results." In the first column, students should list a problem, such as alcoholism, which is common in many families. In the "Creates" column, students should list possible actions, such as violence, that the problem could cause. In the third column, students should list physical, mental, and social results such as hitting, low self-esteem, and introversion. If more than one group listed the same problem, have those groups compare answers. Then have group members present their charts to the class. **(20 min.; Reteach, Reinforce)**

Activity 3.4
Group Murals. Divide the class into groups of four or five students. Give each group two sheets of poster board. Instruct the groups to design two-panel murals showing, on one half, a dysfunctional family, and on the other half, a functional family. Students can use pictures from magazines, newspapers, etc. For added creativity, students may generate original prose, poetry, or drawings describing functional and/or dysfunctional families. **(30 min.; Reteach, Reinforce)**

Activity 3.5
Dysfunctional Trait Posters.

(continued on next page)

shouldering much more responsibility than is appropriate for a child. Another may take on the role of "scapegoat," accepting the blame for everything that goes wrong. A third role is that of "mascot," the one everybody relies on to be cute and funny and bring relief from the family's seriousness. A fourth role is that of "lost child," the one who always needs everyone's help.

In families where people have to play roles, no one can change and grow. No one can just be ordinary. People who adopt these roles as children often find it helpful during adulthood to discover the causes, work out their problems, and shed the roles.

Dysfunctional families have recently received a great deal of public attention. Celebrities have spoken out about how the experiences of their young years affected them in their adult years. Such public statements may have a healing effect on those who finally face and admit their problems. Other victims may need more help of the kinds described later in this chapter to recover completely.

> **Key Points** *Dysfunctional families fail to provide a solid foundation for normal childhood development. Their characteristics may include abuses of many kinds, denial of feelings, hiding of secrets, and failure to trust anyone.*

FIGURE 5-4

Characteristics of a Functional versus a Dysfunctional Family ①

Functional Family:	Dysfunctional Family:
Establishes rules for the sake of smooth functioning; rules are appropriate, consistent, and flexible.	Establishes rules for the sake of control; rules are rigid and irrational.
Encourages its members to develop well-rounded personalities.	Assigns rigid roles to each member, such as the hero, the scapegoat, the mascot, and the lost child.
Accepts its problems and strives to solve them.	Has deep, dark secrets that no one may admit to or work on.
Welcomes outsiders into the system.	Resists allowing outsiders to enter the system.
Values and exercises its members' sense of humor.	Expects members to be serious and discounts humor.
Honors personal privacy, so members can develop a sense of self.	Permits no personal privacy, so that members have difficulty defining themselves as individuals.
Fosters a "sense of family" so that members may leave and re-enter the system at will.	Enforces loyalty to the family; members may not leave the system.
Allows and resolves conflict between members.	Denies and ignores conflict between members.
Welcomes beneficial changes.	Fights against changes.
Enjoys loyalty and a sense of wholeness.	Has no real unity, is fragmented.

Teacher Support Notes

① **Dysfunctional Families:** For enrichment, tell students that various studies suggest there are six major qualities shared by healthy families:

1. *Commitment*—Family members are deeply committed to promoting each other's happiness and welfare.

2. *Appreciation*—Family members appreciate one another and contribute to each other's self-esteem.

3. *Good communication patterns*—Strong families talk to each other, and their members are good listeners.

4. *Desire to spend time together*—Even with individual time commitments, members of a strong family do many things together.

5. *A strong value system*—This quality is often expressed with a high degree of religious orientation.

6. *Ability to deal with crisis and stress in a positive manner*—Strong families are resilient and capable of bouncing back from adversity.

Teach
(Continued)

Have students design posters that show the various dysfunctional traits being acted out in previous activities. These posters can be displayed around the room during the study of families with problems. **(20 min.; Interdisciplinary, Reteach, Reinforce)**

Activity 3.6
Characters and Characteristics. Have the students brainstorm as many characters and characteristics as possible for the following terms: hero, scapegoat, mascot, lost child. An example for scapegoat might be: characteristics—takes blame, always apologizes, gives up easily, has the last choice; characters—Charlie Brown, Bud Bundy, Gilligan, Steve Urkel. **(20 min., Critical Thinking)**

Activity 3.7
Letters and Advice. Divide the class into small groups of six. Ask one half of the groups to write letters from a teen who lives with an addictive parent, feels sad, and wants to run away. Have the other half of the class write letters from a teen who is the family scapegoat and can't stand it anymore. Finally, have the groups switch letters and write advice-oriented answers to each letter.

Teacher Support Notes

① **Teen Views—Follow-Up Questions:** Following are some questions you may want to use to encourage discussion of the ideas expressed by the students in the Teen Views feature:

a. Have any students run away from home? How long were they gone? Would they share with the class their reasons for running away?

b. Do students feel that their parents need to tell them that they love them regularly, or do they feel that this is unnecessary? Tell students that someone once wrote that each time you tell a person that you love him or her, the feeling of love becomes less intense. How would they answer this belief?

c. Several of the teens quoted put most of the blame on the parents, while others think the teens themselves are mostly at fault. Do students think that, in general, one of these two groups is at fault? If so, which one? Which of the comments in the feature most closely matches their opinions?

d. Do students think that running away from home is ever the best solution to a problem? If so, in what types of situations?

118 UNIT 2 Your Emotional and Social Health

TEEN VIEWS

Why do you think teens run away from home? ①

Not enough love! Teenagers need a lot of love and attention, otherwise, they feel like they don't belong and are unwanted. When I was 14 I ran away from home. I felt like killing myself. Parents sometimes don't tell their children enough that they love them—which can really hurt a child. **David Neal, 15, Carter High School, TN**

Teens tend to misinterpret how their families express their love for them. They tend to think their family is against them when they're just trying to lead the teen in the right direction. There is the ever popular argument that "You don't understand me." Teens either don't want to face their problems, or are too chicken to face them. **Brendan Barahura, 16 Hilltop High School, CA**

Teens run away because of pressure, abuse, and neglect. I ran away a couple of months ago. I was gone for 5 days. In that time I saw a lot of stuff. I called my mom. I wanted to come home and since then I haven't thought about doing it again. That experience made me feel good to have a place to call

my home. **Tracy McPhee, 16, Orange Park High School, FL**

They think they can run away from everything bad. They trade old problems for new, maybe even more complex, problems. Teenagers may think they're mature enough to survive on their own, but they usually find they still have to grow up some. **Michelle Stevenson, 14, Thousand Oaks High School, CA**

 As a former runaway, I feel teens run away from home to be free. Every teenager wants to do what they want, when they want. **Ruby Reyes, 16 Robert E. Lee High School, TX**

In today's society, teens have too much freedom and the parents don't have enough authority. A teen will run away because the parent won't give in to the wants of the teenager. **Tracy Tharp, 17, Orange Park High School, FL**

Teens listen to their peers a whole lot and may be using drugs and (or) smoking. Their

parents probably don't approve, so they figure running away will solve those problems. **Angela Hoffmann, 14, Fargo South High School, ND**

Teens feel unimportant and unnoticed. They feel if they run that that'll let them know whether they're missed or not. I know that was the main reason I thought about it when I was younger but never got the nerve to do it. **Heather Feese, 17, West High School, IA**

Teens are confused and don't have anyone to talk to. I think they don't know that there are people they can contact for help. Running away isn't going to solve the problems. **Sueanne Chin, 15, Somerville High School, MA**

Teenagers these days are just misunderstood. Most teenagers do their best to make their families, friends, and others around them happy and proud of them. They go completely insane doing so. Parents should understand their kids are trying their best to make them happy. **Jeri Rodriguez, 15, Woodrow Wilson High School, CA**

Share the letters and advice with the entire class. **(30 min.; Cooperative Learning, Critical Thinking)**

Activity 3.8

Common Characteristics. Write the characteristics from Figure 5–4 onto index cards. Have students take turns drawing a card. After reading the characteristic aloud, have them do *one* of the following: state whether the characteristic is from a functional or dysfunctional family, name a well-known character from movies, TV, or literature who has that characteristic, name the opposite characteristic, or give an opinion as to why that characteristic is positive or negative. **(20 min.; Review, Reteach)**

EVALUATE
SECTION III

Activity 3.9

Home Situations. Using Figure 5–4, have students write a common home situation for each characteristic. Discuss the situations given by students. **(35 min.; Extend, Enrich)**

Activity 3.10

Television Families. Again, using Figure 5–4, have students apply these

(continued on next page)

Revealing one's innermost thoughts to a counselor may be hard, but healing comes through effort.

Codependency

If you live with someone who suffers from an addiction or other dependency problem, can you remain emotionally healthy? Few ever manage to do so. More commonly, the people close to someone with a dependency develop a set of "helping" behaviors called codependency. Codependent people become so focused on the addicted loved one that they forget to tend to their own needs.

Codependency diminishes self-esteem in both the addicted person and the codependent person. The dependent person becomes weaker, and the codependent person feels unloved and unsupported. The codependent person seeks self-esteem from playing a support role, rather than from being worthwhile as an individual. If asked, "How do you feel?" people with codependency will often respond by saying how other people

① feel or by saying what they think the asker wants to hear. It's as though people with codependency aim bright spotlights outward onto people and things outside of themselves. This leaves them hiding alone with their unmet needs in the darkness.

Codependency is especially harmful when the person becomes a parent. A codependent parent is no more able to nurture children than is an addicted parent. Such parents suffer deeply. They say things such as, "If only he would change, I could be happy." "If things weren't so bad, I would do better." "If only I had X, I could do Y." Meanwhile, everything and everyone else suffers from abuse or lack of attention. Children get a false idea that events control individuals. They grow up lacking a sense of control.

Emotionally healthy people, in contrast, know that happiness lies within each individual, that no time is ever perfect, and

Teacher Support Notes

① **Codependent Problems:** As a cause of the problems associated with codependency, some researchers have focused on the intense shame that arises out of the family members' inability to control the dependent person's problems. The family hides the problem, which becomes the family secret. The adult child of one alcoholic reported, "In our family, there were two very clear rules: there is nothing wrong here, and don't tell anyone." The exaggerated shame that develops in the children can be as damaging as the disease itself is to the alcoholic. A predisposition to shame may occur in the first eighteen months of life. A mother may say to her child, "If you're a good girl, Daddy won't be angry." The unspoken message is that the father's drinking results from the girl's behavior. If the drinking continues, the child feels increasingly ashamed.

characteristics to some television families. For example, they could use the Cosby family as the functional family and the Bundy family as the dysfunctional family.

While it is important that students learn to apply this information to their own lives, the teacher must be careful not to imply any criticism of the students' own families. The use of television families allows some emotional distance. **(20 min., Critical Thinking)**

Activity 3.11
  Puppet Shows. Have students write puppet shows focusing on child abuse, family violence, or divorce. Direct the students to write the puppet shows for a young (five–eight-year-old) audience. Make sure the students use situations based on fact. Students may get additional information from current encyclopedias, the local police department, newspapers, and magazines. Have the students perform the shows in class. **(50 min.; Interdisciplinary, Cooperative Learning)**

Activity 3.12
  Legalities of Divorce. Direct stu-

Fast Facts

1 of 3 people in the U.S. is involved in a stepfamily relationship.

Teacher Support Notes

① **Defining Abuse:** Ask students to define the difference between acceptable physical discipline and child abuse. You may want to break the students into groups and have each group define the difference and provide supporting examples of what's acceptable and what's not. Then have the groups compare their definitions.
② **Adjusting to Divorce:** While a discussion of students' personal experiences and feelings regarding divorce may be beneficial, many students may be reluctant to discuss these sensitive issues. A discussion, however, of the way divorces are portrayed in the media may allow students to explore and discuss their own personal feelings. Ask students to write about one positive and one negative relationship or emotion involving divorce that they've observed in movies, television shows, magazine stories, newspaper articles, etc. Discuss their papers in class.

---

that each day must be lived fully. It's been said that "Today is not life's dress rehearsal, but the performance of life itself." To break the chains of codependency, just one person must change and begin to focus on his or her own needs today. After all, one can only change oneself.

> **Key Points** *Codependent people focus all their energy on helping addicted loved ones. They therefore neglect everyone and everything else, including themselves. To recover, such people must begin to focus on themselves.*

Child Abuse and Family Violence

More than a million children in the United States are abused each year by their parents, guardians, or other adults. Almost half a million children die each year at the hands of their abusers. Aside from physical beatings, many more children suffer repeated sexual assaults and the constant emotional abuse of unreasonable expectations, humiliation, and failure to have their needs met.

People who abuse children are emotionally disturbed. They have low self-esteem and little power among adults. Such people may try to bolster themselves by bullying those who are physically weaker. Not only children, but also adults, suffer at their hands. Each year over a million wives in the United States seek medical attention for injuries from attacks by their husbands. An estimated half million to 1 million elderly people are physically abused each year as well.

Family violence most often occurs when outside stresses set in and worsen existing emotional problems. Very young parents, single parents, those who are unemployed, those who fail to manage stress, and those who have few social contacts are especially likely to abuse their children. Alcohol and other drugs are strongly linked with child abuse. If the tendency to abuse exists, intoxication triggers such behavior.

Most important, people who abuse their own children are most likely to have been abused themselves during their childhoods. Abuse runs in families and is passed on from each older generation to the next until someone breaks the chain by seeking and receiving help. A child who is rescued from an abusive situation and who is supported in working through the resulting emotional injuries can recover completely, and can achieve high-level emotional health. Adults who realize that some of their life problems started from abuse in childhood can also get help and recover.

Social services exist to protect children from abuse. However, they cannot do the job alone. People who know of child abuse should report it. You can do this without giving your name.*

> **Key Points** *Child abuse is all too common in the United States. Outside stressors may worsen parents' existing emotional problems, making abuse likely. Alcohol and other drugs also trigger abuse.*

Children of Divorce

Almost half of the families that form today eventually break up in divorce. In cases of severely dysfunctional families, this route may spare family members some further injury. At the same time, however, everyone must adjust to it. Those involved must rearrange everything from home addresses and school locations to emotional ties and future plans. Most children eventually adapt to the changes and live normally. However, some can't adjust and are thrown into long-term problems such as depression.

Both parents and children can feel hurt, shocked, lonely, or angry over a divorce, even if the intact family unit was destructive. However, children need not fear that they will lose a parent. People may divorce

* The national child abuse hotline number is 1-800-4-A-CHILD.

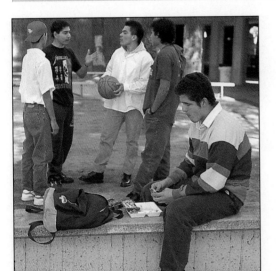

A change may seem hard at first, but a better life may follow.

their spouses, but never their children. Both parents are still parents to their children, regardless of what else happens or whom else they may marry. The first year is always the hardest. With time, relationships become secure in a new way.

In advance of a divorce, it helps to reduce stress if children know where they will live and with whom. A visit to the new location helps to prepare for changes ahead—new schools, new ways of getting around, new friends. If you are facing such changes, ask for some maps of the new area so that you can become familiar with the street names. Ask to be taken to the new school to meet the teachers or just to see the grounds and try to meet as many people, such as neighbors, in the new location as possible. Knowing that you will be safe and loved and that you are not at fault in the breakup are perhaps the most important elements in reducing the stress from the change.

Asking parents to provide these assurances during a time of personal crisis is a tall order. Still, without such assurances, or when parents abuse their children's affections to injure each other, or when they battle openly for their children as "prizes" to be won, the children may end up feeling insecure, anxious, angry, or guilty. These feelings can express themselves as emotional problems with low grades earned in school and poor performance on aptitude tests. A young person who is faced with adults who are unable to cope needs help. An uninvolved family member, the school counselor, a religious leader, or another trusted adult can sometimes provide the needed guidance.

Given time, most children come to accept the split. It helps to know that children **grieve** over a parent who has left the family, just as they would if the person had died. It takes time to build new relationships, especially with **stepparents** who may marry into the family.

Stepparents may seem like intruders at first, each bringing his or her own set of thoughts and family rules. Most times, though, new balances of power can be worked out as long as everyone is permitted a say. Unity of all groups rests on open communication between members. Teens should rely on their assertiveness skills (see Chapter 2) to be sure their views are heard.

①

MINI GLOSSARY

grieve: to feel keen emotional pain and suffering over a loss. The normal stages of grief are described in the Straight Talk section of Chapter 22.

stepparents: people who marry into a family after a biological parent's death or departure through divorce.

In this section students will learn:
1. Various types of therapy for emotional problems.
2. Methods for seeking and finding help.
3. How to help friends with emotional problems.
4. Important information about suicide.

Activity 4.1
Therapeutic Activities. Have students brainstorm a lengthy list of activities that may serve as therapy for mild emotional problems. This list should include any safe, nonviolent, legal activity that brings the participant enjoyment. Discuss. **(15 min., Critical Thinking)**

Activity 4.2
Health Professionals Match.

Write the titles of the emotional health professionals on the next page on a set of index cards and their job descriptions on another set of cards. Have the students play a matching game. This game can be played with the entire class or small groups. Students can even play this game on their own at a learning center in your classroom or as a free-time activity. **(20 min., Cooperative Learning)**

Section III Review
Answers
1. stepparents
2. dysfunctional family
3. grieve
4. Active abuse involves one person's aggression against another, such as hitting or sexual abuse, while passive abuse involves not taking needed actions, such as neglecting to provide food or shelter.
5. members who have alcoholism or other drug addictions or long-term physical illnesses, depend on people who have such conditions, engage in active abuse, and engage in passive abuse
6. Dysfunctional families often have rigid rules; they have family secrets; have no sense of humor; value appearances more than individuals; and lack togetherness.
7. One person must change and begin to focus on his or her own needs.
8. Answers will vary; could include those who are: emotionally disturbed, low in self-esteem and have little power among adults, very young parents, single parents, unemployed, lacking in social contacts, addicted to drugs or alcohol, and victims of abuse.
9. Answers will vary.

122 UNIT 2 Your Emotional and Social Health

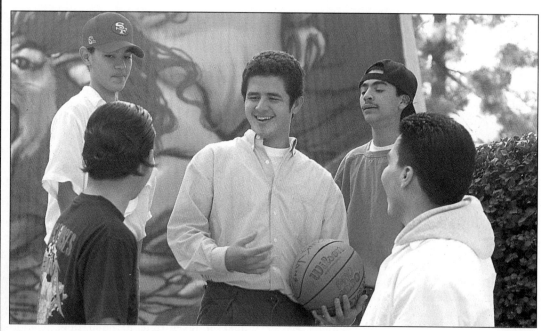

After the adjustment is made, the new life may bring more happiness than the old.

No family, even one that stays together, is perfect. All families require effort and cooperation to succeed.

Key Points *Dysfunctional families sometimes break up through divorce. Although divorce may require an adjustment that is difficult to make, most children soon resume normal life.*

SECTION III REVIEW

Answer the following questions on a sheet of paper.

Learning the Vocabulary
The vocabulary terms in this section are *dysfunctional family, codependency, active abuse, passive abuse, grieve,* and *stepparents.*

1. People who marry into a family after a biological parent's death or departure through divorce are called _____.
2. A _____ has abnormal ways of dealing with problems and erodes the self-esteem and emotional health of its members.
3. To _____ means to feel emotional pain and suffering over a loss.
4. What is the difference between active abuse and passive abuse?

Learning the Facts
5. What types of people are often members of a dysfunctional family?
6. How can you determine if a family is dysfunctional?
7. How can the chain of codependency be broken?
8. List some common traits of child abusers.

Making Life Choices
9. Dysfunctional families have abnormal or impaired ways of dealing with problems. Why do families in trouble often follow an unwritten code of silence? Explain why sexual abuse and family violence are such difficult subjects for victims to talk about. Discuss why it is so important for dysfunctional families to get help.

Activity 4.3

Research and Report. Direct students to do independent research on one of the emotional health professionals discussed in the preceding activity. From this research they are to prepare first-person reports. These reports may be written or oral.

A sample report would begin: "I am a psychiatrist. I have completed medical school and I am an M.D.," etc.

If the report is given orally, the students have the added opportunity to answer questions in the first person. **(Extend, Enrich, Interdisciplinary)**

Activity 4.4

Local Assistance Agencies. Bring in a variety of local phone books. Have students design posters, fliers, and mini phone books with names, phone numbers, and addresses of all local agencies that provide emotional health counseling and assistance.

If possible, post these numbers throughout the school and share them with other schools.

Be sure to have posters in all common

(continued on next page)

SECTION IV

Emotional Healing

You don't have to be sick, and you certainly don't have to be very sick, to ask for help for an emotional problem. You just have to need or want help. The exact moment when a person decides to get help for an emotional problem is often the moment when that person starts to get better. Often, though, people hesitate to ask for help because they are afraid this will be an admission that they are "sick." Actually, emotionally healthy people often make this choice.

Types of Therapy

Any activity that has a healing or health-promoting effect is a form of **therapy**. For one person, going out for a softball team after work may serve as therapy. For another, it may be best to get away from noise and crowds, go home to a quiet kitchen, listen to music, and cut up fresh vegetables for a special dinner. Painting, writing, playing with children, walking on the beach—all these can serve as therapy.

Soothing activities can help relieve many emotional problems, but cannot, by themselves, solve severe problems. A person with a severe emotional problem may benefit from professional help. Professionals who can help may include any of the following:

- A *counselor*—a helping person. Be careful, though. Both qualified and unqualified people practice under this title. Many states require licensing for counselors to practice.
- A *psychiatrist*—a physician (M.D.) who, after completing medical school, received additional special training to treat emotional problems and is licensed to prescribe drugs.

Any activity that has a health-promoting effect is therapy.

① [
- A *psychoanalyst*—a psychiatrist who specializes in seeking the root causes of emotional problems.
- A *psychologist*—a person with a graduate degree (M.S. or Ph.D.) in psychology from a university. Many states require licensing for psychologists to practice.
- A *social worker*—a person with a graduate degree in social work (M.S.W.). This degree includes training in counseling.

Other than these, people who claim to offer therapy may not be trustworthy.

Effective therapy relationships always contain these three ingredients:

1. Respect and trust between the therapist and the client.
2. The exploration of the present problem's causes, effects, or both.
3. The search for new, more productive ways of dealing with the problem.

MINI **G**LOSSARY

therapy: treatment that heals.

languages. **(20 min.; Interdisciplinary, Multicultural)**

Activity 4.5

 Agency Interviews. As a follow-up to Activity 4.4, direct students to call the agencies and ask a series of predeter-

mined questions. When feasible, students may also be encouraged to visit the agencies.

 As a class, develop a list of pertinent and appropriate questions to be asked of the agencies. Have the students share their findings in class. **(Reteach, Reinforce)**

Activity 4.6

 Guest Speakers. Invite guest speakers from some of the agencies from

Activities 4.4 and 4.5 to class.

 Al-Anon and Alateen can be especially valuable to students.

 Encouraging students to prepare questions in advance will bring added value to the time spent with the guest speaker. **(Special Needs)**

Activity 4.7

 Asking For Help. Using the Health Strategies, "Finding Help" (page 125),

---

66 Thoughts on Health 99

If you are physically sick, you can elicit the interest of a battery of physicians. But if you are mentally sick, you are lucky if the janitor comes around.

– Martin Fischer

☎ Where to Call

American Mental Health Fund
1-800-433-5959
Materials about any mental health condition are available.

✉ Where to Write

Mental Health Association
1021 Prince St.
Alexandria, VA
22314

---

124 UNIT 2 Your Emotional and Social Health

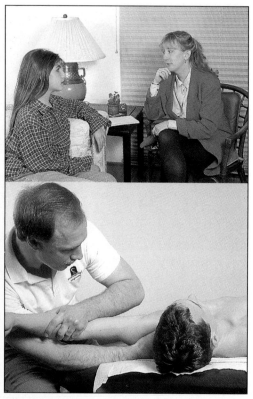

Effective therapy always includes trust and respect. A healing touch can serve as therapy.

 Therapy need not be expensive to be effective. Many public health programs run therapy centers and counseling groups that charge on a sliding scale according to ability to pay. Some schools provide free counseling and may run groups of their own. In addition to formal therapies, many find help in the form of "Anonymous" self-help groups. Alcoholics Anonymous (AA) helps people recover from alcohol addiction. Overeaters Anonymous (OA) helps people recover from eating disorders. Alanon helps the family members of people with addictions, and Alateen helps teens in dysfunctional families. The services of these groups are free, and members support them voluntarily.

Key Points ▶ *Many activities can act as therapy, especially when they are soothing and bring relief from stress. An effective relationship between a professional therapist and client is based on respect, trust, exploration of the problem, and a search for ways of dealing with the problem. Effective therapy need not be expensive.*

About Finding Help

 If you have concluded that you might benefit from having psychological help, be selective. Not all "therapists" are well qualified. Some are even quacks (see the Consumer Awareness box on page 126). Try the possibilities listed in the Health Strategies section on the next page.

 Stick with it. The first source of help you try may not work out well. However, there *is* someone out there for you to talk to. You might start by seeing a counselor for anxiety but end up getting help learning how to deal with peers—which might solve the anxiety problem. Often a single, clearheaded discussion will lead to a simple solution.

 People may hesitate to seek professional help for fear of what they may be forced to discover about themselves. Yet the most earthshaking discovery people are likely to

It's dangerous to go to the wrong person for therapy.

direct the students to role-play asking for help. It is important to orally practice this skill and thus increase the likelihood of using the newly developed skill. **(30 min., Cooperative Learning)**

Activity 4.8

Legitimate Providers vs. Quacks. Have students brainstorm reasons people may decide to visit someone who is considered a quack. Write the list on the board as the students share their ideas.

Next to that list, write, as students brainstorm, reasons for visiting a legitimate emotional health care provider. Discuss and compare the lists. **(30 min., Critical Thinking)**

Activity 4.9

Limericks. Teach students how to write limericks, then have them write emotional health limericks. Limericks are five lines of *approximately* the following number of syllables:

Line 1—8
Line 2—8
Line 3—5
Line 4—5
Line 5—8

Here is an example:
There was a dysfunctional man

(continued on next page)

HEALTH STRATEGIES

Finding Help

If you want some help working on an emotional problem:

1. Tell your parents you'd like to work out a problem. They may be able to help you themselves, or they may have a good idea regarding whom you should see.
2. Check with the teacher of your health or life management skills course. The teacher is likely to be well informed regarding local helping agencies.
3. Ask your family physician to suggest someone to help you.
4. Ask your school guidance counselor whom to see. Or ask for the name of a helpful member of the clergy.
5. Look in your telephone book for a telephone counseling service; call; and ask what to do. You don't have to give your name if you don't want to.
6. Look up "Mental health," "Health," "Social services," "Drugs," "Alcohol," "Family services," "Suicide prevention," or "Counseling" in the telephone book. Call and ask what to do. Again, you can choose whether or not to give your name.

make is that they are not alone—that other people have the same problem and that, with help, they can deal with it.

Key Points   *Seeking professional help for an emotional problem is often the first step towards health. Choose therapists carefully, based on trusted advice and credentials.*

How to Help Another Person

It is sometimes possible to help another person who has an emotional problem. Simply caring and offering support is often enough. Listening is helpful, too. Often a person can work out problems, given enough chances to discuss them.

If you are stuck in a codependent relationship, you may need help getting out of it.

① Helping skills are not inborn, however. The untrained person can do more harm than good by saying or suggesting the wrong things. For example, a person who hopes to help may become codependent, and weaken the other person. A codependent "helper" may allow the troubled person to avoid facing problems. This misguided attempt to help is termed **enabling,** because it supports the continuation of inappropriate behavior. Enablers, with the best intentions in the world, make it possible for other people to continue ② drinking, gambling, or other self-destructive behaviors by rescuing them from the natural consequences of their own actions (see Chapter 14). Without having to face consequences, troubled people have no reason to change.

MINI GLOSSARY

enabling: misguided "helping." An enabler is a person who actually does harm by supporting a troubled person's continued self-destructive attitude or behavior.

125

Who said, "Guess I am what I am."
A counselor said, "Wait!"
"You really are great."
Now he functions as well as he can.

Have the students share their limericks in class. **(45 min., Interdisciplinary)**

Activity 4.10
Creating Their Own Quizzes. Distribute three index cards to each student. Have each student write three questions (one on each card with answers) from Section IV that they feel should be included on a quiz over the section. Put the

cards in a bag or box and choose ten or more of the questions to use as a quiz.

Activity 4.11
School Counselor Interview. Invite a school counselor to class and allow students to interview him/her. You might want to discuss in advance ques-

---

Teacher Support Notes

① **Answers to Critical Thinking:** These questions are not answered directly in the Consumer Awareness feature; they require some brainstorming.
1. Possibilities are to ask for credentials, check with the Better Business Bureau, contact the State Department of Mental Health for licensing information, and ask for recommendations from trusted friends and relatives.
2. They are looking for a quick and easy solution, they need relief, and they are not finding it elsewhere. They want to believe that they can be healed. In many cases they do not have the patience nor the power to pursue genuine help.
3. It's easy; society pressures people to think that medicine can cure all.
4. No product can promise to alleviate such problems. This suggestion implies that lack of the product actually caused the problem, which is unreasonable.

CONSUMER **A**WARENESS **Quack Counselors**

In some states, anyone can hang out a sign that says "Counselor" and collect money in exchange for advice. People who do this without proper training and licensing can do a great deal of harm to those already suffering from the problems that drove them to seek help. A person who seeks help from a quack counselor is likely to wind up with even more problems, and with drained financial resources as well.

Especially dangerous are those who try to sell products or devices that are said to relieve emotional distress. A common example is the sale of vitamin and mineral supplements by "counselors." It is true that many nutrient deficiencies can cause and worsen mental symptoms. It is not true, though, that bottles of pills are the best route to relief. For example, research clearly shows that severe deficiencies of many vitamins and minerals cause reduced mental abilities, weakened memory, and worn-down feelings that seem like depression. However, as the next few chapters show, the nutrient needs of the

body and the brain cannot be met by pill taking. Too much of a nutrient can even be poisonous. If a person lacks nutrients and is suffering mental symptoms, that person is in urgent need of well-planned meals composed of nutritious foods.

Many psychological problems are rooted in life's events. Overcoming them may take hard work. Pills may seem an easy way out, but in the long run they only waste time and money. Pills can even bring on mental problems instead of relieving them.

① **C**RITICAL **T**HINKING

1. *How can you be sure that a counselor is qualified to help you, and is not a quack?*
2. *Why do you suppose that people want to believe in the schemes of quacks?*
3. *Why is it so tempting to try taking pills to solve problems?*
4. *How would you respond to the suggestion that your emotional feelings were due to the lack of a product sold by a "counselor"?*

A person may help another for other wrong reasons. Helping others may be a way of avoiding facing one's own problems. It provides an excuse: "I couldn't go to class because I was helping Jane." People who focus on other people's problems to this extent are often codependent and need help for themselves.

Helping people in crisis requires a special set of strategies. You sometimes have to break out of ordinary social behavior. If a

person is clearly irrational and in danger, you may have to risk the friendship in order to help the person. To tell when to take this risk, ask yourself:

- Do I think that the person's life or health is in serious danger?
- Is the person threatening someone else's life or health?
- If I fail to help, will the situation become dangerous?

RETEACH/BONUS

Here are some activities you could use in conjunction with the Straight Talk feature that begins on the next page.

Secrets and Promises. Teach the students the phrase, "Keep a secret, lose a friend." Tell students that often a suicidal teen will confide in a friend after asking the friend to promise not to tell. Have students brainstorm the feelings they might have if they keep the promise and their friend dies. **(20 min.)**

Responding With Help. As a follow-up to the preceding activity, assist students in writing phrases they might use in responding to a suicidal teen who elicits a promise of silence. Samples:

"I care about you too much to keep this promise. Let's go talk to my mom, my brother, your mom, our teacher, etc.—any trustworthy adult—together. She'll help."

Direct students to use adults only as the choice of a person to go to for help. The adult may be named if desired. (i.e., a favorite teacher) **(30 min.; Reteach, Reinforce)**

If the answer to any of these questions is yes, get involved. It is a risk, but the risk of not helping is worse. Your judgment may not be perfect, but it is the best you have available—so use it.

When a crisis requires professional help, the person who needs help should be the one to call. Mental health agencies will not step in unless the person with the problem makes the request. If your friend is resistant, place the telephone call yourself. Then persuade your friend to talk to a helping person on the other end of the line. If that fails, or in the case of a very sick, weak, or debilitated friend, call the police or an ambulance. The move may be awkward, but its urgency justifies it.

Continue helping until you are satisfied that you have done what you can. Then let go. Should the outcome disappoint you, remember that you did your best.

Be sure to protect yourself. For your emotional well-being, it is important to be aware of the limits of your ability to give support. A depressed person can be a sort of emotional sink into which you pour your energy without getting anything back. Such a relationship drains you, to no useful purpose.

If such a situation drags on for very long, wisdom dictates that it is best for you and the other person if you remove yourself from it. Your continued listening may be postponing a solution. Put the person in touch with expert help, and bow out. Make it clear that you are taking this action to encourage truly effective help for your friend and peace of mind for yourself.

Key Points *Offering emotional help to others is beneficial only if the help does not prevent their recovery. When a person becomes overly dependent, it is best to help the person form a link to professional help, and bow out.*

SECTION IV REVIEW

Answer the following questions on a sheet of paper.

Learning the Vocabulary
The vocabulary terms in this section are *therapy* and *enabling.*
1. Write a sentence using each vocabulary term.

Learning the Facts
2. List all the professionals who are trained to help people with emotional problems.
3. Give three recommendations for finding help for an emotional problem.
4. Why isn't the taking of vitamin and mineral supplements considered to be the best solution for an emotional problem?
5. Why is it important to know your limits when extending yourself to help someone with an emotional problem?

Making Life Choices
6. Many times personal problems are resolved through a discussion with someone in whom you have confidence. Develop a list of people you believe you could go to for help. List the reasons why you chose each particular person.
7. Why do you think people become enablers? Explain how you might discover that you were enabling a friend to keep up a drug problem. Discuss what you might do to stop enabling your friend.

Answers to Fact or Fiction

Here are the answers to the questions at the start of the chapter.

1. False. Emotionally healthy people often benefit from such help, and it is well worth seeking. **2.** True. **3.** True. **4.** True. **5.** False. To express resentment helps resolve conflict. To keep it private can harm a relationship. **6.** False. Assigning blame is not useful; it is destructive.

Section IV Review
Answers
1. Answers will vary.
2. counselors, psychiatrists, psychoanalysts, psychologists, social workers
3. Answers will vary. Refer to Health Strategies on page 125 for possible answers.
4. The nutrient needs of the body and the brain cannot be met by pill taking. Many psychological problems relate to life's events; it takes hard work to overcome them. Pills can bring on mental problems instead of relief.
5. for your own emotional well-being. You can become emotionally drained. Continuing to listen may postpone a solution. Put the person in touch with an expert.
6. Answers will vary; could include: parents, friends, clergy, teacher, relatives.
7. Answers will vary.

Go and Stop Cards. Distribute two cards to each student. One card should be green and one red. Make the cards out of construction paper. Read a variety of responses one may make to a suicidal teen. Have students hold up the green cards for good responses (go) and the red cards for poor responses (stop).

Students may enjoy making up their own responses for the class to evaluate. Use responses from the following list and/or make up your own. Sample responses:

"O.K., I promise to keep your secret."

"Yeah sure, like, I really believe that you'd jump."

"I'm your friend and I'll stand by you."

"Let's go talk to (*trusted adult*), they can help."

"That's dumb, don't worry about it."

"You are making too big a deal of this." **(20 min.; Reteach, Reinforce)**

Reasons for Suicide Discussion. Discuss the most common reasons teens commit suicide. Review the signs students can look for and the ways they can

STRAIGHT TALK — Young People's Suicide

During one average day in the United States, about 20 young people end their own lives. In the same day, 1,000 attempt to do so but fail. Only accidents and homicides kill more teenagers than do suicides, and many deaths listed as accidents may be suicides in disguise. When a young person rides a bike into oncoming traffic on a superhighway, or climbs to a high rooftop and falls, experts suspect the "accidents" may be intentional.

Why would some teenagers want to die?

Suicide attempts seem to mean that the victims want to die. However, except for a tiny percentage, those who attempt suicide truly want to live.

Surprisingly, a suicide attempt is really a call for help. A suicide attempt says, "Look at me, help me, save me!" The person wants desperately to know that someone cares. Suicide may be the nation's number-one preventable cause of death among teens.

The uncertainty of some victims' intentions is clear. Some have been found dead while still clutching the telephone, calling for help. Others have called the police to say they were planning to overdose. The majority of attempts are made in such a way that someone will be sure to save them.

They want to live? Then why would they try to kill themselves?

Most teens who commit suicide suffer from the deep gloom, loneliness, and hopelessness of depression—a fatal despair. Even without clinical depression, teens may feel down moods and have repeated thoughts of death. This chapter stressed the urgency of learning to recognize the symptoms of depression. A reason to do so is that the symptoms of severe depression (on page 110) are the same ones that are associated with suicide.

Young people may attempt suicide because they do not know that life's bad feelings pass with time, and that things almost always improve. Teens may see suicide as the only path out of present circumstances. In reality, of course, many paths lead to the solution of problems. Other reasons teens may attempt suicide include:

- Trying to impress another person with the urgency of their feelings.
- Having an unrealistic, romantic view of death.
- Feeling like a failure.
- Inability to express anger or pain.
- Lacking firm values or rules on which to base life decisions.
- Suffering a loss and seeing no end to deep grief.
- Having a relative or friend commit suicide, which makes the act seem (falsely) reasonable.

Does anything besides depression trigger suicide?

The abuse of drugs or alcohol may play a role. Researchers have studied the lives of suicide victims. They found that two-thirds of those studied abused alcohol or other drugs on a regular basis. It appears that drugs and alcohol can cause or worsen the symptoms of depression that lead to suicide.

(Continued on next page)

✏️ Fast Facts

Approximately 1-1/2% of the deaths of children between the ages of 10 and 14 in 1968 were suicide. In 1991, the percentage had risen to 6%, according to the AMA.

✏️ Fast Facts

More men than women successfully complete their attempted suicides, but women make more attempts. The men use guns or other fatal methods, whereas women more often try a drug overdose, which allows a greater chance of recovery or help.

help. Help students understand that they are not responsible for the actions of a friend, but a friend is more likely to turn to them than to an adult. Learning the options now will help them respond more appropriately if this should ever occur. **(30 min.; Reteach, Reinforce)**

STRAIGHT TALK   *(Continued)*

I've heard that once a person's mind is set on suicide, nothing can change it.

That's a myth. The overwhelming majority of people who survive a suicide attempt are glad they are alive. Only a few repeat the attempt and succeed. The wish to die lasts only a few hours or days, not a lifetime. If victims can be helped through the crisis period, chances are good that life will go on normally, afterward.

I've heard that people who talk about killing themselves never do. They just want attention, and the best thing to do is to ignore their threats.

That, too, is a myth. However, it is widely believed, and it is dangerous. It can lull friends and family even while a person is plainly displaying suicidal intentions. It may even give victims added reasons to follow through—to prove the seriousness of the intent.

I don't want my friends and family to be without help when they need it. How can I tell if someone is about to commit suicide?

It is important to remember that suicide is a possibility.

Otherwise, you may miss the warning signs. Take any of the signs of severe depression seriously.

If I suspect an oncoming suicide attempt, how can I help?

Get involved. Don't wait to see what develops, because tomorrow may be too late. Ask outright if the person is planning suicide. Do not be afraid to mention it. Chances are, your friend already has the idea in mind. Talking about it with a clearheaded person can help your friend. Be careful not to make light of your friend's feelings. If you imply that your friend doesn't mean it, you may unknowingly offer a dare. At the same time as you show your concern, try to offer reassurance that the crisis is temporary.

If the person seems on the verge of making a suicide attempt, the two most important things to do are these:

- Phone a suicide hotline or crisis intervention center immediately. Dial 911, the operator, or the police.
- Stay with the person until help arrives.

What if I fail to prevent a suicide?

Accepting that you may have failed can be one of the

Ask someone to listen to you; you'll be glad you did.

hardest things in life to face. Still, you cannot change what has happened. Emotional support is available for survivors. Learning about the process of grief, described in the Straight Talk section of Chapter 22, can also help.

What if sometimes I feel like ending my own life?

Almost everyone feels that way, sometimes. Those thoughts and feelings come and go, just as others do. Things can seem very bad, but they always get better, given time. You can talk to someone during the bad times without their knowing who you are: call the helping hotline in your area. Or ask someone you trust to listen to your thoughts. You'll both be glad you did.

Fast Facts

Approximately 1 person out of every 100 attempts suicide at some point in his or her life.

Fast Facts

One study, using a representative sample from all 50 states, found that 27% of students in grades 9–12 had thought seriously about suicide.

CHAPTER REVIEW

Answers

Vocabulary

1. **a.** anxiety attack
b. insomnia **c.** guilt
d. Passive abuse **e.** eating disorder
2. **a.** a habit or behavior
b. Anxiety is a state of high energy, and can be beneficial in short spurts. Too much can be disabling. Phobias are a special form of anxiety that are an extreme, irrational fear of an object or situation.
3. **a.** post-traumatic stress disorder **b.** active abuse **c.** shame **d.** emotional problems **e.** resentment **f.** dysfunctional family **g.** schizophrenia
4. Answers will vary.

Recall

Section I
1. social or family relations, performance of tasks, or leisure time activities
2. Society puts heavy pressure on people, and with strong values a person can act according to internal standards and not invite harsh external judgment.

Section II
3. depression
4. Answers will vary; could include: identify the cause, take action, force yourself to do something different, do something physically active, eat a pick-me-up snack, avoid difficult or unpleasant tasks for a while, don't put pressure on yourself to achieve too much too soon, break large tasks into manageable goals, seek out other people, reject negative thinking, find reasons to laugh, go outdoors, and if you feel stuck, get help.
5. Physical activity alters the body's chemistry, lifts mood and attitude, and provides a benefit to those with heart disease, diabetes, alcoholism, and other conditions.
6. Answers will vary; could include: claustrophobia, agoraphobia, acrophobia, and any from the list of phobias on page 112.
7. When a person is made to feel shame, the person learns that he, or she, is bad. This chips away at self-esteem.

CHAPTER REVIEW

LEARNING THE VOCABULARY

emotional problems
schizophrenia
addiction
eating disorder
depression
insomnia
anxiety
post-traumatic stress disorder

anxiety attack
phobia
guilt
shame
resentment
suppress
dysfunctional family

codependency
active abuse
passive abuse
grieve
stepparents
therapy
enabling

Answer the following questions on a separate sheet of paper.

1. **Word Scramble**—*Use the clues from the phrases below to help you unscramble the terms:*
    a. **tyeixna catakt**–A sudden, unexpected episode of severe anxiety with symptoms such as sweating and rapid heartbeat is called an _____ _____.
    b. **niomisan** _____ is a disorder that involves sleep abnormalities.
    c. **luitg**–A feeling a person gets when acting against internal values is called _____.
    d. **siapesv sebua** _____ _____ is abuse that involves not giving love and support.
    e. **geatin resdiodr** Anorexia nervosa is classified as an _____ _____.
2. a. In an addiction, what sorts of things can people become dependent on, other than drugs?
    b. How are anxiety and phobias similar and how are they different?

3. **Matching**—*Match each of the following phrases with the appropriate vocabulary term from the list above:*
    a. a reaction to a stressful event such as rape, arising after the event is over
    b. abuse involving one person's aggression against another, such as sexual abuse of a victim
    c. the extreme feeling of guilt that arises when a person internalizes blame for mistakes
    d. patterns of behavior that impair a person's ability to function in social or family relations, occupation, or use of leisure time
    e. anger that has built up due to failure to express it
    f. a family with abnormal or impaired ways of coping
    g. a serious mental illness that tends to run in families
4. Create a story using as many of the vocabulary terms as you can. Underline each term you use from the vocabulary list.

RECALLING IMPORTANT FACTS AND IDEAS

1. What areas of your life can be affected by emotional problems?
2. Why is it so important to develop a working set of inner values by which to live?
3. What is the most common emotional problem for which people seek counseling?
4. Give four recommendations for coping with mild depression.
5. How does physical activity affect the emotions?
6. Name three phobias.
7. Why is shame destructive to self-esteem?
8. What frequently happens to children in a dysfunctional family?
9. What is the name and phone number of the organization that can offer support to teenage friends and relatives of people with addictions?

10. List three characteristics of a functional family and three of a dysfunctional family.

11. Name some common traits of a codependent person.

12. Approximately how many children in our country are abused each year?

13. What should you do if you become aware of a case of child abuse?

14. Approximately how many marriages end in divorce?

15. What are the three ingredients necessary for an effective therapy relationship?

16. Name a few self-help groups.

17. How common is teenage suicide?

18. What are some reasons why teenagers may attempt suicide?

19. How can you help a suicidal friend?

CRITICAL THINKING

1. Imagine that the community you live in has absolutely no mental health services. Design a comprehensive mental health services program to suit the needs of your community. Consider the different age groups, cultures, and most common emotional problems within your community. What would you advise and why?

2. People who are feeling suicidal often see only one solution to their problems—taking their own life. List as many reasons as you can think of for teenage suicide attempts and for each reason listed develop a healthy way to deal with each problem. It is very important for people to realize there is more than one way to look at a problem. Name some people who could help teenagers in this way.

3. In what ways is your family different from any other? What do you think the "ideal" family would be like? How would family members treat each other? Describe some ways you could show caring and support for each member of your family. To whom could you go for help if your family were in crisis?

ACTIVITIES

1. Analyze a family television show that you watch regularly. How is the family in the show like real families you know? How is it different? Write a one-page report.

2. Locate a song or poem about families in trouble and write a one-page reaction to it. Be sure to include the poem or lyrics to the song you choose.

3. Write a one-page description on what you could do to help a friend whose mom or dad is a substance abuser.

4. Contact a local hotline to find out some of the common problems people call in about. Find out what the staff training involves in order to work on the hotline.

5. Make a chart on poster board that lists the names of ten phobias on one side and their definitions on the other.

6. Find an article or watch a movie about an individual's struggle with an emotional problem. Describe the problem and how he or she dealt with it. Include a copy of the article or the name of the movie.

7. Using your phone book, look up mental health facilities. Call five facilities to find out what services they provide. List each facility, address, phone number, and services provided.

MAKING DECISIONS ABOUT HEALTH

1. Your parents have not been getting along with each other for quite a while. They recently told you they are getting divorced. Although some of your friends have divorced parents, you never thought it would happen to you. Lately, you have been having trouble eating, sleeping, and concentrating on your school work. What steps can you take to help yourself?

CHAPTER 6 PLANNER

OVERVIEW

Chapter 6 is 30 pages long and divided into the 12 sections listed at the right. Major learning outcomes are also listed to the right. The primary purpose of this chapter is to make students more aware of the miraculous workings of the human body and the fact that all the body systems work together, not independently. The chapter can also function as a review of the body systems. It begins with a short discussion of the structure of a system from the simplest cell to the collection of organs that perform a function. Although every system is responsible for a specific function, every system is dependent on all other systems for maintenance, protection, and life processes. It is this integration of all systems that maintains body homeostasis.

MAKING LIFE CHOICES RESOURCES

A variety of activities, handouts, quizzes, and tests to accompany this chapter are available in the *Making Life Choices* supplementary material. You may pick and choose from those materials as appropriate for your amount of class time and the ability levels of your students. Some of the resources you might want to consider using are:

Overheads
- The Spinal Column
- Muscles, Tendons, Ligaments, and Cartilage
- The Organization of the Nervous System
- The Digestive System
- An Overview of the Cardiovascular System
- Delivery of Oxygen by the Heart and Lungs to the Muscles
- The Hormonal System

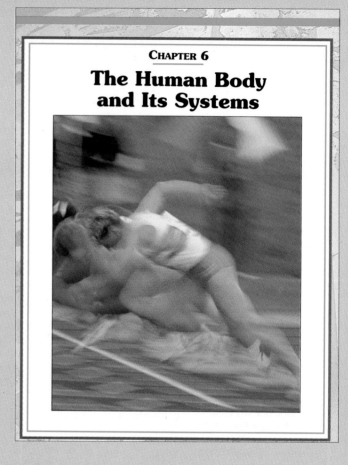

CHAPTER 6

The Human Body and Its Systems

Answers to "Fact or Fiction"

1. False. Adult bones not only break down but also build up their structures throughout life. **2.** True. **3.** True. **4.** True. **5.** True. **6.** False. The lungs lack muscles and, like passive balloons, fill with air only when the diaphragm contracts and creates a vacuum in the chest cavity. **7.** False. Most often, when disease-causing organisms enter the body the immune system destroys them and prevents illness. **8.** True.

Activity To Introduce Chapter

Have students work in pairs to complete the following activity. Assign one member of each pair to perform a simple task, such as opening a book to a certain page and reading a paragraph, or doing a couple of jumping jacks. (All "performers" should do the same activity.) The second member of the pair should carefully observe the performance. The pair should then work together to generate a list of the individual movements that occurred during the performance. They should try to match movements to the body system(s) involved in making that movement. Have all pairs participate to help develop a class list on the board.

OUTCOMES

After reading and studying this chapter, you will be able to:

✓ Differentiate among cells, tissues, organs, and systems.
✓ Describe the importance of muscles and bones.
✓ Identify the brain and spinal cord as the primary organs of the central nervous system.
✓ Explain how the brain's numerous functions are divided among its many physical parts.
✓ Identify the circulatory system as the transportation system of the body.
✓ Describe how the digestive system breaks down food particles.
✓ Compare the endocrine or hormonal system to a communication system.
✓ Identify the male and female reproductive organs responsible for uniting an ovum and a sperm.

CONTENTS

FACT OR FICTION

What do you think? Are the following statements true or false? If you think they are false, then say what is true.

1. Once bones have grown to adult size, they gain no more materials, although they may lose some.
2. Some muscle fibers are striped.
3. The brain is defenseless against the effects of alcohol.
4. If the digestive system did not protect itself, it would be digested by its juices.
5. Everyone's heart has a pacemaker.
6. The lungs are equipped with muscles in their walls that draw air in and out of the lungs' chambers.
7. Once a disease-causing organism enters the body, it is too late to prevent illness.
8. It is normal for men to produce female hormones in their bodies.

(Answers on page 161)

■ **Reminder:** Knowing how to study can increase your knowledge, improve your grades, *and* cut down on your study time. See the *Studying Health* section at the front of your text for some suggestions to help you study this chapter.

SUGGESTED RESOURCES

Student Readings
1. Fekete, Irene and Ward, Peter Dorrington. *Your Body.* New York: Facts on File, 1984.

Teacher Readings
1. Spence, Alexander and Mason, Elliott. *Human Anatomy and Physiology,* fourth edition. St. Paul: West Publishing, 1992.
2. Brunn, Ruth Dowling and Brunn, Bertel. *The Human Body.* New York: Random House, 1982.

Videos
1. *Incredible Human Machine.* Explores human anatomy and physiology. Opportunities for Learning, 800-243-7116.

Software
1. *BodyWorks: An Adventure in Anatomy.* Explore the body's systems, structures and functions. Software Marketing Corporation, 602-893-2400.

NOT ENOUGH TIME?*

You will probably want to use this chapter periodically throughout your course. If you teach the chapter in its entirety, as a review of the body systems, you may want to use the following plan.

TIME	SUGGESTIONS
1 Day	Assign students to read Sections I–VI prior to class. During class have students do the following activities: 2.2 in Section II; 3.1 in Section III; 4.1 in Section IV; 5.2 in Section V; and 6.3 in Section VI. Also, if time permits, use a variety of the Evaluate activities listed for each section.
2 Days	On day 2 assign students to read Sections VII–XII prior to class. During class assign the following activities: 9.3 in Section IX; 10.2 in Section X; 11.1 in Section XI; and 12.1 in Section XII. If time permits, use a variety of the Evaluate activities.

*Please refer to the 18-week daily lesson plans in the supplementary material for additional suggestions.

CHAPTER PROJECT

Have students work in pairs or groups to make lists of risks people take every day. These can include risks people take on their jobs (i.e., electrical workers could be electrocuted, police officers could be shot, etc.), risks people take for recreation (i.e., bungee jumping, skydiving, playing sports, using drugs and alcohol, smoking), or risks people take just living their lives (i.e., driving and riding in cars, eating foods that are not healthful, etc.). After the lists have been generated, have students write, beside each risk, the body system(s) that could be affected by taking that risk. Ask students which system(s) seem to be affected by most of the risks. How could some of these risks be avoided?

In this section students will learn that:
1. The body is made up of cells, tissue, organs, and systems.
2. All cells work in cooperation with other cells to support the whole by performing specific functions according to their genetic makeup.

3. All systems are dependent on each other and work together to maintain a state of homeostasis.

Activity 1.1
   Slides of Cells. Obtain some slides that show the different types of cells. Show the slides during a discussion of cell types.

Activity 1.2
   Class Definitions. In a class discussion have your students define systems as being composed of organs; define organs as being composed of tissues; define tissues as being composed of cells; and, define cells as the basic, sim-

---

Teacher Support Notes

① **The Amazing Body:** Have students brainstorm a list of body functions that they think are remarkable. If they had to list them in order, with the *most* remarkable listed first, how would they list them?

② **Glossary Definitions:** Remind students that all of the parts labeled in the illustrations and discussed in the sections of this chapter are defined in the glossary at the back of this book.

③ **Homeostasis:** You will find another example of homeostasis in Chapter 4. The example in that chapter explains how the body reacts to the stress of cold weather. Depending on whether or not you've already taught Chapter 4, you may want to refer students back to that explanation.

How does your body do the things it does? For example, how can your legs "know" when your mind decides that it's time to walk to the VCR to change a video? What does it mean when you get the hiccups? How does food in your stomach nourish your toes? ①

To answer questions like these you need knowledge, not only of each of the **body systems** individually, but also of the ways the systems work together. The more you learn about the working of the integrated body, the more you will appreciate its miraculous everyday functions.

This chapter is unlike any other in this book. Its mission is to teach you just enough about the body to provide a basis for understanding the chapters that follow. Most sections of this chapter are written as questions and answers centered around figures showing each body system. ③

The figures present all of the structures discussed and named in the text. While reading about each system, look often at the related figure to see the body parts being discussed in the text. This way, learning how the parts work is easy. If you need to see definitions of any of the parts named in the figures, turn to the main glossary at the end of the book. ②

SECTION 1

The Integrated Body

No body system can function all alone, without help from the other systems. Each system depends on all the other systems to maintain the life of the whole person. Each adjusts to changing conditions to keep internal body conditions about the same at all times. This process of the body's striving to maintain constant internal conditions is called **homeostasis**, a word that means "staying the same."

As an example of homeostasis, the urinary system (see Figure 6–8 on page 148) is extremely sensitive to the composition of the blood in the circulatory system. When the body becomes flooded with too much water, the kidneys (in the urinary system) detect the extra water in the blood, draw it out, and release it from the body as urine. These steps bring the blood's water content back to normal. In the opposite case, when water becomes scarce and the blood's water content begins to diminish, the kidneys quickly step in to excrete less water in the urine.

The kidneys' management of the body's water balance is just one among thousands of examples of homeostasis. Each process goes on every minute of every day without your conscious awareness. The beauty of homeostasis is that the sum of its actions is expressed as wellness of the body.

Cells

The body is made up of billions of microscopic **cells**. Each of the body's cells is a self-contained, living unit (Figure 6–1), although each depends on the rest of the body to supply its needs. Each cell keeps itself alive by taking up the substances it needs, such as oxygen, from the surrounding fluid and releasing the wastes it produces into that fluid.

In the human body every cell works in cooperation with every other to support the whole. The cell's **genes** determine the nature of that work. Each gene is a blueprint that directs the cell in making a piece of machinery that helps to do the cell's work. For example, in a nerve cell, the genes guide the cell to make equipment needed to generate nerve impulses.

Each cell contains a complete set of genes inside its **nucleus**. The genes are lined up along slender bodies known as **chromosomes**. This means that all the information plest form of life. **(20 min.; Extend, Enrich)**

Activity 1.3
Homeostasis. Divide the class into groups and have them try to think of machines, or mechanical or electrical systems that are designed to maintain a state of homeostasis. (Examples: cars, with such parts as oil and water gauges that light up; fuse boxes that blow out when overloaded; thermostats, which start furnaces.) **(15 min.; Critical Thinking, Cooperative Learning)**

Activity 1.4
Understanding Cancer. As you discuss cells, students may ask about cancerous cells, which will be discussed fully in Chapter 19. For now, tell them that cancer is an abnormal growth of abnormal cells. Ask students what systems are not affected by cancers. (All systems are affected.) **(15 min., Advanced)**

Activity 1.5
Insurance Plan. Have students devise an insurance plan that rewards participants for being healthy. **(30 min., Advanced)**

Activity 1.6

(continued on next page)

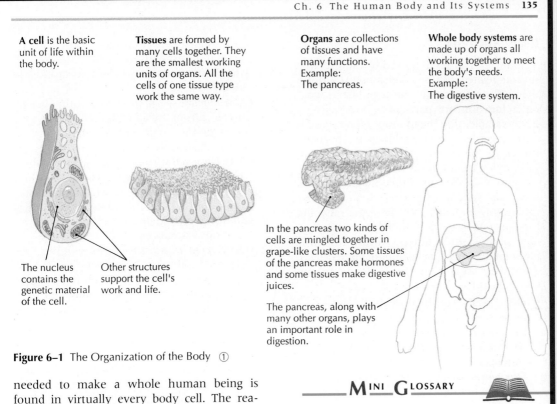

A cell is the basic unit of life within the body.

Tissues are formed by many cells together. They are the smallest working units of organs. All the cells of one tissue type work the same way.

Organs are collections of tissues and have many functions.
Example:
The pancreas.

Whole body systems are made up of organs all working together to meet the body's needs.
Example:
The digestive system.

The nucleus contains the genetic material of the cell.

Other structures support the cell's work and life.

In the pancreas two kinds of cells are mingled together in grape-like clusters. Some tissues of the pancreas make hormones and some tissues make digestive juices.

The pancreas, along with many other organs, plays an important role in digestion.

Figure 6–1 The Organization of the Body ①

needed to make a whole human being is found in virtually every body cell. The reason why cells of different body parts are different from one another is that different genes are active in each kind of cell. For example, in some intestinal cells, the genes for making digestive enzymes are active. In the body's fat cells, the genes for storing fat are active.

Tissues and Organs

Groups of cells that perform similar functions form the **tissues**. Tissues perform tasks for the body. For example, some cells join together to form muscle tissue, which can contract. Tissues also are organized in sets to form whole **organs**. In the heart organ, for example, muscle tissues, nerve tissues, connective tissues, and other types all work together to pump blood.

MINI GLOSSARY

②

body systems: groups of related organs that work together to perform major body functions.

homeostasis (HOH-me-oh-STAY-sis): the maintenance of a stable body environment, achieved as body systems adapt to changing conditions.

cells: the smallest units in which independent life can exist. All living things are single cells or organisms made of cells.

genes (JEENZ): the units of a cell's inheritance, which direct the making of equipment to do the cell's work.

chromosomes: slender bodies inside the cell's nucleus, which carry the genes.

nucleus: inside a cell, the structure that contains the genes.

tissues: systems of cells working together to perform special tasks.

organs: whole units, made of tissues, that perform specific jobs.

Teacher Support Notes

① **Nucleus:** For enrichment, tell students:
a. The nucleus is separated from the rest of the cell by a structure called the *nuclear envelope*.
b. Most cells contain a single nucleus, but some contain two or more nuclei, and mature red blood cells contain no nucleus.
c. DNA is the genetic material of the cell. It is present in the nucleus in the form of chromatin.
② **Cells are Specialized:** For enrichment, tell students about the specialization of cells. For example, muscle cells have a well-developed property of *contractility*, which is the ability to move or contract. Nerve cells are specialized for *conductivity*, which means they have the ability to transmit impulses. Other cells have highly developed properties of *metabolism*, which means they have the ability to process foods, obtain energy, and synthesize products. Still others have the property of *irritability*, which means that they respond to stimuli.

135

Taking Risks. Ask students to defend the statement, "We cannot live life without taking some risks." Then ask, "What are some of the risks we take each day and what body systems are affected?" **(15 min., Critical Thinking)**

Activity 1.7
Body Systems and the Environment. Divide the class into groups. Let each group choose a body system and list the ways your community tries to improve the environment to protect that system. How is that system being harmed? **(Cooperative Learning, Critical Thinking)**

Activity 1.8

Body Systems and Lifestyle. Discuss the following questions with students: How does today's typical lifestyle differ from your grandparents'? How does each difference affect your various body systems? **(20 min.; Extend, Enrich)**

Activity 1.9
Body Systems and the Economy. Have students discuss how the economy affects the health of the various body

Teacher Support Notes

① **Organ Systems:** Some anatomy and physiology texts refer to the systems as *organ systems*. This term may help students see that the different systems in the body consist of different sets of organs working together to perform functions in the body.

② **Circulatory System:** Another name for the circulatory system is the *cardiovascular system*. This is a term that students will learn in Chapter 18.

Section I Review

Answers

1. Answers will vary.
2. When the body is flooded with too much water the kidneys detect the water, draw it out, and release it as urine. When water becomes scarce, the kidneys step in to excrete less water in the urine.
3. by taking up the substances it needs, such as oxygen, from the surrounding fluid and releasing the wastes it produces into that fluid
4. muscle tissues, nerve tissues, connective tissues and others
5. Answers will vary. Refer to the list on this page.
6. Answers will vary.

Body Systems

Some jobs around the body require that several related organs cooperate to perform them. The organs that join together to work on a function are parts of a body system. For example, the heart and blood vessels work together to deliver blood to the body tissues as parts of the circulatory system (also called the cardiovascular system). ①

Figure 6–2 presents simple diagrams of all the body systems. Showing them together this way is intended to convey the meaning that no one system is completely independent of any of the others. All are responsible for functions that maintain homeostasis. Thus they work together to maintain the body's health:

- The *skeletal system* works with the muscular system to produce movement. Its bones release nutrients into the blood when they are needed by other body systems (Fig. 6–3).
- The *muscular system* responds to messages from the nervous system to move body parts. It works with the skeletal system to achieve movement (Fig. 6–4).
- The *nervous system* communicates with all other body systems. It directs activities of all the systems and receives information about the conditions in all other systems (Fig. 6–5).
- The *digestive system* breaks food down into nutrients. It delivers the nutrients to the circulatory system (Fig. 6–6).
- The *circulatory system* pumps blood and carries oxygen and nutrients to all other systems. It cleanses all systems of their wastes. It carries messages of the hormonal system. Its cells come from the bone marrow of the skeletal system (Fig. 6–7). ②
- The *urinary system* works with the circulatory system to maintain fluid and chemical balance in the body. It filters waste products out of the blood into the urine for removal (Fig. 6–8).
- The *respiratory system* delivers oxygen to,

and removes wastes from, the circulatory system. It responds to the nervous and muscular systems to perform its tasks (Fig. 6–9).
- The *immune system* protects all other body systems from infection. Its cells travel through the circulatory system and through all body tissues (Fig. 6–10).
- The *hormonal system* communicates with many body systems to direct their activities. It monitors the blood for indicators of body conditions. It receives information and directions from the nervous system (Fig. 6–11).
- The *reproductive system* works with the nervous and hormonal systems to establish the gender of each human being. It responds to nerves, hormones, and muscles in creating new human beings (Fig. 6–12 and 6–13).

SECTION I   REVIEW

Answer the following questions on a sheet of paper.

Learning The Vocabulary
The vocabulary terms in this section are *body systems, homeostasis, cells, genes, nucleus, chromosomes, tissues,* and *organs.*
1. Use each of the vocabulary terms listed above correctly in a sentence.

Learning the Facts
2. How do the kidneys manage the water balance in the body?
3. How do the cells in the body stay alive?
4. Which tissues in the circulatory system work together to pump blood?
5. List three body systems and describe what they do.

Making Life Choices
6. The body systems can be affected by our behavior. Do you think that some healthy behaviors may benefit many of your body systems? List healthy behaviors that probably offer such benefits. Also list some unhealthy behaviors that you think may harm many systems.

systems. List the systems affected and how they are affected. **(20 min., Critical Thinking)**

EVALUATE
SECTION I

Activity 1.10
   Dependent Body Systems. Have students choose any body organ and list the many systems that require the func-

tion of that organ, or have them choose a system and list the ways in which that system is affected by or affects other systems. For both options, student points are determined by the number of relationships they can list. **(Reteach, Reinforce)**

CLOSE
SECTION I

Activity 1.11

Class Discussion. Ask students to:
1. Tell what makes up a body system.
2. Discuss what makes each cell different and what cells need to function properly.
3. Give an example of a homeostatic process that occurs in the body.
(Reteach, Reinforce)

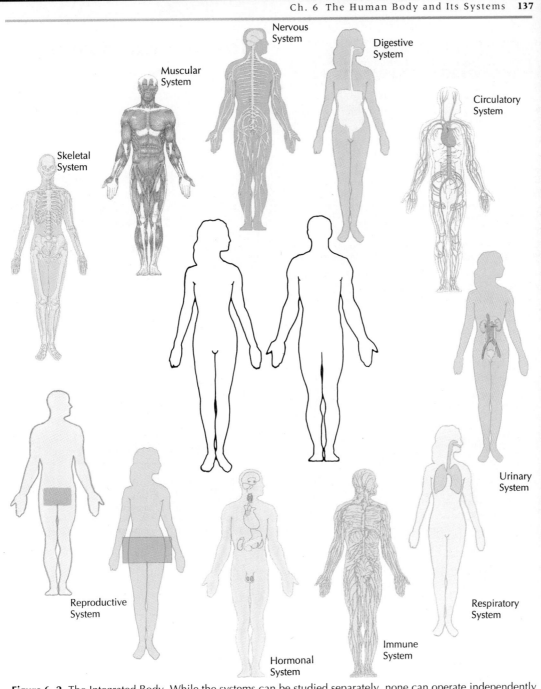

Nervous System

Digestive System

Muscular System

Circulatory System

Skeletal System

Urinary System

Reproductive System

Respiratory System

Hormonal System

Immune System

Figure 6–2 The Integrated Body. While the systems can be studied separately, none can operate independently of the others. ①

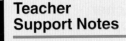

Teacher Support Notes

① **Integrated Body:** Too often students study the body systems separately and never realize how dependent each is on the others. The purpose of this illustration (and one of the purposes of this chapter) is to give you an opportunity to make the point that while students will be studying individual systems in various chapters throughout this text, all the systems work together to maintain the body's desired internal conditions. At this time, you might also want to point out that since students have already studied the body systems in health and science courses prior to taking this course, the information in this chapter is presented in a question–answer format that should help make studying the systems more interesting and relevant than is usually the case.

In this section students will learn that:
1. Bones are living structures four times stronger than concrete.
2. Bones are equipped with both bone building cells and bone dismantling cells.
3. Bones give the body shape, protect vital organs, and help move the body.

Activity 2.1

Chicken Bones. Bring in a couple of chicken or turkey bones and pass them around the room. Have students write down any noticeable characteristics about them. Discuss the properties of bones.

TEACH
SECTION II
(Guided and Independent Practice)

Activity 2.2

Identifying Bones. Using a replica or chart of the skeletal system, ask students to identify specific bones: the largest bone, smallest bone, long bones, flat bones, etc. **(15 min.; Extend, Enrich)**

Teacher Support Notes

① **Fractures:** Ask students if they have had any broken bones. If so, which ones? Make a list of all the bones shown in the figure that the students have broken. Do they know what kinds of fractures they had? Here are some of the more common types of fractures:

a. simple fracture

b. compound fracture (The broken ends of the bone protrude through the skin.)

c. comminuted fracture (The bone is splintered into many fragments at the site of the break rather than being broken in a single plane.)

d. depressed fracture (The broken region is pushed inward.)

e. impacted fracture (The broken ends of the bone are driven into each other.)

f. spiral fracture (The bone is fractured by excessive twisting forces.)

g. greenstick fracture (Only one side of the bone breaks.)

You may also want to introduce the term *hematoma*. A hematoma is a blood clot that forms around the side of the fracture. It is the body's way of beginning the healing process of reconnecting the broken ends of the bone.

SECTION II

The Skeletal System

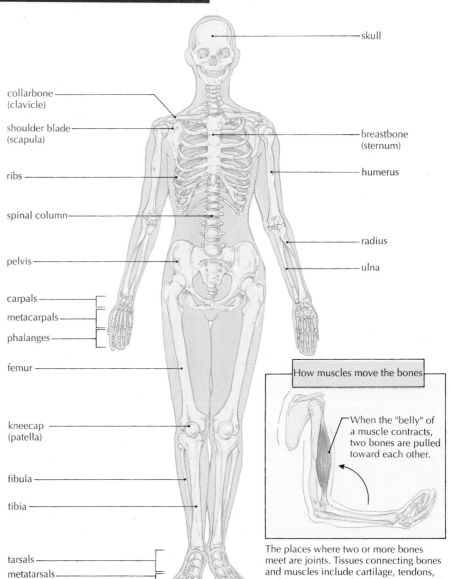

Labels: skull, collarbone (clavicle), shoulder blade (scapula), breastbone (sternum), humerus, ribs, spinal column, radius, ulna, pelvis, carpals, metacarpals, phalanges, femur, kneecap (patella), fibula, tibia, tarsals, metatarsals, phalanges

How muscles move the bones

When the "belly" of a muscle contracts, two bones are pulled toward each other.

The places where two or more bones meet are joints. Tissues connecting bones and muscles include cartilage, tendons, and ligaments. See the glossary at the end of the book.

Figure 6–3 The Skeletal System   ①

EVALUATE
SECTION II

Activity 2.3
Pop Quiz.
1. What are five functions of bones? (They determine the body's shape, protect organs, allow movement, store minerals and vitamins, and manufacture blood cells.)

2. Osteoporosis is a condition caused by bone building cells being [reduced, increased] and bone dismantling cells being [reduced, increased]. (reduced, increased)

3. Name the most important mineral to bone growth. (calcium)

CLOSE
SECTION II

Activity 2.4
Class Discussion. Ask students to:
1. Give an example of the bones that protect, give shape, allow movement, store vitamins, and produce blood cells.
2. Describe the changes that occur in the bones throughout life.

Without a skeleton, people would be made entirely of soft tissues. Like slugs, they would have few distinguishing features. They would be easily injured and would find movement difficult, at best. Bones determine the body's shape. Experts can reconstruct the facial likeness of a person who has died by working from the skull and jawbone alone. Bones also protect soft vital organs, such as the brain and kidneys. They allow movement by acting as levers and anchors to which muscles attach. In addition, bones are warehouses that store many minerals and vitamins. Perhaps the most amazing feat performed by the bones is the manufacturing of all the body's blood cells—millions each day—without which life would come to an immediate halt.

Many people think of their bones as nonliving structures, sort of like the concrete girders that hold up a bridge. The true picture is far more spectacular. Bone tissue is more like solid aluminum or steel; it is four times stronger than reinforced concrete. Bones possess this remarkable strength thanks to a microscopic crystal structure similar to that of diamonds. And unlike concrete, bones are peppered with living bone cells that continuously maintain their solid parts, as well as their honeycombs of chambers and passageways. A rich network of blood vessels and nerves runs all through the bones, bringing nutrients and oxygen to bone cells and picking up stored nutrients to carry to body tissues.

How do bones grow?
Bones are equipped with both bone-dismantling cells and bone-building cells. Babies' bones are made mostly of connective tissue and are soft at first. Gradually, the bone-building cells add crystals of calcium and other minerals, making the bones more and more rigid. As the bones grow longer, they must also be reshaped. Bone-dismantling cells take apart the old structures while bone-building cells put the new ones together.

Once built, do bones ever change?
Throughout life, bone-dismantling cells are active. Whenever the blood needs more of the minerals stored in the bones, the bones give up those minerals. This reduces bone density.

Many older people suffer from a condition of weak bones—osteoporosis—because their bone-dismantling cells remain active while the bone-building cells gradually slow down. If older people also fail to eat diets that provide enough calcium, or if they fail to exercise (along with other factors), their bones' calcium dwindles little by little, day after day over a lifetime.

It is now believed that the teen years are a once-in-a-lifetime opportunity for laying down bone material. Therefore, getting enough calcium in the diet is especially important for you right now. Exercise is also a key.

How do the bones help the muscles to move the body?
Bones are connected to each other at flexible joints, as shown in Figure 6–3. A muscle connected to two bones across a joint can pull the two bones closer together. For example, the largest muscle of your arm (the biceps) is attached to the bone of your upper arm and to a bone of your forearm. The elbow joint separates the two bones. When you want to reach up to touch your shoulder, the muscle contracts. The whole structure works together like a pulley and lever.

Why does it hurt so much to hit your "funny bone"?
"Funny bone" is a nickname for the humerus—pronounced like the word *humorous*—but it hardly seems funny when you feel the intense pain and tingle caused by hitting your elbow against a corner. Actually, the sensation is not caused by the bone itself but by a nerve that nestles in a bony cradle of the humerus bone. When struck, the nerve compresses against the bony structures, sending a bolt of paralyzing pain and sensation from the fingernails through the neck and back—hardly a laughing matter.

Is it harmful to "crack" your knuckles?
The popping noise made when the joints of the fingers (and sometimes other joints) are bent slightly beyond their normal range is probably caused by the release of nitrogen gas that collects in microscopic bubbles inside the joint. The gap between the cartilage pads of each bone end is filled with a thick fluid that lubricates the joint. Physicians disagree whether cracking your knuckles can make them become larger than normal. Knuckle cracking does not seem to be related to arthritis, but it may, if practiced to extreme, cause slight impairment of hand function.

Teacher Support Notes

① **Slugs:** A slug is a slow-moving, slimy animal similar to a snail, usually without a shell.

② **Overhead—Spinal Column:** *The Spinal Column* overhead may help you reinforce the concept of bones protecting soft tissues.

③ **Living Structure:** Emphasize that the bones in the skeletal system are alive. Bones are not lifeless objects, as students might think of them. The skeletal system grows, changes, and repairs itself. Ask students if they think of plants, flowers, and trees as being living things. Point out that the skeletal system is equally alive, constantly growing and changing.

In this section students will learn that:
1. There are three main types of muscles.
2. The body relies on both fast twitch and slow twitch muscles to do most work.
3. Muscle tissues grow with work and shrink without work.

Activity 3.1
Push-Ups. Have students, at their desks, do a back push-up. To do this they should hold onto the edge of their chairs with legs out straight and lower themselves down as far as they can and back to place. (Refer students to Figure 10–8 on page 254.) Have them list the muscles they worked. **(5 min., Critical Thinking)**

Activity 3.2
Examining Muscles. Bring in several different cuts of meat—thigh, drumstick, heart; chicken parts work well. Have students wearing gloves look for how the part is attached to the bone. Examine the fat content around the muscle and identify

---

✍ Fast Facts

The human face has more than 30 muscles in it, and it takes 17 of those muscles to smile. No other animals have this many.

Teacher Support Notes

① **Muscle Names:** Point out to students that some muscles are separated into two, three, or four divisions and this is indicated in their names. For example, the *biceps* have two divisions, the *triceps* have three and the *quadriceps* have four. Other names refer to the size of the muscle. For example, the gluteus *maximus* and gluteus *minimus* muscles of the buttocks are large and small, respectively. Still other muscles include references to their shapes. For example, the *trapezius* muscles are shaped like trapezoids and the *rhomboideus* muscles resemble rhomboids. You may want to have students refer to their algebra or geometry books to recall these shapes.

140 UNIT 3 Your Physical Health

The Muscular System

- neck
- upper back and neck (trapezius)
- shoulder (deltoid)
- chest (pectoralis)
- biceps
- triceps
- back (latissimus dorsi)
- side (oblique)
- abdominals
- buttocks (gluteus)
- inner thigh
- hamstrings
- quadriceps
- calf (gastrocnemius)
- (This tendon, the Achilles tendon, connects the calf muscle to the heel.)

Figure 6–4 The Muscular System ①

Movement of the body is possible thanks in part to the unique structure of muscle tissue. Layers upon layers of muscle tissue form strong sets of paired muscles that pull the bones back and forth in ways that make it possible to dance, ride a bike, and use sign language. Many muscles inside the body are not shown here. Some inner muscles run the length of the digestive organs to move food through the digestive tract. Others surround and grasp the chambers of the heart and squeeze blood from them with each heartbeat.

Are all the muscles the same?

No, they vary. The ones that move your skeleton are under your control. They are called voluntary muscles. The ones that control your internal organs move automatically; they are called involuntary muscles. The voluntary ones appear striped under the microscope, and they are very strong. The involuntary ones appear smooth, and they are less strong.

One set of muscles appears mixed: the muscles of the heart. They are strong, like skeletal muscles, but under involuntary control.

I've heard that some people are born with the right muscles for running or swimming. Is that true?

In a sense, it is. Some of the voluntary muscles are suited for fast action, like the jump of the basketball player. Some are suited for slow action, like the strokes of a long-distance swimmer. Everybody has some of both, but some people inherit more fast-action muscles, and some inherit more of the slow, sustained type.

How do muscles contract?

Muscle cells respond to signals from nerve cells. Nerves release powerful chemicals that create electrical impulses in the muscle cell. The electrical impulses travel along the cell's membrane triggering the long, thin muscle cells to shorten and bunch up. When enough cells get the signal, the whole muscle contracts.

Why is it that the muscles of runners are long and slender, while the muscles of weight lifters are rounded and bulky?

Part of the answer lies in a person's genetic heritage. Some people are just born with bulky or slender muscles. Another part is in the work that each type of athlete does. Each type of work requires different characteristics in the muscle tissues. The body is precise in developing just the equipment it needs for a particular task. For the weight lifter, muscles must be extra strong. Thus each muscle cell builds up its membrane and contracting fibrils to be thick and bulky, providing strength. For the runner, strength is not so urgent as is the ability to contract repeatedly for prolonged times. Therefore, the body does not build bulky muscles in the runner, but packs the cells with the internal structures that sustain effort over a long time.

What does it mean to be "muscle bound"?

A person who trains incorrectly may lose the ability to use certain muscles normally. Muscles come in paired sets. The action of each muscle set opposes another. When one muscle set of the pair becomes greatly more developed than its mate, movement becomes difficult. A bodybuilder who becomes overenthusiastic in developing biceps, for example, may neglect the opposing muscle, the triceps. As a result, the arms begin to hang abnormally when relaxed. Some movements, such as quickly reaching down to catch something, can become almost impossible.

Is it true that to strengthen muscles, you must work them until they are sore?

Years ago the rule for gaining muscle was "no pain, no gain." People thought that injury was the trigger causing muscles to grow. This has been disproved. Scientists now know that muscle contractions themselves send messages to the genetic material of the muscles' cells. The genetic material receives messages about the work: how long it lasts and how intense it is. Based on this information, the cells build the equipment they need to perform the type of work that they are being called upon to do. Even without injury, muscles grow in size and gain in strength after working.

Which body muscle is the strongest?

Strength in a muscle is directly related to its overall size, so it follows that the largest muscle is also the strongest. In the human body, the strongest muscle is the one that pushes the body from a squatting to a standing position and propels a person upward from one stair to the next—did you guess? It's the gluteus maximus, the major muscle of the buttocks (seat).

In this section students will learn that:
1. The central nervous system is composed of the brain and the spinal cord.
2. The brain's many functions are divided among its many physical parts.

Activity 4.1

Eye–Hand vs. Ear–Hand Coordination. Do some reaction tests for eye–hand coordination. Hold the zero edge of a ruler between a student's thumb and fingers. Drop the ruler and record how far the ruler fell before it was caught by the student. (The point at which the student grabs the ruler is the distance.) Now have the subject close his/her eyes and repeat the action when you say, "Now." Discuss which was faster—eye–hand or ear–hand

coordination. **(5 min. for each student)**

TEACH
SECTION IV
(Guided and Independent Practice)

Activity 4.2
Midbrain Stimulation. Create some sounds that are pleasing to the midbrain. (opening a pop can, music) Show some pictures that are pleasing to the midbrain. (beautiful scenery, etc.) Create some

---

66 Thoughts on Health 99

The brain has muscles for thinking as the legs have muscles for walking.

– *Julien Offray de La Mettrie*

Teacher Support Notes

① **Organs:** Students learned what an organ is earlier in the chapter. Check their retention by asking them to define organ. (whole unit made of tissues that perform specific jobs) Ask students if they knew that the brain is an organ. What other organs can they name? (kidney, liver, pancreas, heart, lung, etc.)
② **Overhead—The Organization of the Nervous System:** You may want to use this overhead to help students better understand the system.
③ **Hemispheres:** Some students may have trouble with this word in this context. Point out that a hemisphere is half of a globe, ball, or sphere. Just as the earth can be divided into the northern and the southern hemispheres, the brain is divided into two halves.

SECTION IV

The Nervous System

Top view of the brain

Each half is a hemisphere (cerebrum)

The central nervous system (CNS) consists of the brain and spinal cord.

The peripheral nervous system (PNS) consists of the nerves.

the brain

spinal cord

nerves

Side view of the brain showing where various functions are located

motor cortex (muscle movement)

visual center (visual messages received)

eye field (eyes)

prefrontal cortex (intellect)

hearing center

brain stem (breathing, heart rate, sleep)

spinal cord (receives messages from the body)

cerebellum (coordinates muscle movement)

Cutaway side view of the brain showing the center and one hemisphere

cerebral cortex (outermost layer of the brain)

midbrain (sorts and relays messages to the cerebral cortex and controls basic needs like hunger, thirst, and sex drive)

cerebellum

brain stem (includes the midbrain) (serves as a bridge connecting the spinal cord and higher areas.)

The brain stem controls many basic functions such as breathing, sleeping, and heart rate.

A person whose cortex is injured by an accident or disabled by a disease such as Alzheimer's may live a long time with an intact brain stem.

Figure 6–5 The Nervous System ① ② ③

smells that are pleasing to the midbrain. (perfume, foods, etc.) After each type of stimulation (auditory, visual, olfactory), allow students to share how the stimulation affected them. **(15 min.; Extend, Enrich)**

EVALUATE

Activity 4.3

Pop Quiz. Have students match the terms to the statements that describe them.
1. Master organ of the body (c)
2. Communication line in body (e)
3. Controls thought processes (a)
4. Maintains balance and coordination (d)
5. One of many toxins to the brain (b)
   a. cerebrum; **b.** alcohol; **c.** brain;
   d. cerebellum; **e.** spinal cord

CLOSE
SECTION IV

Activity 4.4
Class Discussion. Ask students to:
1. Name the two major parts of the central nervous system.
2. Explain why our brain is the master organ of our body. **(Reteach, Reinforce)**

The brain, master organ of the body and the seat of the thinking mind, is a 3-pound mass of specialized nerve tissue. With its wrinkled, walnutty appearance, it lies motionless, armored within the skull, just a grey blob with no observable activity. One would never suspect the massive power of the brain which lies not in physical movement but in its chemistry. Without so much as a quiver, it controls almost every physical body function, every thought, and every emotion.

To control things, the brain must obtain information about events and conditions around the body. It must also deliver instructions to tissues about what to do. The spinal cord consists of nerves that connect the brain to all the body parts: it lies safe within the bony spinal vertebrae and provides the body's main communication line. Nerves branch from the trunk of the spinal cord to carry messages back and forth between the tissues and the brain. The brain and spinal cord make up the central nervous system.

Do the different brain parts do different things?

In order to perform the fantastic number of tasks required of it, the brain must be organized. Indeed, its functions are divided among its physical parts. In the outer layer (cortex) of the brain's two large hemispheres, conscious thought takes place. The small bulb lying at the base of the hemispheres, the cerebellum, maintains balance and coordinates muscular activities. The brain stem leading to the spinal cord controls breathing and other basic functions.

Within these large brain areas are smaller divisions, each with specific duties. The prefrontal cortex concerns itself with high intellectual tasks, such as reading a health textbook. When you chat with friends later, an area about the size of a quarter on the left side of your brain will control the muscles of your mouth and throat that produce speech. When you next hear your favorite song on the radio, the hearing center will become active. If the music sends a thrill through you, it has triggered tissues in your midbrain. These tissues create pleasure when stimulated—for example, by viewing a beautiful sight (received by the eye field); when savoring the flavor of a favorite food or the aroma of flowers (the smell center); and more

perilously, from the direct stimulation produced by mind-altering drugs.

Many more functions are known. Some fascinating books have been written about them.

How does the brain protect its chemistry?

The brain maintains a barrier that excludes certain chemicals carried by the blood. The blood-brain barrier is a control system by which the brain's blood vessels control the environment inside the brain. It admits those chemicals the brain needs, but excludes those that could interrupt the brain's work. In this way, the brain's internal chemistry remains balanced, despite changes in the rest of the body's chemistry. The system fails to exclude some harmful chemicals, though, and these enter and affect the brain. Alcohol is a toxin against which the blood-brain barrier provides no defense. Other mind-altering drugs also pass freely into brain tissues.

What if nerve or brain tissues are injured? Do they heal?

Nerve cells, for the most part, cannot reproduce themselves to fully repair injury, as some other tissues do. However, they may be able to grow new parts in a limited way to reconnect with other nerves after being severed. Traditionally, it has been taught that brain cells are not able to reproduce at all. However, recent experiments have shown that at least some types of brain cells can be coaxed to reproduce in the laboratory. Still, many people suffer lifelong damage from injuries to the brain and nerves because regrowth of the tissue is limited.

How does tapping your knee make your whole leg jerk?

The jerk of the leg is an example of a reflex, a sort of intentional short circuit in the nervous system. The nerves that control reflexes form an arc—from tissue to spinal cord back to tissue—that can produce the needed response in a split second. Tapping the knee triggers a reflex that contracts the muscle at the front of the thigh. The thigh muscle jerks the leg.

Reflexes control situations that demand immediate action. They do not wait for judgments by the brain. Reflexes can prevent major damage. For example, when you touch something hot, your hand jerks away uncontrollably before you even feel your finger being burned.

Teacher Support Notes

① **Dysfunctions of the Central Nervous System:** For enrichment, you could give students an example of the types of problems that can occur with the central nervous system, such as *lesions* and *paralysis*. Damage to tissues or organs that results in impairment or loss of function is referred to as a *lesion*. Lesions of the spinal cord generally involve the motor and sensory fiber tracts of which the cord is composed. Lesions of the motor spinal tracts cause paralysis of the structures supplied by the neurons involved.

✎ Fast Facts

Each second, over 100,000 chemical reactions take place in the brain. These require so much energy that intense concentration can cause the brain to burn as many calories as the muscles use during exercise.

FOCUS
SECTION V

In this section students will learn that the digestive system is:
1. Responsible for breaking down food into a form usable by cells.
2. Composed of acids and digestive juices that act on ingested substances.

Activity 5.1
Digestive Actions. Give each student a soda cracker. Have students eat their crackers and describe the action of their digestive systems. (teeth, tongue, saliva, esophagus, etc.) Ask them to name all the digestive organs they can think of.

TEACH
SECTION V
(Guided and Independent Practice)

Activity 5.2
Researching Digestive Systems. Have students research and compare the digestive systems of other animals with humans'. Students should answer these questions: What animals' digestive systems have special characteristics? What are their advantages? (**Extend, Enrich, Interdisciplinary**)

Activity 5.3

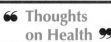

66 Thoughts on Health 99

To eat is human, to digest divine.
— *Mark Twain*

Teacher Support Notes

① **Activities of the Digestive System:** As students look at the illustrations of the digestive system, you may want to give them the basic processes that occur during digestion. There are six basic steps:
1. Ingestion of food into the mouth;
2. movement of food along the digestive tract;
3. mechanical preparation of food for digestion;
4. chemical digestion of food;
5. absorption of digestive food into the blood and lymph for transport throughout the body;
6. elimination of indigestible substances and waste products from the body by defecation.

✎ Fast Facts

Lying down can aggravate heartburn. You can help prevent heartburn by waiting three hours after a meal before lying down or going to bed. This is because gravity helps keep acids down.

SECTION V

The Digestive System

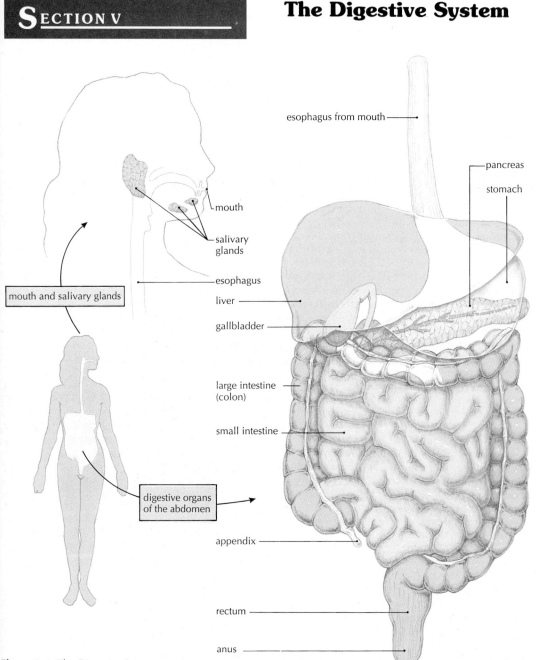

Figure 6–6 The Digestive System ①

"Digesting" Foods. Put a few drops of hydrochloric acid on carbohydrates, proteins, and fats. (cracker, lean meat, and fat) Have students observe how long each takes to be acted upon. Discuss what this tells us about foods we ingest. **(15 min., Critical Thinking)**

EVALUATE
SECTION V

Activity 5.4
Pop Quiz.
1. Everything that enters through the mouth is acted on by enzymes and digested into the intestinal wall. (F)
2. The mucous membrane of the stomach protects the stomach. (T)
3. Alcohol dissolves the mucous membrane of the stomach. (T)
4. Stomach acid is harmful and hinders digestion. (F)

5. Heartburn can be similar to heart attack symptoms. (T)

CLOSE
SECTION V

Activity 5.5
Class Discussion. Ask students to:
1. Identify the organs involved in digestion.
2. Name some ways the digestive system protects itself from harmful substances.

The human body is shaped something like a doughnut, with the digestive tract running through the center to form the hole. If you were to accidentally swallow a small bead, the bead would pass right through your digestive tract and out of your body, never entering the tissues at all. Food in the digestive tract meets a different fate. Glands squirt digestive juices that contain powerful chemicals, called enzymes, into the tract to break the food molecules down into smaller pieces that can be absorbed into the tract's tissues. Only after a substance passes through the intestinal wall tissues is it truly inside the body.

Why doesn't the stomach digest itself?

The powerful acids and juices of the stomach, and the whole digestive tract, would indeed digest the tract if it weren't for a protective layer of mucus that coats the tract's lining. The mucus coating forms a barrier between the system and its contents. If the layer of mucus is too thin to protect the tissue, ulcers can result. Alcohol also dissolves the layer. Ulcers are common in those with addictions to alcohol. Some infections can also cause ulcers.

What causes indigestion, and what is the best cure?

Indigestion is an aching pain in the digestive tract caused from the system's failing to cope with the stomach's contents in a normal way. It can occur when spice in food irritates the tract lining; when too much fat overwhelms the system's ability to digest it; or when too much air, food, or liquid is swallowed and expands the stomach and intestines, causing pain and pressure.

The best cure for indigestion is prevention. Avoid foods that have caused problems for you in the past. Eat mostly low-fat foods with only small portions of high-fat foods. Eat slowly; chew thoroughly; and eat only until you feel full. If you develop indigestion, you might obtain relief from over-the-counter remedies, but it's best to ask a health care provider before turning to use of medicines.

What is heartburn?

At the base of the esophagus, where it meets the stomach, circular muscles squeeze the opening shut to prevent the stomach contents from backing up in the esophagus. Sometimes

the mixture of acid and food in the stomach splashes up through this opening into the esophagus. When this happens, the strong acid burns and irritates the sensitive esophagus lining—heartburn.

Heartburn has nothing to do with the heart. However, the esophagus lies near the heart, so people have been led to think that the pain they feel from heartburn is coming from the heart. The opposite can also happen. Some people have needlessly died from heart attacks because they attributed their chest pains to "indigestion" and failed to get help.

What does the appendix do, and why must some people have theirs removed?

The appendix is the little wormlike sac that hangs from the lower right side of the large intestine. It seems to have no purpose in digestion. It is notable only if undigested food particles and bacteria lodge in it and an infection gets started. Appendicitis is painful. It is also dangerous, because the sac can burst open. If this happens, digestive products and infected material flow into the normally sterile body cavity. This life-threatening condition can be prevented by surgically removing an inflamed appendix before it bursts. The operation carries little risk. If you have a pain in your lower right abdomen that doesn't go away, call a doctor.

Why does my stomach sometimes grumble?

As fluid and gas squeeze past the convoluted folds and turns of the digestive organ tissues, the bubbles produce a gurgling, grumbling sound. The sound may be inconvenient at times, but it is normal, especially when you are hungry.

Why do people "pass gas," and what causes its odor?

Technically, the gas is *flatus* (FLAY-tus). Everyone produces some gas all the time. Not much can be done to avoid it or to help control its release from the intestine. Gases are a normal waste product of digestion. Bacteria of the large intestine consume and thrive on fibers and food particles left in the tract after digestion and absorption. Most odors are from molecules that form when bacteria act on proteins. The nature of the odor depends on the food eaten, and on the type of bacteria in the system.

① The mixture...

② ...

Teacher Support Notes

① **Overhead—Digestive Tract:** You may want to tell students that the digestive tract consists of a tube called the *gastrointestinal tract* or *alimentary canal.* The tube extends from the mouth to the anus. The overhead, *The Digestive System,* will help you illustrate this for your class.

② **Inside vs. Outside the Body:** Most students will think that once something goes in the mouth, it is inside the body. In scientific terms, however, for something to enter the body, it must cross the epithelium that lines the wall of the digestive tract. You could use the earlier comparison with the doughnut to emphasize this point with students. If you put the tube through the hole in the doughnut and drop something through the tube, that object would not "enter" the doughnut. To enter the doughnut, the object would need to be broken down and then would need to seep through the lining of the tube into the doughnut.

In this section students will learn that the:
1. Heart pumps continually to deliver nutrients to the cells and to pick up cellular wastes.
2. Blood can repair damage to the vessel system.

Activity 6.1
"Hearty" Phrases. Have the students think up phrases using the word "heart." (*learn by heart, eat your heart out, get to the heart of the matter, hard hearted*) Do these terms relate to the heart? If so, how?

TEACH
SECTION VI
(Guided and Independent Practice)

Activity 6.2
Animal Heart. Obtain an animal's heart from a local butcher. Describe and point out these characteristics: type of muscle, amount of fat, arteries surrounding it, valves and chambers visible. **(15 min.; Extend, Enrich)**

Activity 6.3
Follow that Blood. Using a diagram of the human heart, trace a drop of blood

Teacher Support Notes

① **Blood Composition:** You may want to tell students that the blood consists of both the liquid component called *plasma* and a nonliquid portion whose structures are collectively called *formed elements*. Plasma is approximately 91% water. The portion of plasma that is not water consists of various dissolved materials. Formed elements include the red blood cells, various types of leukocytes (white blood cells), and cell fragments called *platelets*.

✎ Fast Facts

In June of 1992 the U.S. Army began collecting blood and tissue samples from new recruits in a program that will eventually enable pathologists to identify the smallest tissue specimens by cross-matching to genetic samples stored on file. The Pentagon aims to collect specimens from all two million active service members by the year 2000. The Army says the need for such a system was made clear during the Gulf War, during which a number of soldiers killed in action were unable to be identified.

SECTION VI

The Circulatory System

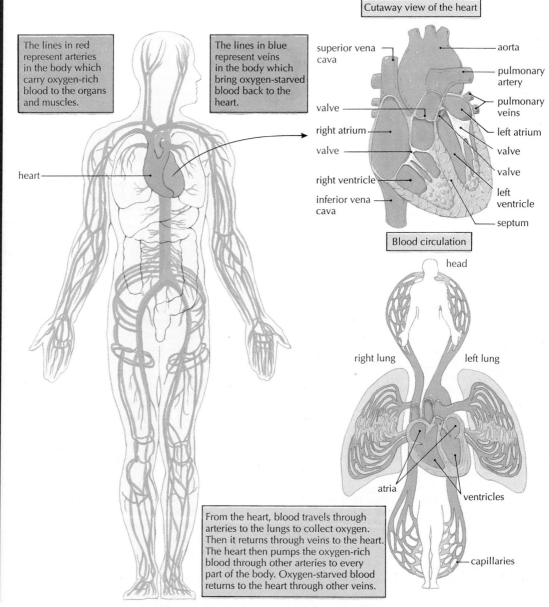

Cutaway view of the heart

The lines in red represent arteries in the body which carry oxygen-rich blood to the organs and muscles.

The lines in blue represent veins in the body which bring oxygen-starved blood back to the heart.

heart

superior vena cava
aorta
pulmonary artery
pulmonary veins
valve
right atrium
left atrium
valve
valve
valve
right ventricle
left ventricle
inferior vena cava
septum

Blood circulation

head

right lung
left lung

atria
ventricles

capillaries

From the heart, blood travels through arteries to the lungs to collect oxygen. Then it returns through veins to the heart. The heart then pumps the oxygen-rich blood through other arteries to every part of the body. Oxygen-starved blood returns to the heart through other veins.

Figure 6–7 The Circulatory System   ①

from the heart, to the lungs, and back to the heart. **(10 min., Extend, Enrich)**

EVALUATE

Activity 6.4
Pop Quiz. Have students use any five of the following terms in a sentence with either *heart* or *circulatory system*: aorta, carbon dioxide, cells, iron, left atrium, oxy-gen, right atrium, transportation system, urinary system. Give extra credit if they can correctly use *inferior vena cava*.

CLOSE
▶ SECTION VI

Activity 6.5
Class Discussion. Ask students to:
1. Describe the function of the circulatory system.
2. Explain how blood helps to eliminate cell waste.
3. List the four blood types.

With its vast network of arteries, veins, and capillaries, the circulatory system provides the transportation system for the body's fluids. Each cell in the body depends on this system's life-sustaining work. Cells dump their wastes into this system. They also pull from its rich abundance all the nutrients and other chemicals they need to live and function.

How does the heart know how fast to beat?

The heart responds to a small area of its upper right chamber (right atrium), its natural pacemaker. This area acts almost as a spark plug does. It sends an electrical impulse through the heart that causes both atria to contract immediately. Within less than a second, the ventricles also contract in response to the signal.

The pacemaker adjusts the heart rate in response to instructions carried by nerves from the brain. Also, when the heart itself detects the need, it can quicken the pace. The heart and blood vessel tissues monitor blood levels of carbon dioxide, the waste product of the tissues. When carbon dioxide reaches a high concentration, this indicates to the heart a need for faster delivery of oxygen from the lungs. The heart also quickens the heartbeat whenever the blood pressure falls, and whenever it receives any of several hormones from body organs.

Does the heart ever rest?

For as long as a person is alive, the heart never takes a break. In a sense, though, the heart rests continuously and efficiently in the moments of muscle relaxation between contractions. During these rest periods, the relaxed heart muscles allow blood to fill the heart's chambers.

When the blood picks up wastes from the cells, how does it get rid of them?

To try to answer this question in a paragraph or two is impossible, for many wastes are deposited in the blood and they are removed by several systems. The urinary system, described next, is wondrously designed to scrub the blood of much of the cells' debris, and it does much more than this, as you will see.

Carbon dioxide waste deposited in the blood trades places with oxygen during gas exchange in the lungs. Other wastes are pulled out of the blood by the liver. The liver processes these wastes and either tosses them out into the digestive tract to leave the body with the feces, or sends them to the kidneys for disposal in urine. Thus the circulatory system, the liver, the digestive system, the lungs, and the urinary system all work together on the task of cleansing the blood.

Blood is red, serum is yellow, and the veins look blue. Why?

Blood outside the body is red because of the enormous number of red blood cells it contains. Take away the red cells, and what's left is not red at all, but a clear, yellowish syrup (serum). The red cells contain hemoglobin, an iron-containing protein that turns red whenever it is in contact with oxygen.

As red cells move through the lungs, they pick up the oxygen of newly inhaled air and attach it to their hemoglobin. The oxygen gives the cells a red color. As they travel through the body, red cells give up their oxygen to the tissues and replace it with carbon dioxide. As they lose oxygen and gain carbon dioxide, the red cells take on a dark purple cast. You can see this blood on its way back to the lungs, because it is traveling through the colorless veins under the skin. If you were to accidentally cut a vein, though, the blood would flow bright red, because oxygen from the air would combine instantly with the hemoglobin.

What makes a wound stop bleeding?

Blood platelets (literally, "little plates") in the blood form a net, which traps still more platelets and other blood cells. This forms a clot, which plugs the wound until it can heal.

What are blood types?

Human blood is classified into four types, depending on which, if any, of two proteins—antigen A and antigen B—are present in the red blood cells. The symbols used to identify the four types of blood—A, B, AB, and O—represent which of the factors are present. Type A contains antigen A, type B contains antigen B, type AB contains both, and type O contains neither.

The categories become important when people need transfusions, because some types of blood are hostile to others. Should blood of the wrong type be given, the native blood would attack the transfused blood as if it were an enemy invader. The blood would clump together within the vessels, with harmful or fatal results.

Teacher Support Notes

① **Overhead— Overview of System:** The overhead *An Overview of the Cardiovascular System* will help you show students how this system is a transportation system.

② **Heartbeat Regulation:** Ask students to reread the paragraph and list the different signals that can alter the heartbeat. (instructions from the brain, carbon dioxide levels in the blood, falling blood pressure, hormones from the body's organs)

✍ Fast Facts

One study done in India suggests that blood type may influence your personality. In a study of 137 male doctors, those with AB+ blood tended to be introverted, while those with A+ or O+ were outgoing and social. A+ subjects were the most impulsive, while B+ doctors were the most emotional.

In this section the student will learn:
1. That the urinary system monitors the composition of the blood and removes wastes.
2. How the urinary systems of men and women differ.

Activity 7.1
Organ Listing. Have students help you list the major organs of the urinary system. **(10 min.; Extend, Enrich)**

TEACH
SECTION VII
(Guided and Independent Practice)

Activity 7.2
Dependent Systems. Ask students to explain how all systems depend on the urinary system.

Activity 7.3
Have students compare how protected the kidneys and bladder are from injury and infection in relation to other organs. Discuss answers to these questions: Can one live without the kidneys? With one kidney? What problems might affect the bladder? **(15 min., Critical Thinking)**

Teacher Support Notes

① **Artificial Kidneys:** For enrichment, you might find students interested in some additional information about the workings of the artificial kidney machine. The artificial kidney employs the principle of *dialysis* (the separation of substances from one another in a solution) to remove waste materials from the blood. In the artificial kidney, the patient's blood is passed through dialysis tubing that allows urea, electrolytes, and other small molecules to move freely across its wall but does not allow the movement of large protein molecules. The dialysis tubing is immersed in a bath that contains various substances. If urea or some other small molecule is present in the blood but not in the bath, it diffuses out of the dialysis tubing and into the bath and thus is removed from the blood. By regulating the composition and concentration of materials within the bath, the types and amounts of materials that leave the blood by net diffusion out of the dialysis tubing can be regulated. In this way, waste products are removed from the blood while needed constituents are retained.

148   UNIT 3 Your Physical Health

SECTION VII

The Urinary System

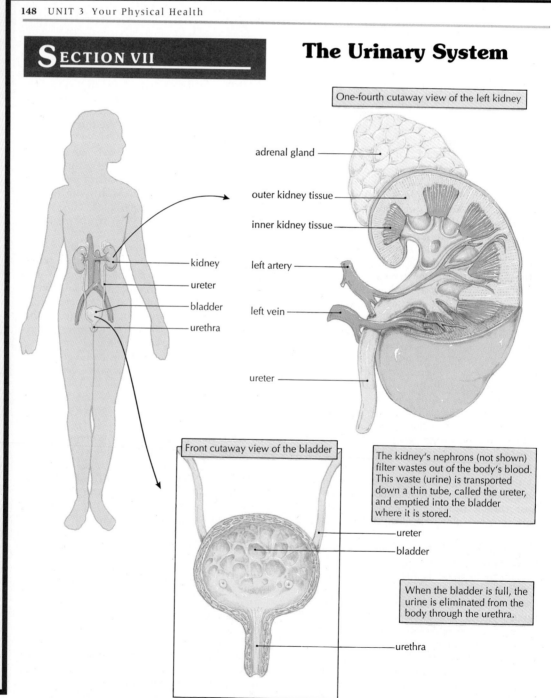

One-fourth cutaway view of the left kidney

adrenal gland

outer kidney tissue

inner kidney tissue

left artery

left vein

ureter

kidney
ureter
bladder
urethra

Front cutaway view of the bladder

The kidney's nephrons (not shown) filter wastes out of the body's blood. This waste (urine) is transported down a thin tube, called the ureter, and emptied into the bladder where it is stored.

ureter
bladder

When the bladder is full, the urine is eliminated from the body through the urethra.

urethra

Figure 6–8 The Urinary System   ①

Activity 7.4
Pop Quiz.
1. All body systems depend on the urinary system. (T)
2. Microscopic units called neurons make up the kidney. (F)
3. It is possible to live with one kidney. (T)

4. You should never drink too much fluid or you will flood the body's cells. (F)
5. Women are more prone to bladder infections than men. (T)

CLOSE
SECTION VII

Activity 7.5
Class Discussion. Ask students to compare the kidneys to a filter or large

net that monitors the composition of blood. **(10 min., Critical Thinking)**

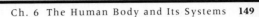

The task of waste removal is the specialty of the urinary system. Although this may seem unglamorous, it is absolutely essential to life. Without the careful monitoring of the blood's composition by the kidneys, toxic wastes would soon build up and interrupt functioning of all the body's tissues.

Among the first signs of kidney failure are confusion, inability to make judgments, and dizziness. Should the situation continue, the person would lose consciousness—pass out. These symptoms demonstrate the connection between the functions of the urinary system and the workings of the brain. The brain—and in fact all the body tissues—depend entirely on the correct composition of the blood, which the urinary system works to maintain.

How do the kidneys know what's inside the blood vessels?

The kidneys are designed perfectly for the job of monitoring the composition of the blood. They are made up of a million microscopic units called nephrons. The nephrons draw fluid from the blood, but they leave the blood cells and large molecules inside the blood vessels. The fluid is then inside the kidneys' units, which detect and measure various substances. These measurements provide the kidneys with information about the condition of the blood.

Once informed of body conditions, the kidneys push some of the fluid—along with some minerals, blood sugar, and other useful substances—back into the blood. Some fluid, along with waste products, stays behind in the kidneys to become urine.

Of all the body's organs, second only to the brain, the kidneys are like a master computer that controls conditions in the body. The numbers of measurements and fine adjustments they make, from moment to moment, are staggering.

How do the kidneys know how much water to put back into the blood, and how much to make into urine?

The water balance of the blood is important. If the kidneys take out too much water, this will dehydrate the body. If the kidneys put too much water back in, the tissues will swell. The kidneys have a partner that helps them to perform this balancing act—the pituitary gland of the brain. This gland also monitors changes in

the blood composition. When the water level begins to drop, the pituitary gland sends a hormone to the kidneys that tells them to conserve water.

The kidneys, on receiving this message, not only use less fluid to make urine but also respond with their own hormone that tells other tissues about the dehydration. One of the tissues that responds to this hormone is the brain, which then lets you know that you're thirsty. You then drink a glass of water to replenish the water in your blood.

Drinking too much fluid causes no problem to the body. The kidneys detect the excess and drain it out as urine. No matter how much water you drink in a day, your body water concentration stays the same, thanks to the skill of your kidneys.

How does the bladder know when to empty?

Urine formed in the kidneys carries the blood's waste products down the tubes, called ureters, that lead to the bladder. The bladder is the holding tank for urine.

The walls of the bladder are stretchy. They allow the bladder to expand as urine collects. When the bladder is full (this takes about 2 cups of urine), nerves in the bladder's walls, known as stretch receptors, inform the brain. The brain then arranges to urinate. On command from the brain, a set of circular muscles at the opening of the urethra relax. Urine then flows through the urethra and out of the body.

Is the urinary system the same in men as in women?

Men and women have similar urinary systems, right up to the urethra. There, however, things change. The male urethra is three times as long as the female urethra. It conducts semen, as well as urine, out of the body. A special valve in the male urethra makes sure that the two functions never happen at the same time.

The female urethra is used for waste disposal only. Because of its short length, it is more prone to allow dangerous infectious bacteria to reach the bladder. Bladder infections are much more common among women than among men. Any infection of the urinary system should be treated immediately, before it has a chance to endanger the health of the kidneys.

①

①

✍ **Fast Facts**

In ancient days, the kidney, not the heart, was thought to be the area of affection.

Teacher Support Notes

① **Symptoms of Kidney Failure:** These symptoms are probably very surprising to students. Ask them what they would have guessed to be symptoms of failure in the urinary system. Ask them what they would have guessed these symptoms were associated with if they had been given the symptoms without being told what they indicated. This should help them realize the importance of the urinary system. Ask students if they know anyone who has had a kidney transplant. What symptoms did they notice in this person prior to the transplant? Was the transplant successful?

✍ **Fast Facts**

Kidney stones can be as large as an inch in diameter.

149

In this section students will learn:
1. The respiratory system is responsible for delivering oxygen to all cells.
2. The functions and potential problems of the sinuses.

Activity 8.1

Respiratory Race. Divide the class into groups. Have groups brainstorm all the organs involved in the respiratory system. The first group finished writes its list on the board. Other groups critique and correct the list on the board. **(10 min.)**

TEACH
SECTION VIII
(Guided and Independent Practice)

Activity 8.2
Exploring Respiration.
1. Have students sit upright and quiet for one minute. Have them count the number of breaths they take in one minute and compare the results with classmates.
2. Have them consciously breathe in and out and explain which muscles seem to be involved in inhalation and exhalation.
3. Discuss the benefits of breathing through the nose.

Teacher Support Notes

① **Respiratory System Problems:** Here's some additional information about some common respiratory problems:
a. *Common Cold*—an inflammation of the mucous membrane of the upper respiratory tract.
b. *Bronchial Asthma*—an allergic response to foreign substances.
c. *Bronchitis*—an acute or chronic inflammation of the bronchial tree caused by bacterial infection or irritants in inhaled air.
d. *Emphysema*—a condition that develops slowly as a secondary response to other respiratory problems. The alveoli become overdistended and eventually break down, reducing the surface area across which gaseous exchange can occur.
e. *Pneumonia*—an inflammation that causes the lung to become solid and airless, which makes it difficult for gaseous exchange to occur. Most cases are caused by viruses.

✏ Fast Facts

One nasal passage is always open wider than the other because every few hours the blood vessels in the nasal passages alternate in size.

SECTION VIII

The Respiratory System

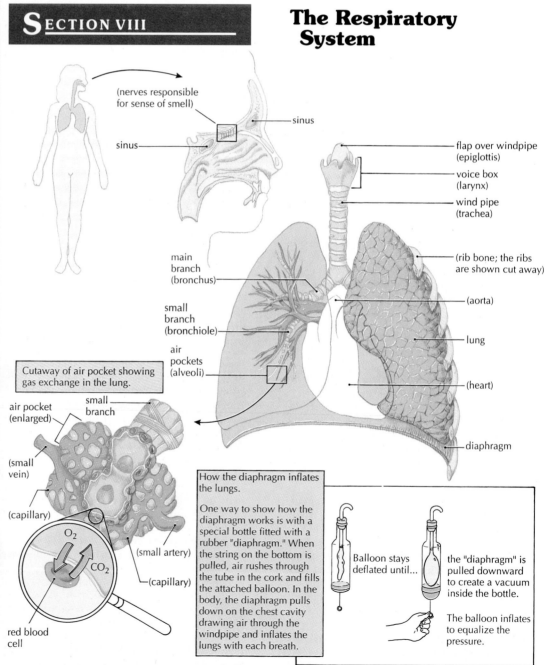

(nerves responsible for sense of smell)

sinus

sinus

flap over windpipe (epiglottis)

voice box (larynx)

wind pipe (trachea)

(rib bone; the ribs are shown cut away)

main branch (bronchus)

(aorta)

small branch (bronchiole)

lung

air pockets (alveoli)

(heart)

diaphragm

Cutaway of air pocket showing gas exchange in the lung.

air pocket (enlarged)

small branch

(small vein)

(capillary)

O_2

CO_2

(small artery)

(capillary)

red blood cell

How the diaphragm inflates the lungs.

One way to show how the diaphragm works is with a special bottle fitted with a rubber "diaphragm." When the string on the bottom is pulled, air rushes through the tube in the cork and fills the attached balloon. In the body, the diaphragm pulls down on the chest cavity drawing air through the windpipe and inflates the lungs with each breath.

Balloon stays deflated until...

the "diaphragm" is pulled downward to create a vacuum inside the bottle.

The balloon inflates to equalize the pressure.

Figure 6–9 The Respiratory System ①

4. Explain what determines the rate of breathing and give some examples of when breathing may be abnormally slow or fast. **(15 min.)**

Activity 8.3
Pop Quiz.
1. Give a short summary on the muscles involved in inhalation and exhalation. (The diaphragm goes down; the chest muscles pull the ribs out to create a vacuum. The diaphragm and chest muscles relax and force air out of the lungs.)
2. Give two important roles of the sinus cavities. (The sinus cavities help lighten the weight of the skull and create the sound of the voice.)

CLOSE
SECTION VIII

Activity 8.4
Class Discussion. Ask students to:
1. Locate and describe the major parts of the respiratory system.
2. State functions of sinuses.

Every day, the lungs breathe in and out the amount of air in an average-sized classroom. With each inhaled breath, the lungs pull from the surrounding atmosphere the oxygen that allows tissues to burn fuels for energy. On exhaling, the lungs return carbon dioxide to the air as the major waste product of the body's fuel use.

To say, as we just did, that the lungs breathe air in and out is not quite accurate. Lungs themselves possess no muscles to move air in and out of their chambers. Instead, the lungs rest like passive balloons within the chest cavity, inflating and deflating thanks to the work of the diaphragm and chest muscles.

When someone takes a breath, the curved diaphragm straightens and pulls downward, as shown in Figure 6–9. Muscles of the chest also pull the ribs outward. The combined effect is to enlarge the chest cavity. As a result, air rushes into the lungs through the only available opening—the windpipe: you inhale. When the diaphragm and chest muscles relax, air flows out of the lungs as the vacuum is released: you exhale. Thanks to this action, life-giving oxygen can be transferred from the surrounding air to the tissues that require it.

What determines how fast I breathe?
The same thing that determines how fast your heart beats—a brain center that measures your need for oxygen. It can tell, from the amount of carbon dioxide in your blood, how fast you need to exchange that gas for oxygen in your lungs. Naturally, it is hard muscular work that creates this need, because muscles burn fuel as they work, and they need oxygen to do it.

Is it true that it is better to breathe through your nose than through your mouth?
The nose is superbly designed for breathing. While the mouth simply pulls air directly from the environment into the lungs, the nose acts as a filter and air conditioner. Nose hairs are the first line of defense against debris entering the lungs. The stiff hairs purify the air of most of the large particles it contains, such as dust or fibers. Any particles that get by this first barrier are likely to be forcefully expelled when they trigger the sneeze reflex. If tiny particles pass by these two defenses, they still must flow over the mucus-coated membranes lining the nasal passageway. Bacteria and other microscopic bits that fall into the mucus produced there are trapped, killed, and swept out into the throat by millions of tiny waving hairs that act as brooms. The mucus and its contents are swallowed, and in the stomach, they are destroyed by acids and digestive enzymes

In addition to filtering the air, the nasal passageways also warm it and add moisture. This protects the lungs from cold or dry air, which could injure the delicate lung tissue. While the mouth is superior for speaking and eating, the nose is indeed the organ of choice for breathing.

What are the sinuses, and why do they cause some people trouble?
Your skull contains eight air spaces—holes in your head, so to speak. The function of the sinuses is to lighten the weight of the skull. They also play a role in creating the sound of the voice as sound waves resonate inside them. The sinuses are located in the facial area—behind the nose, over the eyebrows, and in the cheek area.

The sinuses normally make a thick cleansing liquid known as mucus, which drains into the throat. When infection or allergy causes the membranes to swell, though, the canals become blocked. Painful pressure can build up in the sinuses. This pressure can cause a severe headache. If infection from a cold settles into the sinuses, antibiotics may be needed to help the victim recover.

What is a hiccup?
A hiccup is an involuntary contraction of the diaphragm, caused by irritation. The sound is made when the sudden contraction of the diaphragm sucks air over the vocal cords. The cords then snap shut, cutting off the air flow and the sound.

How can you stop the hiccups?
Most people favor one or another hiccup remedy—drinking water, breathing into a paper bag, being startled. One cure backed by at least some scientific evidence calls for dissolving a teaspoon of sugar on the tongue and letting the sugar soothe the throat. If you cannot take the sugar cure for any reason, be assured that most bouts of hiccups resolve themselves in a few minutes. (Should your case last for a day or more, you may need a medical evaluation.)

① ②

🖉 Fast Facts

An average of seven quarts of air pass through the lungs each minute. There are 300 million air sacs in the lungs to hold all this air. These air sacs have a surface area of 75 square yards, which makes your lungs one of the largest organs in your body.

Teacher Support Notes

① Overhead—Heart and Lungs: The overhead *Delivery of Oxygen by the Heart and Lungs to the Muscles* will help your students better understand how oxygen is delivered to the body simultaneously with the removal of carbon dioxide.

② Do Lungs Breathe? It is a fairly common misconception that the lungs themselves pump air in and out. Ask the students if the lungs push and pull air through the system. If they answer yes, have them reread this paragraph.

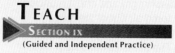

FOCUS
SECTION IX

In this section the student will learn:
1. The functions of the lymphatic system.
2. How the lymphatic system provides immunity.

Activity 9.1
Swollen Glands. Ask students to explain why their glands swell when they are experiencing an illness. **(15 min., Critical Thinking)**

TEACH
SECTION IX
(Guided and Independent Practice)

Activity 9.2
Charting Similarities and Differences. Divide the class into groups. Have each group prepare a chart showing the similarities and differences between the lymphatic system and the circulatory system.

Activity 9.3
Think Yourself Well. Ask students to share experiences they have had to support the theory that one can "think oneself well". **(25 min.; Extend, Enrich)**

Teacher Support Notes

① **Edema:** You may want to provide students with some information about *edema*, which is the accumulation of excess fluid in the tissues, often due to an increased movement of fluid out of blood vessels and into tissues, or to decreased removal of fluid from tissues by the lymphatic system. Edema of the feet and ankles can occur when the person stands upright and perfectly still for a long period of time. Exercise and elevation of an affected limb can help.

② **Exercise and the Immune System:** Many people claim they have fewer infections when they are in good condition than when they are out of shape. There is, however, conflicting scientific evidence. For example, athletes with long, difficult training schedules and intense competition have an increased incidence of respiratory infections. It is possible that athletes who include frequent bouts of exhaustive exercise in their training may have a sustained reduction in mucosal immunity and, therefore, lower resistance to respiratory infection.

---

152   UNIT 3 Your Physical Health

SECTION IX

The Immune System

Organs involved in the immune system

tonsils

thymus gland
(heart)

spleen

(stomach)

bone marrow

The lymph structures of the immune system

lymph duct

lymph nodes

lymph vessels

Lymph and blood capillaries

lymph vessel (returns lymph to the heart through the lymph duct)

(vein)

lymph node
(filters lymph)

lymph capillaries

blood
fluid
lymph

Fluid escapes as blood passes through capillaries. When this fluid builds up enough pressure, it is transferred into the lymph capillaries which transport this fluid, now called lymph, to the lymph nodes for filtration.

Figure 6–10 The Immune System   ① ②

Activity 9.4

Pop Quiz. Write the following terms on the board and tell students to write the correct term as you read the sentences: *lymphatic system, bacteria, disease, immunity, muscles, thymus, vessels, white.*

1. The second circulatory system is the _____ _____. (lymphatic system)
2. Unlike blood, lymph does not need to travel in _____. (vessels)
3. Lymph nodes filter _____ out of the body. (bacteria)
4. The _____ gland is critical to immunity but gets smaller with age. (thymus)
5. _____ cells help fight disease. (White)
6. Lymph travels through the systems by the squeezing action of _____. (muscles)

Activity 9.5

Class Discussion. Ask students to:
1. Describe lymph.
2. Explain the actions of the white cells that attack bacteria and infections.
3. Name factors that negatively affect the immune system.

Each day, the immune system traps, kills, and eliminates many invaders in the body—bacteria, viruses, even cells that could start cancer. Immunity works because its special cells, described in Chapter 16, are busy everywhere in the body. Especially, they congregate in areas where invaders are likely to intrude, such as the throat, digestive tract, and reproductive organs. The lymphatic system is especially active in immunity.

What does the lymphatic system do?

The lymphatic system is similar to the circulatory system, in that it moves fluid around the body. This "second circulatory system" is important in many ways. It helps to clean the cells by carrying their wastes to the blood for removal by the kidneys. It helps to transport fats that have been absorbed from food in the digestive tract. Unlike blood, lymph does not always stay within its vessels. It can travel freely in the tissues.

An extremely important function of the lymph system concerns immunity. The lymph nodes—the structures resembling strung pearls in Figure 6–10—act as filters to remove bacteria from the body. Other lymph tissues also help to produce the body's fighting force of white blood cells that travel throughout the tissues, searching for invaders to destroy.

What good is the thymus gland?

The thymus gland is critical to immunity, especially in infancy, when it is responsible for the development of the immune system. As people age, the thymus shrinks in size. However, it still plays important roles in developing the white blood cells.

Certain white cells, the T cells, are named for the thymus, because they first become functional when they pass through there. White cells are first made by the bone marrow and released in an immature state. They fully develop when they are taken up by other tissues that give them their special functions.

What does the spleen do?

The spleen is a spongy organ that filters blood much as the lymph nodes do. In addition, the spleen destroys old, worn-out red cells. The spleen's spongy structure allows it to act as a sort of reserve for the blood supply. If the body needs more blood to carry oxygen to the tissues, the spleen contracts and squeezes blood ① from its chambers into the bloodstream. Still another talent of the spleen—if the bone marrow becomes unable to produce red blood cells, the spleen can take over this function.

Does the heart pump the lymph around the body?

The heart indirectly moves the lymph, through the action of the blood pressure. However, the heart doesn't pump lymph directly as it pumps blood. Large lymph vessels have valves that keep lymph from flowing backward, and the movement of body muscles helps to squeeze it on its way in the vessels.

Why do people with infections get "swollen glands"?

The swellings detectable at the juncture of the jaw and throat are really lymph nodes responding to infection. Nodes that are working extra hard cleaning up bacteria and fighting infection often become enlarged and painful to the touch. The swellings subside with the infection.

Can anything injure the immune system?

Yes, many things cause injury to the immune system. The virus that causes AIDS (see Chapter 17) is much feared because of its ability to completely disable the immune system of an infected person. Other illnesses can also injure the tissues of the system. Hodgkin's disease, for example, is a form of cancer that attacks lymph tissues.

Nutrition also affects immune system tissues. The body's defenses are sensitive to nutrition status and are soon impaired when a person fails to eat a diet with adequate nutrients, even for a short time. This is why weight-loss dieting, poorly planned, can make a person sick. Another factor that depresses immune response is overexposure to ultraviolet radiation from the sun (sunburn).

Can your mental thoughts make the immune system work better?

An entire new field of psychology, psychoneuroimmunology, is dedicated to finding relationships between emotions, stress, depression, personality, and the physical immune response. Some people would like to believe that people can simply "think themselves well." However, the relationships between the mind's activity and diseases of the body are anything but clear.

Teacher Support Notes

① **The Mind and Immunity:** You may want to continue this discussion of the effect of mental thoughts on immunity. Tell students that common observations suggest that the mind does have an effect on disease development. People under mental stress come down with colds more frequently than others. One study found that unhappy women had smaller numbers of certain immune cells than did women who reported themselves to be happy. The Chapter 4 Straight Talk, "Healing and the Placebo Effect," discusses this issue further.

> **❝ Thoughts on Health ❞**
>
> *What we think and feel and are is to a great extent determined by the state of our ductless glands and our viscera.*
>
> *– Aldous Huxley*

FOCUS
SECTION X

In this section students will learn:
1. How the hormonal system, or endocrine system, operates as a communication system in the body.
2. That hormones can affect growth, basic metabolic rate, and an individual's mood.

Activity 10.1
Gland Study. On a diagram of the human body, have students locate the major endocrine glands and discuss the function of each gland. Glands are defined in the glossary. **(10 min.)**

Activity 10.2
Researching Glands. Divide the class into seven groups. Assign each group a gland to research and report on.

Students should be able to locate the gland, define its function, describe what would happen without the gland, and tell what systems of the body would be affected. **(Extend, Enrich, Interdisciplinary)**

Activity 10.3
Comparing Systems. Discuss with students how the hormonal system differs from the nervous system even though both are communication systems. **(10 min.)**

Teacher Support Notes

① **Hormonal System:** In this text the term *hormonal system* has been used in place of the more traditional, academic term *endocrine system,* because the authors felt that high school students would better comprehend and retain information about a system named for something they have heard about (hormones), rather than something they probably haven't heard of (endocrine).

② **Functions of the Hormonal System:** While the functions of the hormonal system are too many to list, here are a few representative activities for enrichment:
• maintenance of intracellular and extracellular fluid volumes
• acid–base balance
• carbohydrate, protein, lipid, and nucleic acid metabolism
• food and fluid intake
• digestion, absorption, and nutrient distribution
• reproduction and lactation
• immune processors
• blood cell formation
• blood pressure and blood flow
• resistance to stress
• adaption to environmental change

154   UNIT 3   Your Physical Health

SECTION X

The Hormonal System

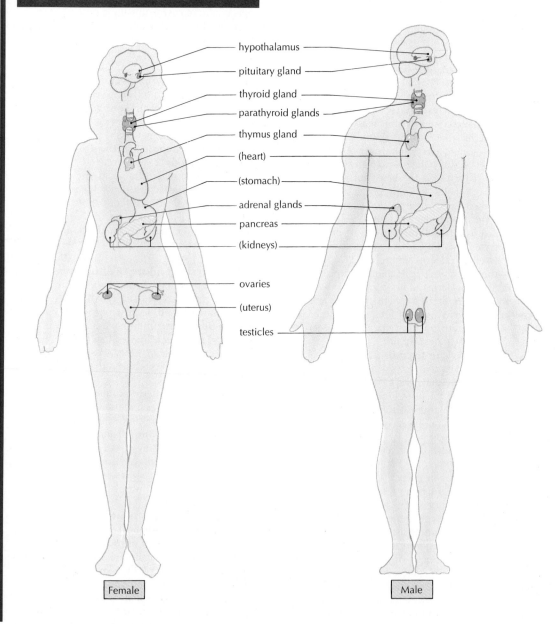

- hypothalamus
- pituitary gland
- thyroid gland
- parathyroid glands
- thymus gland
- (heart)
- (stomach)
- adrenal glands
- pancreas
- (kidneys)
- ovaries
- (uterus)
- testicles

Female

Male

Figure 6–11 The Hormonal System ① ②

EVALUATE
SECTION X

Activity 10.4

Pop Quiz. Have students match these terms to the correct numbered statement: *adrenal glands, pancreas, pituitary gland, thyroid, thymus*.
1. Located in the heart region (thymus)
2. Located at the front of the throat (thyroid)
3. Located above the kidneys (adrenal glands)
4. Located in brain, makes HGH (pituitary gland)
5. Located near the stomach, secretes insulin (pancreas)

CLOSE
SECTION X

Activity 10.5

Class Discussion. Ask students to:
1. Locate the major hormonal glands of the body.
2. Describe the functions of the body's major hormones.

The body has yet another communication system—the hormonal, or endocrine, system. Like the nervous system, it coordinates body functions by sending and receiving messages. Instead of the impulses of the nervous system, which are electrical, the messages of the hormonal system are chemical—hormones released into the bloodstream. Over a hundred hormones are known.

When a gland of the hormonal system releases a hormone, it travels everywhere in the body. However, only the hormone's target organ can respond to it. The target organ is equipped with structures to receive the hormone, and to act in response to it. A message sent along a nerve is like a conversation that travels along a phone wire (the nerve fibers) through a central switchboard (the brain and spinal cord) to one listener. A hormonal message is like a radio talk show broadcast on the airways (the bloodstream). Any organ with the right receiver can pick it up.

What functions do hormones control?

Not all the functions of the many hormones are known. One well-known one is the growth-stimulating effect in children of human growth hormone (HGH). The brain's pituitary gland makes HGH. This hormone then stimulates other glands to make their own hormones. This second fleet of hormones acts on tissues such as the bones and muscles, rebuilding them into more and more adult forms. Later in life, after growth is complete, HGH remains an important regulator of the body's use of protein, as well as its use and storage of fat and carbohydrate.

Does HGH cause young teenagers to grow extra fast?

While growth hormone is produced at a more or less steady rate through the growing years, another set of hormones comes into play at about age 11 or 12, the sex hormones. During the teen years, these hormones act on the growing parts of the body and give growth an extra boost—the adolescent growth spurt. They are also responsible for the development of body hair, the maturation of the reproductive and genital organs, and many other characteristics associated with being male or female.

What would happen if a man or a woman started producing the hormones of the opposite gender?

Years ago, the sex hormones were assumed to be exclusively male or female. However, now scientists know that men normally produce some "female" hormones, and normal women produce some "male" hormones. Male hormones in females are known to stimulate the normal growth of body hair. Female hormones in males help to maintain the appropriate percentage of body fat.

Do thyroid problems make people gain or lose body fat?

The thyroid gland, at the front of the throat, produces thyroxine, a hormone that regulates the use of fuel in the body. Thyroxine is essential both to feeling energetic and to the maintenance of normal body weight. Feelings of energy can reflect the body's basal metabolic rate (BMR, discussed in Chapter 9). When the thyroid produces too little thyroxine, the person feels tired out most of the time. A person whose thyroxine level is just slightly above normal is more likely to feel nervous than extra energetic.

Theoretically, a person with low thyroxine could begin to gain weight if food intake were normal. However, most people with underactive thyroid glands have little appetite, and feel so sleepy and sluggish that they have no urge to prepare food or even to eat. The opposite condition, an overactive thyroid, causes an increased appetite, but an even greater increase in BMR. The weight loss it causes is occasionally so extreme that the thyroid must be destroyed to save the person's life.

How do hormones affect mood?

Hormones may interact with the brain and affect how a person feels. When under stress, people feel hostile, irritable, or angry. These feelings may be related to the release of the stress hormones that make the body ready to fight. Experiments have shown that sex hormones also may partly determine a person's mood. For one thing, aggression is linked to male hormones in rats. For another, some researchers suspect that the ups and downs of female hormones within the menstrual cycle produce mood changes. Many women report feeling anxious or irritable a few days before menstruation, although a direct link to hormonal changes is yet to be proved.

🖊 Fast Facts

The shortest mature human was only 23.2 inches tall. The tallest known human was 8 feet 11.1 inches tall.

Teacher Support Notes

① **Overhead—Functions of Hormonal System:** Check that students understand the basic functions of the hormonal system. Ask if it is more like the nervous system or the circulatory system. (nervous system) Ask why. (The nervous system, like the hormonal system, is a type of communication system; the circulatory system is a transportation system.) Use the overhead *The Hormonal System*.

✉ Where to Write

Association for the Advancement of Health Education
1900 Association Drive
Reston, VA 22091

In this section students learn to:
1. Trace the path of an ovum.
2. Describe the functions of the female reproductive organs.

Activity 11.1
Unhealthy Activities. Have stu- dents generate a list of behaviors that can negatively affect the female reproductive system. **(10 min., Critical Thinking)**

TEACH
SECTION XI
(Guided and Independent Practice)

Activity 11.2
Better Protection. Discuss how the female reproductive system is protected as compared to the male reproductive system. Why is this important? **(10 min., Critical Thinking)**

Activity 11.3
Trace the Journey. On a chart, trace the journey of an ovum from the ovaries to the vagina. **(15 min.; Extend, Enrich)**

Teacher Support Notes

① **Diagnostic Technologies:** For enrichment, you may want to tell students that the desire to bear healthy children has encouraged research and the development of many new diagnostic technologies in recent years. These developments have given health care providers and parents access to information regarding the progression of a pregnancy that was previously unavailable. For example, one fairly new technology is *ultrasound examination*, which uses high frequency sound waves to create a picture of the fetus in the uterus. Results are interpreted on a televisionlike screen. The picture is called a *sonogram*. It is used to determine fetal age and the location of the placenta. Extensive ultrasound techniques can also be used to gain further information if there is a possibility of a problem with the development of the fetus. Another method, *amniocentesis*, draws amniotic fluid from the uterus with a long, thin needle that is inserted through the abdominal wall. Fluid is then examined for evidence of possible birth defects, such as Down's syndrome.

156

SECTION XI

The Female Reproductive System

Figure 6–12 The Female Reproductive System ①

EVALUATE
SECTION XI

Activity 11.4
Pop Quiz. Fill in the blank with the correct word.
A female reproductive system produces reproductive cells known as **1.** __(ova)__ . One of these cells is then swept into the major tube of the reproductive system known as the **2.** __(fallopian)__ tube. Here it may or may not meet **3.** __(sperm)__ . It then travels to the **4.** __(uterus)__ . If not fertilized it is passed through the **5.** __(cervix)__ and out the **6.** __(vagina)__ . If fertilized it travels to the **7.** __(uterus)__ and attaches itself to the wall lining.

CLOSE
SECTION XI

Activity 11.5
Class Discussion. Ask students to:
1. Describe the organs that transport the ova from the ovary to the vagina.
2. Relate menstruation to the cycle of time needed for the journey of the ova to the vagina.

The female reproductive system produces the female reproductive cells, the ova. It also supports each fertilized ovum from the beginning of pregnancy through birth. Starting from the ovaries, the ova travel by way of the fallopian ① tubes to the uterus and vagina.

One of the ovaries releases one ovum, one month; the other ovary releases an ovum the next month (they take turns). The monthly timing is governed by the rise and fall of the female sex hormones.

How do the ovaries produce ova?

Although the ovaries ripen and release the ova, they don't really make any new ones. All of the cells that will ever become ova are present in the ovaries at birth. A baby girl holds approximately one-half million of the immature ova in her ovaries. When she reaches age 12, only a quarter or so of those ova remain alive in her ovaries. At about the midpoint of each month, through all her reproductive life, she releases one of the ova.

Each ovum starts out as an immature cell and is "ripened" by the ovary in a series of stages. The ovary houses the ovum in a small pouch of fluid that develops in stages and ruptures to release the ovum when it's ready. The beating fringe on the end of the ovary sweeps the ready ovum into the major tube of the female system, the fallopian tube.

What does an ovum look like?

An ovum is a large cell, about the size of the period at the end of this sentence. The ova pictured in Figure 6–12 has been greatly enlarged. Ova are like all cells, with one important exception: they possess only half the normal amount of genetic material. Male sperm cells also contain only half the regular amount of genetic material. When the ovum and sperm unite, they form a single cell that possesses two complete sets of genetic material and is unique in its makeup.

Where does an ovum become fertilized?

On being swept up by the gentle, beating fingers at the end of a fallopian tube, the ovum starts a journey. Once in the tube, the ovum may meet sperm that are swimming up from the vagina. The sperm may have been waiting there for a day or two for the ovum. Whether or not sperm are present, the ovum travels through the fallopian tube to the uterus. Unfertilized ova and some fertilized ones just keep on traveling through the cervix and out of the vagina, undetected. Frequently, though, a fertilized ovum will end its travels in the uterus, where it attaches to the wall lining and begins a pregnancy.

What is menstruation?

Each month, the uterus prepares itself to support a pregnancy. It does so by enriching its lining with tissue that can supply blood to a developing ovum that might implant there. If no ovum implants, the uterus sheds its lining by way of menstruation, a period of bleeding that lasts about four to seven days. The 28-day cycle shown in Figure 6–12 is typical. However, cycle lengths vary among individuals, and even in the same woman from time to time.

How does an infant fit through the vagina to be born?

The vagina is very elastic, from the point where it connects to the uterus at the cervix, to the outside of the body. At the time of childbirth, hormones make the vaginal walls especially able to stretch. As the baby's head passes through the cervix, the vagina expands to form a passageway large enough for an infant.

What is a hymen?

In young girls, the vaginal opening is partly or entirely covered by a thin membrane—the hymen. Later, through physical activity, tampon use, or sometimes by way of sexual intercourse, the membrane disintegrates.

What is a hysterectomy, and why might a woman need one?

Hysterectomy is the surgical removal of the uterus, which of course ends menstruation. Sometimes, the ovaries and the fallopian tubes are taken out at the same time. As women age, they may develop tumors or severe menstrual problems that require treatment by hysterectomy. Hysterectomy may also be advised when miscarriage or infection has seriously damaged the uterus.

Teacher Support Notes

① **Infertility:** For enrichment, give students some information about the causes of infertility. The leading cause of female infertility is blocked fallopian tubes, resulting from such factors as pelvic inflammatory disease (PID), septic abortions, or abdominal surgery. The second leading cause is endometriosis. In this disease, uterine tissue grows outside the uterus, often appearing on the ovaries, fallopian tubes, and in the abdominal cavity. Why endometriosis causes infertility is not known. In addition to physical causes, there may be hormonal reasons why a woman is unable to conceive. As many as 20% of women with infertility problems have hormonal abnormalities. Finally, immunological causes may be present, the most significant of which is the production of sperm antibodies by the woman. Other factors are smoking and toxic chemicals.

FOCUS
SECTION XII

In this section, students will learn to:
1. Identify the major organs of the male reproductive system and their functions.
2. Explain why the reproductive organs are external to the body.
3. Describe the properties of semen and sperm.

Activity 12.1
Listing Unhealthy Behaviors. Have students generate lists of unhealthy behaviors that can affect the male reproductive system. **(10 min., Critical Thinking)**

TEACH
SECTION XII
(Guided and Independent Practice)

Activity 12.2
The Parts of the System. Discuss

the advantages and disadvantages of the location of the male reproductive system outside the body. Then have students write down the major organs of the reproductive system and locate and describe each. **(20 min.; Reteach, Reinforce)**

Activity 12.3
Characteristics and Problems. Have students describe the characteristics of a sperm cell. Then have them work

---

Fast Facts

The sperm cell is one of the smallest cells. It would take over 1,000 sperm cells to cover the period at the end of this sentence. The sperm cell will have either an "X" chromosome or a "Y" chromosome, which is the determining factor in the gender of a baby.

SECTION XII

The Male Reproductive System

Cutaway side view through the center of the male body showing male reproductive organs

- (backbone)
- tube to transport sperm (vas deferens)
- vesicle to make semen (seminal vesicle)
- (bladder, urinary)
- gland (prostate)
- gland (Cowper's)
- urethra
- penis
- tube to store sperm (epididymis)
- glans
- foreskin
- testicle
- scrotum

A sperm cell

- head
- nucleus
- middle piece
- tail

- tube to store sperm (epididymis)
- tube to transport sperm (vas deferens)
- tubules that make sperm (seminiferous tubules)

Cutaway side view of the testicle's internal structure

Figure 6–13 The Male Reproductive System

in pairs to list some problems associated with the male reproductive system. **(15 min.; Extend, Enrich)**

EVALUATE

Activity 12.4
Pop Quiz.

1. The testicles are the only human organs that produce male reproductive cells. (T)

2. Sperm production requires a temperature higher than the normal body temperature. (F)

3. In the male reproductive system, most of the organs are well protected. (F)

4. Thousands of sperm are produced daily. (T)

5. Only one sperm can fertilize an ovum. (T)

CLOSE
SECTION XII

Activity 12.5
Class Discussion. Ask students to:

1. Name and describe the organs of the male reproduction system.

2. Identify both differences and similarities between the male and female reproductive systems.

The male reproductive system is made up of a series of organs connected together by tubes that lead out of the body through the penis. The entire unit is designed to continually produce, store, and deliver male reproductive cells to fertilize an ovum. In the male system, most organs, such as the penis and testicles, are external to the body. Most of the transportation route is within the abdominal cavity.

Why are the testicles outside the body?

The testicles are the only human organs able to produce male reproductive cells. Thus it seems surprising that they are located outside the protection of the abdominal cavity. Their location serves an important function, though—temperature regulation.

Sperm production requires a temperature 3 or 4 degrees Fahrenheit lower than normal body temperature. If the testicles were inside the abdomen, the heat of the internal body would bring sperm production to a halt. The scrotum, the tough sac of muscle and skin that contains the testicles, maintains the right temperature. When the testicles become too cool, the scrotum contracts by reflex action to bring them close to the body to warm them with body heat. When the temperature is right, the scrotum relaxes once again. This allows the testicles to drop away from the body.

Men should be aware that anything that holds the testicles too close to the body can interfere with sperm production. Even the wearing of tight pants is thought to interfere with the natural cooling of the testicles.

Where are the sperm produced, and how do they get to the penis?

The sperm are produced inside each testicle by thousands of tiny tubes that make millions of sperm cells each day. These lead to another structure packed with yards of tubing whose function it is to store sperm until it is needed. Many other tubes, one leading to another, wind through the lower abdominal cavity and lead ultimately to the urethra, the passageway through which both sperm (in semen) and urine leave the body.

What is semen?

Semen is a thick mixture of fluids that carry the sperm from the male body. The fluids are produced by several glands. Semen helps to neutralize the normal acid from urine in the male urethra. This is important, because acid kills sperm. The vagina may also be slightly acidic, and seminal fluids neutralize this acid as well. Muscular contractions (ejaculation) propel semen out of the body.

Can sperm really swim?

Sperm are beautifully designed for movement in fluid. As you can see in Figure 6–13, their long, whipping tails make them look something like tadpoles when they are viewed under a microscope. Of course, sperm are as small as bacteria and so are much too small to be seen with the naked eye. Three or four hundred million of them are present in each ejaculation. However, just one sperm fertilizes an ovum.

What is the prostate gland, and why does it cause trouble for older men?

The prostate is one of the glands of the male reproductive system. The urethra, which carries both semen and urine, runs right through the prostate. Occasionally, disease of the prostate partly blocks off the urethra, making urination and sexual activity difficult. After the age of about 50, many men begin to develop enlarged prostate glands. This may lead to bladder and kidney trouble unless the prostate is surgically reduced in size.

Prostate gland enlargement can indicate a risk of cancer. It is important for older men to have periodic checkups to make sure that their reproductive organs are healthy (see Chapter 19).

What is circumcision, and is it medically useful?

A covering of skin, the foreskin, folds over the glans of the penis at birth. Circumcision, the surgical removal of the foreskin, originated in ancient religions and still holds special meaning for some. Most infant boys born in the United States are circumcised soon after birth.

An uncircumcised penis requires extra cleaning under the foreskin during bathing. It is thought that a buildup of bacteria and matter that can ① collect there may increase the risks of infections and cancer in older uncircumcised men. Some physicians recommend circumcision to reduce the risks of these conditions. Others say that the risks are small, that cleaning is easy, and that circumcision should be performed only if the parents request it—not as a routine procedure.

Teacher Support Notes

① **Male Infertility:** The primary causes of male infertility are low sperm count, a lack of sperm ability to move spontaneously, and blocked passageways. As with women, environmental factors may contribute to infertility. Increasing evidence suggests that toxic chemicals are responsible for decreased sperm counts in men and that smoking may reduce sperm counts.

Fast Facts

In spite of the fact that circumcision is not a medical necessity, almost 60% of newborn boys were circumcised in 1985 according to the National Center for Health Statistics. This represents, however, a significant drop from an estimated 93% being circumcised in 1975. It still places the United States far ahead of other Western countries, which circumcise less than 1% of their newborn boys.

Chapter 6 Review

Answers

Vocabulary

1. a. radius b. femur
c. pelvis d. phalanges
e. cerebrum f. right atrium g. aorta h. aorta
i. kidneys j. rectum
k. scrotum
2. a. triceps b. gastrocnemius c. pectorals
d. gluteus maximus
e. testicle f. pulmonary vein g. bladder
3. a. spleen b. veins
c. lymph vessels d. thymus e. lymph nodes
f. large intestines
g. endocrine h. pituitary
i. thyroid j. pancreas
k. scrotum l. vas deferens

Recall

1. Bones determine the body's shape, protect soft vital organs, store minerals and vitamins, and manufacture all the body's blood cells.
2. voluntary, involuntary, and mixed, which are the muscles of the heart
3. It consists of nerves that connect the brain to all parts of the body. It lies safe within the bony spinal vertebrae and provides the body's main communication line.
4. cortex—conscious thoughts take place; cerebellum—maintains balance and coordinates muscular activities; brain stem—controls breathing and basic functions
5. The blood–brain barrier controls the environment inside the brain. It admits those chemicals the brain needs, but excludes those

that could interrupt the brain's work.
6. A reflex is a sort of intentional short circuit in the nervous system. The nerves that control reflexes form an arc from tissue to spinal cord and back to tissue.
7. indigestion—spicy foods irritate the lining, too much fat, or too much air, food or liquid is

swallowed; heartburn—mixture of acid and food in the stomach burns and irritates the lining of the esophagus; appendicitis—particles lodge in the appendix and cause an infection
8. The circulatory system, because each cell in the body depends on this system. Cells dump their waste into this system and pull all the nutrients

and chemicals they need to live and function from it.
9. The heart rests continuously in the moments of muscle relaxation between contractions. During this period, the relaxed heart muscles allow blood to fill the heart's chambers.
10. circulatory system, the liver, digestive system, the

CHAPTER REVIEW

LEARNING THE VOCABULARY

Use the illustrations, the information you learned in this chapter, and the glossary at the end of the book to complete the exercises below.

1. In each group one choice does not belong. List the one that doesn't belong and explain your answer.
   a. radius, hamstrings, triceps, quadriceps, biceps
   b. cerebrum, cerebellum, femur, cortex, brain stem
   c. pancreas, appendix, esophagus, pelvis, liver
   d. aorta, phalanges, ventricle, vein, artery
   e. ureter, bladder, kidney, cerebrum, urethra
   f. radius, ulna, phalanges, tibia, right atrium
   g. voice box, aorta, windpipe, sinus, diaphragm
   h. aorta, lymph node, thymus gland, bone marrow, spleen
   i. mouth, kidneys, esophagus, stomach, small intestine
   j. ovaries, rectum, thyroid gland, hypothalamus, thymus gland
   k. scrotum, cervix, uterus, vagina, ovary

2. Fill in the blank with one of the following vocabulary terms: *pulmonary veins, pectorals, triceps, bladder, testicle, gluteus maximus, gastrocnemius.*
   a. The quadriceps muscle is opposite the hamstrings and the biceps muscle is opposite the _____.
   b. The gluteus maximus is the major muscle of the buttocks and the _____ is the major muscle of the calf of the lower leg.

   c. The trapezius is opposite the _____.
   d. The _____ is the biggest muscle in the body.
   e. The ovary serves the female as the _____ serves the male.
   f. The inferior and superior vena cava attach to the right atrium and the _____ attach to the left atrium.
   g. The rectum is the organ of elimination for the digestive system and the _____ is the organ of elimination for the urinary system.

3. *Matching*—Match each of the following phrases with one of the following vocabulary terms: *lymph vessels, pituitary, pancreas, spleen, thymus, veins, large intestines, thyroid, endocrine, lymph nodes, scrotum, vas deferens.*

   a. filters blood to remove old blood cells
   b. vessels that carry used blood to the heart
   c. vessels that contain lymph nodes
   d. a gland at the base of the heart
   e. small tissues in lymph that contain white cells
   f. responsible for absorption of water and minerals
   g. another name for hormonal system
   h. the gland that makes HGH
   i. gland that controls metabolic rate of cells
   j. secretes insulin
   k. double pouch that contains testicles in males
   l. tube that transports sperm

RECALLING IMPORTANT FACTS AND IDEAS

1. List some functions of the living structures we know as bones.
2. Name three types of muscles present in the body.
3. Describe the spinal cord and its part in the central nervous system.
4. Identify the physical parts of the brain and their functions.
5. What is the blood-brain barrier and why is it important?
6. How does a reflex action work?
7. List three disorders of the digestive system and their causes.
8. Which system is classified as the "transportation system" of the body and why?

lungs, and the urinary system
11. They form a net which traps more platelets and other cells to form a clot so a wound can heal.
12. The nephrons in the kidney draw fluid from the blood. The kidney then detects and measures the substances in the fluid to obtain information about the blood. The kidneys push

minerals, blood sugar, and useful substances back into the blood, while some fluids along with waste become urine.
13. pituitary
14. short length of the urethra allows bacteria to reach the bladder
15. It acts as a filter and air conditioner. The nose hairs filter out debris from entering the

lungs, and purify the air in each breath. It also warms and adds moisture, protecting the lungs from cold or dry air.
16. lighten the weight of the skull, create the sound of the voice as sound waves resonate inside them
17. drinking water, breathing into a paper bag, being startled, dissolving a teaspoon of sugar

on the tongue and letting the sugar soothe the throat
18. It moves the fluid around the body by cleansing cells, carrying wastes, and transporting fat.
19. The spleen filters blood, destroys all worn-out red cells, and if bone marrow is unable to produce red blood cells, it can take over this job.
20. eat a diet with adequate nutrients, avoid overexposure to ultraviolet radiation
21. It sends and receives messages—the messages are chemical hormones released into the bloodstream.
22. *HGH*—human growth; it regulates the body's use of protein and its use and storage of fat and carbohydrate
    sex hormones—responsible for development of hair, maturation of the reproductive and genital organs
    thyroxine—regulates use of fuel in the body, regulates BMR
23. egg travels through the fallopian tube to the uterus through the cervix and out of the vagina
24. Sperm production requires a temperature 3 to 4 degrees Fahrenheit lower than normal body temperatures. If the testicles were inside, the heat of the internal body would stop sperm production.

9. When does the heart rest and what happens during these periods?
10. Name the organs and the systems that work together to cleanse the blood by removing wastes from the cells.
11. What is the function of the blood platelets?
12. Describe how the kidneys act as a filter and tell what is filtered.
13. Which gland helps monitor the amount of water in the blood.
14. Why are women more prone to urinary infections than men are?
15. Why is the nose the preferred organ of breathing?
16. List two functions of our sinuses.

17. List some remedies to stop hiccups.
18. Why is the lymphatic system called the second circulatory system?
19. Why is damage to the spleen a serious injury?
20. What can you do to keep your immune system healthy?
21. Explain how the hormonal system works as a communication system.
22. Name three hormones in the body and describe what they do.
23. Trace the path of an egg from the ovary to the uterus.
24. Why aren't the testicles located inside the body?

C RITICAL THINKING

1. Many people who are hospitalized with heart complications or other infections die, not of heart failure, but of kidney failure. Why does this happen?

2. Even as a young girl, a female should maintain a healthy lifestyle to protect her future children. Why can her actions in her early life affect her children?

A CTIVITIES

1. Take your pulse for 15 seconds and then multiply it by 4. This is your resting pulse rate. Then do two minutes of continuous exercise. Retake your pulse. Compare the two readings. What is the difference? Retake your pulse every minute until it returns to the resting rate. How long did it take to get back to normal? Compare

your results with those of another person in your class. By this standard, who is healthier?
2. Pick a partner in your class to check your lung capacity. Inhale as deeply as you can and then exhale into a balloon. Compare results with your partner. Which one of you has the larger lung capacity?

M AKING DECISIONS ABOUT HEALTH

1. Discuss the subject of organ transplants as a method of prolonging life or curing disease. What organs are most likely to be needed?

What organs would you be willing to donate? How would you feel as the recipient of another person's organ?

Answers to Fact or Fiction

Here are the answers to the questions at the start of the chapter.

1. False. Adult bones not only break down but also build up their structures throughout life.
2. True. **3.** True. **4.** True. **5.** True. **6.** False. The lungs lack muscles and, like balloons, fill passively with air only when the diaphragm contracts and creates a vacuum in the chest cavity.
7. False. Most often, when disease-causing organisms enter the body, the immune system destroys them and prevents illness. **8.** True.

CHAPTER 7 PLANNER

OVERVIEW

Chapter 7 is 22 pages long and divided into the six sections listed to the right. Major learning outcomes are also listed to the right. This chapter introduces students to the nutrients and the ways in which the body uses food to produce energy, and then focuses on the carbohydrates, fats, and protein. The activities in Chapter 7 give students an opportunity to apply the information in the text to their personal nutrition choices. Students will be able to analyze their existing eating patterns and compare what they eat to national guidelines. They will have the opportunity to make changes to meet the recommended amounts of each nutrient.

MAKING LIFE CHOICES RESOURCES

A variety of activities, handouts, quizzes, and tests to accompany this chapter are available in the *Making Life Choices* supplementary material. You may pick and choose from those materials as appropriate for your amount of class time and the ability levels of your students. Some of the resources you might want to consider using are:

Overhead
• Photosynthesis Produced Glucose

Handouts
• Fast Foods Lowest in Fat and Calories
• Recognizing Food Choice Errors
• Analyzing Nutrient Labels

SUGGESTED RESOURCES

Student Readings
1. Yetiv, Jack Z. *Popular Nutritional Practices: Sense and Nonsense.* New York: Dell Publishing, 1988.

Teacher Readings
1. Lauffer, Randall E. *Iron Balance.* St. Martin's Press.

Videos
1. *A Food-Chooser's Guide to the Well-Fed Cell.* (23 min.) Coronet

Films, 65 East South Water Street, Chicago, IL 60601, 800-621-2131.

Software
1. *What Did You Eat Yesterday?* Students enter names of foods they have eaten into the computer. Calorie, protein, fat, and sodium contents are analyzed. Learning Seed Company.

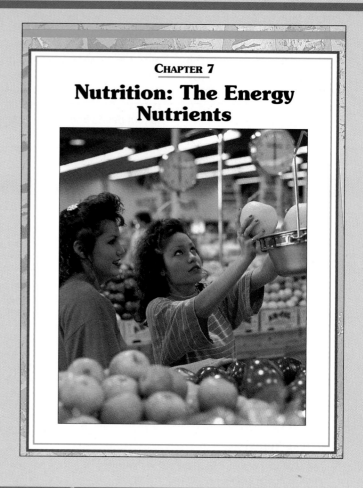

CHAPTER 7
Nutrition: The Energy Nutrients

CHAPTER PROJECT

This project could extend through your teaching of Chapters 7 and 8. Have students write down the foods they eat for a week, including appropriate serving sizes. Then direct them to evaluate their diet records using the six Dietary Guidelines for Americans and the Food Pyramid (see Chapter 8). Have them calculate the percentage of fats, protein, and carbohydrates in their diets for the week. Compare these to the recommended values. Have students analyze their fiber intake daily. Ask

Activity To Introduce Chapter

Copy all vocabulary words from this chapter onto 1/2" by 2" rectangles of paper. Have students cut these out and arrange them on a piece of paper in an order that makes sense to them. They may not know all of the words, but they should attempt to find relationships between words. For example, some words may be topics under which other words will fall. Have students explain their arrangements to you. While you are walking around to check everyone's arrangement of words, have students look through the chapter to define all of the words on a separate sheet of paper. This will also give

OUTCOMES

After reading and studying this chapter, you will be able to:

✓ Identify the six classes of nutrients.
✓ List the six Dietary Guidelines for Americans.
✓ Design a balanced meal.
✓ Estimate your daily fat gram allowance and describe some strategies to control the amount of fat in your diet.
✓ Discuss the impacts that overnutrition and undernutrition have on the body.

✓ Describe the functions and food sources for carbohydrates, fats, and proteins.

CONTENTS

I. Benefits of Nutrition
II. Introducing the Nutrients and Fiber
III. Energy from Food
IV. The Carbohydrates
V. The Fats
VI. Protein

Straight Talk: *Food Choices—What Guides Us?*

FACT OR FICTION

What do you think? Are the following statements true or false? If you think they are false, then say what is true.

1. To be well-nourished is simply a matter of eating foods with enough of the right nutrients.
2. The brain demands the sugar glucose to fuel its activities.
3. Too much protein can make you fat.
4. Foods high in starch are of little benefit to the body.
5. It is almost impossible to eat a diet too high in fiber, because fiber is so good for you.
6. Honey and sugar are the same, as far as the body is concerned.
7. Of all the things in foods that cause diseases, sugar is probably the biggest troublemaker.
8. A teaspoon of fat has twice the calories of a teaspoon of sugar.
9. Once the body has assembled its proteins into body structures, it never lets go of them.
10. To be sure that you get enough protein, you must eat meat.

(Answers on page 179)

■ **Reminder:** Knowing how to study can increase your knowledge, improve your grades, *and* cut down on your study time. See the *Studying Health* section at the front of your text for some suggestions to help you study this chapter.

"What changes, if any, are needed in your diet?" Create a checklist for every area they are to evaluate in their diets, and give time in class for students to present their analyses for a grade. **(Work is done at home. Allow 15 minutes for each student to present.)**

---

them an opportunity to scan the chapter.

Now that they know all of the definitions, ask them to rearrange their terms a second time in a way that makes sense. Have them glue these terms into the final arrangement to turn in to you.

Discuss the various ways that students arranged their terms and what relationships they used as the basis for their arrangements. These will vary. Have them decide which arrangements make the most sense. **(45 min.)**

NOT ENOUGH TIME?*

You could easily spend five or six days teaching this chapter if students read the entire chapter, do a fair number of the suggested activities in the teacher's edition, and complete a sampling of the handouts from the resource material accompanying this text. It is likely, however, that you will have only three or four days to devote to this chapter. Following are some suggestions to help you make sure that you cover the key topics if you have limited time.

TIME	SUGGESTIONS
1 Day	Assign students to read Section I prior to class. Have students complete Activity 1.1. Do the Evaluate Activity 1.4. Assign Section II for reading.
2 Days	On day 2 have students do Activity 2.2 to learn about the nutrients. Have students bring in package labels representing their nutrients and be prepared to discuss how their nutrients function in the body. Do Activity 2.4 (Nutrient Flash Cards). Assign reading in Sections III and IV for homework.
3 Days	Discuss Section III. Have students write down what they ate yesterday. Then have students complete Activity 4.3 to analyze their diets for fiber content. Have students read Sections V and VI for homework.
4 Days	Assign Activities 5.1 and 6.5. Have students complete the Chapter Review.

Please refer to the 18-week daily lesson plans in the supplementary material for additional suggestions.

Answers to "Fact or Fiction"

1. False. Eating foods with enough nutrients is important, but equally important is to keep from eating too much or too little food. 2. True. 3. True. 4. False. Starchy foods provide the body with the glucose it needs. 5. False. Too much fiber can be as harmful as too little. 6. True. 7. False. Fat is by far the biggest culprit. 8. True. 9. False. The body loses proteins from body structures every day. 10. False. You can easily get enough protein from grains, beans, vegetables, milk, and eggs.

In this section students will learn:
1. To identify the benefits of nutrition.
2. The six Dietary Guidelines for Americans.

Activity 1.1
Choosing Nutritious Foods. Write

the following statement on the board or overhead: "A body must be well nourished to be healthy and beautiful." Ask students to answer the questions: "What kinds of foods do you eat that contribute to a healthy, beautiful body? What kinds of foods do you eat that do not contribute to a healthy, beautiful body?" **(5 min.)**

Activity 1.2
Benefits of Good Nutrition. Discuss with students the benefits of nutrition. Ask for concrete examples of each benefit. Perhaps students have had experience with one of the benefits or know someone in the family who has. Which

Teacher Support Notes

① **Understanding Nutrition:** You may want to make sure that students understand the several different forms of the word *nutrition*. Write *nutrition*, *nutrients*, *well-nourished*, and *nourishing* on the board. As a class, develop definitions for each word, then have students write sentences using each word.

② **Food Choices and Diseases:** Examples you may want to give students at this point are risks for developing cancer, high blood pressure, diabetes, heart disease, and intestinal disorders.

③ **More on Dietary Guidelines:** You may want to refer students to the last section of Chapter 8, which contains additional information on the six dietary guidelines.

✏ Fast Facts

The average American consumes 130 lbs. of fat per year. This amount of fat would be equal to eating more than one full stick of butter each day.

You choose to eat a meal about 1,000 times a year. Eating is a voluntary activity, but you probably don't give it a second thought. You will choose when to eat, what to eat, and how much to eat, about 65,000 times in your lifetime (if you live to be 65). You will consume about 50 tons of food. Each day's intake of **nutrients** may affect your body only slightly, but over a period of years, the effects of those intakes will build up. This is why it's important for you to learn how to make wise food choices.

SECTION 1

Benefits of Nutrition

Good nutrition helps make people's bodies strong, fit, and healthy—in short, beautiful. Bodies are beautiful in many different ways. Some people are tall, some short; some have dark skin, some are fair; some have curly hair, some have straight hair. Whatever your body is like, one thing is true: to be its most beautiful, it must be well nourished. Adequate intakes of all the nutrients underlie the health of your complexion, the straightness of your bones, the shape and strength of your muscles, and the gleam in your eye.

Your body is growing and renewing its parts all the time. Each day it adds a little to its tissues as you gain height and strength. It also replaces some old muscle, bone, skin, and blood with new tissues. In this way some of the food you eat today becomes part of "you" tomorrow. The best food for you, then, is the kind that supports normal growth and maintains strong muscles, sound bones, healthy skin, and enough blood to cleanse and nourish all the parts of your body.

The best food also reduces your risks of developing illnesses later in life. Your food

choices weave together with other lifestyle choices you make to either raise or lower your chances of becoming ill. You will learn more about the connections between your food choices and diseases in Chapters 9, 18, and 19.

To manage your nutrition in your own best interest, you have to learn what foods to eat, since not all foods are equally nutritious. The Health Strategies section on this page presents some general dietary guidelines put forth by the government. Although these guidelines are written for adults, they also apply to teens, with one exception—the recommendations about fat. A teen who has trouble eating enough food to grow at the expected rate should not cut fat from the diet, because energy from fat can help promote growth.

Some people do not obtain enough nutrients from their food. They may develop

HEALTH STRATEGIES

Dietary Guidelines for Americans*

1. Eat a variety of foods daily.
2. Maintain healthy weight.
3. Choose a diet low in fat, saturated fat, and cholesterol.
4. Choose a diet with plenty of vegetables, fruits, and grain products.
5. Use sugars only in moderation.
6. Use salt and sodium only in moderation.

*The guidelines also make the recommendation that children and teenagers among others should not drink alcohol. Adults who do drink should limit their intake of alcohol to one or two drinks a day.

benefit is most important to teens? Why? **(10 min.; Extend, Enrich)**

Activity 1.3
Prehistoric vs. Modern Lifestyles. Have students brainstorm the eating habits of prehistoric man. Write their suggestions on the overhead or chalkboard. Students are then to write a story following prehistoric man through a day, telling how he gathers, prepares,

and eats foods (breakfast, lunch, dinner) with his family.

Now have the students write about themselves and how they gather, prepare, and eat foods with their families. Ask them: "What advantages and disadvantages for a healthy lifestyle might there have been in the times of prehistory? What advantages and disadvantages does our modern lifestyle offer in terms of our health status?" Think of at least three

advantages and disadvantages for each. **(30–45 min.; Interdisciplinary, Critical Thinking)**

EVALUATE
SECTION I

Activity 1.4
Vocabulary Quiz. Quiz students on the glossary terms for this section. Read the terms and ask them to write definitions.

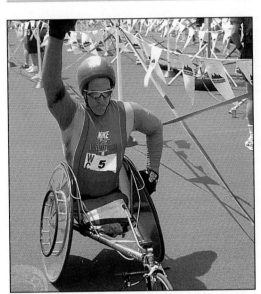
Sound nutrition helps make athletes strong and fit.

nutrient deficiencies or other forms of **malnutrition.** Pregnant women, especially pregnant teens, are very sensitive to nutrient deficiencies. These deficiencies can slow the growth of their infants, both before and after birth. Adolescents and teens are also sensitive to deficiencies because they are growing at astonishing rates. A person who does not receive proper nutrition during the teen years may never reach full height, because all of the nutrients are needed for growth. After the person reaches adulthood growth stops, even if the diet is then excellent. All the groups of people just mentioned are most likely to suffer from **undernutrition**—that is, too few nutrients for health and growth. ①

Another threat to people's health is **overnutrition.** Many people are overweight, or have daily intakes of salt, fat, cholesterol, and alcohol that may be too high for their hearts to remain healthy. Others eat too few vegetables and too much meat, choices linked to many diseases. Even vitamins and minerals can be poisonous if too many are taken in

concentrated form. The key to good nutrition, then, is to eat foods that provide enough, but not too much, energy and nutrients.

Key Points *Good nutrition promotes growth and helps prevent diseases. Both undernutrition and overnutrition threaten health.*

SECTION I REVIEW

Answer the following questions on a sheet of paper.

Learning the Vocabulary
The vocabulary terms in this section are *nutrients, nutrient deficiencies, malnutrition, undernutrition,* and *overnutrition.*
1. Write a sentence using each term.
2. Explain the difference between overnutrition and undernutrition.

Learning the Facts
3. List three benefits of good nutrition.
4. List the six Dietary Guidelines for Americans.

Making Life Choices
5. The food choices we make today influence our health in the future. Take a look at your diet and guess what path your health may be likely to follow in the future.

MINI GLOSSARY

nutrients: compounds in food that the body requires for proper growth, maintenance, and functioning.
nutrient deficiencies (dee-FISH-en-sees): too little of one or more nutrients in the diet; a form of malnutrition.
malnutrition: the results in the body of poor nutrition: undernutrition, overnutrition, or any nutrient deficiency.
undernutrition: too little food energy or too few nutrients to prevent disease or to promote growth; a form of malnutrition.
overnutrition: too much food energy or excess nutrients to the degree of causing disease or increasing risk of disease; a form of malnutrition.

Teacher Support Notes

① **Examples of *Undernutrition:*** Ask students if they consider themselves to be well nourished or undernourished. Can they think of other individuals they know who may be undernourished? Without naming names, ask them to describe the characteristics of these people that might indicate that they are undernourished.

Section I Review
Answers
1. Answers will vary.
2. *Undernutrition* occurs when the body receives too little food energy or too few nutrients for health and growth; *overnutrition* occurs when the body receives too much food energy or too many nutrients, causing or risking disease.
3. helps make people's bodies strong, fit, and healthy
4. Refer to the Health Strategies on page 164.
5. Answers will vary.

CLOSE
SECTION I

Activity 1.5
Guideline Symbols. Divide students into six groups; assign each group one of the dietary guidelines. Have each group draw a simple picture or symbol to stand for its guideline. Share and discuss each picture/symbol. Have students close their books and name the dietary guidelines by using the pictures as a guide. Have students name them without the pictures. **(10 min., Cooperative Learning)**

FOCUS
SECTION II

In this section students will learn:
1. The six nutrients and the roles they play in the body.
2. How to calculate their fat gram allowance and apply it to their eating habits.
3. How to analyze their diets for recommended percentages of carbohydrates, fats, and proteins.

Activity 2.1
Determining Student Knowledge. Before teaching about nutrients in

---

Teacher Support Notes

① **Teen Views— Follow-Up Questions:** Following are some questions you may want to use to encourage discussion of the ideas expressed by the students in the Teen Views feature:

a. Do students think that there is a connection between energy levels and ambition?

b. Do students notice a difference in energy level among their classmates from morning to afternoon? Why do they think this happens? Do they see any connection between their eating habits and their school performance?

c. What does Amnat Chittaphong's story about school closing due to snow suggest with regard to energy levels? Do students think that energy levels are determined more by physical or psychological factors?

d. Do students who eat a lot of junk food believe they have sufficient energy? Would they be willing to change their eating habits if they were guaranteed more energy?

✍ Fast Facts
Two hundred million M&Ms are sold each day in the United States.

TEEN VIEWS ①

Why do you think some people have more energy than others?

It may not necessarily be that some people have more energy, but just that they are more ambitious and hardworking. Getting enough sleep, eating right, and exercising may also be factors. **Jessica Moore, 16, Orange Park High School, FL**

In the mornings, sometimes I feel like I'm walking into a shooting of "The Return of the Living Dead." People who don't eat right may struggle to get through their day. This is true in school because it seems to me that most students aren't "alive" until after lunch. Eating right is probably a major reason why you see some people so active. When people are down and depressed, you probably won't see them jumping around. When you're really happy, you bring your energy level up with you. I've seen kids go to school looking down, and then being told that school's closed because of snow. All of a sudden, they run all the way home without even breaking a sweat. **Amnat Chittaphong, 16, Poughkeepsie High School, NY**

They are more physically fit. People who have a lot of energy work out, play sports, and eat the right foods. **Patrick Leary, 15, Sharon High School, PA**

Being energetic is a state of mind. If you feel lazy, you will act lazy. If you feel energetic, you will be energetic. Emotions also play a part. If you're in a good mood, you are more likely to be energetic than if you're in a bad mood. **Roger Berry, 17, Orange Park High School, FL**

People who eat a balanced and nutritious diet are going to have more energy than someone who eats junk food. I also believe that stress makes people lose their energy. If people could control some of their stress, they might have more energy and feel better. **Rebekah Price, 17, Pine Bluff High School, AR**

SECTION II

Introducing the Nutrients and Fiber

The food you eat supplies nutrients, fiber, and other materials. The nutrients fall into six classes: **carbohydrate, fat, protein,** water, vitamins, and minerals. The first three of these are the main topics of this chapter. Water will be briefly mentioned. The last two are introduced here but are discussed in full in the next chapter.

Three nutrients—carbohydrates, fats, and protein—provide **energy** the body can use. The body uses energy from these nutrients to do its work and to create heat to maintain a steady temperature. Carbohydrates supply the body with one of its main fuels, the sugar **glucose.** The brain and nervous system can normally use only this fuel for energy to fuel their activities.

Fat supplies the body with another main fuel, **fatty acids.** The muscles, including the

TEACH

SECTION II
(Guided and Independent Practice)

Activity 2.2

Nutrient Advertisements. Assign each student a nutrient. Have students create a short radio or TV advertisement. Students are to advertise a nutrient and try to persuade others to try it. Encourage students to choose from a variety of advertising appeals to "sell" the nutrient, such as: bandwagon—everyone uses this so you should, too; celebrity—a famous person endorses this product; sex appeal—a person might be more attractive or have attractive friends if they use that product, etc. Give students time in class to advertise. Have other students rate the advertisement and discuss its effectiveness. **(1 hr., Critical Thinking)**

The brain prefers using carbohydrates for fuel. The muscles use some carbohydrates, but they use much more fat. All body tissue is built from protein, but they can also use protein for fuel.

heart muscle, rely heavily on this fuel. Protein is used mostly to build body tissues. It also can be broken down (into **amino acids**) and used for energy. In difficult conditions, such as starvation or severe stress, the body may burn much more protein for fuel than in normal times. In summary:

- **Carbohydrate**—provides energy as glucose.
- **Fat**—provides energy as fatty acids.
- **Protein**—builds working cell parts; is made from amino acids which can also provide energy.

Recommendations for a healthy diet include holding fat to 30 percent of total calories. Carbohydrates should supply about 60 percent of calories, with protein filling in about 10 percent. Eating this way doesn't have to be complicated. A simple plan of low-fat foods can easily meet these recommendations.

Keep in mind that some foods (like peanut butter) may be very high in fat but also high in nutrients. Include these foods by balancing their fat with low-fat foods at the same meal or in the day's total foods. Peanut butter alone is over 70 percent fat, but when a little peanut butter is spread on two thick slices of bread and is eaten with a banana and a glass of nonfat milk, the fat content of the *meal* is well within recommendations. Figure 7–1 shows how to get a rough estimate of how many **grams** of fat you are allowed each day based on recommendations.

One other substance provides energy: the alcohol of alcoholic beverages. Alcohol is

---

FIGURE 7-1

How to Estimate Your Daily Fat Gram Allowance

1. Determine your daily calorie intake (see Recommended Energy Intakes in Appendix B in the back of the book). Example: 1,800.
2. Divide your total calories by 10. Example: 1,800 ÷ 10 = 180.
3. Divide the answer to Step 2 by 3. Example: 180 ÷ 3 = 60.
4. In this example, the total daily fat intake should not exceed 60 grams.

MINI GLOSSARY

carbohydrate: a class of nutrients made of sugars, that include sugar, starch, and fiber. All but fiber provide energy. Often referred to in the plural, *carbohydrates.*

fat: a class of nutrients that does not mix with water. Fat is made mostly of fatty acids, which provide energy to the body. Commonly referred to as *fats.*

protein: a class of nutrients that builds body tissues and supplies energy. Protein is made of amino acids. Referred to only in the singular, *protein.*

energy: the capacity to do work or produce heat.

glucose: the body's blood sugar; a simple form of carbohydrate.

fatty acids: simple forms of fat that supply energy fuel for most of the body's cells.

amino acids: simple forms of protein normally used to build tissues or, under some conditions, burned for energy.

grams (abbreviated *g*): units of weight in which many nutrients are measured; 28 grams equal one ounce.

Teacher Support Notes

① **Calculating Fat Allowance:** Give students some hypothetical situations to practice calculating the amount of fat a person should have per day. Have them practice reading Figure B-2 in Appendix B on page 676. Ask them how many calories per day are needed for the following:
a. 19–24-year-old males (2,900); **b.** 15–18-year-old females (2,200); Ask them to calculate the maximum fat allowance in grams for each one: **a.** 96-2/3; **b.** 73-1/3.

② **Terminology Distinction:** In this text, you'll find both the singular, scientific usage of *carbohydrate* and *fat*, and the more common, plural forms. *Carbohydrate* and *fat* are often referred to in the plural because individual members of their classes have specific effects on the body. This is not the case with *protein*. Since the body uses all members of the protein class in the same way as amino acids, this class is referred to only in the singular.

Nutrient Review. Have students keep their books open. Start with one student and ask for the name of one nutrient. The next student will add some information about that nutrient, and so on, until you get four items of information on that nutrient. The next student names another nutrient. Repeat until all the nutrients covered in this section have been reviewed. **(10 min.)**

Activity 2.4
Nutrient Flash Cards. Have students make index cards with the name of a nutrient on the front of each card. On the back of each card they will list one important function of that nutrient. They will study these flash cards in pairs until they can tell from memory what each nutrient provides for the body. **(15 min.; Reteach, Reinforce)**

Teacher Support Notes

① **Alcohol:** This paragraph contains quite a few facts, some of which may be confusing to students. You could check their comprehension with the following true/false questions. Alcohol is a nutrient. (F)
Alcohol is a poison. (T)
The body cannot tolerate large quantities of alcohol. (T)
Alcohol is an energy source. (T)
Alcohol promotes growth and repair of the body. (F)

Section II Review

Answers

1. **a.** amino acids
b. energy **c.** toxin
d. carbohydrate
e. glucose
2. carbohydrates, fats, protein
3. 60%
4. Answers will vary. The formula to follow is to first determine daily calorie intake, divide the total by 10, and then divide that answer by 3.
5. You can live only a few days without it. It provides the environment that human tissues need to live, and carries materials from place to place in the body.
6. Answers will vary.
7. Answers will vary.

Water is the most vital nutrient of all.

not a nutrient, because it does not promote growth, maintenance, or repair of the body. In fact, it is a **toxin**: the body can tolerate it in small quantities but in larger quantities is poisoned by it. Still, because people do drink alcohol, and because the body can turn it into fat, it has to be counted as an energy source. ①

The other nutrients, vitamins and minerals, help release the energy that is locked in carbohydrate, fat, and protein.

As for water, it is the major substance of which bodies are made. About 60 percent of your body's weight is water. Water is the most vital nutrient; you can live only a few days without it. Water carries materials from place to place in the body. It also provides the environment that human tissues need to live. Your body loses about six to eight cups of water daily as **urine** and sweat, and in exhaled breath. You must replace all the water you lose, so you need to drink between six and eight glasses of water and other beverages each day.

 Nutrients fall into six classes. Carbohydrates, fats, and protein yield energy the body can use. Vitamins and minerals help with energy release and perform other tasks. Water is the most vital nutrient.

SECTION II REVIEW

Answer the following questions on a sheet of paper.
Learning the Vocabulary
The vocabulary terms in this section are *carbohydrate, fat, protein, energy, glucose, fatty acids, amino acids, grams, toxin,* and *urine.*
1. Match the following phrases with the appropriate terms:
   a. building blocks of protein
   b. ability to create heat
   c. a poison
   d. supplies the body with glucose
   e. the body's blood sugar

Learning the Facts
2. Which nutrients yield energy the body can use?
3. What percentage of the total calories in your diet should be supplied by carbohydrates?
4. Estimate your daily fat gram allowance.
5. Why is water considered to be the most vital nutrient?

Making Life Choices
6. Make a list of the foods you ate for breakfast this morning. How well did your choices agree with the Dietary Guidelines for Americans (page 164)? Which foods were high, and which were low, in fat? in sugar? Discuss any changes that you think you should make.
7. Are you an athlete? Do you drink enough water? Why is it so important for an athlete to replenish his or her body with water?

SECTION III

Energy from Food

The term **calories** is familiar to everyone as a measure of how "fattening" a food is. A more accurate definition of *calorie* is *a unit used to measure energy*. The calorie count of a food does reflect its fattening power. If you consume more carbohydrate, fat, and protein than you need, these nutrients will be stored in your body, mostly as fat. You should remember, though, that calories are more precisely units of energy, not units of body fat. Figure 7–2 below shows the energy contributed by carbohydrate, fat, and protein.

The body gets its energy chiefly from two fuels: glucose and fat. The glucose is stored in the liver and muscles as **glycogen**. The fat, as you know, is stored mostly under the skin as body fat. The body's stores of glycogen are small, so you must eat regularly to maintain them. A regulatory center in the brain known as the **hypothalamus** sends out a hunger signal when blood glucose gets too low. If you don't eat, the body starts to use its four or so hours' worth of glycogen (stored in your liver) to provide glucose. The liver is generous with its glycogen—it releases it into the blood for use by the brain and other tissues. The muscles, on the other hand, keep their glycogen for their own use only. Chapter 10 tells more about the use of glycogen in muscles.

When you eat in response to your hunger, you replenish your fuels. Within seconds after eating carbohydrates, your blood glucose rises. Your liver and muscle cells store some extra glucose as glycogen. If still more glucose is available, the liver changes it, along with any excess protein, to fat and releases the fat into the blood. The fat cells in fat tissue pick up this fat and store it. Fat that comes from food isn't changed much in the body. It is stored in the fat cells as is. As a result of the body's storage of both glycogen and fat you'll have two reserve fuel supplies to draw on the next time you have to postpone eating.

When you get hungry, what should you eat? One obvious choice might seem to be a candy bar "for quick energy." It is true that the body can quickly raise its blood glucose from the concentrated sugar in candy. The only trouble is that a dose of sugar by itself lasts only a short time in the blood. It is quickly used or stored. You'll soon be hungry again, and possibly shaky besides.

A better choice than candy is a **balanced meal**—that is, a meal that contains many kinds of food that offer carbohydrate, fat, and protein all together. Here's why a balanced meal is better:

MINI GLOSSARY

toxin: a poison.
urine: fluid wastes removed from the body by the kidneys.
calories: units used to measure energy. Calories indicate how much energy in a food can be used by the body or stored in body fat.
glycogen: the form in which the liver and muscles store glucose.
hypothalamus (high-po-THALL-uh-mus): a brain regulatory center.
balanced meal: a meal with foods to provide the right amounts of carbohydrate, fat, and protein.

FIGURE 7-2
Energy Contributions of Carbohydrate, Fat, and Protein

- Fat =   9 calories per gram.
- Carbohydrate =   4 calories per gram.
- Protein =   4 calories per gram.

EVALUATE
SECTION III

CLOSE
SECTION III

FOCUS
SECTION IV

Activity 3.3
Balanced Meal/Candy Bar Comparison. Have students write three reasons to eat a balanced meal rather than a candy bar, when hungry. **(15 min.; Reteach, Reinforce)**

Activity 3.4
How Calories Relate to Energy. Have students write a definition of a calorie, explain how calories are related to energy for the body, and tell what happens to extra calories. **(10 min.; Reteach, Reinforce)**

In this section students will learn:
1. The differences between the three types of carbohydrates and the role of each in the body.
2. How much fiber is recommended daily and what foods supply that fiber.
3. How to analyze their diets for the rec-

Teacher Support Notes

① **Foods Contain Mixtures:** Practically all foods contain mixtures of the three energy-yielding nutrients. Foods are sometimes classified, however, by the *predominant* nutrient. It is incorrect to call meat a protein; it is a *protein-rich* food. Beef, for example, contains fat as well as protein. A *carbohydrate-rich* food such as corn also contains fat and protein. Only a few refined foods are pure, single-nutrient foods; the most common ones being sugar, which is almost pure carbohydrate, and oil, which is almost pure fat.

Section III Review
Answers
1. calories
2. glycogen
3. hypothalamus
4. If you consume more carbohydrate, fat, and protein than you need, these nutrients will be stored in your body, mostly as fat.
5. The body uses the glycogen stored in the liver.
6. Answers to this question are contained in the three bulleted items at the top of this page.
7. Answers will vary.

170

- The carbohydrate in the meal provides a quick source of glucose energy.
- The fat in the meal slows down **digestion,** making the glucose last longer. The fat also provides most of the meal's energy (calories).

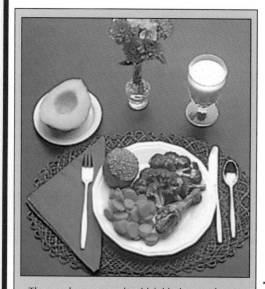

The meal presents a healthful balance of carbohydrate, fat, and protein. Less than 30 percent of its calories are from fat, and about 60 percent are from carbohydrate. The rest come from protein. Note the moderate meat portion and the generous portions of vegetables and fruit. The bread is without butter, and the beverage is nonfat milk. Total calories: about 500.

A mistake people commonly make is to think that if fat should contribute 30 percent of the calories, then it should take up a third of the plate. On the contrary: a spoon of fat contains more than twice as many calories as a spoon of pure protein or of carbohydrate, and much of the fat in a meal is invisible. In this 500-calorie meal, the only visible fat is in the chicken skin, and yet fat contributes almost 30 percent of the calories.

Figure 7–3 A Balanced Meal

- The protein in the meal slows down the body's use of carbohydrates, also making the glucose last longer.

An example of a balanced meal is shown in Figure 7–3.

Key Points ▶ *The body stores any extra energy from dietary carbohydrates, fats, or protein as glycogen or fat. The best source of energy for the body is a balanced meal.*

SECTION III REVIEW

Answer the following questions on a sheet of paper.

Learning the Vocabulary
The vocabulary terms in this section are *calories, glycogen, hypothalamus, balanced meal,* and *digestion.*
Fill in the blanks with the correct answer.
1. The units used to measure energy in food are _____.
2. The body's storage form of sugar is called _____.
3. The _____ sends out the hunger signal.

Learning the Facts
4. Explain how the number of calories in a food reflects its fattening power.
5. How does the body meet its glucose need if you have not eaten?
6. Why is a balanced meal considered the best source of energy for the body?

Making Life Choices
7. Some people become obsessed with counting calories. Have you or anyone you know ever become obsessed with counting calories? What was the result? Explain some of the dangers of such an obsession.

SECTION IV

The Carbohydrates

You have already read about two carbohydrates important in the *body*: (1) the sugar glucose in the blood and (2) the stored

Activity 4.1
Sugar in Soda. Bring a teaspoon, sugar, and a glass to class. Ask students how much sugar they put in coffee or tea. Start putting sugar in the glass and have the students tell you when to stop. Keep measuring until you have put in 10–15 teaspoons. Hold it up, and ask if they would drink something poured into the

glass with that much sugar. Explain that this is the amount of sugar in one can of soda. Discuss. **(10 min.)**

TEACH
SECTION IV
(Guided and Independent Practice)

Activity 4.2
Illustrating Starch, Fiber, and Sugar. Have students draw a diagram illustrating the characteristics that starch,

fiber, and sugar have in common. Then have them illustrate differences between starch, fiber, and sugar. Have students present these to the class, explaining the differences and similarities, and how they chose to represent these on paper. **(45 min.; Reteach, Reinforce)**

---

form of glucose, glycogen, in the liver and muscles. Carbohydrates important in the *diet* are **starch, fiber,** and **sugar.** The body converts the starch and sugars in food into blood glucose. Fiber passes unchanged through the digestive tract. ①

Starch

Starch, the main carbohydrate in grains and vegetables, is the chief energy source for people around the world. Starch serves the human body well. It provides the body with the glucose it needs in a form the body uses best. And that's not all that starch does. If the starchy foods you eat are foods like whole-grain breads (not refined white bread), potatoes (not potato chips), or whole-grain cereals (not the sugary kind), then your body receives many of the *other* nutrients (vitamins and minerals) it needs, along with a steady supply of glucose. ②

Most people would do well to boost their intakes of starchy foods. The brain needs glucose to perform at its best. Studies of schoolchildren show that those who do not eat breakfast cannot concentrate on school work or pay attention as long as their well-fed peers can. It seems that a lack of glucose in the blood plays at least some role in the disadvantage of kids who try to work on empty stomachs. Their bodies run out of glucose. Starchy breakfast foods like cereal, or even just toast, may be enough to keep them going. For the child who has not eaten, though, the morning may be lost altogether.

In another study, college students were unable to pay attention when their blood glucose ran low in the late afternoon. Students who ate a carbohydrate-rich snack in the afternoon performed better on tasks of thinking and memory than other students who ate no carbohydrates. The carbohydrates in foods such as grains, breads, cereals, pasta,

potatoes, and beans, and the sugars of fruits and vegetables, provide the brain with the glucose it needs to perform at its best.

> **Key Points** *Starch is the main source of energy for the world's people. Starchy foods provide the body with glucose and many other nutrients.*

Fiber—Not an Energy Source

Another form of carbohydrate in foods—fiber—is not digestible by human beings and so provides no calories. However, it helps to maintain the health of the digestive tract. As is true for starch, most people would do well to obtain more fiber, too. The body needs about 25 grams of fiber each day to remain healthy. Each serving of any food listed here provides about 2 grams of fiber:

- Fruits in the natural state with skins, 1 piece; ¾ cup berries; ½ cantaloupe; 2 prunes.
- Whole grains including 1 slice whole wheat bread or 2 slices cracked wheat (light brown) bread; 2 Rye Crisp, Triscuit, or other whole wheat crackers; ½ shredded wheat biscuit; ⅓ cup any bran cereal; 1 teaspoon wheat bran or 1 tablespoon All-bran cereal; 1½ cup puffed wheat cereal; 2 cups popped popcorn.

MINI GLOSSARY

digestion: the breaking down of food into nutrients the body can use. The *digestive system* is a series of body organs that break foods down and absorb their nutrients. (See Chapter 6 for details of the system.)
starch: a carbohydrate, the main food energy source for human beings.
fiber: indigestible substances in foods, made mostly of carbohydrate.
sugar: a kind of carbohydrate found both in food and in the body.

Teacher Support Notes

① **Glucose:** Emphasize that glucose is the body's main source of energy. Students might be more apt to remember this if you tell them that, indirectly, the energy they get from food—glucose—originally came from the sun (since photosynthesis, which produces glucose, depends on the sun's energy).
② **Starch:** Tell students that starch is simply a word that refers to glucose as it's stored in plants. Plants can't store glucose in its sugar form because glucose is soluble in water and would be washed away. Starch, however, is insoluble. You may want to use the overhead transparency "Photosynthesis Produced Glucose" to show students how this all-important nutrient is produced by plants.

EVALUATE
SECTION IV

Activity 4.3
Analyzing Diets for Fiber. Have students analyze a friend's diet for sources of fiber. They should calculate the grams of fiber found in food items and make suggestions to add to the diet until the recommended daily intake of

fiber is achieved. **(30 min.; Reteach, Reinforce)**

CLOSE
SECTION IV

Activity 4.4
Benefits of Carbohydrates, Fiber, and Sugar. Have students review the benefits of carbohydrates, fiber, and sugar in a person's diet. Ask for

any negative effects associated with having too much or too little of any of these in your diet. **(5 min., Reteach, Reinforce)**

Activity 4.5
Nutrient Skits. Divide the class into four groups of four or more students. Assign each group one of the four nutrients discussed in this chapter. Tell students to create a skit that shows the importance of the nutrient, and the role it takes in the

---

Fast Facts

The average American consumes about 90 pounds of sugar every year.

Teacher Support Notes

① **Fiber Prevents Disease:** Have students close their books and name diseases that fiber helps prevent. (appendicitis, heart disease, diabetes, cancer) Ask them to explain how fiber does this. (It binds with various materials and carries them out of the body.)

② **Fiber vs. Processed Foods:** Ask students to make a list of the fruit and other foods they eat that are good sources of fiber. In a second column ask them to list foods they eat that have been processed to the point where most of the fiber has been removed, as in the examples given in the text. Ask them whether or not they are getting enough fiber, and what changes they could make to increase their fiber intake.

☎ Where to Call

Alliance for Food & Fiber
Food Safety Hotline
1-800-266-0200

172

- Vegetables, lightly cooked, ½ cup most types; 1 cup raw celery; 2 cups lettuce; ½ cup most cooked dried beans; 1 large tomato; 1 small potato (in jacket); ⅓ cup corn.
- Other sources: 2 1/2 teaspoons peanut butter; 1/4 cup most nuts; 1 large pickle; 1 tablespoon strawberry jam.

Most types of fiber in foods move through the digestive tract almost unchanged—in one end and out the other. They aid in digestion by making the digestive tract contents (stools) soft and bulky. This subject may not be a glamorous one, but it is of interest to anyone who suffers from a lack of fiber. Fiber lack leads to **constipation** (hard, sluggish stools), **hemorrhoids** (swollen, painful veins in the **rectum** that bulge out from straining to pass hard stools), and many other painful intestinal ills.

Fiber also serves the body well in keeping the intestinal contents moving. This can help to prevent infection of the appendix (appendicitis). Also, fiber binds with cholesterol and carries it out of the body in the stools, reducing the risk of heart disease. Fiber also helps to balance the blood glucose and so helps to control the most common form of the disease diabetes. Some fibers bind cancer-causing agents in the digestive tract. This keeps these agents from touching the intestinal walls, and from entering the body, thereby reducing the risk of cancer. In all of these ① ways, fiber helps fight diseases.

Fiber may also help to prevent the accumulation of too much body fat. The person who eats fiber-rich foods chews longer and fills up sooner on fewer calories than the person who eats too little fiber. It is hard to eat a diet high in fiber and also gain weight.

Clearly, fiber benefits the body, but is there such a thing as too much fiber? There certainly is. Some years ago, many college students overdid a high-fiber diet, much to their digestive distress. They suffered dangerously severe diarrhea. Just recently, a man wolfed down a half dozen oat bran muffins. He required emergency surgery to remove a blockage of bran lodged in his intestine. Too much of anything, especially in nutrition, is as harmful as too little.

Plant foods are high in fiber. Plants with their skins and seeds intact are especially rich in fiber. Fiber can be destroyed when foods are refined or cooked. Apples have more fiber than applesauce. Apple juice has none. Baked potatoes with the skins have more fiber than mashed potatoes. Potato chips have almost none. If you want to choose foods with enough fiber for your health, ② choose whole grains, whole fruits, and whole vegetables most of the time. Eat some of these foods cooked lightly, and eat some raw.

> **Key Points** *Fiber is a form of carbohydrate that is not digestible by human beings. Fiber helps maintain the health of the digestive tract.*

Sugars

The last type of dietary carbohydrates is the sugars. All sugars are chemically similar to glucose and can be converted into glucose in the body. The four sugars most important in human nutrition are:

- glucose (the body's fuel),
- fructose (the sweet sugar of fruits and honey),
- sucrose (table sugar),
- lactose (milk sugar).

A spoonful of honey has almost one and a half times as many calories as the same amount of sugar, but in terms of nutrients they are equally poor.

body. The skits should be entertaining as well as instructional for those who are watching. You might require that students use simple visual aids to explain each role in the skit, or to make their points more understandable. Create a set of criteria by which the students can assess the skits. For example: Rate each item on a scale of 1 to 5 with 1 being "poorly done," 3 as "satisfactory," and 5 being "excellent," with the other numbers falling between the rankings

accordingly. **(35 min. to create, 50 min. to perform, Cooperative Learning)**

FOCUS
SECTION V

In this section students will learn:
1. Ways in which too much fat in a person's diet can have a negative effect on health.
2. How to estimate their daily fat gram

allowances.
3. Strategies to lower the amount of fat in their diets.

Activity 5.1
Health Risks Associated With Being Overweight. (This activity is to help students increase their awareness of the emotional as well as the medical aspects of being overweight. The hope is

(continued on next page)

CONSUMER AWARENESS — Honey versus Sugar

Some salespeople market honey as the ideal substitute for sugar. They say it offers nutrients, so it is not empty calories.

It's true that honey contains tiny bits of a few vitamins and minerals. Compared with a person's daily need, however, these nutrients don't add up to much. A tablespoon of honey (65 calories) offers 1/10 milligram of iron, for example. An adult's daily need for iron may be 15 milligrams. To meet the need for iron, then, the adult would need 150 tablespoons of honey in a day—almost 10,000 calories of honey! (Most people can

eat only 2,000 to 3,000 total calories a day without getting fat.)

The nutrients in honey just do not add up as fast as the calories do. Therefore honey, like sugar, is a relatively empty-calorie food.

CRITICAL THINKING

1. *If honey has too many calories and too few nutrients for health, what sorts of sweet foods do you suppose might better provide for the body's needs?*
2. *Why do you think so?*

In foods, the four sugars just named come in diluted form mostly from fruits, vegetables and milk. They come in concentrated form as sugar, honey, and other sweets.

Nutritionists recommend that you consume large quantities of fruits and vegetables that contain sugars, but they urge you in the same breath to "avoid consuming too much sugar." What's the difference?

The answer lies in the phrase **empty calories**. When you eat an apple, you receive about 100 calories from the sugars in it, together with a few of the vitamins, a moderate dose of fiber, and some minerals. By contrast, a 12-ounce regular cola beverage gives you about 150 calories from sugar without any other nutrients. The calories you receive from the cola are empty calories. Another reason experts say to avoid sugar: the bacteria that cause

dental caries (cavities) thrive on sticky sugar.

 Sugars may benefit health when they are consumed in fruits or milk. Sugars may harm health when eaten in the form of too many concentrated sweets.

MINI GLOSSARY

constipation: hard, slow stools that are difficult to eliminate; often a result of too little fiber in the diet.
hemorrhoids: swollen, painful rectal veins; often a result of constipation.
rectum: the last part of the digestive tract, through which stools are eliminated (see Chapter 6).
empty calories: a popular term referring to foods that contribute much energy (calories) but too little of the nutrients.

Teacher Support Notes

① **Critical Thinking Answers:**
1. Fruit is one possible answer. Encourage students to brainstorm other answers and to defend those answers.
2. Fruit also contains fiber, and larger amounts of vitamins and minerals.

Fast Facts

Some examples of empty-calorie foods are soda pop, soft drinks, punches, "sports drinks," candies, sugar, honey, jelly, syrup, marshmallows, candy bars, most granola bars, candy-coated nuts and fruits, frosted toaster pastries, doughnuts, most frosted cakes, fried snacks, tortilla chips, cheese curls, "light" taco shells, butter, margarine, oils, shortening, salad dressings, gravies.

that students will become more sensitive and empathetic toward overweight people. You should consider whether there are any overweight students in your class who might be sensitive about their weight before you assign this activity.) Ask students to name health risks related to being overweight. Ask students to describe feelings that a person might have who is noticeably overweight. Have students read their answers and discuss. Tell them that weight can often be managed by proper nutrition and exercise. Tell them that it is not easy, but it might be the price someone would pay not to go through life being overweight and at an increased risk of health problems. **(10 min.)**

TEACH
SECTION V
(Guided and Independent Practice)
Activity 5.2
Fat as Insulation and Energy.
Have students research the role of fats in arctic animals and migratory animals. Discuss how animals prepare themselves for the cold or for migration by eating extra foods, which convert to fat. (They do not necessarily eat extra fat, but extra foods.)

Section IV Review
Answers

1. Fiber benefits the digestive tract because it softens stools. Lack of fiber leads to constipation.
2. Hemorrhoids develop as a result of straining to pass hard stools. Fiber helps soften stools.
3. empty calories
4. Starchy foods provide the body with glucose which the brain needs to function properly.
5. Answers will vary; could include: lack of fiber leads to constipation, hemorrhoids, and other intestinal ills; fiber helps to prevent appendicitis, reduces risk of heart disease, balances blood glucose, helps control most common form of diabetes, keeps cancer-causing agents from touching intestinal walls, and assists in maintaining balanced weight.
6. Large amounts of sugar equal empty calories. Dental cavities thrive on sticky sugar.
7. Answers will vary; could include: grains, breads, cereals, pasta, potatoes, and beans; broccoli, apples, and pears with skin; regular colas and concentrated sweets.
8. Answers will vary.

___ **S**ECTION **IV** ___ **R**EVIEW ___

Answer the following questions on a sheet of paper.
Learning the Vocabulary
The vocabulary terms in this section are *starch, fiber, sugar, constipation, hemorrhoids, rectum,* and *empty calories.*
1. Explain the relationship between fiber and constipation.
2. What does fiber have to do with hemorrhoids?
3. Foods that contribute a lot of calories but insufficient nutrients contain _____.

Learning the Facts
4. Explain the effect of starchy foods on brain functioning.
5. Why is it beneficial to obtain adequate amounts of fiber in your diet?
6. What danger is there in consuming a large amount of sugar?
7. Give examples for each: foods high in carbohydrates, foods high in fiber, foods high in sugar.

Making Life Choices
8. Make a list of your ten favorite foods. Which ones on your list do you suspect are empty calorie foods? Which ones do you think are the most nutritious?

SECTION V

The Fats

Nearly all the body's tissues (all but the brain and nervous system) can use fat to provide most of the energy they need. Fat is the major source of fuel for the body.

The body has small stores of carbohydrate (glycogen) and not much protein to spare, but it can store fat in almost unlimited amounts. Fat is stored in a layer of cells beneath the skin and also in many pads in the chest and abdomen. As well as providing energy, fat helps to insulate the body from cold and from quick

HEALTH
STRATEGIES

Getting the Fat Out of Foods

To get the fat out of foods:

1. Choose foods that have been grilled, roasted, broiled, boiled, baked, or microwaved. Don't choose fried.
2. Tell the food server "No gravy," or cut your portion of gravy by half.
3. Pizza can be high in fat. Order it with thick crust and more vegetables than meat. Never ask for double cheese.
4. Choose lean meats with no visible fat. Don't eat meats with fat ground in, such as sausages and cold cuts.
5. Reduce meat servings by half. Load up on grains, beans, and vegetables.
6. Use canned tuna or chicken packed in water, not in oil.
7. Trim all the fat you can see from the meat on your plate.
8. Remove skin from chicken or turkey before eating.
9. Use oil-free salad dressings, reduced-calorie mayonnaise, and diet margarine. Use butter-flavored sprinkles instead of butter.
10. If you must fry something, use cooking spray instead of oil or butter.
11. Choose low-fat or nonfat dairy products. Use nonfat yogurt or nonfat sour cream substitute in place of regular sour cream.

These fats insulate them from the cold temperatures and provide energy for their bodies when food is scarce, either in winter, or during a migration when they need extra energy to make the trip. **(1 hr. or more; Extend, Enrich, Interdisciplinary)**

Activity 5.3
Nutrition-Smart Parties. Sometimes the foods served at parties are high in fat. For example, chips and dip are fat-tening. Many people gather around the food table at a party to talk or meet people. Ask students to suggest unique ways to meet people at a party without hanging around the food table. Have students imagine they are planning a party. What could they plan for guests? What activities could they plan so that fattening party foods are not such a major attraction? **(10 min., Critical Thinking)**

EVALUATE
SECTION V

Activity 5.4
Negative and Positive Impacts on Health. Have students describe how being overweight can have a negative impact on a person's health. Have them describe activities that have a positive

(continued on next page)

---

changes in temperature. It also cushions the body, protecting it from bruises, strains, and breaks.

Forms of Fat

The fats you eat come in two forms—**saturated** and **unsaturated** (unsaturated fat includes **polyunsaturated** fat). For people who are developing heart and artery disease, the most important dietary preventive step to take is to reduce their *total* fat intakes. At the same time they should switch from saturated fat to mostly unsaturated fat in foods. Saturated fats come mainly from animal sources, including meats, butter, and cream. They tend to be solid at room temperature. Unsaturated fats come primarily from vegetable oils, including olive oil, corn oil, and canola oil. These tend to be liquid at room temperature. Some foods high in *unsaturated* fats, including the *polyunsaturated* type, are:

- Avocados, nuts, seeds, olives, peanut butter.
- Margarine, mayonnaise, salad dressing, oils (liquid types).

Some foods high in *saturated* fats are:

- Bacon, sausage, cold cuts, lunch meats, hotdogs, hamburgers, chitterlings.
- Butter, lard, coconut and coconut oil, cream (sour or sweet), cheeses, palm oil.

Another form of fat is **cholesterol.** Some cholesterol is made from other fats in the body. Cholesterol is essential for the health of each cell. Too much cholesterol, though, is linked with heart and artery disease. Cholesterol forms deposits that build up along arteries and increase the risk of heart attacks and strokes. People trying to lower blood cholesterol cannot do so by limiting only their cholesterol intakes. They must limit their total fat intakes, and especially limit their saturated fat intakes. Details about dietary fats and blood cholesterol are provided in Chapter 18.

Key Points *Fat is the major source of fuel for the body. Food fat comes in saturated and unsaturated forms. Saturated fats come mainly from animal sources. Unsaturated fats come mainly from plant sources (vegetable oils).*

Benefits of Reducing Fat Intake

More than any other diet factor, a high fat intake contributes to disease. Heart disease and many forms of cancer are linked to high fat intakes. Many other diseases may be too, including arthritis, gallbladder disease, diabetes, and others. The most important dietary steps you can take to prevent these diseases are to control your fat intake and to keep your weight within a healthy range. The Health Strategies features on the opposite page and on page 177 describe some choices you can make to cut down on fat.

Reducing fat intake offers another benefit to people who wish to cut calories. A spoon of fat contains more than twice as many calories as a spoon of sugar or pure protein. By removing the fat from a food, you can drastically cut its calorie count. Figure 7–4 on the next page shows that the single most effective step you can take to reduce the calorie count of a food is to eat it with less fat.

MINI GLOSSARY

saturated: concerning fats and health, those fats associated strongly with heart and artery disease; mainly fats from animal sources.

unsaturated: concerning fats and health, fats less associated with heart and artery disease; mainly fats from plant sources.

polyunsaturated: a type of unsaturated fat especially useful as a replacement for saturated fat in a heart-healthy diet.

cholesterol: a type of fat made by the body from saturated fat; a minor part of fat in foods.

Teacher Support Notes

① **Saturated vs. Unsaturated:** Try the following exercise to help students remember which type of fat they should choose and which type they should avoid. Put the following eight words on the board in random order: *animal, solid, saturated, avoid, plants, liquid, unsaturated, choose.* On a sheet of paper, have each student separate the eight words into two separate columns with the four related words in each column. (the first four words listed should be in one column, the second four words in another column) Have one student come to the front of the class and write the words in the proper columns. Then ask students to brainstorm ways to remember which fats they should choose and which they should avoid.

EVALUATE
(Continued)

impact on their health. **(10 min.; Reteach, Reinforce)**

CLOSE
SECTION V

Activity 5.5

Fat Review. Have students name as many reasons as they can think of to monitor the amount of fats in their diets. **(5 min.; Reteach, Reinforce)**

FOCUS
SECTION VI

In this section students will learn:
1. The functions and importance of protein.

2. The difference between a complete protein and an incomplete protein.

Activity 6.1
Protein Functions. Ask students to write down how protein functions in the body. Then have them call out their responses and make a list on the overhead or blackboard. Students should make their own complete lists. Then have students read this section. Each time they

Teacher Support Notes

① **Trimming Fat:** Ask students to look at the pairs of pictures. Would it be difficult for them to pick the food with less fat in any of the three situations? What choice would be the most difficult for them to make? Have they ever tried that choice? Suggest that they give it a try if they haven't. They could find that they like the choices with less fat just as well.

Section V Review
Answers

1. Saturated fat comes from animal sources and is usually solid at room temperature. Unsaturated fat comes from vegetable sources and is liquid at room temperature.
2. cholesterol
3. major source of fuel
4. reduces diseases, including heart disease, many forms of cancer, arthritis, gallbladder disease, diabetes, and diseases made worse by overweight; it also reduces calorie count of a food
5. Answers will vary. Refer to the Health Strategies on page 174.
6–8. Answers will vary.

176 UNIT 3 Your Physical Health

FIGURE 7-4
Fat and Calories ①

Fat hides calories in food. When you trim fat, you trim calories.

Large pork chop with ½ inch of fat (352 calories).

Large potato with 1 tablespoon butter and 1 tablespoon sour cream (350 calories).

Whole milk, 1 cup (150 calories).

Large pork chop with fat trimmed off (265 calories).

Plain large potato (220 calories).

Nonfat milk, 1 cup (90 calories).

Key Points *A high-fat diet is linked to many diseases. When you remove the fat from a food, you drastically cut its calorie count.*

SECTION V   REVIEW

Answer the following questions on a sheet of paper.

Learning the Vocabulary
The vocabulary terms in this section are *saturated, unsaturated, polyunsaturated,* and *cholesterol.*
1. What is the difference between saturated and unsaturated fat?
2. A type of fat made by the body from saturated fat is called _____.

Learning the Facts
3. What is the main function of fat in the body?

4. List two benefits of limiting the amount of fat in your diet.
5. List three steps you can take to control the amount of fat in your diet.

Making Life Choices
6. Give a few suggestions on how you might best keep your blood cholesterol level down through your dietary choices.
7. Generally speaking, most of the foods from fast-food restaurants are high in fat and lacking in other essential nutrients. Do you find yourself eating at this type of restaurant often? Why or why not?
8. Do you know of any low-fat foods that fast-food restaurants serve? What are they?

TEACH
SECTION VI
(Guided and Independent Practice)

Activity 6.2
Fiber In A Vegetarian Diet. Using Figure 7–5, have students put together a vegetarian diet for a week. Make sure the necessary amino acids are included.

Have students underline sources of protein, circle sources of fiber, and check those that provide carbohydrates. They should put a dot by those that are high in fat. Have students write the answers to the following questions: "Would you eat this diet, why or why not? Does it contain the recommended amount of fiber per day? Do you think it is easier to get your daily fiber requirement on a vegetarian diet?" **(30 min.; Extend, Enrich)**

Activity 6.3
Reports on Countries with Health Problems. Have students research countries that have extensive problems with starvation and malnutrition, and prepare a report on the situation. Include the following information: What, if any, aid does the U.S. government provide? How widespread is the problem? What are the concerns of those directly

(continued on next page)

SECTION VI

Protein

Protein is well known as the body-building nutrient, the material of strong muscles—and rightly so. No new living tissue can be built without it, for protein is part of every cell, every bone, the blood, and every other tissue. Proteins are the body's machinery—they do the cells' work. The energy to fuel that work comes from carbohydrate and fat. Protein itself can be used to provide energy, especially if the other fuels are scarce. However, its role as a fuel source is normally minor.

Proteins are made of building blocks, the amino acids. A set of 20 different amino acids form proteins (much as letters of the alphabet form words and sentences). Your body can make some of the amino acids for itself. The other amino acids, which the body cannot make, are the **essential amino acids.** You must eat foods that contain them.

Your body loses protein every day. Digestive tract cells wear out and exit the body in the stools. Skin cells flake off or are rubbed off. Hair and nails (made of protein) grow longer daily and are shed or trimmed away. An adult loses about one-quarter cup of pure protein a day. People need to eat protein-containing foods every day to replace the protein they lose.

You know you are eating protein when you eat meats, fish, poultry, eggs, cheese, and milk. Plant foods such as grains, beans (chili beans, lima beans, and the like), and other vegetables eaten in quantity also provide protein. In fact, a teenager receives more than a day's protein from one egg, two cups of milk, and an assortment of grains and vegetables—without a single serving of meat. Yet many teens choose

①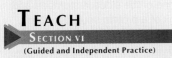

HEALTH STRATEGIES

Nutritious Fast Foods

To select the most nutritious fast foods:

1. Choose broiled sandwiches with lettuce, tomatoes, and other goodies—and hold the mayo. Fried fish and chicken sandwiches are cooked in fat and are at least as fatty as hamburgers.
2. Don't order french fries—order a salad instead.
3. Order chili with more beans than meat. Choose a soft-shell bean burrito over meaty tacos with fried shells.
4. Try a baked potato, light on the toppings, for a change.
5. Drink low-fat milk, not a milk shake.

② two or three eggs for breakfast, a couple of hamburgers for lunch, and a big portion of roast for dinner.

Meats, eggs, and cheese are often high in fat and calories, and all are low in fiber. Too much of these foods can threaten health. Vegetables, beans, grains, and low-fat milk are better choices for providing most of the day's protein.

Well-informed **vegetarians** can easily get enough protein from plant foods alone.

MINI GLOSSARY

essential amino acids: amino acids that are needed, but cannot be made by the body; they must be eaten in foods.
vegetarians: people who omit meat, fish, and poultry from their diets. Some vegetarians also omit milk products and eggs.

Teacher Support Notes

① **Taking Action:** Have students number from 1 to 5 and then rate the five strategies as to how much improvement each would make on their diets if it were implemented. For each number they should write "big improvement," "small improvement," or "no improvement." After completing this, have them go back through the list and write "will do" or "won't do" next to each strategy. If they write "won't do," ask them why.

② **Too Much Protein?** Have students describe whether or not this last sentence describes their eating habits. How many of them think they eat more protein than they need each day? Do they see a negative side to this? (Many protein-rich foods contain high amounts of saturated fat.)

Teach (Continued)

involved? **(1 hr.; Interdisciplinary, Multicultural)**

Evaluate
SECTION VI

Activity 6.4

Essay on Necessity of Protein. Have students answer in essay form, "Why is protein necessary in the diet?" **(10 min.; Reteach, Reinforce)**

Close
SECTION VI

Activity 6.5

Protein Stumpers. Divide the class into two teams. Give each side five sec-

onds to think of a food that is a source of protein-rich food. Have them go back and forth until one of the sides is stumped and cannot think of a protein source in time. The other team wins. **(10 min.; Reteach, Reinforce)**

Activity 6.6

Multicultural Food Fair. Have students pick out a country they would like to represent. Ask them to bring two small

---

Teacher Support Notes

① **Protein's Roles:**
Here is some additional information that should help impress upon students the importance of daily protein intake. In addition to the growth and maintenance of cells, enzymes, and hormones, protein aids in the following:

• Production of antibodies—Antibodies inactivate foreign particles of proteins that invade the body, thereby developing immunity

• Maintain an electrolyte balance—Proteins help to regulate the quantity of fluids in the body. Cell proteins also help to hold fluids and electrolytes in their proper chambers.

• Acid–base balance— Proteins in the blood act as buffers to maintain the proper balance between acids and bases.

✐ Fast Facts

Some bacon substitutes have more fat than the real thing. For example, sizzling pork strips get 80% of their calories from fat, compared to 75% for bacon.

178

---

178 UNIT 3 Your Physical Health

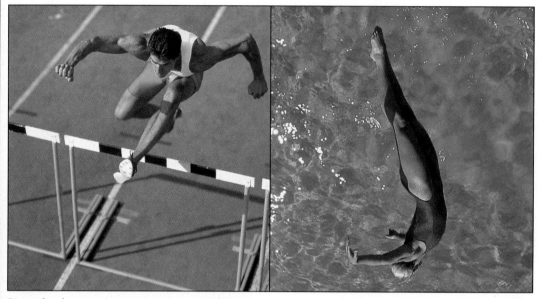

For perfect functioning, every nutrient is needed.

Figure 7–5 below lists some high-protein vegetarian food combinations.

Animal proteins supply all of the essential amino acids in the right amounts for building human tissues, but most plant proteins contain limited amounts of certain of the essential amino acids. To build ① muscles, make new cell parts, and grow, the body needs all of the essential amino acids. Therefore, single plant proteins alone usually won't serve the need. People who eat only plant foods must eat combinations of them each day to receive the full range of needed amino acids. The food combinations

---

FIGURE 7-5

Vegetarian Protein Combinations

Choose from two or more of these columns to obtain the needed amino acids:

Grains	Beans and Peas	Seeds and Nuts	Vegetables
Barley	Dried beans	Sesame seeds	Leafy greens
Bulgur	Dried lentils	Sunflower seeds	Broccoli
Cornmeal	Dried peas	Walnuts	Others
Oats, Rice	Peanuts	Cashews	
Whole-grain breads	Soy products	Other nuts	
Pasta		Nut butters	

food dishes to class: one of their favorite nutritious dishes from home, and one nutritious dish from the country they chose to represent. Have them make a replica of the flag of the country that each dish represents, and lay each dish near its flag. Tell students to write on index cards what makes the dish nutritious. Students will go to each display and take a spoonful to taste. Have students vote on the top ten dishes. Ask those students to

bring the recipes to class and pass them out to students. Or, the top ten recipes of each class can be put into a recipe book which could be printed and sold to raise money for programs at the school. **(1 hr.; Multicultural, Extend, Enrich)**

RETEACH/BONUS

Here are some additional activities for

the various sections of this chapter. You may want to use these activities to reteach certain concepts, or you may choose them as alternatives to earlier activities. Some could also be used in conjunction with the Straight Talk feature below.

Food Choices. Before you assign the Straight Talk, have students brainstorm a list of the causes for their food

(continued on next page)

suggested in Figure 7–5 and others like them provide the full range of essential amino acids, along with starch, fiber, and many more nutrients besides.

A person who fails to consume enough protein is taking a grave risk. The body wastes away its lean tissues and is left defenseless against diseases (the immune cells are made of protein). This often happens in remote places of the world, but it also happens here among neglected and homeless children, sick people in hospitals, substance abusers, and others. Dieters who starve may notice that, within a few months of dieting, their hair begins to fall out or their skin starts to change. For most people who eat a normal diet, though, protein deficiency is almost never a problem.

Key Points *Protein is made of amino acids and serves as the building material for many body structures. The essential amino acids must be obtained from food each day. The consequences of protein deficiency are severe, but most people consume enough protein.*

SECTION VI REVIEW

Answer the following questions on a sheet of paper.

Learning the Vocabulary
The vocabulary terms in this section are *essential amino acids* and *vegetarians.*
1. Write a sentence using each vocabulary term.

Learning the Facts
2. What is the function of protein in the body?
3. What foods are the best sources of protein?
4. What are some signs of protein deficiency?

Making Life Choices
5. How can vegetarians best meet the body's protein needs without consuming animal proteins? Develop your own vegetarian protein combinations.
6. Most teenagers seem to get more than enough protein to meet their bodies' needs. Do you think the protein-rich foods you eat are the best ones for your health? Why or why not?

Answers to Fact or Fiction

Here are the answers to the questions at the start of the chapter.

1. False. Eating foods with enough nutrients is important, but equally important is to keep from eating too much or too little food. **2.** True. **3.** True. **4.** False. Starchy foods provide the body with the glucose it needs in the form it uses best. **5.** False. It is possible, and too much fiber can be as harmful as too little. **6.** True. **7.** False. Of all the things in foods that cause diseases, fat is by far the biggest culprit. **8.** True. **9.** False. The body loses proteins from body structures every day. **10.** False. You can easily get enough protein from grains, beans, vegetables, milk, and eggs without eating any meat.

choices. Then ask them which of these factors they as individuals have direct control over. Ask students to describe situations in which other people may affect their food choices. **(5 min.)**

A Day in the Life of. . . . Show students pictures of people from newspapers or magazines who suffer from overnutrition, undernutrition, and those who are healthy. Brainstorm a list of activities with the class that an overweight, underweight, or healthy person might engage in during the day. Divide the students into ones, twos, and threes. Tell all those who are number one, that they are to write from the point of view of a healthy person, all number twos from the point of view of an overweight person, and all those who are number three from the point of view of a person who is underweight. Students are to describe a day in the life of a person with the health condition they have been assigned. They are to imagine what that person encounters and is feeling. Students should write with as much sensitivity and empathy as possible. **(30–45 min., Interdisciplinary)**

✎ **Fast Facts**

The California Avocado Commission estimated that during Super Bowl week in 1993, football fans purchased 30 million avocados and made 12 million pounds of guacamole.

Teacher Support Notes

① **Hunger vs. Appetite:** Ask students to explain the basic difference between hunger and appetite to make sure they understand this key distinction. (Hunger is *physical*; appetite is *psychological*.)

---

66 **Thoughts on Health** 99

No man in the world has more courage than the man who can stop after eating one peanut.
— ***Channing Pollock***

✉ **Where to Write**

Tufts University Diet and Nutrition Letter
80 Bolyston St.
Boston, MA 02116

STRAIGHT TALK

Food Choices— What Guides Us?

Your food choices greatly affect your health, so they are worth questioning. Why do you eat when you do? Why do you choose the foods you do? And most important, do the foods you choose supply the nutrients you need?

I eat because I'm hungry. Isn't that why most people eat?

Yes, often that is true. But **hunger,** the physical need for food, is not the only reason people eat. Another is **appetite,** the psychological desire for food. Appetite may arise in response to the sight, smell, or thought of food even when you do not need to eat. You may have an appetite when you are not hungry. An example of this occurs when a server offers dessert after you've finished eating, and suddenly you desire a piece of cake. ①

My sister gets nervous before taking her exams, and she can't eat. Why?

It is quite possible to be hungry but to have no appetite. Stress affects different people differently. Some people overeat in response to stress. This is **stress eating.** Others, like your sister, can't eat at all. Her reaction can be explained by the stress response. During stress, the body shuts down digestion, because digestion requires energy. This makes sense in times of physical danger, because muscles must have as much energy as possible to run or to fight.

During times of test taking, however, the response can cause trouble. At the very time people need to think clearly, they may run out of glucose to feed their brains.

Your sister should try to relax enough to eat. If she cannot eat, she may be able to sip a glass of chocolate milk or a milkshake. These can supply enough glucose to feed the brain for a short time.

Why do I sometimes eat when I'm bored or depressed?

People often eat in response to complex human feelings other than hunger or appetite. Sensations such as boredom, depression, or compulsion can sometimes be lessened for a while by eating. It seems that **arousal** from any kind of feelings can cause overeating, because arousal can be mistaken for hunger.

What are some other reasons people eat as they do?

Several reasons come to mind:

- Personal preference (you prefer favorite foods).
- Habit or ethnic tradition (some foods are familiar; you always eat them).
- Social pressure (they are offered; you feel you can't refuse).
- Availability (they are there and ready to eat).
- Convenience (they are quick and easy).
- Economy (you can afford them).
- Emotional needs (foods can make you feel better for a while).
- Values or beliefs (they fit your religious or political views, or honor the environmental ethic).

(Continued on next page)

Philosophical Chairs. Divide the chairs in your room into three sections. Two groups of chairs face each other—these will be pro and con sides. The other group will be against a wall facing the middle of the other two sections. The persons who will sit in the middle group are the undecided individuals.

Make a statement about a controversial issue dealing with nutrition, such as, "There is enough stress in our lives without having to worry about what we eat." Students who agree with the statement sit in the pro section; those who disagree sit in the con section; those who are undecided sit in the middle section and listen to arguments from each side until they are persuaded by their classmates' arguments to take a side. Anyone has the right to change his or her stand on the statement at any time, providing they move only when a speaker is finished speaking.

Speakers from the two sides alternate speaking.

The undecided students can ask a question at any time by raising their hands and being recognized by you. If an undecided person wants to make a statement, he or she needs to move to either the pro or con side and wait his or her turn. You act as the facilitator and fact checker. **(15 min. per topic)**

STRAIGHT TALK   *(Continued)*

- Nutritional value (you think they are good for you).

Of these reasons, only the last one reflects nutrition's importance to your health. But all your reasons for choosing foods are important to you.

I often feel pressured to eat when someone offers me food. How can I resist this pressure?

You are describing a form of peer pressure. You may fear hurting the feelings of the person doing the offering. This is a time to rely on your self-esteem. Practice some assertive behavior by tactfully ① refusing the food. For example, refuse the food, but accept the offer of kindness: "It looks delicious, but I'd really love to have just a glass of water."

You mentioned economy as a reason for people's food choices. Can low-income people get the food they need?

People with low incomes are most likely to suffer from nutrient deficiencies. Government agencies help people in need to buy food by way of coupons such as Food Stamps and by offering children free or low-cost breakfasts and lunches at school.

Some people lack the nutrition knowledge to help them choose wisely on a low budget. Many grocery-store bargains, such as dried beans, pasta, rice and other grains, poultry, breads, milk, and fresh fruits and vegetables, are high in nutrients and low in fat. Expensive foods, such as prepared dinners, sugary cereals, and snack foods are too high in fat and calories and too low in nutrients for most people. A limited budget can sustain a healthy diet. As far as the body is concerned, expensive foods are not often the best ones.

What does "the ① environmental ethic" have to do with food choices?

People who choose their foods according to the environmental ethic strive to choose foods in ways that make them responsible citizens of the planet earth. They follow a few simple rules (in addition to those governing proper nutrition) to make sure their food choices support the health of the earth, as well as their own health.

One such rule is to buy local foods. This means, whenever possible, to avoid buying foods that had to travel a long way to get to your store. Why buy an apple flown in from another state if

fresh local apples cost less and taste as good?

Another rule is to buy fresh food. Food in its natural state is superior in both nutrition and taste to heavily processed varieties. Also, processing requires energy, packaging, processing plants, and transportation systems. All of these generate pollution, and waste resources. Small steps like these, taken by many, can have a big impact on the environment. Choose carefully, for food nourishes not only the body, but the mind and spirit as well. ②

Mini Glossary

hunger: the physical need to eat; a negative, unpleasant sensation.

appetite: the psychological desire to eat that normally accompanies hunger; a pleasant sensation.

stress eating: inappropriate eating in response to arousal.

arousal: heightened activity of the brain with excitement or anxiety.

Vocabulary

1. Answers will vary.
2. a. Calories are units that measure energy to be used by the body, while empty calorie refers to foods that supply much energy, but few nutrients.

b. Glucose is the body's blood sugar, while glycogen is how glucose is stored in the liver and muscles.
3. a. carbohydrate **b.** digestion **c.** sugar **d.** malnutrition **e.** fiber
4. a. amino acids **b.** Overnutrition **c.** Constipation
5. a. Cholesterol **b.** vegetarians **c.** rectum

Recall
Section I
1. Choosing a wide variety helps assure that you receive all the necessary nutrients. Adequate intake of nutrients has an effect over a period of years. The best foods support normal growth, maintain strong muscles, and nourish all parts of the body. Good nutrition pro-

motes health and growth and prevents disease.
2. pregnant women—slows down the growth of their infants; teenagers—may not reach full height
3. eat a variety of foods daily; maintain healthy weight; choose a diet low in fat, saturated fat, and cholesterol; choose a diet with plenty of

---

CHAPTER REVIEW

LEARNING THE VOCABULARY

nutrients	fatty acids	digestion	unsaturated
nutrient deficiencies	amino acids	starch	polyunsaturated
malnutrition	grams	fiber	cholesterol
undernutrition	toxin	sugar	essential amino acids
overnutrition	urine	constipation	vegetarians
carbohydrate	calories	hemorrhoids	hunger
fat	glycogen	rectum	appetite
protein	hypothalamus	empty calories	stress eating
energy	balanced meal	saturated	arousal
glucose			

Answer the following questions on a separate sheet of paper.

1. Write a paragraph or create a story using at least ten vocabulary terms. Underline each term that you use.
2. *Explain the differences between the following terms:*
   a. calorie and empty calorie
   b. glucose and glycogen
3. **Matching**—*Match each of the following phrases with the appropriate vocabulary term from the list above:*
   a. sugar, starch, and fiber
   b. breaking down food into nutrients the body can use
   c. fructose
   d. underweight or overweight
   e. not digestible by human beings

4. **Word Scramble**–*Use the clues to help you unscramble the terms:*
   a. **naomi dcais**–The building blocks of protein are _____ _____.
   b. **vnttoruiioner**–_____ occurs when someone eats an extreme amount of nutrients that can increase disease risk.
   c. **toipnsicotan**– _____ is the result of too little fiber in the diet.
5. a. _____ is a type of fat made from saturated fats by the body.
   b. People known as _____ basically eliminate meat, poultry, and fish from their diets.
   c. The last compartment of the digestive tract is called the _____.

RECALLING IMPORTANT FACTS AND IDEAS

1. Why do you need to include a wide variety of foods in your diet?
2. Name two groups of people who are prone to nutrient deficiencies and discuss the resulting problems.
3. List the six Dietary Guidelines for Americans.
4. Why isn't alcohol considered a nutrient even though it does provide energy for the body?
5. Explain how starchy foods improve the efficiency of the body.
6. Explain how fiber aids the digestive process.

7. Explain the effect that cooking or refining processes have on the fiber in foods.
8. What are the four sugars that are important in nutrition?
9. Which nutrient contains the most calories per gram?
10. List three dangers of a high-fat diet.
11. What is the difference between amino acids and essential amino acids?
12. List four foods that are high in protein but low in fat and calories.

vegetables, fruits, and grain products; use sugars only in moderation; use salt and sodium only in moderation
Section II
4. It does not promote growth, maintenance, or repair of the body. It is a toxin which harms the body.
Section IV
5. Starchy foods supply the body with glucose, which is what the brain needs to function at its best.
6. Fiber keeps the stools softer and bulkier and easy to pass, so that constipation does not occur and hemorrhoids are less likely.
7. The fiber can be destroyed.
8. glucose, sucrose, lactose, fructose
Section V
9. fat
10. Answers will vary; could include: heart disease, many forms of cancer, arthritis, gallbladder disease, diabetes, and all the diseases made worse by overweight.
Section VI
11. The body can make amino acids for itself, but must receive essential amino acids from foods.
12. vegetables, beans, grains, and low-fat milk

CRITICAL THINKING

1. Can you think of any other guidelines to add to the list of Dietary Guidelines for Americans? What are they?
2. According to research, many Americans do not have healthy diets. Discuss some of the barriers people might face in making nutritious food choices. What barriers do you find yourself facing?
3. What influence does advertising exert on our food choices? Do you see this as having a positive or negative impact on your diet? Explain why and give some examples.

ACTIVITIES

1. List all of the foods you consumed in an entire day's meals and snacks. Circle each food you ate that represents "empty calories."
2. List as many factors as you can that have influenced your food choices.
3. List the names, addresses, and phone numbers of three community resources that could provide you with information regarding nutrition.
4. Find a recent article from a newspaper or magazine on the topic of nutrition and write a summary. Be sure to include the date, source, and a copy of the article.
5. Analyze today's lunch menu in the school cafeteria. Does it provide a balanced meal? How can you tell?
6. Interview a nutritionist or dietitian. Find out as much as you can about the person's professional training and the type of work the job involves.
7. Analyze the food selections on your favorite restaurant's menu. Does the menu provide a variety of foods, including low-fat foods? What changes would you make on the menu in order to make the choices more nutritious?
8. Examine one of the latest fad diets (NutriSystem, Slimfast) and determine if it agrees with the Dietary Guidelines for Americans.
9. Choose one nutrient you learned about in this chapter—carbohydrate, fat, or protein. Find four foods that list this nutrient first on their labels. State what each product is and write down exactly how many grams of carbohydrate, fat, and protein it contains.
10. Look through newspapers and magazines for recipes that feature low-fat meals. Choose at least three recipes and prepare these at home. Report to the class on which ones were tasty. Distribute copies of your favorite recipe to the class.
11. Watch TV for two hours. List all the foods you see advertised. Categorize the foods into various groups, such as high-calorie, low-calorie; high-fat, low-fat; healthy, unhealthy, etc. Write a report on your findings and discuss in class.

MAKING DECISIONS ABOUT HEALTH

1. Your friend has decided to go on a starvation diet in an effort to lose weight fast. What advice could you give to help your friend realize what a dangerous choice a starvation diet is? To whom could you recommend that your friend go for advice on diet?
2. You have decided to go on a vegetarian diet and your parents are insisting you eat meat. What strategies could you use to convince your parents that vegetarianism is not necessarily an unhealthy choice?

CHAPTER 8 PLANNER

OVERVIEW

This chapter is 22 pages long and is divided into the three sections listed at the right. Major learning outcomes are also listed to the right. In this chapter students will explore and put to use knowledge about vitamins, minerals, and daily food choices. Activities motivate students and get them actively involved in working with the vitamin and mineral information as well as the guides for nutritious food choices. The evaluations at the end of each section require the student to apply information in a useful and personally beneficial way.

MAKING LIFE CHOICES RESOURCES

A variety of activities, handouts, quizzes, and tests to accompany this chapter are available in the *Making Life Choices* supplementary material. You may pick and choose from those materials as appropriate for your amount of class time and the ability levels of your students. Some of the resources you might want to consider using are:

Overheads
- Nutrients in Bread
- Mistaken vs. Accurate View of Nutrient Intakes
- Daily Food Choices: Milk and Milk Products
- Daily Food Choices: Breads and Cereals
- Daily Food Choices: Vegetables
- Daily Food Choices: Fruits
- Daily Food Choices: Meat and Meat Alternatives
- Daily Food Choices: Miscellaneous Group

Handouts
- Calcium Amounts in Food
- Iron Amounts in Food
- Tips for Reducing Sodium Intake
- Seasoning Without Your Salt Shaker
- Nutrients in Typical Lunches
- Selecting Nutritious Foods
- U.S. Public Health Service Objectives

CHAPTER PROJECT

Have students evaluate six meals at a restaurant or fast food establishment for vitamin and mineral content, fatty foods, and serving sizes. Have all students report on their findings and decide from the results of the reports where some of the most nutritious foods for eating out are being served.

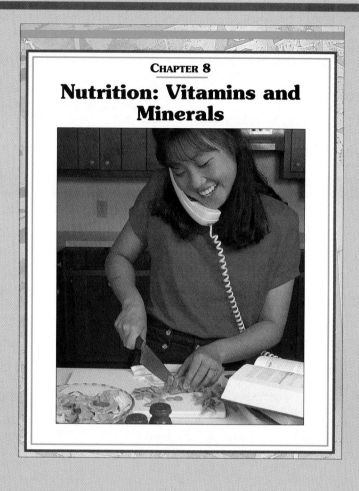

CHAPTER 8
Nutrition: Vitamins and Minerals

Answers to "Fact or Fiction"

1. False. The only disease that a vitamin will cure is the one caused by a deficiency of that vitamin. **2.** False. Vitamins provide no energy to the body themselves. They do help to release energy from carbohydrate, fat, and protein, though. **3.** True. **4.** False. Low intakes of calcium are common, because few foods contain it in large amounts. **5.** False. The tiny amounts of trace minerals in the diet are essential to

Activity To Introduce Chapter

Purchase different types of candy. Get some pill bottles from your local pharmacist and bottle these candies as different "supplements," which you will then need to label. Write on each bottle how that supplement will benefit the user. For example: makes hair shiny, nails strong, bones strong, teeth white, etc., until you have about 20 different pills to fix 20 or more different problems. Read the labels in front of the students and act like a hypochondriac while you extract one "pill" at a time and put it on a table top to take with your glass of water. You might invite students who desire the result on the

OUTCOMES

After reading and studying this chapter, you will be able to:

✓ Identify the essential vitamins, their functions and food sources.

✓ Describe the difference between fat-soluble and water-soluble vitamins.

✓ Identify the essential minerals, their functions, and food sources.

✓ Explain the dangers of consuming high doses of vitamins and minerals.

✓ Discuss the problems associated with a vitamin or mineral deficiency.

✓ List the types and quantities of nutritious foods suggested for teenagers in the Daily Food Choices pattern.

CONTENTS

I. Vitamins
II. Minerals
III. How to Choose Nutritious Foods

    Straight Talk: *Vitamin Supplements—Who Needs to Take Them?*

FACT OR FICTION

What do you think? Are the following statements true or false? If you think they are false, then say what is true.

1. Vitamin supplements can be useful in treating many diseases.
2. Vitamins give you energy.
3. People who snack heavily on foods high in calories, sugar, fat, and salt are likely to suffer from vitamin deficiencies.
4. Most people easily get enough calcium, because it is found in so many foods.
5. The trace minerals are present in foods in amounts so tiny that they are insignificant to health.
6. Electrolytes are dissolved minerals that carry electrical charges.
7. Foods that are eaten cooked provide the same vitamins as those that are eaten raw.
8. Some snack foods from vending machines are more nutritious than others.
9. As far as nutrients are concerned, the more, the better.

(Answers on page 199)

■ **Reminder:** Knowing how to study can increase your knowledge, improve your grades, *and* cut down on your study time. See the *Studying Health* section at the front of your text for some suggestions to help you study this chapter.

Various activities are planned to help students learn about vitamins and minerals. You may want to have students work in groups and assign each group a different set of vitamins and minerals for each activity, allowing students to work with as many different vitamins and minerals as possible.

TIME	SUGGESTIONS
1 Day	After introducing the chapter, have students complete Activity 1.1 and Activity 1.2. Assign the chapter to be read for homework.
2 Days	On day 2 have students complete Activity 1.4 for both vitamins and minerals in which they find what their everyday eating patterns are missing. Have students complete Activity 1.8.
3 Days	On day 3 have students complete Activity 3.5 in class, do Activity 3.3 for homework, and share their reports on diet tips with the class.
4 Days	On day 4 evaluate students using Evaluate Activity 3.9 or Activity 3.3.

*Please refer to the 18-week daily lesson plans in the supplementary material for additional suggestions.

good health. **6.** True. **7.** False. Some vitamins are lost during cooking, and some others become more available. **8.** True. **9.** False. All of the vitamins and minerals can be toxic in large amounts.

bottle to come up and take one of your pills. Tell them quietly what they really are when they get the pill. After you have accumulated your pile of pills to take, ask students if they know anyone like you. Ask them if taking supplements is a healthy thing to do and find out why or why not from those who answer. You can then proceed to explain to them that the supplement industry is a money-making business. Rarely do those supplements really produce the results that they claim to produce.

SUGGESTED RESOURCES

Student Readings
1. Jacobson, Michael F. and Fritschner, Sarah. *The Fast-Food Guide.* New York: Workman Publishing Co., 1986.

Teacher Readings
1. *Tufts University Diet and Nutrition Letter.* New York: William H. White, current issues.

Videos
1. *Eat, Drink, and Be Wary* (Revised) (21-1/2 min.) Includes discussions of fat consumption, high sodium, food processing, additives, and the effects of advertising on what we eat. Churchill Films, 662 North Robertson Blvd., Los Angeles, CA 90069-9970.

Software
1. *The DINE System Nutrient Analysis and Diet Improvement Software.* Students use personal information and their own food choices to learn and understand nutrition. DINE Systems, 716-688-2492.

In this section students will learn:
1. The functions of different vitamins in the human body.
2. How to analyze their diets for vitamin content.
3. The effects of various vitamin deficiencies and overdoses.

Activity 1.1
Deficiencies. Write the word "deficiency" on the board or overhead. Ask students to define the word in their own terms and to give examples of deficiencies (students learned the term *nutrient deficiency* in the last chapter; you may want to refer them back to the Mini Glossary definition on page 165). Discuss student examples and compare with the federal *deficit*. (Most students are proba-bly familiar with this term.) Have students tell you what it would mean to have a vitamin or mineral deficiency. **(5 min.)**

Activity 1.2
Soluble. Ask the students to define the word "soluble" and ask what happens when one chemical is soluble in another. Describe vitamins as being fat and water soluble and what this means. **(5 min.; Extend, Enrich)**

Teacher Support Notes

① **Supplement:** Ask students to read the definition of supplement, then ask them to explain what a supplement is in their own words. Ask them why these pills, powders, and liquids are called *supplements.* (People use them to *supplement,* add to, the nutrients they get from foods they eat.)

② **Protein:** Ask students if they remember (from the last chapter) which nutrient provides building material. (protein)

③ **Too Much or Too Little:** Ask students if it is better to eat too many vitamins and minerals or too few. (neither, both can be harmful)

④ **Vitamins:** Space does not permit discussion of all the vitamins—only a few typical vitamins are discussed in this chapter.

⑤ **Fat Soluble vs. Water Soluble:** The cartoon should help students understand and remember this key difference between vitamins. A, D, E, and K are dissolving in the glob of fat; B and C in a pool of water.

🖎 Fast Facts

57% of youngsters surveyed in a Gallup Poll said they have skipped breakfast.

The discovery of the **vitamins** and **minerals** thrilled people around the globe. Whole groups of people had been unable to walk, or to see, or to stop bleeding. Then, like a miracle, they recovered when one ingredient—a vitamin or a mineral they lacked—was added to their diets. On reading stories like these, people came to believe that vitamins and minerals could cure almost anything. Today we see a stream of advertisements for "miracle vitamins." The quacks say, "Are you nearsighted? Do you have pimples? The right vitamin pill will cure what ails you!" As a result, the **supplement** business is a multi*billion*-dollar industry.

The truth is, a vitamin or mineral can cure only the disease caused by a **deficiency** of that vitamin or mineral. Also, an overdose of any vitamin or mineral can make people as sick as a deficiency. It can even cause death. A balanced diet of ordinary foods supplies enough, but not too much, of each of the vitamins and minerals.

Vitamins and minerals occur in foods in much smaller quantities than do the energy-yielding nutrients. Vitamins and minerals provide no energy themselves. Nor do they provide building material, except for the minerals found in the bones. Instead, many help to release energy from carbohydrate, fat, and protein. Others serve as helpers of other body processes.

The following sections discuss a few of the vitamins and minerals and the importance of meeting your body's needs for them. The end of the chapter shows how to put foods together into an eating plan that will meet your needs for all nutrients.

Key Points *Vitamins and minerals serve as helpers in body processes. Too little or too much of any vitamin or mineral is harmful to health.*

SECTION I

Vitamins

A child once defined a vitamin as "what, if you don't eat, you get sick." Although the grammar could be improved, the definition was accurate. Although small in size and in quantity in the body, the vitamins accomplish mighty tasks, all of which are essential to life.

The vitamins fall naturally into two classes—the **fat-soluble** ones and the **water-soluble** ones. The fat-soluble vitamins dissolve in the body's fats and tend to remain in the body. For this reason, the fat-soluble vitamins can build up to dangerous levels if a person takes supplements of them.

The water-soluble vitamins travel in the body's watery fluids and leave the body readily in the urine. This means that you must be sure to eat foods that provide water-soluble vitamins regularly to replace those that you have lost. Facts about vitamin C (a water-soluble vitamin) and the common cold are presented in the Consumer Awareness on page 189.

Vitamins fall into two classes - fat soluble and water soluble.

Activity 1.3

Menu Analysis. Have students list all of the foods in a complete restaurant meal they have ordered in the past. Have them analyze the meal using Figure 8–2 on page 190 to find out what vitamins the person eating that meal would be receiving. Collect the papers and return them to different students. Have these students compare the vitamin list with the food items from that restaurant to check their classmates' accuracy. You might want to reward those students who are able to come up with additional vitamins that were left out by the originator of the work. Look at all the lists and ask students which meals supply the best variety of vitamins. Ask students' opinions about whether these places always serve a good variety or if this meal is just one of the better balanced meals. Discuss which are the most nutritious places to eat as far as vitamins are concerned. **(30 min.; Extend, Enrich)**

Activity 1.4

Vitamin Contracts. Have students list ten foods that they eat on a regular

(continued on next page)

FIGURE 8-1
Night Blindness

Night blindness is one of the earliest signs of vitamin A deficiency. A person who takes in too little vitamin A might experience this change in vision. Figure 8–2, later in the chapter, lists food sources of vitamin A.

a) In dim light, you can make out the details in this room.

b) A flash of bright light momentarily blinds you.

c) You quickly recover and can see the details again in a few seconds.

d) With too little vitamin A, you do not recover but remain blinded for many seconds; this is night blindness.

Vitamin A

Vitamin A deficiency is the major cause of childhood blindness in the world. More than half a million young children lose their sight each year because of vitamin A deficiency. One of the earliest signs of vitamin A deficiency is **night blindness**, which is illustrated in Figure 8–1 above. As vitamin A deficiency grows worse, it leads to permanent blindness. ①

Vitamin A also helps the body fight infections. It maintains normal, healthy skin and promotes growth. The symptoms of vitamin A deficiency therefore make themselves known not only in the eyes, but throughout the body. Infections occur readily, the skin becomes dry, and growth slows. In short, vitamin A deficiency interferes with many body processes.

MINI GLOSSARY

vitamins: essential nutrients that do not yield energy, but that are required for growth and proper functioning of the body.

minerals: elements of the earth needed in the diet, which perform many functions in body tissues.

supplement: a pill, powder, liquid, or the like containing only nutrients; not a food.

deficiency (dee-FISH-en-see): too little of a nutrient in the body. Severe deficiencies cause diseases.

fat-soluble (SOL-you-bul): a chemist's term meaning able to dissolve in fat.

water-soluble: able to dissolve in water.

night blindness: slow recovery of vision after flashes of bright light at night; an early symptom of vitamin A deficiency.

Teacher Support Notes

① **Permanent Blindness:** The medical term for permanent blindness is *xerophthalmia*. Children deprived of vitamin A do become blind from this preventable condition. If the deficiency is discovered early, it can be reversed by two or three capsules of vitamin A a day.

🖊 Fast Facts

Vitamin A deficiency is the major cause of childhood blindness in the world. More than five million of the world's children suffer from less obvious signs of vitamin A deficiency—stunted growth, poor appetite, and impaired immunity resulting in infections. In Asia, vitamin A deficiency is charged with destroying the vision of 250,000 preschool children each year.

in order to get a variety of vitamins. **(30 min.; Extend, Enrich, Critical Thinking)**

Activity 1.5

Research on Deficiencies. Have students do research on vitamin deficiencies and good sources of foods to supply those vitamins related to the deficiencies. After listening to the research reports, other students should be able to list the

vitamins in which people can easily become deficient and foods that supply those vitamins. **(2 class periods; Extend, Enrich, Interdisciplinary)**

Activity 1.6

Deficiency Illustrations. Have students draw a picture depicting the lack of a certain vitamin in the body. The picture should make an obvious connection between the vitamin and the related symp-

basis. Have them list the vitamins contained in these food sources, then list the vitamins they need to include in their diets and what foods they will eat to include those vitamins. Have them use this list to make a vitamin contract so they will know which foods to add to their existing diets

---

Teacher Support Notes

① **Vitamin A Deficiency:** Ask students to list how often in the past week they have eaten dark green vegetables, deep orange and yellow fruits and vegetables, and milk. How many think they might be deficient in vitamin A intake? Ask them what problems this can cause in addition to night blindness. (Infections occur more readily, the skin becomes dry, and growth slows.)

② **Thiamin Deficiencies:** You may want to tell your students that scientists studied some people who snack heavily on empty-calorie foods and found that these people had below normal thiamin activity in their blood. They also had the mental and physical symptoms of a mild thiamin deficiency. The scientists gave these people thiamin supplements for a month or so. The symptoms disappeared as the thiamin measures in the blood returned to normal. If you give students this information, also caution them against relying on supplements. It is better to obtain vitamins and minerals from foods than supplements. Students will learn more about this later in the chapter.

188

---

188 UNIT 3 Your Physical Health

Vitamin A deficiency often occurs along with protein deficiency. In countries where food is scarce, then, protein and vitamin A deficiencies are major nutrition problems.

In developed nations such as ours, people who take supplements of vitamin A should beware. Vitamin A dissolves into body fat, and can build up to toxic levels. Food sources of vitamin A are chemically different from the vitamin A in supplements. Vitamin A from foods does not cause dangerous buildups to occur. Only vitamin A from supplements does.

The best food sources of vitamin A are dark green vegetables, deep yellow and orange fruits and vegetables, and milk. Fast foods such as burgers and fries are poor sources of vitamin A. It is not surprising that many teenagers' diets tend to be low in vitamin A.

Key Points *Night blindness can be an early sign of vitamin A deficiency. Vitamin A is important to many body processes. Teens must make special efforts to eat enough vitamin-A-rich foods.*

Thiamin

Thiamin is typical of the water-soluble vitamins. It helps the body use energy from other nutrients such as carbohydrates. Your body cannot feel its presence, but its absence makes itself known by causing symptoms.

The victim of a serious thiamin deficiency suffers severe symptoms: paralyzed

Thiamin helps the body use energy from other nutrients.

limbs, loss of muscle tissue, swellings, enlargement of the heart, irregular heartbeat, and ultimately death from heart failure. Luckily, such extreme deficiencies almost never occur, but a mild lack of thiamin also produces symptoms. These include stomachaches, headaches, fatigue, restlessness, problems sleeping, chest pains, fevers, feelings of anger and aggression, and a whole string of symptoms often mistaken for mental illness. It takes a professional diagnosis based on chemical tests to determine the true causes of such common symptoms.

Mild thiamin deficiencies are likely to be seen in people who eat "junk" diets—that is, diets low in nutrients and high in calories, sugar, fat, and salt.

What foods in particular supply thiamin, then? Almost no one food you can eat will supply your daily need in a single serving. In fact, a teenager must eat *sixteen or more servings of nutritious foods each day* to get enough thiamin. The Daily Food Choices pattern advises this number of servings (see Figure 8–5, later in this chapter).

Key Points *Thiamin is essential for health. To get enough thiamin and other nutrients, a teenager must eat sixteen or more servings of nutritious foods each day.*

Vitamin B₆

Vitamin B_6 is a classic example of a nutrient that can be toxic in excess. Whenever people start overusing a nutrient, no matter how harmless the nutrient may seem at first, it is only a matter of time before toxic effects appear. A few years ago, people were "diagnosing" themselves as having vitamin B_6 deficiencies, and then "prescribing" large doses for themselves.

The first major report of toxic effects of high doses of vitamin B_6 described people who had numb feet, then lost sensation in toms of the deficiency. It should contain the name of the vitamin and perhaps some depiction of food sources from which the vitamin is derived. You may want to have the students present their pictures to the rest of the class. They should be able to answer any questions about their vitamins and the related deficiencies. **(45 min.; Reteach, Reinforce)**

Activity 1.7

Vitamin C Questioned. Ask students if they know anyone who takes vitamin C supplements. Have students show the Consumer Awareness feature to those people and ask for reactions. Will they continue to take the supplements? Why? Have students report back to class. **(25 min.; Extend, Enrich)**

Activity 1.8
Vitamin Skits. Assign groups of stu-

dents different vitamins and have them create a skit showing how that vitamin functions in the body. You might also want them to show what happens if too much or too little of the vitamin is consumed. Tell students to be creative and make these funny, but to make sure the information portrayed in the skit is accurate. You may want to have them use visual aids. **(30 min. to create, 30 min.**

(continued on next page)

Vitamin C and Colds: Rumors versus Research

C ONSUMER
A WARENESS

Each day, thousands of people take vitamin C supplements. Many who do so believe that large doses of the vitamin can prevent or cure the common cold. Vitamin C's popularity as a cure for the common cold began in 1970 when the first book on this subject was published. Since that time, vitamin C pills have become cheap and available and great profits have been made through publishing books that make exaggerated claims for vitamin C as a cure for colds. In fact, vitamin C is the most popular vitamin ever. Do vitamin C pills cure colds?

Many scientific studies of the effects of vitamin C on colds have come to one conclusion: the effects of vitamin C on colds, if any, are small. This does not rule out the possibility that for a few individuals, especially those who are deficient in vitamin C, the effects of vitamin C might

be considerable. Still, such people should look to foods, not pills, to provide the nutrients they need.

By the start of the 1990s, researchers were learning more and more about the ways vitamin C works in the body. While enough vitamin C is essential in strengthening the body's defenses against colds, the final word on the vitamin's effect on colds remains to be written. In the meantime, what *is* known is that large doses of vitamin C can be toxic. Avoid supplements, but be sure to eat generous servings of fruits and vegetables to obtain the vitamin C your body needs.

C RITICAL T HINKING

1. *Why are vitamin C supplements so popular?*
2. *Why is it better to eat foods that are rich in vitamin C than to take supplements?*

their hands, and then became unable to work. Later, their mouths became numb. Since then, other reports have shown nervous system damage from overdosing with vitamin B_6.

Not everyone suffers toxicity symptoms with high doses of vitamin B_6. Compared with fat-soluble vitamins and many minerals, vitamin B_6 is relatively nontoxic. However, people vary in how much is too much for them. We cannot say that supplements are "safe" for anyone. This fact holds true for every vitamin, and every mineral, too. Food sources are safe, though. Figure 8–2 on the next page presents the best food

sources of vitamin B_6 and the other vitamins and lists the jobs they do in the body.

Key Points ► *Vitamin B_6 is needed to maintain health. Too much vitamin B_6, like too much of any nutrient, is harmful.*

S ECTION I   R EVIEW

Answer the following questions on a sheet of paper.
Learning the Vocabulary
The vocabulary terms in this section are *vitamins, minerals, supplement, deficiency, fat-soluble, water-soluble,* and *night blindness.*
1. What is the difference between a vitamin and a mineral?

(Continued on page 191)

Teach
(Continued)

to present; Extend, Enrich, Cooperative Learning)

Activity 1.9
Meal Analysis. Instruct students to list their favorite "junk food" meals and a favorite "balanced" meal. Have them ana-

lyze the "junk" meal and "balanced" meals (could be the meal they analyzed in Activity 1.3) for vitamin content. Which food supplies more vitamins? Is the difference significant? **(30 min., Critical Thinking)**

Activity 1.10
Vitamin Bulletin Board. Have students create a bulletin board with the names of the vitamins. They should include pictures and words describing

their toxic effects and related deficiencies. Entitle it: "Vitamins—All in the Balance." **(45 min.; Reteach, Reinforce)**

EVALUATE
SECTION I

Activity 1.11
Balancing the Unbalanced. Create a meal that is unbalanced as far as vitamin content. Have students circle

---

Teacher Support Notes

① **What It Might Do In The Body:** The middle column for this figure gives the established benefits of the individual vitamins. Here are some possible benefits that have yet to be accepted and established by the scientific community. Vitamin A may reduce the risk of breast, lung, colon, prostate and cervical cancer; heart disease; and stroke. Vitamin D may help prevent osteoporosis and kidney disease. Vitamin E may reduce the risk of angina and heart attack, and may prevent spinal cord damage in patients with cystic fibrosis. Vitamin K may have a possible role in cancer prevention. Vitamin C may help reduce the risk of cancer and heart disease. Niacin is a cancer inhibitor. Vitamin B6 may protect against neurotube defects in fetuses. Vitamin B12 may protect against heart disease and nerve damage and possibly prevent neurotube defects in fetuses during the first six weeks of pregnancy.

> 66 **Thoughts on Health** 99
>
> *Never eat more than you can lift.*
> – Miss Piggy

190   UNIT 3 Your Physical Health

FIGURE 8-2
Major Roles and Sources of the Vitamins ①

Vitamin	What It Does in the Body	Major Food and Other Sources
Fat-soluble		
Vitamin A	Maintains normal vision and healthy bones, skin, internal linings, and reproductive system; strengthens resistance to infection	Vitamin A–fortified milk and dairy products; margarine; liver; dark green vegetables (broccoli, spinach, greens); deep orange fruits and vegetables (cantaloupe, apricots, sweet potatoes, carrots)
Vitamin D	Promotes growth and health of bones	Vitamin D–fortified milk; eggs; liver; sardines; sunlight on the skin
Vitamin E	Protects the body's cells from attack by oxygen	Vegetable oils and shortening; green, leafy vegetables; whole grains; nuts and seeds
Vitamin K	Helps with blood clotting and bone growth	Normal bacteria in the digestive tract; liver; dark green, leafy vegetables; milk
Water-soluble		
Vitamin C	Acts as the "glue" that holds cells together; strengthens blood vessel walls; helps wounds heal; helps bones grow; strengthens resistance to infection	Citrus fruits; dark green vegetables; cabbage-like vegetables; strawberries; peppers; potatoes
Thiamin	Helps the body use nutrients for energy	Small amounts in all nutritious foods
Riboflavin	Helps the body use nutrients for energy; supports normal vision; helps keep skin healthy	Milk; yogurt; cottage cheese; dark green vegetables; whole-grain products
Niacin	Helps the body use nutrients for energy; supports normal nervous system functions	Milk; eggs; poultry; fish; whole-grain products; all protein-containing foods
Vitamin B_6	Helps the body use protein and form red blood cells	Green, leafy vegetables; meats; fish; poultry; whole-grain products; beans
Vitamin B_{12}	Helps form new cells	Meat; fish; poultry; shellfish; eggs; milk; cheese
Folate	Helps form new cells	Dark green, leafy vegetables; beans; liver
Biotin and pantothenic acid	Help the body use nutrients for energy	Widespread in foods

Note: The names given here are the official names. Other names still commonly used and seen on labels are *alpha-tocopherol* for vitamin E, *vitamin B₁* for thiamin, *vitamin B₂* for riboflavin, *pyridoxine* for vitamin B₆, *folic acid* and *folacin* for folate, and *ascorbic acid* for vitamin C.

190

(continued on next page)

2. A powder or pill that contains only nutrients is called a _____.
3. A _____ is a condition in which the body lacks an essential nutrient.

Learning the Facts
4. What is the difference between a fat-soluble and a water-soluble vitamin?
5. What is one result of a vitamin A deficiency?
6. What vitamin strengthens resistance to infection?

Making Life Choices
7. Why is it better to obtain the nutrients you need from foods, rather than supplements? Have you ever taken supplements? If so, what were your reasons for doing this?

SECTION II

Minerals

If you could extract all of the minerals from a single human body, they would easily fit into a box about the size of a cracker box and would weigh just a few pounds. Then if you could remove all of the calcium and phosphorus from the box only a small handful of dust would remain. Were you then to separate out of the handful each of the 16 or so remaining minerals, you'd want to close the window before you did so. Most are present in amounts so small that the slightest breeze might blow them away. All minerals, even those present in just tiny amounts, are essential for proper body functioning. A tiny trace of a mineral contains billions of molecules that play vital roles in the body.

Calcium

Calcium is the most abundant mineral in the human body. Most of the body's calcium is stored in the bones and teeth. Milk and milk products are the best food sources of calcium. Everyone knows that children and teens need milk daily to support the growth of their bones. Calcium is not found in many other kinds of foods, however, and low intakes of milk are common. A deficiency of calcium during childhood, and especially in the teen years, threatens the strength of the bones for the rest of the person's life. It sets the stage for loss of bone tissue, **osteoporosis**, which can totally cripple a person in later years. Chapter 22 tells more about who is at risk for osteoporosis and what is known about its prevention and treatment.

The obvious way to meet the need for calcium is to drink milk or eat milk products daily, because they are almost the only foods that contain much calcium per serving. Figure 8–3 shows the amounts of milk that will meet the calcium intake recommendations. A few other foods contain calcium too: almonds, canned sardines (with

---

FIGURE 8-3
Amounts of Milk Needed to Meet Calcium Recommendations

Age	Recommended Daily Intake
Children	2 cups
Teenagers	3 cups
Adults[a]	2 cups
Pregnant women	3+ cups
Pregnant teens	4+ cups
Older women	3 to 5 cups

[a]Nonfat or low-fat milk is recommended for adults.

MINI GLOSSARY

osteoporosis (OS-tee-oh-por-OH-sis): a disease of gradual bone loss, which can cripple people in later life.

FOCUS
(Continued)

students can analyze their diets for mineral content.

Activity 2.1
Milk Drinkers. Discuss with students the idea that young people who drink milk grow up to be big and strong. Ask stu-

dents if this is accurate. Why or why not? **(5 min.)**

Activity 2.2
Hypertension. Define *hypertension.* (high blood pressure) Ask students what mineral is related to hypertension (sodium) and how this mineral creates a problem. **(5 min.)**

TEACH
SECTION II
(Guided and Independent Practice)

Activity 2.3
Mineral Deficiencies. Have students research common mineral deficiencies and report their findings to the class. Also have the students include in their reports foods that supply the mineral. **(1 hr. for research and 45 min. to pre-**

Teacher Support Notes

① **Symptoms of Iron Deficiency:** Ask students to close their books and give you the different symptoms listed for iron deficiency, then ask if any of them feel that they have these symptoms or know someone who does. Do they think there is a chance that the symptoms are caused by a lack of iron? Figure 8–4 on page 194 lists foods that supply iron.

② **Iron Deficiency:** You may want to tell students about an additional cause of iron deficiency—one that's not listed here. Iron deficiency can sometimes be caused by poor absorption of the iron that's in the food. Factors that impair iron availability are tea, coffee, soy protein, wheat bran, calcium supplements, and fiber. Even without these influences, however, a normal, healthy person absorbs only about 10% of the iron from a mixed diet.

③ **Iron Research:** You may want to tell students that certain researchers, such as Randall Lauffer at Harvard Medical School, believe that many people have a disorder known as iron overload which may lead to heart disease and cancer. Their suggestion is to skip the iron-enriched vitamins and foods and cut down on meat.

192

---

192 UNIT 3 Your Physical Health

These foods are rich in calcium.

the bones), leafy greens, broccoli, and beans. Orange juice sometimes has calcium added to it. This can be valuable for people who are allergic to milk. The photo above shows some calcium-rich food choices.

Key Points ▸ *Calcium is the body's most abundant mineral and is needed to form and maintain strong bones. Milk and milk products are its primary food sources.*

Iron

Iron is present in every living cell and is the body's oxygen carrier. In the red blood cells, iron carries oxygen from the lungs to the tissues. Tissues must have oxygen to produce the energy they need to do their work. Too little iron causes **anemia,** with symptoms of weakness, tiredness, apathy, and headaches. A paleness develops that reflects a reduction in the number and size of

the red blood cells. (In dark-skinned people, this paleness can be seen in the corner of the eye.) With too few or too small red blood cells, the person with this anemia grows weak and tires quickly. Energy will return, though, after a few weeks of eating the needed iron-rich foods.

Iron is one of the **trace minerals,** so called because only tiny amounts are needed in the diet. Even so, as many as half of all people—especially children, teens, and women—suffer from iron deficiency. Children and teens are prone to iron deficiency because of their rapid growth. Women in their reproductive years also tend to become iron deficient for two reasons: they lose iron in the blood of menstruation each month, and pregnancy brings extra demands for iron to support the growth of the developing infant.

① People who are low on iron begin to feel tired long before they are diagnosed with iron-deficiency anemia. With no obvious disease, they seem lazy and careless, they work and play without zest, and they become unfit physically. If this one worldwide malnutrition problem could be solved, millions of people's lives would brighten. A person who feels bad day after day should suspect that something is wrong. That something might turn out to be poor nutrition.

② The cause of iron deficiency is usually poor nutrition. Two reasons people may receive too little iron are a sheer lack of food (starvation) or the fact that they eat too many iron-poor foods. Other reasons are medical—blood loss or infection with parasites, for example. Meats, fish, poultry, and beans are rich in iron. An easy way to obtain the needed iron is to eat them regularly. But foods that are rich in iron are poor in calcium and vice versa. Any plan for a balanced diet must provide enough of both. ③ Figure 8–4 on page 194 presents the minerals important in the diet, what they do in the body, and food sources of each one.

sent; Extend, Enrich)

Activity 2.4
Mental Wellness. Instruct students to use poetry or artwork to link proper nutrition or poor nutrition to mental wellness. **(45 min., Interdisciplinary)**

Activity 2.5
Mineral Reports. Assign students to develop an oral report on a mineral. They

should bring in food items when they give their reports to use as visual aids. They should report on deficiencies as well as overdoses of the mineral and what the results of each might be. **(45 min. to write, 45 min. to present; Extend, Enrich)**

Activity 2.6
Mineral Sources. Bring various items to school such as meats, grains,

vegetables, nuts, and candy. Ask students to list all the minerals contained in each food item using Figure 8–4. This will get students used to using the figure. **(30 min.; Reteach, Reinforce)**

Activity 2.7
Candy as a Source? Ask students to use Figure 8–4 to tell you whether or not any type of candy would provide any min-

(continued on next page)

TEEN VIEWS

What prevents you from eating more nutritious meals?   ①

My job after school. I work at a fast-food hamburger restaurant and don't get home until 9:00. Since I get hungry, I have to eat a greasy hamburger instead of a nutritious, well-balanced meal. This has become a habit on the days I work. This happens to many people. They are busy and don't think about how important nutritious meals are. We need to take time out to eat healthier! **Emily Anderson, 16, Robert E. Lee High School, TX**

Embarrassment. I never eat lunch because I mainly feel I am getting fat or that some of my friends would not like the kind of food I like. Also, some of the foods at school aren't very nutritious. In the

morning I don't eat because I normally do not have time. Three nights a week I have dance from 5:30-8:45 and have no time to eat unless I eat directly after school. **Amanda Perrin, 14, Westside High School, NE**

There is a large selection of snack foods on the market. Also, a lot of microwave foods tend to be less nutritious. Sometimes we see something on TV and want to have it. Healthy foods aren't advertised as much as snack or microwave foods. People are caught up in the quest to be cool and commercials tell us we won't be cool unless we eat what is being advertised. **Hope Klinger, 15, Orange Park High School, FL**

I think the taste of a food tempts us to eat what we want. Some unhealthy foods taste much better than healthy foods. To some people it doesn't matter if they eat healthy or not, but to others health is everything. **Laura Fortenbaugh, 14, South Carroll High School, MD**

A lot of the time people lead a fast-paced life and are not able to eat a nutritious, well-balanced meal. Their time for meals is cut short. So they just grab a burger, a sandwich, and go on their way. **Herman Pulliam, 15, Great Falls High School, MT**

Key Points *Iron carries oxygen in the red blood cells. Too little iron in the diet causes anemia. Meat, fish, poultry, and beans are rich sources of iron and should be included in the diet each day.* ②

Electrolytes

Three minerals—sodium, chloride, and potassium—serve as **electrolytes**, minerals that dissolve in body fluids and carry electrical charges. Electrolytes help maintain the proper balance of fluids in the body. Fluid is the environment in which the cells'

MINI GLOSSARY

anemia: reduced number or size of the red blood cells; a symptom of any of many different diseases, including some nutrient deficiencies.

trace minerals: minerals essential in nutrition, needed in small quantities (traces) daily. Iron and zinc are examples.

electrolytes (ee-LECK-tro-lites): minerals that carry electrical charges that help maintain the body's fluid balance.

Teacher Support Notes

① **Teen Views Follow-Up Questions:** Here are a few questions you can use to promote class discussion of the ideas expressed by students in the Teen Views feature:

a. Do any of the students have a problem similar to Emily Anderson's? Have they found solutions?

b. What's Amanda Perrin's main reason for not eating more nutritious meals? What suggestions do they have for Amanda?

c. Do students agree with Hope Klinger, that healthy foods aren't advertised as much as snack foods? What, if anything, could be done?

d. Can students think of healthy foods that taste good?

e. After students read Herman Pulliam's comment, ask them how a busy person can eat nutritiously.

② **Handout—Iron Amounts in Foods:** At this point you may want to distribute the handout that shows the average amounts of iron in selected foods.

erals and, if so, what type. Have students look at the list and name the type of candy bar they think might provide the most minerals. Compare students' results and take a vote with all of the students checking the suggested types of candy bars for accuracy of information. Remind students that

although chocolate does provide a mineral, as do nuts, chocolate candy does have a high fat, sugar, and salt content so it is not really a nutritious food. **(30 min., Critical Thinking)**

Activity 2.8
Electrolyte Illustrations. Have students research the role of electrolytes in the body and draw a graphic representation of how they affect the balance of bod-

ily fluids with their electrical charges. Students should research what events might cause a person's electrolytes to become unbalanced and what would happen as a result. **(2 class periods; Extend, Enrich)**

EVALUATE
SECTION II

Activity 2.9
Mineral Collages. Have students

Teacher Support Notes

① **Calcium Sources:**
Here are some additional food sources of calcium. The US RDA is equal to 1 gram or 1,000 milligrams of calcium. The following numbers are milligrams.
3 oz. sardines = 324
1 oz. Romano cheese = 301
3 oz. canned salmon with bones = 204
1 oz. cheddar cheese = 204
1 oz. Munster cheese = 203
1 cup cooked turnip greens = 198
1 cup raw oysters = 111
1 cup cooked broccoli = 72
1 cup canned kidney beans = 62
1 cup raw shredded cabbage = 32
1/2 cantaloupe = 29
1 slice whole-wheat bread = 25
1 fresh apple, medium = 10
3 oz. lean sirloin steak = 7

✎ Fast Facts

The kinds of pots and pans used in your kitchen can affect the amount of iron in your diet. Acidic foods, such as spaghetti sauces, cooked in cast iron skillets contain 5 to 25 times more iron than the same foods cooked in other pots says the *Journal of Food Science.*

FIGURE 8-4

Major Roles and Sources of the Minerals

Mineral	What It Does in the Body	Major Food Sources
Calcium	Structural material of bones and teeth; helps muscles contract and relax; helps nerves communicate; helps blood to clot	① Milk and milk products; small fish with bones; dark green vegetables; beans
Phosphorus	Structural material of bones and teeth; supports energy processes; part of cells' genetic material	All foods that come from animals
Magnesium	Helps build bones and teeth; helps build protein; helps muscles contract and relax; helps nerves communicate	Nuts; beans; dark green vegetables; seafood; whole grains; chocolate
Sodium	Maintains cell fluids; helps nerves communicate	Salt; soy sauce; processed foods; celery; milk
Potassium	Helps build protein; maintains fluid balance; helps nerves communicate; helps muscles contract	All nutritious foods; meats; milk and milk products; fruits; vegetables; whole grains; beans
Iron	Helps red blood cells carry oxygen; helps tissues use oxygen to release energy; supports normal immunity	Red meats; fish; poultry; shellfish; eggs; beans; dried fruits
Zinc	Helps build genetic material and protein; supports normal immunity; supports growth; helps make sperm; helps wounds heal	Protein-rich foods; meats; fish; poultry; whole grains
Iodine	Part of thyroid hormone needed for growth	Iodized salt; seafood
Selenium	Helps vitamin E protect cells from attack by oxygen	Seafood; meats; vegetables
Copper	Helps make red blood cells; helps build protein; helps the body use iron	Organ meats such as liver; seafood; nuts
Chromium	Helps the body use carbohydrates and fats	Liver; nuts; whole grains; cheese
Fluoride	Helps strengthen bones and teeth	Water; seafood
Manganese	Helps with many processes	Whole grains; fruits; vegetables
Molybdenum	Helps with many processes	Milk; beans

CLOSE
SECTION II

Activity 2.10
Mineral Review. Have students close their books and name minerals as you write them on the board. Have students tell you any information they remember about each mineral, which you might write on the board as well. **(5 min.;**

Reteach, Reinforce)

FOCUS
SECTION III

In this section students will learn:
1. To identify healthier daily food choices.
2. To make sound choices about foods based on factual information.

(continued on next page)

---

work takes place—work such as nerve-to-nerve communication, heartbeats, contraction of muscles, and so forth. When people lose fluid—whether it is in sweat, blood, or urine—they also lose electrolytes. Sometimes too many body fluids and electrolytes are lost, as in heat stroke, diarrhea, or injury. This constitutes a medical emergency and requires expert medical assistance.

Sodium is best known as part of sodium chloride, the most common **salt** in foods. Sodium chloride is ordinary table salt, a much-loved food seasoning. Because salt is so widespread in foods, people easily meet their need for sodium. For this same reason, however, some people must try consciously to reduce salt intakes to avoid making high blood pressure (**hypertension**) worse. Details about hypertension and cutting down on salt are presented in Chapter 18.

Key Points *Electrolytes are dissolved minerals that carry electrical charges and help maintain the proper balance of fluids in the body. Sodium is an electrolyte. Some people must limit salt intakes to control their blood pressure.* ①

SECTION II — REVIEW

Answer the following questions on a sheet of paper.
Learning the Vocabulary
The vocabulary terms in this section are *osteoporosis, anemia, trace minerals, electrolytes, salt,* and *hypertension*.
1. Write a sentence using each term.
2. _____ is a disease of gradual bone loss.
3. _____ is a condition in which a reduction in the number and size of red blood cells is seen.

Learning the Facts
4. Where is most of the body's calcium stored?
5. List four foods that provide calcium.
6. Give an example of a trace mineral and a food source for that mineral.

7. What is an important function of electrolytes?

Making Life Choices
8. List all the ingredients and nutrition information that appear on the label of a popular sports drink. List any other label information you feel might encourage you to buy this product. Are you convinced this drink is the best fluid replacement? Why or why not?

SECTION III

How to Choose Nutritious Foods

Altogether, people need about 40 vitamins and minerals. How can they meet their needs for all of these nutrients? Figures 8–5 and 8–6 on the following pages offer guidance.

Each nutrient has its own unique pattern among foods. It might seem a tricky business, then, to work them all into the meals you eat. Yet people all over the world meet their needs for these nutrients from an astonishing variety of diets.

Happily, eating wisely doesn't require giving up favorite foods and all the pleasures they provide, although it may require limiting yourself in choosing them. Most people's diets just need a little fine-tuning. Eat certain foods more often, and eat other foods a little less often. That's all.

MINI GLOSSARY

salt: a compound made of minerals that, in water, dissolve and form electrolytes.
hypertension: high blood pressure.

Teacher Support Notes

① **Handouts—Salt:** You will find two handouts on salt that you may want to distribute at this point. One is entitled "Tips for Reducing Sodium Intake;" the other is "Seasoning Without Your Salt Shaker."

Section II Review

Answers
1. Answers will vary.
2. Osteoporosis
3. Anemia
4. bones and teeth
5. Answers will vary; could include: milk and milk products, almonds, small fish with bones, leafy green vegetables, broccoli, and beans.
6. Answers will vary; could include: iron (red meats, fish, poultry, shellfish, eggs, beans, dried fruits) and zinc (protein-rich foods, meats, fish, poultry, whole grains).
7. help maintain proper level of fluids in the body
8. Answers will vary.

Focus
(Continued)

Activity 3.1
Vitamin C. Have students write the advantages of getting vitamin C from eating fruits as opposed to taking a vitamin C supplement. Answers should include fiber and other vitamins as well as taste and enjoyment of the food. **(5 min., Critical Thinking)**

TEACH
SECTION III
(Guided and Independent Practice)

Activity 3.2
Balance and Unbalance. Discuss with students the idea of balance and how too little or too much of anything can be unhealthy. Discuss the need for balance in eating, to make sure that a variety of foods are taken in to ensure a variety of vitamins and minerals. Also, make sure students understand that sometimes taking a vitamin or mineral supplement can cause an unbalanced state in a person's diet. Have students guess at the symptoms that might occur with an overdose of any vitamin or mineral. **(5 min.; Extend, Enrich)**

Activity 3.3
Food Choice Posters. Have stu-

Teacher Support Notes

① **Ranking Food Groups:** On a scratch piece of paper, have students list each of the six groups included in this figure in descending order, beginning with the group from which they should have the most servings. Have them list the number of servings next to the group. Ask if they were surprised at which group is the most important in terms of number of servings. You may also want to ask them to make a second listing of the groups in the order in which students think they currently obtain the most servings. How do the lists compare?

② **Point Out Key:** Make sure students notice and understand the key, which indicates the relative number of calories in the different foods.

③ **Overhead—Nutrients in Bread:** This overhead compares the amount of nutrients contained in whole-grain, enriched white, and unenriched white bread.

196   UNIT 3   Your Physical Health

FIGURE ·8-5

The Daily Food Choices Pattern ①

KEY:
- Foods generally lowest in calories.
- Foods moderate in calories.
- Foods generally highest in calories.

Breads and Cereals ③

(For carbohydrate, fiber, others.)
6 to 11 servings per day.
Serving = 1 slice bread; ½ cup cooked cereal, rice, or pasta; 1 ounce ready-to-eat cereal; ½ bun, bagel, or English muffin; 1 small roll, biscuit, or muffin; 3 to 4 small or 2 large crackers.

- Whole grains, enriched breads, rolls, tortillas.
- Rice, cereals, pastas (macaroni, spaghetti), bagels.
- Pancakes, muffins, corn bread, biscuits.

Vegetables

(For vitamin A, folate, others.)
3 to 5 servings per day.
Serving = ½ cup cooked or raw vegetables; 1 cup leafy raw vegetables.

- Bean sprouts, broccoli, brussels sprouts, cabbage, carrots, cauliflower, cucumbers, green beans, and peas, leafy greens (spinach, collard), lettuce, mushrooms, tomatoes, winter squash.

- Corn, potatoes.
- Avocados, sweet potatoes.

② **Fruits**

(For vitamin C, vitamin A, potassium, and other nutrients.)
2 to 4 servings per day.
Serving = ½ cup fresh or canned fruit or typical portion (1 medium apple, ½ grapefruit); ¾ cup juice; ¼ cup dried fruit.

- Apricots, cantaloupe, grapefruit, oranges, orange juice, peaches, strawberries, watermelon.
- Apples, bananas, canned fruit, pears.
- Dried fruit.

Milk and Milk Products

(For calcium, riboflavin, protein, and other nutrients.)
2 servings per day for adults and children.
3 servings per day for teenagers, young adults, and pregnant and nursing women.
Serving = 1 cup milk or yogurt; 2 ounces processed cheese; 1½ ounces natural cheese.

- Nonfat milk, low-fat milk, yogurt.
- Whole milk, cheese, fruit-flavored yogurt, cottage cheese.
- Custard, milk shakes, pudding, ice cream.

dents create a poster in which they show how to trim down their own diets and substitute alternative healthy food choices for those that are high in fat or do not provide many nutrients. Have them list all of the nutrients that they added to their diets and unhealthy items that they took out, such as servings of fattening or sugary foods. **(45 min., Critical Thinking)**

Activity 3.4

Diet Tips. Have students create a report on a diet tip to make a person's diet more healthy. The report should focus on something that people can do to improve the quality of foods they eat and persuasive arguments in favor of adopting this healthy eating habit. Take a vote in class on the four or five best tips to a better diet and put these up on a bulletin board entitled, "Fine Tune Your Diet." **(30 min. to create, 30 min. to present; Extend,**

Enrich, Critical Thinking)

Activity 3.5
Target Foods. Create a target on paper entitled, "Daily Food Choices, Shoot for the Bull's Eye." Have students use Figure 8–5 to write down the foods they eat and where a serving of that food belongs on the target. The bull's eye should be green and contain foods with green dots;

(continued on next page)

Meat, Poultry, Fish, and Alternates

(For protein, iron, and other nutrients.)
2 to 3 servings per day.
Serving = 2 to 3 ounces lean, cooked meat, poultry, or fish; 1 egg, ½ cup legumes, 2 tablespoons peanut butter equal one ounce meat, or about ⅓ serving.
- Poultry, fish, lean meat (beef, lamb, pork), dried peas and beans, eggs.
- Beef, lamb, pork, refried beans.
- Hot dogs, luncheon meats, peanut butter, nuts.

Miscellaneous Group

(Not a food group—few nutrients.)
- Miscellaneous foods not high in calories include coffee, tea, and diet soft drinks.
- Foods high in fat: margarine, salad dressings, oils, mayonnaise, cream, cream cheese, butter, gravy, and sauces.
- Foods high in salt: chips, pretzels, pickles, olives, bouillon, mustard, ketchup, soy sauce, steak sauce, salt.
- Foods high in sugar: cakes, pies, cookies, doughnuts, candy, soft drinks, jelly, syrup, sugar, and honey.

Key
◻ Fat and oils(naturally occurring and added)
◻ Sugars (added)
These symbols show fats, oils, and added sugars in foods.

Fat, oils and sweets — Use sparingly

Milk, yogurt, and cheese group — 2–3 servings

Meat, poultry, fish, dry beans, eggs, and nuts group — 2–3 servings

Vegetable group — 3–5 servings

Fruit group — 2–4 servings

Bread, cereal, rice, and pasta group — 6–11 servings

Figure 8–6 Food Guide Pyramid: A Guide to Daily Food Choices ① ②

Teacher Support Notes

① **Food Guide Pyramid:** Ask students if they can explain why this guide to daily food choices has been drawn in the shape of a pyramid. (The base of the pyramid is its foundation. The foundation must be the most substantial and the largest part of the pyramid, just as the bread, cereal, rice, and pasta group should be the largest and most substantial part of a person's diet.)
② **Overhead:** At this point you might want to use the Food Pyramid overhead from the supplementary material. The overhead includes four overlays.

📖 Fast Facts

According to *The New England Journal of Medicine*, the Tarahumara Indians of Mexico do a lot of running and eat a diet of corn, beans, and small quantities of game and fish. Given a typical American diet for five weeks, their weight shoots up more than eight pounds.

Teach
(Continued)

Activity 3.6
Learning Serving Sizes. Bring the following to school: one bag of chips, ten slices of bread, a jar of peanut butter, a small can of meat, a large soft drink, a box of cereal, measuring spoons, measuring cups, a small food scale, bowls, a butter knife, glasses, and a funnel. Pick pairs of small and large students from your class to volunteer for this activity. Have two students come up and pour into the bowl of their choice the amount of cereal they would eat for breakfast. You might want to bring different sizes of

bowls for them to choose from.
Have two more students come up and pour into a bowl how many chips they might eat as a snack after school. Say, "If you were going to eat some chips, how many would you eat at one time? Pour this amount into a bowl."
Have two more students scoop out the amount of peanut butter that they would use to make a peanut butter and jelly sandwich. Have these students pour

Teacher Support Notes

① **Overheads—Food Groups:** You will find six separate overheads in the supplementary material; one for each of the food groups included in Figure 8–5.

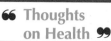
Fast Facts

Only 9% of Americans eat the recommended three servings of vegetables and two servings of fruit daily. Eleven percent of Americans eat no fruits or vegetables at all on any given day.

66 Thoughts on Health 99

Thou shouldst eat to live, not live to eat.
– *Cicero*

✉ Where to Write

World Health Organization
1501 New Hampshire, NW
Washington, DC 20006

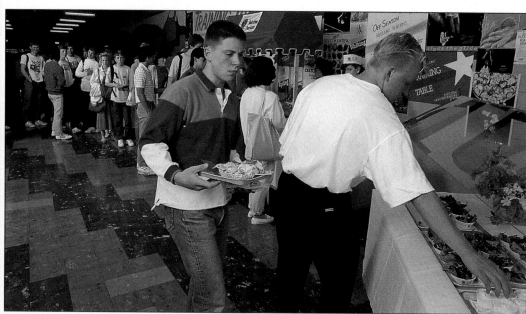
Your food can provide all the nutrients your body needs.

No doubt you've learned about the Four Food Group Plan at an earlier time. The new Daily Food Choices pattern is an improvement on the old plan and can serve as the basis for planning sound diets (see Figure 8–5 on the previous pages). The new pattern divides foods into groups, too, but lists five major groups instead of four.

The pattern goes hand in hand with the Dietary Guidelines for Americans already presented in Chapter 7. People who eat according to the pattern will easily meet their needs for vitamins and minerals while keeping other nutrients in balance. Just choose the recommended number of servings daily from each group. As an example, a teenager could choose 3 servings of milk, 8 servings of breads and cereals, 4 servings of vegetables, 3 servings of fruits, and 2 servings of meat or alternates, to meet daily needs. Figure 8–5 on the previous pages shows some of the major nutrients each food group supplies and offers examples of

foods in each group.

The pattern also helps with calorie control. The foods color-coded with green dots are lowest in calories within the group. Those with yellow dots are intermediate. Those with red dots are highest in calories. ① A person who chooses the smallest recommended number of servings, all from the green-coded foods, will obtain the needed nutrients and only about 1,600 calories. Most people need more energy than this minimum. They can maintain a healthy body weight by choosing more foods coded yellow or red.

The Daily Food Choices pattern is easy to learn, especially in its pyramid form, as shown in Figure 8–6 on page 197. You can use it with great flexibility. For example, you can replace milk with cheese, because both supply the same nutrients in about the same amounts. You can choose dried beans and nuts to stand in for meats. The pattern can also be applied to casseroles and other mixed themselves a soft drink. Have several sizes of glasses for them to choose from.

Talk about serving sizes and how serving sizes are listed on most packages but people do not always eat just one serving. Ask students, "Have you ever noticed how many servings are in a bag of chips? Do you ever eat more than one serving?" Hold up different items and ask students how many servings they think is in each food item, or how big a serving of each item

is. Show students how big a serving of meat is, and what a serving of peanut butter looks like when it is spread on bread.

Measure each item either by weight on the scale or by cups or tablespoons. Compare one serving from the package to what the student volunteers served themselves. How many servings of each item did they actually take as one serving?

Ask them what a calorie is. (If they don't remember, refer them back to

Chapter 7.) Using the labels on the packages, calculate the amount of calories in each student's serving. Compare this to the amount of calories per suggested serving on the package. Have students tell you which nutrients are provided in each food. Have students tell you how many grams of fat per serving, and how many grams of fat in each student's serving.

(continued on next page)

dishes and to different national and cultural foods. A study of the pattern and some thought about the questions asked in this chapter's Life Choice Inventory should help you develop a diet that meets your needs.

Your body is unique. It responds to foods and the energy contained in those foods in its own characteristic ways based on its genetic inheritance and its current needs. No doubt you already know its tendencies. For example, one person may tend to gain weight and may need to take steps to reduce fat intake. Another person may stay thin and may be best advised to ignore at least some fat-reduction suggestions. The overweight person needs to avoid storing excess calories as fat. The thin one needs many calories to help build up body weight.

The point here is to think carefully about your own body and its needs before changing your diet. The next chapter is about weight control for those who need to gain, lose, or just maintain their body weight.

Key Points *Diet planning patterns, such as the Daily Food Choices pattern, help people meet their needs for vitamins and minerals, keep other nutrients in balance, and help with calorie control.*

SECTION III REVIEW

Answer the following questions on a sheet of paper.

Learning the Facts
1. What is the best possible way to meet all of the body's nutrient needs?
2. How can you avoid consuming large amounts of calories and still meet the body's nutrient needs?

Making Life Choices
3. Look at your scores on the Life Choice Inventory. List the areas in which you scored well. List the areas in which you were deficient. List three improvements you could make in your diet. What was your overall rating? Were you pleased with your scores? Why or why not?

Answers to Fact or Fiction

Here are the answers to the questions at the start of the chapter.

1. False. The only disease that a vitamin will cure is the one caused by a deficiency of that vitamin. 2. False. Vitamins provide no energy to the body themselves. They do help to release energy from carbohydrate, fat, and protein, though. 3. True. 4. False. Low intakes of calcium are common, because few foods contain it in large amounts. 5. False. The tiny amounts of trace minerals in the diet are essential to good health. 6. True. 7. False. Some vitamins are lost during cooking, and some others become more available. 8. True. 9. False. All of the vitamins and minerals can be toxic in large amounts.

①

Answers
1. Eat according to the pattern established in the *Dietary Guidelines for Americans.*
2. by selecting foods in Figure 8–5 that are color-coded with green dots
3. Answers will vary.

Teacher Support Notes

① **Handout—Nutrients in Typical Lunches:** You may want to distribute this handout, which shows the amounts of vitamin A, vitamin C, calcium, and iron contained in three standard lunches.

✍ Fast Facts

According to the Gallup organization, half of the 86% of Americans who eat dinners at home during the week are eating prepackaged or take-out food. Spending on take-out food is expected to rise at three times the rate of total food spending.

Remind them of "empty calories" (a lot of calories for very few nutrients) for the soft drinks and chips. Discuss the advantages of eating healthy snacks rather than empty calories. **(50 min.; Extend, Enrich)**

Activity 3.7
Food Pyramid Comparison. Have students write a paper explaining at least two similarities between the new food pyramid and the traditional concept of a square meal using the four food groups. Students should contrast at least two differences. **(25 min.; Interdisciplinary, Critical Thinking)**

EVALUATE
SECTION III

Activity 3.8
Fat Content Chart. Use the target from Activity 3.5. Have small descriptions of food items that are found in Figure 8–5 on a separate sheet of paper. Have students cut these descriptions apart and glue them on the target where they belong. **(20 min.;**

Teacher Support Notes

① **New Labels:** You might tell students that the Health and Human Services Department and the Food and Drug Administration have finalized new regulations regarding food labels. The new labels, which started appearing in mid-1993, list the amounts of nutrients as percentages of the Recommended Daily Intakes (RDI) based on a 2,000 calorie diet.

The new regulations also set standards for the use of the terms "light," "fat free," "low fat," "low calorie," "cholesterol free," and "high fiber."

🖎 Fast Facts

In 1990, 45.7% of the money Americans spent on food was spent at restaurants and fast-food outlets. This compares to just 24.2% in 1950.

LIFE **C**HOICE
INVENTORY

How Well Do You Eat?

How well do you eat? Answer these questions to find out.

Part I. Do you eat nutritious foods from all of these categories? Answer yes or no. For each yes answer, give yourself 2 points. Total possible points = 10. For serving sizes, see Figure 8–5, presented earlier.

Score

1. I have 2 or more cups of milk or 2 servings of milk products every day. _____
2. I have 2 or more servings of meat or meat alternates every day. _____
3. On some days I eat dried peas or beans instead of meat. _____
4. I generally have at least 6 servings of grain products (breads, cereals, rice, and the like) each day. _____
5. I have at least 2 servings of fruits and 3 servings of vegetables every day (total of at least 5). _____

Total for Part I _____

Part II. Do you maintain appropriate weight? If yes, give yourself 20 points, skip Part III, and go on to Part IV. If no, take no points, and complete Part III below.

6. I eat just enough food to stay within 5 to 10 pounds of the weight considered appropriate for my height (see Chapter 9). _____

Part III. Do you choose a diet low in fat, saturated fat, and cholesterol? For each yes answer, give yourself 1 point. Total possible points = 10.

7. My milk and milk-product choices are mostly nonfat or low in fat (nonfat or low-fat milk rather than whole milk); and I eat ice cream or ice milk two or three times a week or less. _____
8. I seldom have more than about 3 teaspoons of margarine or butter per day. _____
9. My meat, fish, poultry, or egg choices usually amount to 2 servings a day or fewer. _____
10. In choosing meats, I eat chicken and fish more often than beef, ham, lamb, or pork. _____
11. I remove fat or ask that fat be trimmed from meat before eating. I avoid meats with fat ground in, such as sausages. _____
12. In choosing meat, I usually choose broiled, boiled, baked, or roasted; I usually don't choose fried. _____
13. On some days I eat dried peas or beans instead of meat. (This is the same as Question 3—it counts under both Part I and Part III.)
14. In choosing or preparing vegetables, I use little or no fat. _____
15. The grain products I use have little or no fat added. _____
16. In buying foods, I read labels for fat content and choose mostly foods with less than 3 grams fat per 100 calories. _____

①

Total for Part III _____

(Continued on next page)

Special Needs, Reteach, Reinforce)

Activity 3.9

Food Pyramid. Have students bring in recipes or descriptions of dishes from other countries. Have them determine what servings from the food pyramid are represented, and ask them to suggest what other foods are still needed to fill in the rest of the day's requirements.
(20 min., Multicultural)

CLOSE
SECTION III

Activity 3.10
Why Poor Nutrition Choices?
Ask students if modifying foods to get proper nutrition is a difficult or relatively easy task. You may want to ask for a show of hands. Ask students why the diet business is such a successful industry.

Address the fact that poor nutrition choices are sometimes a result of ignorance, money, or time, and that poor nutrition also results from behavioral problems. People need to figure out why they eat the less nutritious foods and what causes them to make poor choices. Discuss.
(10 min., Critical Thinking)

How Well Do You Eat? (continued)

Part IV. Do you get plenty of starch and fiber daily? For each yes answer, give yourself 2 points. Total possible points = 10.

17. When I am hungry, I choose starchy foods such as popcorn, cereals, pasta, potatoes, and breads rather than fatty foods such as fried snacks or chips. _____
18. The grain products I use are mostly whole grains (whole-wheat bread, whole-grain cereals, brown rice, and the like). _____
19. I eat abundant fruits and vegetables (this resembles Question 5 above; you get added points for these as high-fiber foods). _____
20. I eat salads or raw vegetables (such as carrots and celery) at least every other day. _____
21. I eat dried beans or peas at least once a week (again, you receive credit for these as high-fiber foods). _____

Total for Part IV _____

Part V. Do you eat reasonable quantities of sugar, honey, and other concentrated sweets? For each yes answer, give yourself 2 points. Total possible points = 6.

22. If I eat sweets (candy bars and the like), it is in addition to, not in place of, the nutritious foods I

need, and only within the limits my weight allows. _____
23. If I drink cola beverages, it is in addition to, not in place of, the milk and fruit products I need, and only within the limits my weight and caffeine tolerance allow. _____
24. I don't let sweets and sugary drinks harm my dental health; I rinse or brush my teeth after eating and drinking them. _____

Total for Part V _____

Part VI. Do you use salt wisely? For each yes answer, give yourself 2 points. Total possible points = 4.

25. I generally choose foods salted lightly or not salted at all. _____
26. I add little or no salt to food after preparation. _____

Total for Part VI _____

SCORING

50	Incredible.
40–49	Excellent.
30–39	Your diet has room for improvement.
20–29	Not so good. Work on your weakest areas.
Below 20	Poor. Make major efforts to improve.

① ②

Teacher Support Notes

① **Handout— Nutritious Foods:** Your supplementary material contains a handout entitled "Selecting Nutritious Foods." This handout pulls together ten strategies that have been mentioned at various points throughout Chapters 7 and 8.

② **Handout—U.S. Public Health Service Objectives:** This handout gives the U.S. Department of Health and Human Services goals for nutrition. You might want to distribute this handout at the conclusion of Chapter 8.

> **❝ Thoughts on Health ❞**
>
> *I told my doctor I get very tired when I go on a diet, so he gave me pep pills. Know what happened? I ate faster.*
>
> **– Joey Lewis**

Advertising Skits. Have students read the Straight Talk, "Vitamin Supplements—Who Needs to Take Them?" Have them create advertising skits for the perfect diet supplements. Tell them to use traditional advertising appeals to get their message across to the audience. Explain to them that not all of the claims that advertisers make are true. Some are made to sell the product to those who never question the validity of the claims. **(1 hr., Critical Thinking)**

Decreasing Impulsive Snacking. Explain that we sometimes eat foods that we do not want or should not eat just because they are readily available. Point out the foods that might be seen as junk foods, and why. Circle all foods that are readily available (need little or no preparation).

Explain that this activity will help students think about those food choices in advance, so they will not make the impulsive decision to eat them just because they are available. Have students brainstorm a list of ways to have nutritious snacks readily available.

Have students write down snacks that

Teacher Support Notes

① **Overhead—Mistaken vs. Accurate View of Nutrient Intakes:** At this point you may want to use the overhead showing the mistake most people make in thinking about how much of a nutrient they should consume. The overhead shows that most people think anything below the RDA is dangerous and everything above it is safe, when in fact the accurate view is that there is a range of safety above and below the RDA and dangerous conditions exist *above* as well as below it.

✎ Fast Facts

In a ten-year study conducted by doctors at Harvard Medical School involving 22,000 male physicians, researchers found that the men with a history of cardiac disease who had been given a beta-carotene supplement of 50 mg every other day suffered half as many heart attacks, strokes, and deaths as those taking placebo pills.

STRAIGHT
TALK

Vitamin Supplements— Who Needs to Take Them?

①

Each year, people spend billions of dollars on vitamin pills. You may be among the almost two-thirds of the population who take some sort of nutrient supplement. You may be wondering, after studying nutrition, whether supplements can really help clear up the skin, make glossy hair and strong nails, build broad chests and strong muscles, or help grow long legs, as many advertisers claim. Read on.

I've read advertisements making fabulous claims for supplements. Are there any supplements that can improve my appearance or physique?

Claims that nutrients can do these things are based on a tiny kernel of truth. Nutrients do support human growth and are absolutely necessary for clear skin, glossy hair, long legs, and all the rest. The trickery comes in when sellers imply that supplements of nutrients, given to people who are already well nourished, will produce even better results. The truth is that supplements do not improve the physical features of a person who eats well.

Can people get the nutrients they need from food alone?

People who haven't learned enough about nutrition think they need supplements as insurance against their own poor food choices. Indeed, their food choices may be poor, but taking supplements is no guarantee that they will get the particular nutrients they need. It's just as likely that they'll get a duplication of the nutrients their food is supplying and still lack the ones they need. The only way to be sure to get the needed assortment of nutrients is to construct a balanced diet from a variety of foods.

Are you saying that no supplement supplies all the nutrients you can get from food?

Yes, that's right. Even if you could get all your vitamins and trace minerals from a supplement, there is no way you can package the bulk of protein, fiber, carbohydrate, calcium, and others you need into a pill. No one knows enough, yet, to construct a synthetic substitute for food. Even hospital formulas that are called "complete" do not equal food. The most these formulas can do is to enable sick people to survive. They won't thrive until they are back on food.

In the chapter I read that fat-soluble vitamins can build up to dangerous levels in the body. How dangerous is this?

Dangerous indeed. Excess vitamin A, for example, can damage the same body systems that are damaged by vitamin A deficiency. Symptoms such as blurred vision, blood abnormalities, organ damage, bone pain, pressure inside the skull, and fatigue can occur with vitamin A excess. Water-soluble vitamins can be toxic as well, but are less likely to cause such severe symptoms.

(Continued on next page)

are waiting for them when they come home from school. Students will find the fat content information on the food package or in a handbook on fat content in foods. Ask and discuss the following questions: Which snacks are good food choices? Which of your favorite snacks are high in fat? Which are high in salt? Which are high in sugar? How many of their favorite snacks does it take to exceed their daily fat allowance? Review what excess fat, sugar, and salt

can cause.

Show students the nutritional information from labels of various snack foods. Ask which of these, if any, would be good snack foods. Why or why not?

Have students brainstorm a list of healthy snacks. Discuss how these snacks could be made readily available for eating.

Ask students if this activity required them to slow down and think about their food choices before letting availability

make their choices for them. Ask, "With this knowledge, who would have a healthy snack that was available and who would choose one that is not as healthy?"

Remind the students to slow down and make a wise decision the next time they open the refrigerator or pantry. **(30 min., Critical Thinking)**

STRAIGHT TALK *(Continued)*

Minerals, too, can be extremely dangerous and even deadly in high doses.

Do people ever have unusually high nutrient needs that require that they take supplements?

No two people have exactly the same nutrient needs. However, people's requirements differ, at the most, only by two or three times. An ordinary diet of mixed foods can easily meet the highest of those needs.

In rare instances, genetic defects may alter nutrient needs considerably, but only 1 person in 10,000 has such a defect. That person needs a diagnosis and treatment by a qualified health care provider.

What about high nutrient needs caused by different lifestyles? I've seen vitamins for stress, for cigarette smokers, for athletes—things like that.

Stresses, including smoking, do deplete people's nutrient stores somewhat. However, which supplements to give stressed people is just guesswork on the part of the manufacturers. The way to supply lost nutrients is still to eat well, not to take supplements. Another way is to learn to control stress. People who smoke should give up smoking, not take

supplements. As for athletes, they need supplements *less* than other people, because their bodies require more food to replace the energy they burn off in exercise. Larger food intakes mean higher nutrient intakes.

Would there ever be a time when I should be taking a vitamin pill?

Yes, when a health care provider recommends it, and yes, in at least two other instances:

- When your energy intake is below about 1,500 calories and you can't eat enough food to meet your vitamin needs. (People who can't exercise have this problem.)
- When, for whatever reason, you are going to be eating irregularly for a limited time.

Remember that if vitamins are needed, minerals are needed, too. A vitamin pill is not enough. A vitamin-mineral supplement is called for.

When I do need a supplement, what kind should I take? I've heard the organic, natural ones are best.

Organic and *natural* are terms that only mean that the product will be expensive. Don't let them fool you. Read

the ingredient lists, and buy the one that contains the nutrients you are looking for at the lowest price.

When selecting a supplement, look for one that contains no more than the RDA for nutrients. (The RDA are listed in Appendix B).

Can taking supplements prevent cancer?

Good nutrition certainly helps protect you. People who eat diets that are *deficient* in nutrients do develop more cancer and many other ills than do well-nourished people. But to say that a nutrient pill will protect you is to overstate the case drastically. You need every nutrient contained in foods, with all the other compounds foods contain, if you really want protection.

Suppose I just want to take a supplement to be sure I get enough nutrients. There's no harm in that, is there?

Perhaps not—if you keep the dose low. But as mentioned, vitamins have toxic effects when taken in large doses. And while overdosing with vitamins is risky, overdosing with minerals is still riskier. Minerals can be toxic—often in doses not far above normal intakes.

Vocabulary

1. **a.** salt **b.** vitamins **c.** trace minerals **d.** night blindness **e.** electrolytes
2. **a.** hypertension **b.** Osteoporosis **c.** Anemia
3. Answers will vary.
4. A supplement is given if a person has a deficiency, too little of a particular vitamin in his or her body.
5. **a.** vitamins **b.** minerals

Recall

Section I

1. A supplement can pro-

vide more of a vitamin or mineral than is necessary, causing an overdose of that vitamin or mineral. Eating a balanced diet provides enough vitamins and minerals.

2. Fat-soluble vitamins dissolve in the body's fat and remain in the body. If excess amounts are taken in supplements, they can build up to

dangerous levels. Water-soluble vitamins travel in the body's fluids and leave the body in urine.

3. Answers will vary; could include: citrus fruits, dark green vegetables, cabbagelike vegetables, strawberries, peppers, potatoes, milk and milk products, whole-grain products, eggs, poultry, fish, protein-

containing foods, meats, beans, shellfish, and liver.

4. Teenagers' diets often consist of fast foods, such as burgers and fries which have little vitamin A.

5. severe—paralyzed limbs, loss of muscle tissue, swellings, enlargement of the heart, irregular heartbeat, and death from heart failure

CHAPTER REVIEW

LEARNING THE VOCABULARY

vitamins	water-soluble	trace minerals
minerals	night blindness	electrolytes
supplement	osteoporosis	salt
deficiency	anemia	hypertension
fat-soluble		

Answer the following questions on a separate sheet of paper.

1. **Matching**—*Match each of the following phrases with the appropriate vocabulary term from the list above:*
   a. the common one contains the mineral sodium
   b. essential nutrients that help release energy from foods
   c. minerals needed only in small amounts daily
   d. an early symptom of vitamin A deficiency
   e. minerals that carry electrical charges
2. **Word Scramble**—*Use the clues from the following phrases to help you unscramble the terms:*

   a. **penthrsiyone**—Another name for high blood pressure is _____.
   b. **tsesopisooro** _____ involves the loss of bone tissue.
   c. **maniea** _____ can be the result of an iron deficiency.
3. Write a paragraph using as many of the vocabulary terms as you can. Underline each vocabulary term you use.
4. Explain the relationship between a supplement and a deficiency.
5. a. Riboflavin, niacin, and thiamin are examples of _____.
   b. Calcium, fluoride, and phosphorus are examples of _____.

RECALLING IMPORTANT FACTS AND IDEAS

1. Explain why taking supplements is not the best way to meet your body's vitamin and mineral needs.
2. Explain why excess amounts of fat-soluble vitamins are more dangerous than excess amounts of water-soluble vitamins.
3. What food groups are particularly notable for supplying water-soluble vitamins?
4. Why do teenagers' diets tend to be deficient in vitamin A?
5. What are the effects of a thiamin deficiency?
6. What are the dangerous effects of high doses of vitamin B_6?
7. Which vitamin promotes blood clotting and bone growth?
8. Which vitamin can be made in the body with the help of sunlight?
9. What is the most abundant mineral found in the body?
10. How much milk do teenagers need to drink to meet daily calcium recommendations?
11. What is a major function of iron in the body?
12. Give two reasons why a person might suffer from an iron deficiency.
13. Which mineral is present in all foods that come from animals?
14. What is the connection between hypertension and salt?
15. List some food selections from the Daily Food Choice pattern that can help you meet your body's needs and at the same time keep your calorie count down.
16. List five foods that provide few nutrients.

mild—stomachaches, headaches, fatigue, restlessness, problems sleeping, chest pains, fevers, feelings of anger and aggression, and a whole string of symptoms often mistaken for mental illness
6. numb feet, loss of sensation to hands, inability to work, numb mouth, and nervous system damage

7. Vitamin K
8. Vitamin D
Section II
9. calcium
10. three cups of milk
11. the body's oxygen carrier
12. Answers will vary; could include: children and teens because of their rapid growth; women in their reproductive years because of loss of blood

during menstruation and extra demands for iron from infants during pregnancy; starvation; eat too many iron-poor foods; blood loss; and infection with parasites.
13. phosphorus
14. Too much sodium, found in salt, causes hypertension.
Section III
15. Answers will vary; could

include: the majority of foods from the color-coded-with-green-dots group, some from the yellow or red group such as fruits, vegetables, grains, and beans.
16. Answers will vary; could include: coffee, tea, diet soft drinks, margarine, salad dressing, oil, mayonnaise, cream, cream cheese, butter, gravy, sauces, chips, pretzels, pickles, olives, bouillon, prepared mustard, soy sauce, steak sauce, cakes, pies, cookies, doughnuts, sweet rolls, candy, soft drinks, syrup, jelly, sugar, and honey.

CRITICAL THINKING

1. Reread the Daily Food Choices pattern on pages 196–197 and answer the following questions. What color-coded area of the Daily Food Choices pattern do most of your food selections come from? In terms of calorie consumption, are your food choices affecting your health mostly positively, or mostly negatively, and why? What changes, if any, do you need to make in your average calorie consumption? On a daily basis, do you generally consume the recommended number of servings in each of the five food groups? In what areas, if any, do you tend to be deficient? What food selections do you need to add and/or omit from your diet in order to meet the recommendations of the Daily Food Choices pattern?

2. According to research, some nutrients that teenagers' diets tend to lack are iron, calcium, and vitamin A. Do you think that at times you do not meet your body's needs for these minerals and vitamins? Why or why not?

3. Food product labels are sources of nutrition information. Do you generally read food labels? Why or why not? What are some of the advantages and disadvantages of reading food labels? How could the information presented in this chapter help you to become a better-educated consumer?

ACTIVITIES

1. Create a set of healthy meal plans for yourself for a full day. Include breakfast, lunch, dinner, and two snacks. Use the Daily Food Choices pattern on pages 196–197 as a guide. Be sure to use only foods that you like when making diet selections. Avoid empty-calorie foods and be conscious of calorie content, especially if you are trying to lose or gain weight.

2. Find a food label and list all the nutrition information it contains. Do you consider this product a healthy food choice? Why or why not?

3. Get copies of four different restaurant menus. One menu must be from an expensive restaurant, one from a place that serves moderately priced food, one from an inexpensive restaurant, and at least one from an ethnic restaurant. Group all the items on the menu according to the Daily Food Choices pattern.

4. Choose one vitamin or mineral you learned about in this chapter and find four foods whose labels show that the foods are good sources of this nutrient. State what the products are and write down all the information listed under "Percentage of U.S. Recommended Daily Allowances" on each label you chose. Each time your nutrient appears on the list, circle it.

5. Find a recent article from a newspaper or magazine on the topic of vitamins and/or minerals. Compare the information in the article with what you learned from this chapter. Did you find any information contradicting this chapter? Include a copy of the article with the date and source.

MAKING DECISIONS ABOUT HEALTH

1. You have noticed that your friend has a habit of skipping breakfast. Your friend is not at all worried because she has been taking a multivitamin every morning. What would you say to her to voice your concern? Describe a more effective meal planning strategy for her to follow.

CHAPTER 9 PLANNER

OVERVIEW

Chapter 9 is 28 pages long and divided into the six sections listed to the right. Major learning outcomes are also listed to the right. This chapter deals with maintaining ideal weight and having realistic expectations about body size. It gives students valuable information that will help them to make good decisions when considering a weight-loss or weight-gain program. It also gives students behavior modification tips and the knowledge to evaluate diet plans.

CHAPTER PROJECT

Dieting is an American obsession. Amazingly, over half of all fourth-grade girls have already been on a diet.

To get feedback on dieting and its problems, have the class develop a survey. In small groups, have students brainstorm questions that could be asked on a questionnaire. Then have the entire class vote on which questions would be most appropriate to use.

Have students survey a set number of females and males. Tally the results in class. See what conclusions the students draw from the results.

SUGGESTED RESOURCES

Student Reading
1. Katch, Frank I. and McArdle, William D. *Nutrition, Weight Control, and Exercise,* 3d ed. Boston: Houghton Mifflin Company, 1988.
Teacher Reading
1. Cannon, Geoffrey and Einzig, N. Hetty. *Dieting Makes You Fat.* London: Century Publishing, 1983.
Videos
1. *Fat Chance in a Thin World* (57 min.) A different approach to weight

control is discussed, which indicates that eating may not be the key for some people. Time-Life Video. 1271 Avenue of the Americas, New York, NY 10020, 303-267-6100.
Software
1. *Lifeline: Nutrition.* This software allows students to analyze the nutrients found in over 1,000 foods. Opportunities for Learning, Inc., 800-243-7116.

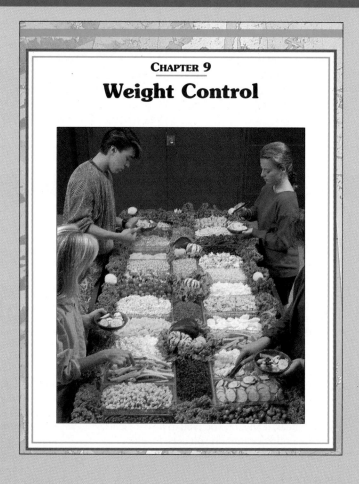

CHAPTER 9
Weight Control

Activity To Introduce Chapter

Students as well as adults are often made to believe false or exaggerated claims for weight-loss diets and products. Billions of dollars are spent on dieting products each year.

To help students evaluate the reliability of advertisers' claims, try this activity.

Ask the class if they think the following diet claim could be true: LOSE 25 LBS. IN ONE WEEK! Take a vote to see how many believe it is possible and how many don't. Then give the class the following information:
1. To lose 1 lb. of body fat a person must go without 3,500 calories.
2. Let's say the imaginary person going on this diet has an energy requirement of 2,500 calories per day.

Ask students to figure out if it would be possible for this person to lose 25 lbs. in one week using the following formula.
7 (days in a week) × 2,500 (daily calorie requirement) = 17,500 calories normally eaten in one week.

OUTCOMES

After reading and studying this chapter, you will be able to:

✓ Explain the problems associated with too little or too much body fat.
✓ Describe a method used to measure body fat and a method used to estimate ideal weight.
✓ Explain the effects of an unbalanced energy budget.
✓ Distinguish between loss of fat and loss of weight.
✓ Identify unsound weight loss programs.
✓ Design a safe plan for weight loss and maintenance.
✓ Design a healthful weight-gain program.

CONTENTS

I. The Problems of Too Little and Too Much Body Fat
II. The Right Weight for You
III. Energy Balance
IV. Weight Gain and Weight Loss
V. Smart Weight-Loss Strategies
VI. Smart Weight-Gain Strategies

Straight Talk: *An Obsession with Thinness: Anorexia Nervosa and Bulimia*

FACT OR FICTION

What do you think? *Are the following statements true or false? If you think they are false, then say what is true.*

1. Being underweight presents a risk to health.
2. The dieter who sees a large weight loss on the scale can take this as a sign of success.
3. The way to lose body fat most rapidly is to stop eating altogether.
4. To succeed in losing weight, you have to stop eating carbohydrates.
5. You can eat any food on a weight-loss diet, as long as you don't eat too much of it.
6. A person who exercises daily spends more calories all day, even during sleep.
7. It is harder to lose a pound than to gain one.

(Answers on page 228)

■ **Reminder:** Knowing how to study can increase your knowledge, improve your grades, *and* cut down on your study time. See the *Studying Health* section at the front of your text for some suggestions to help you study this chapter.

Please refer to the 18-week daily lesson plans in the supplementary material for additional suggestions.

Answers to "Fact or Fiction"

1. True. **2.** False. A weight loss may reflect loss of water or lean tissue rather than loss of fat. **3.** False. Fasting promotes rapid weight loss, but a balanced low-calorie diet can promote more rapid fat loss. **4.** False. Carbohydrate is a necessary part of a healthy, balanced weight-loss diet. **5.** True. **6.** True. **7.** False. It is as hard for a person who tends to be thin to gain a pound as it is for a person who tends to be fat to lose one.

25 lbs. × 3,500 (calories to lose 1 lb.) = 87,500 calories must be burned to lose 25 lbs. Ask students for their answers.

Even if a person ate nothing all week, which would not be advised, the person would still have 70,000 calories to burn before the person could lose 25 lbs. What about exercise? To burn 70,000 calories in one week a person would have to run at a fast rate of speed, 24 hours a day, for all seven days.

This exercise will help students to "see through" some of the outrageous claims diet advertisers make.

NOT ENOUGH TIME?*

Because many teens diet in inappropriate ways and the effects can be lifelong, the entire chapter should be assigned to students as homework. If discussion time for the chapter is limited, follow the suggested plan here, to cover the key concepts of Chapter 9.

TIME	SUGGESTIONS
1 Day	Have the students do "Fact or Fiction" on their own and give the answers in class. Do Activities 1.1 and 1.2 in Section I and in Section II, Activity 2.4.
2 Days	On day 2 do Activity 3.2, the Calorie Quiz in Section III, and Activity 4.3 in Section IV.
3 Days	On day 3 complete Activity 5.6 in Section V and Activity 6.3 in Section VI. Discuss the "Straight Talk" on eating disorders. If time allows, use some of the reviews from the Evaluate sections.

MAKING LIFE CHOICES RESOURCES

A variety of activities, handouts, quizzes, and tests to accompany this chapter are available in the *Making Life Choices* supplementary material. You may pick and choose from those materials as appropriate for your amount of class time and the ability levels of your students. Some of the resources you might want to consider using are:

Overheads
• Percent Nutrients in Food Versus the Human Body
• What Happens Inside the Body During Overeating and Undereating
• Yo-Yo Effect

Handouts
• Calorie Counter and Selected Nutrients in Food
• Calculating Fat Intake
• Fast Foods Low in Fat and Calories
• Evaluating Weight-Loss Diets
• Keeping a Diet Diary
• Ketosis—The Body's Emergency Route
• Diagnosing Anorexia and Bulimia

Teacher Information Sheets
• Fat Cells and Early Onset Obesity's Resistance to Treatment
• Basal Metabolic Rate
• Why Fat Calories May Be the Most Fattening
• Poor Choices for Weight Loss
• Cosmetic Surgery for Fat Removal

In this section students will:

1. Examine the physical, social, and economic factors associated with being underweight or overweight.

Activity 1.1
Reasons for Ideal Weight. Ask

students what they feel is the most important reason ideal weight should be maintained. Write the different responses on the board. Have the class prioritize them by voting on each. **(15–20 min.)**

TEACH
SECTION 1
(Guided and Independent Practice)

Activity 1.2
Circle Chart of Weight Problems.

Draw two very large intersecting circles on the board. Label the left circle "underweight" and the right circle "overweight." Make sure that the space created where they intersect is large enough to write in. Have the students draw the same thing on a piece of paper. Next, have students brainstorm problems. If a problem applies just to being underweight, have them list it in the left circle; if just to being overweight, in the right circle; and, if it could

---

Teacher Support Notes

① **Controlling Behavior:** Ask students to write a sentence stating what it is that a person should be doing if that person is concerned about his or her weight. The sentence should begin, "If I want to weigh more or less than I do now, I should learn to . . . ." Have them complete this sentence, then discuss their sentences in class.

② **Teacher Information Sheet—Obesity:** See the supplementary material for an information sheet on the causes of obesity.

208

---

208 UNIT 3 Your Physical Health

Are you pleased with your body weight? If you answered yes, you are a rare person. Nearly all people in our society think they should weigh more or less (mostly less) than they do. Usually, their main reason is that they want to look good by society's standards. They may know, too, that weight is related to physical health.

People also think they should control their weight. Two false ideas make their task difficult. The first is to focus on *weight*; the second is to focus on *controlling* weight. To put it simply, it isn't your weight you need to control, it's the amount of fat in your body in proportion to the lean. And it isn't possible to control either one, directly. It is possible only to control your *behavior*. ①

SECTION 1

The Problems of Too Little and Too Much Body Fat

Both too little and too much body fat carry health risks. Thin people usually die first during a famine or any time food is in short supply. A fact not always recognized, even by health care providers, is that overly thin people are also at risk in the hospital. They may have to go for days without food so that they can undergo tests or surgery. In fact, people with cancer and other diseases lose their appetites, and so may die from starvation rather than from the disease itself. Women need a certain minimum amount of body fat to menstruate normally. If they become **underweight**, with too little body fat, their cycles are disrupted. Underweight people are urged to gain body fat as an energy reserve and to eat foods that provide all the nutrients.

Underweight and overweight both present hazards to health.

As for too much body fat, for one thing, it makes hypertension (high blood pressure) worse. For another thing, weight gain can bring on diabetes in some people. If hypertension or diabetes runs in your family, you urgently need a sensible program to keep from getting too fat.

Excess body fatness also increases the risk of heart disease. Oversized fat pads crowd the heart muscle within the body cavity. Excess fat demands to be fed by miles of extra capillaries, overworking the heart to the point of damaging it. Meanwhile, fat clogs up the very arteries that bring energy and oxygen to the heart's muscles, starving these muscles.

Many other conditions are brought on or made worse by overfatness. These include breast cancer, diseases of the gallbladder, arthritis, breathing problems, problems in pregnancy, and even a high accident rate. ② The health risks of overfatness are so many that it has been declared a disease: **obesity**. If you are obese, you are urged to reduce your fat intake. You can expect your health risks to lessen as you do this.

Some obese people can escape these health problems, but no one who is fat in our society quite escapes the social and ecoapply to both, it should be written in the space where the two circles intersect. Give students ten minutes. Go around the room and ask each person for one of their answers. Fill in the big chart on the board as they respond. Discuss. **(15–20 min., Advanced)**

Evaluate
SECTION I

Activity 1.3
Weight Lists. Have students close their books and take out a piece of paper. Tell students to write down four problems associated with being underweight, four with being overweight, and four benefits of maintaining ideal weight. **(15–20 min.)**

Close
SECTION I

Activity 1.4
Student Experiences. Lead a class discussion on problems students have had with weight control. **(15 min.)**

Focus
SECTION II

In this section students will learn:

(continued on next page)

---

nomic handicaps. Excess body fatness makes it difficult to be physically active, and so limits people's success in sports. The overweight find it difficult to meet dating partners. They also find it hard to purchase good-looking clothes that fit well. Overweight people pay high insurance premiums, they pay high prices for clothes, and they may be passed over at hiring time when looking for work. Psychologically, too, a body size that embarrasses a person reduces self-esteem. With lowered self-esteem, the person may say, "What's the use in trying to lose weight?" In this way, obesity and low self-esteem worsen each other.

How thin, then, is too thin—and how fat is too fat? The next section helps to draw the lines.

Key Points *Both too much and too little body fat carry health risks. Overfatness carries social and economic handicaps as well.*

SECTION I REVIEW

Answer the following questions on a sheet of paper.
Learning the Vocabulary
The vocabulary terms in this section are *underweight* and *obesity.*
1. What is the difference between being underweight and being obese?
2. Write a sentence using each vocabulary word.

Learning the Facts
3. Why might being extremely thin pose a health risk?
4. List four health problems associated with excess body fatness.
5. Give one economic and one social handicap of obesity.

Making Life Choices
6. Unfortunately many people in our country look down on obese people. How can you help to lessen the social handicaps that obese people experience? Have you ever been in a situation where you or someone you know

discriminated against an overweight person? Explain the situation and describe how it could have been handled more sensitively.

SECTION II

The Right Weight for You

Your body's weight reflects its composition—the total mass of its bones, muscles, fat, fluids, and other tissues. The more of any of these you have, the more you weigh. Each type of tissue can vary in quantity and quality. The bones can be solid or brittle; the muscles can be well developed or underdeveloped; fat can be abundant or scarce; and so on. One tissue, though, stands out as varying the most: your body fat. Fat is the material in which the body can store the most food energy; it is fat that responds most to changes in food intake and exercise; and it is fat that is usually the target of efforts at weight control.

Measuring Body Fatness

Health care professionals would like to measure body fatness, rather than weight, but body fatness is hard to measure directly.

MINI GLOSSARY

underweight: weight too low for health. Underweight is often defined as weight 10 percent or more below the appropriate weight for height.
obesity: overfatness to the point of injuring health. Obesity is often defined as 20 percent or more above the appropriate weight for height.

Section I Review
Answers
1. Underweight is weighing 10 percent below the appropriate weight for height; obesity is weighing 20 percent above the appropriate weight for height.
2. Answers will vary.
3. die first in a famine, at risk during hospitalization, and women do not menstruate normally
4. Answers will vary; could include: hypertension, diabetes, heart disease, breast cancer, diseases of the gallbladder, arthritis, breathing problems, problems in pregnancy, and high accident rate.
5. Answers will vary; could include: economic—pay high price for insurance premiums and clothes, and may be passed over at hiring time; social—difficult to be physically active and successful in sports, difficult to meet dating partners.
6. Answers will vary.

1. There is no way to determine ideal weight for adolescents.
2. There is no perfect way to determine the ideal weight for adults.

Activity 2.1
Determining Ideal Weight. Have

students write on a piece of paper how they determine if their own weights are at a healthy level. They should fold the papers to insure privacy and not put their names on them. Collect the papers in a small box. Read the students' responses and discuss. Also discuss the answers to the following questions: "Do the responses refer to appearance, energy, or health? How much should we be concerned with appearance, if we have ener-

gy and are healthy? Why is a scale not necessarily an accurate measure of how much one should weigh?" **(15–20 min.)**

TEACH
SECTION II
(Guided and Independent Practice)

Activity 2.2
Slaves to Fashion. Tell students that what has been considered a "fashionable" amount for people to weigh has

---

Teacher Support Notes

① **Fatfold Calipers:** Appendix B contains instructions and charts that will enable you to obtain fairly accurate measurements of your students' body fatness using fatfold calipers.

② **Body Fatness vs. Weight:** Even though the point has been made several times, make sure students understand that there is a difference between body fatness and weight. Ask them what components of the body make up their total weight. (as explained in the first sentence of this section—bones, muscles, fat, fluids, and other tissues) Then ask why health care providers are concerned about measuring body fatness rather than weight. (As students read above, because fat responds more than the other materials to changes in food intake and exercise, fat is the target of efforts at weight control.)

📖 **Fast Facts**

Eating one dill pickle can increase your weight by as much as one pound the next day. The salt in the pickle can make you retain an additional pound of water.

A **fatfold test** uses a **fatfold caliper**—a pinching device that measures the thickness of a fold of fat on the back of the arm, below the shoulder blade, on the side of the waist, or elsewhere (see Figure 9–1). When taken by a skilled professional, fatfold measures reflect total body fat fairly well, because about half of the body's fat lies beneath the skin. ①

However, not everyone's body fat is distributed in the same way, and the distribution itself turns out to be meaningful to health. Excess fat around the waist represents a greater risk to the health of the heart than excess fat on the hips, chest, or legs. Some quick but not-too-accurate ways of guessing at body fatness are provided in Figure 9–2.

Key Points   *Body fatness can be measured with a fatfold caliper.*

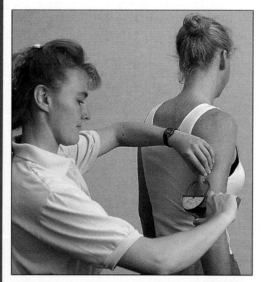

Figure 9–1 Fatfold Test. In a fatfold test, a skilled professional lifts a fold of skin from the back of the arm or other area and measures its thickness. The caliper applies a fixed amount of pressure gently (it doesn't hurt).

FIGURE 9-2

Quick Ways to Estimate Body Fatness

These ways to estimate body fatness are just for fun:

• A crude measure of body fatness is the **pinch test**. (This is a fatfold measure without the equipment to make it accurate.) Pick up the skin and fat at the back of either arm with the thumb and forefinger of the other hand. Keep your fingers still, so as not to lose the "measurement" when you pull them away from your arm. Measure the space between your fingers on a ruler. A fatfold over an inch thick reflects obesity.

• Another shortcut method is to measure your waist compared with your chest (not bust). Every inch by which your waist measurement exceeds your chest measurement is said to take two years off your life.

• Another crude measure: lie down, relax, and place a ruler across your abdomen from one hipbone to the other. If the ruler doesn't easily touch both bones while you're relaxing, you may be carrying too much body fat.

Scale Weight

② Body *weight*, by itself, says little about body *fatness*. A person with strong muscles and bones may not be overweight, but may seem overweight on the scale. Also, a person who doesn't seem overweight on the scale may have too much body fat for health. Even though scale weight is a poor measure of body fatness, it is still the measure people use to get an idea of whether they need to varied throughout the centuries, and from country to country. Also tell them that emphasizing different parts of the body has been popular with clothes designers. Then have students brainstorm to come up with examples of how people have been slaves to fashion, sometimes at the expense of health. Examples: having the lower ribs removed to have a smaller waist; eating arsenic to make the complexion white; binding the bosom to appear flatter (flapper look in 1920s), wearing very tight corsets to have a small waist (it interfered with breathing and women would "swoon" or faint); being overweight was fashionable several hundred years ago, because it was considered a sign of wealth and affluence; some Chinese girls had their feet bound so they would not grow.

Have students discuss why people are willing to risk health for the whims of "here today, gone tomorrow" styles. **(15–20 min., Critical Thinking)**

Activity 2.3
Approximating Ideal Weight. Have students approximate their ideal weights by using some of the examples listed in Figures 9–2 and 9–3. Ask students how many feel these methods are realistic for their weights. If they are not, ask why. Discuss. **(10–15 min.; Extend, Enrich)**

TEEN ① VIEWS

Do teens diet too much or too little?

Girls are more at fault than guys. We always have to watch the way we look. I was always worried about what other people thought about me until it drove me crazy. I was taking diet pills 'til I became somewhat anorexic. I was determined to lose weight and I didn't care. I took two bites of food and it made me sick. I realize I was hurting my body, but I hated myself. I never could accept the way I was. Now I have learned to accept the way I am. Girls need to stop being so concerned about themselves and accept the way they are. Society needs to lend a helping hand in helping teens do that. **Joyce Metz, 15, Carter High School, TN**

They just diet the wrong way. I believe that the word diet is understood incorrectly by most teens. Most teens think of *diets* as short-term ways to lose weight. Really you should make your diet a long-term, life-long commitment, not a way to fit into a dress for a dance in two weeks. Teens should try to eat foods filled with nutrients and low in fat and calories. Two candy bars and a can of soda just don't do it. **Joseph Brooks, 15, Connellsville Senior High School, PA**

I think teens diet too much by far. Today's society makes everyone feel like they have to be thin and beautiful to be accepted. I'm really tired of seeing what today's society does to today's youth. We are all a bunch of robots trying to be accepted by anyone and everyone who's popular. Who really cares more about your image, you or them? Learn to like yourself the way you are. **Andrea Bright, 16, East High School, MN**

You can't just throw all teens in a pot and say "they do this" or "they don't do that." Teens are always changing. One day we're up, the next we're down. One day we're dieting, the next we're not. I think the problem, instead of dieting, is more how we eat in the first place. Yes, teens diet too much, but it's the result of our own stupidity. We eat ourselves to giddy heights on the scale, then crash diet ourselves back to near nonexistence. It's not just teens, though. All of America diets too much. **Kimberly Secora, 15, Great Falls High School, MT**

lose weight. People compare their weights to those listed on height-weight tables to find out what they "should" weigh.

The height-weight tables show the weights of adults who lived long and healthy lives. No one under age 25 is ever included on the tables. Thus, for *adults*, using the height-weight tables is reasonable.

MINI GLOSSARY

fatfold test: a test of body fatness done with a *fatfold caliper.*
fatfold caliper: a pinching device that measures body fat under the skin.
pinch test: an informal way of measuring body fatness.

Teacher Support Notes

① **Teen Views— Follow-up Questions:** Following are some questions you may want to use to encourage discussion of the ideas expressed by the students in the Teen Views feature:
a. Do students agree with Joyce Metz that girls are "more at fault than guys" with regard to dieting too much? Why is this?
b. Have any students taken diet pills? Were they effective? Did anyone regret taking them because of complications?
c. Do students agree that today's society makes everyone feel they have to be thin and beautiful?
d. Andrea Bright says, "Oh, we're all a bunch of robots trying to be accepted." Is Andrea being too harsh? Ask students who agree with Andrea's statement their opinions of the first sentence in Kimberly Secora's comments.
e. Have any students gone on a diet for reasons similar to the ones stated by Joseph Brooks? What were the similar reasons?

EVALUATE
▶ SECTION II

CLOSE
▶ SECTION II

FOCUS
▶ SECTION III

Activity 2.4
   Determining Ideal Weight. Have students give three reasons why it is difficult to determine ideal weight. Students should also be able to name three methods that can help estimate ideal weight.

Activity 2.5
   Criteria for Ideal Weight. Ask students to write a paragraph on what criteria they use in determining their ideal weights.**(20–30 min.)**

In this section students will learn:
1. That calories fuel the basal energy needs and the voluntary activities.
2. How the number of calories taken in vs. those burned off are balanced.

Teacher Support Notes

① **Figure 9–3:** The authors of this text feel strongly that adolescents should not try to gain or lose weight based on information provided in height–weight tables. Those tables were developed for adults and can be extremely misleading for adolescents whose heights and weights are changing rapidly during their teen years. The weight ranges in Figure 9–3 are broad; they don't pinpoint the exact weight a person should be today because that weight can't be determined. The information is from the U.S. Department of Health, Education and Welfare, National Center for Health Statistics. It provides the most meaningful and reliable data available for adolescents. The figure is included here because many students will want to see this information. Refer students to the Life Choice Inventory on page 226 for more information on this topic.

✎ **Fast Facts**

About 40 billion fat cells are distributed throughout the body. The greatest number are in the abdomen, breasts, buttocks, and thighs.

---

212 UNIT 3 Your Physical Health

   For children and teenagers who want to know how much they should weigh, however, the height-weight tables are useless. Children and teenagers are still growing. Weights and heights change rapidly during the teen years. These facts make any guess at what they "should" weigh at a given age or height just that—a guess. The tables of expected weight ranges for teenagers shown in Figure 9–3 are based on measures of many adolescents across the nation. You can use them, together with the Life

FIGURE 9-3 ①
Expected Weight Ranges for Teenagers
(Based on Height and Age)

Females

Height (in inches)	Weight Range (in pounds)					
	12	**13**	**14**	**15**	**16**	**17**
53–54.9	58–78	—	—	—	—	—
55–56.9	76–101	74–98	—	—	—	—
57–58.9	79–106	84–112	84–112	95–127	104–139	86–115
59–60.9	87–116	88–118	95–127	99–132	103–137	99–132
61–62.9	96–128	99–132	102–136	103–137	105–140	109–145
63–64.9	105–140	105–140	108–144	113–151	114–152	114–152
65–66.9	109–145	115–154	116–155	121–161	122–163	121–161
67–68.9	126–168	115–154	128–170	130–173	126–168	123–164
69–70.9	—	—	121–162	126–168	144–192	130–174

Males

Height (in inches)	Weight Range (in pounds)					
	12	**13**	**14**	**15**	**16**	**17**
53–54.9	65–86	65–86	—	—	—	—
55–56.9	68–91	73–97	—	—	—	—
57–58.9	78–104	77–103	80–107	—	—	—
59–60.9	85–114	85–113	91–121	—	—	—
61–62.9	94–125	94–125	94–126	104–139	99–132	108–144
63–64.9	101–134	105–140	103–138	105–140	105–140	114–152
65–66.9	111–148	111–148	115–154	114–152	118–157	124–166
67–68.9	124–166	123–164	124–166	125–167	124–166	133–178
69–70.9	—	135–180	130–173	130–174	133–178	136–181
71–72.9	—	—	144–192	143–191	144–192	146–194
73–74.9	—	—	—	148–197	161–215	151–202
75–76.9	—	—	—	166–221	—	162–216

The numbers in these columns may surprise you. Some older teens weigh less than some younger teens the same height, because gains in weight often don't keep up with gains in height.
Note: The lower number in each weight range was derived by calculating 10 percent *below*, and the higher number was derived by calculating 20 percent *above*, the expected weight for height and age of youths 12 to 17 years old.

Calories and Weight Loss. Small changes in diet may result in large gains or losses in weight, over time. To maintain ideal weight we must exercise more and make good food choices. For instance, if a person left total calories in the diet exactly the same, but increased exercise by walking an additional ten minutes a day, 5 lbs. would be lost in a year. Drinking two less cans of pop per week is equivalent to about 4 lbs. lost in a year. A knowledge of calories in foods can help us make better food choices. Ask students to describe for the class similar calorie comparisons they know about. **(10–15 min.)**

TEACH
SECTION III
(Guided and Independent Practice)
Activity 3.2

Calorie Quiz. Give students the calorie quiz from the supplementary material with these directions: "Number your paper 1 through 15. I will name two foods. By the number, write the food that you think has the most calories, or if you believe they are the same, write SAME." After the quiz, give the students the correct answers and discuss students' reactions to the calories. **(20 min.; Extend, Enrich)**

Choice Inventory, to get a rough idea of how your weight compares to standards.

A rule-of-thumb method for estimating a weight that may be right for you is provided in Figure 9–4. Don't take this too seriously, either. If you are growing normally and your fatfold is average, your weight is probably just right.

FIGURE 9-4
Rule-of-Thumb Method for Estimating "Ideal" Weight

- A quick way to estimate a female's ideal weight is to give the height of 5 feet (barefooted) an ideal weight of 100 pounds. For every inch above 5 feet, add 5 pounds.
  Example: A female who is 5 feet 4 inches tall would add 20 pounds (4 inches times 5 pounds per inch) to 100 pounds, making her ideal weight 120 pounds.
- A quick way to estimate a male's ideal weight is to start with 110 pounds as ideal at 5 feet. Add 5 pounds per inch above 5 feet.
  Example: A male who is 6 feet tall would add 60 pounds (12 inches times 5 pounds per inch) to 110 pounds, making his ideal weight 170 pounds.

Key Points ▶ *Height-weight tables used for adults are useless for children and teenagers. If they are growing normally and their fatfolds are about average, their weights are probably fine.*

SECTION II REVIEW

Answer the following questions on a sheet of paper.
Learning the Vocabulary
The vocabulary terms in the section are *fatfold test, fatfold caliper,* and *pinch test.*

Fill in the blank with the correct answer.
1. A _____ is a device that measures the thickness of the body fat under the skin.
2. A _____ is a fatfold measurement taken without the use of any equipment.

Learning the Facts
3. What methods can be used to measure body fatness?
4. Why are height-weight tables considered inaccurate for teenagers?

Making Life Choices
5. Use the rule-of-thumb method in Figure 9–4 to estimate your "ideal" weight. Are you satisfied with your current weight? Why or why not? Use some of the methods described in this section to estimate your body fat. List the tests you used and discuss the results. Are you satisfied with your body fat test results? Why or why not? Discuss any changes you feel need to be made in your weight and/or amount of body fat.

SECTION III

Energy Balance

Suppose you decide that you are too fat or too thin. How did you get that way? By having an unbalanced energy budget—that is, by eating either more or less food energy than you used up. In other words, your body fat reflects your energy income and expenses in much the same way as your savings account reflects your money income and expenses. In the case of body fat, though, more is not better.

A day's energy budget (in calories) looks like this:

*Food energy taken in (calories) minus
Energy spent by the body (calories) equals
Change in fat stores (calories).*

More simply:

Energy in – Energy out = Change in fat.

① **Estimating "Ideal" Weight:** You may want to give your students some problems to make sure that they can calculate the estimated "ideal" weight on their own. Have them calculate the ideal weights for females standing 5'2" (110), 5'6" (130), 5'10" (150), and 4'10" (90). You may want to tell students, or let them figure out, that they subtract 5 lbs. for each inch *under* 5' for females. Have them calculate "ideal" weights for males at heights of 5'3" (125), 5'7" (145), 6'2" (180), and 4'11" (105).

Section II Review

Answers
1. caliper
2. pinch test
3. fatfold test using calipers; refer to Figure 9–2 on page 210 for answers.
4. Teens are still growing.
5. Answers will vary.

Activity 3.3
Pop Quiz.
1. For every _____ calories a person eats over the amount they burn, a pound of fat is stored. (3,500)
2. The largest proportion of a person's daily energy expenditure is _____ _____ _____. (basal energy needs)
3. The component of a person's daily calorie expenditure under the command of the conscious mind is _____ activities. (voluntary)
True or False
4. The larger people are, the less energy they use to do work. (false)
5. The smaller the active muscle mass, the more energy is needed. (false)

Activity 3.4
Approaches to Weight Loss. Ask students to imagine they have gained 10 lbs. of unnecessary weight due to a broken leg. The cast has now been removed, and the doctor has said it is all right to resume normal activities. Ask students

---

Teacher Support Notes

① **Calorie Counter:** Your supplementary material contains a lengthy handout entitled *Calorie Counter and Selected Nutrients in Food.* For common foods, this handout includes information on calories; the percentages of calories from protein, carbohydrate, and fat; and fiber, cholesterol, and sodium contents of foods.
② **Teacher Information Sheet—Basal Metabolic Rate:** The supplementary material contains background information on several different factors influencing BMR.

✐ Fast Facts

Studies from the University of Arizona reveal that men who spend more than three hours per day in front of the television are twice as likely to be overweight as men who spend less than one hour each day viewing television.

You know about the "energy in" side of this equation. An apple brings in 100 calories; a candy bar, 425 calories. Perhaps you also know that for each 3,500 calories you eat over the amount you spend, you store a pound of body fat. The reverse is also true: for every 3,500 calories you spend beyond those you eat, you will use up a pound of body tissue as fuel.

As for the "energy out" side, the body spends energy in two major ways: to fuel its **basal energy** needs and to fuel its **voluntary activities**. You can change both of these to spend more or less energy in a day, as you will see in a moment.

The basal energy supports the work that goes on all the time, without your awareness. The basal processes include:

• Beating of the heart.
• Inhaling and exhaling of air.
• Maintenance of body temperature.
• Working of the nerves and glands.

These basal processes support life.

Basal energy needs are surprisingly large. A person whose total energy needs are 2,000 calories a day spends 1,200 to 1,400 of them to support basal activities. This means that you use up 1,200 to 1,400 calories a day even if you just sit still and do nothing.

The number of calories a person spends on a voluntary activity depends on four factors:

1. *The number and size of the muscles that are working.* The larger the active muscle mass, the more energy needed. This means that using the large muscle groups of the legs and buttocks to walk upstairs takes more energy than lifting books to a shelf with your arms and shoulders.
2. *The total weight of the body parts being moved.* The heavier the body parts, the more energy required to move them. This explains why a 200-pound person uses

more energy than a 100-pound person does when both are doing the same activity with equal effort.
3. *The length of time of exercise.* The longer the activity lasts, the more calories are spent.
4. *The amount of effort put into the movement—the exercise intensity.* Hard work takes more fuel.

A typical breakdown of the total energy spent by a moderately active person (for example, a student who walks from class to class) might look like this:

Energy for basal activities:	*1,400 calories*
Energy for voluntary activities:	*500 calories*
Total energy needs:	*1,900 calories*

The basal energy is the larger part. You can't change it much, today. You can, however, change the second part—voluntary activities—and so spend more calories today. In addition, you can, if you want to, increase your basal energy output over the long term by making physical activity a daily habit. As you develop lean tissue and drop fat, your basal energy output will pick up the pace as well. The end of this chapter shows how to alter energy spent on both basal and voluntary activities—with diet and physical activity—to regulate body weight.

Key Points *The balance between food energy taken in and energy spent determines how much fat a person's body stores in its fat tissues or how much it uses from storage. Two major ways in which the body spends energy are for basal processes and voluntary activities.*

SECTION III REVIEW

Answer the following questions on a sheet of paper.
Learning the Vocabulary
The vocabulary terms in this section are *basal energy* and *voluntary activities.*

how they would try to lose this weight. What would be the healthiest and most sensible approaches to take? (10–15 min., Critical Thinking)

FOCUS

SECTION IV

In this section students will learn:
1. Body composition and the storage of energy nutrients.

2. The right and wrong ways to lose weight.

Activity 4.1
Significance of Exercise. Ask students to read the first four paragraphs of Section IV. Then give students the following information:

If dieting is done with exercise, 95% of the weight lost will be fat, and 5% will be lean tissue. If dieting is done without exer-

cise, 75% of the weight lost will be fat, and 25% will be lean tissue.

Ask students to explain the significance of exercise as it relates to dieting. Discuss. (10–15 min.; Extend, Enrich)

Activity 4.2
Evaluating Ads. Request that students bring in ads for weight-reduction diets, pills, exercise gadgets, and clothes

(continued on next page)

Fill in the blank with the correct answer.
1. _____ is the sum total of all the energy needed to support the chemical activities of the cells.
2. The smallest component of a person's daily energy expenditure is _____.

Learning the Facts
3. What happens to the calories you eat in excess of those your body expends?
4. What are the two major ways the body spends energy?
5. Name three factors that determine the number of calories a person spends on a voluntary activity.

Making Life Choices
6. Is your body's energy budget balanced, or do you generally eat more or less food energy than you spend? Give specific reasons for your answer. Are you satisfied with your body's energy budget? Why or why not? What changes, if any, would you make?

SECTION IV

Weight Gain and Weight Loss

You step on the scale and note that you weigh a pound more or less than you did the last time you weighed. This doesn't mean you have gained or lost body fat. Changes in body weight reflect shifts in ①

The cautious consumer distinguishes between loss of fat and loss of weight.

many different materials—not only fat, but water, bone minerals, and lean tissues such as muscles. It is important for people concerned with weight control to realize this.

A healthy 18-year-old teenager, who is about 5 feet 10 inches tall and who weighs 150 pounds, carries about 90 of those pounds as water and 30 as fat. The other 30 pounds are the lean tissues: muscles; organs such as the heart, brain, and liver; and the bones of the skeleton. Stripped of water and fat, then, the person weighs only 30 pounds! (A teenager 5 feet tall who weighs 100 pounds has only 20 pounds of lean.)

The body's lean tissue is vital to health. When a person who is too fat seeks to lose weight, it should be fat, not this precious lean tissue, that is lost. And for someone who wants to gain weight, it is best to gain both lean *and* fat, not just fat.

The type of tissue gained or lost depends on how the person goes about gaining or losing weight. Some of the most dramatic weight changes people achieve reflect losses and gains in the body's fluid content, which ideally shouldn't change much at all. Yet people seek to bring about such weight changes because they like to see the quick results. They fail to realize how useless such changes are in changing what really matters—the body's lean and fat tissue.

— MINI GLOSSARY —

basal energy: the sum total of all the energy needed to support the chemical activities of the cells and to sustain life, exclusive of voluntary activities; the largest component of a person's daily energy expenditure.
voluntary activities: movements of the body under the command of the conscious mind; one component of a person's daily energy expenditure.

that are supposed to melt away fat. Have students evaluate the ads' claims. Have volunteers come in front of the class, show their ads, and tell whether or not they think the products would work. **(15 min.; Reteach, Reinforce)**

Activity 4.3
Evaluating Weight-Loss Programs. There are many poor weight-loss programs, and some that are actually dangerous. Have students look at the Health Strategies, "Clues to Identifying Unsound Weight-Loss Programs," on page 219. Then have the students analyze the following diet:
THE STEWARDESS DIET
DAY 1—Eat seven boiled eggs

DAY 2—Eat seven wieners
DAY 3—Eat seven bananas
Drink only water, tea, coffee, or diet soda. Repeat until the desired amount of weight is lost.

Write student responses on the board. If students don't bring it up, tell them each day's calories are below 1,000 calories (Seven eggs = 560 calories, seven hot dogs = 875 calories, seven med. bananas = 560 calories). Students also might not

Teacher Support Notes

① **Quick-Weight-Loss Diets:** Ask students if any of them have participated in any of the quick-weight-loss schemes described here. Were they encouraged by the results? Were the changes permanent? Do they see that changing fluid weight is an easy, but useless, way to change body weight? Why do people continue to use these methods?

② **Teacher Information Sheet—Why Fat Calories May Be the Most Fattening:** Some research indicates that type of calories as well as number of calories may affect weight gain. See the information sheet in the supplementary material for more on this topic.

③ **Overhead—What Happens Inside the Body:** This overhead illustrates how the body handles the different energy nutrients.

66 Thoughts on Health 99

Doctors are always working to preserve our health and cooks to destroy it, but the latter are the more often successful.
– *Denis Diderot*

216

One dangerous way to lose fluid is to take a "water pill" (**diuretic**). These pills cause the kidneys to draw extra water from the blood into the urine. Another quick-weight-loss trick is to exercise heavily in the heat, losing large amounts of fluid in sweat. This practice is dangerous, too, and is not being recommended here.

Most quick-weight-loss diets cause large fluid losses that look like dramatic changes on the scale but are really temporary. Such diets cause little loss of body fat. Later sections of this chapter come back to how *not* to lose weight.

Feasting: Weight Gain

When you eat more food than you need, where does it go in your body? An excess of any energy nutrient—carbohydrate, fat, or protein—can be stored as follows:

- Carbohydrate is broken down, absorbed, and changed into glucose. Inside the body, glucose may be stored as glycogen or body fat.
- Fat is broken down mostly to fatty acids and absorbed. Then these may be stored as body fat.
- Protein, too, is broken down to its basic units (amino acids) and absorbed. Inside the body, these may be used to replace lost body protein. Any extra amino acids are changed into body fat and stored.

Notice that although three kinds of energy nutrients enter the body, they are stored there in only two forms: glycogen and fat. No matter whether you are eating steak, brownies, or baked beans, then, if you eat enough of them, the excess will be stored as fat within hours.

Key Points ▶ *To lose weight safely and permanently, a person must lose fat tissue, not lean tissue or water. The energy from any food can build up in body fat if a person eats more calories than are spent.*

Fasting: A Wrong Way to Lose Weight

When the tables are turned and you stop eating altogether, your body has to draw on its fuel stores to keep going. Nothing is wrong with this. In fact, it is a great advantage to us that we can eat a meal, store fuel, and then use it until the next meal. (Some animals, such as cattle, have to spend almost all their waking hours eating—leaving them little time for daydreaming.)

People can store fuel, but their fuel stores are not unlimited. Every dieter knows that fat is stored abundantly in the body whenever any sort of high-energy food is eaten to excess. A person with just average fat stores has enough fat to provide the body with energy for weeks, even when no food at all is eaten (fasting). On the other hand, carbohydrate, stored as glycogen, is only stored when carbohydrate-rich food is eaten in amounts beyond those needed immediately by the body. When too little carbohydrate is taken in, such as when the eater consumes a diet too low in carbohydrates or fails to eat at all, the glycogen stores last for less than a day. While glycogen runs out, the body's demand for the carbohydrate fuel glucose is as strong as ever.

So how does the fasting body get the needed glucose? It begins to convert protein to carbohydrate. In fasting, the body has no external source of protein, and so it takes apart the protein in its own muscles and organs to keep up the needed supply of glucose. For this reason, dieters should avoid both fasting and diets too low in carbohydrates. People who follow weight-loss schemes that employ fasting or low-carbohydrate diets drop weight quickly, especially at first. This is because they are using up protein from muscles and organs as fuel. Protein contains only half as many calories per pound as fat, so it disappears twice as fast. And with each pound of body protein mention the high cholesterol content of the eggs or the high fat content of the hot dogs.

Discuss the importance of evaluating the healthiness of a diet before going on one. **(30 min., Critical Thinking)**

EVALUATE
SECTION IV

Activity 4.4

Key Points. Without using their books, have students write down five key points they remember from Section IV. Go around the room and have students give an item from their lists. Write the items on the board. **(20 min.; Reteach, Reinforce)**

Activity 4.5
Dieting Don'ts. Put students into groups of four. Each group must have a reporter. Without using their books, have

them write down all of the things Section IV mentioned that people SHOULD NOT do when dieting. Give them five minutes. Come back together as a large group. All reporters should come to the front of the room. Ask each one to read an item from his or her list. After each has contributed, any reporter may add another. Give extra credit to the group that thought of the most correct answers. **(15–20 min.; Reteach, Reinforce)**

Rejecting food can harm health and lead to eating disorders.

used for fuel, 3 or 4 pounds of water are also lost from the body. Because of this, the person who stops eating altogether sees a great change in weight on the scales.

The body is thrown into a crisis—if it were to continue to feed on itself at this rate, death would occur in about 10 days. Instead, it changes gears to an emergency route of energy use that allows it to wring every possible calorie from its stored fuel. In addition, vital functions slow down to reduce the fuel needed for basal activities. The person slows down mentally, too, and feels too tired to exercise.

For the person who wants to lose weight, fasting has drawbacks and is not the best way. A balanced low-calorie, adequate carbohydrate diet has in fact been proved to promote the same rate of *weight* loss and a faster rate of *fat* loss than a total fast. A rule of thumb: to lose weight safely and effectively, do not go below 10 calories per pound of *present* body weight per day.

Key Points *When no food or too little carbohydrate is eaten, the body uses up its glycogen and then breaks down its own protein tissues to supply the brain with glucose. Then the body slows its rate of energy use. Fasting and low-carbohydrate diets are not healthy ways to lose weight.*

Other Wrong Ways to Lose Weight

You can judge a good weight-loss diet not by the speed of weight loss but by how well those who use it maintain their new weight. By this standard, fad diets and fasting are not smart ways to lose weight and true nutrition experts never recommend them.

Other ways *not* to lose weight are water pills, diet pills, health spa regimens, muscle stimulators, passive exercise machines, hormones, and surgery. Water pills (diuretics, mentioned earlier) do nothing to solve a fat problem. They only bring about the loss of a few pounds on the scale for half a day. As for **diet pills** (amphetamines and others), they reduce appetite by triggering the stress response. However, they leave the dieter with another problem: how to get off the pills without gaining more weight back. Health spas may be a nice place to exercise, but you cannot "jiggle" or "melt" pounds away on their special machines. Muscle stimulators reduce body measurements by making muscles tighter, not by reducing their fat content—and only for an hour or so. Hormones are powerful body chemicals, but all have proved useless and often hazardous as weight-loss aids.

Surgery (such as stomach stapling) to treat severe weight problems has dangerous side effects. Most types often lead to digestive tract damage, diarrhea, and malnutrition. Risks of these and other procedures

MINI GLOSSARY

diuretic (die-yoo-RETT-ick): a drug that causes the body to lose fluids; not effective for loss of body fat.
diet pills: medications that reduce the appetite or otherwise promote weight loss. Pills available over the counter usually contain caffeine and other drugs that cause more nervousness than weight loss. Prescription pills include *amphetamines*.

Teacher Support Notes

① **Handout—Ketosis:** For enrichment, you may want to distribute and discuss the handout on ketosis—the body's "emergency route" for fasting.
② **Teacher Information Sheet—Poor Choices for Weight Loss:** In the supplementary material you will find a sheet entitled "Poor Choices for Weight Loss," which provides you with some background information on several unwise choices for weight loss, including water pills and amphetamines.
③ **Teacher Information Sheet—Cosmetic Surgery and Fat:** This background information will help you explain situations in which surgery is and is not appropriate.

Fast Facts

Approximately 50 million Americans went on diets in 1992. Only 5% will keep off any weight that they lost.

CLOSE
SECTION IV

Activity 4.6
Identifying Unsound Programs.
Have the students write, without using their books, five of the eight clues to identifying unsound weight-loss programs. They are listed in the Health Strategies box on the opposite page. **(15 min.;**

Reteach, Reinforce)

FOCUS
SECTION V

In this section students will learn:
1. How to lose weight sensibly.
2. Strategies that help people keep weight off.

Activity 5.1

Diets Are Serious. Have students write down several reasons why a weight-loss diet must be approached seriously. Discuss the students' answers. **(5–10 min.)**

Activity 5.2
Unrealistic Doll Proportions.
Bring to class a tape measure and male and female 11-1/2" fashion dolls.
Explain how children learn from toys

Teacher Support Notes

① **Answers to Critical Thinking:** Answers to these questions will vary depending on how strong the desire is to lose (or gain) weight. Students should realize from the statistics given, however, that the chances are not good. They should offer their own suggestions for a better plan. You may want to refer them to the Health Strategies box on page 222 entitled *Using Behavior Modification for Weight Control.*

Section IV Review
Answers

1. Answers will vary.
2. The body's lean tissues and fluid levels are vital to health.
3. takes apart the protein in its own muscles and organs
4. Answers will vary; could include: fasting, fad diets, water pills, diet pills, health spa regimens, muscle stimulators, passive exercise machines, hormones, and surgery.
5. Answers will vary.

> **❝ Thoughts on Health ❞**
>
> *A little with quiet is the only diet.*
> **– Proverb**

outweigh the benefits. Success, as measured by long-term weight maintenance, is seldom achieved by these methods. As the Consumer Awareness box points out, however, bringing out new diet books and products is a profitable business.

> **Key Points** ➤ *The best form of weight loss is one that is safe and that promotes the maintenance of the person's new weight. Pills, spas, muscle stimulators, and other gimmicks fail by this standard.*

SECTION IV   REVIEW

Answer the following questions on a sheet of paper.
Learning the Vocabulary
The vocabulary terms in this section are *diuretic* and *diet pills.*

1. Write a sentence using each vocabulary term.

Learning the Facts
2. Why is it important to lose mostly fat tissue and not water or lean tissue when you diet?
3. Where does the body get the glucose it needs when a person has not eaten in a while?
4. List four methods that you should not use in attempting to lose weight.

Making Life Choices
5. List as many dangerous methods of weight loss that you can think of. Why is it that so many people try these strategies and invest money thinking they will solve their weight problems? Have you or anyone you know ever tried any of these methods? What was the end result?

CONSUMER AWARENESS   Weight-Loss Schemes

One survey of 29,000 weight-loss schemes found fewer than 6 percent of them effective—and 13 percent dangerous. People may respond to this fact with the question, "Can't the government do something about that?" The government tries to find, and crack down on, health swindles. Watchdog agencies, however, have too few staff members and too little money to handle the huge number of reported cases. They can stop only the most dangerous schemes at best. This results in a free market for others who can rake in billions of dollars on products that are only slightly less dangerous than the worst ones.

It is easy for a swindler to get a product on the market and hard for the govern-

ment or other groups to get it off. That puts the burden of identifying and avoiding frauds on you. To keep from being taken in, remember: if it sounds too good to be true, it probably is. The Health Strategies feature on the next page, "Clues to Identifying Unsound Weight Loss Programs," offers clues to help you recognize bad weight-loss ideas.

① **CRITICAL THINKING**

1. *Do you think it might be worth it to some people to take a risk trying a new diet scheme for weight loss? If so, why? If not, why not?*
2. *Under what circumstances might you try one?*
3. *What might be a better plan?*

and the media what their bodies are "supposed" to look like. Ask students if the images shown in many advertisements are realistic. What about toys? Could real people have bodies like fashion dolls? Show the dolls and tell the students they will do an exercise to find the answer to that question.

You can do this activity yourself or it can be done by groups of students using many dolls and tape measures. Measure the dolls' heights, hips, waists, chests, hands, and feet. Have students multiply each measurement by six. Ask the students for their answers. Doll sizes may vary but the female will be about 5'9" tall with a 34-1/2" chest, 21-1/2" waist, 30" hips, and 4-1/2" hands and feet. The male will be about 6' tall, 36" chest, 27" waist, 34-1/2" hips, 20-1/4" across the shoulders, 8-1/4" feet and 6-3/4" hands. Discuss the findings. Some students will want tape measures to compare their measurements to determine realism.

Add the fact that a leading toy company introduced a new fashion doll with more normal proportions due to consumer pressure. **(20–25 min., Interdisciplinary)**

HEALTH STRATEGIES

Clues to Identifying Unsound Weight-Loss Programs

Don't trust any weight-loss programs that:

- Promise rapid weight loss (that is, more than 1 percent of total body weight per week).
- Use diets that are extremely low in calories (below 1,000 calories per day).
- Use diets that are too low in carbohydrates (providing less than 6 servings of cereals, breads, pasta, or rice in a day)
- Make people dependent upon special products rather than on regular foods.
- Do not teach permanent, realistic lifestyle changes, including regular exercise and behavior modification.
- Misrepresent salespeople as "counselors" supposedly qualified to give guidance in nutrition or general health.
- Require large sums of money at the start or require that clients sign contracts for expensive, long-term programs. Programs should be on a pay-as-you-go basis.
- Fail to inform clients about the risks associated with weight loss in general or with the specific program being promoted.
- Claim that "cellulite" exists in the body. (Cellulite is supposed to be a hard-to-lose form of fat, but in reality, there is no such thing as cellulite. All fat is hard to lose.)

Source: Adapted with permission from *National Council Against Health Fraud Newsletter*, March/April 1987.

SECTION V

Smart Weight-Loss Strategies

With so many weight-loss schemes guaranteed to fail, what works? How can a person lose weight safely and permanently? The secret is a sensible approach (we didn't say *easy*) that uses diet, exercise, and behavior changes. It takes a great deal of effort, at first, for a person whose habits have all led to overfatness to adopt the hundred or so new habits that bring about thinness. When people succeed, they do so because they have used the methods described here.

The following sections are written as advice to "you." This is to give you the feeling that you are listening in on a counseling session in which an overfat person is being given advice about the methods known to be effective.

Diet Planning

No plan is magical. You needn't include or avoid any particular food. You are the one who will have to live with the plan, so you had better be the one who designs it. Don't think of it as a "diet" you are going "on"—because then you may be tempted to go "off." Think of it as an eating plan that you will adopt for life. It must consist of foods that you like or can learn to like, and foods that are available to you. You can see from Figure 9–5 on the next page that even fast foods can undermine weight loss efforts or support them.

Choose a calorie level you can live with. A shortage of 500 calories a day for seven days is a 3,500-calorie weekly shortage— enough to lose a pound of body fat. There is no point in rushing. If you adopt an eating plan rather than a "diet," you can be

Teacher Support Notes

① **Calculating Rapid Weight Loss:** Make sure students understand this strategy. Give them a problem or two. Say that one weight-loss program promises dieters will lose 5 pounds per week. Does this sound reasonable? Students should be able to see that, unless they weigh 500 pounds, this is too much. Ask students what would be the maximum amount of weight they could lose on a sound program given the 1% per week guideline. Each student should calculate 1% of his or her weight and realize that anything over that weight would be unsound.

② **Handouts—Evaluating Weight-Loss Diets:** In the supplementary material, you will find three different handouts that ask students to evaluate weight-loss diets.

Activity 5.3

Weight Maintenance. Tell students that over 30 million Americans are overweight. The U.S. is the most overweight country in the world. On the other hand, 1 in every 100 adolescent girls is anorexic.

Explain to the class that you are going to have them divide into groups of four or five to discuss the following question: Why do so many people experience problems with maintaining proper weight? The group will have ten minutes to brainstorm answers. After the time is up, each group will report back to the class with one idea. **(15–20 min., Cooperative Learning)**

Activity 5.4

Selecting Low-Fat Foods. Ask students to consider the following scenario: Imagine there are two identical twins. One regularly eats 2,600 calories, 50% of it coming from fat. The other also eats 2,600 calories with only 30% of it coming from fat. All other aspects of their lives—exercise, metabolism, etc.—are the same. Ask the class if they would weigh the same. Take a class vote. The answer is that the person with the higher fat content in the diet would weigh more.

Teacher Support Notes

① **Fast-Food Choices:** This illustration should be an interesting one for students. Discuss which foods most students choose most often for each of the four types: tacos, burgers, breakfasts, and pizza. Do any of the students already choose the meals with less fat? You could then have the students calculate the actual calorie differences and calories-from-fat differences. This will help them realize the benefit of the trimmed-down choices. For example, choosing the trimmed meal under tacos would cut the calorie intake by 408 calories. It would cut the fat calorie consumption by 338 calorie. As an additional activity for the students who complain that the trimmed meal is too sparse and not appetizing, have them develop a compromise meal.

② **Handout—Fast Foods:** For enrichment, you may want to distribute the handout found in Chapter 7 that gives both general and specific information about the amount of fat and number of calories in the various types of fast food. Students could use it to develop meals that fall somewhere between those shown in Figure 9.5.

Taco Choices

Loaded
2 regular beef tacos,* cheese nachos

Trimmed
2 bean burritos

856 total calories
53% calories from fat

—OR→

448 total calories
26% calories from fat

*Some tacos, called "light," are higher in fat than the ones used in these calculations. The "lightness" comes from the light texture of a fried flour tortilla as compared to the tougher corn tortillas that are somewhat lower in fat.

Burger Choices

Loaded
Double big cheeseburger on bun, shake,* fries

Trimmed
2 regular hamburgers, low-fat milk, side salad with 1 tbsp ranch dressing

1390 total calories
57% calories from fat

—OR→

676 total calories
36% calories from fat

*McDonald's offers shakes that are low in fat (less than 2 grams of fat per shake). The shake listed here is a regular, ice cream-based shake (over 10 grams of fat per shake).

Breakfast Choices

Loaded
2 bacon, cheese, and egg biscuits, hashbrowns

Trimmed
2 English muffins,* jelly, 1 tsp margarine or butter

1010 total calories
53% calories from fat

—OR→

456 total calories
11% calories from fat

*McDonald's also offers a fat-free apple muffin (most muffins are made with fat).

Pizza Choices

Loaded
2 slices pepperoni, sausage, extra-cheese pizza

Trimmed
2 slices mushroom, onion, green pepper, and cheese pizza

985 total calories
47% calories from fat

—OR→

595 total calories
27% calories from fat

Figure 9–5 Fast Food Choices. Depending on the foods chosen, fast foods can be high or low in calories and fat. ①

practicing positive behaviors all the time you are losing weight. You will be ready to succeed for the rest of your life, once you arrive at your goal weight.

Make your meals meet your nutrient needs. This is a way of putting yourself first. "I like me, and I'm going to take good care of me" is the right attitude. A good pattern to follow is the Daily Food Choices pattern of Figure 8–5 (Chapter 8, pages 196 and 197). ②

Most people could lose weight at a reasonable rate following such a plan and meet their nutrient needs, too. If you resolve to include a certain number of servings of food from each group each day, you may be so busy making sure you get what you need that you will have little time or appetite left for high-calorie or empty-calorie foods. Foods such as fruits, vegetables, and whole grains take a lot more eating, too. Crunchy, wholesome foods offer bulk

Why? Our bodies use the energy nutrients differently. Dietary fat is changed to body fat with little effort. Carbohydrates, on the other hand, require a larger energy expenditure to be changed to body fat.

To give an example of this, Japanese people eat 20% more calories than Americans, but 33% less fat. The Japanese as a group of people do not have the weight problems that Americans do. **(10 min., Critical Thinking)**

Activity 5.5
Repetitious Weight Loss and Weight Gain. It is estimated that between 95% to 98% of people who lose weight, gain it all back, plus a few more pounds. Ask students why they think this happens. Answers will vary. Explain to students that the body, as a survival tactic, lowers its metabolism when it is being starved. If a woman eats less than 1,000 calories per day and a man eats less than

1,200 calories, it is considered starvation-level calories. For each pound of fat lost while eating less than these limits, energy requirements may drop permanently by 10 calories. These permanent changes in metabolism may occur in as little as 72 hours. Ask students, "If a person loses 10 pounds, what happens after the diet is over?" (The weight is gained back because caloric expenditure has dropped

(continued on next page)

---

and a feeling of fullness for far fewer calories than smooth, refined foods. Limit your portions of meats: an ounce of ham contains more calories than an ounce of bread, and many of them are from fat. Remember to drink plenty of water.

Three meals a day is standard for our society, but no law says you shouldn't have four or five meals—only be sure they are smaller, of course. What is important is to eat regularly and, if at all possible, to eat before you are very hungry. When you do decide to eat, eat the entire meal you have planned for yourself. Then don't eat again until the next meal. Save "free" or favorite foods or beverages for a snack at the end of the day, if you need insurance against late-evening hunger.

At first it may seem as if you have to spend all your waking hours planning and eating your meals. Such a huge effort is always needed when a new skill is being learned. (You spent hours practicing writing the alphabet when you were in the first grade.) But after about three weeks, it will be much easier. Reward yourself often, but never with food. Use positive imaging (Chapter 3): see yourself as a person who "eats thin," and visualize your future self as fit and trim. Your new eating pattern will become a habit.

Do not weigh yourself more than every week or two. Gains or losses of a pound or more in a matter of days disappear as quickly; the smoothed-out average is what is real. Don't expect to continue to lose as fast as you do at first. A sizable water loss is common in the first week, but the loss slows down dramatically soon after. If you have been working out lately, your scale weight may show no loss or even a gain. This may reflect a welcome development: the gain of lean body mass—just what you want, if you want to be healthy.

If you slip, don't punish yourself. If you ate an extra 1,000 calories yesterday, don't

Eating sensibly is the best way to control weight.

try to eat 1,000 fewer calories today. Just go back to your plan. On the other hand, you can plan ahead and budget for special occasions. If you want to celebrate your birthday with cake and ice cream, cut the necessary calories from your bread and milk allowance for several days *beforehand*. Your weight loss will be as smooth as if you had stayed with the daily plan. Behavior modification also offers ideas that make sticking with your plan easier, and, the Health Strategies feature on the next page offers some of these.

You may have to get tough with yourself if you stop losing weight or start gaining. Ask yourself honestly (no one is listening in), "What am I doing wrong?" A period of weight gain can usually be explained by a person's own choices. Be aware that you may be choosing that course. Your food behaviors are under your control. Rather than feeling ashamed or guilty, hold your head high and take the attitude, "This is me, and this is the way I am choosing to be right now."

Key Points *To design a successful weight-loss plan, design it to last a lifetime. Be realistic, make it adequate, and reward yourself for following it.*

Physical Activity

Some people who want to lose weight hate the very idea of physical activity. A word to them: weight loss, at least to a point, is possible without exercise. But even

---

✎ Fast Facts

The average amount of food consumed by an American each year is 1,400 pounds.

Teacher Support Notes

① **Planning Your Diet:** Ask students if the burden of planning has ever prevented them from sticking to a diet. How long did they continue with the plan until they gave up? Can they think of other skills they've learned that took more time? How much time should they be willing to devote to changing their eating behavior as compared to learning other new skills?

❝ Thoughts on Health ❞

Fat people who want to reduce should take their exercise on an empty stomach and sit down to their food out of breath.
– Hippocrates (c. 400 BC)

100 calories. Ask students how this might affect someone who was constantly dieting.) **(10–15 min., Critical Thinking)**

Activity 5.6
Measuring Fat Content. Bring to class seven clear eight oz. plastic glasses. Label the glasses with a piece of masking tape and a marker: #1, #2, #3, #4, #5, #6, & #7. Using cooking oil and measuring spoons, fill the cups according to the following list.
#1—1 tsp. oil, represents 1 cup 2% milk; #2—7-3/4 tsp. oil, represents 1/2 cup peanuts; #3—3 tsp. oil, represents 3 slices of a 12" cheese pizza; #4—5-1/4 tsp., represents 15 potato chips; #5—15 tsp., represents a Wendy's triple cheese

burger; #6—9 tsp., represents a Burger King Whopper; #7—2 tsp., represents a McDonald's strawberry shake.
Place the filled cups so all can be seen. Tell the class you are doing an exercise to see how aware they are of fat in their food. Have them number from 1 to 7 on the left side of their papers and give them the number of teaspoons of fat in each cup. Next give them the seven foods the numbers represent, in random order.

Teacher Support Notes

① **Evaluating Strategies:** Twenty-four different general suggestions are given in this box to help students modify their behavior in their attempts to either gain or lose weight. Have them evaluate the strategies for effectiveness and appropriateness in their own lives. You may want to have them do this individually or in groups. Two suggested evaluations are:
a. Have the students make two columns. In one column they should list strategies they think would help them. In the other column, they should list those that they think would be of no help to them personally.
b. Have them rank the 24 strategies in order from most effective to least effective for them personally.
② **Cues.** *Cues* is a term commonly used in behavior modification. It refers to a signal. For a dieter, events or situations that bring about eating are considered cues.
③ **Designated Eating Area:** Ask students where they eat other than the kitchen. Do they consume more calories in these locations than the kitchen or dining room? More empty calories?

HEALTH
STRATEGIES

Using Behavior Modification for Weight Control   ①

1. *To eliminate inappropriate eating cues:*   ②
   - Avoid rich sauces and toppings.
   - Let other family members buy, store, and serve their own sweets. When the television shows food commercials, change channels or look away.
   - Stay away from convenience stores.
   - Carry appropriate snacks from home, and avoid vending machines.

2. *To reduce the cues you cannot eliminate:*
   - Eat only in one place, in one room.   ③
   - Clear plates directly into the garbage.
   - Create obstacles to the eating of problem foods (for example, make it necessary to unwrap, cook, and serve each one separately).
   - Minimize contact with excessive food (serve individual plates. don't put serving dishes on the table, and leave the table when you are finished). Make small portions of food look large (spread food out, and serve it on small plates).
   - Don't deprive yourself (eat regular meals, don't skip meals, avoid getting tired, and avoid boredom by keeping cues to fun activities in sight).

3. *To strengthen the cues to appropriate eating and exercise:*
   - Encourage others to eat appropriate foods with you.
   - Keep your favorite appropriate foods

in the front of the refrigerator.
   - Learn appropriate portion sizes.
   - Save permitted foods from meals for snacks (and make these your only snacks).
   - Prepare permitted foods attractively.
   - Keep your running shoes (hiking boots, tennis racket) by the door.

4. *To practice the desired eating and exercise behaviors:*
   - Slow down (pause for two to three minutes, put down utensils, chew slowly, swallow before reloading the fork, and always use utensils).
   - Leave some food on the plate.
   - Move more (shake a leg, pace, fidget, or flex your muscles).
   - Join in and exercise with a group of active people.

5. *To arrange or emphasize negative consequences of inappropriate eating:*
   - Eat your meals with other people.
   - Ask that others respond neutrally to your deviations (make no comment). This is a negative consequence because it withholds attention.

6. *To arrange or emphasize positive consequences of appropriate eating and exercise behaviors:*
   - Update records of food intake, exercise, and weight change regularly.
   - Arrange for rewards for each behavior change or weight loss.
   - Ask for reinforcement and encouragement from your friends and family.

Have them write those down on the right-hand side of the paper, across from the numbers. Ask students to draw a line from the amount of fat to the food they believe it represents. When they are finished, discuss the correct answers. Explain to students that active teens should limit their fat intake to 18–20 tsp. of fat a day, and adults to 15 tsp. Discuss that some food choices are better than others because of fat content. **(20 min.; Extend, Enrich)**

Activity 5.7

Yo-Yo Dieting. Read to students the newspaper article, "Man Regained 500 lbs. before Dying," from your supplementary material. Discuss the article and the effects of "rollercoaster" or yo-yo dieting. **(10–15 min., Critical Thinking)**

Activity 5.8

Behavior Modification. Have students think of one behavior modification strategy that was not listed in the book. Go around the room and ask each student to give his or her answer. Make a master list on the board. **(10 min.)**

Activity 5.9

Jug Weights. Before class, fill several 1-gallon plastic jugs with water or sand. Ask for students to volunteer to come forward and hold the jugs in their hands.

(continued on next page)

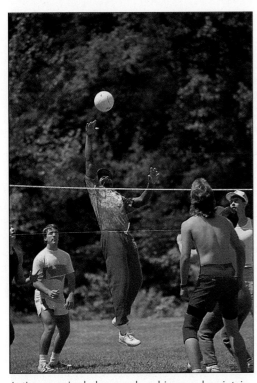

Active exercise helps people achieve and maintain healthy weights.

if you choose not to exercise at first, let your mind be open to the idea. As the pounds come off, moving your body becomes a pleasure. You may want to take up an activity later on.

The next chapter gives many details about developing fitness, but a few points are important here. Physical activity contributes to weight control physically. It develops the body's lean tissue, and it raises the rate of basal energy use. Physical activity also helps mentally. Looking and feeling healthy boosts self-esteem. High self-esteem helps a person to stay with a weight-control effort—a beneficial cycle.

Weight loss without activity can have a negative effect. A person who diets without exercising loses both lean and fat tissue. If the person then gains weight without exercising, the gain is mostly fat. Compared with lean tissue, fat tissue burns fewer calories to maintain itself. The person who slides back into eating the same amount as before the diet gains body fat, but not lean. This cycle of gaining, losing, and gaining again can leave people fatter than if they had not dieted at all. With each turn of the cycle, body fat and weight zoom higher than before. This is the **yo-yo effect** of dieting (Figure 9–6 below).

On the other hand, the more lean tissue you develop, and the more calories you spend, the more you can afford to eat. This brings you both pleasure and nutrients. It must be clear by now that exercise speeds up your body's energy use *permanently*—that is, for as long as you keep your body fit.

Physical activity, of course, also spends energy while you are doing it. Figure 9–7 on the next page lists energy costs of activities.

If an activity is to help with weight loss, it must be active. Being moved passively, as

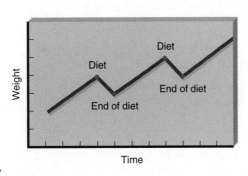

Figure 9–6 The Yo-Yo Effect of Dieting. Each round of dieting, without exercise, is followed by a rebound of body fat and weight to a higher level than before.

MINI GLOSSARY

yo-yo effect: the gain of body fat that results, in the end, from repeated rounds of dieting without exercising.

Teacher Support Notes

① **Overhead—Yo-Yo Effect:** Your supplementary material contains an overhead transparency of this figure.

Each jug represents approximately 8-1/2 lbs. You may want the students to walk back and forth on the side of the room. Meanwhile, explain to the class the relationship between being overweight, exhaustion from carrying the extra weight, and not having the energy to exercise.

Ask the students who have been holding the jugs if they would feel like doing a lot of physical exercise if they had to carry the weights with them wherever they went. **(5–10 min., Special Needs)**

EVALUATE
SECTION V

Activity 5.10
Safe Dieting Summary. Ask stu-

dents to summarize what they have learned in Section V by writing a paragraph. Emphasize that students should interpret what they have read in their own words. Have them write down what they think were the most important things to remember about safe dieting.

CLOSE
SECTION V

Teacher Support Notes

① **Energy Demands of Activities:** This figure gives students the exact amount of calories burned in 15 different activities and for different intensities for three of those activities (bicycling, running, and swimming). For example, a person weighing 110 pounds who bicycles at 13 m.p.h. will burn 5 calories per minute. Using the column that most closely matches their weights, students can find *approximately* how many calories they will burn for each of these activities. To find an *exact* amount for their exact weights, they can use the number factor under the heading *Cal/Lb/Min.* Directions at the bottom of the figure explain the equation the students need to use to find the number of calories spent for their exact weights. Give them the following problem to make sure they understand how to use the equation: Assume a person weighing 98 pounds plays basketball vigorously for two hours. How many calories would be spent? The equation would be 0.097 × 98 = 9.506 × 120 (the two hours must be changed to 120 minutes). The answer would be 1,140.72 calories.

by a machine or a massage, does not help. The more muscles you move and the longer you move them, the more calories you spend.

Weight loss is not the only reward to be won from working out. If you incorporate

---

FIGURE 9-7

Energy Demands of Activities ①

This figure shows how many calories per minute are spent in activities for people at five different body weights. The calories per pound per minute (cal/lb/min) number makes it possible for you to calculate the number of calories for your own body weight, if it is not exactly one of the five weights listed here.

		Calories Spent per Minute (for 5 body weights, in pounds)				
Activity	**Cal/Lb/Min**[a]	**110**	**125**	**150**	**175**	**200**
Aerobic dance (vigorous)	0.062	6.8	7.8	9.3	10.9	12.4
Basketball (vigorous, full court)	0.097	10.7	12.1	14.6	17.0	19.4
Bicycling						
13 miles per hour	0.045	5.0	5.6	6.8	7.9	9.0
19 miles per hour	0.076	8.4	9.5	11.4	13.3	15.2
Canoeing (flat water, moderate pace)	0.045	5.0	5.6	6.8	7.9	9.0
Cross-country skiing (8 miles per hour)	0.104	11.4	13.0	15.6	18.2	20.8
Golf (carrying clubs)	0.045	5.0	5.6	6.8	7.9	9.0
Handball	0.078	8.6	9.8	11.7	13.7	15.6
Horseback riding (trot)	0.052	5.7	6.5	7.8	9.1	10.4
Rowing (vigorous)	0.097	10.7	12.1	14.6	17.0	19.4
Running						
5 miles per hour	0.061	6.7	7.6	9.2	10.7	12.2
7.5 miles per hour	0.094	10.3	11.8	14.1	16.4	18.8
10 miles per hour	0.114	12.5	14.3	17.1	20.0	22.9
Soccer (vigorous)	0.097	10.7	12.1	14.6	17.0	19.4
Studying	0.011	1.2	1.4	1.7	1.9	2.2
Swimming						
20 yards per minute	0.032	3.5	4.0	4.8	5.6	6.4
45 yards per minute	0.058	6.4	7.3	8.7	10.2	11.6
Tennis (beginner)	0.032	3.5	4.0	4.8	5.6	6.4
Walking (brisk pace)						
3.5 miles per hour	0.035	3.9	4.4	5.2	6.1	7.0

[a]*Cal/lb/min* is an abbreviation for *calories* (cal) per *pound* (lb) of body weight per *minute* (min). You can use it to calculate the number of calories you use at *your* body weight for a minute of activity. To calculate the total number of calories you spend for a longer time, multiply the cal/lb/min factor by your exact weight and then multiply your answer by the number of minutes you spend on the activity. For example, if you weigh 142 pounds, and you want to know how many calories you spend doing 30 minutes of vigorous aerobic dance: 0.062 cal/lb/min x 142 lb = 8.8 calories per minute. 8.8 cal/min x 30 minutes = 264 total calories spent.

Source: Values for swimming, bicycling, and running have been adapted with permission of Ross Laboratories, Columbus, Ohio 43216, from G.P. Town and K.B. Wheeler, Nutrition Concerns for the Endurance Athlete, *Dietetic Currents* 13(1986):7–12. Copyright 1986 Ross Laboratories. Values for all other activities: Copyright 1983 by Consumers Union of the United States, Inc., Yonkers, N.Y. 10703-1057. Adapted with permission from CONSUMER REPORTS BOOKS, 1983.

Activity 5.11

Helping Friends. Give students the following scenario. A friend who is over-weight asks your advice about going on a diet. What would you tell your friend? Question students as to what their responses would be. Discuss. **(15 min.; Extend, Enrich)**

FOCUS
SECTION VI

In this section students will learn:
1. How to gain weight wisely.

Activity 6.1
Problems with Being Under-weight. Explain to the class that because so many people have difficulties with being overweight, it is sometimes hard to relate to the problems associated with being underweight.

Have students take out a piece of paper. Give them five minutes to write down drawbacks that would come from being underweight. Tell them not to forget to include social and economic factors, as well as physical ones. Discuss students' answers. **(10–15 min., Critical Thinking)**

the right kinds of workouts into your schedule, your heart and lungs, as well as your muscles, will become and stay fit. The "right kinds" are described in the next chapter.

Physical activity is helpful in weight loss because it increases lean tissue, expends energy, and boosts self-esteem.

Weight Maintenance

Finally, be aware that it can be much harder to maintain weight loss than to lose weight. An appropriate calorie intake for maintenance is higher than the level of intake to promote loss, but it still may take effort not to overeat. (Appendix B at the back of the book includes suggested calorie intakes for people of various ages.) Those who succeed in maintaining appropriate weight have some key traits in common:

• They take responsibility for their weight. They do not place the responsibility on programs, professionals, pills, or potions. (Outside advice can help, but the weight belongs only to the person.)

• They have confidence that they can maintain weight—they believe in themselves. (This sets them free from a self-hate spiral that leads to overeating. Self-discipline is easiest when self-worth supports it.)

• They expect to have **lapses**, times when they fall back into the old patterns.

A word about lapses—people who maintain weight have learned to cope with them. They identify the triggers that lead to lapses and keep learning to avoid them. For example, a person who unexpectedly over-ate at a party would first forgive the lapse, and then get tough. One action might be to promise to eat a balanced meal before attending the next party (to defend against hunger) and to stay away from the buffet

(to reduce temptation). When normal lapses occur, cope by saying, "I'm doing it again, but I do it less often now. I'm making progress."

People who maintain weight take responsibility for their weight. They have confidence in themselves, and they do not let normal lapses bother them.

SECTION V   REVIEW

Answer the following questions on a sheet of paper.

Learning the Vocabulary
The vocabulary terms in this section are *yo-yo effect* and *lapses*.
1. Write a sentence using each vocabulary term.

Learning the Facts
2. List four recommendations for developing a successful weight-loss program.
3. What are some advantages of including exercise in a weight-loss and weight-maintenance program?
4. What is the yo-yo effect of dieting?
5. Give three strategies for using behavior modification for weight control.

Making Life Choices
6. A sound exercise program is important in gaining, losing, and maintaining weight and overall health. Look over Figure 9–7 on the opposite page, "Energy Demands of Activities." Choose several activities on the list that you enjoy. Make up a schedule for a week that includes at least one activity for each day. Calculate the number of calories you'll spend on each activity.

MINI GLOSSARY

lapses: times of falling back into former habits, a normal part of both weight change and weight maintenance.

Activity 6.2

Dietitian Visit. Invite a dietitian to class. Have the dietitian discuss why an underweight person trying to gain pounds has just as difficult a task as an overweight person trying to lose pounds. This will also give students a chance to ask questions from throughout the chapter. **(Extend, Enrich)**

Activity 6.3

Exercising for the Underweight Person. Explain to students that it may seem like a contradiction to have an underweight person exercise while trying to gain weight. Ask students why underweight people need to exercise. **(5–10 min., Critical Thinking)**

Activity 6.4

Determining Calorie Needs. We have learned that weight loss or gain happens when the number of calories we eat does not equal the number of calories we burn. One method of determining calorie requirements for the day is to use the following formula: Multiply your ideal healthy weight by the number below that best describes your activity level. The answer you get will represent your calorie needs

Teacher Support Notes

① **Wrong question:** Point out that not only is this an impossible question to answer, it is the wrong question to ask. For an adult, a wide range of weights is acceptable for a given height, based on the person's health. For young people who are growing, the range of healthy weights is even wider. The more useful question, stated later, is whether or not the person has a reasonable amount of body fat.

② **Appropriate Weight Is Unique:** Stress that some weight-range adjustments must be made for each person. For example, an endurance athlete wants no more than the minimum of body fat. An Alaskan fisherman, on the other hand, needs a blanket of insulating fat to prevent excessive loss of body heat.

✏ Fast Facts

According to *Snack Food Magazine*, from 1980 to 1990 the U.S. consumption of potato chips increased 71%.

LIFE **C**HOICE

INVENTORY

How Much Should You Weigh? ①

The question of how much a person should weigh is hard enough for adults to answer. For young people who are still growing, it is *impossible*. For an adult, the appropriate weight within the acceptable range depends on factors such as family history, occupation, physical and recreational activities, and personal preference. For young people, another factor applies: stage of growth.

For adults, the traditional way of assigning appropriate weights is to use the table of weights for height developed by insurance companies. The height-weight tables do not apply to people who haven't finished growing, however. In fact, no standard applies. How much you should weigh depends on how fast you are growing and on how much more you will grow—factors that could only be determined if you could look both backward and forward in time. The standard to use for comparison is not some ideal person outside yourself. It is yourself as you will end up when you have finished growing and have filled out. The way your body gets to that point (your growth pattern) may be different from another person's growth pattern. One 15-year-old who is 5 feet 2 inches tall may easily weigh many pounds more or less than another, and both may be just fine as far as health and ultimate weight are concerned.

Health care professionals use growth charts to track heights and weights of teens, but they are different from height-weight tables for adults. A growth chart permits comparison between your height and weight today and your heights and weights in prior years. It offers reassurance that height and weight are being added in some consistent fashion during the growing years. If they are not, this alerts the health care provider to see if something may be wrong.

Many teens want to know, though, "What should I weigh?" Growth charts don't answer that question. Figure 9–3 tries to help, by showing the total ranges of weights expected for height at various ages.

② If your weight falls within the range for your height and age, even if it's near one end of the range, that's fine. To be thin compared with others is OK. You may fill out later, or you may be thin all your life, which is fine, too. To be a little fatter than others is also OK. You may be gaining fat to support an upcoming growth spurt, you may slim down later, or you may be near the top end of the range all your life. When you have stopped growing in height and have reached the age of 25, the adult tables will apply.

Meanwhile, you might want to ask a more useful question: Do I have a reasonable amount of body fat? Your teacher, school nurse, or health care provider can help you determine this with a fatfold caliper. Then check the standard in Appendix B to compare your fatfold to the percentiles.

Check your weight against the range of weights expected for a person your height, age, and gender (in Figure 9–3 on page 212). Is your weight within the range? If so, OK. If not, this may still be OK (check with a health care provider).

Determine your fatfold thickness. Is it between the 25th and 75th percentiles on the table of standards in Appendix B? If so, OK. If not, this may still be OK (check with a health care provider).

for the day:

13—very sedentary person, inactive.

14—sedentary, does light housework, moves slowly.

15—average, activities such as doing errands and light yard work, moves at a normal pace.

16—above average, does hard work involving heavy lifting and moving at a brisk pace, exercises regularly for fun.

17—strenuous, has a demanding exer-cise program and works hard physically, moving at a fast pace the major portion of the day.

If weight is above desirable level, try exercising more. About five calories are burned for every minute walked. Remind students that small changes in behavior add up. **(20 min.; Extend, Enrich)**

> **E**VALUATE
> **SECTION VI**

Activity 6.5
Pop Quiz.
1. To achieve a healthful weight gain of 1 to 1-1/2 pounds per week, you must add _____ to _____ calories of nutritious food per day. (700, 800)

(continued on next page)

SECTION VI

Smart Weight-Gain Strategies

It is as hard for a person who tends to be underweight to gain a pound as it is for a person who tends to be overweight to lose one. Like the weight loser, the person who wants to gain must learn new habits and learn to like new foods.

An underweight person must decide whether gaining weight is best for health. If the person is healthy, it may be that weighing less than average is an advantage. Thin people are unlikely to suffer from heart disease, for example. For teens who are still growing, it could be that they will "fill out" naturally in a year or two—the low weight is temporary. But if an underweight person is unwell and eats poorly, trying to gain may be the best course. Some people may want to gain just for the sake of their appearance. This is a personal choice.

Although physical activity costs calories, it is essential for health, and should continue unless body weight is so low as to be life-threatening. The healthy way to gain weight is to build it up by patient and consistent physical training and, at the same time, to eat enough calories to support the weight gain. If you are not dangerously underweight, adopt an activity program designed to build lean body tissue (for more details, see the next chapter).

In addition to exercising appropriately, you must eat enough calories to support weight gain. If you add 700 to 800 extra calories of nutritious foods a day, you can achieve a healthful weight gain of 1 to 1½ pounds per week.

A person who wants to gain weight often has to learn to eat new foods. No matter how many helpings of boiled carrots you

Whether you are trying to gain or lose weight, physical activity is essential for health.

eat, you won't gain weight very fast. Carrots simply don't offer enough calories. The person who can't eat much volume should select high-calorie foods (the very ones the dieter is trying to stay away from). So to gain weight:

- Eat an extra 700 to 800 calories per day.
- Use more high-calorie foods—those items marked in red in Figure 8–5 of Chapter 8 (pages 196–197).

Also, take an independent view of the low-fat diet plan that is recommended for the general U.S. population. Most people are too fat. For you, if you need to gain weight, a

> **66 Thoughts on Health 99**
>
> *One man eats very little and is always full, but another man constantly eats and is always hungry. Why is that?*
>
> *– Zen Riddle*

> ✎ **Fast Facts**
>
> One diet specialist recommends that those people having trouble controlling their calories should tell themselves they will eat only those things that can be eaten with a fork. This will eliminate cookies, potato chips, etc., and also make people more aware of what they eat. The downside of this plan is, of course, that many nutritious foods such as apples, carrots, and bread are also eaten without forks.

(advantage)

5. If you fill up fast, and you are trying to gain weight, eat the _____ calorie items first. (highest)

behavior modification strategies for underweight people. Give students 15 minutes and then discuss their findings. **(20–25 min.; Reteach, Reinforce)**

2. _____ adds calories without adding bulk to the diet. (Fat)

3. A person who wants to gain weight may have to learn to eat _____ foods. (different)

4. If an underweight person is healthy, it may be that weighing less is an _____.

CLOSE
SECTION VI

Activity 6.6
Behavior Modification Strategies. Have students design a list of

RETEACH/BONUS

Identifying Game. Prepare ahead of time pieces of paper with different problems associated with being under-

---

Section VI Review
Answers

1. build up weight by patient and consistent physical training and eat enough calories to support the weight gain

2. 700–800 calories a day

3. Answers will vary; could include: choose milk shakes instead of milk, whole milk instead of non-fat milk, peanut butter instead of lean meat, avocados instead of cucumbers, whole-wheat muffins instead of whole-wheat bread; add margarine to vegetables; use creamy dressing on salads, whipped cream on fruit, sour cream on potatoes; eat more often; plan ahead what to eat at your mealtimes; and plan time for eating each meal.

4. Answers will vary.

✉ Where to Write

The Facts about Weight-Loss Products and Programs
Weight Loss
Federal Trade
Commission
Washington D.C.
20580

diet very low in fat might do more harm than good. Ignore recommendations about fat and calories made to overweight people.

To increase calorie intake:

- Choose milk shakes instead of milk, whole milk instead of nonfat milk, peanut butter instead of lean meat, avocados instead of cucumbers, whole-wheat muffins instead of whole-wheat bread.

- Add margarine to cooked vegetables; use creamy dressings on salads, whipped cream on fruit, sour cream on potatoes, and so forth. (Because fat contains twice as many calories per teaspoon as sugar, it adds calories without adding much bulk.)

Since you need many more calories in a day, you will also need to:

- Eat more often. Make three sandwiches in the morning to eat as snacks between the day's three regular meals.

Most people who are underweight have simply been too busy (sometimes for months) to eat enough to gain or maintain weight. In this case:

- Plan ahead what to eat at your mealtimes and snack times.

- Plan time for eating each meal. If you fill up fast, eat the highest-calorie items first. Don't start with soup or salad. Eat meaty appetizers or the main course first.

Expect to feel full, sometimes even uncomfortably so. Most underweight people usually eat small quantities of food. When they begin eating significantly more food, they complain of being too full. This is normal, and it passes when the stomach adapts.

For the person who tends to be underweight, maintenance of the new weight is a final challenge. The weight-maintenance methods described on page 225 for the person who tends to gain weight work equally well in this case. Just swap strategies—stand *near* the buffet at a party.

Key Points *Healthful weight gain can be achieved by a program of exercise and increased intake of calories.*

SECTION VI REVIEW

Answer the following questions on a sheet of paper.

Learning the Facts
1. What is the healthiest way to gain weight?
2. How many extra calories of nutritious food must be added daily to gain 1 to 1½ pounds per week?
3. Give three recommendations for increasing caloric intake.

Making Life Choices
4. Have you or anyone you know ever had difficulty gaining weight? Explain some of the frustrations involved. How are these problems similar to those of a person who is trying to lose weight? How are they different? Why is it that there are not as many "fad" programs or "gimmicks" on the market targeted at weight gain as there are for weight loss?

Answers to Fact or Fiction

Here are the answers to the questions at the start of the chapter.

1. True. **2.** False. A weight loss may reflect loss of water or lean tissue rather than loss of fat. **3.** False. Fasting promotes rapid weight loss, but a balanced low-calorie diet can promote more rapid fat loss. **4.** False. Carbohydrate is a necessary part of a healthy, balanced weight-loss diet. **5.** True. **6.** True. **7.** False. It is as hard for a person who tends to be thin to gain a pound as it is for a person who tends to be fat to lose one.

weight or overweight (high blood pressure, diabetes, heart disease, clothes, cold, dating, etc.) written on them. Prepare one piece of paper for each student. Without letting the student see the paper, tape it to his or her back. The object of the game is for students, while mingling with their classmates, to ask yes or no questions to find out what the papers on their backs say. For instance, a student might ask someone, "Do I have anything to do with the circulatory system?" The other student may only answer yes or no, nothing else. Allow enough time for most students to guess the problem on their backs. **(15 min.)**

Body Types. Explain to students that each person's body shape is uniquely his or her own. Body types vary due to heredity, exercise, age, and diet.

There are three major body types:

- *Ectomorphs* are lean and lanky.
- *Mesomorphs* tend to be muscular with narrow hips.
- *Endomorphs* have a round look and carry more fat.

In other words, people of the same weight and height may look very different because they have different body types.

Ask students to think about what body types they have.

(continued on next page)

STRAIGHT TALK

An Obsession with Thinness: Anorexia Nervosa and Bulimia

Our society and others like it favor thinness, especially in women. Magazines, newspapers, and television screens display camera-ready women, flaws hidden, unrealistically thin. The message is clear—the way you are isn't good enough. It is as if they are saying, "You should become like the cover girl who doesn't sweat; doesn't grow hair on her slender legs; has a flat stomach, a perfect face, and small feet; and is always perfectly happy. If you, young woman, are not perfectly happy, it is because your body is not perfect by these standards." Acceptance of such unreasonable standards has driven many young women in our society to be obsessed with thinness.

I thought being thin was healthy. Isn't it OK to want to be thin?

Being fit is healthy; being thin may not be. Wanting a healthy body weight is safe and wise. The desire for extreme thinness is linked with two eating disorders, **anorexia nervosa** and **bulimia**.

What happens to someone who has anorexia nervosa? ①

The story of Julie is typical. Julie is 18 years old. She is a superachiever in school and a fine dancer. She watches her diet with great care, and she exercises and practices ballet daily. She is thin, but she is not satisfied with her weight and is determined to lose more. She is 5 feet 6 inches tall and weighs 85 pounds, but she's still trying to get thinner.

It's hard for some young girls to know how thin is too thin.

How could she possibly think she's too fat, weighing only 85 pounds?

Her self-image is false. Against her will, Julie's family took her to see a psychiatrist, who tested her. When given a self-image test, she drew a picture of herself that was grossly oversized. When asked to draw her best friend, Julie drew a fair likeness.

Can't she see that she's starving herself?

Julie is unaware that she is undernourished, and she sees no need for treatment. She stopped menstruating several months ago and has become very moody. Her eyes lie in deep hollows in her face. She is close to physical exhaustion, but she claims never to be tired.

How can someone get so thin and continue to diet?

Julie controls her food intake with great discipline even though she is starving. If she feels that she has slipped and eaten too much, she runs or jumps rope until she is sure she has exercised it off. Her

(Continued on next page)

Teacher Support Notes

① **Anorexia Stories:** Find out what students know, or think they know, about anorexia. Have them write a short story about a case of anorexia. It can be based on a movie they've seen or an article they've read. If it is a true story about someone they know, they should use a fictitious name. Read the stories in class.

Question students to find out if they believe a hereditary trait like body type can be changed. Why or why not? **(10–15 min.)**

Disorder Associations. Help students make the association between eating disorders and other addictive or obsessive behaviors.

Ask students to name things that people become obsessed with or addicted to. (drugs, cigarettes, food, gambling, sex, thinness, money, etc.) List their ideas on the board.

Ask students if they think people with these different addictions have something in common. The answer is that they are all looking for something outside of themselves to make them feel good. Ask students why this doesn't work, or only works temporarily. Explain that it boils down to the fact that people have to be happy with themselves inside. If a person is hurting on the inside, the pain is not relieved by engaging in destructive behaviors even if at first it seems the pain is temporarily gone. Usually people need counseling to solve problems related to addictions, whatever they are. Once they

---

✍ Fast Facts

Close to 50% of anorexics are also bulimic.

Teacher Support Notes

① **Causes of Anorexia:** So many of the problems discussed in the text have been shown to result from low self-esteem. Ask students if they can guess the cause of Julie's disorder. Tell them that many of the emotional problems they read about earlier in the text were attributed to the same cause.

✉ Where to Write

Anorexia Nervosa and Related Eating Disorders (ANRED)
P.O. Box 5102
Eugene, OR 97405

✍ Fast Facts

During any three-month period, 50% of Americans will have had at least one pizza delivered to their homes.

STRAIGHT TALK *(Continued)*

fierce self-control, not lack of hunger, prevents her from eating.

What could have caused her to behave this way? ①

Some think it may have to do with family and social circumstances. The typical family of a person with anorexia is described as being dominated by the mother, with the father absent or distant. The family values achievement and outward appearances more than an inner sense of self-worth. The young person wants her parents to be pleased and works to be perfect for them.

Young women look to their male parents for important feedback on their self-worth. If they don't receive it, they tend to become too sensitive to society's messages. Julie's father's alcoholism makes him an ineffective parent.

What is happening to her physically, and how serious is this condition?

Julie is suffering the physical effects of starvation. Her hormone output has become abnormal. Her blood pressure has dropped. Her heart pumps inefficiently. Its muscle has become weak, thin, and small in size. Her heart's rhythms have changed, with a characteristic abnormality appearing on the heart monitor. Sudden stopping of the heart, due to lean tissue loss or mineral deficiencies, causes many sudden deaths among victims of anorexia nervosa.

Can a person with anorexia be cured?

Julie, as others, is proud of her dieting. She has, after all, made progress toward achieving society's goal for her—to be thin. Treatment is therefore an uphill battle for everyone.

Treatment centers use methods that work better than they used to. Many people are helped to a degree, although two-thirds fail to eat normally after leaving the centers. About 6 percent die, 1 percent by suicide.

You also mentioned bulimia. What happens to someone with this disease?

The case of Sophie shows the plight of the person with bulimia. Like the typical person with bulimia, Sophie is female, single, Caucasian, in her early 20s, well educated, and close to her ideal body weight. Sophie is a charming, intelligent woman who thinks constantly about food. She sometimes starves herself, and she sometimes gets into **binges**. When she has eaten too much, she

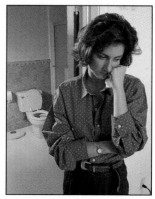

In bulimia, a binge episode ends with shame or self-loathing.

makes herself vomit.

Sophie's periodic binges take place in secret, usually at night. They last an hour or more. She usually starts the binge after having gone through a period of strict dieting, so that she eats with haste from hunger. Each time, she eats thousands of calories of cookies, cake, ice cream, or bread. The binge is not like normal eating. It is a compulsion and occurs in stages: planning, anxiety, urgency to begin, rapid and uncontrollable eating, relief and relaxation, disappointment, and finally shame or disgust.

What are the physical effects of bulimia?

Swollen hands and feet, bloating, fatigue, headache,

(Continued on next page)

can deal with the inner problems they have been hiding inside, they may be able to kick their addictions because they are happier with who they are.

STRAIGHT TALK   (Continued)

nausea, and pain are common. More serious are fluid and electrolyte imbalances caused by vomiting, which can lead to abnormal heartbeat and injury to the kidneys. Vomiting causes irritation and infection of the throat, esophagus, and salivary glands; erosion of the teeth; and dental caries (cavities). The esophagus may rupture or tear, as may the stomach. The eyes become red from the pressure of vomiting.

Some people with bulimia use strong laxatives or **emetics**, which can injure the intestinal tract. Emetics are poisons, and their overuse brings a very real threat of death.

What makes a person become bulimic?

We don't know, but family structure and personality factors may be partly to blame. Much like Julie, who has anorexia nervosa, Sophie has been a high achiever, but dependent on her parents.

Sophie's family often combined hearty eating with socializing around the dinner table. Food was a main focus in celebrations, and was used to console the family during times of grief. Sophie felt it would be disrespectful not to partake of food at such times. Yet as strong as the social pressure on Sophie to eat was,

the opposite pressure—to be thin—was just as strong.

Sophie feels anxious in social settings and has difficulty in making friends and in dating. She is sometimes depressed. Some people with bulimia become antisocial. She may abuse drugs, steal, or become sexually uninhibited. Feelings of failure make her passive with men, to whom she looks for a sense of self-worth. When she is rejected, either in reality or in her imagination, her bulimia becomes worse. In fact, many women point to feelings of male rejection as the event that led to their first binge.

How common are anorexia nervosa and bulimia?

Both anorexia nervosa and bulimia occur only in wealthy nations and are increasing steadily. Women are the most likely victims (although men are not immune).

Many people have symptoms of eating disorders. For example, in one California study researchers found more than 80 percent of girls (age 17–18) feared body fatness, restrained their eating, and occasionally binged. These attitudes and actions are all symptoms of eating disorders. Boys also report such symptoms, but in greatly reduced numbers.

What can be done about this situation?   ①

One school of thought labels both anorexia nervosa and bulimia as social problems. Perhaps they begin when young people develop low self-esteem and adopt the ideal of some false, "perfect" image is portrayed in the media.

Slowly, society is changing. Women are finding honor and esteem in such traditionally male fields as athletics, science, law, and politics. This has raised all women's self-esteem. Perhaps anorexia nervosa and bulimia will disappear as human roles and ideals change. Prevention may be possible if, early in children's lives, they are nurtured to respect themselves. The simple concept—to respect and value your own uniqueness—may be lifesaving for a future generation.

Mini Glossary

anorexia (an-or-EX-ee-uh) **nervosa:** a disorder of self-starvation to the extreme.
bulimia (byoo-LEEM-ee-uh): repeated binge eating, sometimes followed by vomiting (also spelled *bulemia*).
binges (BIN-jez): times of vast overeating.
emetics (em-ETT-ics): drugs that cause vomiting.

☎ Where to Call

Glenbeigh Food Addictions Hotline, 1-800-4A-BINGE

Teacher Support Notes

① **Handout—Diagnosing Anorexia and Bulimia:** Your supplementary material contains a handout that lists some basic criteria for diagnosing both anorexia and bulimia. You may want to distribute the handout at this time.

🖉 Fast Facts

It is estimated that 95% of all cases of anorexia occur in adolescent females (only 5% of the cases occur in males). Approximately 1 in 100 females between 12 and 18 are affected by this disorder.

Answers

Vocabulary

1. **a.** pinch test **b.** diet pills **c.** bulimia
2. **a.** underweight
b. anorexia nervosa
c. diuretic **d.** yo-yo effect
e. fatfold test
3. **a.** Basal energy
b. Emetics

Recall

Section I
1. Answers will vary; could include: they die first in a famine, they are at risk during hospitalization, and women do not menstruate normally.

Section II
2. bones, muscles, fat, fluids, and other tissues
3. A person with strong muscles and bones may not be overweight, but may seem overweight on the scale. Also, a person who doesn't seem overweight on the scale may have too much body fat for health.
4. Teenagers are still growing.

Section III
5. They gain a pound of fat.
6. beating of the heart, inhaling and exhaling of air, maintenance of body temperature, working of the nerves and glands
7. The heavier the body parts, the more energy required to move them.
8. by making physical activity a daily activity

Section IV
9. causes the kidneys to

CHAPTER REVIEW

LEARNING THE VOCABULARY

underweight	basal energy	lapses
obesity	voluntary activities	anorexia nervosa
fatfold test	diuretic	bulimia
fatfold caliper	diet pills	binges
pinch test	yo-yo effect	emetics

Answer the following questions on a separate sheet of paper.

1. **Word Scramble**—Use the clues from the phrases below to help you unscramble the terms:
   a. **chipn sett**—A fatfold measurement taken without the use of equipment is called a _____ _____.
   b. **tied sllip**—Over-the-counter medications that reduce appetite are called _____ _____.
   c. **ailubim**—Repeated binging sometimes followed by vomiting is a disorder known as _____.

2. **Matching**—Match each of the following phrases with the appropriate vocabulary term from the list above:
   a. weight 10 percent or more below the appropriate weight for height
   b. a disorder of self-starvation to the extreme
   c. a drug that causes the body to lose fluids
   d. gain of body fat that results from repeated bouts of dieting without exercise
   e. measurement of body fatness using a fatfold caliper

3. a. _____ makes up the largest component of a person's daily energy expenditure.
   b. _____ are drugs that cause vomiting.

RECALLING IMPORTANT FACTS AND IDEAS

1. List two problems associated with too little body fat.
2. What components make up the sum total of your body weight?
3. Explain why body weight by itself is not an indicator of body fatness.
4. Why are the traditional height-weight charts considered reasonable for adults but useless for teenagers?
5. What happens when a person consumes 3,500 calories more than he or she spends?
6. What are the basal processes that support life?
7. Why does a 200-pound person expend more energy than a 100-pound person does, doing the same activity with equal effort?
8. How can you increase your basal energy output over the long term?
9. Why is the use of a diuretic considered a dangerous weight-loss method?
10. What happens to excess carbohydrates, fats, and protein a person consumes?
11. In order to lose weight safely and permanently, what must a person lose? What must the person retain?
12. Why is fasting a dangerous way to lose weight?
13. Identify some dangerous and some sound weight-loss strategies.
14. How can a person avoid the yo-yo effect when dieting?
15. Give three recommendations for a successful and healthy weight-gain program.
16. What are four common characteristics of a person with anorexia nervosa?
17. List four health problems that can result from bulimic behavior.

draw extra water from the blood into the urine

10. They are stored as either glycogen or fat.

11. lose fat tissues; retain lean tissue or water

12. The body uses up its glycogen and then breaks apart its own muscles and organs to keep the needed supply of glucose.

13. Answers will vary; could include: dangerous—fasting, fad diets, diuretics, diet pills, health spa regimens, muscle stimulators, passive exercise machines, hormones, surgery; sound—diet, exercise, behavior changes.

Section V
14. with physical activity during dieting

Section VI
15. physical training, eating enough calories to support the weight gain, and learning to eat different foods that are higher in calories and fat

Straight Talk
16. Answers will vary; could include: dominated by mother, father absent or distant; family values achievement and outward appearances more than an inner sense of self-worth; and wants to please and be perfect for her parents.

17. Answers will vary; could include: swollen hands and feet; bloating; fatigue; headache; nausea; pain; abnormal heartbeat and injury to kidneys; irritation and infection of the throat, esophagus, and salivary glands; erosion of the teeth; dental cavities; red eyes from pressure of vomiting; hands bruised and cut from scraping on the teeth while inducing vomiting.

CRITICAL THINKING

1. The diet industry makes billions of dollars off the American public. Choose one popular marketed diet plan and evaluate it using the information presented in the past three chapters on nutrition and weight control. Answer the following questions: Do you feel this diet could be effective? Will it meet the body's nutrient needs? Could health problems arise from using this diet? Does this diet include a program for maintaining weight after goal weight is achieved?

2. After reading the Straight Talk about anorexia nervosa and bulimia, answer the following questions: If you were Julie's friend, how would you deal with her anorexic behavior? What do you feel could have been done to prevent Sophie's bulimic behavior prior to her teenage years? What personality traits do Julie and Sophie have in common? Why do you think anorexia nervosa and bulimia appear more often in girls than boys? Why do you think the incidence of eating disorders in our country is steadily increasing?

3. Take a close look at your own personal program of diet and exercise. List four positive and four negative dietary habits you have. List four positive and four negative exercise habits you have.

ACTIVITIES

1. Find some advertisements for weight-loss devices. Analyze each weight-loss method using the Health Strategies section on page 219 entitled "Clues to Identifying Unsound Weight-Loss Programs."

2. Exercise is an excellent way to control weight. Create a collage on poster board that illustrates the different types of exercises. Label each exercise as either low calorie burning, moderate calorie burning or high calorie burning.

3. Devise a list of snack foods you would serve at a party if most of your guests were on diets.

4. Make a list of three positive and three negative diet or exercise habits that you attribute to your parents.

5. Watch television for one hour before dinner. List all the food products that you see advertised during that time. Discuss the possible reasons for airing these commercials at that time.

6. Find three advertisements that seem to encourage teenagers to be thin. Analyze the techniques used in advertising the products that encourage thinness.

7. Visit a local diet center such as Weight Watchers, Jenny Craig, Nutri-System or the like. Write a one-page report discussing your findings.

8. List as many diets and weight-loss devices as you can think of and label each one as either safe or unsound. Explain why you judged them as you did.

MAKING DECISIONS ABOUT HEALTH

1. You get up on a Monday morning determined to start a weight-loss diet. You skip breakfast, and for lunch you have a modest, healthful meal of soup and salad. By midafternoon you are famished, but hold off, exerting your strongest will power. At dinner, the smell of food being served is overwhelming. You eat much more than you had intended, and later that evening, still hungry, you indulge in a sweet dessert.

a. What errors in planning did you make?

b. What could you have done to make it easier to practice moderation at dinnertime?

c. Describe a more effective meal-planning strategy to help you lose weight.

CHAPTER 10 PLANNER

OVERVIEW

Chapter 10 is 34 pages long and divided into the six sections listed to the right. Major learning outcomes are also listed to the right. Briefly, this chapter introduces the physical aspect of health. It stresses the importance of fitness and provides students with factual information about fitness. Students will discover the psychological as well as the physical benefits of fitness. Many practical ideas for becoming fit and staying fit are also covered. At the conclusion of this chapter, the students should be able to properly set up an individual fitness program.

MAKING LIFE CHOICES RESOURCES

A variety of activities, handouts, quizzes, and tests to accompany this chapter are available in the *Making Life Choices* supplementary material. You may pick and choose from those materials as appropriate for your amount of class time and the ability levels of your students. Some of the resources you might want to consider using are:

Overheads
- Oxygen Delivery to Muscles
- How to Take Your Pulse
- Joints and Tissues
- Strength and Endurance Routines
- Diet and Physical Endurance
- Recommended Stretches

Handouts
- Fitness Objectives
- Strategies for Overcoming Fitness Obstacles
- Honoring Your Commitment to Exercise
- The Precompetition Meal

Teacher Information Sheets
- More on the Effects of Steroid Hormones in the Body
- Vitamins and Minerals

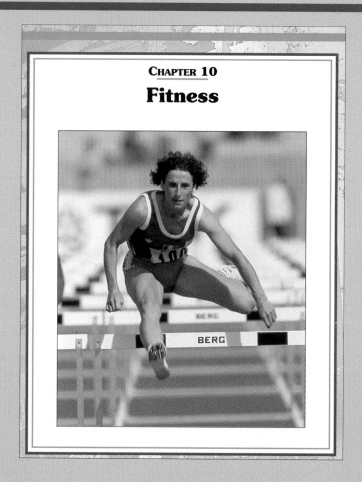

CHAPTER 10

Fitness

CHAPTER PROJECT

Have students keep a daily log of their activity and their inactivity. In their logs they should keep a record of the number of hours for both activity and inactivity. Then have them compare their hours and draw conclusions. Also have them compare their logs and their fitness scores. What conclusions can they draw from this comparison? Finally, have each student prepare an individual fitness program and write an essay on their findings.

Activity To Introduce Chapter

Give the Presidential Fitness Test before teaching this chapter so that students will have a comparative personal learning experience. Allow them time to discover their personal fitness levels and set goals for themselves. You may invite local college students to help test.

OUTCOMES

After reading and studying this chapter, you will be able to:

✓ Discuss how fitness promotes all aspects of health.
✓ Identify the four components of fitness.
✓ Describe how you gain cardiovascular endurance, flexibility, muscle strength, and endurance, and describe the benefits of each.
✓ Recognize the dangers of using steroids and other drugs.
✓ Describe preventive measures for sports injuries and accidents.

FACT OR FICTION

What do you think? Are the following statements true or false? If you think they are false, then say what is true.

1. In gaining fitness, striving to meet goals set by others is not as useful as striving to meet your own internal goals.
2. You should never overload your body, because overload can cause damage.
3. When performing stretching exercises, you should feel tightness but no pain.
4. Weight training is useful mainly to males who wish to build big, bulky muscles.
5. If you feel minor pain in your feet or legs while running, it is best to keep going and try to work through it.
6. You should not stop exercising to satisfy your thirst.
7. On a hot day, if you tend to perspire freely when you exercise, you should take a salt tablet.

(Answers on page 259)

■ **Reminder:** Knowing how to study can increase your knowledge, improve your grades, *and* cut down on your study time. See the *Studying Health* section at the front of your text for some suggestions to help you study this chapter.

CONTENTS

I. Benefits of Fitness
II. The Path to Fitness: Conditioning
III. Gaining Cardiovascular Endurance
IV. Gaining Flexibility
V. Gaining Muscle Strength and Endurance
VI. Preventing Sports Injuries and Heat Stroke

Straight Talk: *Food for Sports Competition*

NOT ENOUGH TIME?*

You could easily spend four or five days teaching this chapter if students read the entire chapter, do a fair number of the suggested activities in the teacher's edition, and complete a sampling of the handouts from the resource material accompanying this text. It is likely, however, that you will have only two or three days to devote to this chapter. Following are some suggestions to help you make sure that you cover the key topics if you have limited time.

TIME	SUGGESTIONS
1 Day	Assign Sections I and II ahead of time. During class assign Activities 1.3, 1.4, and 1.5 in Section I. In Section II assign Activities 2.1 and 2.2. Have students read Sections III and IV before the next class.
2 Days	On day 2, assign Activities 3.2 and 3.3 in Section III and Activities 4.1 and 4.4 in Section IV. Have students read Sections V and VI prior to the next class.
3 Days	On day 3, assign Activities 5.5 and 5.7 in Section V and Activities 6.3 and 6.4 in Section VI.

Please refer to the 18-week daily lesson plans in the supplementary material for additional suggestions.

SUGGESTED RESOURCES

Student Readings
1. Stone, William J. *Adult Fitness Programs.* Glenview, IL: Scott, Foresman and Company, 1988.
2. Darst, P. and Pangrazi, R. *Dynamic Physical Education for Secondary Students.* Macmillan Publishing Co., 1991.

Teacher Readings
1. Heywood, Vivian H. *Designs for Fitness.* Minneapolis: Burgess Publishing Co., 1984.
2. Sweetgall, Whitely, and Neeves. *Walking off Weight.* Clayton, MO: Creative Walking, Inc., 1988.

Videos
1. *Physical Fitness: The New Perspective* (10 min.). The focus of this video is on the positive side of being fit. Professional Research, Inc., 930 Pitner Avenue, Evanston, IL 60202.

Software
1. *Jumping Jack Flash.* After entering basic background information, students learn their basal metabolic rates. Opportunities for Learning, Inc., 800-243-7116.

Answers to "Fact or Fiction"

1. True. 2. False. Although an extreme and sudden exertion can damage the body, a gradual increase in overload will produce a strengthened body. 3. True. 4. False. People of both genders use weight training for trimming and firming the body. Bodybuilders follow special weight-training programs to gain muscle size and bulk. 5. False. You should stop to avoid serious injury. 6. False. It's best to rehydrate as you go. 7. False. You need water, not salt.

In this section students will learn:
1. The difference between fitness and sedentary behavior.
2. The benefits of fitness.

Activity 1.1
Making Fitness Posters. Give small groups of students markers and poster paper. Have them list the characteristics of a person they would consider to be "physically fit" and compare them to characteristics of a person with a sedentary lifestyle. They may want to decorate their lists of characteristics with artwork. **(30 min., Cooperative Learning)**

TEACH
SECTION 1
(Guided and Independent Practice)

Activity 1.2
Group Presentations and Brainstorming. Follow up Focus Activity 1.1 by having the class as a whole compare the lists developed in the small groups. After each group has presented its list (poster) students will brainstorm to determine the number of hours they sit in a day compared to the amount of time they are active. **(1 hr.; Extend, Enrich)**

Fast Facts
79% of American households have remote controls for their TV sets.

Teacher Support Notes

① **Benefits of Fitness:** This paragraph lists many benefits of fitness. Ask students to name them. (graceful movement, strength, appropriate weight, pleasing shape, physical endurance—energy, mental and emotional endurance, confidence) Do students think all of these characteristics apply to them? Are they fit?

66 Thoughts on Health 99

...The most brilliant intelligence of our earliest days—Thomas Jefferson—said not less than two hours a day should be devoted to exercise. If a man who wrote the Declaration of Independence, was Secretary of State, and twice President, could give it two hours, our children can give it ten or fifteen minutes.
— *John F. Kennedy*

---

236 UNIT 3 Your Physical Health

If you are a physically fit person, the following description applies to you. You are graceful and move with ease. You are strong. Your weight is appropriate for your height, and your body's contours appear pleasing. You have endurance; your energy lasts for hours. You meet normal physical challenges with ease and have energy left over to handle emergencies. What is more, you are well able to meet mental and emotional challenges, too. Physical fitness supports not only physical work but also mental and emotional endurance. Your confidence is high in all areas of life: social, academic, work, and athletic—you name it.

If these statements do not describe you today, take heart. You can gain fitness through practice. Activities that help you gain fitness are themselves enjoyable, and they quickly lead to improvement.

Fitness is the reward of a person who leads a physically active life. The opposite of such a life is a **sedentary** life, which means, literally, "sitting down a lot." Today's world permits many people to lead sedentary lives, and even rewards them for doing so. It provides elevators, cars, automatic garage openers, even electric can openers, so that people can exert a minimum of physical effort. Unfortunately, the more people use labor-saving devices, the more weak and unfit they become, and the ① less able to meet life's challenges. The body responds to inactivity by losing muscle and skill, just as it responds to activity by gaining them.

You do not have to become an athlete or a bodybuilder to become fit. Everyone's capacity to develop fitness differs. Some people are born with great potential. Others are born with average or less than average potential or are handicapped. Whoever you are, you have the ability to improve. This is an important concept in fitness: strive to achieve improvements based on your current fitness level and potential. Do not compare yourself to others or to written sets of standards, at least not right away. Your first goal should be to develop and maintain fitness to support your health.

Physical fitness brings many rewards.

Activity 1.3

Analyzing and Developing Magazine Ads. Have magazines available for students to look through. Have them find ads for as many "miracle pills" and other such ploys as possible. Have students design their own ads. Discuss the ads with the class. Show the hidden messages if any. Post the ads around the room. **(1 hr., Critical Thinking)**

Activity 1.4

Writing Essays. Have students brainstorm what their lives would be like if they were completely unfit. Then have them write essays describing how their lives would change. What would they have to give up? What things are they able to do now that they would have to change? They should include physical, social, and mental aspects, and describe what they would be like in 20 years with no fitness. **(50 min., Interdisciplinary)**

Activity 1.5

Making Posters. Have students cut out shapes to describe their mental fitness, social fitness, and physical fitness. Paste the shapes on construction paper with the students' names, then post the sheets around the room. You may assign an essay describing the shapes

(continued on next page)

Fitness:
Makes physical activity easy
   to perform,
Promotes rest, relaxation, sleep,
   and healing,
Aids weight control,
Contributes to nutritional health,
Enhances disease resistance
   (see Figure 10-2),
Strengthens accident resistance.

Physical Health

Fitness:
Strengthens resistance to
   depression and anxiety,
Strengthens defenses against
   stress,
Allows freedom from drug abuse,
Enhances self-esteem,
Enhances ability to learn,
Raises self-confidence,
Instills joy in life,
Inspires courage to face challenges.

**Mental, Emotional, and
Spiritual Health**

Fitness:
Provides social opportunities,
Enhances intimate relationships,
Strengthens family ties,
Opens the way for social
   support,
Encourages citizenship,
Enhances energy for productive
   work.

Social Health

Figure 10–1 Fitness Contributes to All Aspects of Health and Wellness. ①

Then later you can go further if you wish: you can set higher goals.

The term **fitness** means *the characteristics of the body that enable it to perform physical activity.* These characteristics include the flexibility of your joints; the strength and endurance of your muscles, including your heart muscle; and a healthy body composition. Add to that definition *the ability to meet routine physical demands, with enough reserve energy to rise to sudden challenges.* This shows even better how fitness relates to everyday life. Ordinary tasks such as carrying heavy suitcases, opening a stuck window, or climbing four flights of stairs might strain an unfit person. However, such tasks are easy for one who is fit. Add still one more detail to the definition of fitness: *the body's ability to withstand stress,* including psychological stresses. Now the definition is finished. It expresses all the aspects of the wonderful condition of the fit body. You can achieve all of these characteristics through regular physical activity.

> **Key Points** ▶ *Fitness enables the body to perform physical activity, to meet routine physical demands, to meet sudden challenges, and to withstand stress. Fitness is the product of a physically active life.*

SECTION I

Benefits of Fitness

A fit person benefits in all areas of life (see Figure 10–1 above). The most obvious of the benefits are the physical ones. Someone who is physically active, who sleeps soundly, and who eats adequately is one who has every chance for superb health, both physical and mental. Internally, those who are fit have all the advantages—they feel good. Figure 10–2 on the next page shows that physical activity helps defend against physical disorders and also helps promote psychological well-being. If only half of the rewards listed in Figures 10–1 and 10–2 were yours for the asking, wouldn't you step up to claim them?

MINI GLOSSARY

sedentary: physically inactive (literally, "sitting down a lot").
fitness: the characteristics of a body that enable it to perform physical activity, to meet routine physical demands with enough reserve energy to rise to sudden challenges, and to withstand stresses of all kinds.

Teacher Support Notes

① **Fitness Contributions to Health:** This illustration lists twenty separate ways that physical fitness contributes to wellness. To emphasize these factors, divide students into three groups. Assign each group one of the three areas and tell them they are to decide on the two factors in their area that are the most questionable as far as contributions made to overall health. Each group then notifies the group to its left of its two choices, and it's up to that group to develop a list of specific ways in which the two factors chosen by the other group would contribute to health. In other words, each group must prove that the two factors thought to be most questionable definitely do contribute to overall health. Finally, discuss with the class as a whole whether or not they agree that all twenty items listed do contribute to health.

Teach
(Continued)

and explaining their significance as part of the activity. **(1 hr.; Extend, Enrich)**

EVALUATE
SECTION I

Activity 1.6
Writing Essays. Have students write a paragraph explaining the difference between sedentary behavior and fitness. Have them write a second paragraph including the benefits of fitness.

CLOSE
SECTION I

Activity 1.7

Beat the Clock. Students should be able to list the benefits of fitness. Tell the students they have 30 seconds to list as many benefits of fitness as possible. Time them. When you say, "time," ask them to turn them in. Give credit for correct responses. **(5 min.)**

FOCUS
SECTION II

Fast Facts

Only 3% of the average American's lifetime is spent outdoors.

Teacher Support Notes

① **Handout—Fitness Objectives:** In the supplementary material you will find a handout listing the U.S. Public Health Service's objectives for the nation for the area of physical activity and fitness.

Section I Review

Answers

1. Fitness
2. sedentary
3. Answers will vary; could include: graceful and moves with ease; strong; weight is appropriate for height; body's contours appear pleasing; endurance, energy lasts for hours; meets normal physical challenges with ease, has energy left over to handle emergencies; able to meet mental and emotional challenges; and confidence is high in all areas (social, academic, work, and athletic).
4. Answers will vary. Refer to Figure 10–2 above for possible answers.
5. Answers will vary.

238   UNIT 3 Your Physical Health

FIGURE 10-2

Benefits of Physical Activity

Regular Physical Activity Helps Protect Against These Conditions:

Physical
- Acne
- Backaches
- Cancer (colon cancer, breast cancer, and others)
- Diabetes
- Digestive disorders (ulcers, constipation, diarrhea, and others)
- Headaches
- Heart and blood vessel disease (heart attacks and strokes)

- High blood cholesterol and triglycerides, high blood pressure
- Infections (colds, flu, and many others)
- Infertility (some forms)
- Insomnia (sleep disorders)
- Kidney disease
- Menstrual irregularities, menstrual cramps, and mood swings associated with the menstrual cycle
- Obesity
- Osteoporosis (adult bone loss)

Psychological
- Physically active people experience less anxiety and depression than do sedentary people.
- Fit people deal better with emotionally stressful events than do sedentary people.
- Depressed people who adopt a routine of regular running become as well and stay as well as others who obtain psychotherapy.

Imagine for a moment that the benefits in Figure 10–2 are associated not with regular physical activity, but with a newly discovered "miracle pill." A stampede of people would try to buy it. In fact, miracle products claim to offer many of these benefits. People spend billions of dollars each year in hopes of obtaining them yet they won't spend effort to exercise. Why is money so much easier to spend than effort?

Sadly, regular physical activity requires more effort than pill taking, and more time. The choice is personal, but this chapter will, of course, try to influence your decision.

Key Points ➤ *Physical activity promotes fitness. Fitness promotes all aspects of health.*

SECTION I   REVIEW

Answer the following questions on a sheet of paper.
Learning the Vocabulary
The vocabulary terms in this section are *sedentary* and *fitness*.

1. _____ enables the body to perform physical activities.
2. A person who is basically inactive is considered _____.

Learning the Facts
3. Describe a physically fit person.
4. List four benefits of physical activity.

Making Life Choices
5. What do you think has caused the fitness boom in our country? Has the fitness boom influenced your attitudes and behavior in any way? Why or why not? What do you have to gain by becoming more physically active?

SECTION II

The Path to Fitness: Conditioning

① The path to fitness is physical conditioning, which you can achieve through practice or training. Conditioning is the microscopic nuts and bolts of fitness: the hundreds of small changes that cells make so that the body can do the work that training demands.

Even routine daily activities can help condition the body. Small choices you make each day can either add to your fitness or take away from it. The person who chooses to walk upstairs gains more fitness than the one riding an elevator, for example. Parking the car a mile from your destination, or getting off the bus several stops early and walking the rest of the way, is a fitness-promoting strategy. Many other such strategies are listed later in the chapter, and all can help you become more fit.

Components of Fitness

Fitness expresses itself differently in different body systems. With respect to the heart and lungs, endurance is important. This type of endurance is **cardiovascular endurance.** With respect to the joints, **flexibility** is important. With respect to the muscles, **muscle strength** and **muscle endurance** are important. Fitness also expresses itself in **body composition**—the proportions of muscle, fat, bone, and other tissue that make up a person's body weight. As you become physically fit, improving your cardiovascular endurance, flexibility, muscle strength and endurance, and body composition, you improve the health of your entire body.

Physical activity leads to fitness. You can get an estimate of how physically active you are by answering the questions in this chapter's Life Choice Inventory. The way to get a truly accurate measure of your own fitness is to visit an **exercise physiology** laboratory and have measurements taken by a professional.

The sections that follow give general principles that govern training and show how to train for a fit body. Before actually starting an activity, though, make sure it is safe to begin. Ordinary physical activity is not hazardous to any healthy person, especially to a young person. However, if you answer yes to any of the questions that follow, you should proceed with caution. A fitness professional can test you to make sure you start your program at a level high enough to bring about the desired changes but not so high as to be dangerous. The key questions for a young person seem to be:

- Have you been sedentary for a long time?
- Are you more than 20 pounds heavier than you should be?
- Do you have any chronic illness?
- Has a health care provider ever said you had heart trouble?
- Did you ever have, or do you now have, a heart murmur?
- Have you ever had a diagnosed or suspected heart attack?
- Do you ever have chest pains at any time?

Mini Glossary

cardiovascular endurance: a component of fitness; the ability of the heart and lungs to sustain effort over a long time.
flexibility: a component of fitness; the ability to bend the joints without injury.
muscle strength: a component of fitness; the ability of muscles to work against resistance.
muscle endurance: a component of fitness; the ability of muscles to sustain an effort for a long time.
body composition: a component of fitness; the proportions of lean tissue as compared to fat tissue in the body.
exercise physiology: the study of how the body works and changes in response to exercise. An exercise physiology laboratory has equipment to measure the components of fitness and to take other measurements.

markers are their identities.) For the next minute have the groups write injuries that could occur if the exercise technique is not done correctly. Again have them trade papers so that there is a new group with a new component. For the next minute, have students list as many results as pos-

sible from not meeting this component. Trade again for the last time. In the last minute, have groups list positive results for that component. Have the recorders bring the posters to the front for discussion. **(45 min., Cooperative Learning)**

Activity 2.3
Warm-up and Cool-down. Write the words *warm-up* and *cool-down* on the board. Have students list on their own

papers as many activities as they can for each topic. Encourage individual work. You will also want to emphasize that we have to warm up and cool down all of the major muscle groups, so we need a variety of each kind of activity. Examples would be: *Warm-up:* 15 arm circles, touch toes for count of ten, ten inverse hurdlers, 20 jumping jacks, and jogging one lap. *Cool-down:* 10 arm circles, jog two laps, touch toes for count of 15. (Once warm

Teacher Support Notes

① **The Use-Disuse Principle:** Talk to students who score in the inactive range about the Use-Disuse Principle, which says that fitness develops in response to demand and decreases when demand stops. Muscles enlarge after being called upon repeatedly to do a certain type of work. This muscle growth is called *hypertrophy.* (hi PER tra fe) When the activity is stopped for a few days and the muscles shrink and lose strength, it is called *atrophy.* Unused muscles do not "turn to fat," as many people believe. However, with food intake remaining constant, the less a body works, the more fat it collects and the more muscle it loses.

✍ Fast Facts

Participating in ballroom dancing for 15 to 30 minutes can raise your heart rate to 60 to 70% of its maximum potential and burn off calories. Waltzing, for example, can burn 5–7 calories per minutes or up to 210 calories in a half hour.

L IFE   C HOICE
I NVENTORY

How Physically Active Are You?

For each question answered yes, give yourself the number of points indicated.

Occupation and Daily Activities

1. I usually walk to and from school and work (at least ½ mile each way). 1 point.
2. I usually take the stairs rather than use elevators or escalators. 1 point.
3. My typical daily physical activity is best described by the following statement:
   a. Most of my day is spent walking to class, sitting in class or at home, or in light activity. 0 points.
   b. Most of my day is spent in moderate activity such as fast walking. 4 points.
   c. My typical day includes several hours of heavy physical activity (football, volleyball, basketball, gym workout, or the like). 9 points.

Leisure Activities

4. I spend a few hours in light leisure activity each week (such as slow canoeing or slow cycling). 1 point.
5. I hike or bike (at a moderate pace) once a week or more on the average. 1 point.
6. At least once a week, I participate for an hour or more in vigorous dancing, such as aerobic or folk dancing. 1 point.
7. I play racquetball or tennis at least once a week. 2 points.
8. I often walk for exercise or recreation. 1 point.
9. When I feel bothered by pressures at school, work, or home, I use exercise as a way to relax. 1 point.
10. Two or more times a week, I perform calisthenic exercises (sit-ups, push-ups, etc.) for at least 10 minutes per session. 3 points.

11. I regularly participate in yoga or perform stretching exercises. 2 points.
12. Twice a week or more, I engage in weight training for at least 30 minutes. 4 points.
13. I participate in active recreational sports such as volleyball, baseball, or softball:
    a. About once a week. 2 points.
    b. About twice a week. 4 points.
    c. Three times a week or more. 7 points.
14. At least once a week, I participate in vigorous fitness activities like jogging or swimming (at least 20 continuous minutes per session):
    a. About once a week. 3 points.
    b. About twice a week. 5 points.
    c. Three times a week or more. 10 points.

Total points earned _____

S CORING

① 0 to 5 points—inactive. This amount of physical activity leads to a steady decline in fitness.

6 to 11 points—moderately active. This amount of physical activity slows fitness loss but will not maintain fitness.

12 to 20 points—active. This amount of physical activity will build or maintain an acceptable level of physical fitness.

21 points or over—very active. This amount of physical activity will maintain a high level of physical fitness.

Source: Adapted with the permission of Russell Pate (University of South Carolina, Dept. of Exercise Science).

and loose, an increase in time may help flexibility.) Challenge the students to think of new exercises for the warm-up and cool-down, and then use the good ideas for your fitness classes. You may want to consider giving extra credit for new ideas. The students will feel they have more input in the program. **(40 min., Critical Thinking)**

EVALUATE
SECTION II

Activity 2.4
Pop Quiz.
1. If you have good flexibility as a youth, you will have it forever. (F)
2. Muscular strength and muscular endurance are the same thing. (F)
3. Riding an elevator is a good way to develop cardiovascular fitness. (F)
4. Improper exercise often results in proper fitness. (F)
5. A person should have a balance of the four components of fitness. (T)
6. A person should get a physical from the doctor before participating in strenuous activity. (T)
7. Cool-downs can be skipped unless a person feels dizzy. (F)

(continued on next page)

If, during activity, you become uncomfortable, have trouble breathing, or feel any pain, stop exercising and consult your health care provider before continuing. The rest of this chapter assumes your fitness program will go well.

 Key Points *The components of fitness are cardiovascular endurance, flexibility, muscle strength, muscle endurance, and body composition. Before beginning a fitness program, check your health.*

The Overload Principle

Every day your body works. The stronger and more fit you are, the less you must strain to do that work. If your body is weak, you can't trade it in as you might trade in a car too run-down to do its job. But fortunately, you don't have to put up with a weak body. Unlike a run-down car, which will break down when overloaded, your body responds to **overload** in a positive way. It gets itself into better shape to meet the demand next time.

You can apply overload by using the **progressive overload principle** in several different ways. You can do the activity more often—that is, increase its **frequency.** You can do the activity more strenuously—that is, increase its **intensity.** Or you can do it for longer periods of time—that is, increase its **duration.**

All three strategies work well. You can pick one or a combination, depending on your preferences. For example, if you love your workout, do it more often. If you run out of time, shorten your workout time, but increase its intensity. If you hate hard work, take it easy and go longer. Any way you apply it, the progressive overload principle improves fitness.

This doesn't mean that you should try to do too much too soon. It's better to progress slowly than to risk serious injury

by pushing yourself too hard. To safely increase the frequency, intensity, or duration of your workout, exercise to a point that is only *slightly* beyond what is comfortable.

 You've probably heard the expression "No pain, no gain." However, pain won't help you gain fitness; sustained effort will. It doesn't make sense to start with activities so demanding that pain stops you within two days. Learn to enjoy the small steps along the way, because fitness builds slowly. A worthwhile goal is to develop a fitness program that you can stick with, year in and year out.

You have to overwork just a little. Pushing your body a little beyond its normal level of demand releases hormones that stimulate muscle and bone growth. In a day or two, nature repairs any slight injuries to the muscles although injury is not required or desirable. It also remodels and strengthens the muscles and bones so that next time the body will meet the more vigorous challenge more easily.

At the top of the next page are some other pointers about applying overload:

MINI GLOSSARY

overload: an extra physical demand placed on the body.
progressive overload principle: the training principle that a body system, in order to improve, must be worked at frequencies, durations, or intensities that increase over time.
frequency: the number of activity units per unit of time (for example, the number of exercise sessions per week).
intensity: the degree of exertion while exercising (for example, jogging takes more exertion than walking and so is more intense).
duration: the length of time spent in each exercise session.

Teacher Support Notes

① **Progressive Overload:** Have students demonstrate their understanding of the concept of progressive overload by picking an activity of their choice and then writing an imaginary training program that includes all three types of progressive overload. They should write sentences such as "In week 2, I will begin swimming three days instead of two." Have them write nine to ten sentences, enough for each of the three types of overload, to make sure that they understand and remember that overload can be broken down into these three types.

② **Too Much Too Soon:** Ask students for examples of new activities they've tried but discarded because they tried to do too much too soon. Were they unrealistic and unprepared for the difficulty of the task? You may want to refer the students back to the discussion of motivation and planning for behavior change in Chapter 1.

242

EVALUATE
(Continued)

8. Warm-ups are important in preventing injury. (T)
9. Proper technique of exercise can prevent injuries. (T)
10. Potential heart attacks may be prevented or delayed through exercise. (T)

CLOSE
SECTION II

Activity 2.5
Developing an Exercise Program.
Have the students set up an exercise program for themselves, or for the entire family. Have students set and write a goal to exercise for one week. The goal must include the types of exercise, number of repetitions, when and if each will be increased, and time of day they will be completed. Help students include exercises for each muscle group.

At the end of the week, have students orally present their goals. Then have the students describe how the program actually went, if anything had to be changed, if their goals were set too high or too low, and what health improvements they have seen.

Teacher Support Notes

① **Pay Attention:** Make sure students reread this sentence: *"Listen to your body and cooperate."* Emphasize the fact that no one can tell another person exactly how much he or she can do.

Section II Review
Answers

1. Muscle strength is the muscle's ability to work against resistance, while muscle endurance is the muscle's ability to sustain that effort for a long time.
2. Cardiovascular endurance
3. progressive overload system, frequency, intensity, duration
4. cardiovascular endurance, flexibility, muscle strength, endurance, and body composition
5. Answers will vary; could include: if you love your workout, do it more often; if you run out of time, shorten it but increase intensity; if you hate hard work, take it easy and go longer. Exercise regularly, train hard only once or twice a week, listen to your body and cooperate.
6. to get the body's fuels ready and warm up the muscles and connective tissues, so that they will stretch without tearing
7. Answers will vary.

- Exercise regularly.
- Train hard only once or twice a week, not every time you work out. Between times, do light workouts.
- Listen to your body and cooperate. If you feel energetic, work hard; if you are tired or in pain, go lightly or stop, even if that was not in your original plan. ① ①

Also, keep in mind that work that develops one component of fitness usually does little to improve other components. For example, stretching develops flexibility, but has no effect on cardiovascular endurance. Strive for balance in your fitness program. Plan your activity program to include work of different kinds, so as to develop all the components of fitness.

> **Key Points** *Overload is extra physical demand that improves fitness. The progressive overload principle states that to improve, one must increase the frequency, intensity, or duration of exercise over time.*

Principles of Warm-Up and Cool-Down

Before starting to work hard, the body needs to prepare for activity in two ways. It needs to get its fuels ready. It also needs to warm up its muscles and connective tissues, so that they will stretch without tearing. A warm-up activity helps to do both. It frees the needed fuels from storage, and it sends extra blood through the tissues, warming them.

To warm up, take a brisk walk, take a light jog, or do some easy cycling or other light exercise followed by a stretching routine. Another way to warm up is to do a light version of what you plan to do intensively later. A runner may start out walking; break into a jog; and finally, when it feels right, pick up the pace to an outright run. A person who bodybuilds may start with light weight repetitions; a tennis player, with a few lobs. This strategy is thought to best prepare the muscle groups that will be needed to perform the task ahead.

After exercise the body also needs to cool down so it can begin to relax again. A few minutes of light activity after a workout helps relax tight muscles and allows blood to circulate freely, cooling the body. This is also a good time to stretch the muscles. Stretching helps to prevent muscle cramps and soreness that might otherwise occur. Cool-down activities can also help to prevent symptoms—dizziness, for example—that people sometimes feel when they suddenly stop exercising.

Now that you know what fitness is and have learned some general principles about conditioning, you are ready to start some physical activities. The next few sections provide pointers on how, exactly, one goes about getting fit.

> **Key Points** *Warm-up activities help the body get ready for exercise. Cool-down activities help muscles to relax and cool off.*

SECTION II REVIEW

Answer the following questions on a sheet of paper.
Learning the Vocabulary
The vocabulary terms in this section are *cardiovascular endurance, flexibility, muscle strength, muscle endurance, body composition, exercise physiology, overload, progressive overload principle, frequency, intensity,* and *duration.*
1. What is the difference between muscular strength and muscular endurance?
2. _____ is the ability of the heart and lungs to sustain effort over a long time.
3. The _____ states that to improve fitness, one must increase the _____, _____, or _____ of an activity over time.

Learning the Facts
4. What are the five components of fitness?
5. Give some pointers about applying overload in a fitness program.

Encourage students to use this knowledge to develop a permanent exercise
program.

FOCUS
> SECTION III

In this section students will learn to:
1. Identify the differences between aerobic and anaerobic exercise.
2. Take their pulses.

3. Name several activities that benefit
cardiovascular endurance.

Activity 3.1
Activity Cards. Hang two posters
from the board, labeled *Aerobic* and
Anaerobic. Have an index card for each
student and a piece of tape. On each
index card list an activity such as walking,
basketball, tennis, etc. Have students
tape their index cards under the appropri-

ate sign. Have the student explain the
reasons for the placement. When all have
placed their cards, discuss them thoroughly. **(45 min., Critical Thinking)**

TEACH
> SECTION III
(Guided and Independent Practice)

Activity 3.2
Fitness Essays. Have students

(continued on next page)

6. What is the purpose of warming up before
you begin an activity?

Making Life Choices
7. Determine how physically active you are by
taking the Life Choice Inventory on page
240. Then answer the following questions:
What was your score? Are you satisfied with
your score? Why or why not? Discuss any
changes you feel need to be made in your
physical activity level. At this point, what
effect does your activity level have on your
overall health?

SECTION III

Gaining Cardiovascular Endurance

You're exercising. Your heart beats faster,
your blood quickens through your arteries,
your breathing delivers great lungfuls of air.
How long can your heart and lungs keep
going? How developed is your cardiovascular endurance?

Cardiovascular endurance training demands that the heart and lungs work extra
hard to deliver oxygen to the muscles for as
long as the exercise lasts. Cardiovascular
endurance training is therefore **aerobic**—it
demands oxygen. The more a person performs cardiovascular endurance exercises,
the better the heart and lungs become at
delivering oxygen.

Not all exercises are aerobic. Activity that
lasts just a short time, but that is very intense, doesn't require as much oxygen as
aerobic activity does. This type of activity is
called **anaerobic** activity.

A way to think of the difference between
the two types of activity is to imagine two
athletes. The first is a distance runner on
an endless stretch of beach. The runner
strides steadily across miles of sand. Now

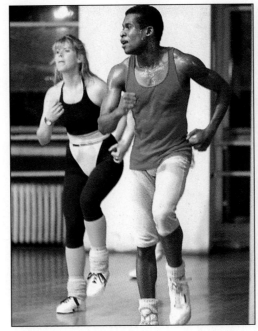

Sustained muscular efforts involve aerobic work.

imagine a track meet. A sprinter bursts
across the starting line in an explosion of
energy. The burst lasts only a few seconds,
followed by exhaustion at the finish line.

The distance runner is performing mostly
aerobic work, the kind that requires endurance. The ability to continue swimming
until you reach the far bank, to continue
hiking until you are at camp, or to continue pedaling until you are home reflects aerobic fitness.

MINI GLOSSARY

aerobic (air-ROE-bic): refers to energy-
producing processes that use oxygen (*aero* =
air).
anaerobic (AN-air-ROE-bic): refers to energy-
producing processes that do not use oxygen
(*an* = without).

Teacher Support Notes

① **Aerobic vs. Anaero-
bic:** Have students develop a list of physical
activities in which they participate. Then have them
classify the activities as
primarily aerobic or anaerobic. Question individual
students about which type
they tend to do more or
less of. If they tend to favor
one or the other, why do
they think this is?

Fast Facts

Most jogging ailments
result from overexer-
tion, an inadequate
warm-up, bad running
technique, or wearing
improper footwear.
Common sense will
prevent most of these
injuries.

write an essay on one of these topics: **1.** "Building Self-Esteem Through Fitness." **2.** "Insomnia vs. Fitness" **3.** "Lean Body Weight or Body Fat." Have students share their essays with the class. Post the best essays on a bulletin board to share with all classes. **(40 min.; Extend, Enrich)**

Activity 3.3

Devising Workouts. Have students devise their own aerobic or anaerobic workouts. These can be performed in class, or written, but must show that the student knows the differences between the two. The aerobic workout should include a target heart rate activity, such as an aerobic routine with music. The anaerobic workout should include the amount of time and the number of repetitions, if

required. For example, in a weight-training routine, the student will need to list reps and sets for the workout, as well as the time of rest between each. **(one class period to present; Reteach, Reinforce)**

Activity 3.4

Heart Rate Check. Demonstrate the proper way to check for pulse. Have students figure their RHRs. Have students stand by their desks, jump for 30 sec-

---

Teacher Support Notes

① **Different Muscle Fibers:** For enrichment, tell students their muscles are made up largely of two different types of contracting cells called *muscle fibers*. The two types are *slow-twitch muscle fibers* and *fast-twitch muscle fibers*. The slow-twitch fibers are best suited to aerobic work; fast-twitch fibers to anaerobic work. The slow-twitch fibers are best suited for activity of lower intensity and longer duration and, therefore, depend most on fat, the body's main source of fuel to provide energy aerobically. Fast-twitch fibers are best suited for high intensity, short-duration activity and, therefore, depend mostly on glucose, the body's sugar for their anaerobic energy fuel. Depending on the type of activity the person participates in, he or she will develop more fully either the slow-twitch or the fast-twitch muscles. A person's fitness potential or athletic talent is inborn, partly because every person is born with a set number of each type of fiber. In a sense, an individual is born to be either a sprinter or a long-distance runner.

---

244 UNIT 3 Your Physical Health

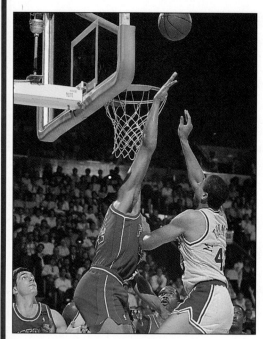

Split-second surges of power involve anaerobic work.

The sprinter is performing mostly anaerobic work, which requires strength, agility, and split-second surges of power. The jump of the basketball player, the slam of the tennis serve, the weight lifter's heave at the barbells, and the fullback's blast through the opposing line are all anaerobic work.

At the start of this chapter, Figures 10–1 and 10–2 listed some of the health benefits of physical activity. All of the benefits listed there can be credited to cardiovascular endurance training. Some of the benefits, such as sound sleep, building of lean body tissue, and improved self-image, can also be gained by way of flexibility and strength training. But cardiovascular endurance training promotes each and every one.

A poorly conditioned cardiovascular system limits a person's ability to perform daily activities more than a lack of flexibility or muscle strength does. For this reason,

cardiovascular endurance is the part of fitness most important to health and life. However, stretching to keep the joints flexible and strength training to build stronger muscles are important to total fitness, too, as later sections show.

> **Key Points** *Cardiovascular endurance training demands oxygen—it is aerobic. With cardiovascular endurance training, the heart and lungs become better at delivering oxygen to the body.*

Principles of Cardiovascular Endurance Training

With cardiovascular endurance training, the blood increases in volume and can carry more oxygen. The heart muscle gains size and strength. The larger, stronger heart pumps more blood with each beat, so fewer beats are necessary to support a given task. The heartbeat (**pulse**) rate slows. The muscles that work the lungs gain strength and endurance, and breathing becomes more efficient. Blood moves easily through the body's arteries and veins, and the blood pressure falls. Muscles throughout the body ① become firmer. Figure 10–3 on the next page shows how the heart, circulatory system, and lungs all work together to deliver oxygen to the tissues and carry away the waste product carbon dioxide.

A slow resting pulse rate means the cardiovascular system is healthy. You may want to check your pulse right now. As a rule of thumb, the average resting pulse rate for teenagers and young adults is around 70 beats per minute. However, the rate can be higher or lower. Active people can have resting pulse rates of 50 or even lower. Instructions for taking your pulse are given in Figure 10–4.

Professional athletes surround themselves with technical trappings—stopwatches, graphs, and charts—to measure improve-onds, and recheck their pulses. This is simply to show the difference in heart rate. You can also use a student to demonstrate the correlation between RHR and exercise. First check the student's RHR. Exercise the student for one minute. Recheck the pulse. This will help the students see the difference in the heart rate (not just in breathing). Sometimes people think that if they are breathing hard they are working hard. Although breathing can be an indicator, it's not a reliable measure. The person could also be working hard, but the person wouldn't know for sure without taking his or her pulse. **(20 min.; Reteach, Reinforce)**

Activity 3.5
Cardiovascular Discussion. Lead the class in a short discussion on the differences in cardiovascular endurance and muscular strength. Have them give examples of each. **(10 min.; Reteach, Reinforce)**

Activity 3.6
Body Image. Invite someone to speak about "body image." Ask the speaker to include discussions about self-esteem, our perceptions of ourselves, advertising, and stereotypes in the presentation.

(continued on next page)

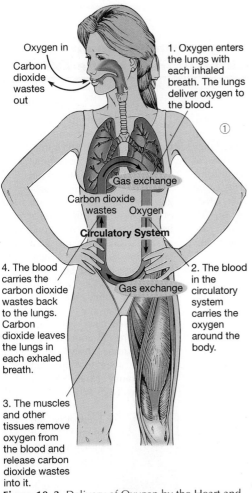

Oxygen in

Carbon dioxide wastes out

1. Oxygen enters the lungs with each inhaled breath. The lungs deliver oxygen to the blood. ①

Gas exchange

Carbon dioxide wastes   Oxygen

Circulatory System

4. The blood carries the carbon dioxide wastes back to the lungs. Carbon dioxide leaves the lungs in each exhaled breath.

Gas exchange

2. The blood in the circulatory system carries the oxygen around the body.

3. The muscles and other tissues remove oxygen from the blood and release carbon dioxide wastes into it.

Figure 10–3 Delivery of Oxygen by the Heart and Lungs to the Muscles. The more fit a muscle is, the more oxygen it draws from the blood. That oxygen is provided to the blood by the lungs. Chapter 6 presented details of the circulatory system. Here, an oval-shaped diagram represents the body's blood vessels.

ments in their pulse rates. The next section discusses the details of such measurements for those who want them. However, you need not get tangled up in all this. To improve your pulse rate, just get up and run, dance, or do any physical activity you'd

like. Do it again every other day forever. A guideline for those who wish to gain fitness but who do not aspire to compete in the Olympics is to walk, jog, or run for 20

Figure 10–4 How to Take Your Pulse ③

Get a watch or clock with a second hand. Rest a few minutes for a resting pulse. Place your hand over your heart or your finger firmly over an artery in any pulse location (shown by the yellow circles) that gives a clear rhythm. Start counting your pulse at a convenient second and continue counting for 10 seconds. If a heartbeat occurs exactly on the tenth second, count it as one-half beat. Multiply by 6 to obtain the beats per minute. To ensure a true count:

- Use only fingers, not your thumb, on the pulse point (the thumb has a pulse of its own).
- Press just firmly enough to feel the pulse. Too much pressure can interfere with the pulse rhythm.

MINI GLOSSARY

pulse: the number of heartbeats per minute.

Teacher Support Notes

① **Oxygen for the Muscles:** This illustration shows how the circulatory system delivers oxygen to the muscles. For a review of the circulatory system as a whole, refer students back to Chapter 6, page 146. Tell students that the person with more fit muscles extracts from the inhaled air more oxygen than a person with less fit muscles. The cardiovascular system responds to the demand for oxygen by building up its capacity to deliver oxygen. Researchers can measure cardiovascular fitness by measuring the maximum amount of oxygen a person consumes per minute while working out—a measure called VO_2 max.

② **Overhead—Oxygen Delivery to Muscles:** There is a transparency of this illustration in the supplementary material.

③ **Overhead—How to Take Your Pulse:** You will find a transparency of this illustration in your supplementary material.

Activity 3.7

Activity Review. Write the activities described on pages 247 and 248 on index cards. Add other activities until you have a card for each student. Distribute a card to each student. Have each student tell if the activity is aerobic or anaerobic. Also have

each student express which component of fitness that activity works the most. **(30–40 min.; Reteach, Reinforce)**

Activity 3.8

Expressive Paragraphs. Have the students write a paragraph expressing what life would be like for a person who was perfectly fit, or as fit as possible. Also describe what a normal day would include. (exercise, work, fun activities,

social activities, etc.) In a second paragraph, have students write what life would be like for a person with no cardiovascular endurance. Examples could include going nowhere, having to have someone wait on them, social group changes, high body fat percentage, low self-esteem, etc. For the last paragraph have the students compare the two lives and decide which is the smart life to live. **(40 min., Critical Thinking)**

Teacher Support Notes

① **Teen Views Follow-Up Questions:** Here are some questions that may help you promote discussion of the issues raised in the Teen Views comments:
a. Do students believe that Americans are "addicted" to television, as does Maryanne Rektorik?
b. Do students believe that decisions should be made at the national level to restrict television broadcasting to certain hours?
c. Should the development of new technologies for games and entertainments be restricted?
d. Do students believe that today's teenagers are more interested in being amused and less interested in work than were teenagers of previous generations?
e. Would the elimination or restriction of TV time help solve family problems?
f. Do adults think teens watch more television than they really do?
g. Does television help relieve stress?
h. Has television had a negative effect on the morality of Americans?
i. Felix Valadez says that even "noneducational" television programs are educational and show people how to "deal with real life." Do students agree?

TEEN **V**IEWS

Do teenagers spend too much time sitting in front of the TV? ①

Television has almost become an addiction to Americans—we cannot seem to live without it. Many teenagers would rather watch TV than do homework. This may be one reason why American teenagers aren't as focused on their school work as teens in other countries. In some Asian countries, for example, TV stations only have TV programming in the mornings and evenings, so teens can do their work without any distractions during the day. If this were incorporated into American television, I think grades of the average teen would increase, and our country would have more successful, smarter people in our future. **Maryanne Rektorik, 17, Frontier Central High School, NY**

After a hard day at school, teenagers come home and grab a snack, but instead of relaxing with music or reading a book, what do they do? They park their fannies in front of a television or Nintendo. This has become more of a problem as technology advances. The more television shows and video games that come out, the more couch potatoes there will be. In today's society, there is an

obsession with being amused. Few teenagers are able to amuse themselves, so they rely on electronic devices to do it for them. This discourages teens' creativity and learning ability. The adults should put a limit on TV time. **Julie Johnson, 16, Orange Park High School, FL**

There are few entertainment options today that do not cost money. Television, home video games, and home movies are very cheap and convenient. If everyone would spend at least one hour of his or her TV time communicating with their family, maybe there would be fewer dysfunctional families and fewer problem children. **Robert McMillan, 17, Robert E. Lee High School, TX**

Most adults would say yes. Because a lot of students are not participating in extracurricular activities, adults assume they are at home sitting in front of a television. A lot of students are starting to think about their futures, thinking about how they want to be successful, and are doing something called *studying*. **Alisha Jill Irwin, 15, Carter High School, TN**

I think watching television can be both good and bad for teenagers. If all homework and chores are done, it's a nice way to wind down or relax. Good programs can get your mind off of things that might have been stressful. A good movie always puts me in a good mood. Some people think that TV can be a bad influence, but I believe you act on and think about your morality from the way you were raised and your beliefs. We're old enough now to determine how much time we need to spend on what. **Renee Thies, 16, Orange Park High School, FL**

Teenagers do spend too much time in front of the television. But even though they do, they are being educated. Many TV shows deal with real life and show how people cope with hard times. Video games make people think and solve puzzles. Many games are difficult and people develop new ways of solving problems. **Felix Valadez, 16, Robert E. Lee High School, TX**

Activity 3.9

Fitness Papers. Plan a research trip to the library. Assign a fitness topic to each student. (Fitness Crazes, Walking vs. Running, Effects of Exercise, Effects of Not Exercising, etc.) Help the students find recent articles and books on the topics. Allow the students enough time to begin their research. Give the students one week to complete the research and writing of their fitness papers. Allow time in class for students to share their findings. **(Extend, Enrich)**

Activity 3.10

Sport Benefits. Divide the class into groups of four or five. Assign each group a sport to research. They will research the following areas:

1. How physical is this sport?
2. How fit are the players?
3. Is fitness important in this sport?
4. Does this sport have fitness benefits for any person who chooses to participate in it?

Allow time in class for the groups to share their findings. **(Cooperative Learning)**

EVALUATE
SECTION III

Activity 3.11

(continued on next page)

---

minutes or more at a rate at which you can talk but not sing. If you can't talk, you're going too fast—slow down. If you can sing, your pace is too slow to build fitness—speed up.

Key Points *Cardiovascular endurance enlarges the blood volume, improves the heart muscle's size and strength, slows the pulse rate, makes breathing more efficient, lowers the blood pressure, and firms muscles throughout the body.*

Activities for Cardiovascular Endurance

To improve cardiovascular endurance, you must work up to a point where you can perform aerobic activity for 20 minutes or more at a session. This means you must raise your heart rate (pulse) for that long. You should shoot for a heart rate that is quite a bit faster than your resting rate to "push" the heart, but not one so fast as to strain it. Athletes call this the **target heart rate.** You can calculate yours from your age.

To calculate your target heart rate, first subtract your age from 220. The resulting number is close to the absolute *maximum heart rate* for a person your age. You should never exercise at this rate, of course. Now multiply your maximum heart rate number by 0.75 to get your target heart rate. For example, to calculate the target heart rate for a 16-year-old person:

- Maximum heart rate = 220 − 16 = 204.
- Target heart rate = 204 x 0.75 = 153 beats per minute.

When you first work out at this rate, you may find that even mild exercise will push your heart to the target rate. As your cardiovascular fitness improves, you will have to work harder to push your heart to beat this fast. When you can work out at the target heart rate for 20 to 30 minutes, you know that you have arrived at your fitness goal.

You can develop cardiovascular fitness only if you choose aerobic activity. This activity must:

- Be steady and constant.
- Use large muscle groups, such as legs, buttocks, and abdomen.
- Be uninterrupted and last for more than 20 minutes.

Walking, aerobic dancing, running, swimming, and cycling all fit this description. You probably know something about these activities already. However, a few more facts about them might help.

Walking is good exercise, but the walker must put some "oomph" in the pace to achieve an aerobic workout. Strolling along at a pace of 1 or 2 miles per hour might help you to warm up, but striding along at 3.5 to 5 miles per hour is the way to get a workout for your heart. Walking practically never injures people (so long as they wear supportive walking shoes and watch for traffic), because walking is easy on the joints.

Aerobic dancing can provide a balanced, full-body workout, as well as a cardiovascular workout. In dance, a good pair of shoes is a must for the safety of the feet and legs. Equally important is the choice of fitness center. Check the flooring to make sure that it is made of materials that absorb shock, such as wood platforms. (Cement, even when under carpeting, shocks the lower back.) Flooring becomes less critical in **low-impact aerobic dance,** in which

MINI GLOSSARY

target heart rate: the heartbeat rate that will condition a person's cardiovascular system—fast enough to push the heart, but not so fast as to strain it.

low-impact aerobic dance: aerobic dance in which one foot remains on the floor to prevent shock to the lower body.

①

Teacher Support Notes

① **Fitness Training:** Tell students that in building up to the 20–30 minute workout, they may want to use a pattern for aerobic conditioning that involves exercising at the target heart rate for longer and longer periods of time with breaks between. For example, a jogger might run at the target heart rate for two minutes, then rest by walking until ready to jog again, run another two minutes, then rest by walking, and so on for 20 minutes. At each session, the jogger can make the running periods longer and the resting periods shorter. Eventually, the rest periods will no longer be needed at all.

> ❝ **Thoughts on Health** ❞
>
> *Those who think they have not time for bodily exercise will sooner or later have to find time for illness.*
>
> – Edward Stanley, Earl of Derby

Pop Quiz.

1. An example of aerobic exercise is sprints. (F)
2. Self-esteem can be built during fitness training. (T)
3. An example of anaerobic exercise is distance running. (F)

4. Dance routines are the only form of aerobic exercise. (F)
5. You should know your target heart rate before exercise. (T)
6. The purpose of target heart rate is to assure benefits of exercise without overexertion. (T)
7. We need to be fit because the media says we do. (F)
8. Fitness is a personal choice. (T)
9. Walking can benefit fitness as much

as running. (T)
10. Body fat percentage is not important as long as you look good. (F)

CLOSE
SECTION III

Activity 3.12
  Video Quiz. Collect videos of athletic activities. Collect as many as possible, representing a wide variety of activities.

Teacher Support Notes

① **Swimming:** You may want to refer students back to Figure 9–7 on page 224 in Chapter 9 that shows how many calories per minute are burned in various activities. While swimming is an excellent fitness activity, it does not burn as many calories per minute as some other activities, and, therefore, will not be as productive for people trying to lose weight.

② **Exercise Strategies:** Discuss the fifteen strategies listed here with students. How many are they participating in now? How many could they implement into their daily routines? Caution them not to try to do too much too soon, but to pick out one or two at a time.

🖾 Fast Facts

Research at Florida State University indicates that if you're planning to lose weight by walking, do so for at least 45 minutes per session. The longer the exercise is sustained, the more fat is burned. This isn't true, however, until you pass the 3/4-hour mark.

---

one foot always remains in contact with the floor. In dance, move around the room and change directions freely, take long strides, and lift your legs high. These movements, performed with control and vigor, provide the work your heart needs.

Running is a passion for some. The challenge, simplicity, freedom, and mental and physical well-being that come with running keep many people returning to the road, day after day. However, with the joys come risks. Running injuries are common.

The right shoes are essential, of course. A runner hits the ground with a force of about two to three times the weight of the body, hundreds of times per mile. Running shoes stabilize the feet and cushion the enormous impact of each stride. Most injuries in running result from pushing too hard and too fast, trying to get fit too quickly. To begin a program, start slowly. Do not rush your progress. Watch and listen for traffic (don't wear a headset). If you are a female, run or walk with a partner. Heed the advice on rape prevention in the Straight Talk section of Chapter 20.

As for swimming and cycling, these, too, provide work that strengthens the heart. These activities are almost stress-free for joints and connective tissues. Swimming not only develops cardiovascular endurance, but also develops strength and endurance in the upper body. However, swimming may not improve body composition as much as some other aerobic activities do. Cycling, on the other hand, superbly develops the lower body while it improves cardiovascular endurance, and it promotes a lean body composition effectively. Taken together, the two activities make a nice conditioning package—swimming for upper body and heart, and cycling for lower body, heart, and body composition.

The activities just described are only a few of many that people enjoy while gaining cardiovascular endurance. Don't limit your-

self. Just use your imagination and go for it. For a lifestyle that encourages general fitness, the Health Strategies feature on this page offers some novel ideas.

Key Points *Activities that promote cardiovascular endurance are those that raise the heart rate, are sustained for 20 or more minutes, and are performed every other day or more often. Many activities fit this description.*

HEALTH STRATEGIES

Including Exercise in Your Day

To include exercise in your day:

1. Join a school fitness program (or take a physical education class, even if it's not required).
2. Join a social exercise club.
3. Make friends with others who help one another stay fit.
4. Play sports in school or city leagues.
5. Sign up for dance, sports, or conditioning courses.
6. Improve your swim strokes.
7. Join a hiking, biking, or rowing club.
8. Join a YMCA program.
9. Walk to nearby stores.
10. Take stairs instead of elevators.
11. Stretch often during the day.
12. Lift small weights while watching TV or talking on the phone.
13. Garden or do yard work.
14. Play with children.
15. Wash your family car with extra vigor, or bend and stretch to wash your toes in the bath. Be imaginative.

Use these videos for a quiz. Have the students number on their papers, 1 to whatever number of videos you will be showing. Play a 30-second spot of each video. The students must write whether the activity is aerobic or anaerobic.

FOCUS
SECTION IV

In this section students will learn the:

1. Fundamentals of proper stretching.

Activity 4.1
Exercise Class. Have an athletic trainer take the class through some stretching exercises. Ask the trainer to discuss each exercise and its importance, as it is being done by the students. Ask the trainer to share updated information on any changes in traditional exercises. **(50 min.; Extend, Enrich)**

TEACH
SECTION IV
(Guided and Independent Practice)

Activity 4.2
Exercise Questionnaire. Have students, as a class, prepare a questionnaire of five to ten questions. Students will interview ten people (not students in the same class) using the questionnaire.

(continued on next page)

SECTION III REVIEW

Answer the following questions on a sheet of paper.

Learning the Vocabulary
The vocabulary terms in this section are *aerobic, anaerobic, pulse, target heart rate,* and *low-impact aerobic dance.*

1. Your _____ rate is the number of times your heart beats per minute.
2. Your _____ is fast enough to push the heart, but not so fast as to strain it.
3. What is the difference between aerobic and anaerobic activity?
4. Write a sentence using each vocabulary term.

Learning the Facts
5. Name two aerobic and two anaerobic activities.
6. Give three effects of cardiovascular endurance.
7. What are the three principles that a person must follow to achieve cardiovascular fitness?

Making Life Choices
8. After taking your resting pulse (Figure 10–4), answer the following question: Is your pulse below average, average, or above average? Now calculate your target heart rate (see page 247). Do you generally reach your target heart rate when you exercise? Why or why not? What activities do you regularly participate in to improve your cardiovascular endurance? Identify any changes you feel need to be made in your program.

SECTION IV

Gaining Flexibility

Have you noticed that some people find reaching movements difficult? For a person who lacks flexibility, it is uncomfortable even to reach to the feet to tie the shoes. Contrast this person with a dancer of the

Full Range of Motion

Figure 10–5 Range of Motion of the Hip Joint

same age taking a graceful bow after a performance, hands almost brushing the floor. These people represent both ends of the flexibility spectrum. The first person is stiff from years of limited movement. The second person has worked for years to maintain flexibility.

If the body is flexible, it can move as it was designed to move and will bend instead of tearing or breaking in response to sudden stresses. Flexibility depends on the **elasticity** of the muscles and connective tissues and on the condition of the joints.

Each body joint has its own limits on its movements and on how far it can move, its **range of motion** (see Figure 10–5). A joint's range of motion is determined by the shape of its bones, and the placement and condition of its connective tissues. The bones and connective tissues of knees and elbows, for example, limit their movements to two

MINI GLOSSARY

elasticity: the characteristic of a tissue's being easily stretched or bent and able to return to its original size and shape.
range of motion: the mobility of a joint; the direction and the extent to which it bends.

Following are some examples of questions:
1. Do you exercise? If so, how often? If not, is there a reason?
2. Do you think exercise is important? Why or why not?
3. Do you know the difference between aerobic and anaerobic exercise?

4. Why is flexibility important?
5. How much exercise do you get in one week?
Have students share their findings in class. **(30 min. preparation, 30 min. presentation; Extend, Enrich)**

Activity 4.3
Stretching Techniques. Have students stand beside their desks. Take them through range of motion exercises for their

arms and hips. (arm circles and bending over) After taking the students through the motions, use a rubber band to show how it stretches in the same way as our muscles. Show the proper technique with the rubber band—use a smooth, not jerky, pull. Explain that this is how we should stretch. We are not supposed to bounce. While you are discussing bouncing, continually jerk on the rubber band. As you discuss the proper, smooth, one-motion stretch,

---

Teacher Support Notes

① **Exercises to Avoid:** Ask students if they have done any of these stretches and exercises. Has doing these exercises resulted in any injuries?

✉ **Where to Write**

National Recreation Association
8 W. 8th St.
New York, NY 10011

250

---

250 UNIT 3 Your Physical Health

direction only. The design of the shoulder joint, on the other hand, permits movements in many directions. If a joint is flexible and healthy, it moves smoothly through its entire range of motion.

Stretching improves flexibility. When you stretch, remember that your goal is to get limber, not to push your joints beyond their range of motion. (Observe a cat stretching, and notice the technique. The stretch is long and lazy, a few moments of pure pleasure.) Choose easy stretches, and stretch only to the point where you feel tightness but not pain. As you hold the stretch, even the feeling of tightness should gradually ease. If the tightness does not ease, or the stretch becomes painful as you hold it, you are overstretching.

Stretch in smooth motions—do not bounce. Bouncing can easily overstretch or tear a ligament until it can no longer support its joint, making the joint prone to in-

jury. Nerves can overstretch painfully, too, if you are only slightly too enthusiastic. Figure 10–6 below lists some stretches and exercises that are dangerous to the joints.

Never stretch a cold muscle. Warm up first with five minutes of light activity or with a hot shower. Then, to get a full stretch, relax the muscles, allow each body part to move slowly through its full range of motion, and hold each stretch position for 10 seconds. Breathe normally. Repeat each stretch once or twice. To improve, add 2 seconds to the time you hold each stretch until you are holding it for 30 seconds. Choose stretches that work all body areas: neck, shoulders, back, pelvis, thighs, calf muscles, and ankles. Figure 10–7 illustrates some recommended stretches.

Key Points *Flexibility depends on the elasticity of the muscles and connective tissues, and on the condition of the joints. A joint's range of motion sets limits on its movements. Stretching improves flexibility.*

FIGURE 10-6

Stretches and Exercises to Avoid ①

Which Ones to Avoid?	Why Avoid Them?
Unsupervised yoga	May cause many types of injury
Hurdler's stretch (sit with one leg bent under at the knee, reach for toe of outstretched leg)	May cause knee injury
Toe touching with straight knees	May overstretch tendons and damage major nerves and vertebrae
Deep knee bend; duckwalk (thighs touch heels)	May cause knee injury
Straight-leg lift (lie on back and lift both legs)	Aggravates lower back problems
Hyperextension of the back (arch the back and then let it sag, performed to extremes)	May injure the lower back
Toe standing	May damage the foot arch
Straight-leg sit-up	Aggravates lower back problems
Ballet stretch (designed for dancers)	May cause many types of injuries

pull the rubber band gently. **(20 min.; Extend, Enrich)**

EVALUATE

Activity 4.4
Vocabulary Match. Divide the class into five teams. Give each team all the Mini Glossary definitions in Sections I–IV. Without using books, have the groups write the correct word for each definition. The first team with all the definitions matched with the correct words, wins. You may also write the words to choose from on the board. A more challenging variation of the activity is to give the words and ask for the definitions. **(30 min.)**

CLOSE

Activity 4.5
Using tape on the floor and a ruler, have each student sit on the floor and reach as far with the ruler as possible. Make sure both hands are on the ruler. Have the students set a goal for them-

(continued on next page)

Whole-body stretch

Neck stretches

Lower back stretch

Lower back stretches

Calf muscle stretch

Quadriceps and hip flexors stretch

Buttocks stretch

Hamstring stretch

Inner thigh stretch

Upper body stretches

Upper back and side stretch

①

Figure 10–7 Recommended Stretches. These stretches can help you meet flexibility goals safely. The muscles being stretched are highlighted.

Teacher Support Notes

① **Overheads—Recommended Stretches:** In your supplementary material, you will find overhead transparencies of this illustration, which you may want to use in your classroom presentation of this lesson.

☎ Where to Call

U.S. Bicycle Polo Association
1-212-369-3599
Bicycle polo is a relatively new sport that might help some students improve their fitness. The game is played on a 100' by 45' field with six play periods. Each is about 7-1/2 minutes long. Teams are currently competing in major cities.

selves and develop a plan to achieve that goal. If the students retest themselves in two weeks and improve (can reach farther), give them extra credit. Express the concern that many people say they want to improve, but in order to improve you must work hard and make a commitment

to fitness. This could be the beginning of a regular program for the students. Give them these guidelines for goal setting:
1. Set a goal you are interested in reaching.
2. Make your goal small and realistic at first.
3. Make changes in your environment. Surround yourself with positive influences for your goal. Be patient with change.
4. Choose and establish reinforcements.

5. Evaluate your success and failures to reset the next goal.

FOCUS

SECTION V

In this section students will:
1. Determine proper ways to gain muscle strength and endurance.

Activity 5.1

Section IV Review
Answers
1. Answers will vary.
2. do not push joints beyond their ranges, choose easy stretches, stretch in smooth motions, never stretch a cold muscle
3. *Avoid*—Answers will vary. Refer to Figure 10–6 on page 250 for possible answers.
   Safe—Answers will vary. Refer to Figure 10–7 on page 251 for possible answers.
4. Answers will vary.

Teacher Support Notes

① **Opportunities to Develop Strength:**
Have students brainstorm to develop a list of activities that people used to do regularly that would help them develop their strength, but which people today are able to avoid due to advances in technology. How have these lost opportunities affected athletic performance? As an example, you could cite a professional baseball pitching coach's theory that pitchers today, as a whole, are not throwing as fast because they don't have the upper body and arm strength of pitchers who grew up in earlier years doing more physical labor.

SECTION IV REVIEW

Answer the following questions on a sheet of paper.
Learning the Vocabulary
The vocabulary terms in this section are *elasticity* and *range of motion.*
1. Write a sentence using each vocabulary term.

Learning the Facts
2. Give three recommendations for safe stretching.
3. Name one stretching exercise to avoid and one safe stretching exercise.

Making Life Choices
4. Try each of the recommended stretches in Figure 10–7 on page 251. Be sure to follow the guidelines for stretching listed in this section. Which exercises did you find the easiest and which did you find the hardest? What parts of your body seem to need the most work in terms of improving flexibility? Why? Do you stretch on a regular basis? Why or why not? How might you safely measure improvements in your flexibility?

SECTION V

Gaining Muscle Strength and Endurance

Strength is a familiar concept. It is the ability of the muscles to work against **resistance**: to pull weeds from the ground, to push a stalled car, or to open a jar of jam. Strong muscles, tendons, ligaments, and bones also best protect the body's internal organs from injury. Many of today's mechanical helpers spare us effort but also rob us of opportunities to develop strength. For example, a thermostat makes it easy to turn up the heat without chopping firewood.

Muscle endurance is closely related to strength. Muscle endurance is the ability of a muscle to hold a contraction for long periods of time or to contract repeatedly.

Strength Conditioning

Two ways people gain muscle strength and endurance are through **weight training** and **calisthenics.** Weight training is the most efficient way. It uses weights or machines to provide resistance against which the muscles can work. Calisthenics are exercises that develop muscle strength and endurance by using the body's parts as weights pulled or pushed against gravity. Familiar examples are sit-ups, push-ups, and pull-ups.

Weight training is not for males only. It can be an ideal workout for both males and females, and it need not produce big, bulky muscles. Bodybuilders can follow programs designed to do just that, but you can tailor your weight routine to meet other goals. To gain strength without bulk, you can use light weights and more repetitions. Rumor has it that weight training will lead to muscle-bound inflexibility; it does not. Inflexible joints do not result from weight training, but from unbalanced training and from leaving stretching exercises out of any fitness routine.

Remember to breathe when you work with weights. Holding your breath puts pressure on the heart and lungs and can damage them. Exhale as you raise or push the weight away. (A way to remember this is to "blow the weight away from you.") Inhale as you lower the weight. Also, raise and lower the weight smoothly. Jerking it up or letting gravity pull it down fails to improve strength and threatens to injure your joints.

To develop maximum strength from the smallest number of repetitions, lower the weight especially slowly. A group of ten

Physical Stereotypes. On the board write the words *females* and *males*. Have students brainstorm physical characteristics of each, as you write them under the proper heading. Include items such as *weight lifting*, *strong*, *powerful*, and *aerobics*. Review the lists and discuss any stereotypical responses that were made. Discuss the fact that we all have different body frames and muscular ability, and how, as we try to achieve our personal best, stereotypes sometimes inhibit us. **(20 min., Critical Thinking)**

Activity 5.2
Conveniences and Laziness. As the students brainstorm, list on the board the conveniences that encourage laziness (such as remotes for TVs and stereos). Discuss how modernization does not encourage exercise. **(15 min.; Extend, Enrich)**

Activity 5.3
Resistance. Have the students experiment with resistance. A few examples you could use are to have them do the following:

1. Place their books between both hands

(continued on next page)

Weight training is not for males only.

repetitions of a particular exercise should take about a minute. Such a group of repetitions is called a **set.** Performing many sets with lighter weights mostly increases endurance. Doing fewer sets with heavier weights favors bulk and strength.

Small muscles fatigue quickly, and this can stop your workout. Therefore, strengthen the larger muscle groups first, then the smaller ones. Make sure to distribute the weight work equally over the arms and legs, both sides—all the muscles. Overdeveloped muscles in one part of the body, combined with weak muscles in another part, can cause damage. For example, strong back muscles and weak stomach muscles can pull the back out of line, injuring the spine. An overdeveloped muscle that opposes a weak one can also interfere with movement—the person becomes muscle bound. The muscular system in Chapter 6 shows all the major muscles of the body.

Heavy weights can be dangerous. A wise beginning exerciser seeks guidance from a seasoned, professional trainer who has a reputation for getting results safely. (New employees of spas and gyms may be long on enthusiasm but short on knowledge and experience.)

Figure 10–8 on the next page shows exercises that build strength and endurance. Some use small weights, called dumbbells, to provide resistance. Others use parts of the body working against gravity for resistance (calisthenics). One repetition of any of these exercises is easy to do, so the exerciser must apply overload by repeating the exercise many times in a set. Another way is to perform many sets in an exercise session. Remember, overload just a little—not so much as to injure yourself.

Whether your goal is strength, endurance, or improved body composition, weight training every other day or so seems to produce the best results. Rest is as important as work. Muscles use the time between workouts to repair small injuries, to replenish their fuel supplies, and to build themselves up. If you like to work out every day, just be sure to work different muscle groups today from those you worked yesterday. Give each muscle group a day off.

Some false "short cuts" to strength, such as taking nutrient drinks, pills, and powders

MINI GLOSSARY

resistance: a force that opposes another; in fitness, the weight or other opposing force against which muscles must work.

weight training: exercise routines for strength conditioning that use weights or machines to provide resistance against which the muscles can work.

calisthenics: exercise routines for strength conditioning that use the parts of the body as weights.

set: a specific number of times to repeat a weight-training exercise.

Teacher Support Notes

① **Weight-Training Advice:** Please caution students against reading this section and then running off to a gym to work with weights or weight machines without first obtaining instruction from a knowledgeable coach/trainer or weight specialist. Emphasize the possibility of serious injury in working with weights improperly.

② **Repetitions and Sets:** If you have students in the class who have participated in weight-lifting programs, have them talk about their routines. At what pace did they increase repetitions and/or sets?

❝ Thoughts on Health ❞

Whenever I feel like exercise I lie down until the feeling passes.
– Robert Hutchins

and press together.
2. Push both hands against the desk.
3. Hook arms at the elbow with a partner and pull.

After students have reviewed the information in this section, have them experiment with other ways to create resistance. **(20 min.; Extend, Enrich)**

Activity 5.4
Equipment Evaluation. Explore your school training room and weight room. If a variety of equipment is available, hold one class period in that room. Give each student enough index cards to evaluate each piece of equipment. Plan and explain an orderly rotation process, so that every student views each piece of equipment. As they rotate, have them write the name of the equipment, which muscle group it works, and which component of fitness it develops. (could be more than one muscle group or component) **(one class period; Extend, Enrich)**

Activity 5.5
Advertisements. Have the students read the Consumer Awareness article on page 255. Have them assume roles as

---

Teacher Support Notes

① **Overhead— Strength and Endurance Routines:**
Your supplementary material contains an overhead with selected routines from this illustration. Use it to stress the importance of doing different exercises to develop different muscle groups.

📢 Fast Facts

Studies show that the typical sedentary person has a 35 to 52% greater risk of developing high blood pressure than someone who exercises regularly.

✉ Where to Write

American Running and Fitness Association
P.O. Box 4704
N. Hollywood, CA 91607

①

Figure 10–8 Muscle Strength and Endurance Routines. Some of the exercises show people using dumbbells. Should you wish to use other equipment to achieve the same effects, consult a qualified trainer. The muscles worked by each exercise are highlighted.

advertising agents. The students must advertise one of the pills or powders. Encourage students to create their ads using selling points that companies use in selling products. Display the advertisements. **(30 min.; Extend, Enrich)**

Activity 5.6
Steroids. Discuss how steroids are a short-term method of self-esteem building. Include in this discussion the reasons

people want quick methods instead of long-term gains. Also discuss how steroids can be dangerous. You can approach this from the standpoint of side effects, as well as the deadly effect of AIDS (from the needles). **(30 min.)**

Activity 5.7
Pro and Con Chart. Have the students write a pro and con list for the use of steroids. After completing their lists,

have students cut their lists so that each pro and con is on a separate slip of paper. They should then cut off the pro and con headings. In small groups have the students paste their lists on poster board under the proper headings. This activity will reinforce knowledge as well as encourage small-group discussion. Their lists should contain many more cons than pros. Emphasize that even if

(continued on next page)

CONSUMER AWARENESS

Pills, Powders, and Potions for Fitness ①

Athletes and other active people can be easy targets for quacks who sell an endless river of products—herbal steroid-drug substitutes, protein or amino acid supplements, vitamin or mineral supplements, "complete" drinks, "muscle-building" powders, electrolyte pills, and many other so-called **ergogenic** aids. The term *ergogenic* claims to mean that such products have special work-enhancing powers. Actually, no food or supplement is ergogenic.

Advertisements for commercial products may read as these do: "SWINDLE amino acids deposit slabs of muscle bulk"; "HOODWINK enzymes ram the body into turbo charge"; "Ultrapotent TECHNO-HYPE vitamins and minerals blast carbs through your system." Many ads like these are easy to see through. They are trying to pick readers' pockets. Others are harder to see through, though just as false.*

If potions do seem to work, they probably work by the power of suggestion. Don't discount that power, because it is awesome. In fact, use it instead of the potions. Imagine yourself as a winner, and visualize yourself as capable in your sport. You don't have to rely on magic for an extra edge. You already have a real advantage—your mind.

② CRITICAL THINKING

1. Taking pills and other supplements may seem like a scientific approach to athletics, but experts recommend against it. Especially with regard to the herbal steroids, why do you think experts say to avoid supplements?
2. Why is it so easy for some people to believe false advertising claims for improved athletic performance?
3. What motivates the sellers of such fake products?

*If you have questions about a fitness product, book, or program, write to the American College of Sports Medicine, P.O. Box 1440, Indianapolis, IN 46204.

without hard work always fail as the Consumer Awareness box points out. Muscles grow in response to work. Muscles do not helplessly build tissue whenever extra nutrients float by. Hard work itself triggers the muscles to grab what they need from the bloodstream to build themselves up. Muscle building is an active process, started by activity itself. A few hormones can also signal muscles to build tissue, but the price to health of taking them is high.

Key Points ▶ *Strength develops when muscles work against resistance.*

Strength Sought from Steroids and Other Artificial Means

It is unwise to use hormones or other drugs to improve strength. Hormones and drugs that athletes take to gain strength or improve endurance have many dangerous side effects. Despite the hazards, these prod-

MINI GLOSSARY

ergogenic: (ER-go-JEN-ick): a term that claims to mean "work-enhancing." In fact, no products enhance the ability to do work.

Teacher Support Notes

① **No Easy Solutions:** Emphasize to students that no product has any special beneficial effects on either muscles or athletic performance. People must learn to defend themselves against the lies told by sellers of fitness products and schemes. Students must be knowledgeable and think critically.

② **Answers to Critical Thinking:**

1. The herbs may contain toxins and can have unexpected side effects. Tell students not to make the mistake of equating "natural" with "harmless."

2. Answers will vary, but students should realize that many people want the benefits of fitness without doing the work. Advertisers realize this and develop their ads around the idea of quick and easy fitness and performance.

3. Making a profit.

255

they think there are some pros, steroids are dangerous—they should not use them. **(30 min.; Reteach, Reinforce)**

Activity 5.8

Interviews. Have students investigate, through articles and interviews at health clubs, how our society idolizes professional athletes, their performances, and their salaries. Students should also investigate how society's view of these athletes affects the use of steroids. **(Extend, Enrich)**

EVALUATE
SECTION V

Activity 5.9

Pop Quiz. Have cue cards prepared, each with one positive or one negative effect of muscle strength, muscular endurance, or steroids. (feel better, last longer, grow other body hair, liver ruptures) Have students number their papers according to the number of prepared cards. Hold up the cards one at a time (numbered in order on the back of the card). Quiz the students by asking them to write if: **1.** the effect is positive or neg-

---

Teacher Support Notes

① **Teacher Information Sheet—Steroids:** Your supplementary material contains information on steroids entitled "More on the Effects of Steroid Hormones in the Body."

② **Steroid Abuse:** A highly publicized case of steroid abuse was that of Lyle Alzado, a professional football player whose cancer death was attributed to his heavy use of steroids during his football career. Major articles appeared in early 1992 in national news magazines. Have students research Alzado's case and report back to the class on the impact steroids had on his life and death.

✎ Fast Facts

A person's energy level can be increased and fatigue decreased by exercise.

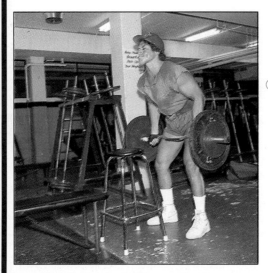

Men generally develop bulkier muscles than women do, in response to exercise.

ucts often tempt those who want to gain a competitive advantage over others.

Men generally develop bulkier muscles than do women, in response to exercise. This is because men produce larger amounts of certain hormones known as **steroids** in their bodies. These hormones are also available as drugs, which were developed to treat children born lacking in the ability to produce the hormones. Like all drugs, steroids can be abused. Some athletes, both men and women, take steroid drugs in the attempt to develop bulky muscles. Many studies of these practices show that steroid drugs can indeed increase body weight (especially lean body weight). The drugs can increase muscle strength in some highly conditioned athletes who also exercise intensely.

Athletes struggling to be the best are tempted by the promise of muscles bigger and stronger than those that training alone can produce. Athletes who are not born superstars, and who normally would not be able to compete at high levels, can suddenly compete with born champions. This tempts other athletes to abuse the drugs, too. Especially among professionals for whom enormous salaries reward excellent performances, illegal steroid abuse is common.

Steroid abuse comes at a very high price, however. For one thing, all steroid abusers experience a sharp change in their blood fats that reflects an increased risk of heart disease. In addition, steroids are known to interrupt the normal work of the liver; cause cancerous liver tumors, liver rupture, and hemorrhage (bleeding); produce permanent changes in the reproductive system; and alter the structure of the face. In males, steroids cause the testicles to shrink. In females, they cause mustaches and other body hair to grow, and the breasts to shrink. Steroids stunt growth in those who haven't yet reached full height. They also may cause acne. Steroids also affect the mind, bringing on mood swings, aggressive behavior, and changes in the sex drive. Some steroid users suffer deadly effects right away. Others may live longer. The effects on the body of years of abuse are unknown.

For now, serious athletes are forced to make a hard choice. They can use no steroids and face a field full of artificially gifted opponents, or use the drugs and risk death or disease. Judging from how many athletes choose steroids, they must consider the drug risks less of a threat than the risk of losing competitions.

Steroids are illegal in competition and can be detected in urine tests. Therefore, some athletes have switched to other unsafe hormones that are not detectable— **human growth hormone,** for example. Then they develop symptoms of the disease **acromegaly**—huge body size, widened jawline, widened nose, protruding brow and teeth, and an increased likelihood of death before age 50. The American Academy of Pediatrics and the American College of Sports Medicine speak out against the use of all hormones by athletes.

CLOSE
SECTION V

Activity 5.10
Article Presentations. Have students bring to class one article from a magazine or newspaper that pertains to

this section. Have the students present the article orally to the class.

FOCUS
SECTION VI

In this section students will learn:
1. Ways of preventing heat stroke and sport injuries.

Activity 6.1

Injury Reports. Without using their books, ask the students to describe as best they can shin splints, stress fractures, and tennis elbow. Ask for other examples of injuries they have heard about. List them on the board as they are mentioned. Have students select one of the listed injuries to report on the next day. Each presentation should not take more than three minutes. If there are not

(continued on next page)

Remember that the start of this chapter talked about miracle pills for fitness? If there were such a thing, people would no doubt gobble them like candy. The use of steroids is just one example of the type of thinking that hooks people into seeking easy ways to hard achievements.

 Key Points *Hormones promote muscle growth, but the taking of hormone drugs to improve strength and endurance for athletic competition is illegal and dangerous to health. There is no quick road to fitness.*

SECTION V REVIEW

Answer the questions on a sheet of paper.
Learning the Vocabulary
The vocabulary terms in this section are *resistance, weight training, calisthenics, set, ergogenic, steroids, human growth hormone,* and *acromegaly.*
1. What is the difference between weight training and calisthenics?
2. Drugs that are abused by some athletes seeking a shortcut to large muscles are called _____.
3. High doses of _____ can cause a disease known as _____.
4. Strength develops when muscles work against _____.

Learning the Facts
5. What are the two ways people gain muscle strength and endurance?
6. How frequently should weight training be done?
7. What are four dangerous physical side effects of steroid use?
8. Name some products that are marketed as ergogenic aids.

Making Life Choices
9. Have you or anyone you know ever used steroids or any pills, powders, or potions for fitness? What were the results, both positive and negative? If someone offered you a newly discovered "miracle pill" to improve your strength, would you try it? Why or why not? Assuming there is no such "miracle pill," set up a personal strength

conditioning program for one week that you would enjoy following. Don't make it too demanding—assume you will add to it as time goes on.

SECTION VI

Preventing Sports Injuries and Heat Stroke

① Fitness-minded people talk a lot about **shin splints, stress fractures, tennis elbow,** and other athletic injuries. These and other injuries can be avoided by exercising properly and by building fitness slowly. You can become a marathon runner in

MINI GLOSSARY

steroids: hormones of a certain chemical type that occur naturally in the body , some of which promote muscle growth. Available as drugs, they are abused by athletes seeking a shortcut to large muscles.

human growth hormone: a nonsteroid hormone produced in the body that promotes growth; taken as a drug by athletes to enhance muscle growth; also called *somatotropin.*

acromegaly (ack-ro-MEG-a-lee): a disease caused by above-normal levels of human growth hormone.

shin splints: damage to the muscles and connective tissues of the lower front leg from stress. Such damage usually heals with rest.

stress fractures: bone damage from repeated physical force that strains the place where ligament is attached to bone.

tennis elbow: a painful condition of the arm and joint, usually caused by strain, as from poor form in playing tennis.

enough injuries listed for each student to report on one, have them report in pairs. **(One class period for presentations; Extend, Enrich)**

TEACH
SECTION VI
(Guided and Independent Practice)

Activity 6.2

Wrestler Interviews. With permission, have students watch a school wrestling team during its workout. Afterwards, have students talk to the wrestlers to find out the importance of "making weight." Ask them what types of things they do to make weight. Ask about wrestlers losing water weight and any other myths they may have heard. After watching and discussing, have your students bring

their findings back to share with the class. Discuss the positive and negative aspects of wrestling that they have learned. Ask whether or not they view wrestling as a healthy sport. (The purpose here is not to put any sport down; only to expose the importance of water weight and possible effects in relation to dehydration.)

Teacher Support Notes

① **Handouts—Strategies for Overcoming Fitness Obstacles:** In your supplementary material you will find a handout for students that lists barriers to obtaining fitness and suggested solutions for each of the barriers. You will find another handout in your supplementary material entitled "Honoring Your Commitment to Exercise." This handout is similar to the one described above, but is different in that the solutions to the various excuses are not given. Students have to supply their own. You may want to do this handout before the other or in place of the other depending upon the ability levels of your students.

Where to Write

President's Council on Physical Fitness
400 6th St., SW
Washington, DC
20201

time. However, you can do it without joint damage only if you build slowly. Another obvious measure is to use proper equipment, such as supportive shoes designed specifically for your sport.

Be consistent, too. An "occasional athlete," one who is inactive for days and then suddenly plays hard, invites injury. Vigorous and sudden demands on out-of-condition muscles, ligaments, and tendons lead to sprains. Take on a regular program of fitness to develop the strength that safe play demands.

Pain during activity is a signal that something is wrong. For example, if a jogger feels leg pain, a change of posture may be needed. If the pain continues or gets worse, stop jogging until the pain goes away. Then try again slowly, increasing just a little at a time.

Be alert to the dangers of overheating and **dehydration.** Muscles heat up during exercise because they are burning fuel. To help control the body's temperature, blood flows through the muscles and carries heat to the skin. There the surrounding air and the evaporation of sweat can carry the heat away. On humid days, though, sweat does not evaporate well. Heat builds up. Then the body sweats even more heavily in an attempt to cool itself. This heavy sweating can be extremely dangerous, because fluid and electrolyte losses beyond a certain point cause cells to stop functioning. It can even be fatal.

Overheating progresses through several stages. Early symptoms may be just swelling of the hands and feet or cramps in the legs or other muscles. Then comes **heat exhaustion**, and finally **heat stroke**.

The symptoms of heat exhaustion are signals of distress, such as headaches, nausea, chest pains, or diarrhea, and they warn that heat stroke may be threatening. Extreme fatigue, intense dizziness, and fading-out consciousness are signs of heat stroke.

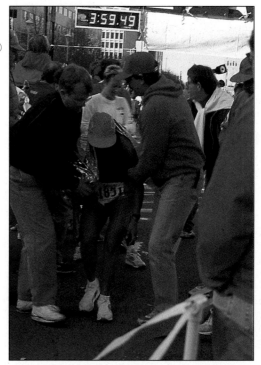

Pain during an activity means that something is wrong. If you feel pain, stop and seek relief.

The most important preventive steps are to stop the activity immediately, seek out shade and a cool place, rest, and drink water. For the same reasons, it is unwise to exercise in a plastic or rubber suit in hopes of losing pounds. The waterproof material stops evaporation, causing the body to sweat heavily. This can lead to heat stroke. Similarly, too long a stay in a hot whirlpool bath, hot tub, or sauna can cause heat stroke. To avoid heat stroke:

- Rest during times of high humidity, high temperature, or both.
- Limit exposure to any source of heat.
- Wear lightweight, loose-fitting clothing.
- Drink several extra glasses of water in the hours before you exercise heavily. Drink enough to cause you to urinate (this

EVALUATE
SECTION VI

Activity 6.3
Posters. Have students make posters teaching ways to avoid heat stroke. (see text) Display the posters around the room, gym, and school. **(40 min.; Reteach, Reinforce)**

CLOSE
SECTION VI

Activity 6.4
Resource List. As a class, compile a resource list of local places to call for preventive methods or treatments for athletic injuries. For example: fitness club, fitness director of a company, nurse, doctor, athletic trainer.

RETEACH/BONUS

Here are some additional activities for the various sections of this chapter. You may want to use these activities to reteach certain concepts, or you may choose them as alternatives to earlier activities. Some could also be used in

(continued on next page)

---

means your tissues are full to the maximum with water).

- Replace water lost during the activity with about a half-cup of a dilute, cold beverage every 15 to 20 minutes. Cold, plain or lightly flavored water is recommended.
- Listen for your body's distress signals, and if you have to, stop exercising. Take a rest in the shade.

Dehydration interferes with the body's ability to exercise. Muscle weakness and unusual fatigue on a hot day may mean you need more fluids. You do not need salt tablets or other forms of salt. These may make dehydration worse, because they pull water from the tissues into the digestive tract. Some people like commercial sports drinks, but these are usually unnecessary. (In the case of endurance athletes, though, who work out for more than an hour without stopping, the sugar in sports drinks may be of some benefit.) You do not need supple-

mental vitamins and minerals, either. Ordinary foods and beverages replace losses naturally.

Key Points *Most sports injuries are preventable. The most important preventive measures are to follow proper form, stop working if you feel pain, and take precautions against dehydration, heat exhaustion, and heat stroke.*

SECTION VI REVIEW

Answer the following questions on a sheet of paper.

Learning the Vocabulary
The vocabulary terms in this section are *shin splints, stress fractures, tennis elbow, dehydration, heat exhaustion,* and *heat stroke.*

1. How are dehydration and heat exhaustion related?
2. _____ involve damage to the muscles and connective tissues of the lower front leg due to stress.

Learning the Facts
3. What is the problem with being an "occasional athlete"?
4. How can heat stroke be avoided?
5. Name three steps you can take to prevent injury.

Making Life Choices
6. What do you consider to be some of your fitness strengths? What are some of the barriers and limitations you face in setting up and following through on a personal fitness program? List what you believe to be a workable solution to each obstacle you are facing.

MINI GLOSSARY

dehydration: loss of water. The symptoms progress rapidly from thirst to weakness to exhaustion, confusion, and even death.
heat exhaustion: a serious stage of overheating which can lead to heat stroke.
heat stroke: a life-threatening condition that results from a buildup of body heat; can be fatal.

Answers to Fact or Fiction

Here are the answers to the questions at the start of the chapter.

1. True. **2.** False. Although an extreme and sudden exertion can damage the body, a gradual increase in overload will produce a strengthened body. **3.** True. **4.** False. People of both genders use weight training for trimming and firming the body. Bodybuilders follow special weight-training programs to gain muscle size and bulk. **5.** False. You should stop to avoid serious injury. **6.** False. It's best to rehydrate as you go. **7.** False. You need water, not salt.

Section VI Review
Answers

1. Heat exhaustion is a serious stage of overheating. The loss of water and the buildup of body heat can be fatal.
2. Shin splints
3. Vigorous and sudden demands on out-of-condition muscles, ligaments, and tendons lead to sprains.
4. Answers will vary; could include: rest during times of high humidity or high temperature; limit exposure to any source of heat; wear lightweight, loose-fitting clothing; drink several extra glasses of water in the hours before you exercise heavily; replace water lost during the activity; and listen to your body's distress signals and stop exercising.
5. follow proper form, stop working if you feel pain, take precautions against heat exhaustion
6. Answers will vary.

conjunction with the Straight Talk feature below.

Increasing Fitness. Divide the students into four groups: cardiovascular endurance, flexibility, muscular strength, and muscular endurance. Each group will need a blank overhead transparency and pen. Students are to list as many exercises as they can that would increase fitness in their assigned areas. Also, have the students tell which component, in the physical fitness test, they are testing for. (Match the component of fitness with the fitness test to understand the purpose of fitness testing.) **(20 min., Cooperative Learning)**

Analyzing Injuries and Conditions. Before class, make index cards that list various injuries and conditions that may exist if a person lacks the four components of fitness. (muscle soreness, heart attack, tears in the muscle area, hyperventilation, and headaches) Place the four components on the board as column headings. Give each student a card. Have the students tell which column their cards should be placed under and

---

Teacher Support Notes

① **Nutrition Review:** To introduce this Straight Talk you might remind students that to perform any basic physical act, their bodies need nutrients. Ask them which nutrients they need to produce energy. (mostly carbohydrates and fats; to a much lesser degree and in special circumstances, protein) Which nutrient is necessary to build new tissues? (protein) What do vitamins and minerals do? (help the body regulate and support its functions) Which of these nutrients are needed then to engage in the strenuous physical activity of sports competition? (all of them)

📣 Fast Facts

According to the Amateur Athletic Union in Indianapolis, two out of three American children between the ages of 6 and 17 cannot pass a basic fitness test.

STRAIGHT TALK _____ Food for Sports Competition

You may wonder if athletes need special foods or nutrients to help them perform. Right away, you should know that no supplement or nutrient product has ever proved helpful in this way. On the other hand, the foods athletes choose at every meal matter greatly. The meals they eat can help or hinder their performance. ①

I work out each day, and I'd like to go out for the track team. Can my diet help me make the team?

While the right diet can help you in your efforts, it would be an exaggeration to say that diet alone can help you make the team. Rather, a balanced diet that provides adequate nutrients and fuels can support your efforts. Once these things are in place, dedication and hard work can win your spot on the team. Without the needed raw materials, though, your efforts will be an uphill battle.

What fuels are best to support my activity? I've heard that carbohydrates are the best.

Yes, carbohydrate-rich foods are best.

Why?

The way your body handles fuels during exercise plays a major role. At rest, your body uses a fuel mix of about equal parts of fat and carbohydrate.

However, when you begin to work physically, the fuel mix changes. The type of work you choose—aerobic or anaerobic—determines the fuel mix your body uses. Fat "goes with" aerobic exercise. Activities such as jogging or distance running use mostly fat for fuel. Glucose "goes with" anaerobic activities. Sprinting, tennis, and football use much more glucose for fuel.

If you are a jogger or distance runner, you'll use mostly fat to provide your energy (but you'll still use some carbohydrate). On the other hand, sprinters and weight lifters use mostly carbohydrate (although they still use some fat). Athletes of both kinds depend on their storage form of glucose, glycogen, to provide the carbohydrate they need.

How does glycogen in the working body relate to carbohydrate in the diet?

To see the relationship, try to imagine the body packing away into storage some of the nutrients it receives from foods. It will draw on these stored nutrients later, during activity. Your body can store unlimited amounts of fat, and fat is abundant in the diet, so you needn't worry about obtaining enough fat. Carbohydrate is a different story. The body's glycogen stores are very small. Also, they run out quickly, after only an hour or so of intense activity. You must fill your glycogen stores from food daily. And most people rarely include enough carbohydrate-containing foods in their days' meals to keep their glycogen stores full. They must make special efforts to eat enough carbohydrate-containing foods.

What would happen if I ran out of glycogen?

Most times, when glycogen runs out, a person just feels tired and hungry. During physical activity, though, to run out of glycogen is to "hit

(Continued on next page)

why. Tell them to put their cards under the most common component for that condition since some may be placed under more than one component. Have the students tape the card under the proper heading. Remind the class that they can agree to disagree. Allow time for class discussion so that they can develop some opinions about what these components are, and some consequences of not being physically fit. **(50 min., Critical Thinking)**

Designing Ads on T-shirts. Have the students bring old T-shirts to class. Give students markers and allow them to design an advertisement for exercise, on their shirts. You may assign groups if you don't have enough shirts. Explain to them that advertising can be used as a method to promote fitness, the same way it is used to promote products. **(20–30 min.; Extend, Enrich)**

Balance Beam. Set up an obstacle course in an open classroom, or go to the gym area. Use a balance beam if available, or stacks of wood that can be walked on. Have weights available. Ask volunteers to hold objects and walk the beam. The beam represents your travel through life. The weights represent body fat, lack of cardiovascular fitness, and lack of strength. Have the students carry

(continued on next page)

STRAIGHT TALK   *(Continued)*

the wall." Continuing activity beyond this point is possible only through great effort, and the quality of performance is lowered. Figure 10–9 shows that a high-carbohydrate diet can triple an athlete's endurance.

For people who exercise lightly for an hour or less, such as casual joggers, glycogen stores rarely matter much. These people simply do not go long or hard enough to run out of glycogen. For distance runners, others who exercise for more than an hour at a stretch, and for people who work anaerobically, such as weight lifters and sprinters, glycogen is important.

I've heard of a method called glycogen loading to improve performance. What is glycogen loading?

Athletes who compete in long-distance endurance events want to have as much stored energy in their muscles as they can. Glycogen loading tricks the muscles into storing more glycogen than normal. Old ways of doing this were dangerous, but the plan described here is safe.

Exercise physiologists recommend this glycogen-loading plan. First, about two or three weeks before competition, the athlete increases exercise intensity while eating a normal, high-carbohydrate diet. Then,

Figure 10–9 The Effect of Diet on Physical Endurance. A high-carbohydrate diet can triple a person's endurance.

Maximum endurance time

Fat and protein diet — 57 min

Normal mixed diet — 114 min

High carbohydrate diet — 167 min

during the last week before competition, the athlete does two things. With respect to exercise, the athlete gradually cuts back and, on the day before competition, rests completely. Meanwhile, with respect to foods, the athlete eats carbohydrate as usual until three days before competition, and then eats a very-high-carbohydrate diet. Endurance athletes who follow this plan can keep going longer than their competitors.

In hot weather, extra glycogen has one more advantage—it holds water. As glycogen breaks down, it releases its water, which helps to meet the athlete's fluid needs.

I'm sold. What's the best high-carbohydrate food?

Candy bars have sugar, and sugar is a form of carbohydrate, right?

From the standpoint that candy provides carbohydrate, candy bars might seem, at first glance, to be useful. Candy is available, needs no preparation, and tastes delicious. But before you load up on candy, you should know that most candy also contains a lot of fat. In fact, most types contain many more calories of fat than of carbohydrate.

Another thing about candy—while it provides concentrated sugar and fat for energy, it provides almost no other nutrients with them. Vitamins and minerals are just as important to performance as is carbohydrate. So consider candy, always, as a treat, not as

(Continued on next page)

(Continued on next page)

Teacher Support Notes

① **Hitting the Wall:** Ask students if any of them have ever experienced this sensation. If so, ask them to describe the situation and the feeling. If not, ask a marathon runner who has "hit the wall" to visit your class and describe his or her experiences with this sensation.

② **Who Benefits?** Point out here that extra glycogen benefits only those athletes who exercise long enough (90 minutes or more) and hard enough to use up their stores of glycogen. The regular, everyday exerciser does not benefit from having extra stores of glycogen.

③ **Overhead—Diet and Physical Endurance:** You will find an overhead of this illustration in your supplementary material.

different weights across the beam, and have the others in the class observe their balance. (Use spotters if needed.) After each person has crossed the beam carrying the added weight, have them cross the beam without a weight, and note balance change. Explain that we cannot, at

will, place body fat where we want or take it away. We cannot add endurance and strength only when we want. We must obtain a balance of all these components and work hard to keep them. **(30 min.; Reteach, Reinforce)**

Health Speakers. Invite a speaker from the YMCA or community wellness center to speak on the components of fitness. Have the speaker include informa-

tion pertaining to the proper age group.

Questionnaires. Have the students prepare individual questionnaires (ten questions) that a doctor could give to a patient before beginning an exercise program. Have the students explain why each question is important. Ask if the students can see the importance of athletic physicals before competition. Have the students make a list of other times that physicals

Teacher Support Notes

① **Choices Do Affect Performance:** Point out to students that the following information in the text gives them specific recommendations of how the foods they eat and the liquids they drink in the hours before physical activity do affect performance.

② **Handout—The Precompetition Meal:** Your supplementary material contains a handout that summarizes this information about pregame meals and provides, in addition, some sample meals.

✍ Fast Facts

A University of Maryland Research Center survey says that the leisure-time activities at which Americans spend most of their time are, in order: TV viewing, eating, and shopping.

STRAIGHT TALK (Continued)

a food to support health and performance. Bread, baked beans, potatoes, and pasta provide carbohydrate as starch, plus many other nutrients along with it.

Are you telling me I should eat more bread, beans, potatoes, and pasta to provide carbohydrate?

Yes, those are the foods to choose, along with fruits (almost pure carbohydrate), low-fat milk products, cereals, grains, and vegetables. Olympic training tables are laden with such choices.

Are there special foods I should be sure to include?

It's a mistake to think in terms of special foods. No one food must be either included or avoided. Try to adopt an athlete's diet as part of your lifestyle, something you do every day—all three meals and all snacks eaten every day of every week. Instead of "special foods," try to think in terms of "special diet."

Is there anything I can do before competition to help me perform my best?

On the day of competition, carefully plan your pregame meal. Eat it three to four hours before the event. The meal should be light (300 to 1,000 calories) and easy to digest. The meal should

provide carbohydrate-rich foods such as potatoes, beans and lentils, refined pastas and breads, and fruit juices. Not only do these foods supply glucose, but they are quickly absorbed. The juice provides fluids to help guard against dehydration and heat stroke.

Stay away from foods high in fat (such as meat) or foods high in fiber (such as raw vegetables). These require long times for digestion and can cause nausea during exercise. Tradition may call for a steak-and-salad dinner before a big game, but the needs of the players are better served by a new tradition—pasta or other high-carbohydrate meal to support performance. (See Figure 10–10.)

Speaking of steaks, you haven't mentioned protein. Don't athletes need more protein than other people do?

① Athletes need just slightly more protein than other people do. They use much of the extra to build muscles, and a little of it for fuel. While exercising, the muscles use more of certain amino acids for fuel, because these ② can provide energy in much the same way as glucose.

This does not mean, though, that athletes need to take amino acid pills or powders or eat more meat. A

diet of regular high-carbohydrate foods provides all of the protein and amino acids that athletes need, and in just the right amounts. Vegetarian athletes don't need amino acid pills either. They do need to be careful to include generous servings of protein-rich foods such as beans, seeds, whole-grain bread, pasta, and cereals, and low-fat milk and milk products in their diets.

Almost every athlete I know takes vitamin C pills. Do athletes need more vitamin C than the amount in their diets?

Your question is part of a large issue: whether athletes need more of *any* vitamin. It goes without saying that athletes need *enough* vitamins and minerals to do what they do. However, they do not need *more* than the RDA (Recommended Dietary Allowance) amount of any of them (Appendix B at the back of the book lists the RDA). Much research supports this statement, and virtually no true scientific evidence exists to oppose it. As for vitamin C, it follows the same rule as for all the other vitamins (although faddists say otherwise). Studies show that more is not better. Athletes who take vitamins in addition

(Continued on next page)

are needed in life. (marriage, insurance, jobs) **(45 min.–1 hr., Critical Thinking)**

Exercises to Avoid. Have students research stretches and exercises to avoid. Have them complete their own charts similar to Figure 10–6. Provide resources, a speaker, or a trainer to help the class that day. It is important that the students get updated material, as guidelines change constantly. It is also impor-

tant to understand the reasons we don't do certain exercises. Allow time in class to discuss the charts thoroughly. **(40–60 min.; Extend, Enrich)**

Letters. Have students write letters to local doctors and companies that sell supplement drinks. Have the students ask for nutritional information on these drinks. Compare and discuss responses and display the materials collected. **(40 min.,**

Extend, Enrich)

Interviews. Have students interview five older adults and get their opinions on fitness in later years. Have students ask how important fitness really is to them as they grow older. Have students share their interview findings with the class. Discuss any similarities and differences. **(40 min.; Extend, Enrich)**

(continued on next page)

STRAIGHT TALK *(Continued)*

to an ample diet do not perform any better than those who get enough from food.

Besides, for vitamin C, anyone eating a reasonable diet would find it almost impossible *not* to receive two or three times the RDA. A person who drinks a small glass of orange juice and eats a baked potato and a serving of broccoli in a day receives about five times the RDA for vitamin C from these foods alone. When they learn this fact, athletes have been known to throw away their pills and learn to cook broccoli.

Are you saying that no supplements have any effects on performance at all? ①

No, that's not quite true. Some concentrated nutrients may hurt an athlete's performance. For example, niacin supplements interfere with the body's release of fat. Without enough fat to use as fuel, the muscles are forced to use extra glycogen in place of fat. This may make the body run out of glycogen sooner, and it makes the work seem more difficult to the exerciser.

Can I relax my diet and rely on the drinks and candylike bars that claim to provide "complete" nutrition to supply the

FIGURE 10-10	
Pregame Meal Tips ②	
Some Good Ideas for a Pregame Meal	**Not Recommended:**
Angel food cake	Biscuits
Apricot nectar	Butter
Baked beans	Cheeses
Baked white or sweet potatoes	Creams
Black beans	Croissants
Blackeye peas	French fries
Dried fruit	Frosted cakes
Frozen yogurt	Gravy
Graham crackers	Ice cream
Grape juice	Margarine
Jell-O	Mayonnaise
Lentils	Meats
Pancakes	Muffins
Pasta	Nuts
Pineapple juice	Onion rings
Popsicles	Pies
Sherbet	Potato Chips
Sponge cake	Salad dressings
Tortillas	Stuffing

nutrients I need?

Such bars and drinks usually taste good and provide extra food energy. However, they do not come close to providing "complete" nutrition, as they claim. They lack fiber, many nutrients, and other important constituents of real food.

In one case, though, a liquid meal may be useful. An athlete who gets nervous and so cannot eat before a game might try such a drink to supply some of the needed fluid and carbohydrate.

However, a homemade milk shake of nonfat milk, ice cream, and a banana blended with flavorings can do the same thing, and less expensively.

Can the athlete find any other help in the diet?

Yes, there are two more things to be aware of. One is the use of caffeine. A moderate dose of this mild ③ stimulant (the amount of one

(Continued on next page)

Teacher Support Notes

① **Teacher Information Sheet—Vitamins and Minerals:** Your supplementary material contains additional information about the effects of vitamins and minerals on athletic performance.

② **Assessing Current Habits:** Have students who compete in athletic activities list on a sheet of paper the foods in this figure in two columns, as shown. Have them write Yes or No next to each food to indicate whether or not they've ever eaten that food in the two to three hours before competition. Have them total the yes's and no's in both columns. Are they eating more of the "Recommended" or "Not Recommended" foods?

③ **Moderate Amounts:** Stress with students the importance of the word *moderate* in this sentence. Remind them of what they've read repeatedly in this text—too much of a nutrient can be as damaging as too little.

264 UNIT 3 Your Physical Health

STRAIGHT TALK   (Continued)

This is a body that vegetables built. Andreas Cahling is a vegetarian.

or two cola beverages or glasses of iced tea) one hour prior to exercise seems to help some people's performance. Caffeine stimulates the body's release of fat. Exercise does too, but caffeine taken before exercise gets the fuel flowing before the exercise begins.

Remember, though, that a warm-up activity stimulates fuel release, too. Also, caffeine has adverse effects—upset stomach, nervousness, sleeplessness, irritability, headaches, breast disease, and diarrhea, among others. It also has a diuretic (water loss) effect that is potentially hazardous. Finally, caffeine in amounts greater than in 5 or 6 cups of coffee is illegal in competition and can disqualify a competitor. Use caffeine-containing beverages, if at all, with extreme care, as you would use any medical drug. Also, use them *in addition* to other fluids, not as substitutes. The example on the next page shows how to modify your diet to meet your needs as an athlete.

You said there were two things concerning diet and exercise to be aware of. What's the other?

The other help that comes from diet is a real advantage in sports for the athlete who eats right. A diet that is low in fat, high in complex carbohydrates, and adequate in protein and other nutrients serves all the needs of human beings. Such a diet meets the needs of those who place physical demands on their bodies especially well.

The meal plans on page 265 show how a normal, high-carbohydrate diet can be boosted with nourishing foods to meet an athlete's energy needs while providing abundant nutrients. Athletes need extra helpings of cereals, rice, beans, and bread; more milk and fruit; and even some sweet snacks such as angel food cake or puddings. Meats provide important nutrients, but athletes need only the same amounts as do other people.

Training and genetics being equal, who would win a competition—the person who habitually consumes too few nutrients or the one who arrives at the event with a long history of full nutrient stores and well-met needs? Be sure you give your active body the food it needs if you expect it to perform its best.

(Continued on next page)

cuss the information they've accumulated. **(Extend, Enrich)**

Sports Directory. Have students gather advertisements, phone books, and other resources for the purpose of identifying all the sports and fitness establishments in your community. Have students compile and organize the information and then have them design and produce a booklet listing all the facilities and pertinent information, such as location, hours, costs, etc. Students can either distribute the end product free of charge to members of the student body or sell the booklet and donate any profits to the school physical education department.

Normal Diet and an Athlete's Diet—How to Modify a Regular Day's Meals to Meet an Athlete's Needs

Regular Meal Choices ————→ To Modify: ——→ ① Athlete's Meal Choices

The regular breakfast plus:
2 pieces whole-wheat toast
4 teaspoons jelly
1/2 cup orange juice
2 teaspoons brown sugar on the oatmeal
2-percent-fat milk instead of nonfat milk

Both enjoy a snack

The regular lunch plus:
1 more beef and bean burrito
1 banana
Plus an afternoon snack:
1 cup 2-percent-fat milk
1 piece angel food cake

The regular dinner plus:
1 dinner roll
2 teaspoons butter
¼ cup more noodles
½ cup more sherbet
2-percent-fat milk instead of nonfat milk

Total calories 1,759
57 percent calories from carbohydrate
24 percent calories from fat
19 percent calories from protein

Total calories: 3,119
61 percent calories from carbohydrate
24 percent calories from fat
15 percent calories from protein

Teacher Support Notes

① **Comparing Meals:** Ask student athletes to look at these photos and compare the meals shown with the meals they typically eat. Are there major differences?

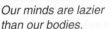 **Fast Facts**

Active people should be drinking more than the recommended eight glasses of water a day. One study suggests that athletes drink two-thirds of an ounce of water per pound of body weight daily. A 120-pound woman athlete, for example, should drink 80 ounces, or ten glasses of water daily.

CHAPTER REVIEW
Answers

Vocabulary

1. **a.** frequency
b. anaerobic **c.** fitness
d. heat exhaustion
e. flexibility **f.** set
2. **a.** Exercise duration is how long an exercise is performed—exercise intensity is the degree of exertion with which an exercise is performed. **b.** Target heart rate is the heartbeat rate that will condition a person's cardiovascular system.
3. **a.** Overload **b.** Stress fractures **c.** elasticity
d. Tennis elbow
4. **a.** Cardiovascular endurance, flexibility, muscles strength, endurance, and body composition
b. Low-impact aerobic dance

Recall
Section I
1. Answers will vary; could include: protection against acne; backaches; cancer; diabetes; digestive disorders; headaches; heart and blood vessel disease; high blood cholesterol and triglycerides; infections; infertility; insomnia; kidney disease; menstrual irregularities, menstrual cramps, menstrual mood swings; obesity; and osteoporosis.
Section II
2. If you love your workout, do it more often. If you run out of time, shorten your workout time, but increase intensity. If you hate hard work, take it easy and go longer. Exercise regularly, train hard only once or twice a week, and listen to your body.
3. A warm-up helps the body to get needed fuels ready and warms up muscles and connective tissues, so that they will stretch without tearing. A cool-down helps relax tight muscles and allows blood to circulate freely, cooling the body.
Section III
4. It demands that the heart and lungs work extra hard to deliver oxygen to the muscles for as long as the exercise

---

CHAPTER REVIEW

LEARNING THE VOCABULARY

sedentary	duration	set
fitness	aerobic	ergogenic
cardiovascular endurance	anaerobic	steroids
flexibility	pulse	human growth hormone
muscle strength	target heart rate	acromegaly
muscle endurance	low-impact aerobic dance	shin splints
body composition	elasticity	stress fractures
exercise physiology	range of motion	tennis elbow
overload	resistance	dehydration
progressive overload principle	weight training	heat exhaustion
frequency	calisthenics	heat stroke
intensity		

Answer the following questions on a separate sheet of paper.

1. *Matching*—Match each of the following phrases with the appropriate vocabulary term from the list above:
   a. the number of weight training sessions per week
   b. energy-producing processes that do not use oxygen
   c. the characteristics that enable the body to perform physical activity
   d. serious stage of overheating
   e. ability to bend the joints without injury
   f. a specific number of times to repeat a weight-training exercise
2. a. What is the difference between exercise duration and exercise intensity?
   b. What is the relationship between target heart rate and cardiovascular endurance?

3. *Word Scramble*—Use the clues from the phrases below to help you unscramble the terms:
   a. **devaorol** _____ is an extra physical demand placed on the body.
   b. **ressts cusrafret** _____ _____ are bone injuries caused by repeated physical shocks at the point of ligament and bone attachment.
   c. **tacyilesit** The ability to be stretched or bent and then return to the original size and shape is known as _____.
   d. **nenits below** _____ _____ is a painful condition of the arm joint usually caused by strain.
4. a. _____, _____, _____, and _____ are all components of fitness.
   b. _____ is a dance exercise in which one foot always remains on the floor to prevent shock to the lower body.

RECALLING IMPORTANT FACTS AND IDEAS

1. List four physical benefits of fitness.
2. Offer some pointers for applying the overload principle.
3. Explain the principles of warm-up and cool-down.
4. Why must cardiovascular endurance training involve aerobic activities?
5. How does cardiovascular endurance affect the heart?
6. How long must aerobic activity last to improve cardiovascular endurance?
7. How do you determine your target heart rate?
8. Give three strategies for including daily exercise in your schedule.

lasts. Cardiovascular endurance training is aerobic.
5. The heart muscle gains size and strength and pumps more blood with each beat.
6. at least 20 minutes
7. Subtract your age from 220 and multiply that number by .75.
8. Answers will vary; could include: join a school fitness program; join a social exercise club; make friends with others who help one another stay fit; play sports in school or city leagues; sign up for dance, sports, or conditioning courses; improve your swim strokes; join a hiking, biking, or rowing club; join a YMCA program; walk to nearby stores; take stairs instead of elevators; stretch often during the day; lift small weights while watching TV or talking on the phone; garden or do yard work; play with children; and be imaginative.
Section IV
9. Answers will vary; could include injuries to knees, damage major nerves and vertebrae, aggravate lower back problems, injure the lower back, and damage the foot arch.
10. Bouncing can easily overstretch or tear a ligament until it can no longer support its joint. Nerves can also overstretch with bouncing.
Section V
11. use small weights to provide resistance, repeat exercises many times in a set, perform many sets in a session, and train every other day
12. they produce larger amounts of certain hormones known as steroids in their bodies
13. Answers will vary; could include mood swings, aggressive behavior, and changes in sexual drive.
14. urine test
Section VI
15. extreme fatigue, intense dizziness, and fading-out consciousness
16. It stops evaporation, causing the body to sweat heavily, which can lead to heat stroke.
17. exercise properly, build fitness slowly, and use proper equipment

---

9. What are some signs and symptoms of overstretching?
10. Why is gentle stretching recommended over bouncing?
11. How can you best increase muscle firmness and endurance when weight training?
12. Why do men generally develop larger muscles than women when they exercise?
13. What are some psychological side effects of steroid use?
14. How can steroid use be detected?
15. What are the signs of heat stroke?
16. Why is exercising in a plastic or rubber suit dangerous?
17. How can injury best be prevented when you exercise?

CRITICAL THINKING

1. List some of the reasons why being physically fit is especially important in today's world. Do you need to join a fitness center in order to keep in shape? Why or why not? What are some of the advantages and disadvantages of belonging to a fitness center? List some ways to become physically fit at a minimal expense. In your community, what sports activities can you participate in without paying any fees?

2. List your personal fitness goals. Make a list of all the physical activities you participate in within a one-week period. Identify which fitness component is promoted by each activity and which activities are anaerobic and aerobic. Will these activities help you to develop all your fitness goals? Now that you have read this chapter, what changes do you think you need to make in your program?

ACTIVITIES

1. Interview a podiatrist or a doctor whose specialty is sports medicine and write a one-page report on your findings.
2. Investigate a particular type of exercise equipment: for example, Stairmaster, Nordic Track, stationary bike, or the like. Discuss which fitness components the machine is designed to improve. Explain the different features of the equipment and state the approximate cost.
3. Write a letter to the President's Council on Physical Fitness to obtain literature about fitness. The address is: President's Council on Physical Fitness and Sports, 450 Fifth St. NW, Suite 7103, Washington, DC 20001.
4. Interview someone over 50 and ask about the person's involvement in physical activities. Write a short report about the person's participation in sports as a child, teen, and adult. Ask the person about activities he or she plans to take up in the future. Ask the person how physical activity has affected his or her life.
5. Investigate the different types of steroids that are commonly abused and write a one-page report.
6. Visit a local fitness center. Find out about the types of facilities, programs, classes, and instructors the center offers. What is the fee for joining? Overall, would you consider joining this center? Would it be a worthwhile investment? Why or why not?
7. Make a poster of newspaper and magazine advertisements for physical fitness devices. Label one half of the poster "Safe and Effective Devices" and the other half "Dangerous and Suspicious Devices." Place each advertisement under the appropriate title, forming a collage.

MAKING DECISIONS ABOUT HEALTH

1. Your classmate considers himself to be in "perfect health." He rarely gets sick, eats right, is not overweight, and has cholesterol and blood pressure measurements within the acceptable range. He insists there is no need for him to participate in any type of exercise program. Do you agree with your classmate? Why or why not?

267

CHAPTER 11 PLANNER

OVERVIEW

Chapter 11 is 22 pages long and divided into the four sections listed to the right. The major learning outcomes for the chapter are also listed to the right. This chapter is designed to acquaint the students with the knowledge and skills for proper care of the body, through good hygiene, self-exams, and proper posture.

MAKING LIFE CHOICES RESOURCES

A variety of activities, handouts, quizzes, and tests to accompany this chapter are available in the *Making Life Choices* supplementary material. You may pick and choose from those materials as appropriate for your amount of class time and the ability levels of your students. Some of the resources you might want to consider using are:

Overheads
• Brushing and Flossing the Teeth and Gums
• Testicular Cancer Self-Exam

Handouts
• Some Terms Used on Cosmetic Labels
• Personal Care Products Shopping Analysis

SUGGESTED RESOURCES

Student Readings
1. Alter, Judy. *Surviving Exercise: Judy Alter's Safe and Sane Exercise Program.* Boston: Houghton-Mifflin, 1983.

Teacher Readings
1. Cooper, Kenneth. *The Aerobics Program for Total Well-Being.* Leisure Press, 1985.

Software
1. *Health Maintenance.* Preventive health measures and questions to assess the students' lifestyle are included. MECC, 800-685-6322.

Videos
1. *Taking Control.*

American Cancer Society, 1986.

Pamphlets
1. "What Everyone Should Know About Personal Hygiene" is a scriptographic student pamphlet published by Channing L. Bete, Co., Inc., South Deerfield, MA 01373. For phone orders, call 800-628-7733 and request booklet number 12666.

Oversized Models
1. Health EDCO, Division of WRS Group, Inc., P.O. Box 21207, Waco, TX 76702-1207, 817-776-6461.

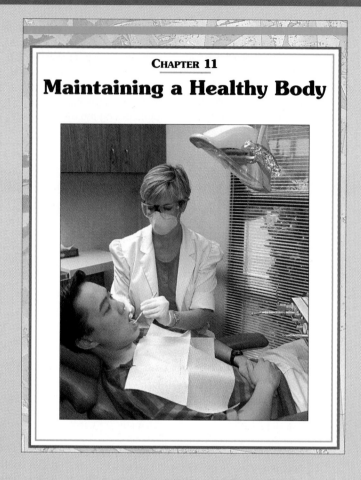

CHAPTER 11
Maintaining a Healthy Body

CHAPTER PROJECT

Assign the students to keep a personal diary of their daily health maintenance schedules. It should include: each practice, when it was done, and how it was done. They are to do this for each and every activity they do for their health every day. Have them analyze this diary after one week and design a personal maintenance plan for themselves to follow for the next week. As the final phase of the project, they are to write a brief synopsis of the experiences and behavior modifications they will implement in their lives.

OUTCOMES

After reading and studying this chapter, you will be able to:

✓ Identify self-care practices to maintain healthy teeth, hair, nails, ears, and skin.
✓ Identify sales gimmicks and quackery.
✓ Explain self-examination procedures for breasts, testicles, and skin to protect against cancer.
✓ Identify immunizations you have received and those you still need.
✓ Determine when medical help is necessary.

CONTENTS

I. Healthy Teeth and Clean Breath
II. Personal Cleanliness Concerns
III. Essential Self-Exams
IV. When to Visit a Health Care Provider

Straight Talk: *Posture and Image*

FACT OR FICTION

What do you think? Are the following statements true or false? If you think they are false, then say what is true.

1. A dental plaque is an award given to students of dentistry at graduation.
2. Flossing is more important to the fight against gum disease than is brushing tooth surfaces.
3. People who get acne simply need to keep their faces cleaner.
4. Acne often clears up during summer vacations.
5. Douching is not necessary.
6. For every one product people truly need, a hundred other unneeded ones are for sale.
7. The advertising tricks used to sell unneeded products are easy to see through.

(Answers on page 283)

■ **Reminder:** Knowing how to study can increase your knowledge, improve your grades, *and* cut down on your study time. See the *Studying Health* section at the front of your text for some suggestions to help you study this chapter.

NOT ENOUGH TIME?*

You could easily spend four or five days teaching this chapter if students read the entire chapter, do a fair number of the suggested activities in the teacher's edition, and complete a sampling of the handouts from the resource material accompanying this text. It is likely, however, that you will have only one or two days to devote to this chapter. Following are some suggestions to help you make sure that you cover the key topics if you have limited time.

TIME	SUGGESTIONS
1 Day	Assign students to read Sections I and II prior to class. In class do Activity 1.6 in Section I, and Activity 2.6 in Section II. Also include a variety of Evaluate activities if time permits.
2 Days	On Day 2, assign students to read Sections III and IV prior to class. In class do Activities 3.2 and 3.4 in Section III and Activity 4.3 in Section IV.

Please refer to the 18-week daily lesson plans in the supplementary material for additional suggestions.

Answers to "Fact or Fiction"

1. False. Dental plaque is a sticky substance that builds up on teeth, damaging them. **2.** True. **3.** False. Although cleanliness is important, there are no simple answers to preventing or curing acne. **4.** True. **5.** True. **6.** True. **7.** False. False advertising sounds convincing, but many fail to see through it.

Activity To Introduce Chapter

Divide the class into groups of four or five students each and give them ten minutes to list all the strategies that they use to maintain healthy bodies. Have them record these on chart paper. Allow each group to share and discuss their lists with the entire class. Then post their charts around the room.

In this section students will learn:
1. The benefits of proper dental care.
2. The consequences of improper dental care.
3. To identify dental diseases, procedures, and terminology.

Activity 1.1
   Questioning Technique. Ask the class to respond to the following questions before you have them read this section or do any of the activities:
1. Why would brushing back and forth be better than brushing up and down?
2. Why should the upper teeth be brushed first?
3. What difference does it make how you hold a toothbrush?

4. Why should we not "saw" with dental floss? What could be some of the consequences of sawing?
5. Why is it important to use a long section of floss?
Allow time for students to explain their answers; let others make additional comments. Discuss each question thoroughly. **(20 min.)**

Teacher Support Notes

① **Health Care Providers:** Make sure students know what a health care provider is. Ask them to name as many different kinds of health care providers as they can. (pediatricians, family doctors, surgeons, nurses, x-ray technicians, etc.)

② **Self-Care Technique:** Ask students if they routinely do anything for the purpose of maintaining good health and preventing disease. List all the behaviors they mention on the board. Many of the students will overlook some of the basic procedures such as bathing and brushing their teeth.

③ **Toothaches:** Ask if any students have had severe toothaches. Can they describe the pain to their fellow students? How did this pain compare to other types of pain the students have experienced?

④ **Gum Disease:** Do any of the students know adults who have had serious gum problems? What actions had to be taken to solve these problems? Are the students aware of the costs involved? Were any of the procedures painful? Try to elicit enough stories to help impress the students with the importance of preventive care now and throughout their lives.

270

Advice about health care usually has more to say about curing illnesses than it does about staying healthy. Such advice emphasizes other people—health care providers, who help cure illnesses. Usually, though, the most important aspect of health care is *self*-care. Doing a few simple things for your body can enable you to maintain it at least as lovingly as you would maintain a fine car.

This chapter starts by going over the body head-to-toe and instructs you in some simple self-care techniques. If you faithfully follow its advice, you can spend less time trying to cure illnesses and more time doing the things you like doing. There are times, though, when you must seek out help from a health care provider. The last section tells when you should do so.

SECTION I

Healthy Teeth and Clean Breath

A bright smile says something about its owner—that the person has high enough self-esteem to tend daily to tooth care. You probably already know how to brush your teeth, but you may not know that tooth decay can lead to major illness of the whole body. Even without decay, teeth that collect food particles and **dental plaque** create unpleasant mouth odor.

The bacteria that live in plaque break down food particles and create acid. The plaque holds this acid like a sponge. This acid dissolves away the tooth's outer layer, its **enamel.** The person may not feel a **cavity** forming in its early stages. However, as the decay advances into the tooth's middle layer, its **dentin,** it eats into nerves. The pain at this stage can be shocking. Should

the decay infect the tooth's deepest layer, its **pulp cavity,** it might kill the tooth. If a cavity is discovered in the early stages, a dentist can drill away the damaged part of the tooth surface and replace it with a substance that seals and saves the tooth. Some dentists recommend filling and sealing cavities of healthy teeth to prevent decay. Figure 11–1 shows how cavities form.

Brushing the teeth after each meal and flossing once each day can remove particles and plaque—if, that is, brushing and flossing are done correctly. Some people brush and floss wrong, every day, all their lives, and suffer tooth and gum disease despite their efforts. It is important to angle your brush to get at the gum line, as well as to brush the surfaces of your teeth. Dental plaque takes hold at the gum line and beneath it. The gums themselves become diseased if plaque gets out of hand.

Gum disease causes mouth odor. It also causes more tooth loss than tooth decay does. Fifty percent of all adults will develop gum disease. An early symptom is gums that bleed easily. Treatment of advanced gum disease often involves the dentist's

Figure 11–1 How Cavities Form in Teeth. Cavities begin when acid dissolves away the tooth's enamel (A), its outer layer. At this stage, a cavity is easily treated. As the decay advances through the dentin (B) to the pulp cavity (C), hope for saving the tooth diminishes.

Activity 1.2
Teacher Demonstration—Cleaning Teeth. Use an oversized model of teeth and a toothbrush (can be purchased from Health EDCO; see resources) and the steps illustrated on this page to demonstrate the steps to cleaning teeth

properly. **(20 min.; Reteach, Reinforce)**

Activity 1.3
Creative Writing. Assign the students a creative writing paper on their visits to the dentist. Ask them to create some metaphors (i.e., The dentist's drill sounds like. . . . The office reminded me of. . . . My clean teeth felt like. . . . The lights were as bright as. . . . The hygienist was like. . . . [which animal], etc.) **(30 min.,**

Interdisciplinary)

Activity 1.4
Oral Presentations. Prepare a set of cards with dental procedures, problems, diseases, and terms on them. Have the class divide into partners. One partner should draw a card. Each team should then research the term and prepare an oral presentation for the class. In addition

(continued on next page)

Brush tooth surfaces back and forth, not up and down, so as not to push food particles below the gum line.

Brush the gums, especially beneath the gumline (gently), to dislodge plaque there.

Use floss to pull plaque up from below the gum line between the teeth.

Use a toothpick or brush to dislodge plaque from below the gum line along the teeth.

Figure 11–2 Brushing and Flossing the Teeth and Gums ①

cutting away diseased gum tissue and scraping the teeth below the gum line. But even then, gum disease often returns, especially if the person fails to floss. Happily, gum disease is a problem everyone can avoid by brushing and flossing according to the directions in Figure 11–2.

To ensure that your flossing is effective, use the floss to pull plaque up from below the gum line, between the teeth. If you do this only once a day, you will be doing more to protect your teeth and gums than you can do by any amount of brushing of your tooth surfaces.

By the way, you need not buy expensive toothpastes and mouthwashes for a clean mouth. They do taste good and freshen the breath for a few minutes. Some even provide a little of the mineral fluoride, which helps protect teeth against decay. However, the fluoride in a mouthwash is not nearly so effective as the treatments given by dentists. It may be wise to avoid mouthwashes

of more than 25 percent alcohol. While they have not been proved to *cause* cancer, their use has been associated with oral or throat cancer in some scientific studies. It is wise to avoid teeth-whitening products such as the kits sold in drugstores, too. Products sold as teeth whiteners contain bleaching substances and acids that may damage the teeth, gums, and tongue.

MINI GLOSSARY

dental plaque (PLAK): a buildup of sticky material on the surfaces of the teeth; a forerunner of tooth damage.
enamel: a tooth's tough outer layer.
cavity: a hole in a tooth caused by decay. (Tooth decay is also called dental *caries.*)
dentin: a tooth's softer, middle layer.
pulp cavity: a tooth's deepest chamber that houses its blood vessels and nerves.

Teacher Support Notes

① **Overhead—Brushing and Flossing:** You may want to use the overhead "Brushing and Flossing the Teeth and Gums" at this point. Go through each of the drawings, asking students to describe what they see. Discuss the right way and the wrong way to do each procedure. Encourage students to ask questions. Try to get a commitment from the students to implement and continue using the brushing and flossing procedures if they are not already doing so.

Fast Facts

Research by the Academy of General Dentistry in England indicates that eating cheese at the end of the meal helps prevent tooth decay. If you drink or eat anything else with the cheese, however, you weaken the protective effect. The best cheeses to eat are Edam, Gouda, mild cheddar, and Danish blue.

Research should include a complete description/definition, procedures for prevention (for those terms that apply), and treatments for those that would apply. Have the partners present their research to the whole class. **(1 hr.; Extend, Enrich, Cooperative Learning)**

EVALUATE
SECTION 1

Activity 1.5
Class Challenge. Prepare a set of cards, each with a question, vocabulary word, or dental problem. Have students draw a card, prepare a quick answer or response, and then recite that to the class. The class should evaluate whether or not the statement given by the student is correct. The student giving the response may intentionally give an incorrect response to challenge the class. Use

Teacher Support Notes

① **Teeth and Gum Products:** Ask students to name the teeth and gum products that they buy and use regularly. How much do they or their parents spend monthly? Why do they buy the toothpaste they buy? Do different people in the household feel that they need different toothpaste? If so, why?

② **New Expectations:** Make sure students read this first sentence—"Years ago people expected to lose their teeth in old age." Ask them if they have older relatives who have false teeth. Then have them read the second sentence in this paragraph. Why do they think this change has occurred? (more knowledge and more preventive health care)

③ **Comparing Snacks:** Have students label a sheet of paper with the same two column headings in Figure 11–3. For each food that they eat regularly, have them put a check mark in that column. When they're finished, they can see whether they have more check marks in the "Foods Do Not Promote Tooth Decay" column or the "Foods Do Promote Tooth Decay" column. Discuss what changes they can make to help prevent tooth decay.

Many adults develop gum disease.

For everyday cleaning, a toothbrush, clean water, and baking soda or toothpaste is all you need. Tablets or solutions that temporarily color existing plaque may be useful to show you where to concentrate your cleaning efforts.

To support your daily efforts, you should visit a dentist. A professional cleaning about once every six months and a full examination about once a year can go a long way toward helping you keep your teeth for life. Of course, you should also follow your dentist's advice about fluoride rinses or supplements.

One more thing about tooth care: choose snacks with care. The delicious snacks listed in the left column of Figure 11–3 do not promote dental decay. The sticky sweet foods and other snacks listed in the right column cling to the teeth and are used by the bacteria in plaque to make acid.

② Years ago, people expected to lose their teeth in old age. Today, teens who care for their teeth have every reason to expect to be chewing with them at age 90.

Key Points ▸ *Brushing and flossing teeth and gums properly are needed to prevent tooth decay and gum disease. Some snacks help to support dental health, while others damage it.*

FIGURE 11-3 ③

How to Choose Snacks for Dental Health

Some foods are more likely to cause tooth decay than are others. Sugar is one factor, but it's not just the sugar in foods that makes the difference. Other factors, such as fat, fiber, and stickiness matter as well.

These Foods Do Not Promote Tooth Decay

- Milk, cheese, plain yogurt
- Popcorn, toast, hard rolls, pretzels, corn chips, pizza
- Fresh fruits, fruits canned in water, salad greens, cauliflower, cucumbers, radishes, carrots, celery
- Lean meats, fish, poultry, eggs, beans
- Water, sugarless gum, sugar-free drinks

These Foods Promote Tooth Decay; Brush Your Teeth after Finishing Them

- Chocolate milk, ice cream, milk shakes, sweetened yogurt
- Cookies, sweet rolls, pies, cakes, cereals, potato chips, crackers
- Dried fruits, fruits canned in syrup or juice, jams, jellies, fruit juices
- Peanut butter with added sugar, most luncheon meats (with added sugar), glazed meats, hot dogs
- Candies, sugar-sweetened gum, fudge

all the terms covered previously in Activity 1.4. You may want to give extra credit for knowledge of terms in addition to the glossary terms. **(30 min.; Reteach, Reinforce)**

CLOSE
SECTION I

Activity 1.6
Dental Review. Students should be able to do at least one of the following:
1. Have a class discussion on the steps to proper dental care. Have students explain why each step is important.
2. Name and describe in writing two dental problems that can occur from improper care. Tell what procedures or treatments are followed to remedy the problems. **(Reteach, Reinforce)**

FOCUS
SECTION II

In this section students will learn:
1. The structure of hair and proper care procedures.
2. The structure of skin and proper care.
3. Routine cleanliness techniques for all-around body maintenance.

(continued on next page)

SECTION I   REVIEW

Answer the following questions on a sheet of paper.

Learning the Vocabulary
The vocabulary terms in this section are *dental plaque, enamel, cavity, dentin,* and *pulp cavity.*
Fill in the blanks with the correct answer.
1. The _____ is the deepest chamber of a tooth that has blood vessels and nerves in it.
2. The tough outer layer of a tooth is called the _____.
3. Another name for dental caries is a _____.

Learning the Facts
4. How do cavities form?
5. How can gum disease be avoided?
6. How often should you schedule dental visits?

Making Life Choices
7. How often do you visit the dentist? Based on your answer, do you anticipate that in the future you will have problems with your teeth and gums? Why do you think some people avoid going to the dentist? What could you tell such people to convince them to go? How might a person's dental health affect the person's physical, mental, and social health?

SECTION II

Personal Cleanliness Concerns

Along with tooth care, the care of your hair, nails, and skin is important for both appearance and health. Some things such as daily bathing are too obvious to mention. Others, however, may not be learned during childhood and are important.

Care of Hair and Nails

For many, hair makes a personal statement—from dramatic shaved heads to long, glossy curls. People often choose hairstyles that reflect their personalities and lifestyles. During the identity-seeking teenage years, hairstyles can become almost an obsession. This is normal, but sellers of hair-care products may take advantage of the interest placed on hair. Learning something about hair and hair products can save you many wasted dollars. ①

Each hair strand is a fiber made of long, parallel strands of protein. Hair is a product made in the skin's **follicles,** vessel-like structures that contain the oil glands, the muscles that control hair movement (and also goose bumps), and the roots of hairs (see Figure 11–4 on the next page). In cross-section, a strand of hair may be round (straight hair), oval (curly), or flat (wavy). Hair is a product of living tissue but is not alive itself. Therefore, it has no real needs of its own. It contains cells, but they are dead cells, woven into strands of protein.

Products that claim to "nourish" the hair are using the term *nourish* loosely. At best, most product ingredients sit atop the hair strands, and their effects are usually temporary. The exceptions are permanent coloring, hair straighteners, and permanent waves. These enter hair strands to change the chemical nature of the treated parts of hair.

To keep normal hair healthy, simple cleansing is all that is needed. Soap would do the job, but it tends to make hair sticky. Shampoos are mild detergents that leave the hair cleaner. Shampoos vary in their effects because of their chemistry. Some are more acid, and this smoothes hair down. Some are more alkaline, and tend to fluff

---

MINI GLOSSARY

follicles: vessel-like structures in the skin that contain the oil glands, the muscles that control hair movement (and also goose bumps), and the roots of hairs.

Section I Review

Answers
1. pulp cavity
2. enamel
3. cavity
4. The bacteria that live in plaque break down food particles and create acid that dissolves away the tooth's outer layer (enamel).
5. by brushing and flossing properly
6. every six months for a cleaning and once a year for a full examination
7. Answers will vary.

Teacher Support Notes

① **Cost of Hair Care:** Ask each student to estimate how much he or she spends on hair-care products and services monthly. Have them list the products they buy and the services they pay for. Compile the numbers and compute a class average. Discuss the results.

4. To identify cosmetic quackery and unneeded or fake health products.

Activity 2.1

Group Assignment. Divide the class into four groups. Assign each group one of the following topics: hair, skin, spe-

cial care areas, quackery. Distribute instruction sheets for each topic, and tell students their assignment is to create a way to present their topics to the class. Choices may be an oral report, skit, center display, charts, posters, panel discussion, etc. Give a set time to prepare and present. Instruction sheets might require that the group deal with the following aspects of its topic: natural body maintenance, personal care procedures, prob-

lems, diseases, professional help resources, drugs used, consequences of improper care, hereditary factors, and statistics applicable. Encourage the use of visual aids in presentations. **(1 hr. for preparation, 1 hr. for presentations; Extend, Enrich, Cooperative Learning)**

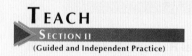

TEACH
SECTION II
(Guided and Independent Practice)

Teacher Support Notes

① **Artificial Nails:** You may want to tell students that according to Dr. Lawrence Norton, a dermatology professor at Boston University, artificial nails can easily get water under them. This creates a prime growing condition for bacteria. Most infections can be successfully treated with antibiotics and steroids, but sometimes the damage is permanent. Medical problems do develop as a result of the individual's failure to properly maintain the acrylic nails. Other experts say that the infections begin with negligent, poorly trained or completely untrained nail technicians. Students should be careful when searching for and identifying a good manicurist. Factors to take into consideration are whether or not the shop is licensed, do the premises look clean, and whether or not the manicurist seems to have good personal hygiene.

☎ Where to Call

The American Medical Hair Replacement Directory answers questions on treatment options for men with thinning hair. 1-800-456-8090

274 UNIT 3 Your Physical Health

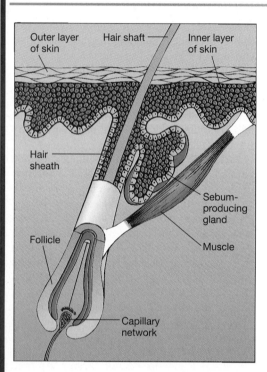

Figure 11–4 Skin and Hair Structures

hair up. Choose an inexpensive one that works for you.

Shampoos for oily hair have more or stronger detergents. Those with protein additives that supposedly "repair damage" can do no such thing. Protein can be added to hair only during its creation within the hair follicles. The protein in shampoos just rinses down the drain, along with "herbal ingredients," "botanicals," and the extra money the user spent to buy them. Conditioning products may be useful, however, because they coat the hairs, making them slide freely against one another rather than tangling. If hair becomes split or roughened from hot hair dryers, rough brushes, curling irons, or harsh chemicals (such as permanent waves, colorings, or the chlorine in swimming pools), the only cure is to trim off the damaged parts.

Some people worry about dandruff—do they need to use dandruff-fighting shampoos? The scalp is like other skin in that it sheds bits of its thin outer layer each day. When these bits of skin are washed away daily or almost daily, they are unnoticeable. When they are allowed to build up and mix with the scalp's oils, they cling together into flakes (dandruff) and become an embarrassing social problem. By the way, no harm comes from washing your hair each day, and this alone often prevents or clears up a dandruff buildup. If regular washings with ordinary shampoo fail to control flaking, ask a pharmacist for an effective treatment.

As for nails, they are much like hair in composition. Like hair, nails grow from a root structure. Under the **cuticles** (see Figure 11–5), nail-forming cells bind together the protein **keratin** into sheets that form the nails. Once formed, nails can no longer accept protein. People who use polishes, hoping to strengthen their nails, may actually weaken them, because the solvents in polish and removers can disrupt normal nail protein structures.

Biting the free part of the nails isn't really harmful. Biting or clipping below the line of attachment may start an infection that is difficult to treat and may linger for years. To stay healthy, nails need only be kept clean and trimmed.

While products do little to enhance hair and nails, proper diet helps a great deal. No nutrient supplement, not even gelatin, improves hair or nails so long as the person receives an adequate diet. But too few nutrients from food can exert dramatic effects on nails. The body conserves nutrients when they run low by meeting essential functions, such as making immune system cells, before it spends resources making "optional" products such as hair or fingernails. Young people who go on "crash" weight-loss diets often begin losing their hair after

Activity 2.2

Classroom Demonstration. Invite a cosmetologist to your classroom or visit a cosmetology classroom or salon. Have the cosmetologist wash and fix a volunteer's hair, explaining proper hair care procedures as the class observes. Have the cosmetologist perform a facial. Ask him/her to speak on proper skin care as the class observes. Hold a question-and-answer session following the demonstra-tion. Ask the class to share what they have observed and learned from the demonstration. Ask the class to share some ideas for better hair and skin care, which they can include in their daily hygiene routines. **(Extend, Enrich)**

Activity 2.3

Designing Care Pamphlets. Distribute copies of "What Everyone Should Know About Personal Hygiene." (See resources for information to obtain these.) Have the students spend about ten minutes reading the pamphlets. Tell them to remember or make notes on the contents. Collect the pamphlets. Number the class off one–six until everyone has his or her own number. On the board or overhead list the assignments for each number group: **1.** skin; **2.** special care areas—feet, hands, nails and ears; **3.** hair;

(continued on next page)

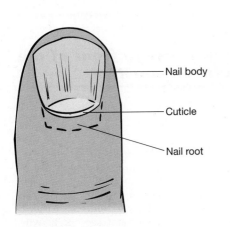

Figure 11–5 How Fingernails Grow. Underneath the cuticle, in the nail root, nail-forming cells collect the protein keratin. The cells then flatten and die to form the nail body.

Labels: Nail body, Cuticle, Nail root

a few weeks or months. Their fingernails may also become cracked or odd-shaped.

Hair loss and changes in fingernails are two early signs of malnutrition. Dietitians in a hospital are trained to watch for these signs. The most effective way to ensure that hair and nails look their best is to nourish the whole body. If the cells that make hair and nails are in top condition, and are given plenty of materials with which to build, the healthiest possible hair and nails are assured.

Key Points *Hair and nails grow from root structures and are made mostly of protein. Once formed, they do not have the same needs as living tissues do. Cleanliness of hair and nails is important, but cosmetic products are unnecessary. During their formation, both hair and nails are sensitive to malnutrition.*

Help for Acne

No one knows why some people get **acne** and others do not. However, it is known to run in families. If both your parents had acne, the odds are high of your having it, too. The hormones of adolescence also play a role by making the glands in the skin more active.

① Acne is related to the skin's natural oil, **sebum.** Sebum is made all the time in deep glands and is supposed to flow out of the glands to the skin's surface through the tiny ducts around the hairs. In acne, the oil is not brought to the surface of the skin.

Each of the ducts is lined with a skinlike tissue that normally sheds by scaling and flaking. The oil carries these scales and flakes to the surface of the skin. At times, the scales stick together and form a plug, halting the flow of oil and allowing bacteria to migrate down into the duct. As the plug grows bigger, it weakens the duct, allowing oil and bacteria to leak into the surrounding skin. The oil and bacteria irritate the skin and cause redness, swelling, and **pus** formation—the beginning of a **whitehead,** or pimple. A **cyst** may be formed—a sort of enlarged, deep pimple. Or the skin may open above the plug, revealing an accumulation of dark skin pigments just below the surface—a **blackhead.**

Mini Glossary

cuticles: the borders of hardened skin at the bases of the fingernails.

keratin: the normal protein of hair and nails.

acne: a continuing condition of inflamed skin ducts and glands, with a buildup of oils under the skin, forming pimples.

sebum (SEE-bum): the skin's natural oil—actually a mixture of oils and waxes—that helps keep the skin and hair moist.

pus: a mixture of fluids and white blood cells that collects around infected areas.

whitehead: a pimple filled with pus, caused by the plugging of oil-gland ducts with shed material from the duct lining.

cyst (SIST): an enlarged, deep pimple.

blackhead: an open pimple with dark skin pigments (not dirt) in its opening.

Teacher Support Notes

① **Sebum:** For enrichment, you may want to tell students that the sebum develops in the sebaceous glands. The purpose of the sebum is to oil the skin and the hair to prevent them from drying. Sebum also contains substances that are toxic to certain bacteria. Students should see that the sebum is not the body's way of playing a cruel trick on them; it really does serve several valuable functions. Unfortunately, the sebaceous glands are stimulated by the presence of sex hormones, which can cause excess sebum to accumulate and form pimples. You may want to ask students if there are any areas of the body that do not form pimples. (hairless regions of the body such as the palms of the hands and the soles of the feet) Why do they think this is? (These areas do not have sebaceous glands.)

4. teeth; **5.** diet; **6.** fitness. Give each group some plain white paper. Instruct them to design their own pamphlets about their assigned areas of hygiene. They should use content, color, creative design for attractiveness and readability, cartoons, pictures, or charts to make the pamphlet one that will teach others proper care of the assigned hygiene area and be interesting and easy to read and use. Display the finished products on a classroom bulletin board. You may want to have a contest with them. **(30 min.; Reteach, Reinforce, Cooperative Learning)**

Activity 2.4
Ingredient Analysis. Have all students bring an empty container or package of a personal care product to analyze and research the ingredients. They are to determine whether or not their products are effective. Have students prepare a report, or have them chart their findings. They should then recommend or discourage the use of the product, and give their rationale to the class. **(research—at home, presentations—1 hr.)** Note: If you plan to complete Activity 2.5, you will

Teacher Support Notes

① **Teen Views Follow-Up Questions:** Following are some questions you may want to use to encourage discussion of the ideas expressed by the students in the Teen Views feature:

a. Do students agree with Dirk Johnson, that the reason people spend too much time in front of the mirror is because they are overly self-conscious?

b. Does anyone disagree with Dirk and think it's more important to look nice than be nice?

c. Does appearance affect whether or not people like you? Can spending time in front of the mirror make a person more popular?

d. Can you feel good about yourself without spending a lot of time making yourself look good?

e. Is everyone self-conscious to some degree? Is there any way of telling if a person is too self-conscious? How?

f. In general, is our society too concerned with appearances? If so, how could this be changed?

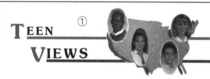

TEEN **V**IEWS ①

How much time in front of the mirror is too much?

Teenagers should spend enough time in front of the mirror to look clean and well put together. They need enough time to comb their hair, wash their face, brush their teeth, and do any other necessities. The problems start when a person gets self-conscious. If every hair needs to be in place, every pimple neatly covered by goop, and every article of clothing in the coolest position possible, these kids are spending too much time in front of the mirror. As soon as you walk to your next class everything isn't going to be in perfect order. Everyone should try to look nice, but the most important thing is to be nice. **Dirk Johnson, 15, Great Falls High School, MT**

Looks aren't everything. You shouldn't be stuck on yourself. You should keep yourself clean by taking showers and combing your hair. I am not a person who spends a lot of time in front of the mirror and people like me. **Sean Morrissey, 16, East High School, MN**

I think that people who have to carry a mirror with them everywhere they go are going to extremes. Everyone wants to look good, but looks aren't everything. What counts is if you feel good about yourself as a person and not so much that your lipstick is still on. **Wendy Joy Miller, 17, Connellsville Senior High School, PA**

I do not think that there is a specific time period that could be considered too long. I think it is healthy to look in the mirror and sometimes admire yourself. We all sometimes feel a little self-conscious about the way we look or act. Usually if we don't like what we see, we can change it until we do, whether it be our hair, make-up, clothes, or even attitude. I think that it is a wonderful feeling to be able to look in the mirror and say to yourself, "Yeah, I like what I see." **Kelli Wilson, 15, Orange Park High School, FL**

For teenagers of this generation, standing in front of a mirror has become a learned behavior. Though not necessarily a negative one, the behavior has become a problem for this society. Today, the emphasis and stress is to look good. Society should concentrate on other important things instead of what kind of shoes someone is wearing. **Susan Crawford, 17, Orange Park High School, FL**

Many people think skin bacteria cause acne, but they do not. Bacteria make it worse, once the process has begun. Also, the color of a blackhead is caused by pigments, not by dirt, so cleanliness alone isn't the answer. Squeezing or picking at pimples to try to remove their contents does not help. In fact, it can cause more scars than the acne itself does.

How, then, can you treat acne? Most young people with acne are willing to go to considerable trouble and expense to find a want to assign personal care product areas for Activity 2.4. This will ensure that the display in Activity 2.5 will have products from each care area: hair, skin, eye, ear, and cosmetic.

Activity 2.5
Product Analysis Display. Have students create a display based on the product analysis they did in Activity 2.4. The display should be titled "Products to Buy—Products Not to Buy." Allow students to "browse" the displays. Have them choose a product for each body area, and defend their choices. **(1 hr., Critical Thinking)**

Activity 2.6
Class Collage. Have students compile a class collage of advertisements that give inaccurate or deceiving information about a product. Have them highlight the inaccurate parts of the advertisements. **(30 min., Critical Thinking)**

Activity 2.7
Shopping Analysis. Distribute the "Personal Care Products Shopping Analysis" handout from your supplementary material. Instruct the students to go "shopping" for personal care products. They must choose one for skin, hair,

(continued on next page)

remedy. Many remedies have been suggested: washing constantly, sunbathing, taking antibiotics, spreading vitamin A acid (Retin-A) on the skin, taking prescription acne medicines (such as Accutane), avoiding certain foods and beverages, avoiding **comedogenic** cosmetics, or obtaining relief from stress. Each of these has helped some people. However, everyone responds differently to them. Nothing works for everyone.

Some products are worth a try. Among the over-the-counter treatments for mild acne are those that contain one of the following effective ingredients:

- Benzoyl peroxide.
- Salicylic acid.
- Resorcinol.
- Sulfur.

These ingredients have been proved safe and effective. However, they may have side effects such as drying or irritating the skin. Careful washing twice daily with mild soap helps remove skin-surface bacteria and oil and helps to keep the oil ducts open.

People who fail to find relief from their acne will try almost anything. Before trying unproved "therapies," read this chapter's Consumer Awareness (on the next page) for hints about tricks used by quacks. The price of valid medical help is small when compared with the dangers that may lurk in a fraud's potions.

If nonprescription methods fail to clear up acne, see a **dermatologist** for a prescription medication. Antibiotics may be either applied on the skin's surface or taken internally. Retin-A (the vitamin A acid mentioned earlier) works in skin creams and lotions because the acid loosens the plugs that form in the ducts, allowing the oil to flow again so that the ducts will not burst. Skin clearing may begin within a month or so of using the products. Retin-A makes the skin more easily damaged by sunlight and may cause drying or peeling. These side effects may make the acne look worse at first.

② Accutane is an internal medicine reserved for severe acne that scars the skin. Its effectiveness for reversing severe acne is so high that for some people the drug is hailed as a miracle.

① The miracle can involve risks, though. Side effects range from irritation and drying of the nose, mouth, and skin to miscarriage in pregnant women. Birth defects in infants of women who take Accutane during pregnancy are also possible.

Better than to treat acne is to prevent it, but this is not always possible. Many people think that certain foods and drinks worsen their acne. ③ Chocolate, cola beverages, fatty or greasy foods, nuts, sugar, and foods or salt containing iodine have all been blamed for worsening acne. It's not proved that these foods do worsen acne. If they do seem to affect your skin, however, there's no harm in avoiding them.

④ Some cosmetics do cause acne flare-ups in susceptible people, so a change of products may be worth a try. Stress clearly worsens acne by way of the hormones that are secreted in response to it. Vacations from school or other pressures slow secretion of stress hormones and so help to bring relief. The sun, the beach, and swimming also seem to help. The sun's rays kill bacteria, and swimming can help cleanse the skin. Avoid excessive sun exposure, though; it can cause skin cancer.

One remedy always works: time. Acne is most common among teenagers and young adults. While waiting for acne to clear up,

M̲INI G̲LOSSARY

comedogenic (coh-MEE-doh-JEN-ick): causing acne.
dermatologist: a physician (M.D.) who specializes in treating conditions of the skin.

Teacher Support Notes

① **Acne Remedies:** How many students have tried the different remedies mentioned here? What additional remedies have students tried? Which products seem to be most effective?

② **Accutane:** You may want to tell students that women who require Accutane should take a test to rule out the possibility of pregnancy before starting use of the drug. Women who use Accutane and are sexually active should use an effective contraceptive method to avoid pregnancy-related risks.

③ **The Cause of Acne:** Ask students if they have been told that any foods in addition to those listed here can cause acne.

④ **Stress and Acne:** Having read this sentence, students concerned about an acne problem may be more highly motivated to read the information about stress. You may want to refer students back to Chapter 4 at this point.

277

eyes, ears, and one cosmetic/make-up type item. Have them complete the worksheet on their choices. Labels will have to be read and information recorded at the store, with research of the ingredients done thereafter. Products do not have to be purchased. Encourage the students to

choose items they do not usually use or have at home, in order to increase consumer awareness. **(Advanced)**

EVALUATE
SECTION II

Activity 2.8
Diagram and Discussion. Provide a cross-section diagram, or have the students draw their own, of a hair follicle and

skin structure. Have them label the parts: blood vessels, oil gland, hair follicle, sweat gland, and skin layers. Have a class discussion about the effect these glands and parts play in the cleanliness of the body. Ask students to consider which ingredients in the personal care products they have learned about in this section affect the parts. **(30 min.)**

Activity 2.9

Teacher Support Notes

① **Quack Medical Devices:** Tell students that the FDA has grouped quack medical devices into nine categories:
a. Figure enhancers (Examples: fanny shapers, waist cinchers, muscle developers)
b. Arthritis and pain-relieving gadgets
c. Sleep aids
d. Hair and scalp devices (Examples: most baldness cures)
e. Youth prolongers (Examples: wrinkle removers, royal jelly)
f. Sex aids
g. Air and water purifiers
h. Disease diagnostics
i. Cure-alls (Examples: anemia cures)
② **Unneeded Medical Products:** Give students the following list of unneeded or fake products upon which people spend millions of dollars:
a. Mouthwashes and teeth-whitening products
b. Sleeping pills and potions
c. Cancer preventives and "cures"
d. Health foods and nutrient supplements
e. Fad diets and diet aids
f. Vaginal deodorant sprays and douches
g. Herbal cures
③ **Critical Thinking Answers:**
1–3. Answers will vary.

CONSUMER
AWARENESS — **Cosmetic Quackery and Health Products**

Many advertisements twist the truth to dream up problems for us, or to make small problems seem large. Then they twist the truth again to make us think that they have just the solutions we need for these problems. Suppose you have a few freckles (or a thousand). A television commercial might start there, and take these steps:

• You have freckles. (So far, that's true.)
• Freckles make you look younger than you are. (This is, at most, only partly true, and it's not a problem.)
• That's a problem. (The commercial wants you to think freckles are a problem, so that it can go on to say . . .)
• You need Product X to hide those freckles.

People buy many Product Xs they don't need because they believe the twisted advertisements.

A common case of created problems is premenstrual syndrome (PMS), which has been said to "disable" women before their menstrual periods each month. PMS is not a made-up problem. It does seriously affect some women (see pages 280–281). Advertisers make it out to be more common than it is, though, and claim that it needs treatment when it does not. Women are led to think that anyone who menstruates needs to buy PMS remedies. Only an informed critical thinker can recognize the difference between a real need and a created one.

Other gimmicks to get your attention include personal reports, opinions, exaggerations, vague statements that hide the

facts, and glowing reports from people who have tried products. Other claims familiar to television watchers are:

• Our product is better than theirs (brand loyalty appeal).
• Everyone uses our product (peer pressure appeal).
• Rich and famous people use our product (snob appeal).
• You'll receive bonuses and free items if you buy our product (bribery).
• Our product is new and improved (newness appeal).
• Ordinary people use our product (just-plain-folks appeal).
• Funny, happy people use our product (smile appeal).
• Beautiful people use our product (beauty appeal).
• Scientific people approve our product (appeal to reason).

Quacks also offer special machines (special technology), secret formulas (mysterious chemistry), and medical "breakthroughs" (miracles and magic for the child in everyone). These selling techniques work. Otherwise, they would not be used.

CRITICAL THINKING

1. *Do you think such advertisements have ever worked with you or someone you know?*
2. *Have you ever bought useless products because of an advertisement?*
3. *With so many grasping fingers reaching for your wallet, how can you protect yourself?*

(continued on next page)

keep the symptoms under control with treatments that work for you.

Key Points *Acne results from a buildup of sebum and flakes of skin that get trapped in the skin's ducts. Cleanliness and relief from stress may help control it. Nothing but time is a permanent cure.*

Eyes and Ears

The eyes and ears care for themselves most of the time. The eyebrows, eyelids, and eyelashes help keep debris out of the eyes. If debris enters the eyes despite the lashes, lids, and brows, the flow of tears from special tear glands usually washes the debris away. Commercial eyedrops are not necessary for healthy eyes. When tears fail to remove debris, hold the eye open under a gentle stream of clean, plain water for a second or two to wash debris out safely. Tap water that contains chlorine may cause a slight burning feeling in the eyes, so people whose water source is chlorinated may prefer to use one of the commercial eyewash solutions available for purchase over the counter. These solutions are sterile and contain no chlorine. A pharmacist can recommend one.

As for the ears, occasionally a waxy secretion begins to build up in the outer chambers. Normal showering usually removes most of this buildup. A wipe with a facial tissue may help remove any excess left behind. Do not place cotton swabs or other objects inside the ear canal. The delicate inner structures of the ear, which are involved in hearing and balance, are easily damaged (see Figure 11–6). Besides, the swab can easily pack wax down inside the ear, promoting infection.

Should any problems develop with eyes or ears, see a physician immediately. Vision and hearing can be permanently damaged by infections or injuries.

Key Points *The tears wash the eyes; use soft tissues to wipe wax from external ear parts.*

Ear canal

Outer ear   Middle ear   Inner ear

Figure 11–6 Cleaning the Ears. Use a soft tissue or washcloth to clean the outer part of the outer ear. Never push cotton swabs or other objects into the ear canal.

Avoiding Body Odor

Everyone knows to bathe daily to remove the collected sweat and grime of the day. Some may wonder, though, whether they need products to help them stay clean: underarm antiperspirants or deodorants, vaginal sprays, douches, scented powders, or cologne. The truth is that none of these products are needed for *health*. Most simply mask odors for a while.

When you purchase items at a drugstore, do you assume they have been tested for safety? In the case of medicines, you would be right in thinking you are protected. The FDA makes sure that medicines sold are safe to use. The story is different for cosmetics, though. For them, safety testing is recommended but optional. Also, only a few cosmetic ingredients, such as colorants, are restricted. The use of others needs no approval. Cosmetic labels must list their ingredients, though, and they offer other information as well.

Teacher Support Notes

① **Handout—Cosmetic Label Terms:** In your supplementary material you will find a handout for students entitled "Some Terms Used on Cosmetic Labels." This handout lists some commonly used terms and provides definitions and explanations for students to help them become more informed about what they are buying. Some of the terms included are *allergy-tested*, *natural cosmetics*, *hypoallergenic* and *astringents*.

10. What is the internal medicine for acne, which is considered by some to be a miracle? (Accutane)

CLOSE
SECTION II

Activity 2.10

Oral Presentations. Utilize the students' displays, reports, collages, and analyses to review. If you have kept cooperative groups the same throughout the series of assignments, assign each group a specific personal care area (hair, skin, etc.) to report on. The group will compile its resources on that area. Each group will give an oral presentation of its findings. **(preparation, 1 hr., presentations, 1**

hr.; Reteach, Reinforce)

FOCUS
SECTION III

In this section the student will learn:
1. The importance of self-exams.
2. Step-by-step procedures for self-exams.
3. Consequences of untreated breast or testicular cancer.

" Thoughts on Health "

Henry IV's feet and armpits enjoyed an international reputation.
– Aldous Huxley

Teacher Support Notes

① **Menstruation:** Students will learn more about menstruation in Chapter 21. You may want to refer them to that discussion at this point.
② **PMS Products:** You may want to refer students back to the "Consumer Awareness" feature on page 278, which discussed advertiser attempts to sell products for PMS.

✎ Fast Facts

A survey conducted by the USC School of Medicine and the American Orthopaedic Foot and Ankle Society determined that 88% of women wore shoes smaller than their feet. Eighty percent said their feet hurt.

280   UNIT 3 Your Physical Health

Plain soap and water are all you need to keep your skin clean.

Body odor is caused by the action of normal skin bacteria on sweat and skin debris. Soap makes bacteria slippery enough to be washed away. While no threat to health, unpleasant odors may make others withdraw and damage a person's self-esteem. People who perspire heavily may want to use antiperspirants to reduce the sweat that feeds the bacteria that cause body odor. Also, a deodorant may help a little to mask any odor that may form during the day. Antiperspirants and deodorants are not substitutes for cleanliness, though. Even the most aromatic ones cannot mask an unclean odor. Both male and female external reproductive organs require a careful daily washing to keep them free of infections and odors. An unpleasant discharge or bad odor may indicate an infection and should be checked out by a physician.

Key Points ▶ *Cleanliness is the key to freedom from body odors. Some people may want to use antiperspirants, but most other products are unneeded.*

Menstrual Concerns

A healthy vagina cleans itself. Even during **menstruation**, gentle external cleaning is all that is needed. "Personal deodorant" sprays are not needed and **douches** can be downright dangerous. Douching interrupts the normal cleaning cycle and may wash bacteria up into the normally bacteria-free areas of the reproductive tract. (Douching has been linked with reproductive tract cancer, but it is uncertain whether douching can *cause* cancer.) Girls should know that the vagina can easily become infected with the normal bacteria from the digestive tract. Soiled toilet paper should be kept away from the vaginal area.

Many women use tampons to absorb menstrual flow internally. They should be aware that while using tampons is convenient, the user stands a risk of developing **toxic shock syndrome (TSS)**. TSS develops when bacteria begin to break down the menstrual blood trapped inside the vagina. These bacteria release dangerous poisons that are absorbed into the blood, causing high fever and a sunburn-like rash. Tampons must be changed at least every four hours to prevent TSS.

Pads or sanitary napkins are used to collect menstrual flow externally. Pads, too, should be changed at four-hour intervals to prevent bacterial growth. Bacteria cause odor when they break down menstrual blood externally.

Girls and women who menstruate may experience normal contractions of the muscular uterus—**menstrual cramps**. The over-the-counter drug *ibuprofen* is especially effective in relieving them. Should cramping become severe, a health care provider should check for problems.

Some symptoms, such as nervousness, cramping, moodiness, and fatigue, may announce the menstrual period several days in advance of bleeding. Called **premenstrual syndrome (PMS)**, such symptoms

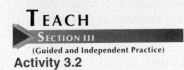
can be a problem for some women. PMS often responds to simple remedies such as getting enough rest, exercise, relaxation, and nourishing food. No vitamin pills of any sort are effective against PMS, but reducing intakes of colas, iced tea, and other caffeine sources may help.

Many other products are on store shelves, sold for many reasons. Don't be misled by sellers trying to force unneeded products on you.

> **Key Points** *For health, bodies need only routine cleansing. Feminine sprays, powders, and perfumes may be enjoyable, but are not essential.*

SECTION II   REVIEW

Answer the questions on a sheet of paper.

Learning the Vocabulary

The vocabulary terms in this section are *follicles, cuticles, keratin, acne, sebum, pus, whitehead, cyst, blackhead, comedogenic, dermatologist, menstruation, douches, toxic shock syndrome (TSS), menstrual cramps,* and *premenstrual syndrome (PMS).*

1. A _____ is a physician who specializes in treating conditions of the skin.
2. An enlarged deep pimple is a _____.
3. _____ is the protein of hair and nails.
4. How are acne and sebum related?
5. Physical discomfort, moodiness, and nervousness can be signs of _____.

Learning the Facts

6. Why are protein additives in shampoos ineffective in repairing damaged hair?
7. How does malnutrition affect hair?
8. Name two over-the-counter treatment ingredients that are effective for acne.
9. List three gimmicks that are commonly used to sell health products.
10. Why is it important to change tampons at least every four hours?

Making Life Choices

11. List all the skin care products you have purchased within the last six months including lotions, creams, soaps, make-up,

and acne medications. Which products did you find made a difference and which ones would you term useless?

SECTION III

Essential Self-Exams

Once a month a young woman should check her breasts and a young man should check his testicles for cancer. If you start testing now, while you are young, it will be a habit that will serve you well throughout life. The breast test is easy, especially when it is done in the shower, while the skin is slippery (see Figure 11–7). Lumps are most often not cancerous. However, they should be checked by a health care provider nonetheless. You'll soon easily tell the "normal lumpiness" that occurs before the menstrual period from an unusual lump. Many

MINI GLOSSARY

menstruation: the monthly shedding of the uterine lining in nonpregnant females.

douches (DOOSH-es): preparations sold to cleanse the vagina. Actually, vaginas clean themselves constantly with no help, and douches can wash dangerous bacteria into the reproductive tract.

toxic shock syndrome (TSS): a type of poisoning that can occur when bacteria break down menstrual blood; often associated with use of super-absorbent tampons.

menstrual cramps: contractions of the uterus, during and a few days before menstruation, that may cause pain.

premenstrual syndrome (PMS): symptoms such as physical discomfort, moodiness, and nervousness that occur in some women each month before menstruation.

woman feels much like a marble. In the male it feels like a small dried bean.

Breast procedure:
1. Raise each arm, in turn, above head, turn from side to side, look for any change from normal appearance.
2. Gently squeeze the nipple, checking for any discharge.
3. Examine the skin surface; orange peel texture could indicate the presence of a lump.
4. Lie on your back with a pillow under head and shoulders, arm at side. Using the flat of your hand, work around the outer parts of the breast in a clockwise direction.
5. Raise your arm above your head and examine the inner parts. Stretching the skin and tissue makes it easier to detect a lump. Feel up to the collarbone and under the arm.

Testes procedure: Gently feel all the skin surface on the testes. This skin moves freely, making palpation easy. **(30 min.; Extend, Enrich)**

Activity 3.3
Field Trip. Female students could be scheduled to visit a local health facility to

---

Teacher Support Notes

① **Overhead—Testicular Cancer Self-Exam:** Your supplementary material includes an overhead that graphically illustrates how males should check for testicular cancer. You may or may not want to use this overhead with your class, depending upon their ages and maturity level.

② **Moles:** If students ask what a mole is, tell them that they are elevations of the skin that are generally pigmented. They are very common. Almost everyone has at least one mole and the average person can have as many as twenty on various parts of the body. Most moles are benign (do not develop into tumors). Some may, however, become malignant, or capable of spreading to other parts of the body. This change is indicated by an increase in size and pigmentation, a reddening of the skin around the mole, and itching.

---

282   UNIT 3   Your Physical Health

1. Stand before a mirror. Inspect both breasts for anything unusual, such as any discharge from the nipples or puckering, dimpling or scaling of the skin.

2. Watch closely in the mirror. Clasp hands behind your head, and press hands forward. The purpose of these steps is to find any changes in the shape or contour of your breasts. As you do them, you should be able to feel your chest muscles tighten.

3. Next, press hands firmly on hips and bow slightly toward the mirror as you pull your shoulders and elbows forward.

Parts 4 and 5 of the exam are easy to do in the bath or shower where fingers glide over soapy skin.

4. Raise your left arm. Use three or four fingers of your right hand to explore your left breast firmly, carefully, and thoroughly. Beginning at the outer edge, press the flat part of your fingers in small circles, moving the circles slowly around the breast. Gradually work toward the nipple. Be sure to cover the entire breast. Pay special attention to the area between the breast and the armpit, including the armpit itself. Feel for any unusual lump or mass under the skin.

5. Gently squeeze the nipple and look for a discharge. Repeat the exam on your right breast.

6. Repeat steps 4 and 5 lying down. Lie flat on your back with your left arm over your head and a pillow or folded towel under your left shoulder. This position flattens the breast and makes it easier to examine. Use the same circular motion described earlier. Repeat on your right breast.

Figure 11–7 Breast Self-Examination

times, a cancerous lump feels like a little pea buried in the breast. Report anything unusual to a health care provider right away.

If you are a young man, you can help protect yourself from cancer of the testicles through self-examination. Although it occurs less frequently than breast cancer, cancer of the testicles can be deadly, because it advances rapidly. Report any large lump, enlargement, or change in shape to a health care provider.

One more test to perform at bath time is a visual check of your entire skin. Skin cancer is a real threat. The more familiar you become with any moles or freckles you may have, the better you will be able to detect changes in them that could mean the start of cancer. Stand in front of a large mirror, and take a look at your skin. Use a hand mirror to help with the back view. If a mole has changed its shape or color or has begun ① bleeding, have it checked right away. And protect your skin from the sun. The burns you get now, can set you up for skin cancer in years to come. Another reason to cover up: nothing ages and wrinkles the skin so fast as overexposure to the sun. Use sunscreen, take along a shirt, and wear a big ② hat or visor.

view a mammogram. You may wish to ask for a volunteer from the class to be the model. Ask the technician to orally explain the procedure as she does it, explain the reasons for the steps, and the functions of the machine. Ask them to allow the students to see a printout and to explain how they are read. **(Extend, Enrich)**

EVALUATE

Activity 3.4
Pop Quiz.
1. How often should a young man or woman examine themselves for lumps that might indicate cancer? (once a month)
2. Which is more common, breast or tes-

ticular cancer? (breast)
3. Which progresses more rapidly, breast or testicular cancer? (testicular)
4. What is the major cause of skin cancer? (sun exposure)
5. What is average size of a breast lump in the early stages? (approximately the size of a pea)

Ch. 11 Maintaining a Healthy Body 283

LIFE CHOICE ①
INVENTORY

Are Your Immunizations Up to Date?

Check yes (Y) if you've been immunized for all that apply to you. If you check no (N) and the description applies to you, ask a parent or the school nurse about it.

Age:	Vaccine:	Response:	
2 months	DPT (diphtheria, pertussis, tetanus), HIB (haemophilus influenza, type b), oral polio	Y	N
4 months	DPT, HIB	Y	N
6 months	DPT, HIB (Some physicians also recommend an additional dose of oral polio.)	Y	N
12 months	Tuberculin test	Y	N
15 months	MMR (measles, mumps, rubella), HIB	Y	N
18 months	DPT booster, oral polio	Y	N
5 to 6 years	DPT booster, polio booster	Y	N
14 to 16 years	Tetanus-diphtheria toxoid, adult type; booster every ten years or after a contaminated wound if more than five years have passed since the previous injection.	Y	N
16 to 18 years (before entering college)	MMR	Y	N

Key Points ▶ *Self-examinations of the breasts, testicles, and skin can help protect against cancer. Protection from the sun can, too.*

SECTION III REVIEW

Answer the following questions on a sheet of paper.
Learning the Facts
1. How often should the breasts, testicles, and skin be checked for cancer?
2. If a lump is detected in a breast or testicle, what course of action should be followed?
3. Name three precautions to take against skin cancer.

Making Life Choices
4. A monthly self-examination of breasts or testicles, and skin could save your life. Do any of these types of cancers run in your family? Do you perform self-examinations on a regular basis? Why or why not?

Answers to Fact or Fiction

Here are the answers to the questions at the start of the chapter.

1. False. Dental plaque is a sticky substance that builds up on teeth, damaging them. 2. True. 3. False. Although cleanliness is important, there are no simple answers to preventing or curing acne. 4. True. 5. True. 6. True. 7. False. False advertisements sound convincing, and many fail to see through them.

Section III Review
Answers
1. once a month
2. have it checked by a health care provider
3. use sunscreen, wear a shirt when out in the sun, wear a big hat or visor
4. Answers will vary.

Teacher Support Notes

① **Life Choice Inventory:** Students may or may not be able to obtain the information they need to complete this inventory. If not, ask them why not. How much of a problem do they think this is? Which sources do they rely upon for obtaining information? Why is it so important to keep their own personal records on immunization? Can they think of situations when it might be necessary to show these records? (enrolling in a new school, signing up for athletic programs, etc.)

CLOSE
SECTION III

Activity 3.5
Daily Diaries. Assign the students to do self-exams for a period of time and record findings, emotions, and outcomes in a daily diary. **(Reteach, Reinforce)**

FOCUS
SECTION IV

In this section the student will learn:
1. When a person needs to see a doctor.
2. When a person does not need to consult a professional physician.

Activity 4.1
Identifying Health Care

Providers. Ask students to name and describe the duties of as many health care providers as possible (see Appendix A). **(10–15 min.)**

TEACH
SECTION IV
(Guided and Independent Practice)

Activity 4.2
Researching Health Care
Providers. Have students choose one

Teacher Support Notes

① **Seeing Health Care Providers:** Ask students to explain this sentence: Why is it just as important to know when *not* to go to a health care provider? (excessive, unnecessary costs)

Section IV Review
Answers
1. Answers will vary.
2. Answers will vary. Refer to Figure 11–8 on this page for possible answers.
3. Answers will vary.

✎ Fast Facts

Only about 33% of all doctors today are family physicians, general internists, and pediatricians. Only 17% of all medical school graduates are choosing to become generalists. These numbers are different in other countries. For example, in England 73% of the physicians are generalists; in Germany and Belgium the figures are 54% and 53%, respectively.

---

284   UNIT 3 Your Physical Health

SECTION IV

When to Visit a Health Care Provider

Part of caring for yourself involves seeking help from a health care provider when needed. For one thing, growing children and teens need to be checked to make sure they are growing as expected and to receive their **immunizations** on time. This chapter's Life Choice Inventory challenges you to think about your own immunization history.

Almost as important as knowing when to go see a health care provider is knowing when *not* to go. One time not to go is when you have an ordinary cold. You also need not go if you have: ①

- A mild rash without other symptoms.
- A single episode of vomiting or diarrhea without abdominal pain.
- A fever of less than 102 degrees Fahrenheit (39 degrees centigrade).

As for when *to* see a health care provider, Figure 11–8 provides some guidelines.

Key Points *Knowing when to get medical help is an important part of maintaining your body.*

SECTION IV REVIEW

Answer the following questions on a sheet of paper.
Learning the Vocabulary
The vocabulary term in this section is *immunizations.*
1. Write a sentence using this term.

Learning the Facts
2. List some symptoms of illnesses or injuries that indicate the need to seek medical help.

Making Life Choices
3. Take the Life Choice Inventory on page 283. Were you able to obtain all the necessary information to complete this inventory?

FIGURE 11-8
When to Ask for Medical Help

See a health care provider for:
1. Fever above 104 degrees Fahrenheit.
2. Any serious accident or injury.
3. Any fall with possible injury.
4. Sudden severe pain in the abdomen.
5. Breathing difficulty.
6. Loss of consciousness, even if brief.
7. Severe headache for more than two hours.
8. Intense itch.
9. Bleeding with unknown cause. (Blood in vomit or stools may appear dark; blood in urine may appear pink.)
10. Faintness; dizziness; abnormal pulse; abnormal breathing; cold or clammy skin; bluish cast to lips or fingernails.
11. Sudden loss of mental ability, vision (especially a halo effect), hearing, touch, or ability to move.
12. Any symptoms after taking medication.
13. Diarrhea or vomiting for a day or more.

MINI GLOSSARY

immunizations: injected or oral doses of medicine that stimulate the immune system to develop the long-term ability to quickly fight off infectious diseases; also called *vaccinations.*

of the health care providers identified in Activity 4.1 and research that occupation. Students should report back to class on the education requirements, the duties, and any other interesting facts they can find about the particular health care provider. **(30 min. for presentations; Extend, Enrich)**

EVALUATE
SECTION IV

Activity 4.3
Designing Pamphlets. Divide students into pairs. Give each pair two pieces of paper. Have them fold the paper pamphlet-style. Then have them design a cover and develop interior information on the topic, "When to See a Doc-

tor." **(40–60 min.; Reteach, Reinforce, Cooperative Learning)**

CLOSE
SECTION IV

Activity 4.4
Interviewing. Divide the class into pairs. Give each pair the name of one

(continued on next page)

STRAIGHT
TALK — Posture and Image

Have you ever wondered why it is that some people seem to radiate energy, have a bounce in their step, and seem to be a picture of high self-esteem? One of the best things good posture does is give a person that energetic look. By the same token, a person who slumps or sways appears tired, bored, or negative. Since you have to stand, sit, walk, and lie down anyway, why not align your body for its best posture?

Does posture have anything to do with a person's health?

Yes, especially skeletal health. The way you walk, sit, and sleep greatly affects your skeleton over the years. The bones and cartilage disks of your **spine** are sensitive, as those who have had even a twinge of back pain are keenly aware. Think of your spine as a set of 33 delicate hollow bones (**vertebrae**) ① stacked up on one another like doughnuts with pads between them (the cartilage disks). Think of your spinal cord running right up through the holes in the doughnuts. (A difference from doughnuts is that the holes in the vertebrae are near their edges, not at the center.) Major nerves exit and enter the spaces between the vertebrae—and if the bones or cartilage disks are damaged, they can bulge out and pinch those nerves (see Figure 11–9). The result is stabbing pain, like an electric

A. Normal disc (leathery connective tissue)

Vertebra (bone)

B. Damaged disc pressing on nerves

Spinal nerves

Normal curve of the spine. When the bones are stacked this way, the discs bear the weight evenly, and the nerves feel least pressure.

Figure 11–9 The Spinal Column

shock, torturing the muscles of the neck, shoulders, back, or legs. There is a good chance that it can happen to you. During adulthood, eight out of ten people have back pain bad enough to send them to a doctor. Most cases are preventable through proper posture and exercise. ②

That's not likely to happen to me—I don't do strenuous work using my back.

There's a catch—people who are sedentary (sit down a lot) are the most likely victims. If they don't exercise, their back and abdominal muscles

(Continued on next page)

Teacher Support Notes

① **More on the Spinal Column:** Some students may question this number. They may think that there are 26 vertebrae in the spinal column rather than 33. If so, tell them that at birth their spinal columns consisted of 33 vertebrae separated into five different types: 7 cervical, 12 thoracic, 5 lumbar, 5 sacral, and 4 coccygeal (kok SIJ e al). In adults, the sacral vertebrae will fuse into a single *sacrum* and the coccygeal vertebrae will fuse to form a *coccyx*. The result is an adult spinal column of 26 separate bones.

② **Adult Survey:** Have students survey their parents and adult relatives and friends to find out how many have had back problems. When they report back to class, compile the results. Do your results match the 80% figure in the text? Also have students ask for remedies or activities the adults use in easing their pain.

health care provider in your local area. Have them conduct a short, person-to-person interview, or phone interview, to get a "Do's and Don'ts" list for when to see a doctor. Then have each pair make a poster of the "Do's and Don'ts" they learned. Display the posters around the school. **(30 min.; Extend, Enrich)**

RETEACH/BONUS

Create a Dental Care Center.
Have each student bring a dental care item (or package) to class. Create a "Good Dental Health Care Center" for the classroom. Invite some elementary classes to visit the "Center." Pair your students with the visiting youngsters to explain the care items and demonstrate proper dental care to their "partners." **(Extend, Enrich)**

Spine Construction. Assign the students to construct a model of a human spine using household materials. (blocks, matchsticks, pieces of wood, bottle caps, popsicle sticks, etc.) Instruct them to simulate a head on top of the 7 cervical, 12 thoracic, and 5 lumbar vertebrae, plus the

---

Teacher Support Notes

① **S Curve:** Many students may fail to see the S curve unless you point it out to them. Refer them back to the illustration on the preceding page. Have them trace the contours of the spinal column with their fingers. Do they see the S curve?

☎ Where to Call

The San Francisco Spine Institute, San Francisco, CA 1-800-523-BACK. Information and materials on back care. Referrals to spine specialists in your area also available.

STRAIGHT TALK   (Continued)

become weak, and their spines tend to become less and less well supported and slip out of shape. Poor posture combined with weakened muscles is practically a guarantee of major back trouble.

Which exercises are best for working the back?

For the health of the back, the stomach muscles are as important as the back muscles. The back muscles can pull your spine out of shape unless you have strong abdominal muscles to work against them. For this reason, sit-ups and leg lifts are as important for the back as they are for the belly.

Well, I need to do sit-ups to help me stay trim, anyway. What else should I know about posture and back care?

How you sit, stand, and walk also matter a lot. The image to keep in mind is of that stack of doughnuts. Keep it in its normal S curve so that it will not topple; so that it will hold your heavy head up by balancing, not by straining; and so that the nerves can run freely through it.

How you sleep is important, too. You spend a third of your life sleeping. By the time you have lived 75 years, you will have spent a quarter of a century lying down. Whatever position you choose to lie in for 25 years is bound to affect the shape of your skeleton permanently.

This doesn't mean that you necessarily must change the position you like to sleep in. No one position is right for sleeping, but there are some to avoid. In general, the idea is to keep your spine in its normal curve while sleeping,

just as you would try to do while awake. If you sleep on your back, support your knees, so as not to develop a ① swayback, and do not use too high a pillow under your head. If you sleep on your side, use a pillow just high enough to keep your neck straight. Do not sleep on your stomach. Figure 11–10 on the next page shows how to sit, stand, and walk, too.

Mini Glossary

spine: the stack of 33 vertebrae that form the backbone and hold the spinal cord, whose nerves enter and exit through spaces between the bones.

vertebrae (VERT-eh-bray; singular, **vertebra**): the delicate, hollow bones of the spine.

sacrum and coccyx to show the normal curve and weight-bearing construction of the back. **(Reteach, Reinforce)**

Teacher Instruction. Use a student model or model of the back to teach the parts of the vertebrae structure, names of its parts, and the weight-bearing responsibility of the back. Instruct on which muscles surround the back area and the physiology of these. Point out the rela-

tionship of these and the abdominal muscles, as well. **(Reteach, Reinforce)**

Student Interviews. Have the students design a questionnaire to interview someone about common back ailments. Have them assume the role of a physician questioning about ailments, movement and pain associated with various moves, and suspected cause of the ailment. Have the student write an analysis of the interview

and a personal diagnosis of the problem. Have students do research on the ailment and use the research to complete the following: Have them suggest treatment for the ailment and suggest possible preventative measures that may have been done prior to the ailment. **(Extend, Enrich)**

Don't

Sleeping Lie flat on your back: this arches the spine too much.

Use a high pillow.

Sleep face down.

Do

Lie on your back and support your knees.

Lie on your side with knees bent and pillow just high enough to keep your neck straight.

Sitting Leave your lower back unsupported when not upright.

Sit straight with back support, knees higher than hips.

Standing Let your back bend out of its natural curve.

Stand upright, hips tucked, knees slightly bent.

Walking Lean forward or wear high heels.

Lead with chest, toes forward.

Figure 11–10 Care of the Spine ①

To avoid backaches, remember this rule: For every 20 minutes you are seated, get up and walk or stretch for 20 seconds.

Teacher Support Notes

① **Self-Assessment:** Four different areas in which students can evaluate and possibly correct improper posture are shown in this illustration. Have students write the four areas (sleeping, sitting, standing, and walking) down the left side of a sheet of paper leaving several lines of space between each heading. For each heading have them pick the illustration that most closely matches their most typical posture. They should then describe whether or not they are satisfied with their posture in that area, whether or not they've had any trouble with their backs, and what they will try to do if they are not satisfied with their posture or have experienced back pain.

Vocabulary

1. **a.** dermatologist
b. follicles **c.** Cuticles
2. **a.** Douches **b.** Dental plaque
3. **a.** pus **b.** comedogenic **c.** dentin **d.** Immunizations **e.** toxic shock syndrome
4. **a.** A cavity is a hole in the tooth caused by decay, while a pulp cavity is the tooth's deepest chamber that houses its blood vessels and nerves. **b.** The spine is made up of 33 vertebrae which are delicate, hollow bones stacked on each other.

Recall

Section I

1. brush tooth surfaces back and forth, not up and down; brush the gums, especially inside at the gum line; use floss to pull plaque up from below the gum line between the teeth; use a toothpick or brush to dislodge plaque from below the gum line along the teeth
2. They contain bleaching substances and acids that may damage the teeth, gums, and tongue.
3. Promote tooth decay— Answers will vary; could include: chocolate milk, ice cream, milk shakes, sweetened yogurt, cookies, sweet rolls, pies, cakes, presweetened cereals, potato chips, dried fruits, fruits canned in syrup or juice, jams, jellies, peanut butter with added sugar, glazed meats, hot dogs, candies, and sugar-sweetened gum.

CHAPTER REVIEW

LEARNING THE VOCABULARY

dental plaque	acne	douches
enamel	sebum	menstruation
cavity	pus	toxic shock syndrome (TSS)
dentin	whitehead	menstrual cramps
pulp cavity	cyst	premenstrual syndrome
follicles	blackhead	immunizations
cuticle	comedogenic	spine
keratin	dermatologist	vertebrae

Answer the following questions on a separate sheet of paper.

1. **Word Scramble**—*Use the clues from the phrases below to help you unscramble the terms:*
   a. **temogdrolitas** A _____ is also known as a skin doctor.
   b. **celilolfs** The structures that contain the roots of hairs are called _____.
   c. **ciuctsel** _____ are the borders of hardened skin along the bases of the fingernails.
2. a. _____ are preparations used to clean the vagina.
   b. _____ is material that builds up on the tooth.

3. **Matching**—*Match each of the following phrases with the appropriate vocabulary term from the list above:*
   a. a mixture of fluid and white blood cells around an infected area
   b. acne-causing
   c. a tooth's soft middle layer
   d. also called vaccinations
   e. dangerous poisoning that can occur when bacteria break down menstrual blood.
4. a. What is the difference between a cavity and a pulp cavity?
   b. What is the relationship between the spine and the vertebrae?

RECALLING IMPORTANT FACTS AND IDEAS

1. Describe correct flossing and brushing techniques.
2. Why should teeth-whitening products be avoided?
3. Identify two foods that promote tooth decay and two foods that do not promote tooth decay.
4. What is the only cure for damaged hair?
5. What happens when oil and bacteria irritate the skin?
6. How can foreign particles best be removed from your eye when tears fail to remove them?
7. Why shouldn't cotton swabs be used to clean the ear canal?
8. What is the Food and Drug Administration's role in regulating the sale of cosmetics?
9. What causes skin to age and wrinkle at a rapid rate?
10. What should you do if you notice a change in a mole on your body?
11. Why is performing regular breast self-examinations so important?
12. Why do children and teenagers need to go for regular medical check-ups?
13. List four situations that would require a visit to the doctor.

Do not promote tooth decay—Answers will vary; could include: milk, cheese, plain yogurt, popcorn, toast, hard rolls, pretzels, corn chips, pizza, fresh fruits, fruits canned in water, salad greens, cauliflower, cucumbers, radishes, carrots, celery, lean meats, fish, poultry, eggs, beans, water, sugarless gum, and sugar-free drinks.

Section II
4. trim off the damaged parts
5. redness, swelling, and pus form, the beginning of a whitehead or pimple
6. hold eye open under a gentle stream of clean, plain water for a second or two
7. The inner structures of the ear are easily damaged and the swab can easily pack wax down inside the ear, promoting infection.
8. Safety testing is recommended but optional and only a few cosmetic ingredients, such as colorants, are restricted. Cosmetic labels must list their ingredients.

Section III
9. overexposure to the sun
10. have it checked by a health care provider right away
11. for early detection of cancer, making the cancer more treatable

Section IV
12. to make sure they are growing as expected and to receive immunizations on time
13. Answers will vary. Refer to Figure 11–8 on page 284 for possible answers.

CRITICAL THINKING

1. What are the benefits to the medical profession when people become more involved in self-care? What are some of the specific benefits of practicing self-care? Are there any risks involved in self-care?
2. Compare and contrast personal health care today with personal health care in the nineteenth century. Give specific examples.
3. Why is quackery such a profitable business? Why do so many people fall victim to deceptive practices? List some examples of products quacks might sell based on fear. How can you avoid spending your money on worthless products?

ACTIVITIES

1. Submit a copy of an advertisement and analyze the gimmicks used based on the Consumer Awareness feature on page 278.
2. Interview a dental hygienist or a dentist about the dental care practices they recommend. Hand in a short report or a tape recording of the interview.
3. Make a list of various activities that damage hair and some precautions that will help minimize the risk of damage.
4. Write a one-page report on the responsibilities of the Food and Drug Administration.
5. Produce an original video commercial. Pretend to be a quack and use some of the deceptive practices listed on page 278 in the Consumer Awareness feature.
6. Submit a copy of a newspaper or magazine advertisement for a health care product you suspect is making a false claim. Attach a one-page report explaining the reasons for your suspicions.
7. Research sunscreen products and write a brief report comparing and contrasting different brands in relation to cost, ingredients, and sun protection factors.
8. Contact some local community health agencies and make a list of educational programs they have available on self-care.
9. Call your water district and find out if the water in your community is fluoridated, the cost of fluoridation, and when this practice began.
10. Make a poster of the do's and don'ts of personal health care by either collaging pictures you cut out from magazines or creating original drawings.
11. List all the ways to protect eyes to keep them healthy. Identify what occupations and sports commonly use protective eyewear.
12. Write a report on how your life would be different if you could not hear or see.

MAKING DECISIONS ABOUT HEALTH

1. You have the nagging feeling that something is wrong with your body. There's pain here, discomfort there, and a feeling of nausea that's almost overwhelming sometimes. These symptoms seem to come and go and you wonder if you should see a physician. What course of action should you follow?
2. You recently discovered that your mother does not do a monthly breast self-examination and does not go for regular check-ups at the gynecologist. You are worried that due to her negligence she will fall victim to breast cancer. Do you feel comfortable discussing this with her? If you are comfortable, how can you convince her that this self-examination is essential? If you are uncomfortable with discussing this issue, whose help can you enlist?

289

CHAPTER 12 PLANNER

OVERVIEW

Chapter 12 is 20 pages long and divided into the four sections listed to the right. Major learning outcomes of the chapter are also listed to the right. Briefly, this chapter describes the effects of medicines on the body and the regulatory role of the FDA. It stresses the importance of the proper selection and use of medicines. It also gives students guidelines to follow for taking medicine.

MAKING LIFE CHOICES RESOURCES

A variety of activities, handouts, quizzes, and tests to accompany this chapter are available in the *Making Life Choices* supplementary material. You may pick and choose from those materials as appropriate for your amount of class time and the ability levels of your students. Some of the resources you might want to consider using are:

Overheads
- The FDA
- Risk/Benefit Ratio

Handouts
- How New Drugs Are Discovered
- Attitudes About Over-the-Counter Drugs
- Analyzing Medicine Use
- Caffeine Contents of Beverages, Foods, and OTC Drugs

Teacher Information Sheet
- Food/Drug Interactions

Answers to "Fact or Fiction"

Here are the answers to the questions at the start of the chapter.
1. False. All drug use involves risk. **2.** False. Everyone who takes aspirin receives all of its effects, whether or not they seek them. **3.** True. **4.** True. **5.** False. Generic drugs contain the same active ingredients as name brands, but may contain different inactive ingredients that can affect their actions in the body.

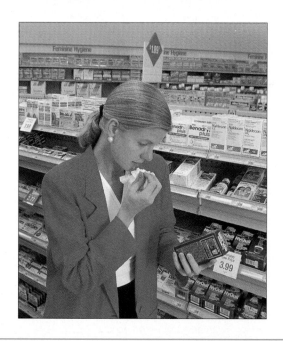

CHAPTER 12

Drugs as Medicines

CHAPTER PROJECT

Have students create a new medicine, working in teams of four. Teams should do the following: identify an ailment or condition for which there is currently no satisfactory treatment, describe how their medicine will help, name their medicine, create the packaging for it (with labels and inserts), and develop an advertisement to promote it. Possibilities for ads include a billboard, a poster, a cartoon, a magazine ad, a poem, jingle or rap, a TV commercial, a skit, or any means of promoting their product that is appropriate.

OUTCOMES

After reading and studying this chapter, you will be able to:

✓ List five ways medicines benefit people.
✓ Describe the factors that alter or influence the effects of drugs.
✓ Explain the procedures the FDA must follow in order to approve a drug.
✓ Describe the differences between over-the-counter drugs and prescription drugs.
✓ Explain how advertising affects the sales of over-the-counter drugs.
✓ Describe the purpose of over-the-counter drugs.
✓ Discuss the purposes of prescription drugs.
✓ Describe the effects of caffeine on the body.

CONTENTS

I. The Actions of Drugs
II. Drug Testing: Risks and Safety
III. Nonprescription (Over-the-Counter) Medicines
IV. Prescription Medicines

    Straight Talk: Caffeine

FACT OR FICTION

What do you think? Are the following statements true or false? If you think they are false, then say what is true.

1. Prescription medications can be dangerous, but over-the-counter medicines are safe.
2. The effect aspirin has on the body depends on why a person takes it.
3. The action of a drug can depend on whether or not it is taken with meals.
4. People who drink alcohol often need higher doses of certain drugs than other people.
5. Generic drugs are exactly the same as their brand-name equivalents, only cheaper.

(Answers on page 305)

■ **Reminder:** Knowing how to study can increase your knowledge, improve your grades, *and* cut down on your study time. See the *Studying Health* section at the front of your text for some suggestions to help you study this chapter.

NOT ENOUGH TIME?*

You could easily spend four or five days teaching this chapter if students read the entire chapter, do several of the suggested activities in the teacher's edition, and complete a sampling of handouts from the resource material accompanying this text. It is likely, however, that you will have only two or three days to devote to this chapter. Following are some suggestions to help you make sure that you cover the key topics if you have limited time.

TIME	SUGGESTIONS
1 Day	Assign Section I prior to class. During class have students do Activity 1.1 and Activity 1.4. Conclude the class with Activity 1.7, the Pop Quiz.
2 Days	On day 2 have students read Sections II and III. During class have students do Activities 3.1 and 2.2. Conclude with Activity 3.3. Assign Section IV.
3 Days	On day 3 during class have students do Activities 4.2 and 4.7.

*Please refer to the 18-week daily lesson plans in the supplementary material for additional suggestions.

Activity To Introduce Chapter

Have students inventory sections of a local drug store. This inventory should include: names of medicines, purpose, active and inactive ingredients, classification (generic or brand name, over-the-counter or prescription), costs, and expiration dates.

SUGGESTED RESOURCES

Student Readings
1. Burger, Alfred. *Drugs and People*. Charlottesville, VA: University Press of Virginia, 1986.
2. Flodin, Kim C. "Bitter Pills; Teens and Appetite Suppressants." *American Health: Fitness of Body and Mind*. 10 (July–August 1991): 64.
3. Kittredge, Mary. *Prescriptions and Over-the-Counter Drugs*. New York: Chelsea House Publishers, 1989.
4. Sommi, Roger, "What's Your Drug IQ?" *Current Health*. 2.17 (September 1990): 11–13.
5. "Over-the-Counter Drug Abuse." *USA Today*. 118 (February 1990): 9.
6. *The New Medicine Show*, 6th ed. Mount Vernon, NY: Consumers Union, 1989.

Teacher Readings
1. Long, James W., M.D. *The Essential Guide to Prescription Drugs*. New York: Harper Collins Publishers, 1992.
2. Loeb, Stanley. *Nursing 92 Drug Handbook*. Pennsylvania: Springhouse Corporation, 1992.
3. *Physicians Desk Reference*. New Jersey: Medical Economics Co., 1992.

Software
1. *PDR Drug Interactions and Side Effects Diskettes*. New Jersey: Medical Economics Data, 1992.
2. *Drugs: Their Effects on You*. Opportunities for Learning, Inc., 800-243-7116.

In this section students will learn the:
1. Actions of drugs.
2. Side effects of commonly used medicines.
3. Factors that change medicines' effects.

Activity 1.1
Brainstorming Medicines. Write the word "medicine" on the chalkboard. Have students call out the names of all the medicines they can think of. Write the students' responses under the word "medicine." To encourage class participation in this brainstorming activity, reserve comments until all students are satisfied with the list. Discuss the list. Suggest medicines that may have been omitted.

(penicillin, cortisone, polio vaccine, etc.) Divide the class into teams of four. Have each team examine the list of medicines and incorporate each medicine into one of the five categories: prevents disease, cures disease, makes the disease less severe, relieves symptoms, or brings about other desired effects. Discuss their choices. **(15–30 min.; Special Needs, Cooperative Learning)**

Teacher Support Notes

① **Drugs:** Because students are so used to hearing the word *drugs* used to mean the drugs of abuse, you should emphasize the actual meaning of the term, which is any substance taken into the body that changes one or more of the body's functions. Have students write sentences using the word *drug* or *drugs*, without referring to the drugs of abuse. Ask students to volunteer their sentences to be read aloud.

② **Symptom:** Check students' knowledge of *symptom*, which means any phenomenon experienced by an individual as a departure from normal function, sensation, or appearance, generally indicating disorder or disease. A symptom is a sign—it suggests visible evidence of an adverse condition. Have students compose sentences to make sure they understand the distinction between the symptom and the disease.

✎ Fast Facts

Americans consume ten billion aspirin annually, or one every three seconds.

292 UNIT 4 Drug Use and Abuse

Within this century, remarkable discoveries of **drugs** that help prevent, cure, or relieve symptoms of disease have spared much suffering and saved countless lives. Today, people use thousands of different drugs as **medicines** to treat hundreds of different illnesses or symptoms of illnesses. The health effects of such widespread use of medicines are not always those that people expect.

This chapter presents drugs used as medicines. The Straight Talk discusses one of the most common of all drugs—caffeine. The next chapter focuses on drug abuse.

SECTION I

The Actions of Drugs

Medicines benefit people in these ways:

- They may help *prevent* disease (example: vaccines are used to convey immunity to diseases).
- They may help in the *cure* of disease (example: penicillin kills the bacteria that cause pneumonia).
- They may make diseases less severe without helping cure them (example: steroid hormones reinforce the body's defense against incurable arthritis).
- They may relieve symptoms (example: aspirin relieves inflammation, aches, and pains).
- They may bring about other desired effects (example: minoxidil, rubbed on a balding scalp, helps promote hair growth).

Notice that drugs do not cure diseases by themselves, although they can help. Only the body can actually cure diseases, and drugs can only help the body in its efforts.

All drugs work by changing the body's own processes. One familiar drug illustrates this concept. It may be available in tiny, portable boxes, sometimes found right next to a candy counter. Or it may be available in huge bottles of a thousand tablets from the pharmacy. The drug is **aspirin,** one of the oldest known painkillers, and still the best drug available to relieve certain kinds of pain.

Most people think they understand aspirin. Their reasoning goes something like this: "Aspirin is cheap and familiar. Many people take it for headache or fever. It's not addictive, and it certainly can't be as powerful as the drugs physicians prescribe. It must be safe." If this is how you think about aspirin, then you may be surprised by its far-reaching chemical effects on the body. All drugs (whether drugs used medically or abused drugs) affect users physically. Their use always involves risks.

A fever can help the body fight infection.

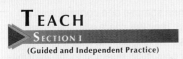

TEACH
SECTION I
(Guided and Independent Practice)

Activity 1.2
Definitions. Write "prevent," "cure," and "relieves symptoms" on the chalkboard. As a class, develop definitions for each term. Have the students write sentences using each term to make sure they understand the proper use of each.

(15 min.; Reteach, Reinforce)

Activity 1.3
Discussion. Discuss the text statement, "Drugs do not cure diseases by themselves." Have students describe how drugs *help the body* cure diseases.
(10 min., Critical Thinking)

Activity 1.4
Vocabulary Circles. Have students

stand in pairs in two concentric circles. The inside circle faces out, the outside circle faces in. Students hold flash cards with definitions from Section I: *aspirin, inflammation, acetaminophen, ibuprofen, tolerance, addiction, drugs, medicine, side effects, antihistamines,* and *antagonistic drugs*. One side of the card has the word, the other side the definition. Each student holds a card up to the person he

(continued on next page)

Aspirin works by blocking the actions of powerful body chemicals. These chemicals exist in all body tissues. They produce fevers, cause **inflammation**, make nerves sensitive to pain, and cause the blood to clot. Aspirin changes all these body responses through its actions on body chemistry. Thus aspirin reduces fever and inflammation, relieves pain, and prevents the blood from clotting.

You cannot use aspirin for any one purpose without bringing on all its other effects. A person might take aspirin to prevent blood clotting, but this same effect also occurs in people who take aspirin to treat pain. For people who do not expect it, the anticlotting effect may be dangerous, since it can prolong bleeding. A single two-tablet dose of aspirin doubles the bleeding time of wounds, an effect that lasts from four to seven days. For this reason, it is important not to take aspirin before any kind of surgery or in the weeks before childbirth.

Another thing you should know about aspirin is that its use is associated with a rare, but often fatal, disease: Reye's (pronounced "RISE") syndrome, which damages the liver and brain. The most likely victims of Reye's syndrome are children under 15 years of age who are given aspirin to relieve symptoms of chicken pox or flu. The lives of victims who are promptly treated can sometimes be saved, but they may be left mentally retarded or with disorders of voice and speech.

Almost all cases of Reye's syndrome can be prevented by treating children's symptoms of flu or chicken pox with pain relievers other than aspirin. For example, **acetaminophen** (sold under brand names such as Tylenol or Datril) or **ibuprofen** (whose brand names are Advil, Motrin, and others) can reduce fever and relieve pain. Those medicines are not associated with Reye's syndrome. Warning signs of Reye's syndrome are listed in Figure 12–1. In a

---

FIGURE 12-1
Warning Signs of Reye's Syndrome

A child may seem to be recovering from flu or chicken pox when these symptoms appear:

- Nausea with severe vomiting.
- Fever.
- Inactivity.
- Loss of consciousness.
- Uncontrollable behavior while unconscious.

---

child recovering from chicken pox, any of those signs means that a medical emergency is developing. See a health care provider right away.

Aspirin is typical of all drugs: they all have **side effects.** Some are harmful (see Figure 12–2 on the next page). For example, many drugs impair driving ability. Cold medicines

---

MINI GLOSSARY

drugs: substances taken into the body that change one or more of the body's functions.

medicines: drugs used to help cure disease, lessen disease severity, relieve symptoms, prevent disease, help with diagnosis, or produce other desired effects.

aspirin: a drug that relieves fever, pain, and inflammation.

inflammation: pain and swelling caused by irritation.

acetaminophen (ah-SEET-ah-MIN-o-fen): a drug that relieves fever, pain, and inflammation.

ibuprofen (EYE-byoo-PRO-fen): a drug that relieves fever, pain, and inflammation.

side effects: effects of drugs other than the desired medical effects.

Teacher Support Notes

① **Pain Relievers:** Ask students what acetaminophen, ibuprofen, and aspirin have in common. (pain relievers) Have students think of some brand names for aspirin and other pain relievers. Then write those brand names and those in the text on one side of the board, and the three pain relievers on the other. Have students draw lines to show which brand names go with which drugs. This should help students see that "Bufferin" and the like are not generic terms.

② **Nausea:** Ask students if they know what nausea means. (stomach distress with distaste for food and an urge to vomit; feeling sick to the stomach)

③ **Side Effects:** Ask students why the effects of drugs other than the desired effects are called "side effects." As the word *side* refers to something that's "off to the side," something that is not in the "center" of your attention, a side effect is an effect other than the main effect.

or she is facing. The person viewing the card must give the correct definition. The card holders may coach in this review activity. After thirty seconds the circles rotate in opposite directions, moving to the next person. **(15 min.; Reteach, Reinforce)**

Activity 1.5
Aspirin's Side Effects. Have students list the dangerous side effects of aspirin. Students work in pairs within teams of four. In pairs, students alternate; one describes all the dangerous side effects he or she can think of, while the partner listens and compiles a list. After two minutes, the partners switch roles. After two additional minutes, the pairs share with their teammates. The four team-

mates then compile one comprehensive list, which they will share with the class. The class will discuss the lists and check them for accuracy, referring to the information on pages 293 and 294 in the students' books. **(25 min.; Reteach, Reinforce, Cooperative Learning)**

Activity 1.6
Hazards Search. Referring to the information in Figure 12–2, prepare six-

---

Teacher Support Notes

① **Side Effects:** Tell students that they should not be frightened of the list of possible hazards associated with each of these drugs. In almost all cases, the drugs are perfectly safe. They were tested extensively before the government permitted their sale. These are potential problems and reactions that take place, which people should be aware of. Some additional side effects that you might want to give to students are:
a. acetaminophen—difficulty in diagnosing overdose because reaction may be delayed for up to a week after taking medication.
b. antacids—possible concealment of ulcer, prevention of certain antibiotics' functioning (for example, antacids that contain aluminum).
c. aspirin—excessive bleeding during surgery or childbirth.
d. diet pills—nervousness and crabbiness.

294

---

294 UNIT 4 Drug Use and Abuse

F**IGURE** 12-2

Side Effects of Commonly Used Medicines ①

Medicine	Possible Hazard
Acetaminophen	Bloody urine; painful urination; skin rash; bleeding and bruising; yellowing of the eyes or skin (even at normal doses); severe liver damage and death from overdose; liver damage from chronic low-level excesses
Antacids	Reduced mineral absorption from food; reduction of effectiveness of other medications; possible worsening of high blood pressure; aggravation of kidney problems
Aspirin	Stomach bleeding; vomiting; worsening of ulcers; enhancement of the action of anticlotting medications; severe allergic reactions in some people; association with Reye's syndrome in children and teenagers; prolonged bleeding time
Cold medications	Loss of consciousness (if taken with prescription tranquilizers)
Diet pills	Organ damage or death from bleeding of the brain
Ibuprofen	Allergic reactions in some people with aspirin allergy; fluid retention; liver damage similar to that from acetaminophen; enhancement of action of anticlotting medications; digestive disturbances (half as often as with aspirin)
Laxatives	Reduced absorption of minerals from food; creation of dependency
Toothache medications	Destruction of the still-healthy part of a damaged tooth (for medications that contain clove oil)

and **antihistamines** can cause drowsiness. Other drugs can slow down a driver's reaction time. If there is any question about a drug's effect on driving, talk with a pharmacist or health care provider. All drugs have many effects. All of them occur when you take the drugs, whether you expect them and want them to occur or not.

Key Points *Medicines help prevent disease, cure disease, make disease less severe, relieve symptoms, or prevent or produce other desired*

effects. Drugs act by altering body processes. All drugs have side effects.

Factors That Change Medicines' Effects

When you take a drug, many factors work together to determine its effects on you. One is the nature of the drug itself—the substance. Another factor is the form in which you take the drug. Liquid drugs, for example, may be absorbed faster than cap-teen flash cards. Write eight medicines on eight separate index cards. On the remaining eight index cards, list the potential hazards. Shuffle the sixteen cards and distribute to sixteen "teams." A team may consist of one or more players, depending on class size. At your signal, each team is to find the corresponding team that holds the word or definition that complements their cards. **(15 min.; Reteach, Reinforce)**

Activity 1.7
Pop Quiz.
1. Drugs do not cure diseases by themselves. (T)
2. All drugs work by changing the body's own process. (T)
3. The use of aspirin involves no risk. (F)

4. A person who takes aspirin to reduce fever will not experience aspirin's anticlotting effect. (F)
5. Children under 15 years of age who are given aspirin to relieve symptoms of chicken pox or flu are the most likely victims of Reye's syndrome. (T)
6. Aspirin is the only nonprescription drug that can reduce fever and relieve pain. (F)

(continued on next page)

Foods can slow down the absorption of drugs from the digestive tract.

sules or tablets, so liquids tend to go to work faster. Another factor is the route by which the drug is taken. Drugs taken by mouth must travel through the digestive tract to be absorbed. Those injected into the bloodstream go to work right away. When you take the drug is another factor. For example, whether or not the drug is taken at mealtimes affects how fast it can act on the body. Food in the digestive tract can slow down the absorption of medicines. Still another factor is you—your body and mind. Your age, your weight, and what you expect the drug to do modify its effects.

Probably the strongest factor affecting the actions of medicines is the use of other drugs, such as alcohol, nicotine (the drug of tobacco), drugs of abuse, medicines, and others. Two or more drugs taken at the same time can strongly affect one another's actions. They may slow down one another's absorption. They may work against one another in the tissues. Or one drug may get in the way of the other's breakdown and removal from the body. A person's history of drug use also affects a medicine's action. This is so important that the next section tells of its effects on the body. Figure 12–3 sums up factors that affect the action of drugs.

> **Key Points** *Factors that alter a drug's effects on you include the drug itself, the form in which it is taken, the route by which it is taken, whether or not it is taken with food, your age, your weight, your expectations, and what other drugs you may take with it.*

FIGURE 12-3
Factors That Change Medicines' Effects

1. The nature of the drug.
2. The form in which it is taken.
3. The route by which it is taken.
4. When it is taken (with or without food, for example).
5. You (your age, weight, expectations, etc.).
6. Other drugs taken with it.
7. The taker's history of drug use.

Previous Drug Use, Other Drug Use

A drug may produce one set of effects when used for just a few days but produce an entirely different set of effects when used over weeks, months, or years. Often, after taking a drug over a long time, a person will need higher doses to get the desired effect. This is because the body has developed **tolerance** to the drug.

Tolerance means the body has grown used to being exposed to the drug. The longer the exposure, the better the body becomes at breaking the drug down, and the faster it gets rid of it. Many organs work together on this. The liver breaks down the

---

MINI GLOSSARY

antihistamines: drugs that counteract inflammation caused by histamine, one of the chemicals involved in allergic reactions.
tolerance: a state that develops in users of certain drugs that makes larger and larger amounts of the drugs necessary to produce the same effect.

Teacher Support Notes

① **Effects of Drugs:** Five general factors that determine the effects of a drug are listed and explained in this paragraph. Two more are given in the next paragraph. Students may also refer to Figure 12–3. Have them close their books, name the factors, and give examples of each.
② **Teacher Information Sheet—Food/Drug Interactions:** In your supplementary material, you will find an information sheet entitled "Food/Drug Interactions." This sheet will give you more in-depth information about some of the ways that foods can affect the actions of drugs in the body.
③ **Tolerance:** Ask students if any of them have had to take a particular drug long enough to build up a tolerance to it, or if anyone in their families has. What has been the result? Has the physician prescribed heavier doses, changed drugs, or attempted some other strategy?

may need higher doses of medicines to treat their illnesses. (T)

EVALUATE
(Continued)

7. All drugs have side effects. (T)
8. The form in which you take a drug (liquid or tablet), partly determines its effect on you. (T)
9. The liver can tell one drug from another. (T)
10. People who smoke or drink alcohol

CLOSE
SECTION I

Activity 1.8
Question Review. Students should be able to complete the following: **1.** List five ways medicines benefit people. **2.** Describe the advantages and disad-

vantages of aspirin. **3.** Describe the factors that influence the effects of drugs.
(10–15 min.; Reteach, Reinforce)

FOCUS
SECTION II

In this section students will learn:
1. The role of the FDA.
2. The purpose of drug testing.
3. How antibiotics work.

Teacher Support Notes

① Cross-Tolerance:
For enrichment you may want to explain *cross-tolerance.* It is the tolerance developed by the body to one drug, which in turn, affects the body's reactions to one or more other drugs as well. This happens when one drug causes the liver to develop equipment to break down other chemical relatives of the first drug. Due to cross-tolerance, people who smoke or drink alcohol may need higher doses of medicines to treat their ills. A wise physician always asks about tobacco, alcohol, or other drug uses before writing a prescription for medicine.

Section I Review

Answers

1. **a.** aspirin **b.** side effects **c.** drugs
d. addiction **e.** medicines
2. when they are used to help prevent, cure, or relieve symptoms of disease
3. reduces fever and inflammation, relieves pain, prevents blood from clotting, and doubles the bleeding time of a wound; four to seven days
4. drowsiness
5. Answers will vary.

296

drug faster. The kidneys throw it out in the urine faster. Other tissues begin to ignore the drug—they no longer respond to it.

Tolerance varies from person to person. One person may come to tolerate a certain drug well, but another may hardly adjust to it at all. When you understand the body's tolerance to a drug, you begin to catch a glimpse of how drug **addiction** can set in.

Drugs also interact, sometimes dangerously. An example is that of a person who takes sleeping pills with an alcoholic beverage. The person needs to know that the body breaks down both of these drugs in the same way. Taken by itself, the dose of the sleeping medicine is broken down little by little as it enters the body. The presence of alcohol changes things, though, because the body gives highest priority to breaking down alcohol. Meanwhile, the body ignores the sleeping medication which could build up in the blood to high, or even deadly, levels. Many accidental deaths occur in this way and many drugs, taken with alcohol, cause dangerous reactions. ①

One drug can also prevent the action of another, acting as an **antagonist.** Such drugs are often useful in the treatment of accidental overdoses or poisonings. Drugs

that block the action of snake venoms are examples of antagonists. Some forms of addiction therapy use antagonist drugs to oppose the effects of the addictive drug.

> **Key Points** *Tolerance to a drug develops when the body gets used to exposure to the drug. Tolerance sets the stage for the development of addiction and for accidental overdoses. Alcohol and medicine can be a dangerous combination.*

SECTION I   **REVIEW**

Answer the following questions on a sheet of paper.
Learning the Vocabulary
The vocabulary terms in this section are *drugs, medicines, aspirin, inflammation, acetaminophen, ibuprofen, side effects, antihistamines, tolerance, addiction,* and *antagonist.*
1. Match each of the following phrases with the appropriate term:
   a. A drug that relieves fever, pain, and inflammation that should not be given to children.
   b. Effects of a drug other than the desired medical effect.
   c. Substances taken into the body that change one or more body functions.
   d. A physical or psychological craving for higher and higher doses of a drug.
   e. Drugs used to help cure diseases, lessen disease severity, and relieve symptoms.

Learning the Facts
2. When do drugs become medicines?
3. What are the effects of a single, two-tablet dose of aspirin? How long do the effects of this dose last?
4. List a side effect of cold medicines and antihistamines.

Making Life Choices
5. Your father is a smoker and has a beer every night. He has a bad cold with a fever. He decides to treat his cold with over-the-counter antihistamines. With his smoking and drinking, what do you now know about the dose he takes? Why is it dangerous to take drugs when you drink or smoke?

This person might have an unexpected reaction to medicine.

Activity 2.1

Drug Evaluation Analysis. Write the following statements on the chalkboard: "Miracle drug discovered. It has been claimed that this drug will raise the IQ of those who take it by 20 points. The FDA stands in the way, refusing distribution to the public." Have students list the pros and cons of the FDA's drug evaluation policies. Provide a forum for debate. **(35–45 min., Critical Thinking)**

TEACH

SECTION II
(Guided and Independent Practice)

Activity 2.2

Media Releases. Have students discuss the following statement: "News of 'new' medicines often hits the media years before the drugs are ready for use. This raises false hopes in those who urgently need drugs for medical problems

such as cancer or AIDS." Have students work in teams of four. Each team represents a different TV station's editorial staff, responsible for what news goes on the air and what is omitted. After discussing the above statement, they are to decide whether to release news of a new drug not yet approved by the FDA, or to wait for FDA approval of the drug. The maker of the drug claims that this drug will cure

(continued on next page)

SECTION II

Drug Testing: Risks and Safety

Ingredients in medicines must be proved both safe and effective before the Food and Drug Administration (FDA), a watchdog agency of the federal government, allows the medicines on the market. The term **safe** means that an ingredient will not hurt you. The term **effective** means that the ingredient will do what the maker claims it will do. The FDA evaluates drug safety and effectiveness by keeping tabs on drug companies as they develop new drugs and bring them to market. The FDA checks to make sure the company has followed all the right scientific procedures before it approves a drug. Then, after the drug is on the market, the FDA continues to check for side effects. The research and checking procedures drug companies must go through to bring a new medicine to market have been "streamlined," but can still take many years.

News of "new" medicines often hits the media years before the drugs are ready for use. This raises false hopes in those who urgently need drugs for medical problems such as cancer or AIDS. It is best to wait, though: testing is a must before marketing. Otherwise, drugs that looked good in early tests might turn out to be harmful when used by people. They might be useless and delay treatment by other, less revolutionary but proven, drugs. Proper drug testing is important to ensure that a drug's effects and side effects are known before people begin using it.

No drug is totally safe for all people at all times at any dose. The safety of any substance depends on its dose. Part of the evaluation of a drug's safety compares the

Some drugs must walk a narrow line. They must be effective, but they must also be safe.

dose that presents risks to health with the dose needed for the medical effect.

Drugs that are safe to use in the amounts that work are the best ones for treating diseases. Among the safest drugs are many **antibiotics.** Antibiotic drugs stop all living cells from dividing. Antibiotic drugs can be used to work against bacteria in the body because bacteria normally divide more rapidly than most body cells. Because they divide faster, the bacteria die off faster than the body's own cells do when exposed to an antibiotic. Once the drug is out of the system, the body's own cells soon recover. This is why antibiotics are relatively safe for human beings, but deadly to bacteria. As you can see, the dose and length of treatment have to be

MINI GLOSSARY

addiction: a physical or psychological craving for higher and higher doses of a drug that leads to bodily harm, social maladjustment, or economic hardship.

antagonist (an-TAG-uh-nist): a drug that opposes the action of another drug.

safe: causing no undue harm; part of the legal requirement for a drug.

effective: having the medically intended effect; part of the legal requirement for a drug.

antibiotics: drugs used to fight bacterial infection.

Teacher Support Notes

① **Handout—How Drugs Are Discovered:** For enrichment your supplementary material contains a handout entitled "How New Drugs Are Discovered."

② **Overhead—The FDA:** Your supplementary material contains an overhead that gives an overview of the FDA's process for checking and approving drugs.

③ **Overhead—Risk/Benefit Ratio:** Explain to students that scientists use a formula to compare the risks of a drug to its benefits. This formula is called the *risk/benefit ratio*. The risk/benefit ratio answers the question, "How much drug does it take to help a person compared with the amount that will kill that person?" The greater the difference, the greater the drug's margin of safety. Your supplementary material contains an overhead that illustrates this concept.

AIDS. Have each team report its decision and reasons to the class. **(30–50 min.; Cooperative Learning, Critical Thinking)**

Activity 2.3
Pop Quiz.
1. The watchdog agency of the Federal Government, which evaluates drugs before allowing them to go on the market is the (FDA) .
2. The term that means that an ingredient will not hurt you: (safe) .
3. The term that means the ingredient will do what the maker claims it will do: (effective) .
4. Proper drug testing is important to ensure that a drug's effects and (side effects) are known before people begin using it.
5. (No) drug is totally safe.
(10–20 min.; Reteach, Reinforce)

Teacher Support Notes

① **Lethal Doses of Alcohol:** Many students may not be aware of the fact that alcohol can cause death. Make sure they read this paragraph carefully.
② **Handout—Attitudes About OTC Drugs:** In your supplementary material you will find an activity entitled "Attitudes About Over-the-Counter Drugs." The activity provides students with an opportunity to explore their own attitudes about OTC drugs.
③ **OTC Purchases:** Ask students to estimate how much money their families spend on OTC drugs a year. They'll need to talk to their parents and make some guesses. Have them report back to the class and compare the averages.

Section II Review

Answers

1. lethal dose
2. anesthetics
3. effective
4. They stop all living cells from dividing. They work against bacteria, because bacteria divide faster and, therefore, die off sooner.
5. The amount of alcohol needed for the anesthetic effect is dangerously close to a lethal dose, making it unsafe to use.
6. Answers will vary.

298   UNIT 4   Drug Use and Abuse

just right to wipe out the bacteria and leave the person able to recover.

Some drugs are less safe. An example is the drug alcohol, which was used to kill pain during wartime, in surgery, and in childbirth before the development of safer **anesthetics.** A little alcohol dulls pain. More alcohol produces unconsciousness, and only a little more stops the heartbeat and breathing. The amount of alcohol needed for the anesthetic affect is dangerously close to a **lethal dose** (one that causes death)—making alcohol unsafe to use in this way. Today, better, safer drugs are used for pain management instead.

Key Points > *Companies must prove that ingredients in medicines are safe and effective before the Food and Drug Administration (FDA) allows their sale. Scientists study the risks of each drug compared with its benefits. Drugs that carry low risks to health in comparison to their benefits are most desirable in the treatment of disease.*

SECTION II REVIEW

Answer the following questions on a sheet of paper.
Learning the Vocabulary
The vocabulary terms in this section are *safe, effective, antibiotics, anesthetics,* and *lethal dose.* Fill in the blank with the correct answer.
1. A _____ is the amount of a drug necessary to produce death.
2. Drugs that kill pain, with or without producing loss of consciousness, are called _____.
3. An _____ drug is one that has the medically intended effect.

Learning the Facts
4. How do antibiotic drugs work to fight infection?
5. What are the medical problems associated with the use of alcohol as an anesthetic?

Making Life Choices
6. You are going to a party to celebrate your friend's 16th birthday. He is planning to

drink 16 shots of alcohol. What do you think could happen to him? How are you going to react? Will you try to stop him? How would you argue your opinions?

SECTION III

Nonprescription (Over-the-Counter) Medicines

The FDA divides medicines into two classes: **over-the-counter (OTC) drugs**, sold freely; and **prescription drugs** (which you will read about in the next section), sold only with a physician's prescription.

People buy over-the-counter (OTC) medicines in the belief that they will bring relief from medical problems. Fortunately, buyers often choose correctly and obtain relief from minor and **chronic** medical problems at reasonable costs. Many ailments respond to the OTC treatments people choose for themselves. Sometimes, though, people buy medicines that are not necessary and may be quite costly. Net sales for OTC medicines are in the many billions of dollars every year.

Unlike prescription drugs, which need a doctor's prescription, OTC drugs are freely available. This is because they are relatively safe. Also, most people require about the same doses, so OTC drugs can be used without individualized guidance. The instructions are easily understood. Finally, OTC drugs are not abused in the usual sense. That is, although they may be misused, they do not produce sensations that drug abusers seek. All of these factors make them safe to use, and easy to use correctly, without a physician's help.

Many people, however, use too many OTC medicines, too often. Advertisers seek-

CLOSE
SECTION II

Activity 2.4
Review Questions. Students should be able to answer these questions: 1. What is the function of the FDA? 2. What are the qualities of a safe and effective drug? **(10–15 min.; Reteach, Reinforce)**

FOCUS
SECTION III

In this section students will learn the:
1. Difference between active ingredients and inactive ingredients.
2. Difference between over-the-counter and prescription drugs.
3. Difference between brand-name and generic drugs.

Activity 3.1
Comparing Generics. Display the packages of a variety of generic and brand-name medicines. If possible, include packages from over-the-counter and prescription medicines. Ask students which drugs they think are most effective and which they would prefer to use. Have students compare the ingredients and the prices. Have students examine their

(continued on next page)

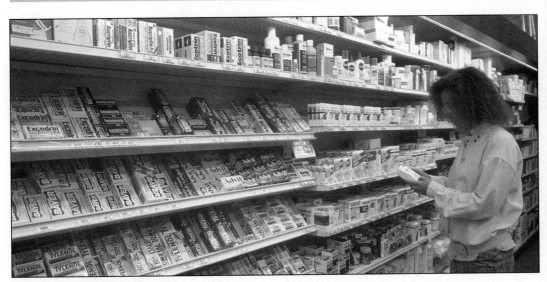

Medicines can be overused.

ing to sell their products suggest that people pay attention to feelings in their bodies, label them as "problems," and then seek cures through pills. For example, a person who has a headache may quickly take a dose of aspirin rather than trying to identify the cause of the headache. Maybe the person's headache is from hunger or tension. Maybe the person needs to rest more, to eat better, to exercise more, or to learn and use stress-reduction techniques. This chapter's Consumer Awareness section on the next page warns you of other tricks advertisers use to sell OTC medicines.

Pain or discomfort is a signal from your body that something is out of balance. Before heading for the medicine cabinet for every minor ailment, stop and listen to your body and try to find and relieve the *cause* of the pain. Instead of taking a tablet for indigestion, try eating more slowly or eating smaller portions. See if that relieves your discomfort.

Many people misuse OTC diet pills in an

① effort to lose weight. As Chapter 9 discussed, the way to lose weight safely and permanently is to eat an adequate, balanced diet and be physically active. Diet pills contain stimulants that raise the heart rate and blood pressure. Misuse of diet pills has been linked to seizures and bleeding inside the head.

MINI GLOSSARY

anesthetics (an-us-THET-icks): drugs that kill pain, with or without producing loss of consciousness.
lethal dose: the amount of a drug necessary to produce death.
over-the-counter (OTC) drugs: drugs legally available without a prescription.
prescription drugs: drugs legally available only with a physician's order.
chronic: in relation to illness, this term refers to a disease or condition that develops slowly, shows little change, and lasts a long time.

Teacher Support Notes

① **Selecting OTC Medicines:** Among many suggestions for selecting OTC medicines are:
a. Consult a home medical guide to determine the condition you're trying to treat.
b. Ask a pharmacist to help you guess what is wrong.
c. Do not buy a nasal decongestant spray for a runny nose.
d. Be careful about using two medicines at the same time.
② **Your Body's Signals:** This is a key sentence: "Pain or discomfort is a signal from your body that something is out of balance." Emphasize the point being made here. Students should not be in the habit of taking medicine the second they experience discomfort. They should stop and think about what's causing the discomfort.

medicine: the cost or the fact that it has been advertised. **(10–15 min.; Advanced, Critical Thinking)**

the past year. When the lists are complete, have the teams categorize the medicines as prescription or over-the-counter. After teams have categorized their lists, have a class discussion. Make a class chart, listing the drugs as prescription or over-the-counter. Discuss the chart. Which medicine is taken most often? Discuss. **(15 min., Cooperative Learning)**

motives for selection. Does packaging influence their selections? What role does product identification play in their choices? Is someone more likely to buy a medicine advertised on TV, on the radio, or in a magazine? Ask students to examine which is more important when buying

TEACH
SECTION III
(Guided and Independent Practice)

Activity 3.2
Class Chart. Have students work in teams of four. Allow students two minutes to list the medicines they have taken in

---

Teacher Support Notes

① Answers to Critical Thinking:

1. to protect everyone's right to freedom of the press

2. Answers will vary; students may think that a large segment of the population would be in favor of such laws. They should realize, however, that it would be difficult to write laws in such a way that they would eliminate the "information" that needs to be eliminated while still allowing valuable, accurate information to be published.

3. Again, answers will vary, but students should realize that they are responsible for their own protection. The government can do a great deal to make advertising honest, but as students have seen, there are limits to what the government can do. Finally, each individual must make wise decisions and read information critically.

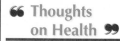

66 Thoughts on Health 99

When you buy a pill and buy peace with it you get conditioned to cheap solutions instead of deep ones.
– Max Learner

---

300 UNIT 4 Drug Use and Abuse

CONSUMER
AWARENESS

OTC Medicine Advertising

Although the law states that labels *on* products must be truthful, dishonest companies may place "information" sheets or cards of *mis*information *near* the display shelf where products are being sold. This trick is especially common in places that sell "health" or "natural" products, but such sheets can appear in regular drugstores and grocery stores, too. Be suspicious of claims of cures or benefits displayed near products for sale.

A similar trick is used in some magazines. You might open a magazine and start reading a scientific-looking article written by Dr. Rip Off, M.D., who boasts that vitamin X pills clear up acne. Already you think this is strange—*the claim seems too good to be true.* As you read on to the next page, an advertisement jumps out at you: "BALLYHOO vitamin X tablets—only $6.95 per bottle." The advertisement says only that the company sells vitamin X tablets, a legal claim. But if you were to

search for the origins of the article on the previous page, chances are you would find that the BALLYHOO Company sent it, as well as the advertisement, to be published.

The article is full of lies, but it is legal to print it. The FDA prevents companies from printing lies in advertisements, but no law forbids lies in other writing. Lies on labels are illegal, but "information" sheets can say anything and claim the constitutional right to freedom of the press. Your first clue to the hoax is the claims in the article. Your second is the advertisement for the product nearby.

① CRITICAL **T**HINKING

1. *Why do you think the government allows these tricks of publishing?*
2. *What would happen if the government tried to stop people from writing them?*
3. *Who protects consumers from falling for such tricks?*

Sometimes, though, medicines are truly needed. When they are, how can you tell which medicines to buy? You need to know how to read their labels to find what's in them.

By reading labels of OTC drugs, you can protect yourself against ingredients that may harm you. If you are allergic to the yellow dye tartrazine, for example, you can choose drugs not colored with it. The FDA makes sure that medicine companies tell the truth on labels. A drug label must list

approved uses for drugs—that is, conditions against which the drugs have been proved effective. If products have other, unproved claims on their labels, they can be removed from store shelves. While you're reading the label, check the expiration date. Medicines change with time into other substances that are not effective in treating illnesses. Do not buy medicines if they've passed the date stamped on the label. Throw away medicines you bought earlier, if they've passed their expiration dates. Fig-

EVALUATE
SECTION III

Activity 3.3
Pop Quiz.
1. Drugs legally available without prescription: __(over-the-counter)__
2. Drugs available only with a physician's order: __(prescription drugs)__
3. The chemical names for drugs: __(generic)__
4. Drugs that are given names by the companies that make them: __(brand names)__
5. Ingredients in a medicine that produce physical effects on the body: __(active ingredients)__
6. Ingredients that give medicine qualities other than medical effects: __(inactive ingredients)__
7. A disease that lasts a long time is a __(chronic)__ disease.
8. The federal agency that divides medicines into two classes: __(FDA)__
9. You can save money by using a __(generic drug)__ rather than the same drug sold with a brand name.
10. The person you need to see if OTC drugs don't bring relief: __health care provider__

TEEN VIEWS

Do people take too much medicine?

Some people take medicine like it is candy. People who do that can very easily take an overdose (O.D.). I have experienced someone in my family having an overdose. It is not a pretty sight. It's really scary to the person who took the overdose and to the family. **Lisa Nicole Delk, 15, Fern Creek High School, KY**

Yes, I think that doctors are prescribing too much medicine. I have a friend who has cystic fibrosis. When she came to stay the weekend, she was taking about five pills at every meal, and even more in between meals. It scares me to watch her take handfuls of pills every day. Right now there is no cure for cystic fibrosis.

She has to take the medicine prescribed or she would die. **Jill Schmidt, 14, Fargo South High School, ND**

Most people take too much medicine. People who have psychological illnesses believe that the more medicine they take, the better they will feel. Many doctors overprescribe medicine. My grandmother has diabetes and heart problems. Every time she went to the doctor, he would give her at least two more pills to take. She was taking about ten pills until her doctor realized that her problem was probably due to overmedication. Even

though medicine is good for you, taking too much can also be harmful. **Tyrisha Holloway, 16, Orange Park High School, FL**

I think people take too much medicine. They do not rely on themselves for healing. There are medicines people must take for a cure or for reduction of pain, but there are many others that do not fall in that category. People who have a cold often overlook rest, fluids, and nutritious food. They opt for a couple decongestants and a lot of cough medicine. The same applies to a headache. Instead of relaxing, many people will just take a few aspirin. **Alecia McKay-Jones, 15, East High School, MN**

ure 12–4 on the next page shows what else you might find on a medicine label.

Both OTC drugs and prescription drugs are referred to by two terms. First, **generic names** are the chemical names of drugs. These generic names never begin with capital letters. Second, **brand names** are the names given to drugs by the companies that make them. They are always capitalized. (They also have a circled *R* by their names, meaning "registered trademark.")

One generic drug may have several brand names.

MINI GLOSSARY

generic (jeh-NEHR-ick) **names:** the chemical names for drugs, as opposed to the brand names; the names everyone can use.
brand names: the names companies give to drugs; the names by which they are sold.

Teacher Support Notes

① **Teen Views Follow-up Questions:** Here are some questions you may want to use to encourage discussion of the ideas expressed by the students in the Teen Views Feature:
a. Have any of the students or any people they know taken an overdose of a medical drug? What were the results?
b. Do students agree with Lisa Delk that some people take medicine "like it is candy"? If so, why do people do this?
c. Are doctors guilty of prescribing too much medicine, as Jill Schmidt thinks? Do students have any personal experiences that would support this idea?

The vast majority of students polled responded "yes" to this question, yet the fact that people purchase billions of dollars worth of drugs every year suggests that many people have a different view. Ask students if any of them would like to argue that people do *not* take too much medicine.

CLOSE
SECTION III

FOCUS
SECTION IV

Activity 4.1
Prescription Drugs. Have students call out illnesses and disorders that are treated with prescription drugs. Compile the list on the chalkboard. Discuss what life would be like without prescription drugs. **(10–15 min., Critical Thinking)**

Activity 4.2
Discussion. Have students discuss the benefits of having a doctor prescribe

Activity 3.4
Questions. Students should be able to answer the following questions: **1.** What is the difference between over-the-counter drugs and prescription drugs? **2.** What are the advantages of using generic drugs? **(15–30 min.; Reteach, Reinforce)**

In this section students will learn:
1. Why prescription drugs are not freely available.
2. What to ask the physician before taking a prescribed drug.
3. How to take medicines safely.

Section III Review
Answers

1. a. Active ingredients produce physical effects on the body, while inactive ingredients give a medicine qualities such as flavor, color, or any others that don't affect the body.
b. Over-the-counter drugs are available legally without a prescription, while prescription drugs are available only with a physician's order.
2. saving money
3. hard for people to misuse them, most people require about the same doses, instructions are easy to understand, not abused in the usual sense as they do not produce sensations that drug abusers seek
4. Answers will vary. Refer to Figure 12–4 for possible answers.
5. They contain stimulants that raise the heart rate and blood pressure. The misuse of diet pills has been linked to seizures and bleeding inside the head.
6. the companies that make them
7. Answers will vary.

✉ Where to Write

Food and Drug Administration
5600 Fishers Lane
Rockville, MD 20857

You can often save money by using a generic drug rather than the same drug sold with a brand name. Ask your physician or pharmacist first, though. A generic drug contains the same **active ingredients** as the brand-name drug. However, it may have different **inactive ingredients**—which may affect its use in the body.

While OTC drugs can help relieve symptoms, they do nothing to treat the underlying illness. Sick people who take OTC drugs can be tempted to carry on with their regular routines instead of resting in bed until they are well. This makes it likely that they'll be sick longer. They may even suffer **relapses**.

If OTC medicines don't bring you the relief you seek, it's time to visit your health care provider. Any health care provider can advise you on what actions to take. If you need prescription medicine you'll need to consult a physician. To see how well you choose OTC medicines, try this chapter's Life Choice Inventory on page 305.

> **Key Points** *Medicines are divided into two classes: over-the-counter (OTC) drugs and prescription drugs. OTC drugs are safe if used correctly and according to directions. OTC drugs can be overused, however. Both OTC and prescription drugs are given two names: generic names and brand names. Drugs have both active and inactive ingredients.*

SECTION III REVIEW

Answer the following questions on a sheet of paper.
Learning the Vocabulary
The vocabulary terms in this section are *over-the-counter (OTC) drugs, prescription drugs, chronic, generic names, brand names, active ingredients, inactive ingredients,* and *relapses.*
1. Explain the differences between the following terms:
   a. active ingredients and inactive ingredients
   b. over-the-counter drugs and prescription drugs

Learning the Facts
2. What are the benefits of buying generic drugs?

FIGURE 12-4

What You'll Find on a Medicine Label

The drug label lists:
- Name and statement of identity of the product.
- What the product will do.
- Quantity of contents.
- Active ingredients and, usually, inactive ingredients.
- Name and address of the manufacturer, distributor, or packer.

It also lists directions:
- The correct amount of each dose.
- How frequently it should be used.
- How to use it (take by mouth, with water, and so on).

- How to store it.
- When to throw it away (the expiration date).

Finally, it lists warnings:
- A limit on the duration of use.
- Side effects, if any (drowsiness, constipation, and the like).
- Circumstances that may require a health care provider's advice before use.
- A warning to the pregnant woman to seek the advice of her health care provider before using the product.

medicines. **(10–15 min., Critical Thinking)**

TEACH

SECTION IV
(Guided and Independent Practice)

Activity 4.3
Reasons for Prescriptions. In teams of four, have each student in turn give one reason prescribed drugs can be obtained only by a physician's order. Have students check this page of their texts to ensure that they listed all the reasons. **(10–15 min., Cooperative Learning)**

Activity 4.4
Medical Treatment Barriers. Have students discuss the reasons a person might not seek treatment from a physician. Some reasons that you might suggest are: lack of opportunity (no doctors available), inadequate insurance, lack of money, ignorance, fear, and religious or cultural taboos. This activity provides an opportunity to promote an understanding, and an appreciation for various cultures in our society. Have students discuss ways of overcoming the barriers that keep those who want medical care from receiving it. **(15–30 min., Multicultural)**

(continued on next page)

---

3. What makes over-the-counter drugs relatively safe?
4. List at least five things you find on a medicine label.
5. Describe the problems associated with the misuse of diet pills.
6. Who gives brand names to drugs?

Making Life Choices

7. Angela has a cold and sore throat. At the drug store she buys a night-time cold medicine so she can sleep, something to take during the day so she won't be drowsy, a cough medicine, nasal spray, and throat gargle. Should she be taking all these together? What advice would you give Angela?

SECTION IV

Prescription Medicines

Prescription drugs are drugs that are not freely available. You can't buy them over the counter. They can be obtained only if prescribed (ordered) by physicians, because:

- They may be dangerous. They can easily be misused.
- The doses must be adjusted to body weight, age, drug use, or other factors.
- They require guidance to use them correctly. They may have complicated directions.
- They can be abused. They can cause addiction or have other serious side effects.

Prescription drugs are true miracles of our time, when they are used correctly. As an example, for a person whose cells can not properly use the sugar glucose in the blood, insulin is a lifesaving medicine. Another miracle: a person whose heart can no longer use calcium may take a calcium channel blocker, so that the life-giving heartbeat can go on.

When using prescription drugs, follow safety guidelines.

Prescription medicines can be misused, though. A physician may prescribe these drugs, but the taker has a part to play, too, in using them correctly.

Suppose your cold symptoms do not go away, but instead grow worse after two weeks of rest and OTC medication. You begin to wonder if your illness is more serious than a cold. You wisely decide to see a health care professional, who prescribes a medicine for you. Before leaving the physician's office with your prescription, be sure that you know:

- The name of your condition.
- The name of the prescribed medicine.

MINI GLOSSARY

active ingredients: ingredients in a medicine that produce physical effects on the body.

inactive ingredients: ingredients that give a medicine qualities other than medical effects. For example, oils and waxes may be mixed with a medication to be used on the skin; water, colorants, and flavors may be added to liquid medicines taken by mouth.

relapses: illnesses that return after being treated and almost cured. Relapses are often more severe than the original illnesses.

Teacher Support Notes

① **Physician's Diagnosis:** Ask students if they have ever been examined by a doctor and then left the office not really knowing any more about their conditions than before the visit. If this happened, was it because the doctor did not explain the condition, or did the student not understand the doctor's explanation? You might tell students that it's not uncommon for people to be intimidated by doctors. People are reluctant to ask questions. Students should remember that they are paying the doctor for a service and that they should receive the service they want. The bulleted list is a good checklist to use in making sure that they have all the information they need when they leave the doctor's office.

Activity 4.5
Physician/Patient Role-Playing. Students role-play in pairs; one is the prescribing physician, the other the patient who asks all the right questions. The physician should check pages 303 and 304 in the text to ensure that the patient

has not omitted any questions. When the patient has finished asking questions, reverse roles. **(10–15 min., Special Needs)**

Activity 4.6
Medicinal Guidelines. Have students work in teams of four to list as many of the guidelines for taking medicines safely as they can think of. Each student in turn describes a guideline to his or her

teammates. Allow 15 minutes for this review activity, then have one representative from each team report its results. Compile a class list. Discuss which team offered the most comprehensive list, and if any guidelines were omitted. **(30–45 min.; Cooperative Learning, Special Needs)**

EVALUATE
SECTION IV

---

66 Thoughts on Health 99

Medicine is a collection of uncertain prescriptions, the results of which, taken collectively, are more fatal than useful to mankind. Water, air, and cleanliness are the chief articles in my pharmacopeia.

– Napoleon

Teacher Support Notes

① **Handout—Analyzing Medicine Use:** As you conclude the chapter, you may want to use the handout that presents students with two different scenarios involving medicines and asks students to analyze the situations.
② **Strategies for Taking Medicine Safely:** Have students evaluate their behaviors for each of the strategies listed in this box. For each strategy they should say *yes, no, not sure, sometimes* to indicate how often they use the strategy.

✍ Fast Facts

According to a recent study, zinc lozenges taken soon after cold symptoms begin reduced the length and severity of the cold.

---

304   UNIT 4 Drug Use and Abuse

- How often, how long, and in what doses you should take the medicine.
- Whether to take the medicine with meals or between them.
- What side effects you should look for and report.
- What you should do if you forget to take a dose on time—double the next one, take it late, or leave it out entirely.

Also, be sure that your physician knows about other medicines you are taking. Other strategies for taking medications, both OTC and prescription, are summed up in the Health Strategies section on this page, "Taking Medicines Safely."

Key Points ①   *Taking prescription medication safely requires that you understand the diagnosis, know what medicine is being prescribed, and follow instructions. Follow recommended guidelines for use, storage, disposal, and replacement of medicines, too.*

SECTION IV   REVIEW

Learning the Facts
1. Prescription drugs are true miracles of our time, when they are used correctly. What are the two examples discussed in this section?
2. List four reasons why prescription drugs can only be obtained with a physician's order or prescription.

HEALTH STRATEGIES

Taking Medicines Safely   ②

To take medicine safely, follow these guidelines:

1. Check with your physician or pharmacist before substituting generic for brand-name prescription medicine.
2. Read and follow instructions on labels or on package inserts.
3. Do not share prescription medicine with other people who seem to have the same illness that you did. Their illnesses could be different. Furthermore, a drug or dose that is safe for you may be dangerous for someone else.
4. Do not mix drugs (including OTC and other drugs) without checking first with your physician or pharmacist.
5. Avoid alcohol when using medicine.
6. Throw away any unused prescription medicine or an OTC drug that has expired. Drugs break down into unknown, untested chemicals as they age.

7. Store drugs in a cool, dark place. Be especially careful in the summertime—medicines left in a hot car can turn into who-knows-what. Some drugs must be refrigerated and others protected from light.
8. Call your physician if the drug isn't doing what you expect it to.
9. Call your physician if you develop side effects.
10. Keep the drug in its original container.
11. When taking medicine at night, turn on the light to see the label and your dose.
12. Take the entire prescription of medicine, even if you feel better right away. After the symptoms are gone, the underlying cause remains, and the drug must wipe it out completely.
13. Keep all medicines where young children cannot get them.

Activity 4.7
Pop Quiz.

1. Drugs that are not freely available: _(prescription drugs)_ .
2. Before substituting a generic medicine for a brand-name prescription consult your _(physician)_ .
3. Unused prescription medicine should be _(thrown away)_ .
4. Store drugs in a _(cool, dark)_ place.

CLOSE

> SECTION IV

Activity 4.8
Questions. Students should be able to answer these questions: **1.** List three reasons prescription drugs are not freely available. **2.** List five questions one should ask the doctor before taking a prescribed medicine. **3.** List ten guidelines to follow when taking medicine. **(Reteach, Reinforce)**

RETEACH/BONUS

Interviews—Home Remedies. Have students research home remedies by interviewing one another. Students will

(continued on next page)

Ch. 12 Drugs as Medicines **305**

LIFE CHOICE INVENTORY

How Wisely Do You Choose OTC Medications?

Answer yes or no to these questions to find out how smart an OTC drug shopper you are.

1. When I have an ailment, I do not go straight to the drugstore. First, I ask myself honestly if there's a lifestyle change I need to make, such as getting more sleep, eating better, or exercising more. If so, I make the change. 4 points
2. If I have an ailment that I think would respond to an OTC medicine, I first consult a medical book or a pharmacist to confirm my suspicions. 3 points
3. I buy only the medicines I need to relieve my symptoms. (Example: a cough suppressant, not an inflammation reliever, for a cough). 3 points
4. I read drug labels and buy by chemical names, not by brand names. 3 points
5. In taking medicines, I read their labels and follow directions as to dose, timing, and duration. 3 points
6. I do not overbuy, and I throw away drugs after their expiration dates have passed. 2 points
7. Before taking two or more drugs, I check with my health care provider or pharmacist to be sure there is no cross-reaction. 3 points
8. If my symptoms persist, I see a health care professional. 2 points

SCORING

For each yes answer, give yourself the number of points indicated.
23: Perfect score! You are a wise user of OTC medicines.
18–22: Very good. Identify the questions you missed, and raise your score to 23.
13–17: Not so good. You could be harming your health or wasting money by using OTC drugs unwisely or unnecessarily.
12 or under: Improvement needed. Think, revise your behaviors, and take this quiz again.

---

3. The Health Strategies feature "Taking Medicines Safely" offers thirteen guidelines for taking medicines. List five of them.

Making Life Choices

4. After taking the Life Choice Inventory on this page, are you satisfied with your results? What will you do to improve your results? What guidelines can you offer to your family and friends who use over-the-counter drugs to help insure that they do so safely and effectively?

Answers to Fact or Fiction

Here are the answers to the questions at the start of the chapter.

1. False. All drug use involves risk.
2. False. Everyone who takes aspirin receives *all* of its effects. **3.** True.
4. True. **5.** False. Generic drugs contain the same active ingredients, but may contain different inactive ingredients.

Section IV Review
Answers

1. insulin and calcium channel blockers
2. they may be dangerous; doses must be adjusted to body weight, age, or drug use; require guidance to use them correctly; can be abused
3. Answers will vary. Refer to Health Strategies, Taking Medicines Safely, on page 304 for possible answers.
4. Answers will vary.

 Fast Facts

Some experts recommend eating yogurt while taking antibiotics. The antibiotic kills good bacteria as well as bad ones. The acidophilus in yogurt may introduce beneficial bacteria back into your system.

305

need to question their parents about family remedies beforehand. This activity is designed to foster understanding and acceptance among students from diverse backgrounds, to help build an awareness of one's cultural heritage, and to promote an understanding and an appreciation for the culture and contributions of all members of our society. Remind students to compile the information and refrain from negative comments. Students interview each other in pairs, first one way, then the other. Students each share with the class information they learned in the interview. You may want to refer students to the Chapter 24 Straight Talk, which discusses home remedies. Compile a class list. Have a class discussion. **(Extend, Enrich, Multicultural)**

Panel Discussions. Have the class work in teams of four. Each team represents a panel of personal health consultants. They are to recommend treatment for a cold. Allow the teams 15 minutes to formulate their recommendations. Have one spokesperson per team describe its recommendations to the class. Have a class discussion. Ask the students to describe

---

✏ Fast Facts

The National Coffee Association in New York City estimates that the average American drinks 3.4 cups of coffee each day. They also estimate that 385,000 Americans drink at least ten cups of coffee each day.

Teacher Support Notes

① **Handout—Caffeine Contents of Foods and Drugs:** In your supplementary material you will find a handout entitled "Caffeine Contents of Beverages, Foods, and OTC Drugs." This handout gives the caffeine content in milligrams for various food and drug items. You may want to distribute this handout to the students or make a transparency to use during your presentation of this topic.

✉ Where to Write

National Clearinghouse for Drug Abuse Information
5454 Wisconsin Avenue
Chevy Chase, MD 20015

STRAIGHT TALK

Caffeine ①

*In our society, people start using **caffeine** during youth with their first cola drink, chocolate bar, or glass of iced tea. Caffeine in coffee and other medications comes later, as adults look for a wake-up effect. Lately, though, some people have been cutting back on their caffeine use because they fear that caffeine may cause harm.*

What exactly does caffeine do?

Caffeine is a **stimulant** drug, so it peps up the activity of the central nervous system (the brain and spinal cord). Some of its effects feel like a pick-me-up, with reduced drowsiness and fatigue and a sharpened focus on tasks at hand. The effect on you depends on how much you take in and how much you're used to, as well as your individual makeup. Most people notice a speeded-up heart rate and feel their muscles tense when they take in the amount contained in two to five cups of brewed coffee. More than this can cause abnormal symptoms.

What symptoms does caffeine produce?

It produces signs of stress. Prolonged stress can weaken the body. Caffeine also acts as a diuretic—a drug that makes the body lose water through frequent urination. Caffeine also stimulates stomach acid secretion. This means that it will irritate the stomach, especially in a person likely to get ulcers. The most severe effect of caffeine is fatal poisoning, but that occurs only with huge doses. For example, if a child accidentally ate 30 or so wake-up pills (which contain caffeine), emergency treatment would be required to save the child's life.

Scientists are studying links between caffeine and heart disease, adult bone loss, and a painful breast condition called fibrocystic breast disease.

How can I tell if I'm getting too much caffeine?

If you take more caffeine than the amount in about five cups of coffee, your heartbeat may become irregular, and you may feel your heart pounding. You may have trouble sleeping. You may have headaches, trembling, nervousness, and other symptoms of anxiety.

When a person reports these symptoms to a physician, the condition may be hard to diagnose because the symptoms are like those of mental anxiety. The physician who is unaware of a person's caffeine use may mistakenly prescribe calming tranquilizers or recommend a psychiatrist. All the person really needs is to cut down on caffeine intake.

All of caffeine's symptoms seem to hit children the hardest. Children love colas and chocolate, but these must be strictly limited. As people age, they once again become sensitive to caffeine and must restrict intakes.

I've heard a friend say, as a joke, "I'm addicted to cola!" Is caffeine addictive?

Your friend may have built up a tolerance to caffeine by taking in large amounts daily. Caffeine resembles many

(Continued on next page)

how they formulated their decisions. Discuss the source of treatment. Was it based on personal experience, factual knowledge, or influenced by ads? **(Critical Thinking, Cooperative Learning)**

Role-Playing. Students role-play in pairs. One partner plays the role of a medical consultant, the other plays the role of a parent of a sick eight-year-old. The parent describes the symptoms the child has just developed: nausea with severe vomiting, a temperature of 103°, inactivity, loss of consciousness, and uncontrollable behavior while unconscious. The parent tells the medical consultant that the child is recovering from the flu. The consultant must give a diagnosis and prognosis. **(15 min., Critical Thinking)**

STRAIGHT TALK *(Continued)*

other drugs in this way. The more you take in, the more your body builds equipment to dispose of it, and the more you need for an effect.

If your friend were to suddenly stop using caffeine, withdrawal symptoms might

WOW... WEE...

The caffeine withdrawal headache is a symptom of addiction.

start: anxiety, muscle tension, and a headache that no painkiller can relieve. A dose or two of caffeine can reverse withdrawal symptoms. Thus people soon learn that they can relieve their symptoms by taking more caffeine.

Is that why they put caffeine in headache medicines, then?

Yes. Someone with a caffeine-withdrawal headache

may try plain pain relievers, but these fail to cure the headache. When the person tries an "extra-strength" kind that include caffeine, the headache disappears. The person is led to believe (wrongly) that those pills are indeed stronger against pain in general, and so buys them regularly, thus increasing caffeine intake even more.

If caffeine is addictive, as you say, is my friend engaging in drug abuse?

You may want to read the next chapter and then ask yourself that question. Certainly, if your friend takes caffeine *pills* to avoid withdrawal, then yes, your friend is abusing drugs. However, if your friend drinks only colas, then the caffeine is a food component, not officially a drug. That is why caffeine can be added to soft drinks—it occurs naturally in the kola nut and is an expected part of the product.

Do you think we should all do without caffeine?

Most likely not. The equivalent of one cola beverage a day is almost certainly safe for any teenager. For healthy adults, caffeine seems to be relatively harmless in moderate doses (the equivalent of about two

cups of coffee a day). Pregnant women and young children might be wise to do without it, though, just because some questions about caffeine are still unanswered.

Can you suggest some alternatives to beverages that contain caffeine?

Certainly. All sorts of sodas are caffeine-free these days. Decaffeinated coffee is an old standby. (By the way, there is no truth in the rumor that decaffeinated coffee contains dangerous chemicals.) Decaffeinated tea and teas made from mint or other herbs are delicious. Be careful about using herbal teas, though. Many herbs contain *other* chemicals that are harmful. Don't forget the best thirst quencher—a glass of ice-cold water. Also, juice and milk are "natural" drinks with a health bonus—nutrients your body needs.

Mini Glossary

caffeine: a mild stimulant of the central nervous system (brain and spinal cord) found in common foods, beverages, and medicines.

stimulant: any of a wide variety of drugs, including amphetamines, caffeine, and others, that speed up the central nervous system.

Teacher Support Notes

① **Caffeine and Hyperactivity:** For enrichment you may want to tell students that excess caffeine can overstimulate children. Two or more 12-ounce cola beverages could contain as much as 100 milligrams of caffeine. In a 60-pound child this amount of caffeine is equivalent to the caffeine contained in eight cups of coffee for a 175-pound man. Chocolate bars can also be a source of excessive caffeine for children.

✒ Fast Facts

Caffeine raises body temperature because it stimulates metabolism. When running a fever avoid fluids with caffeine in them. That's why hospitals use 7-Up.

Vocabulary

1. Answers will vary.
2. Generic names are the chemical names of drugs and never begin with capital letters. Brand names are the names given to the drugs by the company that makes them and are always capitalized.
3. a. caffeine **b.** antagonist **c.** prescription drugs **d.** relapses
4. a. Active ingredients **b.** stimulant **c.** addiction
5. a. Antibiotics **b.** aspirin, acetaminophen, ibuprofen **c.** safe **d.** Over-the-counter drugs

Recall

Section I

1. Answers will vary; could include: prevent disease, help in the cure of disease, make diseases less severe, relieve symptoms, and bring about other desired effects.
2. aspirin
3. reduces fever, reduces inflammation, relieves pain, prevents the blood from clotting
4. nausea with severe vomiting, fever, inactivity, loss of consciousness, uncontrollable behavior while unconscious
5. Answers will vary. Refer to Figure 12–2 on page 294 for possible answers.
6. Answers will vary; could include: nature of the drug; form in which it is taken; route by which it is taken; whether or not it is taken with food; age; weight; expectations; other drugs taken; and taker's history of drug use.
7. a state that develops in users of certain drugs that makes larger and larger amounts of the drugs neces-

---

CHAPTER REVIEW

LEARNING THE VOCABULARY

drugs	addiction	chronic
medicines	antagonist	generic
aspirin	safe	brand names
inflammation	effective	active ingredients
acetaminophen	antibiotics	inactive ingredients
ibuprofen	anesthetics	relapses
side effects	lethal dose	caffeine
antihistamines	over-the-counter drugs	stimulant
tolerance	prescription drugs	

Answer the following questions on a separate sheet of paper.

1. Write a paragraph using at least ten vocabulary terms. Underline each term used.
2. Explain the differences between a drug's generic name and its brand name.
3. *Matching*—Match each of the following phrases with the appropriate vocabulary term from the list above:
   a. a stimulant drug
   b. a drug that opposes the action of another drug
   c. drugs available only with a physician's order
   d. illnesses that return after being treated and almost cured
4. *Word Scramble*—Use the clues given to help you unscramble the words:

   a. **aiectv iieegtsdrnn** _____ _____
      produce physical effects on the body.
   b. **aiuttslmn** _____ any of a variety of drugs that speed up the central nervous system.
   c. **aiioddctn** _____ physical or psychological craving for higher doses of drugs.
5. a. _____ are drugs used to fight bacterial infections.
   b. There are three different drugs that are used to relieve fever, pain, and inflammation. They are _____, _____, and _____.
   c. A drug that is _____ causes no undue harm.
   d. _____ are legally available without a prescription.

RECALLING IMPORTANT FACTS AND IDEAS

1. List three ways in which medicines benefit people.
2. What is one of the oldest known painkillers?
3. Name four things aspirin does to the body.
4. List the five warning signs of Reye's Syndrome.
5. Refer to Figure 12–2, "Side Effects of Commonly Used Medicines." Name one severe hazard from each type of medicine.
6. Describe the factors that alter a drug's effects on the body.
7. Define *tolerance* (to a drug). What body organs are affected by an increase in drug tolerance?
8. Many accidental deaths occur when two particular drugs are taken together. What are the two drugs?
9. What is the purpose of a drug that acts as an antagonist?
10. List three things the FDA must do in order to approve a new drug.
11. Why are antibiotic drugs the safest drugs?
12. What is the difference between generic drugs and brand name drugs?
13. How much money is spent yearly on over-the-counter drugs?

sary to produce the same effect; liver, kidneys

8. sleeping pills and alcohol

9. to prevent the action of another drug, in cases such as an overdose, poisoning, or snake bite

Section II

10. They must evaluate drug safety and effectiveness; check to make sure the company has followed all the right scientific procedures; and after the drug is on the market, they continue to check for side effects.

11. Once the antibiotic is out of the system, the body's own cells soon recover after the bacteria has been killed.

Section III

12. The generic name is the chemical name of a drug, while the brand name is the name given to a drug by the company that makes it.

13. many billions of dollars

14. The FDA regulates what is printed on the labels, but not what is printed on information sheets. This allows for lies to be printed on information sheets.

14. What is the legal difference between information sheets and printing on drug labels?

15. What information should you know before leaving the physician's office with your prescription?

16. What effects does caffeine have on the central nervous system?

17. List three side effects of caffeine.

18. Describe the withdrawal symptoms of caffeine addiction.

CRITICAL THINKING

1. Discuss some of the problems people may face from taking aspirin regularly. How can healthier alternatives to aspirin be promoted? How could you publicize this information in your school?

2. Other countries put drugs on the market faster than the United States. Many people go out of the country for these drugs. The Food and Drug Administration has strict guidelines. Do you think the FDA's guidelines are too strict? Do you think it is safe for many Americans to use other countries' drugs? What possible problems could occur?

3. On Friday night, Kyle suffered a painful swollen shoulder during the football game. To relieve the pain he took a friend's prescription drug containing codeine. Soon Kyle experienced nausea. What should he do? What should he have done after the injury?

ACTIVITIES

1. Make a chart of all the prescription drugs you find in your medicine cabinet at home. The chart should contain a list of the following categories: the name of the prescription drug; the expiration date; the dosage; and any warnings listed on the bottle (i.e., Do not take without food, May cause drowsiness, etc.) How many different drugs did you find? Compare your findings with those of others in your class. What was the average amount of drugs found per household?

2. Watch TV for one hour and write down all the advertisements that relate to drugs. How many advertisements are for over-the-counter drugs? What does that tell you about our society and the use of drugs? Take an advertisement that promotes the use of a drug to relieve a health problem and change it to an advertisement that promotes no drugs, but healthful activities, for relief.

3. Bring in one article from a newspaper or magazine about the problem(s) of over-the-counter drug use. Highlight information the class has discussed. Read aloud parts of the article the class has not discussed.

4. Keep a list of all the over-the-counter drugs or prescription drugs you use in a week. Go back over the list and see which drugs you take without even thinking about it. Which drugs could you omit from your weekly intake? How could you eliminate all of the drugs you are taking?

5. Make a video for local elementary schools and high schools showing the effects caffeine has on the body and explain why it's the most widely used over-the-counter drug.

MAKING DECISIONS ABOUT HEALTH

1. You have been feeling tired and run-down lately. Your hectic schedule, which includes school full-time, work part-time, and participation on a softball team, leaves no time for adequate rest or proper nutrition. You decide to make a trip to the health food store to see if you can buy something to give you more energy. You spot a bottle that looks interesting. An information sheet nearby promises to give you renewed energy, stamina, and mental alertness, and to clean toxins out of your blood. Are such remedies more effective or safer than non-prescription, over-the-counter drugs? Why or why not? What can you say about the reliability of the information presented on the information sheet next to the remedy?

309

Chapter 13 Planner

Overview

Chapter 13 is 36 pages long and is divided into the seven sections listed to the right. Major learning outcomes are also listed to the right. The chapter explains the difference between drug use, misuse, and abuse. It introduces students to all the personal problems associated with these national problems, and explains why people still use drugs. The chapter then gives students effective tools to use to help kick the habit of drug abuse and to replace it with their own drug-free highs. This chapter includes opportunities for students to acknowledge how drug abuse might affect their future goals. It provides them opportunities to practice refusing drugs, tobacco, or alcohol, and to protect others from drug, alcohol, and tobacco abuse.

Making Life Choices Resources

A variety of activities, handouts, quizzes, and tests to accompany this chapter are available in the *Making Life Choices* supplementary material. You may pick and choose from those materials as appropriate for your amount of class time and the ability levels of your students. Some of the resources you might want to consider using are:

Handouts
• Attitudes About Drug Abuse
• Mini Glossary of Drug Abuse Terms

Overheads
• The Downward Spiral of Physiological Addiction
• The Cycle of Psychological Addiction
• Stimulation to Depression

Teacher Information Sheet
• Stopping Drug Addiction

Answers to "Fact or Fiction"

1. True. **2.** False. Even people who are fully aware of the hazards abuse drugs. **3.** False. People continue abusing drugs to avoid the pain of withdrawal symptoms. **4.** False. Psychological addictions can be as powerful as physical ones. **5.** False. Smoking marijuana is associated with harmful health effects. **6.** True. **7.** False. Amphetamines impair driving ability. **8.** False. People rarely recover from drug dependency on their own.

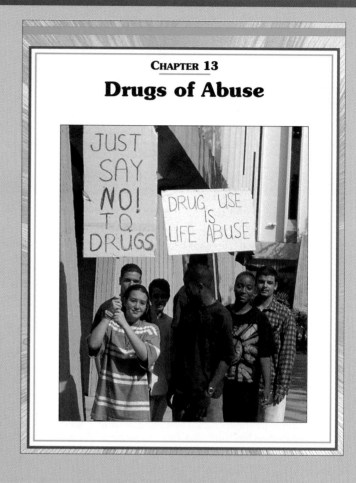

Chapter 13
Drugs of Abuse

Chapter Project

Have students work together in groups to produce their own antidrug public service announcement videos. Offer suggestions—choose a central theme, target an audience (such as elementary-school children), and use creativity to make the message appealing. Show the videos to the class, then select one or two to show the entire school and possibly other schools, such as junior high and elementary schools.

Activity To Introduce Chapter

To emphasize to students just how big a problem drug abuse is in our society, invite a judge or lawyer to visit your class and explain how drug abuse affects all aspects of our society. This should introduce the chapter as well as establish why students should learn how they can help on an individual level. Also have students brainstorm a list of why students take drugs. Follow up by reading current event articles related to crime or death as a result of drug abuse. **(1 hour)**

OUTCOMES

After reading and studying this chapter, you will be able to:

✓ Define and differentiate among drug use, drug misuse, and drug abuse.
✓ Describe the three factors that lead people to drug abuse.
✓ Explain the problems associated with physical and psychological addiction.
✓ Identify the effects of marijuana and related drugs.
✓ Define and discuss the abuse of narcotics, depressants, and stimulants.
✓ Describe the effects of inhalants, look-alike drugs, and designer drugs.
✓ List the signs of drug abuse.
✓ Describe ways to enjoy a drug-free high.

CONTENTS

I. Drug Abuse Defined
II. Why Do People Abuse Drugs?
III. Addiction
IV. Commonly Abused Drugs
V. Drugs and Driving
VI. Kicking the Habit
VII. Helping Someone Else Kick the Habit

Straight Talk: *Teens and Social Problems*

FACT OR FICTION

What do you think? *Are the following statements true or false? If you think they are false, then say what is true.*

1. People with low self-esteem are more likely to abuse drugs than people with high self-esteem.
2. People who abuse drugs are unaware of the hazards the drugs present.
3. When people become addicted to drugs, the primary reason they continue to take them is to experience pleasure.
4. A physical addiction is more powerful than a psychological addiction.
5. Smoking marijuana provides a harmless high.
6. Smoking marijuana is more damaging to the lungs than smoking tobacco cigarettes.
7. Amphetamines improve people's driving because they speed up the nervous system.
8. People usually recover from drug dependency on their own.

(Answers on page 339)

■ **Reminder:** Knowing how to study can increase your knowledge, improve your grades, *and* cut down on your study time. See the *Studying Health* section at the front of your text for some suggestions to help you study this chapter.

SUGGESTED RESOURCES

Student Readings
1. Dusek, D. E., and Girdano, D. A. *Drugs: A Factual Account.* 4th ed. New York: Random House, 1987.

Teacher Readings
1. Witters, Weldon and Venturelli, Peter. *Drugs and Society.* Boston: Jones and Bartlett Publishers, 1988.

Videos
1. *The Danger Zone: Substance Abuse.* AAVIM, 745 Gaines School Road, Athens, GA 30605, 800-228-4689.

Software
1. *Drug Abuse Learning Environment (DALE).* Substance Abuse Education, Inc., 913-441-1868.

NOT ENOUGH TIME?*

This is a very important chapter. You will probably want to spend four or five days teaching it. Following are some suggestions to help you make sure that you cover the key topics if you have limited time.

TIME	SUGGESTIONS
1 Day	Have students read Sections I and II prior to class. Have students practice the refusal skills found in Section II. Complete Activity 2.2. Assign students to read Section III for the day 2 lesson.
2 Days	On day 2, have students develop a drug-free plan for their futures. Spend any remaining time going over students' answers to Activity 3.2 orally. Assign students to read Section IV for homework for the day 3 lesson.
3 Days	On day 3, briefly discuss the drug categories and their effects listed in Section IV. Have student groups read about and present information about each drug category. Assign students to describe the nine groups of drugs by writing a paragraph for each group. Assign Section V as reading homework for the day 4 lesson.
4 Days	On day 4, take a few minutes for Activity 5.1. Assign students to answer the Section V review questions. Go over answers, then have students complete the Close activity from Section V. Ask students to read Sections VI and VII for the day 5 lesson.
5 Days	Have students answer the essay question in Activity 7.5. Have students explore the issue of protecting their friends from drug abuse by using activities found in Section VII, such as 7.3 and 7.6.

*Please refer to the 18-week daily lesson plans in the supplementary material for additional suggestions.

In this section students will:
1. Define drug use, abuse, and misuse.
2. Explore society's views of drug use and abuse.

Activity 1.1
Use, Abuse, and Misuse. List some drug use, abuse, and misuse situations on the board. An example of each would be taking aspirin for a headache, snorting cocaine at a party, and taking sleeping pills each night. Ask students to add to each list. **(10–15 min., Critical Thinking)**

TEACH
SECTION I
(Guided and Independent Practice)

Activity 1.2
The Prices People Pay. Have students brainstorm a list of positive and negative consequences that can result from drug use, abuse, misuse, and even recreational or social use. If any positive consequences are listed, discuss them with the class and decide under what circumstances they might be positive. **(10 min., Critical Thinking)**

Teacher Support Notes

① **Debates About Drugs:** Ask students if they have ever been involved in emotional discussions about drugs and drug abuse. What points were being argued? Which side were they on? Why do they think that the drug abuse topic is such an emotional one?

② **Handout—Attitudes About Drugs:** As students begin the chapter, you may want to use the handout in your supplementary material entitled "Attitudes About Drug Abuse" to help students evaluate their present attitudes about drugs, before they begin the chapter. Be sure they realize there are no right or wrong answers.

③ **Drug Use:** To help reinforce the definition of drug use for students, ask them to give examples. (taking aspirin for a headache according to the directions on the bottle, taking antibiotics prescribed by a doctor, etc.)

④ **Drug Abuse:** Now ask students to give examples of drug abuse. Seek examples involving both medicines and illegal drugs. (smoking marijuana, taking too many tranquilizers for the purpose of obtaining an emotional high)

312

312   UNIT 4   Drug Use and Abuse

A concerned mother tells her husband that she is upset about her son's smoking marijuana—his drug abuse. She is so uptight that she takes a double dose of prescribed sleeping pills to calm her nerves.

A young man comes home from a stressful day at his high-pressure job and drinks a six-pack of beer to relax. On the 11 o'clock news, he hears a report of a local cocaine drug bust. He thinks to himself, "Those people who abuse drugs are such a problem to our society."

You've probably guessed that in the two scenes just described, the people concerned about drug abuse were also engaging in it. A discussion of drug abuse with these people could lead to heated debate. People trying to define drug abuse often disagree and end up in emotional discussions. What is drug abuse? Let's try to define it in an objective, nonemotional way.

SECTION I

Drug Abuse Defined

Definitions of drug abuse vary. Medical experts and the Food and Drug Administration (FDA) have created one set of formal definitions. Society has created another set of definitions. Individual people have created still others, based on their own drug histories and attitudes.

The FDA's definitions are these. **Drug use** is the taking of a drug, as medicine, correctly—that is, for its proper medical purpose and in the right amount, frequency, strength, and manner. In contrast, **drug abuse** is the taking of a drug for a nonmedical purpose, and in a manner that can damage a person's health or ability to function. All drugs can be abused, even those

prescribed by physicians. The FDA also defines **drug misuse** (of medical drugs only) as the taking of a drug for its correct medical purpose, but not in the right amount, frequency, strength, or manner. These definitions classify any use of drugs for nonmedical reasons as drug abuse. There is no such thing as mere "use"—for example, to socialize with friends—of a nonmedical drug.

Some individuals try to define drug abuse differently. Many people who take mind-altering drugs call themselves drug users, not abusers. They use the label **recreational drug use**. They claim to suffer no harmful health effects and no problems on the job, in the family, or in society. (People who call themselves *social drinkers* make these same claims.) The term *recreational drug use* does not hold much meaning, because abusers of drugs are not able to judge themselves fairly—their opinions are slanted.

Society's view of drug abuse can be seen in its laws. Society clearly displays its disapproval of mind-altering drugs—except for alcohol for adults—by making it illegal to possess, use, or sell them. By making these laws, society has defined the use of mind-altering drugs, except alcohol, as abuse.

Key Points *Drug abuse is the taking of a drug for a nonmedical purpose and in a manner that can damage a person's health or ability to function. Both legal and illegal drugs can be abused.*

SECTION I   REVIEW

Answer the following questions on a sheet of paper.
Learning the Vocabulary
The vocabulary terms in this section are *drug use, drug abuse, drug misuse,* and *recreational drug use.*
Match each of the following phrases with the appropriate term.
1. taking a drug for its medically intended purpose but not in the proper dose

Activity 1.3
Review Sentences. Have students finish the following sentences without using the book:
1. A drug abuser is . . . ; **2.** A drug misuser is . . . ; **3.** A drug user is . . . ; Students should be able to give descriptions that help define these classifications of drug usage.

CLOSE
SECTION I

Activity 1.4
Paragraphs on Drug Abuse. Have students describe, in a few short paragraphs, the different ways in which drugs are abused in our society.

FOCUS
SECTION II

In this section students will:
1. Practice refusal skills in situations involving drug and alcohol abuse.
2. Learn why people take drugs.
3. Learn the consequences of drug abuse.

(continued on next page)

---

2. a term made up by people who claim their drug taking produces no harmful social or health effects
3. deliberate taking of a drug for other than medical purposes
4. taking of a drug for its medically intended purpose

Learning the Facts
5. What two groups have gotten together to define drug abuse?
6. Why doesn't the term *recreational drug use* hold much meaning?
7. Describe how society's views of drug abuse are reflected in its laws.

Making Life Choices
8. The neighbors are growing marijuana in their backyard. They have told your parents that they use marijuana as a recreational drug. You have just learned about this drug in school that this drug is illegal and can harm health. How do you feel about confronting the neighbors? What will you do about the neighbors, if anything? Why?

SECTION II

Why Do People Abuse Drugs?

Different factors lead different people to abuse drugs. Among them are the nature of the person, the nature of the drug, and the possible consequences that await the abuser from both the family and the larger society.

The Nature of the Person

A person's physical or genetic nature affects the way that person relates to drugs. Scientists are studying people's genetic makeups in hopes of finding clues as to what makes some people abuse drugs.

Personality traits, too, may play a role in a person's tendency toward or away from

drug abuse. For example, some people are naturally curious, and curiosity can be a strong motivator. Many people try drugs to see what they are like. Most of these people don't, however, become chronic drug abusers. A few do continue trying drugs, and some become unable to stop.

A strong factor that motivates people to abuse drugs is peer pressure, already discussed in the Straight Talk section of Chapter 3. Drugs are often a part of social events, and the desire to fit in socially is strong, especially among the young. It is normal for a person to want to belong to a group. Belonging is a human need throughout life. The problem comes when drug-taking provides all or part of the reason that a group gets together. So strong is the human need to be a "member"—to fit into a group—that a person may abandon common sense, override internal warnings (fear), and go ahead and take drugs. The drive to belong is also responsible for other dangerous decisions, such as gang membership.

While it is important to have friends, it is more important to resist the pressure to fit

M**INI** G**LOSSARY**

drug use: the taking of a drug for its medically intended purpose, and in the appropriate amount, frequency, strength, and manner.

drug abuse: the deliberate taking of a drug for other than a medical purpose and in a manner that can result in damage to a person's health or ability to function.

drug misuse: the taking of a drug for its medically intended purpose, but not in the appropriate amount, frequency, strength, or manner.

recreational drug use: a term made up, to describe their drug use, by people who claim their drug-taking produces no harmful social or health effects; a term not defined by the FDA.

①

Section I Review
Answers
1. drug misuse
2. recreational drug use
3. drug abuse
4. drug use
5. medical experts and the FDA
6. because the abusers of drugs are not able to judge themselves fairly—their opinions are slanted
7. clear disapproval of mind-altering drugs—except for alcohol—by making it illegal to possess, use, or sell them
8. Answers will vary.

Teacher Support Notes

① **Reasons for Abusing Drugs:** Three reasons for abusing drugs are given on this page. (a person's physical or genetic nature; personality traits; peer pressure) Ask students to identify these reasons and then state what they believe is the most common reason of these three and why. Discuss.

use refusal skills and still keep their friends by following these steps:

1. Be direct, friendly, and confident in refusing.

2. List the consequences of getting caught.

3. Offer a fun alternative that will not get you in trouble.

4. If they refuse your alternative, leave an open invitation and walk away.

Divide the class into groups to role-

Activity 2.1

Brainstorm Why? Ask students why people abuse drugs. List their reasons on the board. Emphasize euphoria as a reason people continue to abuse drugs. **(5 min.)**

Activity 2.2

Role-Play. Ask for volunteers to role-play. Ask them to steal something from a store, or do drugs. When they refuse, have them give their reasons for refusing. Try to focus on a valid argument to combat peer pressure. Show students how to

Teacher Support Notes

① **Why People Take Drugs:** Five different mental or emotional reasons for abusing drugs are given in this paragraph. Ask students to identify the reasons (focus attention on self, pride in "differentness," fun and excitement, substitute for money or love, escape) and then discuss what they believe is the most common of these reasons.

② **Self-Esteem:** Do students agree that people with high self-esteem do not abuse drugs, whereas people with low self-esteem do? This is an extreme statement, but it might help to stimulate conversation. If they don't agree with the extreme, would they agree that people with high self-esteem are less likely to abuse drugs than people with low self-esteem?

✉ Where to Write

National Clearing House for Drug Abuse Information 5454 Wisconsin Ave. Chevy Chase, Maryland 20015

314 UNIT 4 Drug Use and Abuse

into a group by taking drugs. Often, when one or two key people stand up for their own rights, the behavior of a whole group can change. Relationships among groups of people are complicated, but the rewards they bring are worth some effort in getting them right.

Are you wondering how you can stand up for yourself among friends who are taking drugs? A place to start is to ask why your friends take them.

People who focus their attention on themselves rather than on other people or activities are likely to abuse drugs. People may also abuse drugs because they pride themselves on their "differentness" from the rest of society. Drugs fit their image of themselves as different. Others may lack excitement or fun and look to drugs to fill this void. Still others may lack money or friends or parental love, and they look to drugs as a substitute for these things. Drug abuse may temporarily distract the person—feel like an escape—from life's problems, whatever they may be.   ①

Unfortunately, when the drug is gone, the person is still left with the original problems—problems now complicated by a drug problem. The "escape" is really a trap. It prevents people from recognizing and solving their problems. People who see this clearly can better take a stand in behalf of their own well-being. The Health Strategies section on this page, "How to Say No," offers suggestions to help teens say no to drugs.

Self-esteem is another factor. A person with high self-esteem finds it easy to refuse drugs, even when a group offers them. A person with low self-esteem needs more approval from others and may use drugs to win approval and so boost self-esteem.   ②

Key Points ▶ *People's natures affect whether they abuse drugs. Curiosity, a desire to fit in with peers, and self-esteem play major roles.*

HEALTH **S**TRATEGIES

How to Say No

- **Practice.** Plan what you will say if someone offers you drugs *before* you are actually in such a situation. Practice by yourself in front of a mirror, or get together with some friends and do some role playing. Here are some example situations and responses:

Person who abuses drugs:
   "Come on, just try a little coke (or pot, or speed). It'll make you feel good."

Person who does not abuse drugs:
   "No, I already feel just fine."
   "No, I have a test (or game or job interview) tomorrow, and I want to be at my best."
   "No, I'm driving tonight."

Person who abuses drugs:
   "Don't be such a chicken. Try something new."

Person who does not abuse drugs:
   "I'm not a chicken. I like to try new things, but not things that are harmful."
   "I'm not a chicken. I can make my own choices, and I choose not to take drugs."

Person who abuses drugs:
   "Here, take a hit off this joint."

Person who does not abuse drugs:
   "No, I'll pass. I'm going running tomorrow, and I don't want anything to slow me down."
   "No, I've had a cold, and I don't want to do anything to make it worse."
   "No, I don't like the way it tastes."
   "No, I think I'll just watch you guys get stupid."

play. Give them the following scenario and have the groups develop skits using their refusal skills. "You are walking down the street with a group of friends. One of them pulls out a marijuana cigarette and asks you to join in smoking." **(1 hr.)**

Activity 2.3
   Interview Questions. Have the class work together to prepare a list of interview questions to mail to a prisoner in jail for drug-related crimes. Then go over the replies orally with the class. **(30 min., Critical Thinking)**

EVALUATE
SECTION II

Activity 2.4
   Refusal Skills. To check students' refusal skills, have the students write a few short paragraphs explaining their answers to the following situation: One of your friends asks you to do cocaine. What is your reply to the persistent invitations? **(20 min.)**

CLOSE
SECTION II

Activity 2.5
   Other Influences. Have students

(continued on next page)

- **Stay busy and involved.** Take up a new hobby. Play a sport or two. Volunteer your time to help those in need. When you are busy and involved in activities you love, you'll meet people who enjoy the same things you enjoy. You'll have fun, and you'll find that drugs have no place in your life.
- **Be strong, and believe in yourself.** Every time you say no, give yourself credit for standing up for yourself and doing what is in your own best interest. It takes commitment, skill, and self-esteem to say no. Be proud of your accomplishment.
- **Think about the consequences.** It is against the law to smoke marijuana or to take any other illegal drug. For minors, alcohol is against the law. Even more important, alcohol and all other drugs can be dangerous to your well-being.

The Nature of the Drug

   In addition to the nature of the person, as just described, the nature of the drug itself partly determines whether people abuse it. Drugs that give feelings of pleasure—that is, drugs that produce **euphoria**—are most likely to be abused.

   When animals are given access to a device to let them receive cocaine, they visit the device often. In fact, when they are offered either food or the drug, they choose the drug over food, until they starve. The drug itself makes them return for more, and makes them forget to eat or sleep. Cocaine can have that effect on people, too. Animals feel no peer pressure or social problems; the drug itself produces their addictive behavior.

Key Points *A drug that produces euphoria is likely to be abused.*

The Consequences from Society

   A person's nature and the nature of the drug itself are not the only factors affecting the choice to abuse drugs or not. The choice is also affected by how severely the person thinks society or the family punishes people for drug abuse. A society or family that tolerates drug abuse encourages it.

   People may think that education about the harm drugs cause is enough to prevent people from abusing drugs, but this is not true. Education alone is not effective against drug abuse. We know this because physicians, even with their superior knowledge, have narcotic addiction rates 30 times higher than the general population.

   Anyone who is considering trying any illegal drug should know that harsh punishment awaits those who possess or sell such drugs, or who are even in the same room with them. At the same time, entertainers, movies, songs, magazines, and books may portray drug abuse as "funny" or "cool." People may become confused and begin to think the views they see in print or other media are those of the society as a whole. This is the wrong idea. Society condemns drug abuse, but it also protects the rights of individual expression through writing and the arts. Therefore, while society severely punishes drug *abusers*, it also fiercely defends the right to make public individual points of view on drug abuse.

   Don't be confused by mixed messages from different segments of society. The expression of different views is an important part of our personal freedom. However,

MINI GLOSSARY

euphoria (you-FORE-ee-uh): a sense of great well-being and pleasure brought on by some drugs; popularly called a *high*.

Teacher Support Notes

① **Staying Busy:** Tell students that there is a correlation between people who abuse drugs and people who have few obligations on their time. Ask them how much free time they have during a typical day. Is it too much? Not enough? Can they think of any enjoyable or productive activities that they could be doing in this spare time?

② **Euphoria:** Ask students what other drugs they think have this euphoric effect on people. What drugs do they think have the strongest euphoric effect?

③ **Tolerant Societies:** As enrichment, to emphasize this point, you may want to tell students that countries such as England and Sweden have tried to combat addiction by making heroin legally available. These countries have since reversed their laws because epidemics of addiction resulted from the legalization of the drug.

315

think of songs that talk about drug and/or alcohol abuse. Write these song titles or lyrics on the board. Is the abuse of drugs and alcohol "put down" in the songs or glorified? Is taking drugs shown to be mysterious or "cool?" Have students discuss the appearance of the beer drinkers in the

beer commercials. Are beer drinkers really like this? Discuss students' opinions. Should there be more control over these messages? **(20 min., Critical Thinking)**

FOCUS
SECTION III

In this section students will learn about the:

1. Physical nature of withdrawal

symptoms.

2. Difference between physical and psychological addiction.

Activity 3.1
Withdrawal Symptoms. Ask the class if anyone has ever seen a person on TV or a character in a movie who is addicted to a drug, and who is having to go without his or her drug. Have students describe what behaviors they observed.

Teacher Support Notes

① **Biochemistry of Addiction:** As background you will be interested to know that part of the secret of addiction may be in the person's biochemistry. In response to certain stimuli, the brain produces its own endogenous opiates. These substances relieve pain and soothe anxiety—they act like the pain killer morphine. The drug causes the level of endogenous opiates to drop below normal. When the drug is suddenly removed, too few opiates of any kind are present and the symptoms of withdrawal ensue.

Section II Review

Answers
1. Answers will vary.
2. Answers will vary. Refer to the Health Strategies on pages 314–315 for possible answers.
3. People with high self-esteem find it easy to refuse drugs. A person with low self-esteem needs more approval from others and may abuse drugs to gain others' approval.
4. because the feeling of pleasure blocks the feeling of need for food or sleep
5. Answers will vary.

316 UNIT 4 Drug Use and Abuse

you must be aware that society's views and the views of individuals may differ.

This chapter is about some of the most commonly abused illegal drugs. Keep in mind, though, that the most-abused drug in the United States is still the legal one, alcohol, the topic of the next chapter.

> **Key Points** *A society or family that tolerates drug abuse encourages it. Harsh punishment awaits people who possess or sell illegal drugs.*

SECTION II   REVIEW

Answer the following questions on a sheet of paper.
Learning the Vocabulary
The vocabulary term in this section is *euphoria.*
1. Write a one-sentence description of euphoria.

Learning the Facts
2. List at least three "How to say No" responses you learned from the Health Strategies section.
3. Describe what self-esteem has to do with drug use.
4. Drugs that produce euphoria are most likely to be abused. Why?

Making Life Choices
5. Entertainers, movies, songs, magazines, and books may portray drug abuse as funny or cool. What can you do to change this image? How can we as a society change the media's outlook on drugs?

SECTION III

Addiction

Drugs produce euphoria by imitating the brain's natural way of producing feelings of pleasure. The acts of eating, exercising, and

relaxing produce pleasure naturally by way of **endorphins**, pleasure-producing chemicals of the brain. The lack of these chemicals produces an unpleasant feeling, known as **dysphoria.** In this way, nature encourages people to engage in health-promoting behaviors. These natural chemicals are similar to mind-altering drugs, but there is a key difference. The natural chemicals are produced in response to *healthful activities*.

① The taking of mind-altering drugs produces pleasure directly in the brain, with no healthful activity associated with it. At the same time, the brain of the drug-taker produces fewer and fewer of its own endorphins. Thus after each round of drug-taking, when the pleasure from the drugs wears off, the person is left with the unpleasant sensation, dysphoria. The person may then take more drugs to chase away the dysphoria, unaware that still more unpleasant feelings will follow, along with the desire for still more drugs—and so on.

When people take drugs to ease dysphoria, they may be headed toward **drug**

Many people who use drugs to chase away unpleasant feelings are unaware that eventually the unpleasant feelings may be the aftereffects of the drugs themselves.

What did the person do to get money for drugs? Have students read the third paragraph below, aloud. Ask if there is anyone who thinks withdrawal symptoms would be easy to overcome. Why or why not? **(15 min.)**

TEACH
SECTION III
(Guided and Independent Practice)

Activity 3.2

Stress-Free Activities. Have students develop their own stress-free, endorphin-releasing activities. Tell students to develop a list of ten activities that give them a natural high. Tell them that what one person enjoys, another may not like at all. Sometimes friendships between two people are based on activities that both enjoy, such as playing a particular sport. Interests like this can serve to help you "fit in" with a group whose members enjoy the

same kinds of things as you.

Have students read their lists. Write down several suggestions that come up frequently. At the end, ask students who wrote down those activities, one by one, to raise their hands. Tell them to look around the room and see who the other people are who share the same interests. You might want to give students time to organize an outing of those people who

(continued on next page)

addiction (also called **dependence**). Drug addiction can be either physical or psychological.

Most of the drugs that cause addictions are euphoria-producing drugs. A few drugs, though, produce addictions without euphoria. Nicotine, the active drug in tobacco, is one. Caffeine is another.

In **physical addiction,** the body chemistry actually changes. The body must have the drug—not for pleasure, but just to be able to function normally. As the body begins to clear the drug from the system, the altered body chemistry is unable to function normally. The symptoms of **withdrawal** begin.

The symptoms of withdrawal vary from drug to drug. They may include abnormalities in vision, muscle activity, digestion, brain function, temperature regulation, or many other processes (see Figure 13–2, later in this chapter). Withdrawal symptoms create an urgent need for more of the drug.

A physical addiction to a drug is detectable from the withdrawal symptoms it produces. Withdrawal changes brainwave patterns, affects mood, and makes the person crave the drug (just as withdrawal of food makes people crave food). Physical addiction is also involved when the person develops a tolerance to the drug—when the person needs to take higher and higher doses. The craving created by withdrawal, followed by the need to take higher and higher doses, creates a spiral of physical addiction, as shown in Figure 13–1 on the next page. Recovery from addiction is described on pages 335–336.

Physical addiction always has a psychological effect, too—a strong mental craving for the drug. But **psychological addiction** can occur without physical addiction. Habits or behavior other than drug-taking—such as overworking, overeating, or overexercising—can also set up a craving. People who never

learned to cope with emotional pain often develop psychological addictions to drugs. This happens because these people have learned they can use drugs to relieve emotional pain for a while. However, this too can set up a cycle of worsening addiction. Psychological addictions can be, for some people, as powerful as physical addictions.

The craving for a drug can last for years after the person has stopped taking the drug. Curing psychological addiction has been compared to trying to cure someone's appetite for food, except that the drug craving is stronger. Imagine to what lengths people may go to get food when they are hungry. The drug-addicted person will go much farther. Attachment to the drug becomes almost like a great love relationship with another person. Addicted people defend,

MINI GLOSSARY

endorphins: chemicals in the brain that produce feelings of pleasure in response to a variety of activities.

dysphoria (dis-FORE-ee-uh): unpleasant feelings that occur when endorphins are lacking; they often follow drug-induced euphoria.

drug addiction (dependence): a physical or psychological need for higher and higher doses of a drug.

physical addiction: a change in the body's chemistry so that without the presence of a substance (drug), normal functioning begins to fail, and withdrawal symptoms set in; also called *physical dependence.*

withdrawal: the physical symptoms that occur when a drug to which a person is addicted is cleared from the body tissues.

psychological addiction: a craving for something; mental dependence on a drug, habit, or behavior; also called *psychological dependence.*

☎ **Where to Call**

National Institute on Drug Abuse Help Line 1-800-662-HELP.

Teacher Support Notes

① **Withdrawal:** Ask students if they know anyone who has gone through withdrawal. How did the person describe the withdrawal experience? Was the experience successful?
② **Overhead—Psychological Addiction:** Your supplementary material contains an overhead that shows the cycle of psychological addiction. You may want to use this overhead for enrichment.

✎ **Fast Facts**

The odds that a first-time user of crack cocaine will become addicted are one in three.

share similar interests to get together and have fun. **(30 min.)**

Activity 3.3
  Guest Speaker. Bring a recovering drug abuser to the class to describe the daily fight with drugs and addiction. The

person should also discuss how he or she became addicted, overcame the addiction, and fought the withdrawal symptoms caused by the drug. As a class, prepare questions to ask the guest speaker. **(1 class period; Extend, Enrich)**

Activity 3.4
  Physical vs. Psychological. Have students write a page explaining the difference between physical addiction and

psychological addiction. **(20 min., Interdisciplinary)**

EVALUATE
SECTION III

Activity 3.5
  Pop Quiz.
1. The pleasant feeling produced by some chemicals is dysphoria. (F)
2. Drug addiction can be either physical

Teacher Support Notes

① **Overhead—Physiological Addiction:** In your supplementary material you will find an overhead of this illustration, which you may want to use in your classroom presentation of this lesson. Ask students to talk their way through the illustration explaining in their own words what happens at each point. Have them create an imaginary character so as to explain what happens in a storylike manner. As they tell their stories, you should be able to determine whether or not they understand the terms *euphoria, dysphoria, tolerance, elevated drug doses, withdrawal,* and *addiction.* If students are having trouble, have them reread the preceding pages.

② **Teacher Information Sheet—Stopping Drug Addiction:** The background information sheet in your supplementary material entitled "Stopping Drug Addiction" will help prepare you for questions the students might ask about different strategies our society is using, and could use, to help stop drug addiction.

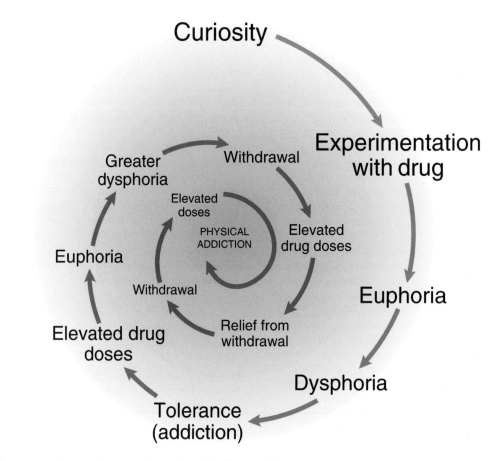

Figure 13–1 The Spiral That Leads to Physical Addiction ①

cherish, and protect the drug habit as they would defend and protect a loved one.

  Drug addiction is unexpected. No one who starts out taking a substance intends to get hooked, but it still happens. A person tries a drug for one reason, but continues taking it because addiction has set in. For example, a young teen may begin to take a drug to feel grown-up and to impress friends. Ten years later, however, the adult person is still fighting an addiction to the drug. The original reason is long gone. The addiction has taken over and may last a lifetime.

  People who experiment with drugs often want to believe that the craving won't get to them—only to others who "can't handle it." In truth, no one who is exposed repeatedly to an addictive drug can remain free from addiction. Remember that even laboratory animals helplessly become addicted when given such drugs. This is why sellers of drugs often give new drug-takers the first few doses for free. Once the drug has a person hooked, the seller's job becomes easy.

  The only sure way to escape drug addiction is never to experiment with taking or psychological. (T)

3. Physical addiction causes a change in the body's chemistry that creates a dependence on a drug. (T)

4. The chemicals in the brain that produce feelings of pleasure are called endorphins. (T)

5. Psychological addiction often occurs in people who have never learned to cope with emotional pain. (T)

in their own minds without drug use. **(10 min.)**

Activity 3.6
Review. Before moving on to the next section, check to be sure that students are able to:
1. Describe both physical and psychological addiction.
2. List ways to stimulate endorphin release

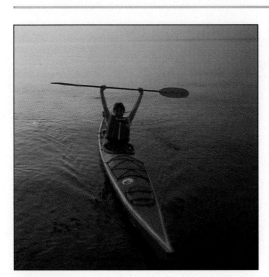

Natural highs are preferable to drug-induced highs.

drugs that produce it. Groups who invite their friends to join them in drug-taking don't have the same motivation as those who sell drugs, but the effect is the same. A few doses into the habit, and the new member no longer has a choice. Groups do pressure people to join them, however, because any outsider who refuses to join in threatens the group's assumption that their behavior is OK. Get the outsider hooked, and the threat is gone.

Key Points ▶ *Dysphoria is the unpleasant feeling that follows when the euphoria produced by a drug wears off. Addiction can be physiological, psychological, or both. The only sure way to escape drug addiction is never to experiment with drugs that produce it.*

SECTION III REVIEW

Answer the following questions on a sheet of paper.
Learning the Vocabulary
The vocabulary terms in this section are *endorphins, dysphoria, drug addiction (dependence), physical addiction, withdrawal,* and *psychological addiction.*

Fill in the blank with the correct answer.
1. The physical symptoms that occur when a drug to which a person is addicted is cleared from the body tissues are called _____.
2. A craving for something; mental dependence on a drug, habit, or behavior is called _____.
3. _____ are chemicals in the brain that produce feelings of pleasure in response to a variety of activities.

Learning the Facts
4. What can people do to naturally produce endorphins?
5. Define physical addiction.
6. List the withdrawal symptoms from physical addiction.
7. List the three different psychological addictions discussed in this section.

Making Life Choices
8. Your little sister Renee has been hanging around a group of high school kids. Her attitudes about school, friends, and family have changed. She has a large amount of money in her piggy bank. You are sure that the high school kids she hangs around with use drugs. You are afraid she may be using drugs and selling them to other junior high students. How will you feel if your suspicions are true? What will you do in this situation? Who can help you?

SECTION IV

Commonly Abused Drugs

① This section discusses a few commonly abused drugs and compares their actual effects with popular beliefs about them. Figure 13–2 on the following pages presents many more details about abused drugs.

Section III Review
Answers
1. withdrawal
2. psychological addiction
3. Endorphins
4. eat, exercise, and relax
5. condition in which the body chemistry changes and the body must have the drug to function
6. abnormality in vision, muscle activity, digestion, brain function, temperature regulation, etc.
7. overwork, overeating, overexercising
8. Answers will vary.

Teacher Support Notes

① **Handout—Drug Abuse Terms:** Your supplementary material contains a handout listing several of the more common drug abuse terms that students will encounter.

In this section students will learn about:
1. The effects and dangers of commonly abused drugs.
2. The impact of drug abuse in the school and community.
3. How dangerous it is to take drugs that are bought on the street.

Activity 4.1
Drug List. Have students call out drugs and street names of drugs that can be bought at school. Write the drug names on the board. **(10 min.)**

TEACH
SECTION IV
(Guided and Independent Practice)

Activity 4.2
Guest Administrator. Invite a

school administrator to visit your class and discuss what types of drugs are most commonly sold and abused in school. Ask the administrator to inform students about the school district's policy on controlled substances. Also have them speak on ways that they catch students abusing and selling drugs. **(1 hr.; Extend, Enrich)**

Activity 4.3
Refusal Steps. Have students tell

Teacher Support Notes

① **Abused Drugs Table:** Point out to students that this table covers four pages and that they should use the table for reference as they work their way through the rest of the chapter. The table, in many cases, does not contain as much information as is provided within the body of the text, but it also contains some information, such as street names and medical uses, that are not included in the body of text. Because there is so much information in the table, you may want to ask students a few questions to help them familiarize themselves with the table and the information contained in it:
a. How many different classes of drugs are included in the table and what are the names of those classes? (six plus "other"—narcotics, depressants, stimulants, psychedelics, inhalants, and cannabis)
b. Ask if all of the drugs have a medical use. (no, most of the psychedelics do not; the "other" drugs do not)
c. Tell students that not all drugs are physically addictive. Ask them to name the drugs that experts either are uncertain about or know to be nonaddictive

FIGURE 13-2

Abused Drugs ①

Class	Drug (with selected brand or other names)	Medical Use	Physical/Psychological Dependence
Narcotics	**Opium** (Dover's Powder, paregoric, Parepectolin), **morphine** (Pectoral Syrup), **codeine** (Empirin with Codeine, Robitussin A-C), others (Levo-Dromoran, Percodan, Tussionex, Fentanyl, Sublimaze, Darvon, Talwin, Lomotil)	Pain reliever, antidiarrheal, cough reliever	Yes/Yes
	Heroin (diacetylmorphine, H, black tar, horse, smack)	Pain reliever	Yes/Yes
	Hydromorphone (Dilaudid), meperidine (pethidine) hydrochloride (Demerol)	Pain reliever	Yes/Yes
	Methadone hydrochloride (Dolophine, Methadone, Methadose)	Pain reliever, heroin substitute	Yes/Yes
Depressants	**Barbiturates** (phenobarbital, Alurate, Butisol, Nembutal, Seconol, Tuinal), chloral hydrate (Noctec)	Anesthetic, anticonvulsant, sedative, hypnotic	Yes/Yes
	Glutethimide (Doriden), Methaqualone (Quāālude, Sopor)	Sedative, hypnotic	Yes/Yes
	Benzodiazepines (Ativan, Clonopin, Dalmane, Diazepam, Librium, Serax, Tranxene, Valium), others (Equanil, Miltown, Noludar Placidyl, Valmid)	Anxiety reliever, anticonvulsant, sedative, hypnotic	Yes/Yes
Stimulants	**Cocaine** (base, coke, crack, flake, rock, snow)	Local anesthetic	Yes/Yes
	Amphetamines (biphetamine, speed, uppers, black beauties, white crosses, Desoxyn, Dexedrine, Mediatric), phenmetrazine hydrochloride (Preludin), methylphenidate hydrochloride (Ritalin), others (Adipex, Bacarate, Cylert, Didrex, Ionamin, Plegine, Sanorex, Tenuate, Tepanil)	Control of hyper-activity in children, sleep disorders, weight	Possible/ Yes

you the steps in refusing an offer to do drugs. Ask each student to take a drug and have them refuse your offer directly, pleasantly, and confidently. Reinforce the fact that they need to be firm, be direct, and maintain eye contact with you while refusing. For those students who cannot maintain confidence in refusing, pressure them until you force them to be direct and firm with you. Point out to students that they look like they can be persuaded if they are not direct and appear confident. **(20 min.; Extend, Enrich)**

Activity 4.4
Choose Not to Be Sick. Ask the class, "If you have a choice to feel sick or feel well, how many would choose to be sick?" Hopefully no one will choose to be sick. Explain that this is why drug abusers keep taking drugs, in order to avoid withdrawal symptoms that make them sick.

(5 min.)

Activity 4.5
Stereotypes. Have students close their eyes and imagine a drug abuser, then describe him or her. Then have students imagine a drug misuser and describe him or her. Finally, have them imagine a recreational drug user and describe him or her. Discuss with students

(continued on next page)

physically. (amphetamines, LSD, amphetamine variants, psilocybin, phencyclidine hydrochloride and "others" in the psychedelic group, marijuana, designer drugs, clove cigarettes)
d. Which classes of drugs potentially can cause death? (all but cannabis)

Fast Facts

In 1990, the anti-drug budget of the federal government totaled 10.6 billion dollars. 71% of that total went to law enforcement, 13% to education.

Where to Write

National Association of Drug Abuse Problems
355 Lexington Ave.
New York, NY 10017

Ch. 13 Drugs of Abuse **321**

Usual Method of Administration	Possible Effect	Effect of Overdose	Withdrawal Syndrome
Oral, smoked, injected			Watery eyes, runny nose, yawning, loss of appetite, irritability, tremors, panic, chills and sweating, cramps, nausea
	Euphoria, drowsiness, respiratory depression, constricted pupils, nausea	Slow and shallow breathing, clammy skin, convulsions, coma, possible death	
Injected, sniffed, smoked			
Oral, injected			
Oral, injected			
Oral, injected	Slurred speech, disorientation, drunken behavior without odor of alcohol	Shallow respiration, cold and clammy skin, dilated pupils, weak and rapid pulse, coma, possible death	Anxiety, insomnia, tremors, delirium, convulsions, possible death
Oral, injected			
Oral, injected			
Sniffed, injected, smoked	Increased alertness, excitation, euphoria, increased pulse rate and blood pressure, insomnia, loss of appetite, skin lesions	Agitation, increase in body temperature, hallucinations, convulsions, kidney failure, possible death	Apathy, long periods of sleep, irritability, depression, disorientation
Oral, injected			

321

the idea that "recreational" drug users and hard-core drug abusers are all drug abusers. A person who is abusing drugs loses the ability to make sound judgments and to decide when recreational drug use becomes a real addiction. **(15 min.)**

Activity 4.6
Family Changes. Assign students to write a story about how their families would change if a family member started abusing drugs or was addicted. **(20 min., Critical Thinking)**

Activity 4.7
Empathetic Listening. Ask students what the word "empathy" means. "What does it mean to be empathetic to someone?" A good, understandable definition is that empathy means trying to put yourself in someone else's shoes; seeing the world from another's point of view. Then have students tell you what qualities a good listener has. (maintains eye contact, blocks out distractions, gives feedback such as facial expressions and nods, etc.) Tell the students that you want them to listen with empathy and understanding while you read something to

✉ **Where to Write**

National Organization for the Reform of Marijuana Laws
530 8th Street, SE
Washington, DC
20003

Fast Facts

In 1985, it was estimated that 45% of the marijuana smoked in the United States was imported. In 1992, it was estimated that 70% was imported. The portion of the U.S. marijuana crop that is grown indoors is estimated to be 25%.

Fast Facts

52% of Americans say they approve of searching homes without a warrant in order to combat drugs.

FIGURE 13-2

Abused Drugs (continued)

Class	Drug (with selected brand or other names)	Medical Use	Physical/Psychological Dependence
Psychedelics (hallucinogens)	**Lysergic acid diethylamide,** or **LSD** (acid, microdot), mescaline and peyote (mesc, buttons, cactus)	None	No/Unknown
	Amphetamine variants (2,5-DMA, PMA, STP, MDA, MMDA, TMA, DOM, DOB)	None	Unknown/Unknown
	Psilocybin and related mushroom species (mushrooms, shrooms)	None	Unknown/Yes, Rarely
	Phencyclidine hydrochloride (PCP, angel dust, hog)	Veterinary anesthetic	Unknown/Yes
	Others (PCE, PCPy, TCP, DMT, DET, morning glory seeds)	None	No/Unknown
Inhalants	**Hydrocarbon vapors** from many sources, such as plastic cement, gasoline, spray can vapors (glue, gas, poppers, locker room, rush, odor of man, Aspirols, Vaporal, amyl nitrite, butyl nitrite, nitrous oxide, laughing gas)	Amyl nitrite relieves heart pain; nitrous oxide relieves anxiety	Yes/Yes
Cannabis	**Marijuana** (pot, Acapulco gold, grass, weed, dope, reefer, sinsemilla, Thai sticks), tetrahydrocannabinol (THC), hashish (hash), hashish oil (hash oil)	Relief of glaucoma and cancer therapy side effects	Unknown/Yes
Other	**Designer drugs** (Ecstasy, Ex, MDMA)	None	Varies/Varies
	Clove cigarettes rolled from high-nicotine and high-tar tobacco, clove oil, cocoa, licorice, and other ingredients (Djarum, Kreteks)	None	Unknown/Unknown

them. Read the last paragraph under psychological addiction, which begins at the bottom of page 318 and continues to 319. Discuss what you have read with the students. Remind them that they are being empathetic. Ask if they understand how this might happen to someone rather suddenly and how he could come to regret the first time he ever experimented with drugs. What type of friend would get someone started on something that might

eventually kill him or ruin his life? Ask students to share any bad situations that may have occurred to one of their friends or family members as a result of drug abuse. Remind students that they are to be good listeners and have empathy for the person who is sharing and for the person that the story is about. If the main character of anyone's story is known to others, have students keep that person's identity anonymous. **(30 min.; Extend, Enrich)**

Activity 4.8
Posters. Assign students to make posters of a particular drug. Include street names, effects, side effects, withdrawal effects, and if possible, price of the drug and punishment for having and selling the drug. Students may use Figure 13–2 for information. **(20 min.; Reteach, Reinforce)**

(continued on next page)

Usual Method of Administration	Possible Effect	Effect of Overdose	Withdrawal Syndrome
Oral, injected Oral, injected Oral Smoked, oral, injected Smoked, oral, injected, sniffed	Illusions and hallucinations, poor perception of time and distance, nausea, vomiting	Longer, more intense "trip" episodes; psychosis; death by accident or suicide	None reported
Sniffed, vapors concentrated and inhaled	Altered time sense; brief euphoria; nausea; vomiting; dizziness; headache; liver, brain and kidney cancer	Loss of consciousness, death by suffocation, cerebral hemorrhage	None reported
Smoked, oral	Euphoria, relaxed inhibitions, increased appetite, disoriented behavior	Fatigue, paranoia, possible psychosis	Insomnia, hyperactivity, decreased appetite
Varies Unknown	Varies. Nausea, vomiting, respiratory dysfunctions and bleeding, allergic reaction,	Varies Possible death from severe lung infection	Varies None reported

Where to Write

National Family Council on Drug Addiction
401 West End Ave.
New York, NY 10024

" Thoughts on Health "

Despair is better treated with hope, not dope.
– Richard Asher

Activity 4.9

Speaker. Bring in a law officer to discuss the legal aspects of drug abuse. Ask the officer to bring a drug board that shows drugs and drug paraphernalia. Have the officer explain exactly what will happen to a minor and an adult if they get caught selling or abusing drugs. Have the officer explain what a minor in possession charge is and how these situations might affect a person's future.

Activity 4.10

Role-Play. Assign students to role-play the following characters in the life of a kilo of cocaine. The manufacturer of the drug produces a kilo of pure cocaine. What does he then do to make money? The courier then dilutes the kilos before selling to the distributor. Finally, what will the distributor do before selling it on the street? With all of this diluting going on, what happens to the original pure cocaine? Is there any way to guess how pure the end product is? Be sure that students understand that the drug is not regulated as legal drugs are. If a person is used to taking a drug that is not pure, taking the same amount of a pure drug

Teacher Support Notes

① **THC:** As enrichment you may want to tell students that the percentage of THC in marijuana today is considerably higher than in the 1960s when marijuana's use became popular. Today's marijuana averages 3%–4% THC with some samples exceeding 10%, compared with the marijuana of the 1960s, which usually contained less than 0.5%. Many of the studies of marijuana's effects were made using the older, weaker drug. It is unknown whether today's marijuana has the same effects as the marijuana of the 1960s.

② **Additional Risks:** Another risk associated with marijuana abuse is that of escalation to the use of more powerful drugs. Users looking for a "better high" sometimes shift to hashish and then possibly on to other, more dangerous drugs.

 Fast Facts

50% of the inmates in federal prisons in the United States are serving a sentence for drug dealing.

324

You'd be surprised to hear how many people take illegal drugs without first learning about their risks. They think that illegal (street) drugs are about the same as legal ones in their purity and safety. This is completely false. With street drugs, no amount of learning can ensure that the taker knows all the risks in advance. Street drugs can contain anything, even pure poisons, as the Consumer Awareness section, "Greed and Street Drugs," makes clear.

Marijuana

To get marijuana to market, sellers harvest and dry the plants. They then sell the flowers, as well as some of the leaves and small stems. Marijuana smokers roll the mixture into cigarettes (joints) or smoke it in pipes.

The chemicals in marijuana that produce euphoria are all related to the chemical delta-9-tetrahydrocannabinol, or THC for short, which the plant produces as it grows. When inhaled by smoking, the active chemicals are rapidly and completely (90 percent) absorbed from the lungs. They then travel in the blood to the various body tissues that process them—the brain, liver, and kidneys.

THC affects sensitive brain centers. It alters hearing, touch, taste, and smell, as well as the sense of time, the sense of space, and feelings of the body. THC also produces changes in sleep patterns. Marijuana is unique among drugs because it seems to bring about great enjoyment of eating, especially of sweets ("the munchies"). (It is not known how this effect occurs.)

The THC from a single marijuana cigarette can linger in the body's fat for a month before being removed in the urine. Drug tests can detect trace amounts of THC for as long as six months afterward.

In addition to THC, scientists have identified at least 400 different chemicals in marijuana. Further, the chemicals vary with each genetic strain of plants, within the same strain from season to season, and even from one part to another of the same plant. These differences in chemical makeup affect the different experiences people have when using marijuana.

Another factor that affects marijuana abusers' experiences is their expectations. How people expect to feel, along with their surroundings and their history of marijuana use, all combine to vary their reactions. Reactions range from a mild euphoria and uncontrollable laughter to **hallucinations.** Users may feel more confident than usual. Or, on the other hand, they may feel unfounded fears and be less confident. They may feel graceful (but act clumsy). They may feel like excellent drivers (but actually drive dangerously). They may feel brilliant or witty (but make no sense). Marijuana may dull sexual pleasure and is likely to make people feel sleepy, not sexy.

The morning after an evening of smoking marijuana is, for many, a morning of feeling tired and down. And for many, this is a time to roll another joint to get rid of the unpleasant feelings of dysphoria. This is the road to psychological addiction and habitual abuse of marijuana.

Most people who smoke marijuana have the idea that since it has been around for thousands of years, it must provide a harmless high. Unfortunately, they are wrong. Research indicates that harmful health effects are associated with marijuana use. These include short-term memory loss and a shortened attention span.

Marijuana also changes the heart's action, causing rapid and sometimes irregular heartbeats. Marijuana may also impair the body's immune response. In young men, it may reduce both hormone levels and sperm count. Like other drugs, marijuana can pose the greatest hazard to those who use it most heavily and frequently.

could kill the person. **(20 min.; Extend, Enrich)**

Activity 4.11

Developing Plans. Have students develop a drug-free plan to follow for life. The plan should start with students writing all of the goals they wish to accomplish. They should tell by what age they would like to meet each goal.

The next section of their plans should identify roadblocks, things that might come up in their lives that will stand in the way of their meeting each goal. Beside each roadblock, have students write a way around each block or a way to cope with it if they can't go around it.

Finally, have students write what role drug and alcohol abuse will play in their lives from the present on. They should develop a plan with alternative activities, activities other than drug abuse, to help them not get addicted to drugs. They need to have a plan for social interaction, coping with stress, and developing and improving self-esteem without the abuse of tobacco, drugs, or alcohol. Ask for volunteers to share their plans with the class. **(2 days outside class to develop, 1 class period to present; Extend, Enrich)**

Activity 4.12

(continued on next page)

CONSUMER AWARENESS

Greed and Street Drugs

No watchdog agency such as the FDA screens illegal drugs for safety or purity. This affects those who abuse drugs. Street drugs are unpredictable in their contents. They vary from batch to batch.

Each person who handles an illegal drug makes a profit. To make the most money, sellers mix drugs generously with other substances at every turn. For example, "consumer-quality" cocaine is expected to be "cut" (diluted) with some quantity of white powder other than pure cocaine, usually talcum powder or a type of powdered sugar. However, some sellers of cocaine are more greedy than others, and they add enormous quantities of powders. Then they mask the weakened effect of the cocaine with cheaper drugs, such as prescription stimulants, caffeine, or anesthetics that copy some of cocaine's effects.

As great a danger as the drugs themselves may pose to the takers, greater still may be the dangers from unknown substances they contain. Medical drugs are pure and reliable. Street drugs often contain nasty surprises.

① **CRITICAL THINKING**

1. *Can the taker of street drugs know for sure exactly what is in the drugs?*
2. *What motivates sellers of drugs to "cut" their drugs with other powders?*
3. *Which government agencies watch over the contents of street drugs?*

Hashish is a concentrated marijuana resin collected from the flowering top of the plant. The resin is smoked or sometimes eaten. With hashish, the risks are higher, because the taker receives a stronger dose.

Marijuana smoking, even more than cigarette smoking, damages the lungs and so can lead to lung cancer. Smoking three to four marijuana cigarettes damages the lungs as much as smoking more than 20 tobacco cigarettes. Other hazards exist: marijuana may be contaminated with pesticides, poisonous molds, or herbicides. It may contain dangerous drugs. An example is the animal tranquilizer phencyclidine hydrochloride (PCP, or "angel dust") added to marijuana by sellers to trick buyers into thinking that its potency is high.

② A dangerous side effect of marijuana is that it impairs driving ability. Even after a small dose, a person's driving performance is impaired. The effect lasts long after the high is gone.

Some people respond to long-term marijuana abuse by losing ambition and drive—the so-called **amotivational syndrome.**

MINI GLOSSARY

hallucinations: false perceptions; imagined sights, sounds, smells, or other feelings, sometimes brought on by drug abuse, sometimes by mental or physical illness.
amotivational syndrome: loss of ambition and drive; a characteristic of long-term abusers of marijuana.

Teacher Support Notes

① **Critical Thinking Answers:**
1. no
2. the prospect of making more money
3. none

② **Marijuana Use:**
Many people think of marijuana as a fairly safe drug in comparison to the drugs that will be described on the following pages. After reading this section on marijuana, however, students should be aware of the risks and dangers involved in smoking marijuana. Ask them to describe their general impressions of marijuana. Have those impressions changed after reading this section?

Party Situations. Have students brainstorm in groups a list of situations in which young people might find themselves in a position to abuse drugs or alcohol. These situations might be related to a person, place, or event. Have each group go over its list orally, or write them on the board. Tell the class that we know where we might run into drug abuse so we need to use this to our advantage and develop a mind-set that will allow us to stay in touch with our own personal goals and expectations for ourselves.

Ask them, "How many of you know in advance what parties or other situations might involve drugs or alcohol?" (Most of the students will raise their hands.) Tell them that we are usually aware of the types of situations that we allow ourselves to become a part of. The first decision you need to make to stay drug-free is whether or not you want to attend a party or event where drugs or alcohol have a good chance of being abused. If you decide to go to a party like this or with a group of people who abuse drugs or alcohol, you need to develop a positive mind-set so that you will take charge of your life, make decisions for yourself in

---

Teacher Support Notes

① **Overhead—Stimulation to Depression:** Your supplementary material contains an overhead that you might want to use for enrichment. It shows several drugs and their effects on a range from high stimulation to low depression. At this point you may want to discuss with students that most drugs can be placed on a scale ranging from stimulation to depression. Drugs such as the amphetamines stimulate the central nervous system, while drugs such as the barbiturates have just the opposite effect. While some drug abusers take a variety of drugs, many tend to favor either the stimulants or the depressants.

Others find that they've come to crave the drug and require therapy to give it up.

Marijuana is the most often abused illegal drug in the United States today. THC was once used to fight the intense nausea people suffer when they undergo cancer treatments. It also can reduce eye swelling from the disease glaucoma. Because marijuana is illegal, other drugs are used for these purposes.

> **Key Points** *Marijuana affects hearing, touch, taste, and smell. It alters the sense of time, the sense of space, and the feelings of the body. Its use can cause abnormal heart action; reduced immunity; a lowered sperm count in men; lung damage, including cancer; and amotivational syndrome. It also impairs driving ability.*   ①

Amphetamines

In this high-speed society, a drug that claims to provide some extra get-up-and-go might tempt even a cautious person. The **amphetamines** are said to be just such drugs. They are stimulants—drugs that stimulate the nervous system and so increase activity, block fatigue and hunger, and produce euphoria. Amphetamines are used to treat diseases such as life-threatening obesity; constant sleeping; or in children, **hyperactivity**. This last seems an unlikely use for a stimulant. However, in the case of hyperactivity, the drug does not stimulate the child. It stimulates a brain center that helps the child sit still and pay attention.

Peer pressures can be strong, but don't give in—Don't take drugs.

advance, and not let peer pressure make your important decisions for you.

Tell students, "First, remember all of your positive reasons for not abusing drugs or alcohol, then think of all the possible negative consequences that might occur for people who abuse drugs or alcohol in this situation. Be aware of what you are saying to yourself when you are at the party. An example of a positive mind-set is, 'I am an athlete, I want to perform at my personal best so I will not abuse drugs or alcohol.' An example of a negative mind-set is, 'I need friends and I will do anything to get them.' "

Have students brainstorm a list of negative mind-sets that people often have at social events that may make them more likely to abuse drugs or alcohol, such as, "Everyone else is doing it," or "I look like a nerd with this can of soda in my hand," or "People won't like me if I don't join." List all negative mind-sets on the board or overhead. Divide students into groups and have them take the entire list and turn each negative mind-set into a positive one. Have each group present their positive mind-sets in the same order as the negative ones that they have changed. **(30 min., Critical Thinking)**

(continued on next page)

People may start taking amphetamines to lose weight or to combat fatigue so they can stay awake at night. They may also take amphetamines to reduce the sleepiness brought on by alcohol, marijuana, or **sedatives.** Sometimes a daily cycle develops in which people take sedatives to relieve the effects of amphetamines and then take more amphetamines to pick themselves up again. The body builds up tolerance to amphetamines in just a few weeks. Soon, the taker may need several hundred times the original dose to get an effect. At this point, drug addiction is severe.

When used as medicine, amphetamines are taken by mouth. The usual route for abuse is injection into a vein. The risks of abusing any drug increase dramatically when the drug is injected. Overdoses are likely. Needles may not be sterile. The skin may not be properly cleansed. The needle puncture may carry life-threatening microbes or a fatal air bubble into the bloodstream. People who share needles share infections such as AIDS (a fatal disease) and hepatitis (a dangerous, often incurable liver infection).

A person injecting amphetamines experiences an intense, but short-lived, euphoria. The drug-taker may feel unusually strong. This, combined with the drug-induced overactivity and euphoria, can lead to dangerous behavior. An addicted person may inject the drug ten times a day for days, with no sleep and very little food.

The euphoria wears off much more quickly than the drug's other effects. The taker cannot sense tiredness until suddenly overwhelmed by it, perhaps while driving or crossing the street. Severe dysphoria and mental depression follow amphetamine abuse. Thus the person may turn again to the drug for relief. Side effects of injecting amphetamines include extreme anxiety, temporary mental illness, and malnutrition.

High doses can cause convulsions, lack of oxygen, loss of consciousness, dangerously high temperature, bleeding of the brain, high blood pressure, and death.

People taking amphetamines sometimes think that the drugs make them better in some way. They think their drugged selves compare favorably with their undrugged selves. In continuing to take the drugs to maintain their illusions, they abandon real life, in which they could become genuinely more sensitive, more fun, more intelligent, more physically fit, or whatever else might improve the quality of their lives.

① **Key Points** *Amphetamines are stimulants. They increase activity, block fatigue and hunger, and produce euphoria. Amphetamines are addictive drugs, because tolerance to them develops quickly. Withdrawal from amphetamines causes severe dysphoria and psychological depression.*

Sedatives and Barbiturates

Sedatives slow down body systems; they are depressants. Some sedatives slow the heart; some act on the brain and nervous system; some do both. They may be used

 Mini **G**LOSSARY

amphetamines (am-FETT-ah-meenz): powerful, addictive stimulant drugs. Because they suppress appetite, they are reserved for use in cases where overfatness threatens health. Also called *speed.*
hyperactivity: a condition in children that makes them overly active, unable to pay attention, aggressive, and easily distracted.
sedatives: drugs that have a soothing or tranquilizing effect.

327

Activity 4.13

Interviews. Assign students to interview one of the following: **1.** A pharmacist about the danger of look-alike drugs. **2.** A coach about the effects of drugs on athletic performance. **3.** A counselor or minister about the drug abusers they

have counseled. **4.** A police officer about the laws concerning drugs. **5.** An FBI agent about drug cultures. **6.** A judge about sentences for drug abusers. Then have students give brief oral reports about their interviews to the class. **(1 hr.; Extend, Enrich)**

Activity 4.14

Speaker. Invite an emergency room doctor or nurse to speak to your class

about drug overdoses or drug-related injuries that they have seen or treated. Emphasize how many patients get treated, have no money, and are paid for by the students' parents' tax dollars. **(1 hr.)**

Activity 4.15

Antidrug Posters. Assign students to make their own antidrug posters or notebook covers to be displayed around the classroom. **(30 min.; Reteach, Reinforce)**

Teacher Support Notes

① **The Cocaine Craze:** You may want to give students some additional information about cocaine. Contrary to popular belief, cocaine is not a new drug. The U.S. experienced its first cocaine epidemic in the late 1880s. Sigmund Freud tested and praised the drug in 1884. Coca-Cola contained minute amounts of cocaine, enough to act as a significant stimulant, which has since been replaced by caffeine. Coca-Cola was marketed as a "brain tonic" to relieve headaches, cure all nervous afflictions, and act as an antidote to toothache pain. It was offered to treat asthma and became the official remedy of the American Hay Fever Association. In 1910 President Taft presented a State Department report to Congress declaring cocaine a public enemy. In 1914 Congress passed the Harrison Act, which tightly regulated the distribution and sale of the drug. Cocaine overdoses have killed several celebrities including actor John Belushi and college basketball star Len Bias.

328 UNIT 4 Drug Use and Abuse

to calm an upset person, to dull sensation, or to put a person to sleep. Thus they are useful tools in the hands of medical professionals. But they can be dangerous when taken without medical care. Some are more dangerous than others, but none are safe.

The **barbiturates** are a group of drugs that depress the central nervous system, slow the heart rate, slow the respiration rate, and lower the blood pressure and body temperature. They, too, have their medical uses, but they are easily abused. Long-term abuse can cause depression, forgetfulness, reduced sex drive, and many other harmful effects, including addiction. Overdoses kill.

Key Points *Sedatives and barbiturates act as depressants, slowing the body's systems. Long-term abuse causes many dangerous effects, including addiction.*

Opiates

Opiates come from the seed pods of the opium poppy. Most **narcotics**—drugs that relieve pain and cause sleepiness—are forms of opiates. Narcotics come in different strengths, from **codeine** and **opium,** which are less dangerous painkillers, to **morphine** and **heroin,** which are strong and highly addictive.

Physicians sometimes prescribe codeine for pain relief or to calm a cough. Codeine is weak, compared with other narcotics. However, codeine is still abused for the euphoria it produces, and can cause addiction. Opium is also a pain reliever, but it has side effects such as slowed breathing, slowed heart rate, loss of appetite, and loss of mental abilities.

Morphine is one of the strongest painkillers in medicine. Since it is extremely addictive, its medical use is limited to those with diseases such as cancer, who are in desperate need of pain relief. Morphine is often abused. It often causes addiction

This seed pod from the opium poppy yields a powerful narcotic drug.

with withdrawal symptoms so painful that most addicted people need professional help to stop abusing the drug.

The narcotic abused most often in the United States is heroin, a concentrated form of morphine. It is not used as a medicine in this country because it is so addictive. In fact, heroin is illegal in the United States. Heroin dulls the senses and seems to make the abuser's worries disappear. After addiction sets in, though, the person must have heroin to avoid the pain of withdrawal.

Key Points *Narcotics are drugs that are used to relieve pain, but they are also very addictive. Codeine can relieve minor pain and coughing. Morphine is used rarely in medicine. Heroin is illegal in the United States because it is so addictive.*

①☐ Cocaine

Cocaine's effects are like those of two groups of medical drugs: the local anesthetics and the stimulants. In fact, experienced cocaine abusers cannot tell injected amphetamine from injected cocaine.

The drug cocaine is taken from the leaves of the coca bush. In coca-growing cultures, people chew the leaves to receive small doses of the stimulant to help them work longer. In other cultures, pure cocaine is usually mixed with other white powders—

328

Activity 4.16

Group Research. Divide your class into six groups for a group research/ presentation project. Assign each group a different class of drugs. Have them give reports on each of the drugs in that class and the street names and paraphernalia as well as dangers involved with each drug. You might have them include the source of each drug. **(one class period for presentations, Cooperative**

Learning)

Activity 4.17

Review of Helpful Sources. Have students explain who they would ask for help if they found themselves addicted to drugs and wanted to get off them.

Activity 4.18

Probation Speaker. Invite a parole or probation officer to visit the class and speak about how he or she deals with

those on parole or probation for drug abuse. Ask the officer to describe the signs that indicate potential violations are about to occur. Also ask how the system helps people get off drugs. **(1 hr.)**

Activity 4.19

TV Characters. Have students describe drug abusers and drug misusers they see on TV. Point out that the drug

(continued on next page)

some active, some not—before it is sold. If an unwary consumer happens upon pure cocaine and takes it in the same quantity as the diluted product, the reactions are severe or fatal.

People may use any of a number of methods to take cocaine. One route is snorting—that is, sniffing the powder into the nose. Other routes are injecting or smoking the drug. Many a person who starts by snorting a little soon increases the doses, goes on binges, and moves to the more direct routes—injection or smoking.

Cocaine in its smokable forms ("base," "crack," or "rock") is an extremely addictive drug. Smokable cocaine now rivals marijuana in frequency of abuse in some areas of the United States. Crack opened whole new cocaine markets because of its low price. Widespread addictions and deaths from the drug followed.

The short-lived burst of euphoria from cocaine is mixed with a feeling of being out of control. It is followed by intense dysphoria. The intensity of the high and the low depends partly on the drug dose, partly on the route of administration, and partly on the abuser's expectations. Repeated use of the drug shuts off all drives, including the hunger and sex drives. It replaces them with a drug-seeking drive.

Cocaine stimulates the nervous system and brings on the stress response—constricted blood vessels, raised blood pressure, widened pupils of the eyes, and increased body temperature. It also drives away feelings of fatigue.

Cocaine taken into the nose destroys the nasal tissues, leaving a hole internally between the nostrils. Over half of chronic snorters report nasal problems. Many more cocaine abusers suffer chronic fatigue, inability to perform sexually, and severe headaches. Cocaine occasionally causes death—usually by heart attack, stroke, or

seizure in an already damaged body system.

Pregnant women who abuse cocaine risk permanent birth defects and death of their infants. In hospitals throughout the country, doctors are seeing more and more crack-damaged babies. Many of these babies are born too small, too early. The pregnant woman who smokes crack cuts off the flow of oxygen and nutrients to her baby, stunting the baby's growth during pregnancy. Crack babies may also suffer seizures and malformations of organs such as the kidneys, intestines, and spinal cord. Some women who have abused cocaine during pregnancy and damaged their unborn babies have been sued to pay for the damage.

① Cocaine abuse is a problem for over 1 million people in the United States. Between 60 and 80 percent of takers questioned believe themselves to be addicted, unable to turn the drug down if offered, and unable to limit their abuse of cocaine. A person who is addicted to cocaine loses the ability to work, to play, to keep a job, or to stop abusing the drug.

MINI GLOSSARY

barbiturates: depressant drugs that slow the activity of the central nervous system.

opiates: a group of drugs derived from the opium poppy, that relieve pain and induce sleep; also known as *narcotics*.

narcotics: habit-forming drugs that relieve pain and produce sleep when taken in moderate doses; also called *opiates*, because most are derived from the opium poppy.

codeine: a narcotic drug that is commonly used for suppressing coughs.

opium: a narcotic drug that relieves pain and induces sleep, made from the opium poppy.

morphine: a narcotic drug that doctors prescribe as a painkiller.

heroin: a narcotic drug derived from morphine.

Teacher Support Notes

① **Penalties for Crack Convictions:** In recent years many critics have charged that federal crack laws are subjecting thousands of African Americans to unfairly long prison sentences while treating whites with comparative leniency. Some studies suggest that more than 90% of all federal crack defendants are African American (about 5% are white) and many are serving mandatory prison sentences of five years or more for as little as 5 grams. Each gram of crack is considered the equivalent of 100 grams of powder cocaine according to federal law. To trigger the same minimum sentence for a defendant using powder cocaine, the criminal would have to be convicted of trying to sell 500 grams. (About 45% of powder cocaine defendants are white.) Some argue that the penalties are justified because crack is much more dangerous than snorted cocaine.

abuser on the show usually ends up dead, in jail, or in rehabilitation for the drug problem. Explain that these negative outcomes can be avoided by not getting involved with drugs. **(10 min.)**

Activity 4.20

Commercials. Discuss antidrug commercials that are seen on TV. Determine what their messages are. Explain to students that these public service announcements do cost money to produce and air. No companies pay for these advertisements because they do not promote any products. Emphasize that their sole purpose is to inform society of a great danger. **(5 min.)**

EVALUATE
SECTION IV

Activity 4.21
Matching Quiz. Write the following terms on the board, then read the nine descriptions. Have students number their papers 1–9 and write the correct term for each number.

Teacher Support Notes

① **Hazards of PCP:** As enrichment you may want to share the following information with your students. More people taking PCP die from injuries resulting from drug-induced behavior than from the drug itself. Auto accidents and falling from roofs and windows are some of the accidents linked to PCP. It is reported that people on PCP have drowned in shallow water because they were unable to tell which way was up. Also linked to PCP use are suicides, self-inflicted wounds, and drownings from sedation.

② **Availability:** Following is some background information, which you may or may not choose to share with your students. One of the most disturbing characteristics of inhalants is their availability. Currently, there are in excess of 300 products offered in aerosol form. Because of the relative ease with which these products can be obtained (and abused), and to discourage abuse, many of the products have certain chemical additives, which result in unpleasant side effects to inhalants.

---

330 UNIT 4 Drug Use and Abuse

Key Points ▶ *Cocaine is a stimulant and an anesthetic that produces a short-term, intense high followed by extreme dysphoria. Side effects include eroding of nasal tissues, chronic fatigue, severe headaches, birth defects, and deaths of users.*

Hallucinogens

While many drugs can produce false sensations in the mind, **hallucinogens** produce vivid visions, sounds, smells, and other sensory experiences that are out of touch with reality. One of the best known of the hallucinogens is **LSD (lysergic acid diethylamide).** So powerful is the pure chemical LSD that just a tiny drop of solution, ingested with sugar or other food, sends the taker on a mental "trip" of distorted visions that lasts for hours, and that cannot be stopped until the drug wears off. Some people say that trips have given them new ideas. Others, though, have experienced nightmarish "bad trips." A person having a bad trip may become irrational and do dangerous things to try to escape an imaginary pursuer. A taker of LSD may experience a temporary resurfacing of the drug's effects, called a flashback, days or even years after the original trip has subsided.

A drug that causes frightening hallucinations and violent tendencies is **PCP (phencyclidine hydrochloride).** It was first made as a tranquilizer for animals. People who take it for its hallucinogenic effect suffer dangerous and unpredictable side effects. PCP causes some abusers to become so violent that they commit murder or suicide; others suffer seizures, coma, and death. ①

Some hallucinogenic drugs are made in the tissues of plants. The **peyote** cactus produces the drug **mescaline.** Mescaline's effects have been compared to a mild LSD trip, but one accompanied by vomiting, sweating, and painful abdominal cramping. The taking of Peyote is part of the religious ceremonies of some Native Americans of the southwestern United States. Two other hallucinogens, **psilocybin** and **psilocin,** are part of the tissues of a strain of mushrooms. Many wild mushrooms look alike, but some contain deadly poisons. Even expert mushroom hunters have been fooled by appearances.

Key Points ▶ *Drugs that produce false sensations in the mind, such as vivid and distorted visions, are called hallucinogens. LSD, PCP, mescaline, psilocybin, and psilocin are hallucinogens.*

② Inhalants

Three types of chemicals are sometimes inhaled to produce a high. The first type, solvents, are liquids that vaporize at room temperature. They include fumes from gasoline, glue, lighter fluid, cleaning fluid, and paint thinner. A second type, propellants, are substances added to products such as paint, deodorant, hair spray, whipped cream, and oil to make them sprayable. A third type is intended for medical use: chloroform, ether, nitrous oxide (laughing gas), and others. Amyl nitrite, a heart pain medicine, is sometimes abused this way. So is butyl nitrite, sold legally as a "room odorizer."

Products of the first two types bear labels that warn against inhaling their fumes because of the hazards they present. A person who experiments with them, even once, risks permanent brain damage or death from heart failure or suffocation. Chemicals of the third type bring on headache, dizziness, a quickened heart rate, nausea, nasal irritation, or coughing. In high doses, they may cause a heart attack or stroke.

The effects of inhalants on brain cells are unpredictable. The effects depend on the chemicals inhaled and the dose. In general, even short-term abuse disrupts vision, impairs judgment, and reduces muscle and

marijuana   opiates
amphetamines   cocaine
barbiturates   hallucinogens
inhalants   look-alikes
designer drugs

_____ **1.** block fatigue and hunger, increase activity, and stimulate the central nervous system (amphetamines)

_____ **2.** induce sleep and relieve pain (opiates)

_____ **3.** cause unpredictable results such as vision disruption, impair judgment, and cause loss of muscle control (inhalants)

_____ **4.** resemble other drugs but have unknown effects (designer drugs)

_____ **5.** is similar to both anesthetics and stimulants (marijuana)

_____ **6.** alters hearing, touch, taste, and feelings (cocaine)

_____ **7.** have similar effects as other drugs, but are legally sold over the counter (look-alikes)

_____ **8.** depress the central nervous system (barbiturates)

_____ **9.** produce sensory experiences that are not real (hallucinogens)

Some play with deadly toys . . . and some choose health-promoting activities.

reflex control. These effects may be permanent. Many cases of permanent brain and nerve damage have resulted from sniffing. The kidneys, blood, liver, and bone marrow also suffer damage. When the lungs fill with gases that contain no oxygen, or when the product coats the lungs' surfaces and blocks oxygen's path to the blood, suffocation results.

> **Key Points**   *Three categories of chemicals are used as inhalants: solvents, propellants, and medicines such as chloroform and nitrous oxide. People who experiment with inhalants risk permanent disability or death.* ①

Look-alikes

Another group of easily purchased drugs is the so-called **look-alikes.** Drug pushers, posing as companies, combine OTC drugs and other legal substances to produce pills and powders that look like the illegal drugs that abusers seek. For example, magazines publish ads for "legal stimulants" ("mail-order speed") that look exactly like amphetamines, but with one important difference: the pills contain a mix of over-the-counter stimulants, decongestants, caffeine, and other drugs instead of amphetamines.

Because look-alikes are weaker than the drugs they look like, takers tend to take a lot of them and then experience sleep disturbances, abnormal heartbeat, and sudden rises in blood pressure. The most dangerous situation is when a taker can't tell the difference between the look-alike and the real thing. When such a person gets some of the real, high-powered drugs

M ini G lossary

hallucinogens (hal-LOO-sin-oh-jens): drugs that cause visions and other sensory illusions.
LSD (lysergic acid diethylamide): a powerful hallucinogenic drug; also called *acid.*
PCP (phencyclidine hydrochloride): an animal tranquilizer, abused by human beings as a hallucinogen.
peyote: a cactus that produces the hallucinogen mescaline.
mescaline: the hallucinogen produced by the peyote cactus.
psilocybin (sill-oh-SI-bin), **psilocin** (sill-OH-sin): two hallucinogens produced by a type of wild mushroom.
look-alikes: combinations of OTC drugs and other chemicals packaged to look like prescription medications or illegal drugs.

Teacher Support Notes

① **Psychological Effects:** Many people experience very pronounced psychological effects from inhaling volatile substances. Among the effects experienced are tenseness, retarded motor-coordination skills, lack of behavioral control, confusion, hyperactivity, impaired judgment, and in some cases, acute psychosis and permanent brain damage.

331

CLOSE
SECTION IV

(30 min.; Reteach, Reinforce)

Activity 4.22
Section Review. Students should be able to describe each of the groups of drugs from this section. This should include effects, side effects, method of administration, and whether or not the drug causes psychological and/or physical addiction.

Activity 4.23
Essay. Assign students to write an essay describing how three of the nine groups of drugs would adversely affect their lives if they abused each of them. **(30 min.; Interdisciplinary, Critical Thinking)**

Teacher Support Notes

① **More About Ecstasy:** You might want to share the following information with your students for enrichment purposes. Ecstasy is chemically known as MDA (methylenedioxyamphetamine). It has two structural relatives, MMDA and MDMA, which also go by the name *Ecstasy*. Researchers feel that one of the greatest hazards of using Ecstasy (besides the negative side effects) is that it stimulates further use, which is likely to lead to addiction.

Section IV Review

Answers
1. barbiturates
2. heroin
3. morphine
4. for a month, six months
5. relief of glaucoma and cancer therapy side effects
6. extreme anxiety, temporary mental illness, and malnutrition
7. birth defects; death of infants; stunted growth; suffer seizures and malformations of organs such as kidneys, intestines, and spinal cord
8. LSD
9. Answers will vary.

---

and takes the same number of pills, a fatal overdose results.

The look-alikes are legal, so there are no limits on their sale. Those who sell them make huge profits at the expense of the taker's health. But so it is with all street drugs—no one is looking out for the consumer.

> **Key Points** ▶ *Look-alikes are made from legal substances and look like drugs that abusers seek. As with all street drugs, no agency checks the contents of these drugs, so the taker risks harm.*

Designer Drugs

Laboratory-made drugs that closely resemble illegal drugs in chemical structure are called **designer drugs.** *Ecstasy*, for example, is a designer drug that closely resembles cocaine. Each drug is defined as legal or illegal based on its exact chemical formula. Because designer drugs have new formulas, they are legal, at least for a while. They are similar enough to illegal drugs so that they produce similar effects in the body—at least, that is the maker's plan.

A story of what actually can happen with designer drugs was told in an episode of the public television series "Nova." A fumbling amateur chemist, using a crude basement laboratory in California, tried to produce a batch of designer heroin. His attempt at chemistry produced, instead, a substance toxic to brain cells. When the heroin addicts who purchased it injected the stuff, they were immediately and permanently paralyzed. The substance left them with Parkinson's disease—destruction of the parts of the brain that control muscle movements. When the police found and arrested the "chemist," he, too, had developed Parkinsonism from his creation. He had absorbed the chemical through his skin and lungs while making it.

This story shows the problem all takers of street drugs face: lack of testing. People

who take street drugs, or even simply handle them, are risking exposure to highly toxic chemicals.

> **Key Points** ▶ *Designer drugs are laboratory-made drugs that closely resemble illegal drugs in chemical structure. Lack of testing presents an enormous risk to the taker.*

SECTION IV   REVIEW

Answer the following questions on a sheet of paper.

Learning the Vocabulary
The vocabulary terms in this section are *hallucinations, amotivational syndrome, amphetamines, hyperactivity, sedatives, barbiturates, opiates, narcotics, codeine, opium, morphine, heroin, hallucinogens, LSD (lysergic acid diethylamide), PCP (phencyclidine hydrochloride), peyote, mescaline, psilocybin, psilocin, look-alikes,* and *designer drugs.* Use the clues given to help you unscramble the term.

1. **rraaeiubbstt** Depressant drugs that slow the activity of the central nervous system.
2. **eiohnr** A narcotic drug derived from morphine, illegal in the United States.
3. **eiohmnpr** A narcotic drug that is used by doctors as a painkiller.

Learning the Facts
4. How long does THC linger in the body?
5. Describe how THC can be used medically.
6. What are the side effects of injecting amphetamines?
7. What are the risks for the unborn baby and the newborn when the mother uses cocaine?
8. What is the best known hallucinogen?

Making Life Choices
9. Reread the Consumer Awareness section on Greed and Street Drugs on page 325. Discuss some of the problems associated with illegal drugs on the streets. Why do some sellers dilute their drugs more than other sellers? How do street drugs differ from medical drugs?

FOCUS
SECTION V

In this section students will learn that:
1. Drugs affect judgment needed for driving.
2. Marijuana and alcohol affect driving long after the high has worn off.
3. Amphetamines actually cause a decline in driving ability.
4. Over-the-counter medicines can impair driving ability.

Activity 5.1
Effects of OTC Drugs. Have students brainstorm a list of OTC drugs they have at home that could affect driving. List these on the board. This will get students thinking about drugs that could affect drivers in their own families.
(15 min.)

TEACH
SECTION V
(Guided and Independent Practice)

Activity 5.2
Effects on Driving. Have students investigate how different drugs affect the nervous system and a person's judgment in such a way that would impair the ability to drive. Have different groups research

(continued on next page)

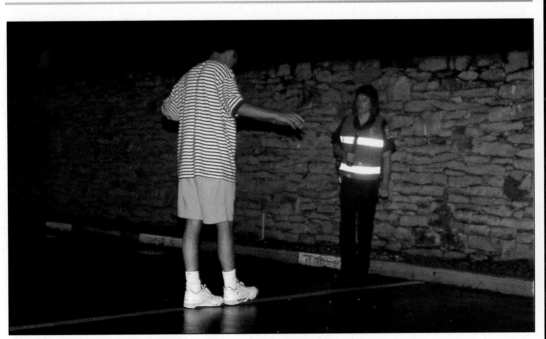

A person who is too impaired to walk should certainly not drive.

SECTION V

Drugs and Driving

One more hazard of all the drugs just described is their effect on driving ability. Mind-altering drugs, including alcohol, marijuana, and others, slow people's reactions and make them unable to judge how fast they are going. In simulator tests, people on drugs crash often. In the cases of alcohol and marijuana, the impairment of driving lasts for hours *after* the high from the drug has worn off—even into the next day.

You might think amphetamines would improve people's driving, because they speed up the nervous system. Accident studies show otherwise, though. Heavy amphetamine doses allow fatigued people to override their feelings of exhaustion. Their driving ability, however, declines even though they think they are doing well.

Even many over-the-counter medicines can impair a person's ability to drive. Many needless accidents and fatalities could be prevented each year if people who take drugs or medicines that affect driving would stay away from the wheel.

MINI GLOSSARY

designer drugs: laboratory-made drugs that closely resemble illegal drugs in chemical structure, but that are different enough to be legal until ruled illegal.

Teacher Support Notes

① **Marijuana Flashbacks:** In addition to the fact that impairment of driving abilities can last for hours after taking marijuana, these abilities can also be impaired by flashbacks. Some people who have taken marijuana have reported recurrences of feelings and perceptions (flashbacks) not unlike those produced when the drug was just taken. These recurrences are spontaneous and can include a vivid reliving of a drug-related experience, or milder forms of recall.

marijuana, alcohol, OTC medications, and amphetamines. **(one class period for presentations, Interdisciplinary)**

Activity 5.3
OTC Drug Posters. Have students make posters displaying over-the-counter

drug labels and ads for drugs that should not be taken before driving. Display posters around the room. This will show students just how many commonly used OTC drugs should not be taken before driving. **(Reteach, Reinforce)**

EVALUATE
SECTION V

Activity 5.4

Pop Quiz.
1. How do drugs affect judgment that is needed for driving? (They slow people's reactions and make them unable to judge how fast they are going.)
2. In what ways do marijuana and alcohol affect driving long after the high is gone? (They continue to impair judgment and reaction time.)
3. Can over-the-counter medications affect driving ability? How? (Yes. They

---

Teacher Support Notes

① **Teen Views Follow-Up Questions:** Here are some questions that should help you promote class discussion of the comments made by students to the question "How has drug abuse affected your school or community?"
a. Have any of the students witnessed the type of community change described by George Watson?
b. George Watson suggests that the government's actions regarding drug abuse are affected by racial concerns. Do students agree or disagree?
c. Do students feel that it is dangerous in their neighborhoods? If so, how much of this is due to drugs, in their opinions?
d. Do students believe that the federal government should be spending more to fight drug abuse even if it means cutting money from such places as defense? How can money be used to fight drugs?
e. Are drugs as common in students' social lives as they seem to be in Keith Levy's?
f. Ask students if they can tell that other people have been abusing drugs. If so, how?

334

334 UNIT 4 Drug Use and Abuse

TEEN
VIEWS

How has drug abuse affected your school or community? ①

Drug abuse has changed my community a great deal. When I was younger, it was easier growing up in my neighborhood. People were more concerned for every child. Times have changed. You have to be careful walking down the street because a crackhead might try to kill you. Little ones have to stay in the house. Everywhere you go, people are selling and using drugs. Death is everywhere, in the parks, at home, and in the schools. Drug abuse is killing innocent people. Government spends so much money on defense, but they can't invest money on America's future. Drugs in the community have brought my community down. It seems like the government doesn't care as long as drug abuse stays in the Black community. **George Watson, 17, Woodrow Wilson High School, CA**

Drug abuse is a serious problem in all communities, not just mine. I know of people who have used drugs, and have even sold them. Drugs have become a normal thing. It is common to hear people discussing their plans for the weekend and hear them say

they are going to get high, trip, or go out drinking. Because of drug busts in our community, people have stopped, or they have become more aware. You can get drugs as easy as buying a newspaper. They are being sold on every corner. **Keith Levy, 18, Orange Park High School, FL**

 We go to school with people selling drugs. The principal and teachers who know keep asking to make unexpected searches to see if you have drugs on you. When they find out that a student has drugs, they call the cops. In our community little kids can't go out and play because of all the drug traffic. There could be a cross-fire shooting or even a dealer trying to sell drugs to them. **Shay Murphy, 18, Poughkeepsie High School, NY**

I have seen the dangers of using drugs firsthand. Every day I can tell that at least one person at my school had used drugs. It is a scary situation. I promised myself a long time ago that I never

would use drugs. What parents and other adults may not realize is that this community is just as involved in drugs as any other. **Angie Palmesano, 15, Westside High School, NE**

Drugs are a big deal in our school. Many kids have tried drugs because they are pressured into saying yes or they want "to look cool." There are many people that sell drugs to kids in our school. Drugs are not a major issue in my own community, but in other communities around Newman, drugs are big. **Mattie Chisolm, 14, Newman High School, CA**

Kids talk out loud at school about what kind of pot they smoked over the weekend. People are crazy when they end up doing drugs. A guy I knew did PCP. My friend found him three blocks away from the school. He had no idea where he was or what day it was. I never thought that he would be the one to fall into the peer pressure of drugs. **Amy Enriquez, 16, Hilltop High School, CA** impair driving ability.)

4. Do amphetamines affect driving ability? How? (Yes. They allow people to override their feelings of exhaustion, but the driving ability continues to decline.)

CLOSE
SECTION V

Activity 5.5
Paragraph on Drugs and Driving.

Have students write a paragraph describing how drugs can affect driving. They should be sure to include how marijuana and alcohol affect a person long after the high is gone. **(15 min.; Reteach, Reinforce)**

FOCUS
SECTION VI

In this section students will learn:

1. How hard it is to give up a drug problem.
2. That the first step to beating drug abuse is admitting to a drug problem.
3. To name agencies that help with drug problems.
4. How the revolving door of drug treatment works.

Activity 6.1
How to Begin to Help. Present this

(continued on next page)

Honest talk helps people face problems.

 Key Points *Mind-altering drugs slow people's reactions and impair their judgment of speed. Therefore, mind-altering drugs impair driving ability.*

SECTION V   REVIEW

Answer the following questions on a sheet of paper.

Learning the Facts
1. List the effects drugs have on driving.
2. How do amphetamines impair a person's ability to drive?
3. Could marijuana and alcohol have an effect on your ability to drive the next day? Explain your answer.

Making Life Choices
4. You are visiting an aunt's house and she wants to take you out to her favorite restaurant. Before you go she has to take a diet pill. She also has been sipping on wine most of the afternoon. You have a long drive to get to this special restaurant. What are some of the problems that may occur on your way? How can you help prevent these problems? What will you do to protect yourself from danger? What can you do differently the next time you go to visit her?

SECTION VI

Kicking the Habit

When people realize they have a drug problem, they have taken one important step: admitting it. Now comes a hard choice: suffer on and on, or quit. To quit involves suffering, too, but the suffering ends. Recovery requires much more than is presented here. The process is described in the next chapter.

A person who faces up to a drug problem has taken the important first step.

Section V Review
Answers
1. slow people's reactions and makes them unable to judge how fast they are going
2. They allow fatigued people to override their feelings of exhaustion. Their driving ability has declined even though they think they are doing well.
3. Yes. In cases of marijuana and alcohol the impairment of driving lasts for hours after the high has worn off, even into the next day.
4. Answers will vary; could include: discussion of aunt's driving ability, offering to drive or skip the special dinner, or calling a taxi.

> ❝ **Thoughts on Health** ❞
>
> *Heaven ne'er helps the man who will not help himself.*
> **– Sophocles**

problem to the class: How do you help a drug abuser who does not want to quit or even acknowledge that there is a problem? Evaluate and discuss students' answers. Emphasize that the person first must admit to the problem and want help. **(3 min.)**

TEACH
SECTION VI
(Guided and Independent Practice)

Activity 6.2
Making Choices. Assign students to create a list of people and/or things in their lives that drug abuse could cause them to lose. Then list things that they would not give up, things that would cause them to kick a drug habit if choices

had to be made. **(15 min., Critical Thinking)**

Activity 6.3
Role-Play. Assign one student to be a son or daughter who has to admit to his or her parents that he or she has a drug problem. Have three students role-play this situation for the rest of the class. Assign the class to explain on paper how they would do this differently than the

---

Teacher Support Notes

① **Getting Help:** If you or one of your students knows someone who is looking for a treatment program for a drug problem, encourage that person to discuss the following questions with a trained professional to determine the best treatment program:
a. How serious is the abuse problem? Is the person out of control and unable to stop abusing? Are large amounts of drugs being taken?
b. Is there an addiction to several drugs? If so, is detoxification necessary?
c. Has the drug abuse resulted in serious behavioral and psychiatric problems? Have medical problems resulted? Is the person violent or suicidal?
d. Can the person still function on a daily basis? (go to work, relate to people, etc.)
e. Has the person tried and failed in other attempts at treatment?

336

If you think a drug may be causing you a problem, here is a way to recognize it: give up the drug for a month. (Of course, if the drug is a medicine, the physician should decide whether it is safe to do without it.) Coffee, colas, cigarettes, OTC drugs, prescriptions, and alcohol, as well as illegal drugs, all qualify for this test. Try doing without one, and write down your responses to this chapter's Life Choice Inventory. The first step in solving a drug problem is to face the fact that you have one.

For those who face the problem and choose to quit, the next step is to get help. Rarely do people recover from drugs on their own. Figure 13–3 lists sources of help. Help comes in many forms—hospitalization, drug-quitting groups such as **Narcotics Anonymous (NA),** psychological therapy, and drug therapy.

An example of drug therapy is the use of **methadone** as treatment for heroin addiction. Methadone is an addictive drug, as heroin is. However, it is cheaper, and its effects are milder and longer lasting. Taking a "maintenance" drug such as methadone allows people addicted to heroin to recover socially. That is, they no longer must struggle to buy high-priced illegal drugs to hold off withdrawal.

Other useful drugs are the **narcotic antagonists,** which the person takes daily. The antagonists block the effects of the problem drugs. By taking the antagonists, the person commits to staying drug-free that day. This once-a-day commitment is easy to make. Then, when the urge to take the drug strikes, the person is protected from giving in to it. The same drugs are used to treat overdoses.

Few people who attempt recovery make it all the way. Most people who seek treatment get caught in something like a revolving door: getting treatment, giving up the drug, getting out of treatment, taking the drug again, going back into treatment—and

① Many agencies stand ready to help teens with drug problems or just to answer questions. You don't have to give your name. A few examples are Covenant House, Just Say No International, National Cocaine Hotline, and National Institute of Drug Abuse. To find these agencies and others:

Look in your telephone book under Drug Abuse, Drug Addiction, Alcohol Treatment, or Rehabilitation Services.

Go to the local library and ask the reference librarian for the addresses and telephone numbers of drug abuse agencies.

Ask someone you trust, such as your parents, a favorite teacher, or the school guidance counselor for help in finding a drug abuse agency.

Figure 13–3 Help Resources

so on. The addicted person may fail to make needed lifestyle changes. When the person first becomes free of the drug, he or she faces many more problems than ever, and now they must be handled without the escape of the drugs. The person who develops a support system has the best chance of staying free of drugs.

Still, some people make it. The first part is the hardest, for life seems empty without the drug. But later, looking back, the recovered person finds that the rewards of sanity and health outweigh by far whatever the drug seemed to offer. The Health Strategies section on the next page, "Drug-free Highs," shows that life is full of natural highs available to everyone.

Key Points Admitting a drug problem is the first step to overcoming it. Help comes in many forms: hospitalization, Narcotics Anonymous, psychological therapy, and drug therapy. Not everyone who attempts recovery makes it all the way. Those who do, however, are always glad they did.

role-players and how their parents would react. **(20 min., Critical Thinking)**

EVALUATE
SECTION VI

Activity 6.4
Essay. Assign students to answer the following essay question: How would you help one of your parents if the parent admitted a drug problem to you and asked for your help? **(20–30 min.)**

CLOSE
SECTION VI

Activity 6.5
Life Choice Inventory. Have students take the Life Choice Inventory entitled "Do You Have a Drug Problem?" Even though they might not abuse drugs, these questions might be answered for a family member or friend, or they might have relevance to other compulsive behaviors such as overeating, gambling, shopping, or overexercising.

Activity 6.6
No Stopping? Ask students when was the last time they did something wrong that they knew was wrong. Why did they do it? Explain that everyone

(continued on next page)

HEALTH STRATEGIES

Drug-free Highs

Pleasure is there for the taking, for those who know where to look.

- Run, walk, or skip across an open field or along a beach.
- Ask a grandparent what life is about.
- Play with a baby.
- Give a friend a gift that you made with your own hands.
- Work hard at something, and see it through to completion.
- Have a good cry about that thing you have been hiding from for too long.
- Learn to meditate.
- Eat a delicious, nourishing food.
- Write some poetry for yourself (it doesn't have to rhyme).
- Climb a mountain; or visit a river, ocean, or lake.
- Say "thank you" more often.
- Beat the feathers out of a pillow next time you are very angry.
- Stop biting your nails (or another bad habit).
- Read a good book.
- Give someone a long hug.
- Tell your parent, "I love you."
- Volunteer your time to help others (serve food at a soup kitchen, or collect needed items for your favorite charity).

Source: Adapted from S. J. Levy, *Managing the "Drugs" in Your Life* (New York: McGraw-Hill, 1983), p. 104.

SECTION VI REVIEW

Answer the following questions on a sheet of paper.
Learning the Vocabulary
The vocabulary terms in this section are *Narcotics Anonymous, methadone,* and *narcotic antagonists.*
Fill in the blank with the correct answer.
1. _____ oppose the actions of other drugs.
2. A 12-step program that promotes personal growth and leads to the person's helping others to recover is called _____.
3. A drug that is used to treat heroin addiction is _____.

Learning the Facts
4. What is one important step in kicking a drug habit?
5. List some of the drugs to which the Life Choice Inventory on page 338 applies.
6. Name the different agencies that can help people with drug problems.
7. Explain what is meant by "the revolving door syndrome" in drug treatment.

Making Life Choices
8. After completing the Life Choice Inventory on page 338, are you satisfied with your results? Do you have a drug problem? Give a few suggestions on how you could go about making more healthful choices. What benefits might you gain by making these choices?

MINI GLOSSARY

Narcotics Anonymous (NA): a free, self-help program of addiction recovery. It uses a 12-step program, promotes personal growth, and leads to the person's helping others to recover.
methadone: a drug used to treat heroin addiction; it holds off withdrawal and helps people recover socially.
narcotic antagonists: drugs that oppose the actions of other drugs. The word *antagonist* means something or someone who struggles with, or opposes, another.

Teacher Support Notes

① **Drug-free Highs:** Ask students to expand the list in this Health Strategies box.

Section VI Review
Answers
1. Narcotic antagonists
2. Narcotics Anonymous
3. methadone
4. admitting it
5. caffeine found in coffee and colas, cigarettes, OTC drugs, prescriptions (with physician's approval), alcohol, and illegal drugs
6. Covenant House "9-Line", Just Say No International, National Cocaine Hot Line, National Institute of Drug Abuse Hot Line
7. getting treatment, giving up the drug, getting out of treatment, taking the drug again, going back into treatment, and so on, with the person failing to make lifestyle changes
8. Answers will vary.

knows that drug abuse is wrong and illegal, but this does not stop some from experimenting, and it does not stop them once they are addicted. **(5 min.)**

Activity 6.7
Healthful Activities. Tell students that for young people, the need to fit in is a very strong part of establishing one's own identity. Have students brainstorm a list of ways to become an active part of a group that promotes healthful activities— activities that will boost a person's self-esteem. Answers might include sports, band, clubs, church groups, etc. You might want to ask for a show of hands to see how many of your students are involved in any such activities. This would be a good opportunity to have young people see the value of becoming involved with an organization. **(15 min.)**

Activity 6.8
Short Stories. Ask each student to write a short story about a teenager who gets caught up in drug abuse and the selling or smuggling of drugs. **(20 min., interdisciplinary)**

Teacher Support Notes

① **Overcoming Cravings:** Many people going through withdrawal feel that it is not possible to resist the cravings that are part of the withdrawal process. However, the most severe cravings are temporary and behavior modification methods can help overcome them. Changing environment, finding family or friends who can help overcome these feelings, and avoiding people who might trigger thoughts of drug abuse are some effective behavior modification methods.

> 66 **Thoughts on Health** 99
>
> *It is easier to be wise for others than for ourselves.*
> – *Francois de La Rochefoucauld*

LIFE CHOICE
INVENTORY

Do You Have a Drug Problem?

This exercise is an informal way to find out if any drug is a problem for you. Give up the drug for a month, and answer these questions:

1. Do you miss the drug?
2. Are you experiencing withdrawal effects?
3. Does life seem less full or less fun without the drug?
4. Are you suddenly aware of problems in your life that you had been ignoring?
5. Are you feeling more tense or anxious than usual?
6. Are you feeling depressed?
7. Do you feel better without the drug?
8. Do you have more problems concentrating or meeting goals and due dates than usual?
9. Do you find that you spend a lot of time thinking about the drug?

① 10. Did you make sure you could get some of the drug quickly, just in case you missed it too much?

SCORING

If you were unable to give up the drug for a month, you have a drug problem.

If you answered yes to many of these questions, you may have a drug problem.

If you gave up the drug for a month, you may want to kick the habit permanently now. You need not figure it out alone. You may want to get someone to help you.

Source: Adapted from S. J. Levy, *Managing the "Drugs" in Your Life* (New York: McGraw-Hill, 1983), p. 41.

SECTION VII

Helping Someone Else Kick the Habit

You may know someone who has a drug problem and feel the need to reach out to that person. First, you may want to take a look at Figure 13–4 on the next page, to help you determine whether the person really is a drug abuser.

Extreme caution should be used in attributing any of the signs to drug abuse. They may be caused by hundreds of other things as well. Probably the best way to find out for sure if a person is abusing drugs is to express concern and ask questions. If you care, this is a way to show it.

Another way to show you care about a person with a drug problem is to make the effort to help, even if this means being tough. You may have to risk confronting the person, standing against your peers, and maybe even losing a friend in the effort to save the person's health or life. Things you can do include:

• Making sure the person knows you won't approve of the drug habit.

FOCUS
SECTION VII

In this section students will learn:
1. Why blame or judgment will not help give the drug abuser more will to quit.
2. To see that the drug abuser's will to quit is the only thing that will help him or her quit.

Activity 7.1

Breaking Habits. Ask students to think of habits that they have. How could someone make them quit their habits, even if they did not want to? Discuss some of the habits and ways to break them. **(10 min.)**

Activity 7.2

Want to Quit? Have the class try to convince you (a drug abuser) that you

should stop abusing drugs. Be strong. Have some responses prepared in advance. Show them that the drug abuser must want to quit. **(5–10 min.)**

TEACH
SECTION VII
(Guided and Independent Practice)

Activity 7.3

Role-Play. Assign students to role-

(continued on next page)

- Making available all the information you can gather on the health effects of the drug.
- Making sure the person knows, on choosing to seek help, where to go for it.

Drug addiction does not mean someone is a bad person. Blame is a useless concept. It can make people feel guilty, but it can't help them get better. Drug-addicted people pay heavily enough for past choices. If you want to help, you won't judge, and you won't blame.

No amount of effort on your part, however, can supply the key ingredient in someone else's choice to give up drugs: the will to quit. In fact, the toughest job for many people whose lives are affected by drug abusers is to learn to enjoy their own

lives without being dragged down. Often they have to learn simply to accept the other person's choice, painful as that may be. Beyond caring, you have to let go. Live your own life as fully as possible while it is yours to live.

> **Key Points** *You cannot make someone quit a drug habit. The person has to have the will to quit. The toughest part for those close to an addicted person is to learn to enjoy their lives without being dragged down.*

SECTION VII REVIEW

Answer the following questions on a sheet of paper.

Learning the Facts
1. List the signs of drug abuse given in this section.
2. What are three things you can do to help a person with a drug problem?
3. What is the crucial ingredient needed for a person to give up drugs?

Making Life Choices
4. There are many agencies that work with drug addictions. How could you help a friend choose the right agency? What are some of the advantages and disadvantages about each of the agencies?

FIGURE 13-4

Signs of Drug Abuse

How can you tell whether someone close to you is abusing drugs? Here are some signs to look for:

- Paleness and perspiration.
- Dilated pupils.
- Runny nose and nosebleeds.
- Jitters and hyperactivity.
- Ability to go without food or sleep for long periods of time.
- Anxiety or unreasonable suspiciousness.
- Loss of memory.
- Unexplained increases in energy and talkativeness, followed by lethargy and depression.
- Sudden carelessness about personal appearance.
- Broken appointments, broken promises, lying.
- Inability to explain what happened to money.

Answers to Fact or Fiction

1. True. **2.** False. Even people who are fully aware of the hazards abuse drugs. **3.** False. People continue abusing drugs to avoid the pain of withdrawal symptoms. **4.** False. Psychological addictions can be as powerful as physical ones. **5.** False. Smoking marijuana is associated with harmful health effects. **6.** True. **7.** False. Amphetamines impair driving ability. **8.** False. People rarely recover from drug dependency on their own.

Teacher Support Notes

① **Signs of Drug Abuse:** Ask students if they know anyone with these symptoms. If so, what do they think they should do? Emphasize that they should not jump to conclusions. As the text states, many other causes can bring about these symptoms.

Section VII Review
Answers
1. Refer to Figure 13–4 on this page for answers.
2. make sure the person knows you don't approve of the drug habit, make available all the information you can gather on the health effects of the drug, make sure the person knows where to go for help
3. the will to quit
4. Answers will vary.

(15 min., Critical Thinking)

Activity 7.4
Community Resources. Assign students to make a list of people from whom they would seek help or would refer a family member to in their community for a drug abuse problem. Combine all the lists to make a master list on the board to show students just how many sources of help are available. **(10–15 min.)**

EVALUATE
SECTION VII

Activity 7.5
Essay. Assign students to answer the following essay question: A good friend of yours is abusing drugs. How do you help? Students should include showing disapproval, making information available, and making sure the drug abuser knows

---

play. One student's job is to show that he does not approve of another student's drug abuse problem. Enforce the rules, however, that they cannot blame and they cannot judge the individual. The drug abuser is to try to justify his habit. Invite the class to interact and help both!

Teacher Support Notes

① **More on Violence:** Of course, teens are not the only ones committing acts of violence. If students point out or ask about violent acts committed by adults, you may want to give them some of the following unfortunate statistics:
• One American kills another every 23 minutes.
• More than 1.4 million American children are subjected to physical abuse by parents each year.
• Over 25% of all the married men and women in the U.S. have attacked their spouses.

STRAIGHT **T**ALK

Teens and Social Problems

Abuse of drugs and other substances is many times linked with other problems of society—especially the problems of youth. The violence that characterizes some groups of teens today triggers fear in almost everyone near them, and rightly so.

Statistics show that hundreds of thousands of youths carry guns to school at least occasionally to protect themselves from fellow students. Closer to a million carry knives for that purpose. Homicide is now the leading killer of black males aged 15 to 24. It is second only to auto accidents among causes of death of white youngsters. One news reporter puts it this way: Disputes once settled with fists are now settled with guns. Every 100 hours, more youths die on the street than were killed in the Persian Gulf War. ①

More adolescents are confined in correctional institutions today than ever before. Some 100,000 are confined, adding up to millions each year. This prompts some experts to declare the situation a national emergency.

I know gangs are a problem, but is everybody in trouble? Where do regular kids fit into the picture?

Luckily, the majority of teenagers are emotionally strong, socially healthy, and on a path that leads to a successful life. Those named in the statistics above are most often "repeat offenders." These are teens with long-standing social problems, and who are chronically in trouble at home, at school, and with the law. As you might suspect, many are members of gangs that traffic in drugs and violence. Many times the gangs imitate the images created by movies and television of "tough guys" or "the cool people." These offenders do create problems for others, too, because they disrupt schools and drain limited resources. In certain areas they may threaten local people and peers with assault, rape, robbery, and sometimes even death.

I've heard of some kids like that. What makes them act that way?

Many theories attempt to explain the progression of events leading to a first arrest. One theory involves heredity. Social problems seem to run in families. A child who has one or more parents, or even grandparents, with social problems is far more likely to become delinquent than are others.

A widely accepted theory holds that social problems in the teen years stem from the events of early life. The series of events begins with a child who has a tendency to act out aggression, and whose parents are ineffective in exerting control.

When such a child begins acting aggressively with the parents, they unknowingly reinforce the child's tendency. Parents who discipline only inconsistently, or who "give in" to tantrums or other aggression, teach the child that aggression is a tool to use in getting one's own way.

(Continued on next page)

CLOSE
SECTION VII

Activity 7.6
Avoiding Consequences. Have students list negative consequences of drug abuse. Have several students share their lists. Ask students the following questions. Do you want to be protected from these things happening to you? Why or why not? Do you feel the need to protect your family members and friends from these things? Why or why not? What things might stand in your way as you try to protect family and friends from situations involving drug abuse?

RETEACH/BONUS

Decision Making. Have students brainstorm a list of major decisions that they have to make in their lifetimes. You might receive answers such as what college to attend, who to marry, where to live, etc. Then ask students if drug abuse might impair a person's ability to make sound and responsible decisions. Tell students that a good decision is made when a person considers positive and

(continued on next page)

STRAIGHT TALK *(Continued)*

Parents who are abusive in their discipline convey the same message: that violence controls people. Social and economic disadvantages, common in such families, worsen the problem by adding to the parents' burden of stress. Stress may make them unresponsive or hostile to their children.

A naturally aggressive child who is rewarded for being aggressive at home will also try this tactic in other settings. At school, though, aggressive behavior earns the child rejection from peers. The child then suffers from social isolation. Growing up without normal friends, the child misses out on important social lessons taught by peers, becomes disruptive, and fails in school.

If the cycle of aggression and isolation continues year after year until adolescence, then the child may become a **juvenile delinquent.** By the teen years, the aggressive antisocial child is likely to join gangs, to commit crimes, to abuse substances and become addicted, or to have to deal with pregnancies. As a teen, the child may leave home and become a **runaway,** or the parents may push the child out. The child is then a **"throwaway."** Such teens are likely to give up on school and become **dropouts.**

Almost without fail, an adult with such a history will eventually commit serious crimes and be jailed. Such people may lack strong social ties and have no support groups. People who lack social connections also become ill more often, die earlier from all causes, and have more accidents. How sad that some live life without the full enjoyment of the very things that make life worth living—love, happiness, creativity, accomplishments, and contributions—and suffer more of life's mishaps as well.

Actually, I think I once did something antisocial. I was with some friends, and. . .

Wait. Whatever you've done, it doesn't mean that you are headed for a life of violence and crime. Studies show that almost everyone, including the most loved and respected people of the community, did something in early life that authorities would have considered to be delinquent or illegal. But people who are socially healthy learn from their experiences, and do not chronically repeat delinquent behaviors. The antisocial people seem to choose a life of delinquency over one based on social health.

From the way you describe it, some kids don't seem to have much choice. Is it certain that a child like the one you described will turn out to be delinquent as a teen?

It is likely.

Is there any way to help such children lead a normal life?

① Yes, especially if their parents seek help in the early years of parenting. Studies of antisocial, aggressive preschool children show that they improve greatly when their parents learn to discipline them effectively at home. As long as the parents use effective parenting techniques, the children keep improving in their interactions with others and learn to make friends.

Unfortunately, no program seems to provide lasting help to isolated aggressive teens. Some programs seem to help for a while, but then the effect seems to "wear off." The children once again take up their old aggressive ways. However, even teenagers on this road are not hopeless or lost forever. They can reach a point in maturity where they decide

(Continued on next page)

Teacher Support Notes

① **Causes of Aggression:** For enrichment you may want to give students some additional theories about the causes of aggression. For example, you could tell them that some physiological studies have shown that there are brain areas capable of beginning or ending aggressive behavior. Biological causes of aggression can include the abuse of some drugs, such as crack and alcohol. In some cases brain damage can also cause aggression.

negative consequences of any decision before making a decision. Have them look at their lists of decisions and speculate on poor decisions that might be made by a person who is abusing drugs. Ask them if they or people they know ever make a decision without considering the consequences. Make sure they understand that frequently you have to live with the consequences of a decision even if you do not like it.

Ask students: "In what ways might a drug abuser have to live with the consequences of a decision? Does a person on drugs ever make decisions?" Students need to realize that indeed they do and the real problem with young people abusing drugs and altering the ability to make good decisions is that they are preparing for the future and that every decision they make is important and may affect their happiness.

Have students work with a decision-making model (Chapter 2) to make an important decision such as choosing a college, buying a car, whether to spend or save money, where to live when they are on their own, or what occupation to choose.

Teacher Support Notes

① **Night and Day Stories:** Ask students if they know anyone, or if they've heard their parents talk about, a friend or relative who made one of these dramatic changes in behavior. If so, ask students to tell what caused the change. Did the person simply decide to change one day, or was there a particular event that prompted the change?

② **Denial:** The term *denial* is not used here, but is discussed in more detail in the next chapter.

③ **Assertiveness Training:** Students were given some tips on developing more assertive behavior in Chapter 2. You may want to refer them back to that chapter to review what they learned about being assertive, rather than passive or aggressive. Tell students that it helps to *rehearse* assertive behavior. Practicing in front of a mirror, for example, can be helpful. Students can ask a friend to role-play the type of behavior that most challenges them. Other tips are to *overlearn* the assertive behavior so that it happens automatically, and to repeat statements, like a broken record, so as not to become aggressive.

STRAIGHT TALK *(Continued)*

to change their own courses, permanently.

Do you mean that even really bad kids can choose to turn out OK?

Sometimes, yes, but only with a great deal of dedication and personal effort. Human beings are capable of dramatic life changes. Stories abound of folks who, once committed to a course of action, have found the will and perseverance to change completely and permanently.

Sometimes, I have some trouble socially. Can I change the way I interact with people to make sure they like me?

Right away, you must change your expectation that everyone must like you. This is not realistic. Then realize that the most important person to please is yourself. If you want to make some changes in yourself, this can be a positive sign, because you accept that it may be *you* who needs to change. When teens with serious social problems were questioned as to causes of their problems, they named parents, peers, poverty, school, neighborhood, and drugs. But none of them, not even one, found the slightest fault with themselves.

The first step in making any change is to own the problem. Once it's yours, you can do with it what you will. Once over this hurdle, you can use the information presented in the early chapters of this book to assist you in making your change. Perhaps you should strive to be more assertive. Or maybe your relationships would benefit if you were a better listener. Whatever area you decide to work on, be assured that you can gain a high level of social health by committing now—today—to make the needed changes.

Mini Glossary

juvenile delinquent: a youth under age 18 who has committed illegal acts.

runaway: a youth who voluntarily leaves and lives away from home to escape an adverse environment, real or imagined.

throwaway: a youth who leaves home at the demand of his or her parent. Throwaways often seek help from shelters and social agencies.

dropouts: students who were enrolled in school, but who no longer attend and are not seeking diplomas or equivalents, and who have not left because of illness or other school-approved reasons.

After students have made a responsible decision, tell them they will be unable to check the results until the decision has been put into effect. Explain how this is a responsible way to make a decision based on what is important to you. You do not have to follow a plan like this every time you make a decision; this just helps you consider everything involved before making a decision. People who abuse drugs often do not make decisions that are responsible. Ask students what things might influence a drug abuser's decision. **(Critical Thinking)**

Underlying Behaviors. Direct students' attention to page 315, "The Consequences from Society." Tell students that although education about drugs is enough to keep some people from ruining their lives, it is not effective for everyone. Therefore, it is important that students understand the behaviors underlying drug abuse and be honest with themselves to see if they might exhibit some behaviors such as low self-esteem, need to fit in with a group, need to stand out, appear different, etc., of a person who would abuse drugs.

CHAPTER REVIEW

LEARNING THE VOCABULARY

drug use	amphetamines	PCP (phencyclidine hydrochloride)
drug abuse	stimulants	peyote
drug misuse	hyperactivity	psilocybin/psilocin
recreational drug use	sedatives	look-alikes
euphoria	barbiturates	mescaline
endorphins	opiates	designer drugs
dysphoria	narcotics	Narcotics Anonymous (NA)
drug addiction (dependence)	codeine	methadone
physical addiction	opium	narcotic antagonists
withdrawal	morphine	juvenile delinquent
psychological addiction	heroin	runaway
hallucinations	hallucinogens	throwaway
amotivational syndrome	LSD (lysergic acid diethylamide)	dropout

Answer the following questions on a separate sheet of paper.

1. Explain the differences between the two terms in each of the following sets:
   a. physical addiction and psychological addiction
   b. drug abuse and drug misuse
   c. look-alike drugs and designer drugs
2. *Matching—Match each of the following phrases with the appropriate vocabulary term from the list above:*
   a. the physical symptoms that occur when a drug to which a person is addicted is cleared from the body tissue
   b. drugs that have a soothing or tranquilizing effect
   c. a cactus that produces the hallucinogen mescaline
   d. a sense of great well-being and pleasure brought on by some drugs
   e. a youth under age 18 who has committed illegal acts
3. Write a paragraph using at least ten vocabulary terms. Underline each term that you use.
4. *Word Scramble—Use the clues from the following phrases to help you to unscramble the terms:*

   a. **raicntocs** _____ habit-forming drugs that relieve pain and produce sleep when taken in moderation
   b. **aeiichprttvyy** _____ a condition that makes children overly active
   c. **aaiiouchlnnstl** _____ false perceptions; imagined sights, sounds, smells, or other feelings
   d. **ooudprt** _____ a student who was enrolled in school but no longer attends
   e. **aeeodhmnt** _____ a drug used to treat heroin addiction
5. a. _____ is a narcotic drug that is commonly used for suppressing coughs.
   b. An unpleasant feeling that often follows a drug-induced euphoria is called _____.
   c. The narcotic drug _____ is used by doctors as a painkiller.
   d. A person who loses energy and ambition as a result of marijuana use is said to have _____.
   e. A _____ is a dependent child who voluntarily leaves and lives away from home to escape an adverse environment.

CHAPTER REVIEW
Answers
Vocabulary
1. **a.** Physical addiction produces a change in the body's chemistry so that normal functioning begins to fail without the drug, while psychological addiction is a mental dependence on a drug, habit, or behavior. **b.** Drug abuse is the deliberate taking of a drug for nonmedical reasons, while drug misuse is taking drugs for a medical purpose, but not in the correct amount, frequency, strength, or manner. **c.** Look-alikes are a combination of OTC drugs and other chemicals packaged to look like prescription medications or illegal drugs, while designer drugs are laboratory-made drugs that closely resemble illegal drugs in chemical structure, but are still legal.
2. **a.** withdrawal **b.** sedatives **c.** peyote **d.** euphoria **e.** juvenile delinquent

3. Answers will vary.

4. a. narcotics **b.** hyperactivity **c.** hallucinations **d.** dropout **e.** methadone

5. a. Codeine **b.** dysphoria **c.** morphine **d.** amotivational syndrome **e.** runaway

Recall

Section I

1. Drug use is the taking of a drug for its medically intended purpose; drug abuse is the deliberate taking of drugs for a nonmedical purpose that could be harmful; drug misuse is taking of a drug for the correct medical purpose, but not in the right amount, frequency, strength, or manner.

Section II

2. nature of the person, nature of the drug, and possible consequences that await the abuser from family and society

3. different from the rest of society, drugs fit image, drugs fill void of excitement and fun, substitute drugs for friends, parental love, an escape from life's problems

4. Harsh punishment awaits those who possess or sell drugs, while entertainers, movies, songs, magazines, and books may portray drug abuse as "funny" or "cool". Society condemns drug abuse, but also protects rights of individuals' expression through writing and the arts.

Section III

5. nicotine, caffeine

6. dysphoria

7. curiosity, experimentation, euphoria, dysphoria, tolerance, elevated drug doses, euphoria, greater dysphoria, withdrawal, elevated drug doses, relief from withdrawal, withdrawal, elevated doses, and physical addiction

8. Addicted people defend, cherish, and protect the drug habit as they would a loved one.

9. Never experiment with drugs that produce it.

10. Once a person is hooked, they will do almost anything for the drug they are addicted to.

Section IV

11. It alters hearing, touch, taste, and smell, as well as sense of time, space, and feelings of the body.

12. short-term memory loss, shortened attention span, rapid and irregular heartbeats, reduces body's immune response, reduces hormone levels and sperm count in men, damages the lungs

13. life-threatening obesity, constant sleeping, and hyperactivity in children

14. depress the central nervous system, slow the heart rate, slow the respiration rate, lower the blood pressure and body temperature

---

RECALLING IMPORTANT FACTS AND IDEAS

1. Define drug use, abuse, and misuse.
2. Name the factors that lead people to abuse drugs.
3. People who focus their attention on themselves rather than on other people or activities are likely to abuse drugs. List the reasons these people give for abusing drugs.
4. How is society sending us mixed messages about drugs?
5. A few drugs produce addictions without euphoria. What are they?
6. What is the unpleasant sensation people may feel after taking drugs?
7. Describe the spiral that leads to physical addiction.
8. How does drug addiction compare to a great love relationship?
9. What is the *only* sure way to escape drug addiction?
10. Explain why a drug seller's job is so easy.
11. THC affects sensitive brain centers. In what ways does THC affect the body?
12. Research indicates that harmful health effects are associated with the use of THC. What are they?
13. What are the medical uses for amphetamines?
14. List the effects of barbiturates on the body.
15. What can long-term abuse of barbiturates cause?
16. What is one of the strongest painkillers and why is its use so limited?
17. What is the most often abused narcotic in the United States and why is it illegal?
18. What are the three ways to take cocaine?
19. List the effects of cocaine on the nervous system.
20. Describe the various hallucinogens and the side effects each one causes.
21. What are three types of chemicals inhaled to produce a high?
22. Why are look-alike drugs so dangerous to users?
23. Explain how methadone and narcotic antagonists help in the treatment of drug addiction.
24. Of the 17 "drug-free highs" listed on page 337, write down the ones you've experienced.

CRITICAL THINKING

1. Suppose a friend who was anxious about getting into college confided in you that she was taking increasingly greater amounts of speed to enable her to study more hours. What advice would you offer your friend? What action would you take to help your friend?
2. The use of marijuana in junior high is on the rise. About 6% of the students in these grades smoke marijuana. What are some of the reasons why so many more young students are using marijuana? What do you think should be done to solve this problem?
3. The Straight Talk section of this chapter deals with teens and social problems. What are some of the factors contributing to teen problems? How can aggressive behavior be changed? How can you educate parents in discipline training? What kind of help can you give children to enable them to lead normal lives? What can you do to help teens own up to their problems?

ACTIVITIES

1. Put together a list of community resources for people seeking help for drug problems. Provide the name, address, and phone number of each agency. Describe the services the agencies provide, the basic costs of their services, and details of services to school-age children and adolescents.

344

15. depression, forgetfulness, reduced sex drive, addiction, death in cases of overdose
16. morphine; it is extremely addictive
17. heroin; because it is so addictive
18. snorting, injecting, smoking
19. It stimulates the nervous system bringing on the stress response—constricted blood vessels, raised blood pressure, widened pupils of the eyes, and increased body temperature.
20. LSD: In its purest chemical form it causes mental "trips" of distorted visions that cannot be stopped until drug wears off; flashbacks of bad trips can resurface even years after original trip.

PCP: Originally a tranquilizer for animals; has dangerous and unpredictable side effects that may cause some to become so violent that they commit murder or suicide, or suffer seizures, coma, and death.

mescaline: made from tissues of peyote cactus; produces mild LSD trip accompanied by vomiting, sweating, and painful abdominal cramping

psilocybin and psilocin: made from tissues of a strain of mushrooms; cause hallucinations
21. solvents (fumes from gasoline, glue, lighter fluid, etc.); propellants (paint, deodorant, hair spray); those intended for medical use (chloroform, ether, nitrous oxide)
22. Takers use a lot of them and experience sleep disturbances, abnormal heartbeat, and sudden rises in blood pressure. They're most dangerous when a person can't tell the difference between the look-alikes and the real thing and accidentally takes the same number as the real thing, thus producing a fatal overdose.
Section VI
23. Methadone is a "maintenance" drug that is cheaper, milder, and longer lasting than heroin. It helps people addicted to heroin to hold off withdrawal and recover socially. Narcotic antagonists block the effects of the problem drug. With daily dose, a person commits to staying drug free that day, protecting them from giving in when the urge to take a drug strikes.
24. Answers will vary. Refer to the Health Strategies, Drug-free Highs on page 337 for possible answers.

---

2. Find as many articles as you can about people who have died from drug abuse. Make a poster to share with the rest of the class. Then make a list of all the people your class has come up with that have died from drug abuse. Have any of these people affected your life? How?
3. Make a video for your class or community about drug abuse. In your video describe the different types of drugs, ways that any drug may be misused, the physical and emotional dangers of drug abuse, and the treatments for various types of drug abuse.
4. Interview a local law enforcement official and find out about illegal drug activity in your area. What are some of the dangers and problems these officers face in their investigations? Report these findings to the rest of the class.
5. Research the drug laws in your state and prepare a chart that summarizes these laws. Compare the laws in 1992 with the laws in 1982. What changes have occurred in the last 10 years? What are your predictions for the next 10 years?
6. Debate whether marijuana should be legalized. Write an article for the school newspaper about the debate on marijuana. In your article list all the effects of marijuana on the body.
7. More and more companies are requiring that their employees take drug tests. Call the personnel office of a company in your area to find out if they require their employees to take a drug test. Who is tested and how often? What procedures are followed? If someone tests positive for drugs, are they terminated? Compare your findings with those of your class and discuss the similarities or differences you have found.
8. Federal, state, and local laws relating to drug abuse are written to protect the general public. The punishments seem to vary. What do you think the punishments should be for abusers, and for drug dealers? Do your punishments differ for these two groups? Explain why you think the punishments should be the same or different for these groups.
9. Write a public television or radio announcement that describes the physical and emotional dangers of drug abuse. Share these announcements with your local elementary school.
10. Explain why just saying no to drugs is not enough. Write a proclamation for a drug-free society. On the proclamation, write five ways to stay drug free.
11. Keep a journal for two weeks. In your journal, underline all the drug-free highs you had during that time. What causes most of your drug-free highs?

MAKING DECISIONS ABOUT HEALTH

1. One of your relatives complains of fatigue and depression. The person is also overweight and under a lot of stress at work. The person's health history indicates no regular exercise routine, and a poor diet. The doctor has run extensive tests and no physical abnormality has turned up, but in hopes of bringing the patient some relief, the doctor reaches for his/her pad to prescribe a stimulant.

a. What might be at the root of your relative's complaints?
b. Why might the prescription of a stimulant for your relative be an unwise decision, given the circumstances?
c. What might you suggest to your relative so that he or she may get some relief?
d. What can you tell your relative about the use of stimulants? What are some of the risks of stimulant use?

CHAPTER 14 PLANNER

OVERVIEW

This chapter is 24 pages long and divided into the five sections listed to the right. Major learning outcomes are also listed to the right. This chapter defines alcohol as the most widely used and abused drug in the U.S. It stresses the impact of alcohol abuse on the judgment centers of the brain and on the liver both immediately and over an extended period of time. This chapter emphasizes the effect alcohol has on everyone in society and the difficulty in overcoming alcoholism. It stresses the importance of saying no and feeling good about the decision. Some excellent tips are included to aid in entertaining without alcohol.

MAKING LIFE CHOICES RESOURCES

A variety of activities, handouts, quizzes, and tests to accompany this chapter are available in the *Making Life Choices* supplementary material. You may pick and choose from those materials as appropriate for your amount of class time and the ability levels of your students. Some of the resources you might want to consider using are:

Handouts
- Classify Your Drinking Behavior
- Blood Alcohol Concentration by Number of Drinks and Body Weight
- The Disguises of Alcoholism
- Characteristics of Alcoholism
- Attitudes About Drunk Driving
- Myths About Alcoholism
- Test Your Knowledge
- The Progression of Alcoholism

Overheads
- Alcohol's Effects on the Brain
- The Liver
- The Hangover
- The Fates of Two Drinkers
- Comparing Excessive vs. Moderate Drinking

Teacher Information Sheets
- Withdrawal from Alcohol
- The Family Dynamics of Alcohol Abuse

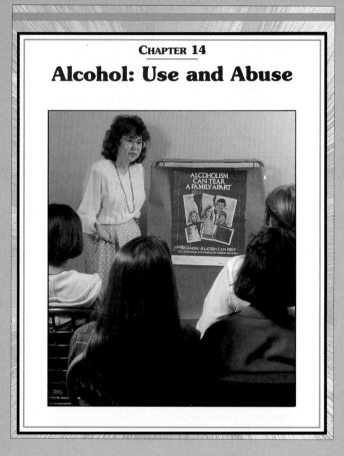

CHAPTER 14
Alcohol: Use and Abuse

Activity To Introduce Chapter

The Life Choice Inventory (on page 352) is an excellent activity to begin this chapter. Students can answer for themselves or for a friend they are concerned about. Another effective activity for beginning the chapter would be to discuss the Consumer Awareness on page 350. Discuss some of the most popular ads, shows, and entertainers that influence our thoughts on alcohol. Then use the Critical Thinking questions to provoke thoughts on our society's promotion of alcohol.

CHAPTER PROJECT

Give the students one week to complete the following homework assignment: Find a magazine article that deals with alcohol. The article can cover accidents, violence, family life, etc. They are to read the article and list the facts brought out in the article. Each student must have from 10 to 20 facts.

On the day the assignment is due, put the students into groups based on common topics. Give the students poster board, typing paper, markers, crayons, glue, scissors, etc. Their task is to develop an educational tool that can be used at their level or lower (middle school, elementary). The tool must

OUTCOMES

After reading and studying this chapter, you will be able to:

✓ List three reasons why young people start to drink alcohol.
✓ Explain what alcohol is and how it affects the body.
✓ Identify the immediate effects of intoxication.
✓ Discuss what is meant by Fetal Alcohol Syndrome.
✓ Describe the effects of drinking on driving.
✓ Explain why alcoholism is a family disease.
✓ Identify how an enabler's behavior affects the person with an alcohol problem.

✓ List what kinds of help are available to the alcohol-dependent person.

CONTENTS

I. Why People Drink
II. Effects of Alcohol
III. Accidents and Alcohol
IV. The Way Back: Strategies for Recovery
V. How to Refuse Drinks, How to Give a Great Party

Straight Talk:
Alcoholism, the Disease

FACT OR FICTION

What do you think? Are the following statements true or false? If you think they are false, then say what is true.

1. Alcohol is a drug.
2. A person who drinks two drinks every day may be a moderate drinker.
3. In the body, alcohol is digested just as food is.
4. Alcohol is a depressant drug; it slows people down.
5. Impaired driving performance occurs when the blood alcohol level is 0.10 percent or higher.
6. A person who has had too much to drink should walk around so the muscles will burn off the alcohol more quickly.
7. Drinking black coffee can help a drunk person sober up.

(Answers on page 364)

■ **Reminder:** Knowing how to study can increase your knowledge, improve your grades, *and* cut down on your study time. See the *Studying Health* section at the front of your text for some suggestions to help you study this chapter.

Answers to "Fact or Fiction"

1. True. **2.** True. **3.** False. Alcohol does not have to be digested. It is immediately absorbed into the blood. **4.** True. **5.** False. Driving is impaired at blood alcohol levels lower than 0.10 percent. **6.** False. Muscles do not use alcohol for fuel, so walking does not affect the body's rate of alcohol breakdown. **7.** False. Coffee can wake up, but not sober up, a drunk.

include a minimum of 10 facts on their topic. They should start by sharing their information and then deciding what facts are most important for others to know. Their tools can be posters, advertisements, true/false quizzes, songs or raps, cartoons, etc.

Time: allow one full class period—then give them two to three days to work on it outside of class.

When this project is done, have a circle discussion on the tools and the facts. Some groups may want to "teach" the class. Then decide how and where these tools will be used. **(Extend, Enrich, Cooperative Learning)**

NOT ENOUGH TIME?*

You could easily spend four or five days teaching this chapter if students read the entire chapter, do a fair number of the suggested activities in the teacher's edition, and complete a sampling of the handouts from the resource material accompanying this text. It is likely, however, that you will have only two or three days to devote to this chapter. Following are some suggestions to help you make sure that you cover the key topics if you have limited time.

TIME	SUGGESTIONS
1 Day	Assign Sections I and II prior to class. At the beginning of the class do the Fact or Fiction on this page to evaluate students' comprehension of the information. During class have the students do Activity 1.1 in Section I and Activity 2.2 in Section II. Use Activity 2.1 as a quick reteach lesson or review.
2 Days	Discuss Section III and use the "Making Life Choices" on page 363 as a role-playing activity. Use Activity 3.2 to start students thinking about drinking and driving.
3 Days	Assign Sections IV and V. During class have students complete Activities 4.1, 4.3, and 4.4. Close the lesson on alcohol by using Activities 5.2 and 5.3 in Section V.

Please refer to the 18-week daily lesson plans in the supplementary material for additional suggestions.

SUGGESTED RESOURCES

Teacher Readings
1. Finn, P. and O'Gorman, P.A. *Teaching about Alcohol.* Boston: Allyn and Bacon, 1981.

Student Readings
1. Pinkham, M.E. *How to Stop the One You Love from Drinking.* New York: The Putnam

Publishing Group, 1986.

Videos
1. *MADD, The Story of Carrie Lightner.*
2. *The Bill Wilson Story.*
3. *24 Hours on America's Highway.*

Software
1. *Alcohol: Making the Choice.* Focus Media, 516-931-2500.

In this section students will learn the:
1. Reasons people choose to drink alcohol.
2. Difference between drinking in moderation, abusive drinking, and addictive drinking.
3. Media's influence on people's drinking

choices.

Activity 1.1

Drug Continuum. Ask the students to call out all the drugs that come to their minds. As they do, list them on the board. If alcohol is *not* mentioned, add it to the list and ask them why they didn't list it. Explain that it is our most used and abused drug. Then draw a continuum on the board. On one end put the word

"Bad;" in the middle put "Neutral;" and on the other end put "Good." Ask the students to pair up in twos and threes. They are to draw the same continuum on a sheet of paper and then put each drug (listed on the board) on the continuum where they believe it belongs. If the drug list is too long, star ten drugs they are to place on the continuum. Be sure alcohol and penicillin are in the list of ten.

When they are done, choose a drug

Teacher Support Notes

① **What Is Moderate:** Tell students that conditions such as body size and weight, age, gender, genetics, general health, and pregnancy status determine what is a moderate amount of alcohol. The young, the elderly, and women are usually more sensitive to the effects of alcohol than are middle-aged men, for example. Women are more sensitive even after adjusting for body weight. According to one recent study women have less of an enzyme *alcohol dehydrogenase* in their stomachs, which deactivates alcohol before it reaches the bloodstream. This could mean that per drink more alcohol reaches the bloodstream in women than in men. There is also some evidence that the way alcohol affects people is genetically predetermined.

348 UNIT 4 Drug Use and Abuse

In chemistry, the term **alcohol** refers to a class of chemical compounds. One of these compounds is the active ingredient of alcoholic beverages—**ethanol**, or **ethyl alcohol**, often called just *alcohol*. Alcoholic beverages contain a lot of water and other substances, as well as alcohol. Wine and beer have relatively low percentages of alcohol. In contrast, whiskey, vodka, rum, and brandy may contain as much as 50 percent alcohol. The percentage of alcohol in alcoholic beverages is stated as **proof**. For example, 100-proof liquor is 50 percent alcohol. Thus, proof is equal to twice the percentage of alcohol.

Ethanol, the alcohol that people drink, is poisonous, although it is less poisonous than some of the other alcohols. If it is diluted and taken in small enough doses, it has effects on the body that people seek. These effects are not achieved without risks. However, people may not know the risks they face when they drink.

Medically, alcohol is a drug—that is, a substance that can change one or more of the body's functions. Ethanol is the most widely used—and abused—drug in our society. It is also the only legal, nonprescription drug that produces euphoria. Drinking alcohol is legal, however, only for those who are 21 years of age or older.

SECTION I

Why People Drink

Drinkers will give lots of reasons why they drink alcohol: to celebrate, to unwind, because they like the taste of alcoholic beverages, because it's the custom. Young people drink because peer pressure encourages it, or because they think drinking makes them look grown up, or because it is a way of rebelling against authority. The advertisers of

alcohol also promote drinking, of course, and they appeal to many aspects of people's self-image (see the Consumer Awareness section, "Advertisements for Alcohol" on page 350).

For whatever reasons people drink, they derive drug effects by doing so. Like other addictive drugs, alcohol produces euphoria, changes mood, relieves pain, and releases tension.

① Alcohol, taken in **moderation** by healthy adults, can be compatible with good health. Drinking may encourage people to relax and be social. Of course, people might benefit more from learning how to relax in the face of life's pressures without alcohol.

The key to people's using alcohol wisely is moderation. Just what does this mean? No one exact amount of alcohol per day is moderate for everyone, because people have different tolerance levels. The Health Strategies section "Dietary Guidelines for Americans" in Chapter 7 recommends that adults who drink limit their intake of alcohol to one or two drinks a day. This amount is supposed to be enough to produce euphoria periodically without risking harm to health over the long term. Some people might be able to consume slightly

Servings of alcohol equal to a standard drink.

and ask them where they placed it. Write the drug on the continuum reflecting one or numerous student choices. Do this with five drugs, including alcohol and penicillin. Hopefully you will end up with a variety of answers. When done with the five, tell the students that almost *all* drugs belong in the middle (neutral). Ask them why. The point is that the drugs aren't the problem, people are the problem. It's the way people use the drugs that make them "bad" or

"good." Penicillin, for example, can help cure disease, but it can be harmful to those allergic to it. LSD can prove harmful to many, but some psychiatrists say it has helped certain clients, including the terminally ill. Alcohol can be used socially by many without any negative problems, yet it is the cause of many accidental deaths and the disease alcoholism. Even the most dangerous drugs are neutral if people say "no." **(30 min., Critical Thinking)**

Activity 1.2
Advertisements. Have each student bring in an ad for an alcoholic beverage. You should have five to seven of your own. Tape the ads to the board. Ask the students to look them over and then have each student choose one to discuss. In the discussion, ask the students to answer the following questions:
1. What is the ad stating?

(continued on next page)

more than one or two drinks a day. Others could definitely not handle nearly so much without danger.

People measure alcohol in servings they call "a **drink**." However, the serving any one person considers to be a drink may not match the standard "drink" amount used by experts to define moderation. A standard drink delivers ½ ounce of pure ethanol:

- 12 ounces of beer.
- 3 to 4 ounces of wine.
- 1 (10 ounce) wine cooler.
- 1 ounce of hard liquor (whiskey, gin, brandy, rum, or vodka).

The photo on the preceding page shows what these servings look like.

A wide range of drinking patterns falls between not drinking at all and alcoholism. The most danger lies at the extreme of excessive alcohol intake. The more a person drinks, the closer to that dangerous extreme the person is.

People who drink must monitor and evaluate their own drinking behaviors. Figure 14–1 lists terms that describe people who drink, together with their definitions. Figure 14–2 on page 351 compares some behaviors of people who drink moderately with behaviors of problem drinkers.

Those people who succeed in drinking moderately drink at appropriate times and in appropriate settings only. They limit their intakes, and they enjoy being in control. Among the skills they report they've had to learn are the following:

- "I decide in advance how much I'm going to drink. If it's BYOB (bring your own bottle), I take only two drinks with me."
- "If they're serving beer by the pitcher, I still order it by the glass. That way, I don't feel I must drink more than I want to."

FIGURE 14-1
Terms Used to Describe People Who Drink Alcohol

A **moderate drinker** does not drink excessively. The person doesn't behave inappropriately because of alcohol and the person's health is not harmed by alcohol over the long term.

A **social drinker** drinks only on social occasions. Depending on how alcohol affects the person's life, the person may be a moderate drinker or a problem drinker.

A **problem drinker**, or an **alcohol abuser**, suffers social, emotional, family, job-related, or other problems because of alcohol. This person is on the way to alcoholism.

An **alcohol addict** (**alcoholic**) has the full-blown disease of alcoholism. This person's problems, caused by alcohol abuse, are out of control.

MINI GLOSSARY

alcohol: a class of chemical compounds. The alcohol of alcoholic beverages, *ethanol* or *ethyl alcohol*, is one member of this class.
ethanol (ethyl alcohol): see *alcohol.*
proof: a measure of the percentage of alcohol in alcoholic beverages. *100 proof* means 50 percent alcohol, *90 proof* means 45 percent, and so forth.
moderation: an amount of alcohol that causes no harm to health: not more than one to two drinks a day for healthy adults.
drink: the amount of a beverage that delivers ½ ounce of pure ethanol—12 ounces of beer, 3 to 4 ounces of wine, 1 (10 ounce) wine cooler, or 1 ounce of 100 proof liquor.

Teacher Support Notes

① **Distilled Liquor:** Tell students distilled spirits have a higher concentration of alcohol than beer or wine because green fermentation is followed by the distillation process—condensation of a vapor obtained from a liquid heated to the volatilization point. Some distilled liquors and their carbohydrate sources: bourbon (at least half from corn); rye (rye); scotch (barley); vodka (wheat, rye, corn, or potatoes); rum (cane products such as molasses); brandy (wine).

❝ **Thoughts on Health** ❞

I can abstain; but I can't be moderate.
– Samuel Johnson

2. To whom is the ad appealing?
3. How realistic is the ad?
4. What does the ad NOT show?

Be sure to stress how unrealistic the ads for alcohol are. **(30 min., Critical Thinking)**

Activity 1.3
Proof vs. Percent. Bring in a couple of labels from alcohol products that show proof and percentage. Ask the students to describe the difference between the two. (Proof equals twice the percent of alcohol present. Example: 90 proof = 45% alco-

hol.) Put five items on the board and ask the students to convert them.
Example:
20 Proof = _____%
50% = _____ proof
100 Proof = _____ %
(15 min.; Extend, Enrich)

Activity 1.4
Questionnaire. Develop your own drinking questionnaire (or use the "Think-

---

Teacher Support Notes

① **Answers To Critical Thinking: 1.** Answers will vary but students should see that the images projected through the media make a connection between drinking and popularity. **2.** Students will have different opinions. This would make a good debate topic. **3.** After students have discussed #2, ask them if their responses would be different if they were personally involved in the situation. Challenge students opposed to the athletes endorsing alcoholic products to come up with rationalizations for accepting large sums of money. Pretend to give them a check for a large sum and ask them how they might convince themselves that it would be okay to take the money. For example, they might say to themselves that regardless of what they say and do in the commercial, it's up to individuals to make their own decisions.

📣 Fast Facts

Children of alcoholics are four times more likely to become addicted to alcohol than the rest of the population.

CONSUMER **A**WARENESS
Advertisements for Alcohol

Magazines, television, and other media project an image of alcohol drinkers as members of an exclusive clique. The drinkers wear expensive clothes and drive plush automobiles. They are smiling, healthy, beautiful, strong, and young. The message is that everybody who's somebody drinks, and you'd better drink, too, if you want to be somebody. This is one sort of advertising appeal for alcohol.

Drinking alcohol can also be a way to belong to a group. For example, drinking alcohol has become linked with certain sports, partly because famous athletes appear in liquor advertisements. Such ads glorify the athletes. Both fans and athletes are drawn to the glorious images and to the alcohol that goes with them. The tragic result: alcoholism sometimes destroys athletes early in their careers. A famous ex-baseball player who opened an alcoholism clinic says, "We just . . . winked at each other as we drank each other to death."*

Appeals to drink alcohol have found their way into almost every area of life. A sign that hangs over a bar at a golf club in New Hampshire reads: "You can't trust a man who doesn't drink." Greeting cards and comedy routines make drinking and even drunkenness socially acceptable and funny.

Actually, though, alcohol use hinders attainment of all the qualities used to promote it. A person striving for rewarding social interactions needs not to lose control, but to gain it by practicing social skills. A person seeking sports success will find it not by drinking beer on the couch, but by faithfully practicing the sport.

All such appeals fail to mention any possibility of harm, and all of them set you up to want to drink alcohol. Learn to watch out for advertising appeals. Remember, it's up to you to decide whether you really want what is offered.

① ⌐ **C**RITICAL **T**HINKING

1. *Why do you think that teenagers connect drinking with popularity?*
2. *Do you feel that athletes, as role models for many young people, should earn large sums of money promoting alcohol use?*
3. *If you were the athlete or the company wanting to pay the athlete to advertise your product, how would you feel about athletes' receiving financial rewards to push alcohol?*

*Ryne Duren, as quoted by L. Herberg, *Alcoholism: The National Pastime*, *Arizona Republic*, 30 March 1980. p. f1.

• "I allow time for my body to break down the alcohol I've drunk before I drive."
• "I sip my drinks: I add ice cubes or water; I drink water or soft drinks if I'm thirsty."
• "Now and then I skip a round. I don't

accept drinks I don't want."
• "I go slowly with unfamiliar drinks."
• "If I need sleep, I sleep—I don't drink. If I need to relax, I relax—I don't drink."
• "I know my capacity, and I don't exceed it."

ing about Drinking" questionnaire in your supplementary material) for students to answer as homework. Remind them that they should answer the questions honestly and thoroughly. Then use the questionnaire as the content for a circle discussion. Go over each question, allowing students to answer freely. Be sure each question is processed with a closure statement or fact before going on to the next. **(20 min.; Extend, Enrich)**

Activity 1.5
Life Choice Inventory. Have students turn to the Life Choice Inventory on the next page. Ask them to privately complete the inventory. Give them three to four minutes to complete the inventory. Ask them to read over the scoring. Remind them to be aware of the "yeah, buts" and to seriously think about their relationships with alcohol. **(20 min.; Extend, Enrich)**

EVALUATE
SECTION I

Activity 1.6
Pop Quiz. Have students match the following terms to the statements that describe them: *addict, drug, ethyl alcohol, moderation, proof.*

(continued on next page)

FIGURE 14-2

Behaviors of Moderate Drinkers and Problem Drinkers ①

Behaviors typical of moderate drinkers include these:	*Those who are problem drinkers have different behaviors, such as these:*
• They drink slowly (no fast gulping).	• They gulp or "chug" their drinks.
• They eat before or while drinking.	• They drink on an empty stomach.
• They know when to stop drinking.	• They drink to get drunk.
• They respect nondrinkers.	• They pressure others to drink.
• They know and obey laws related to drinking.	• They drink when it is unsafe or unwise to do so.
• They avoid drinking alcohol when solving problems or making decisions.	• When they have problems to solve, they turn to alcohol.
• They do not focus on drinking alcohol—they focus on other activities.	• They maintain relationships based solely on alcohol.
• They do not view drunkenness as stylish, funny, or acceptable.	• They believe that drunks are funny or otherwise admirable.
• They do not become loud, violent, or otherwise changed by drinking.	• When drinking, they may become loud, angry, violent, or silent.
• They cause no problems to others by drinking.	• They physically or emotionally harm themselves, family members, or others.

How *much* people drink is not the only question to ask in determining whether people have drinking problems. Other important questions are the *reasons* for their drinking and the *consequences* (results) of it. This chapter's Life Choice Inventory asks questions that are used to identify alcoholism. Although it is written in terms of "you," you can apply these questions to anyone you are concerned about. If the answer is yes to three or more of the questions listed, the person may be on the road to alcoholism.

Key Points ▶ *People may drink for many reasons. Alcohol taken in moderation may relax people. A moderate drinker differs from a problem drinker in how much the person drinks, the reasons for drinking, and the consequences of the drinking.*

SECTION I   REVIEW

Answer the following questions on a sheet of paper.
Learning the Vocabulary
The vocabulary terms in this section are *alcohol, ethanol, proof, moderation,* and *drink.*
1. Fill in the blank with the correct response.
   a. _____ is a term used to describe the percentage of alcohol in alcoholic beverages.
   b. To drink an amount of alcohol that causes no harm to health is to exercise _____.
   c. A _____ is the amount of a beverage that delivers ½ ounce of pure ethanol.

Learning the Facts
2. List three reasons that young people give as to why they drink alcohol.
3. What is the key to safe alcohol use?
4. List and define the terms used to describe people who drink alcohol.

Teacher Support Notes

① **Comparing Moderate and Problem Drinkers:** The two columns correspond to each other. Have one student read aloud an item from one column, then another student read the corresponding item from the other column. This should help students see the differences between moderate and problem drinking.

Section I Review
Answers
1. **a.** Proof **b.** moderation **c.** drink
2. peer pressure encourages it, drinking makes them look grown-up, a way to rebel against authority
3. moderation
4. Refer to Figure 14–1 on page 349 for possible answers.
5. Answers will vary. Refer to Figure 14–2 on this page for possible answers.
6. Answers will vary.

EVALUATE
(Continued)

1. _____ Acceptable alcohol use in society (moderation)
2. _____ Twice the percent of alcohol (proof)
3. _____ Alcohol we drink (ethyl alcohol)
4. _____ Changes one or more body functions (drug)

5. _____ Has the disease alcoholism (addict)
(5 min.)

CLOSE
SECTION I

Activity 1.7
Review. Before proceeding to Section II, the students should be able to answer these questions:

1. What impact can alcohol abuse have on your life?
2. Why is moderate use of alcohol important?
3. What are some signs that alcohol is becoming a problem?

FOCUS
SECTION II

In this section the students will learn the:

> ## ❝ Thoughts on Health ❞
>
> *We drink to one another's health and spoil our own.*
> *– Jerome Jerome*

Teacher Support Notes

① **Life Choice Inventory:** You may want to restate the text comment on the preceding page regarding the fact that the inventory is written in the second person "you," but it's assumed that most students do not have a drinking problem. Students can read and answer the questions as though they are a parent, a friend, relative, or someone else who might possibly have a drinking problem. Doing the inventory should help the students become more familiar with the behaviors associated with alcoholism.

② **Handout—Classify Your Drinking Behavior:** After students have completed the Life Choice Inventory, you may want to distribute the handout in your supplementary material entitled "Classify Your Drinking Behavior." This handout describes six levels, or types, of drinking.

LIFE CHOICE INVENTORY

Do You Have a Drinking Problem? ①

Give yourself 1 point for each yes answer.

1. Do you feel you drink more than most people?
2. Do friends or relatives think you drink more than most people?
3. Are you unable to stop drinking when you want to?
4. Do your parents or other near relatives ever worry or complain about your drinking?
5. Have you ever attended a meeting of Alcoholics Anonymous?
6. Has drinking ever created problems between you and a parent or other near relative?
7. If you have a part-time job, have you ever gotten into trouble at work because of drinking?
8. Have you ever neglected your obligations, your family, or your schoolwork for two or more days in a row because you were drinking?
9. Have you ever gone to anyone for help about your drinking?
10. Have you ever been in a hospital because of drinking?
11. Do you ever feel guilty about your drinking?
12. Have you ever been arrested for drunken driving, driving while intoxicated, or driving under the influence of alcoholic beverages?
13. Have you ever been arrested, even for a few hours, because of other drunken behavior?

SCORING

A score of 0 or 1 indicates no alcohol problem. A score of 2 indicates possible alcoholism. A score of 3 or more indicates alcoholism. This test is highly accurate but is for screening purposes only. Final diagnosis should be made by an alcoholism expert.

Source: Michigan Alcoholism Screening Test (MAST), developed by Dr. Melvin L. Selzer. There are longer tests, but this short one is valid. It detects from 94 to 99 percent of people with alcoholism.

②

5. Describe the skills that moderate drinkers of alcohol use.

Making Life Choices
6. Reread the Consumer Awareness box, "Advertisements for Alcohol," on page 350. What does this tell you about our society and drinking? Describe the different ways alcohol is being advertised. What could you do to change how alcohol is being advertised?

SECTION II

Effects of Alcohol

The drug alcohol has both immediate and long-term effects on the body. These effects depend on the size of the dose of alcohol. As with other drugs, all of alcohol's effects on

1. Short- and long-term effects of alcohol on the body.
2. Effects of alcohol on the brain and the various thought processes.
3. Long-term effects of alcohol on unborn children. (fetal alcohol syndrome)

Activity 2.1
Descriptions of "Drunks"

1. Have the students write a short paragraph describing a typical "drunk" using personal experience or popular belief as depicted on TV or in movies.
2. List some of the most common descriptions of "drunks" on the board. As you discuss the chapter, continue to remind students that these characteristics result from the use of alcohol. **(15 min.; Extend, Enrich)**

Activity 2.2
Influencing Factors. Have students list the answers to one of the following questions on a sheet of paper: "What factors influence the different reactions to the same amount of alcohol in two different people?" or "John and Sue each have had four drinks tonight. What will determine how they react to these four drinks?"

List the questions on the board, then ask for volunteers to give the correct answers. Important ones to include are:

(continued on next page)

TEEN VIEWS

Should teens be allowed to drink alcohol if supervised by an adult? ①

No!!! Teens should never be allowed to drink alcohol! Any parent who would supervise must not care too much about their son or daughter. How could you watch your children kill themselves? **Jayme Deck, 15, Great Falls High School, MT**

Teens should be allowed to drink if supervised by adults. They can prevent us from driving or hurting ourselves in some way. If our parents say it's okay, it should be legal. **Fred Pistorius, 17, Sharon High School, PA**

If you let them drink with a parent, they start to believe it's o.k. to drink without one. **Isabel Gonzaba, 16, Hilltop High School, CA**

What adult would let teens drink alcohol, supervised or unsupervised? Society is trying to stop alcohol abuse, not promote it. **Runya Marta Bedrosian, 14, Thousand Oaks High School, CA**

The law is age twenty-one. If adults are allowing teens to drink, they are helping to break the law. **Chris Collins, 14, South Carroll High School, MD**

The big reason most people drink is because they're not allowed to. If kids were allowed to drink, some would probably get sick of it. If they just made it legal, it would solve so many problems. **Nathan Delgros, 16, Sharon City High School, PA**

---

the body occur when a person drinks it, no matter which effect the drinker is seeking.

Moderate Drinking: Immediate Effects

Alcohol is a special molecule in many ways. It is extremely small, as molecules go. It can move fast, and it can mix with both fatty and watery substances. This means that it meets with no barriers in the body. It can go anywhere. Alcohol affects every cell of the body.

Alcohol begins acting on the body the moment a person swallows it. From the stomach and intestines, it moves rapidly into the bloodstream (alcohol does not have to be digested). From the blood, it enters every cell. Within minutes after the first sip of a drink, ethanol is affecting the brain, muscles, nerves, glands, and the small blood vessels of the skin. It also passes through the liver.

The liver is the organ most well-equipped with the machinery to change alcohol into harmless wastes that the body can excrete. The liver goes to work on alcohol right away, but can handle only about one drink an hour. If a person drinks faster than this, the excess keeps building up, affecting all the cells more and more.

The effects the drinker can feel are from alcohol's action on the nervous system. Alcohol first depresses the action of some of the brain's fine-tuning nerves—those that usually set limits on behavior. A person slightly under the influence of alcohol will talk or laugh more loudly and gesture more

1. *Time*—How fast did each one drink? If John drank four drinks in one hour, and Sue drank four drinks in four hours, John will have a more severe reaction.
2. *Tolerance*—If John is used to drinking and Sue has never had a drink, then Sue will have a more severe reaction because her body has not developed tolerance to the drug.
3. *Body weight and size*—If John is 170 lbs. and Sue is 115 lbs., Sue will have the higher BAC level because she has less blood. The smaller the person, the less blood, and the less blood the higher the blood alcohol concentration. (This is one reason parents can accidentally overdose young children with cough syrup.)
4. *Food in the Stomach*—If there is no food in the stomach, the effect will be quicker and stronger.
5. *Concentration of the Drink*—Was it four shots of whiskey or four 12-oz. beers? The four shots will give a more severe effect because there is less fluid to interfere (dilute) with absorption of the alcohol into the bloodstream.
6. *Mental Disposition*—If the person is depressed to begin with, the alcohol will exaggerate the depression. If the person

① **Warming Effect of Alcohol:** Tell students it's a myth that alcohol helps to warm people up when they are cold. It's never a good idea to try to warm up a person who has been exposed to cold weather by feeding the person alcohol. Alcohol will open the skin's blood vessels and make the person *seem* warmer, but the extra blood that flows through the skin will allow extra heat from the inner body to be transferred into the air, chilling, rather than warming, the person.

② **Positive Effects of Alcohol:** You may want to give students some information about the possible benefits of drinking alcohol. Some evidence indicates that people who use alcohol moderately over their lifetimes have a lower risk of heart attack, probably because of a life full of friendships and social stimulation. A person who relaxes with friends may suffer less tension.

③ **Overhead—Alcohol's Effects on the Brain:** In your supplementary material you will find an overhead of this illustration.

354 UNIT 4 Drug Use and Abuse

Alcohol meets with no barriers in the body; it can go anywhere.

widely after these controls are gone. A loud buzz of conversation starts to rise a half hour into a party where alcohol is served, because alcohol has depressed people's fine-tuning nerves.

The loosening-up effect of one drink has given people the impression that alcohol is a stimulant. It is not; it is a depressant. After drinking alcohol, a person might feel socially stimulated. However, the molecule itself never stimulates any process within the body. In fact, it acts like the anesthetics that are used to put people to sleep for surgery.

Alcohol is a poor choice among anesthetics, though. Like heroin, the amount of alcohol that causes unconsciousness is close to the amount that causes death. It does not reliably keep people under, and yet it can kill them. (It is still sometimes used in emergencies, however, when no better anesthetic is available.)

Soon after a few sips of alcohol, the drinker can feel it warming the skin. Nerves normally keep the blood vessels of the skin narrow to prevent the body's losing too much heat. Alcohol relaxes these nerves, and the blood vessels of the skin widen. The skin of a person who has been drinking may appear flushed and feel warm.

Another early effect of alcohol in the brain is to sedate the cerebral cortex (see Figure 14–3), where conscious thinking takes place. The drinker loses certain kinds

of awareness, including awareness of unpleasant recent events, worries, insecurity, discomfort, and pain. At the same time, the brain's speech and vision centers are being put to sleep.

Alcohol also disturbs sleep and reduces the ability to perform mental tasks. The brain normally helps to shut out distractions. Alcohol, however, puts this function to sleep, allowing attention to wander easily.

In addition, alcohol reduces the brain's ability to inhibit the awareness and expression of emotions. Thus the person expresses love, joy, sorrow, anger, and hatred more easily than before.

At this point, a person who decides to drink no more alcohol can easily recover from these effects. Recovery becomes complete as soon as the liver clears the last of

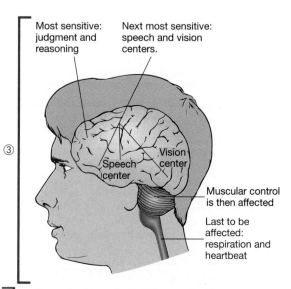

Most sensitive: judgment and reasoning

Next most sensitive: speech and vision centers.

Speech center

Vision center

Muscular control is then affected

Last to be affected: respiration and heartbeat

Figure 14–3 Alcohol's Effects on the Brain. Alcohol is rightly termed an anesthetic, because it puts brain centers to sleep in the following order: first the frontal lobe, the reasoning and judgment centers, then the speech and vision centers, then the centers that govern muscular control, and finally the deep centers that control respiration and heartbeat.

7. *Setting*—Where the person is and with whom will affect the person's reaction to alcohol. (school, home alone, at a party with friends, at a party with strangers)

Although evidence is still not conclusive, students could also say that the sex and genetic differences between John and Sue could also have an effect. **(40 min., Critical Thinking)**

Activity 2.3
Effects of Alcohol. Divide the class into four groups. Assign one of the following systems to each group: circulatory, respiratory, nervous, and muscular. Have each group research the assigned system and then do a class presentation on how alcohol affects that system. **(50 min., Cooperative Learning)**

Activity 2.4

Effects on Internal Organs. Display a chart of the body's internal organs. Explain to students how the liver is the first major organ to be affected by alcohol. Emphasize that the blood goes from the stomach immediately to the liver and brain and then throughout the body. Remind them of the part played by fat production in the liver. Describe "fatty

(continued on next page)

---

the alcohol from the body. If the person decides to drink still more, though, alcohol's depressant effects start to add up.

> **Key Points** *Alcohol affects every cell. In moderate amounts, it depresses the brain's fine-tuning nerves, opens the blood vessels of the skin, disturbs sleep, impairs mental abilities, dulls awareness, clouds vision and speech, and intensifies emotional expression.*

Excessive Drinking: Immediate Effects

With increasing doses of alcohol, behavior becomes unpredictable. People may act against their own desires and wishes, because their awareness of those desires and wishes is now gone. Against all reason and judgment, a person may pick a fight; or may become sexually aggressive; or may attempt a dangerous physical exploit—with painful or even tragic results. The reason these things can happen is clear from the map of the brain in Figure 14–3. The person's judgment might have prevented the behavior, but the judgment center has been put to sleep.

Judgment would also tell the person not to have another drink—but again, judgment is gone. This is why a person may go on to drink to the point of passing out. The person can no longer see the need to stop.

Next, speech, vision, and coordination are disabled. The drinker should not drive. However, many do so, because at this point, drinkers cannot tell that they should not drive. Everyone has seen the out-of-control driver, weaving back and forth on the highway, unable to tell how fast to go and how to steer. The driver doesn't see that the risks are life-threatening, and may be more entertained than frightened.

With still more drinking, the conscious brain is completely depressed, and the person passes out. Figure 14–4 shows the

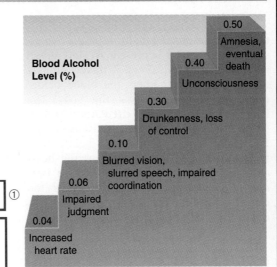

Blood Alcohol Level (%)

- 0.50 Amnesia, eventual death
- 0.40 Unconsciousness
- 0.30 Drunkenness, loss of control
- 0.10 Blurred vision, slurred speech, impaired coordination
- 0.06 Impaired judgment
- 0.04 Increased heart rate

Figure 14–4 Effects of Various Blood Alcohol Levels. *Note:* Data are for an average-sized person under ordinary circumstances. Effects vary greatly from person to person, from day to day, and from one circumstance to another.

blood alcohol levels that correspond with progressively greater **intoxication**.

During these events, the drinker's body is processing alcohol as fast as it can. Alcohol is a toxin (a poison). The body protects itself against toxins in several ways. For one thing, the throat stings as straight alcohol goes down and triggers the choking reflex. This keeps the drinker from swallowing too much in a gulp. A second protective device is the stomach, which rejects a too-large dose. The drinker vomits and expels at least part of the dose before it can be absorbed. Third, the body breaks down any alcohol that does get into the blood as quickly as possible.

MINI GLOSSARY

intoxication: literally, a state of being poisoned; often used to mean drunkenness.

🔎 Fast Facts

140 million Americans use alcohol, and an estimated 14 to 18 million of these people have a serious drinking problem.

Teacher Support Notes

① **Overhead—Comparing Excessive vs. Moderate Drinking:** An overhead in your supplementary material graphs the differences between a social drinker and an alcohol abuser, showing the amount of alcohol needed to achieve euphoria and how that relates to the amount of alcohol the body will tolerate.

② **Unpredictable Behavior:** Ask students for stories, without naming names, of people who have had too much to drink and acted in unpredictable, irrational ways.

③ **Handout—Alcohol Concentration:** Your supplementary material contains a handout showing blood alcohol levels by number of drinks and body weight.

liver" and "cirrhosis of the liver." **(30 min.; Reteach, Reinforce)**

Activity 2.5
Hangovers. Have students define a hangover in terms of what happens inside the body to produce the symptoms most

familiar to us. Emphasize that time is the only cure. Discuss the terms *cogeners*, *dehydration*, and *formaldehyde* and ask students what relationship each has to hangovers.

Borrow a small amount of formaldehyde from the science department and pass it around the room. Allow students to smell the formaldehyde. Point out that this is a by-product of the breakdown of alcohol. Ask the science teacher to talk to

your class about the uses of formaldehyde and its other properties. **(15 min.; Extend, Enrich, Interdisciplinary)**

Activity 2.6
Alcohol During Pregnancy.
Emphasize that many young women are pregnant for up to two months before they realize it. How does this impact the development of a healthy fetus? You may want to have your students read the Straight

---

Teacher Support Notes

① **Teacher Information Sheet—Withdrawal:** Withdrawal occurs every time someone has a hangover. For background information on this topic consult the information sheet entitled "Withdrawal from Alcohol" in your supplementary material.

② **Demonstrate the Effects of Alcohol:** To demonstrate the effects of alcohol in the brain, mix a cup of pure alcohol with a cup of water. Note that the mixture measures less than two cups because the alcohol absorbs the water. Alcohol has the same effect on the liquid in the brain. After a night of excessive drinking, blood vessels and their associated nerves expand and stretch causing the headache pain associated with a hangover.

Alcohol entering the stomach and intestines is absorbed rapidly into the bloodstream unless food is present to slow down its absorption. From there, it travels directly to the liver, which filters the blood before releasing it to the rest of the body. The liver's location in the circulatory system permits it to remove toxic substances carried there from the intestines before they reach other body organs, such as the heart and brain. But the liver itself faces a hazard. When a person eats or drinks too much of any toxin, the liver is the first organ to be damaged.

> **Key Points** *Excessive drinking makes people unaware of their desires and wishes and steals judgment. Still more alcohol puts the conscious mind to sleep. The body protects itself from toxic doses of alcohol through the choking reflex, vomiting, and the breakdown of alcohol by the liver. The liver itself can be damaged by alcohol.*

The Hangover ①

The hangover—the awful feeling of headache pain, unpleasant sensations in the mouth, and nausea that a drinker suffers the morning after drinking too much—is a mild form of withdrawal. (A much worse form is a **delirium** with severe **tremors**, which warns of a danger of death and demands medical treatment.) Hangovers are caused by several factors. One is the toxic effects of ingredients other than alcohol in alcoholic beverages—**congeners**. The congeners in gin are different from those in vodka, which in turn are different from those in bourbon or rye whiskey. Some people are more sensitive to the congeners in some liquors than to those in others. More important than the type of congeners in bringing on hangovers, though, is the total amount of alcohol drunk.

Dehydration of the brain is a second factor causing a hangover. Alcohol causes the ②

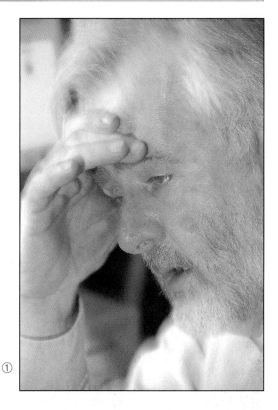

Nothing relieves a hangover but the passage of time.

body to lose water. It actually reduces the brain cells' water content, too. When they rehydrate the morning after, the nerves hurt as they swell back to their normal size. Another reason for the hangover is the effects of **formaldehyde**, a chemical familiar as the stuff biology labs use to preserve dead animals. Formaldehyde forms when the body breaks down alcohol.

Nothing helps the headache pain, the nasty taste in the mouth, and the nausea of a hangover. Popular remedies such as vitamins, tranquilizers, aspirin, drinking more alcohol, breathing pure oxygen, exercising, eating, or drinking something awful do not work. Time alone is the cure for a hang-

Talk on FAS in Chapter 21 at this time. Review with the class how a fetus develops by weeks of growth. Correlate this to the damage of alcohol on the development of the fetus. **(45 min.; Reteach, Reinforce)**

EVALUATE

SECTION II

Activity 2.7

Pop Quiz.

1. Alcohol can travel freely in the blood but mixes only with water. (F)
2. Alcohol does not need to be digested in the small intestines. (T)
3. The liver can process only 1 oz. of alcohol per hour. (T)
4. Alcohol is a stimulant. (F)
5. Alcohol makes you think you are warm, but you are really losing body heat. (T)
6. Alcohol affects the deeper brain cen-

ters that control emotions. (T)
7. Alcohol is a toxin that affects the heart first. (F)
8. Formaldehyde forms when the body breaks down alcohol. (T)
9. FAS is the longest-term damage done to the fetus by alcohol. (T)
(10 min.)

over. The problem comes simply from drinking too much.

Key Points → *A hangover is a mild form of withdrawal that causes headache, unpleasant sensations in the mouth, and nausea. The extreme form is delirium with tremors. Time is the only cure.*

Long-Term Effects of Excessive Drinking

The reason some people can drink excessively for years and not suffer obvious damage is that they allow their systems time to recover. The damage done by each bout of drinking is repaired before the next bout. Long-term drinking in excess, without sufficient recovery periods between times, however, wrecks the health of body systems. It may damage one person's heart, another person's pancreas, and another person's brain the most. However, it always affects all organs to some extent.

Probably the most common disease to occur among abusers of alcohol is liver disease. One effect of excessive drinking is that the liver cells start to fill with fat. If time between drinking bouts is not long enough to permit this fat to be removed, then the fat-stuffed liver cells stop functioning. The liver cells die and harden, and lose their function forever.

When the liver is injured, the whole body suffers. One of the worst effects of liver damage is high blood pressure. High blood pressure makes heart attacks and strokes likely. Liver damage also weakens the body's defenses against infection. The liver makes fat from alcohol that collects in the blood vessels and heart muscle, as well as in the liver and other places. Wherever it collects, the fat interferes with function. The fat also collects in fat's regular storage sites—under the skin at the hips, belly, legs, and other fatty areas.

Nerve and brain tissues are especially sensitive to alcohol. The brain shrinks, even in people who drink only moderately. Excessive drinking over many years can cause major, permanent brain damage affecting vision, memory, learning ability, and other functions.

Alcohol abuse also increases the risk of cancer of the mouth, throat, lungs, liver, pancreas, and rectum. Abusing alcohol also directly causes the pancreas to stop producing insulin. Thus some people develop diabetes from alcohol abuse.

② Other long-term effects of alcohol abuse:

- Ulcers of the stomach and intestines.
- Shrinking of all the body's muscles, including the heart muscle.
- Abnormal changes in the blood.
- Kidney damage; bladder damage; gland damage.
- Skin rashes and sores.
- Shrinkage and damage to the testicles, causing men to become feminine and develop sexual problems.
- Failure of the ovaries and menstrual problems in women.
- Lung damage leading to flu, pneumonia, or tuberculosis.
- Psychological depression and mental illness.

MINI GLOSSARY

delirium: a state of mental confusion, usually with hallucinations and continual movement.

tremors: continuous quivering or shaking.

congeners (CON-jen-ers): ingredients in alcoholic beverages, other than the alcohol itself, that may irritate the nervous system.

formaldehyde: a substance related to alcohol. Formaldehyde is made by the body from alcohol and contributes to hangovers.

Teacher Support Notes

① **Overhead—The Liver:** You may want to use the overhead in your supplementary material showing how the liver works as students begin to read about the effects of alcohol on the liver. Tell students that should the liver cells become fatty, the second state of liver disease, *fibrosis*, begins and the scar tissue replaces fat. The last stage of liver disease is *cirrhosis*, in which liver cells die and lose their function. The liver cells can no longer regenerate, and the person may die.

② **Handout—Disguises of Alcoholism:** In addition to having students read the following list of long-term effects of alcoholism, distribute the handout in your supplementary material entitled "Disguises of Alcoholism." This handout lists several illnesses and problems that often result from alcoholism.

Writing Explanations. Before going to the next section make sure that students can write explanations of the following:
1. Alcohol is toxic to the brain and liver and has immediate effects on all body systems, behaviors, and perceptions.

2. The liver is the organ that processes alcohol at a rate of 1 oz. per hour.
3. Hangovers are the result of toxic cogeners, dehydration, and the formation of formaldehyde in the system.
4. Alcohol has many long-term effects, including Fetal Alcohol Syndrome.

FOCUS
SECTION III

In this section the students will learn the:
1. Correlation between alcohol abuse and accidents.
2. Skills in dealing with an intoxicated friend.
3. Agencies and groups available to help friends and family members.

Activity 3.1

Newspaper Search. Bring in a num-

Section II Review
Answers
1. **a.** delirium
   b. formaldehyde
   c. cogeners
2. every cell of the body
3. talk or laugh more loudly and gesture more widely
4. The amount of alcohol that causes unconsciousness is close to the amount that causes death.
5. It inhibits the awareness and expression of emotions; person expresses love, joy, sorrow, anger and hatred more easily.
6. Answers will vary.

✎ Fast Facts
Nearly 8,000 young people die each year in automobile accidents that are alcohol related. An additional 40,000 are either disfigured for life or crippled.

Teacher Support Notes
① **Overhead—Comparing Drinkers:** Your supplementary material contains an overhead that compares the fates of two drinkers: one who manages to drink socially in moderation, another who begins as a social drinker and ends up an alcoholic.

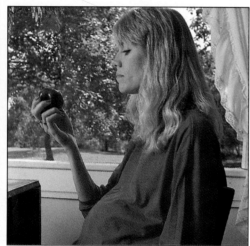

The pregnant woman who loves her baby-to-be will abstain from alcohol use.

Then there are the risks to the fetus when a pregnant woman abuses alcohol—the longest-term risks of all. The effects of **fetal alcohol syndrome (FAS)** are severe. They include mental and physical retardation and birth defects that last a lifetime. The Straight Talk section of Chapter 21 describes FAS in more detail.

In short, alcohol abuse damages health in every possible way. Even social drinking is linked with a higher than normal risk of death. Social drinkers who drink to excess are at risk, even though they may never appear drunk. Add, to all these risks, one other. This risk crosses over the boundaries of self-destruction to destroy the lives of other innocent people—the risk of accidents due to drinking. ①

Key Points *The effects of excessive drinking add up over the years to cause severe health damage. The liver, brain, and nerves suffer most, but all organs suffer to some extent. The longest-term damage is suffered by the infant born to a woman who abused alcohol during pregnancy—fetal alcohol syndrome.*

SECTION II REVIEW

Answer the following questions on a sheet of paper.

Learning the Vocabulary
The vocabulary terms in this section are *intoxication, delirium, tremors, congeners, formaldehyde,* and *fetal alcohol syndrome.*
1. Match each of the following phrases with the appropriate vocabulary term from the list above.
   a. a state of mental confusion
   b. made by the body from alcohol and contributes to a hangover
   c. ingredients in alcoholic beverages that may irritate the nervous system

Learning the Facts
2. Alcohol affects which cells?
3. Name the effects of alcohol when a person is slightly under the influence.
4. Why is alcohol a poor choice for an anesthetic?
5. How does alcohol affect the deeper brain centers?

Making Life Choices
6. How would you react to the following statements: "My parents won't allow me to drink alcohol. They say it's illegal and that it can lead to other drug addictions. All of my friends are drinking. I don't see anyone taking other drugs. Recently, I discovered my parents drinking at their parties. They are saying one thing but doing another. How can I make up my mind? I'm getting mixed messages and things are so confusing." What would you tell the writer? How would you feel if it were you? How would you deal with your parents?

SECTION III

Accidents and Alcohol

Drinking slows reactions. Drinking before and while driving is the single greatest hazard on the road. Of all fatal automobile and

TEACH
SECTION III
(Guided and Independent Practice)
Activity 3.2

The Six Ds. Put the following on the board—one underneath the other:

1. *D&D* **2.** *D* **3.** *D* **4.** *DD*. Start the activity by saying, "Okay, we've been talking about alcohol. Tell me what these Ds are about." Inevitably, someone will bring up "drinking and driving" (#1). Ask the students to tell you what they know about drinking and driving. Then ask them how many of them have ever ridden in a car with a driver under the influence (driver had more than two drinks in two hours). Ask them why they did it. The reason is

the second D—Denial. We really don't think anything will happen to us and drunk drivers definitely deny they are drunk. So, #1 D&D plus #2 D equals #3 D—Death. People drink, they drive, they deny, they die or cause others' deaths. What is #4, DD? It is one prevention all drinkers can agree to—Designated Drivers. **(20 min., Critical Thinking)**

---

motorcycle accidents on the roads today, about half involve alcohol. There is no better way to display friendship than to keep a friend who has been drinking off the road.

Drinking, Driving, Accidents, and Violence

The dangers of drinking and driving are so great that states have passed laws that forbid driving under the influence of alcohol. Under these laws, it is a crime to be **DWI** (**D**riving **W**hile **I**ntoxicated) or **DUI** (**D**riving **U**nder the **I**nfluence of alcohol or any other mind-altering substance). The "influence of alcohol" is proved if the driver's blood alcohol level is 0.10 percent or above. The alcohol content of the blood is reflected in the alcohol level in a person's breath. Therefore, the **breathalyzer test** is one method used to measure the blood alcohol level of a person suspected of driving under the influence of alcohol.

Lobby groups such as MADD (Mothers Against Drunk Drivers) and SADD (Students Against Driving Drunk) are pressuring the government to make the laws stricter. They have lost too many cherished sons, daughters, and friends to alcohol-related accidents on the highways and are trying to prevent other needless losses.

A drinker cannot drive safely for several hours after the blood alcohol level has fallen back to zero. Even moderate drinkers are advised not to drive the *morning after* an evening of drinking. They may feel fine, but their driving ability may still be abnormal.

Not only auto accidents, but all accidents, are more likely when people drink alcohol. Violent crimes are more likely, too. Most are committed by people who have drunk heavily enough to produce blood alcohol levels from 0.10 to 0.30 percent. (With levels higher than that, people pass out.) Remember, these people are not necessarily

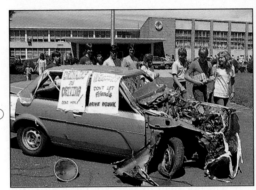

Don't do it. Don't ever drink and drive.

violent people to begin with. Under alcohol's influence, however, they become violent. Violent behavior attributed to the effects of alcohol accounts for one-third to two-thirds of all murders, assaults, rapes, suicides, family violence, and child abuse.

 Key Points ▷ *Alcohol makes auto accidents and other accidents much more likely. DWI and DUI laws punish people who drink or take drugs and drive. Violent behavior is strongly linked to alcohol use.*

MINI GLOSSARY

fetal alcohol syndrome (FAS): a cluster of birth defects, including permanent mental and physical retardation and facial abnormalities, seen in children born to mothers who abuse alcohol during pregnancy.

DWI: driving while intoxicated with alcohol or any abusable substance—a crime by law. Intoxication is defined by blood alcohol level (a level of 0.10 percent in most states).

DUI: driving under the influence (of alcohol or other mind-altering substances). See *DWI.*

breathalyzer test: a test of the alcohol level in a person's breath, which reflects the blood level of alcohol.

Teacher Support Notes

① **Handout—Attitudes about Drunk Driving:** The supplementary material contains a handout entitled, "Attitudes About Drunk Driving."

② **Alcohol-Related Accidents:** To emphasize this point, tell students that driving under the influence of alcohol is especially hazardous for young drivers who are inexperienced in both driving and drinking. Drivers younger than 20 represent fewer than 8% of the nation's licensed drivers, but they are involved in more than 25% of all collisions, and drinking and driving accidents are the leading cause of death.

③ **Violent Crime Percentages:** Give students the following percentages for violent crimes in which alcohol abuse is a factor: 64% of murders, 41% of assaults, 34% of rapes, 29% of other sex crimes, 30% of suicides, 50% of fights in the home, and 60% of child abuse cases.

Activity 3.3
Pop Quiz. All six of the following statements are false because of the underlined word or phrase. You may want to give students extra credit if they can change the underlined word or phrase in each sentence to make it a true statement.

1. A blood alcohol level of _1.0_ (in most states) is considered under the influence. (F)
2. Caffeine is a _depressant_. (F)
3. Alcohol is a _stimulant_. (F)
4. _Black coffee_ is the only real cure for a hangover. (F)
5. MADD stands for _mentally addicted drunk drivers_. (F)
6. DWI stands for _drunk without identification_. (F) **(5 min.)**

Activity 3.4
Review. Before proceeding to the next section, students should be able to:
1. Write the definitions of DWI and DUI.
2. Name three support groups of victims of alcoholism.

Teacher Support Notes

① **Handout—Progression of Alcoholism:** Distribute the handout in your supplementary material entitled "The Progression of Alcoholism," which shows the behavior that occurs in five stages of developing full-fledged alcoholism. Discussing the behaviors listed on the handout will help increase student interest in Section IV.

Section III Review
Answers

1. a. sober **b.** breathalyzer test
2. drinking before and while driving
3. breathalyzer test
4. don't respond to emotions stirred by alcohol; show concern; do not trust your friend's judgment about further drinking; take your friend's car keys away
5. Answers will vary.

☎ Where to Call

Al-Anon and Alateen Family Group Headquarters, Inc.
1-800-356-9996

When a Friend Has Drunk Too Much

If a friend has drunk too much, you can't speed up the recovery process by taking your friend for a walk. The muscles have to work to walk, but since they cannot use alcohol for fuel, they cannot help clear it from the blood. Time alone can do the job of making your friend **sober** again. Each person's blood is cleared of alcohol at a steady but limited rate.

It will not help to give your friend a cup of coffee. Caffeine is a stimulant, but it won't help break down alcohol. The police say, "A drunk who drinks a cup of coffee won't get sober but may become a wide-awake drunk."

Other suggestions for dealing with someone who is intoxicated:

- Don't respond to emotions stirred by alcohol.
- Do show concern.
- Do not trust your friend's judgment about further drinking.
- Take your friend's car keys away.

For someone who has had too much to drink, we repeat: time is the only real cure. One-half pint of alcohol takes 10 hours to leave the system. A person who has passed out from drinking needs 24 hours to sober up completely. Let such people sleep. (Let them lie on their sides, rather than on their backs. That way, if they vomit, they won't choke.) Don't let them drive, and never let them take a drink for the road.

A great weight of evidence shows alcohol is harmful to health. The only points in its favor seem to be the social effects mentioned at the start of this chapter. There, the question of why people drink was asked. Perhaps an even more important question is, "How can people who become addicted to alcohol stop drinking?"

Key Points *Time alone restores a person who is drunk to a sober state.*

SECTION III REVIEW

Answer the following questions on a sheet of paper.

Learning the Vocabulary
The vocabulary terms in this section are *DWI, DUI, breathalyzer test,* and *sober.*
1. Match the following phrases with the appropriate terms.
   a. free of alcohol's effects and free of addiction
   b. a test which reflects the blood level of alcohol in a person's body

Learning the Facts
2. What is the single greatest hazard on the road?
3. What is one method for measuring a person's blood alcohol level?
4. List four suggestions for dealing with someone who is intoxicated.

Making Life Choices
5. What would happen in this situation? After a party, Tim, who has had two beers, gets into his car to drive home. He claims to feel just fine and doesn't need your advice. What would you say to him to stop him? What other action would you take?

SECTION IV

The Way Back: Strategies for Recovery

We know a great deal about the addictive nature of alcohol. We also know a great deal about recovery from alcohol addiction. Some of the struggles to recover from addiction apply only to alcohol. Many, though, apply to all drugs.

How can we add up all the misery caused by addiction to alcohol, or **alcoholism**?

In this section the students will learn the:
1. Symptoms of alcoholism.
2. Impact of alcoholism on family, friends, and society.
3. Symptoms of enabling an alcohol addict.

4. Tools for coping with and surviving alcoholism in the family.

Activity 4.1
Symptoms. Draw an outline of a person on the board. Ask the students to give symptoms of an alcohol addict. As they give the correct ones, fill in the head, arms, torso, etc., with the symptoms. Stress the difference between a functional alcohol addict and a nonfunctional alcohol

addict. **(40 min., Critical Thinking)**

TEACH
SECTION IV
(Guided and Independent Practice)
Activity 4.2
Test Your Knowledge. Have each student fill out a copy of the "Test Your Knowledge" worksheet from the supplementary materials. This worksheet con-

(continued on next page)

One way is to measure the impact in terms of losses to society. People who are addicted to alcohol and other drugs take many sick days from work or school. They may lose their jobs or quit school. This limits their ultimate contributions to society. Not only do they fail to contribute; they also draw heavily on society's resources. They require more hospitalization, placing a burden on insurance companies to pay for services. They cause avoidable accidents and injuries, and they commit crimes. These behaviors require the services of public support systems such as police, ambulances, courts, prisons, lawyers, and rehabilitation centers. The true dollar costs of alcoholism, if added up in this way, are colossal.

For some, the costs in dollars may be far outweighed by the other costs of alcoholism. Another way to measure the tragedy of alcoholism is to look at the effects upon one family in which a member is addicted to alcohol. The family suffers losses of income, of status in the community, of physical and mental health, and even of life itself. Both the person with alcoholism and the people close to that person suffer these losses. However, only one individual can put an end to the misery—the addicted person. The day that person admits to having a dependency problem is the first day on a long road to recovery. With recovery, though, comes an end to the losses and miseries suffered by the family and the community.

You may be wondering why, when faced with all these losses, the addicted person does not simply quit drinking. The reason is that a person who is addicted to alcohol is in the grip of a powerful force that nonaddicted people cannot possibly imagine.

The addicted person may want to quit drinking, may promise to do so, but may drink secretly and then feel guilty and worthless. More promises unkept and more drinking lead to physical, mental, and moral deterioration until the addiction becomes life's only reality. Finally, one day, the person may admit complete defeat in the face of physical, financial, and emotional losses. This is the point of surrender for many who then seek out helping programs and begin their way back. Others may begin recovery at earlier points.

Recovery from addiction occurs in stages. First, the person has to accept that the problem exists and "own" the problem. Then the person must quit using the drug and (usually) get help. Then the person must "stay quit." This sounds simple, and it is, but it is not easy. Some people will not make it.

> **Key Points** *People who are addicted to alcohol and other drugs not only fail to contribute to society; they also draw heavily on society's resources. People addicted to alcohol and members of their families suffer financial, physical, and emotional losses. Recovery from alcohol addiction occurs in stages.*

Don't Enable

You may know someone in the recovery process. Let's assume you are another family member, or a helper such as a counselor. Let's also assume that the person with the problem is still drinking. The most important thing you can do is *not* **enable** the person to escape the problems that come along with excessive drinking.

An enabler is a rescuer—a person who tries to save the alcohol abuser from the consequences of his or her behavior. The

MINI GLOSSARY

sober: free of alcohol's effects and of addiction; not drunk.
alcoholism: the disease characterized by dependence on alcohol, which harms health, family relations, and social and work functioning.

① **Handout—Myths About Alcoholism:** Your supplementary material contains an activity for students that requires them to correct myths about alcoholism. Twenty myths are stated and space is provided for students to write the facts. Also included is an answer sheet with the facts to correct the myths.

✏ **Fast Facts**

Recent studies have found that 9% of women suffer from alcoholism (up from 3% in past years), and another 8.3% from problem drinking. Researchers have thought that men were five times as likely as women to be alcoholics. The ratio now seems to be closer to 2-1/2 or 2 to 1.

tains ten true/false statements about alcohol addicts and alcoholism. Go over it, asking how they answered, then give the correct information. **(full class period, Critical Thinking)**

Activity 4.3

Enabling. Write the word *Enabling* on the board. Ask the students to give sample definitions. Then ask the following questions:
1. How do family members enable parents who are alcohol abusers? (They call work and make excuses, clean up after them, accept their apologies, and cover up for them.)
2. How do teens enable their friends who are problem drinkers or alcohol abusers?

(They let them copy homework, lie for them, and drink with them.)
3. What is the #1 way teens enable their friends? (*The Code of Silence.* They keep their mouths shut even though they know there is a problem. They know facts and conceal them from adults. The teen alcoholics rely heavily on the unspoken Code of Silence.)

Use this activity to lead in to a discussion of the guidelines to prevent enabling (on

Where to Write

National Institute on Alcohol Abuse and Alcoholism
Bethesda, MD 20205

Teacher Support Notes

① **Teacher Information Sheet—Family Dynamics:** Your supplementary material contains background information entitled "The Family Dynamics of Alcohol Abuse," on the relationship between the alcohol abuser and family.
② **Dysfunctional Families:** You may want to refer students back to the discussion of dysfunctional families on page 114.

Fast Facts

According to the U.S. Surgeon General, more than half the students in the junior and senior high schools in the United States are alcohol drinkers. Of those who drink, 8 million consume alcohol weekly, 5.4 million have binged on occasion, and nearly one-half million go on weekly binges, guzzling five or more drinks in a row.

HEALTH **S**TRATEGIES

How Not to Enable   ]①

These strategies will help you keep yourself from enabling someone else's drug-addicted behavior:

• Stay concerned. (Give the message, "I care about you. I think your behaviors are wrong, but I see you as a worthwhile person.")
• Be prompt. Speak up as soon as possible after each drinking or drug episode.
• Speak about the behavior, but do not attack the person. (Say, "You got drunk last night." Don't say, "You are a no-good, worthless drunk.")
• Be specific; name and describe behaviors. Don't judge. (Say, "You fell and broke the standing lamp." Don't say, "You made a fool of yourself.")
• Act as a mirror—tell what you see. ("Your eyes are red; your hands are shaking.")
• Don't try to smooth things over. (Say, "Go ahead and cry. Here's a tissue." Don't say, "There, there, it'll be all right.")
• When you are angry, cool off before you talk to the person. (Don't let the other person "make" you angry. That's letting yourself be controlled.)

AL-ANON Family Group Headquarters   1-212-302-7240
P.O. Box 862, Midtown Station
New York, NY. 10018-0862

Alcoholics Anonymous World Service Office   1-212-870-3400
475 Riverside Drive
New York, NY. 10115

Figure 14–5 Resources for People with Alcohol-Related Problems

Enabling takes many different forms—coming up with money when it's owed, helping make excuses ("I'm sorry to have to tell you this, Boss, but my brother is sick today"), doing the other person's work. Enablers can be family members or helpers outside the family (religious leaders, health care providers, counselors, lawyers, and others). A support group for codependents, Al-Anon, is similar to Alcoholics Anonymous (for people addicted to alcohol). Al-Anon helps enablers learn how not to get in the way of lessons that lead to recovery. Alateen, a support group sponsored by Al-Anon, is for young people whose lives have been affected by alcoholism in a family member or a close friend. Figure 14–5 lists resources for people with alcohol-related problems. The Health Strategies section on this page provides rules to prevent enabling.

Beyond these strategies, family members and friends should go about living and enjoying their own lives as best they can. The alcohol problem is not their problem. They cannot solve it, change it, take it away, or take responsibility for it. They can, though, take the responsibility for their own lives.

rescuer seems good-hearted. In the case of alcoholism, however, rescuing blocks recovery. By blocking the consequences of the alcohol abuser's behavior, the enabler prevents the learning that would otherwise take place. The alcohol abuser never has to face the music as long as the enabler is around. An enabler within the same family as the alcohol abuser is sometimes called a **codependent**.

Key Points ▶ *Enabling feels like rescuing, but it blocks recovery. It doesn't help. Concerned people should be careful not to enable, but*

②

EVALUATE
SECTION IV

Activity 4.4
Pop Quiz. Have students write answers to the following statements and questions:
1. Identify the stages of recovery from addiction. (Admit the problem, quit using the drug, stay clean.)
2. Define the role of the codependent as an enabler. (Covers for the alcohol addict so he doesn't feel the consequences of his behavior.)
3. How is the recovering alcohol addict like a person suffering from grief? (They both experience denial, bargaining, anger, guilt, and acceptance.)

CLOSE
SECTION IV

Activity 4.5
Before going to the next section, students should be able to explain in their own words that:
1. We are all victims of alcoholism in some way.

(continued on next page)

---

should make their feelings known. Family members and friends of alcohol-dependent people must live their own lives as best they can.

Recovery

Traveling the road back to normal life from alcohol addiction may take years. It's hard, and not everyone succeeds. After all, in most cases the damage done by alcohol has progressed for years. All parts of life have been changed by it. During recovery, the person must take these steps: stop drinking, become able to sleep, regain an appetite, begin to function better socially, return to work, and recover health.

A person giving up a drug goes through the same emotional stages as someone who is grieving over the loss of a loved one. An early stage is **denial**. Another is bargaining. Then come anger and guilt, and finally acceptance. The person giving up addiction needs the respect given to any grieving person.

It helps if the person is in touch with other people who have recovered. No one is as powerful in helping a person who is recovering from substance abuse as another person who has already traveled that road. The worldwide self-help recovery group Alcoholics Anonymous (AA) works this way. The AA program takes a positive approach—12 steps to recovery and spiritual growth that end in the person's helping others. In AA, thousands of people have helped one another recover from alcoholism.

In the beginning of the recovery process, the ex-user is "dry." The person doesn't drink or take drugs, but still craves the substance, and doesn't enjoy life without it. Only later does the person become "sober." The person who is sober actually prefers life without the substance.

Key Points *The road to recovery from alcohol or other drug abuse is long and hard. Not all who try to quit succeed. AA helps many people,*

first to overcome their grief at giving up the addiction, and then to become sober.

SECTION IV REVIEW

Answer the following questions on a sheet of paper.

Learning the Vocabulary
The vocabulary terms in this section are *alcoholism, enable, codependent,* and *denial.*
1. What is the difference between an enabler and a codependent?
2. _____ is a disease of dependence on alcohol.

Learning the Facts
3. What losses does a family suffer when one of its members is addicted to alcohol?
4. Describe how an enabler affects a person addicted to alcohol.
5. What does giving up alcohol have in common with grief?
6. Name three health agencies that help those recovering from addiction to alcohol.

Making Life Choices
7. You have made a date with a very good-looking, popular student at your school. You have heard that this person likes to have a good time and goes to parties where other people drink alcohol and use other drugs. You are worried that you might be asked to use drugs or alcohol. How would feel about being asked to use alcohol? What would you do? Why would you take that action?

MINI GLOSSARY

enable: make possible. In addiction, enabling means "helping" by trying to "save" the addicted person from the consequences of the behavior. This makes possible continued alcohol or other drug abuse.
codependent: an enabler who is a member of the family of, or has a close relationship with, a person addicted to a drug.
denial (dee-NIGH-al): refusal to believe the facts of a circumstance—for example, to deny that a person is a problem drinker in the face of clear evidence that it is so.

2. Only the alcohol addict can take the first step to recovery, but it is up to others to show compassion without enabling.
3. The goal of a recovering alcohol addict is to enjoy life without alcohol.

FOCUS
SECTION V

In this section the students will learn:
1. Skills for giving and participating in a successful nonalcoholic party.

Activity 5.1
Party Time. Have students brainstorm things that are usually done at par-

ties they attend. List their ideas on the board and discuss.

TEACH
SECTION V
(Guided and Independent Practice)
Activity 5.2
Drug-Free Activities. Divide students into three groups, with equal numbers of males and females in each group. Ask them to draw a line down the middle

---

Teacher Support Notes

① **Refusing Drinks:** Have students role-play a party at which drinks are served, after they have read this section. Select one person to be the "host;" then pass out slips of paper to the rest of the class, the "guests," telling them whether to accept drinks enthusiastically (most should do this) or refuse (a few should be selected to do so). The host passes a tray of glasses (pretend cocktails). Host and guests then pressure the refusers in various ways to go ahead and accept an alcoholic drink while refusers practice their assertiveness skills. Afterwards have the refusers describe their feelings about the experience, telling what was most difficult for them and why. Have the drinkers describe their feelings about why it was important that the nondrinkers accept a drink and how it felt to pressure them into drinking.

Section V Review

Answers

1. not to drink at all
2. don't apologize, expect others to respect your choice
3. Answers will vary; could include mentioning contacting Al-Anon or Alateen.

SECTION V

How to Refuse Drinks, How to Give a Great Party

①

The only way to be completely protected against alcohol addiction is not to drink at all. The choice is personal. Those who choose not to drink have every right to make that choice. It is no one else's business. It is perfectly OK to say, "I don't drink because I don't want to drink."

Unfortunately, some social groups give people a hard time for refusing to drink, because drinking is a shared experience. Two useful pointers for the nondrinker are:

• Don't apologize.
• Expect others to respect your choice.

The Health Strategies section on this page, "How to Give a Great Party without Alcohol," offers suggestions.

SECTION V REVIEW

Answer the following questions on a sheet of paper.
Learning the Facts
1. What is the only way to be completely protected against alcohol addiction?
2. Name the two useful pointers for a nondrinker.

Making Life Choices
3. Your best friend's parents are addicted to alcohol. Your friend has come to you many times about this problem. You have told her several times to go to the counselor at your school. You want to go to her parents and talk to them, but you don't really know what to say. What would you do in this situation? How can you help your friend? How would you feel if you were the person with the alcohol problem and with parents like hers? Would your responses be different?

HEALTH
STRATEGIES

How to Give a Great Party without Alcohol

To give a great party:
1. Make it known that this is to be a party with no alcohol.
2. Offer interesting nonalcoholic beverages, such as punch.
3. Provide plenty of food and snacks—make-it-yourself sandwiches can be fun.
4. Remember, if anyone is disappointed, that's a reflection on their drinking problem, not on your hospitality.
5. Keep the music low. Loud music makes people anxious.
6. Arrange activities, such as badminton or swimming, as the focus. Or provide a dress theme (such as entertainment or sports celebrities). Or plan games.
7. Get your guests involved—ask them to bring musical instruments or their favorite music tapes or compact discs.

Answers to Fact or Fiction

Here are the answers to the questions at the start of the chapter.

1. True. **2.** True. **3.** False. Alcohol is not digested. It is immediately absorbed into the blood. **4.** True. **5.** False. Driving is impaired at blood alcohol levels lower than 0.10 percent. **6.** False. Muscles do not use alcohol for fuel, so walking does not affect the body's rate of alcohol breakdown. **7.** False. Coffee can wake up, but not sober up, a drunk.

of a sheet of paper. On one side, they are to list all the things that could be done to have fun at a *drug-free* (alcohol-free) party. On the other side they are to list the things nondrinkers need to remember or can do if criticized or pressured by drinkers. Once they've developed a list they can all agree on, give each group two pieces of posterboard. Ask the groups to use markers to transfer their lists onto the poster pieces (party list on one sheet, nondrinker list on the other). Then put the pieces together and display the posters on the wall.
(40 min., Cooperative Learning)

EVALUATE
SECTION V

Activity 5.3
Pop Quiz.
1. List five suggestions for giving a party without alcohol. (See Health Strategies on the opposite page for possible answers.)
2. The only way to be completely protected from alcoholism is _____. (abstinence) **(10 min.)**

CLOSE
SECTION V

(continued on next page)

STRAIGHT TALK

Alcoholism, the Disease

Alcoholism is one of the nation's most serious health problems. About two-thirds of all U.S. adults drink. Of these, about one in every ten is addicted to alcohol. The annual cost to the nation, including work time lost to alcohol abuse, is estimated in the tens of billions of dollars. Worse still, the rate of alcoholism is on the rise.

I know people who drink alcohol, but I don't think I know anyone who is addicted to it.

If you know ten people who drink, chances are that at least one of them is addicted to alcohol or is on the road to addiction. Teenagers have an even higher rate of alcoholism than do adults. One in every five teenagers who drink (aged 14 to 17) is already becoming dependent on alcohol.

I know more than ten people who drink, but not one has the reputation of being addicted.

Many people would rather not see the problem of alcohol addiction. In fact, people can choose not to see it. They can convince themselves that it doesn't exist, or that it is a minor problem. Such blindness is even found in hospitals. Physicians may list on patients' records many alcohol-related illnesses, such as liver disease, but never suggest the possibility of alcoholism. Yet anywhere from 33 to 95 percent of all patients may be in hospitals because of alcohol-related illnesses—including diseases of every body organ, broken bones, and emotional problems. Any of these disorders may be due to other causes, but alcoholism is often a contributor. Whenever the problem underlying any of these diagnoses is alcoholism, this has to be dealt with first. To deal with alcoholism, we have to acknowledge it and face it. Denial blocks recovery.

Isn't alcoholism easy to recognize? Isn't it drunkenness?

No, to be drunk is not the same thing as to be a person with alcoholism. Anybody can get drunk, simply by drinking too much alcohol. However, that does not necessarily reflect alcoholism. (It may, but you would have to look at other factors to identify the disease.)

Many misconceptions attached to the term *alcoholism* need to be corrected. For example, alcoholism is not related to the kind of beverage drunk. Even wine coolers and beer can produce it. Nor is alcoholism tied to a particular age. As mentioned, even teenagers can develop it. It is not always obvious. It is easy to hide, even in its advanced stages. People have been amazed to learn that a good friend, whom they thought they knew well, had reached a late stage of alcoholism before they found out about it. The addiction had been developing for years, but friends had no clues.

You have told me what alcoholism is not. Now, please tell me what it is.

The American Medical Association (AMA), the American Psychiatric Association (APA), and other

(Continued on next page)

✉ **Where to Write**

National Clearing House for Alcohol Information
P.O. Box 2345
Rockville, MD 20852

Teacher Support Notes

① **Moderate Blood Alcohol Levels:** You may want to tell students that some researchers have observed that drinking makes people feel good as long as the blood alcohol remains at a level of about 0.05. In this range people feel relaxed, euphoric, and sociable. At higher levels, they go from moderately intoxicated to thoroughly drunk. A 140-pound person could consume only 1-1/4 drinks per hour and still maintain the blood alcohol level of .05 or lower, with one drink equaling 12 ozs. of beer, 4 ozs. of wine, 2-1/2 ozs. of brandy, or 1-1/4 ozs. of 80 proof liquor.

CLOSE
(Continued)

Activity 5.4

Before going to the next chapter, students should know:

1. That drinking within the acceptable limits of the law or abstinence is a personal choice.

2. They should expect others to respect

their choice of abstinence.

RETEACH/BONUS

Here are some additional activities for the various sections of this chapter. You may want to use these activities to reteach certain concepts, or you may choose them as alternatives to earlier activities. Some could also be used in conjunction with the

Straight Talk feature below.

Speaker. Invite a CAC (Certified Alcohol Counselor) who works with teens addicted to alcohol to come in and discuss "How do I know my friend is becoming an alcohol addict?" and "What can I do if I think my friend is in trouble with alcohol?" Take notes to develop a list of symptoms and do's and don'ts. Develop an information sheet for the students. The

66 Thoughts on Health 99

'Tis not the drinking that is to be blamed, but the excess.
– John Selden

Teacher Support Notes

① **Food and Alcohol:** As enrichment you may want to explain to students why failure to eat prior to drinking can increase the effects of alcohol. Enzymes in the liver that metabolize alcohol are made of protein, and like all body protein, they break down when a person fails to eat. Fasting for as little as one day can reduce the rate of alcohol metabolism by half. Therefore, drinking on an empty stomach not only lets the drinker feel the effects more promptly but also raises the blood alcohol level higher for longer times and anesthetizes the brain more profoundly.

✍ Fast Facts

Approximately 35% of Americans do not drink alcohol at all. About 10% of the people who drink account for half of all the alcohol consumed in this country.

366

STRAIGHT TALK   *(Continued)*

authorities define alcoholism as a disease of dependence on alcohol. It is chronic (long-lasting), progressive (gets worse over time), and potentially fatal. It involves tolerance, physical addiction, and organ damage caused by alcohol.

The path of worsening symptoms is well known. Alcoholism progresses from the first drink, usually in the teen years, to more involvement with alcohol. It goes on to a point where alcohol comes to dominate the person's life, damaging family ties and friendships, work life, and physical health. Alcoholism at its worst typically takes from three to ten years to develop after heavy drinking has begun. For young abusers, less time is required. Some teenagers are clearly already addicted to alcohol.

How is alcoholism identified?

Usually, the person with the problem identifies it by taking a quiz such as the one in this chapter's Life Choice Inventory. The person answers yes to three or more questions and faces the result squarely. This is important to understand, because people with alcoholism try to deny the problem exists. Someone else may see that a person has a problem with alcoholism.

However, until the person has accepted that fact, nothing can be done.

What sorts of people suffer from alcoholism?

Just as people with diabetes or cancer come in all sizes, shapes, and varieties, so do people with alcoholism. The disease does not respect income, education, social class, or physical attractiveness. The person you most admire is just as likely to be addicted to alcohol as the person you most dislike. All people may be susceptible to alcoholism.

It is useful to separate the *person* from the *condition*. Think of the person as worthwhile, even though you disapprove of what the person *does*. Use words that show this attitude. Speak of "the person with alcoholism," not of "the alcoholic." After all, if treatment is successful, the person will recover (that is, the person will become a person without active alcoholism). It is probably not correct to think alcoholism can be cured. However, the disease is treatable, and it can be arrested, as long as the person steers clear of alcohol. The person is not "an alcoholic" any more than the person with cancer is "a canceric."

How can I tell whether someone I know is becoming addicted to alcohol?

A telling event on the way to alcoholism is the occurrence of **blackouts**—episodes of **amnesia**. Some authorities say that blackouts are the single most notable sign to warn of alcoholism. This statement is open to question, but blackouts are certainly common in people with alcoholism.

A friend of my brother's drank so much that he passed out. Was that a blackout? ①

No. In fact, blacking out bears no resemblance to passing out. A person who has had too much to drink may pass out—that just means losing consciousness. A person having a blackout, on the other hand, may show no outward signs of it at all. The person acts normal, although drinking. The next day, however, the person is unable to remember anything that happened beyond a certain time.

An example may help make this clear. Judy eats dinner with her family and then sits down at the sewing machine with a drink by her side, to make a dress. She

(Continued on next page)

next day, ask the students what they remember from the presentation. Give them time to bring out the major points, then distribute the information sheet and discuss. **(Extend, Enrich)**

Role-Play. Ask for volunteers to role-play a friend (or friends) confronting another friend about his/her drinking. Coach the drinking role to be manipulative ("You drink with me—what about your

drinking?"; "You're just jealous because of all the friends I have"; "If I have a problem, you have a problem"; "I have it all under control, you're imagining things"). The friend(s) tries to convince the friend to go for help.

At one point in the role-play, freeze the scene. Discuss the frustration of the friend(s), then pinpoint guidelines:
1. Never confront alone.
2. Confront with the facts.

3. Confront with love and concern.
4. Don't let the person change the subject—"We're not talking about me (us) right now, we're talking about you."
5. Give ultimatums—"Either go with me (us) to get help, or we'll go without you."
6. Don't drink with them anymore and tell them why. Otherwise it gives them the idea you approve of their drinking. **(20 min.; Extend, Enrich)**

STRAIGHT TALK *(Continued)*

finishes the first drink, goes and gets a second one, and continues making the dress. Several hours later she has had five drinks, has finished the dress, has ironed it and hung it up in the closet, has put away her sewing machine, and has gone to bed. The following morning she remembers nothing beyond the time when she started to sew. To see what she has done, she has to go back and look around. She finds the completed dress in the closet and a half-empty bottle in the cabinet.

As you can see, a person's behavior can be completely normal during a blackout. Of course, some terrible thing may happen instead. Rather

than simply having completed a dress, Judy might have taken the car, gone out to buy another bottle, and killed someone on the way. The following morning, as before, she would have awakened completely unaware of what had happened the evening before. A dent and some blood on the front of her car might have been her first clues to what went on. ①

Blackouts often mark a turning point for people on their way to alcoholism, because blackouts are scary. Realizing that their lives are out of control, people come to recognize their condition. The disease of alcoholism can progress far beyond

blackouts, but people can stop drinking at any time along the way. The beginning of blackouts is one excellent place to stop.

Mini Glossary

blackouts: episodes of amnesia regarding periods of time while drinking. The person may act normal during a blackout, but later be unable to recall anything about it. Blackouts are likely to occur in the life of a person with alcoholism.

amnesia: loss of memory.

Teacher Support Notes

① **Blackouts:** Tell students additional stories about blackouts. For example, a drug counselor tells the story of a patient becoming angry after a blizzard cancelled his plans to see a professional football game in Minnesota. The patient began to drink and the next thing he remembered, he was coming out of his blackout on a park bench. The grass was green, the temperature mild, and none of the surroundings familiar. Embarrassed to ask anyone where he was, he finally bought a newspaper and discovered that he was in a southern state, hundreds of miles from his home in Minnesota. The only clue he has as to how he got there is the bus tickets he found in his pocket.

Answers

Vocabulary

1. a. DUI b. sober
c. tremors d. blackout
e. codependent
2. a. alcohol b. proof
c. enable d. amnesia
3. a. Formaldehyde
b. denial
4. a. Ethanol is the alcohol in alcoholic beverages, while cogeners are ingredients other than alcohol that may irritate the nervous system. b. Moderation is an amount of alcohol that causes no harm to health, family, and social functioning, while alcoholism is a disease that harms health, family relations, and social and work functioning. Moderation means a person has control over alcohol. Alcoholism means that alcohol has control over the person.

Recall

Section I
1. alcohol
2. to celebrate, to unwind, they like the taste of alcoholic beverages, it's the custom

3. Answers will vary. Refer to Figure 14–2 on page 351 for possible answers.
4. Answers will vary. Refer to Figure 14–2 on page 351 for possible answers.

Section II
5. brain, muscles, nerves, glands, the small blood vessels of the skin, the liver
6. one drink an hour

7. Alcohol relaxes the nerves of the blood vessels of the skin. These widen, making the drinker appear flushed and feel warm.
8. The drinker loses certain kinds of awareness. The brain's speech and vision centers are being put to sleep. People may act against their own desires and wishes, may

pick a fight, may become sexually aggressive, and may attempt a dangerous physical exploit.
9. The person passes out.
10. The throat stings and triggers the choking reflex. The stomach rejects too large a dose and causes the drinker to vomit. Finally, the body breaks down any alcohol that does get

CHAPTER REVIEW

LEARNING THE VOCABULARY

alcohol	tremors	sober
ethanol (ethyl alcohol)	congeners	alcoholism
proof	formaldehyde	enable
moderation	fetal alcohol syndrome (FAS)	codependent
drink	DWI	denial
intoxication	DUI	blackouts
delirium	breathalyzer test	amnesia

Answer the following questions on a separate sheet of paper.

1. *Matching*—Match each of the following phrases with the appropriate vocabulary term:
   a. driving under the influence of alcohol
   b. free of alcohol's effects and of addiction
   c. continuous quivering or shaking
   d. temporary amnesia linked to alcohol abuse
   e. an enabler who is a member of the family of a person addicted to a drug
2. *Word Scramble*—Use the clues from the phrases below to help you unscramble the words:
   a. **aoocllh** _____ a class of chemical compounds
   b. **oofpr** _____ term used to describe the percentage of alcohol in alcoholic beverages
   c. **aeebln** _____ make possible; in addiction, to "help"
   d. **aaiemns** _____ loss of memory
3. a. _____ is a substance made by the body from alcohol, and it contributes to hangovers.
   b. Refusal to believe the facts of a circumstance is called _____.
4. Explain the relationships between:
   a. congeners and ethanol
   b. moderation and alcoholism

RECALLING IMPORTANT FACTS AND IDEAS

1. What is the most widely used and abused drug in our society?
2. List four reasons that drinkers give as to why they drink alcohol.
3. List five behaviors that are typical of moderate drinkers.
4. List five behaviors that are typical of problem drinkers.
5. Within minutes after the first sip of a drink, ethanol is affecting what body parts?
6. How much alcohol can the liver handle?
7. Explain why people think alcohol warms them up when they drink it.
8. What happens to a person who has drunk enough to affect the judgment centers of the brain?
9. Describe what happens when the conscious brain is completely depressed.
10. How does the body protect itself from toxins?
11. What are three symptoms of a hangover?
12. What are the effects of liver damage on the body?
13. Excessive drinking over many years can cause severe and permanent brain damage. What are three things most affected by this type of brain damage?
14. Identify and describe five other long-term effects of alcohol abuse.
15. How long does it take for someone who has passed out from an alcohol overdose to sober up?
16. Describe how alcoholism costs society colossal amounts of money.
17. List the seven rules to keep from being an enabler.
18. What are the five emotional stages someone has to go through in giving up a drug?

into the blood as quickly as possible.
11. headache pain, unpleasant sensations in the mouth, nausea
12. The whole body suffers. One of the worst effects is high blood pressure, which can lead to heart attacks and strokes. Liver damage also weakens the body's defenses against

infection.
13. vision, memory, learning ability, and other functions
14. Answers will vary; could include: ulcers of stomach and intestines; shrinking of all the body's muscles, including the heart muscle; abnormal changes in the blood; kidney damage; bladder damage; gland damage; skin rashes and

sores; shrinkage and damage to the testicles; failure of the ovaries and menstrual problems in women; lung damage leading to flu, pneumonia, tuberculosis; and psychological depression and mental illness.
Section III
15. 24 hours
Section IV
16. require more hospitaliza-

tion, placing a burden on insurance companies; cause avoidable accidents and injuries; commit crimes; require the services of police, ambulances, courts, prisons, lawyers, and rehabilitation centers
17. stay concerned; be prompt; speak about the behavior, but do not attack the person; be specific—name and describe behaviors—don't judge; act as a mirror—tell what you see; don't try to smooth things over; when you are angry, cool off before you talk to the person
18. denial, bargaining, anger, guilt, acceptance
Straight Talk
19. alcoholism is not related to the kind of beverage drunk—even wine coolers and beer can produce alcoholism; alcoholism is not tied to a certain age—even teenagers can be alcoholics; and it is easy to hide
20. three to ten years

19. List at least three misconceptions about alcoholism.

20. Alcoholism at its worst typically takes how many years to develop?

CRITICAL THINKING

1. Movies and other entertainment media often show an intoxicated person as a joke and a funny individual. But, is it a joke? Do all who drink become hilariously funny, agreeable, and friendly? What can we do to change this image?

2. After reading the Straight Talk, "Alcoholism, The Disease," why do you think so many

people who are aware of the dangers of alcohol still drink? Why is it that so many people fall victim to alcoholism? How long does it take to become addicted to alcohol? What group of people are most likely to become addicted to alcohol? What is a sure-fire sign of alcoholism? What did you learn from reading this Straight Talk?

ACTIVITIES

1. Write a report profiling a candidate for alcoholism. Include a description of the person's personality and family background.

2. Interview a local law enforcement agency about the problems associated with teenage drinking. What are the problems? Has changing the legal age of drinking to 21 helped? What do they think will help stop teens from drinking?

3. Attend a local Alcoholics Anonymous meeting. What happened at the meeting? What are the goals of the people who attend the meetings?

4. Write a radio announcement to convince the public not to drink and drive.

5. Identify different groups at school or in the community that encourage responsible drinking behavior. A few examples might be Students Against Driving Drunk (SADD), a safe-ride program, and Mothers Against Drunk Drivers (MADD). Call these local agencies and make a poster showing each one's name, address, phone number, and hours of operation. Display these posters around the school.

6. Plan an alcohol-free party. Give the party a clever name. Plan healthful activities and a healthful menu. Design an invitation on a sheet of poster board. Discuss with your class the party you have planned.

MAKING DECISIONS ABOUT HEALTH

1. Randy and Colleen are both college seniors. Randy is taking Colleen to a dance in his new Z-28. All of Randy's friends are drinking at a party before the dance. Randy decides to drink with them. He has had four beers in one hour and Colleen has had one glass of champagne.

Randy and Colleen go to the dance for two hours and then go to another party. At the party they drink and dance for about two hours. In that time period, Randy has six more

beers and Colleen has two more drinks. It is getting late and Colleen is nervous because Randy has drunk too much to drive. Colleen is from out of state and doesn't have a current driver's license.

a. What advice would you give Colleen in this situation?

b. How should Colleen get home?

c. What should Randy do in this situation?

CHAPTER 15 PLANNER

Chapter 15 is 28 pages long and is divided into the five sections listed to the right. Major learning outcomes are also listed to the right. This chapter addresses a major health problem in our society, the use of tobacco. The chapter explains why people continue to smoke, even though they may be well informed of the dangers that accompany their bad habit. This chapter then gives specific details about how smoking affects the smoker's and non-smoker's health. The effects of smokeless tobacco are also discussed in the chapter. The last section explains why and how a person should quit smoking. It also explains how to help a person quit smoking. The chapter focuses on tobacco as a problem of our society, and states that it should be addressed on a personal level.

Answers to "Fact or Fiction"

1. False. The main reason for continuing to smoke is addiction to nicotine. **2.** True. **3.** True. **4.** False. Nicotine is a highly addictive drug. **5.** True. **6.** True. **7.** True. **8.** False. The risks of cancer of the mouth and throat are greater for people using smokeless tobacco products than for smokers.

SUGGESTED RESOURCES

Student Readings
1. Blum, Alan, ed. *The Cigarette Underworld—A Front Line Report on the War Against Your Lungs.* Secaucus, NJ: Lyle Stuart, 1985.
Teacher Readings
1. Rucker, William B., ed. *Drugs, Society and Behavior.* Guilford, CT: The Dushkin Publishing Group, 1987.
Software
1. *Smoking: It's Up To You.* Several smoking-related topics are investigated. MECC; 800-685-6322.

CHAPTER 15
Tobacco

Activity To Introduce Chapter

In order to get students thinking about how their life choices and behaviors affect their lives, ask them to write a paragraph describing how they plan to spend the last 20 years of their lives, or how they would like to live after they retire. After they have completed this part of the assignment, ask them to turn their papers over and write how smoking would affect their retirement plans. Remind students that smoking may cut as many as 18 years from their lives. They now have two years of retirement to write about. This will help students realize how devastating the smoking habit can be to them and their plans.

OUTCOMES

After reading and studying this chapter, you will be able to:

✓ Describe the immediate effects of nicotine on the body.
✓ Describe the effects of smoking on the respiratory system.
✓ Describe the effects of smoking on the cardiovascular system.
✓ List negative aspects of tobacco use other than health hazards.
✓ Identify strategies to avoid other people's tobacco smoke.
✓ Identify the health problems associated with the use of smokeless tobacco.

✓ Describe the changes that occur in a person's body when the person quits smoking.

CONTENTS

I. Why People Use Tobacco
II. Health Effects of Smoking
III. Passive Smoking
IV. Smokeless Tobacco
V. The Decision to Quit

Straight Talk: *Tobacco Advertising and Ethics*

FACT OR FICTION

What do you think? Are the following statements true or false? If you think they are false, then say what is true.

1. After someone has started smoking, enjoyment is the reason he or she continues to smoke.
2. One of nicotine's chief effects is to elicit the stress response.
3. A sign of nicotine withdrawal is an inability to concentrate.
4. Nicotine is not an addictive drug.
5. In emphysema, the lungs first become damaged not because people can't breathe in but because they can't breathe out.
6. Smoking wrinkles the skin.
7. To live with a smoker is to run the risk of contracting lung cancer.
8. One effective way to reduce the risk of getting cancer is to switch from smoking cigarettes to chewing tobacco or snuff.

(Answers on page 393)

■ **Reminder:** Knowing how to study can increase your knowledge, improve your grades, *and* cut down on your study time. See the *Studying Health* section at the front of your text for some suggestions to help you study this chapter.

NOT ENOUGH TIME?*

You could easily spend four or five days teaching this chapter if students read the entire chapter, do a fair number of the suggested activities in the teacher's edition, and complete a sampling of the handouts from the resource material accompanying this text. It is likely, however, that you will have only one or two days to devote to this chapter. Following are some suggestions to help you make sure that you cover the key topics if you have limited time.

TIME	SUGGESTIONS
1 Day	Assign students to read the chapter prior to class. Ask students to answer the Section II Review questions on page 384 and the Section III questions on page 386. Next, assign the Section IV Review questions on page 387. After students have completed the section review questions, go over their answers aloud. If reteaching activities are needed, choose some of the activities that are provided, such as Activities 2.7, 3.3, and 4.4.
2 Days	On day 2, assign students to answer the Sections I and V Review questions. Activities 1.3 and 5.6 will provide additional reinforcement for these sections.

*Please refer to the 18-week daily lesson plans in the supplementary material for additional suggestions.

MAKING LIFE CHOICES RESOURCES

A variety of activities, handouts, quizzes, and tests to accompany this chapter are available in the *Making Life Choices* supplementary material. You may pick and choose from those materials as appropriate for your amount of class time and the ability levels of your students. Some of the resources you might want to consider using are:

Overheads
• Normal Lung
• Normal Lung vs. Lung with Emphysema
• Carbon Monoxide

Handouts
• Smokers and Their Smoking Habits
• Smoking Facts
• Analyzing Advertisements for Tobacco
• International Smoking
• Public Health Objectives

CHAPTER PROJECT

Ask the girls in the class to imagine they are dating a guy who uses smokeless tobacco. Ask them to make a list of all of the things about smokeless tobacco use that would irritate them. They might include bad breath, spitting, yellow teeth, and the image projected by the guy to her friends and family.

Then ask the girls to state how they would react. (Break up. Try to get him to quit. If so, how? Ignore it.)

At the same time the girls are considering the above questions, have the guys imagine they are dating a girl who smokes. List the negative aspects and how they would react. Do the majority say they would tolerate it, try to change the girl, or stop dating her?

In this section students will learn that the following are causes of people using tobacco despite knowing there are problems associated with its use on a regular basis:

1. Advertising strategies aimed at a young impressionable public.

2. Physical addiction to nicotine.

3. Using tobacco to avoid nicotine withdrawal.

4. Psychological dependence on the smoking habit and the mannerisms that accompany it.

Activity 1.1

Personal Habits. Ask students to tell about a habit they have, such as biting their nails. Then ask the students to

explain why they continue their habits, even though they may not be desirable. Explain to students that smoking is similar to these habits, only worse because of the addictive drug nicotine. **(5–10 min.)**

TEACH
SECTION I
(Guided and Independent Practice)

Activity 1.2

Impact Essays. Ask students to

" Thoughts on Health "

For thy sake, tobacco I would do anything but die.

– Charles Lamb, A Farewell to Tobacco

Teacher Support Notes

① **Health Hazards of Tobacco:** Ask students if it is possible that there are still people unaware of tobacco's drawbacks. Do students know any such people? Tell students that one poll showed that 13 to 17 percent of smokers did not know that cigarette smoking is hazardous at all. A survey of more than 15,000 high school seniors revealed that nearly 1/3 did not perceive any great risk associated with smoking and nearly half of all teenagers are unaware that nicotine is an addictive drug.

② **Nicotine:** As enrichment, give students some more information about nicotine. When pure, it is a colorless, oily fluid with little odor but a sharp burning taste. Nicotine is one of the most toxic and addicting of all poisons. It acts as swiftly as cyanide. The fatal dose for an adult is estimated to be less than 5 milligrams per kilogram of body weight.

372   UNIT 4   Drug Use and Abuse

Without a doubt, tobacco offers something people seek. Otherwise they wouldn't use it, because, as nearly everyone knows, many health hazards accompany tobacco use. This chapter begins with the question of why people use tobacco. It then goes on to look at the health effects of smoking and smokeless tobacco. The last section tells how to quit using tobacco and how to help the quitter. It tries to present all the facts—both for and against—with honesty. The health evidence, though, is one-sided—against. ①

SECTION I

Why People Use Tobacco

The tobacco industry uses highly effective advertisements. Ads suggest that tobacco users are handsome, macho cowboys; suc-

cessful executives; or athletic, dynamic-looking women. These images are not realistic, but people don't always see through them.

Cigarette company ads deliver double messages. They are required to say in print that smoking harms health, but then they show healthy people smoking. They also falsely link smoking with healthy activities. This confuses people—especially children—about the unhealthy effects of tobacco use. Young people, searching for role models, imitate the images they see in tobacco ads and take up smoking or chewing tobacco. Then they show off their new behavior, enticing their peers into the same habits.

A person whose mind is open to using tobacco begins by trying it once. That one time may be followed by another. In a short while, the person becomes a regular user, because tobacco's active ingredient, **nicotine**, is a powerfully addictive drug. Tobacco companies know that once they've got people started, they've got them hooked. Thus they aim their ads at the young. They must attract children and young teenagers in order to re- ②

To make smoking or chewing tobacco, tobacco leaves are cured in barns full of smoke.

choose the statistic, from the following list, provided by the American Cancer Society, that has the most impact on them. Assign them to write about their choice in an essay explaining why they chose the one they did.
— Smoking is the #1 preventable cause of death in the nation.
— Every 13 seconds, someone dies from a tobacco-related illness.
— Cigarette smoking is responsible for one out of every five American deaths.
— More people die from tobacco-related illnesses than from alcohol, traffic accidents, illicit drugs, murder, and suicide.
— 85 percent of teenagers who smoke two or more cigarettes, and overcome the initial discomfort, will become addicted smokers.
— Nicotine is a deadly poison, which if taken in high doses can kill.
(15 min., Interdisciplinary)

EVALUATE
SECTION 1

Activity 1.3
Pop Quiz
1. List as many reasons that people smoke as you can.
2. Describe as many of nicotine's effects on the body as you can. Be sure to mention body systems, hormones, and mental

(continued on next page)

---

place the more than 2 million adult smokers who die each year worldwide from lung cancer and other smoking-related diseases.

Statistics on smoking are disturbing. Each day, 5,000 children light up for the first time—some of them only seven or eight years old, in a hurry to grow up. About one in five high school seniors smokes regularly. More than 3,000 teenagers become regular smokers each day. If the current rate of tobacco use by young people continues, the surgeon general warns that 5 million of today's children will die of smoking-related illnesses in their later years.

A folder written by young people for young people describes how smokers try to explain their choice to smoke:

- I'm young now. I can quit later.
- I don't inhale. Smoking can't hurt me.
- Smoking makes me look grown-up.
- I smoke filter cigarettes. Filters protect me.
- My parents (friends) smoke. Why shouldn't I?
- If I don't spend the money on cigarettes, I'll spend it on something else.
- It keeps me from biting my nails, putting on weight, or being mad or bored or hurt or unhappy.

All of these reasons are unrealistic. However, the new smoker believes them.

The first use of tobacco is, to most people, a sickening experience. Chewing tobacco in the mouth tastes unpleasant. The body reacts to inhaled smoke as to any smoke—by coughing to expel the irritating substance.

If this were all there were to it, no one would get hooked. Why, then, do people keep on using tobacco? Users keep coming back for more, mainly for the drug nicotine, to which they have become addicted. The addiction is so strong that when users suddenly can't get their form of tobacco, they helplessly switch to other forms— from cigarettes to a pipe, pipe to chewing, chewing to smoking.

An editorial in a journal about tobacco use made the addiction point clearly:

"How can I tell you how serious smoking is? Look: the 350,000 premature deaths *per year* caused by cigarette smoking exceed all other drug and alcohol abuse deaths combined, seven times more than all automobile deaths per year . . . and more than the combined American military deaths in World War I, World War II, and Vietnam. More than 60 percent of these yearly deaths represent persons who became addicted to nicotine as adolescents, before the age of legal consent."

Nicotine has many effects on the body. It affects the body's major organ systems: the nervous and hormonal systems, the circulatory system, and the digestive system. It triggers the release of stress hormones, so it speeds up the heart rate and raises the blood pressure. It changes the brainwave pattern. It calms the nerves, but some people may feel stimulated. It reduces anxiety, reduces feelings of pain, helps the person concentrate, dulls the taste buds, and reduces hunger. Nicotine acts on many different brain centers, so different people respond differently to it. As a result, the reasons why people use tobacco (other than addiction) differ.

The user of tobacco notices the pleasant effects of nicotine immediately. Even more noticeable, however, are the unpleasant effects of withdrawal as the dose wears off.

MINI GLOSSARY

nicotine (NICK-oh-teen): an addictive drug present in tobacco.

Teacher Support Notes

① **Tobacco Quote:**
This quote was chosen because of the strong impression it should make on high school students. Some might question the accuracy of the numbers involved since some sources put the total military deaths in the three wars mentioned at approximately 390,000 (54,000; 292,000; 47,000 respectively). The authors chose to retain the quote, however, because of its impact and because the 350,000 number appears to be conservative. In 1989 the Surgeon General's report put the number of premature deaths caused by smoking at 390,000 and in *PRIORITIES*, Dr. Elizabeth Whelan estimated the number of Americans dying prematurely each year due to smoking at 485,000.

EVALUATE
(Continued)

effects. **(15 min.)**

CLOSE
SECTION I

Activity 1.4
My Plan As Surgeon General. To show mastery of the information in the first section, students are to develop a plan for the following assignment. "The President just named you as the new Surgeon General. Your first assignment is to significantly lower the number of teenagers starting to smoke in America. What reasons that cause people to smoke do you attack first, and how?" After giving students time to draw up their plans, ask students to present short oral summaries of their plans to the class. **(1 hr.; Extend, Enrich)**

FOCUS
SECTION II

In this section students will learn:
1. How smoking damages the human body.
2. How smoke affects the lungs, heart, and circulatory system.

✍ Fast Facts

In the United States, 1.4 billion cigarettes are smoked each day.

Teacher Support Notes

① **Handout—Smoker's Survey:** You may want to distribute to students the handout in your supplementary material entitled "Smokers and Their Smoking Habits." This handout contains 17 questions that the students can use in interviewing smokers about their smoking habits.

Section I Review

Answers

1. Answers will vary.
2. Answers will vary; could include: I'm young now; I don't inhale, smoking can't hurt me; smoking makes me look grown-up; I smoke filter cigarettes; my parents smoke; if I don't spend the money on cigarettes, I'll spend it on something else; all my friends smoke; it keeps me from biting my nails; it keeps me from putting on weight; or being mad, bored, hurt or unhappy.
3. more than 2 million
4. 350,000
5. the nervous and hormonal systems, the circulatory system, and the digestive system
6. Answers will vary.

374

The tobacco companies know that once they've got you started, they've got you hooked.

Withdrawal is signaled by a slowed heart rate, lowered blood pressure, nausea, headache, irritability, restlessness, anxiety, drowsiness, inability to concentrate, and a craving for another dose.

Many users take the next dose of nicotine in order to avoid the letdown from the last one—a pattern that points to addiction. The addiction becomes so strong that they cannot quit even if they know that their health is suffering in the ways described in the next section.

Physical addiction is not the only reason people continue to use tobacco, although it is the most important reason. Psychological dependence also plays a role, because nicotine both brings pleasure and reduces pain. People enjoy the behavior itself. It provides an excuse, in a busy routine, to take a break and relax. Important, too, is that it provides an escape from small stresses. A person who is embarrassed and doesn't know what to say can light up a cigarette. A person who is angry and needs to cool off before speaking can pack a pipe. For

these and many other reasons, people use tobacco, but they pay a tremendous price.

Key Points *People begin using tobacco for a variety of reasons: influence of advertisements, peer pressure, or boredom. All people continue to use tobacco because they become addicted to the drug nicotine. Withdrawal from nicotine causes unpleasant symptoms.*

SECTION I   REVIEW

Answer the following questions on a sheet of paper.
Learning the Vocabulary
The vocabulary term in this section is *nicotine*.
1. Write a sentence using the vocabulary term.

Learning the Facts
2. List five statements that describe how smokers try to explain their choice to smoke.
3. How many adults die each year from smoking-related diseases?
4. How many premature deaths are caused each year by smoking?
5. Identify the major systems of the body that are affected by nicotine.

Making Life Choices
6. Make a list of the immediate effects nicotine has on the body. How might these affect health?

SECTION II

Health Effects of Smoking

Anything being burned releases many chemicals not present in the original raw material. The damage people cause themselves by smoking is primarily from the *burning* ingredients of cigarettes. More than 4,000 hazardous compounds make their way into the lungs of smokers and into the air that everyone breathes.

3. Why smoking is the single greatest cause of preventable death in America today.

Activity 2.1

Effects on Appearance. Ask students to describe the physical appearance of people they know who have smoked for years. How many negative effects can they name? Students should start to list how smoking affects a person's appearance after years of exposure to the 4,000 different chemicals that make up cigarette smoke. **(5 min.)**

Activity 2.2

Personal Experiences. Ask students if they have any relatives or friends who have died or been sick from smoking-related problems. Have them describe how the illness affected the individual, and how long the person had been smoking. **(10 min.)**

TEACH
SECTION II
(Guided and Independent Practice)

Activity 2.3

Experiment on Effects. To demonstrate the effects of smoking, obtain the following equipment: one gallon jar, two-hole stopper, cigarettes, two delivery

(continued on next page)

TEEN ① VIEWS

Why do so many teens think smoking is cool?

For a lot of people smoking simply starts out as a small rebellion. They start smoking to prove that they, not their parents, are in control. The big problem is that the more and more addicted the smoker becomes, the less and less control they have. Although I smoke myself, I think it's wrong and admire anyone who can successfully beat the habit. **Erika Karlsson, 17, Orange Park High School, FL**

I'm from Germany, and over there, smoking is very popular. It's not allowed, but everyone is doing it. If you talk to 100 people, 30 will say that they don't like to smoke, but they're doing it because it's "cool"! 50 will say that they are doing it because if they don't do it, everybody will laugh at them. 10 might say they smoke because it is the only way they can relax and it tastes good. Finally, 10 might say that they feel like adults if they smoke. I can live a cool and healthy life without smoking. **Ralf Buyna, 15, Wilson High School, CA**

Many teenagers I am associated with smoke because they think that it is cool. They smoke just to have something to do. Everybody is curious about smoking; almost everybody is going to try it sometime in their life. Everybody says that peer pressure makes people do it, but nowadays, nobody could care less whether you smoke or not. Nobody can make you do anything that you do not wish yourself to do. **Kristina Mayberry, 14, Orange Park High School, FL**

Teenagers assume the people that are big, bad, and popular are cool. These people that they look up to usually smoke. They watch M.T.V. and see their favorite band smoking cigarettes. What teenagers forget when they see their peers smoking is that it can kill you. **David E. Proudfoot, 14, South Carroll High School, MD**

I don't think teens actually think smoking is "cool." Most of my friends started because of the curiosity, not the image. Those people with low self-esteem think that if they see other people doing it that they will fit in too. I believe that teenagers know the risks involved and don't do it to be "cool." **Mackenzie O'Connor, 15, Westside High School, NE**

Kids don't smoke because they think it's "cool." They do it because they tried it once and got hooked. Smoking is a waste of money, time, and energy. I choose not to smoke or do drugs because I want to live to be healthy. I have better things to do than waste all my money on something that can end up killing me. **Brenda Weiler, 15, Fargo South High School, ND**

They feel like everybody is doing it. Teens also have parents who smoke and it gives them easier access to cigarettes. Many teens smoke just to get the attention of others, often the opposite sex. They think smoking makes them look good and they don't care how it affects their health. **Michael Madriaga, 15, Farrington High School, HI**

Teacher Support Notes

① **Teen Views Follow-up Questions:** Following are some questions you may want to use to encourage discussion of the ideas expressed by the students in the Teen Views feature:

a. Do the students agree with Erika Karlsson that many people begin smoking as a rebellion against their parents?

b. Ask students if they are influenced by famous athletes, musicians, and other well-known personalities. Would seeing a member of their favorite band smoking cigarettes increase the chances they might try smoking?

c. Is curiosity more of a factor than peer pressure in causing people to try smoking?

d. Do students believe that they can become "hooked" by smoking just one cigarette? If not, how many does it take?

e. Do students believe that smoking increases a person's sex appeal? Why or why not?

tubes (glass), cigarette holder, vacuum pump. (Your supplementary material contains a diagram that explains how to set up this demonstration.)

Fill the gallon jar half full of water. Place an unfiltered cigarette in the holder (attached to the jar with a glass bend) and

light it. Using the vacuum pump (attached to the jar with the other glass tube) draw smoke from the cigarette into the gallon jar and watch the water as the smoke enters. Continue pumping until the cigarette is completely burned. Examine the color of the water and allow students to smell it.

Repeat the experiment with a filtered cigarette and note there is little difference. Smoking machines may be obtained from

the Cancer Society or purchased from health education supply companies.

Activity 2.4
Guest Speaker. Invite a doctor or nurse to speak to the class about the effects of smoking that he or she treats daily. Ask them to focus the message on the irreversible damage and the end result caused by this bad habit. Also, ask them to speak on how smoking will affect

Teacher Support Notes

① **Carcinogen:** Make sure students know this word, which may look and sound difficult to them, but simply means "something that causes cancer."

② **Overhead—Normal Lung:** Your supplementary material contains an overhead of the normal lung, which you may want to use during this lesson.

🖎 Fast Facts

In a University of Arizona study it was found that children from lower-income families had 2-1/2 times the chance of contracting asthma as children from middle-class families. Researchers attributed the difference to second-hand smoke from mothers in the lower-income families who smoked more than the mothers in the middle-class families.

The most harmful of these are the **tars**, which are similar to the tars used on roads. These are well-known **carcinogens**, known to cause most cases of lung cancer and many cancers of other organs. Smokers who puff 20 to 60 cigarettes per day collect anywhere from one-fourth to one and one-half pounds of the sticky black tar in their lungs each year. Tars are also the principal cause of **emphysema**, another major disease of the lungs.

Many other ingredients in cigarettes also harm smokers. Cigarette makers select from over a thousand additives to enhance their products—flavoring agents, moistening agents, agents to prevent cigarettes from going out once lighted, and others. Among the flavoring agents are cocoa, licorice, prune juice, and raisin juice. You might think these would be harmless. However, both cocoa and licorice, when burned, form carcinogens.

When people smoke, they inhale many harmful compounds. Naturally, the organ most affected by smoke is the lungs.

Key Points ① *More than 4,000 hazardous compounds make their way into the lungs of smokers and into the air that everyone breathes. Tars in cigarettes are the most harmful compounds.*

The Lungs

② A detailed diagram of the lungs appeared in Chapter 6. Figure 15–1 serves as a reminder of the lung structures of concern here. The lungs receive blood pumped from the heart and add oxygen to it. Then the blood, with its oxygen cargo, returns to the heart to be pumped to all the body's cells. Every cell has to breathe. The lungs provide oxygen to the cells so they can stay alive.

The lungs are huge, compared with the heart. They are rich with blood vessels, and they fill the chest. Twelve to fourteen times a minute they draw in air deeply and, like a sponge, soak up oxygen and squeeze out carbon dioxide.

Healthy **bronchi**, the major breathing tubes leading to each lung, are coated

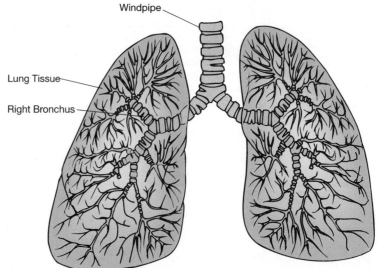

Windpipe

Lung Tissue

Right Bronchus

Figure 15–1 The Lungs. The windpipe branches to form the right and left bronchi. These branch again and again, finally ending in tiny passageways that conduct air into the air sacs (shown in Figure 15–2).

with slippery **mucus** and little waving hairs (**cilia**). The mucus catches dirt and bacteria that would otherwise lodge in the lungs. The cilia sweep the mucus in a constant stream, up to the windpipe (also lined with cilia) and then all the way up to the throat. When you clear your throat and swallow or spit, you remove a bit of this mucus with its burden of debris from your air passages.

Smoking damages the lung tissue in many ways. The tars in cigarette smoke make the coat of mucus abnormally thick. They also slow the action of the cilia in sweeping out the mucus. Irritation builds, making the smoker feel like coughing. But each puff on a cigarette paralyzes the cilia and numbs the throat for a while, so the smoker experiences *relief* from irritation. As a result, the need to cough feels like a need to smoke, and the smoking, which harms, also soothes.

Some people who smoke ultimately get one or more chronic diseases of the lungs, such as **bronchitis** or emphysema. Bronchitis is familiar to most people as an infection of the bronchi, which become clogged with heavy mucus. The resulting irritation causes deep, harsh coughing and wheezing. Bronchitis develops in almost all cigarette smokers after about ten years.

Emphysema takes longer to develop than bronchitis, and its effects are more life-threatening. Emphysema does not strike only smokers. Some people who live in smoggy cities or who are exposed to polluted air for other reasons (for example, coal miners or workers in smoky factories) may get it, too. A few people will develop emphysema whether they smoke or not. Most, however, get emphysema from smoking.

Figure 15–2 shows normal lung tissue and lung tissue damaged by emphysema. As you can see by comparing the two, the normal tissue has many tiny, bubblelike air

sacs. A tiny air tube leads to each little sac. As the lung expands, the sac expands and draws air in through the tube. As the lung deflates, the sac gets smaller and squeezes air back out.

In emphysema, the fine dividing walls between the tiny air sacs break and the sacs balloon out to become large pockets of air with hard, inflexible walls. (This is much like what happens when 50 tiny soap bubbles merge to form one big bubble.) As the lung expands, the pockets still draw air in. As the lung deflates, however, the stiffened tissue around the airways blocks air from escaping. The air trapped in the lungs bursts and tears lung tissue, making the pockets larger and worsening the condi-

M ini G lossary

tars: chemicals present in (among other things) tobacco. Burning tars release many carcinogens.

carcinogens: (car-SIN-oh-gens): cancer-causing agents.

bronchi (BRONK-eye): the two main airways in the lungs; branches of the windpipe (trachea). The singular form is *bronchus*.

mucus (MYOO-cuss): a slippery secretion produced by cells of the body's linings that protects the surfaces of the linings.

cilia: hairlike structures extending from the surface of cells that line body passageways, including the trachea and upper lungs. The cilia wave, propelling a coating of mucus along to sweep away debris.

bronchitis (bron-KITE-us): a respiratory disorder with irritation of the bronchi; thickened mucus; and deep, harsh coughing.

emphysema (em-fih-ZEE-muh): a disease of the lungs in which many small, flexible air sacs burst and form a few large, rigid air pockets.

dents vote on the best two or three videos, to be shared with some local elementary and junior high schools. (**Cooperative Learning**)

Activity 2.7
Effect Cards. Give each student an index card. Students are to print one negative effect of tobacco use on the card. Half the class should be instructed to write "diseases and health effects" and the other half to write "negative effects on appearance, image, etc." (aesthetic effects) Then, on an outline drawing of the body, which you have prepared on the board, students should tape their cards near the area of the body affected. For example:

Physical: Throat cancer, lung cancer, bladder cancer, kidney cancer, emphysema, heart disease, cold hands and feet, birth defects, leukoplakia, decrease in taste and smell, ulcers.

Aesthetic: Stained fingers, bad breath, smelly hair, smelly clothing, red eyes, burned clothing, yellow teeth, wrinkled skin, hoarse voice.

Discuss which group of effects would be more likely to persuade students not to

Teacher Support Notes

① **Breathing Difficulty:** Students could try the following activity to get an idea of what it's like to try to breathe with emphysema. Have them run up a long flight of stairs and then clap a wet towel over their noses and mouths. They will be out of breath, their chests will be heaving, but they will not be able to get enough air.

📖 Fast Facts

Children of smokers are hospitalized for bronchitis and pneumonia at twice the rate of children of nonsmokers.

378

378 UNIT 4 Drug Use and Abuse

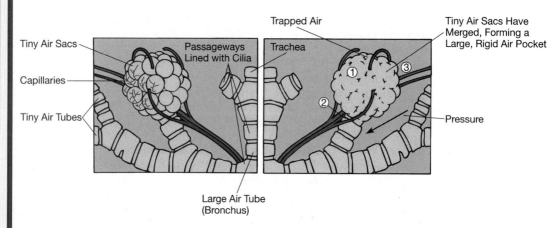

In a normal lung, tiny sacs at the ends of the air passageways permit release of the body's carbon dioxide into the air and recharging of the blood with oxygen from the air.

In emphysema, air sacs have burst to form a single, rigid, balloonlike pocket (1). The tiny air tube leading to this portion of lung tissue opens to bring in air, but then closes under pressure from the surrounding tissue so that the air is trapped (2). The capillaries are breaking down (3).

Figure 15–2 Normal Lung versus Lung with Emphysema

tion. Lung damage occurs not because people can't breathe in but because they can't breathe out.

Emphysema makes it hard to breathe, and each breath delivers less oxygen to the person panting for it. The person with emphysema breathes fast—30 times a minute at rest, compared with the normal adult's 20 times. But the person with emphysema never gets to take a deep breath. Emphysema is a crippling, depressing, ever-worsening condition. It ruins the quality of life, and finally it kills. Death is from slow suffocation—or from heart failure. The heart muscle itself cannot get the oxygen it needs at the same time it is asked to pump harder to provide oxygen to the other tissues.

Bronchitis, emphysema, and a few other diseases of the lungs are often termed **chronic obstructive lung disease**

(COLD), because less and less air flows in and out of the lungs. Smoking-related COLD kills an estimated 57,000 people a year in the United States. The surgeon general concludes that "the contribution of cigarette smoking to COLD deaths far outweighs all other factors."

Another disease of the lungs—cancer—is much more common in smokers than in nonsmokers. The carcinogens in cigarette smoke cause cancer not only in the lungs but also in the nose, lips, mouth, tongue, throat, and esophagus. Some of the carcinogens get into the bloodstream and travel freely, so they can cause cancer in any other organ as well. Smokers have higher rates of cancer of the bladder, pancreas, and kidney than do nonsmokers (see Figure 15–3). Lung cancer now causes more deaths in women than does breast cancer. Women are said to be the victims smoke. In many cases the list of aesthetic effects is more of a deterrent to teens than the list of physical effects because they are less likely to believe tobacco use could cost a person his or her life. **(30–35 min.; Reteach, Reinforce)**

Activity 2.8
Money Better Spent Elsewhere. Have a student who is interested in math calculate the weekly, monthly, and yearly cost of smoking for a pack-a-day smoker. Determine the amount spent over 40 years. Then make a list of items the students would buy if they had the weekly, monthly, or yearly amount of money available to them. Have the students work in groups to prepare posters with pictures of all the items one could buy in a week, month, and year with the smoker's money. **(30 min., Interdisciplinary)**

Activity 2.9
Guest Speaker. The American Cancer Society can often provide former cancer patients to speak to classes. Some have obvious physical impairments such as no larynx, as a result of surgery for cancer. Some may be willing to speak to classes about their experiences and their present attitudes about smoking. **(Extend, Enrich)**

(continued on next page)

FIGURE 15-3

The Risks of Smoking ①

Disease	Smokers Increase Their Risks of Dying By:[a]
Lung cancer	7 to 15 times
Throat cancer	5 to 13 times
Oral cancer	3 to 15 times
Esophagus cancer	4 to 5 times
Bladder cancer	2 to 3 times
Pancreatic cancer	2 times
Kidney cancer	1½ times
Heart disease	1½ to 3 times
Emphysema and other chronic airway obstructions (excluding asthma)	10 to 20 times
Peptic ulcer disease	2 times

[a]The risks of a person who smokes one pack of cigarettes or less per day are at the lower end of the spectrum. Risks of those who smoke more than a pack a day are at the higher end. Most important, *the smoker has risks of all these diseases at the same time.*

---

of an "epidemic of smoking." African-Americans suffer the highest rates of lung cancer of any group in the country. As a result of all this, cigarette smoking is the major single cause of cancer deaths in the United States.

Smoking combined with other risk factors creates a far greater hazard than smoking by itself. For example, the risk of developing many types of cancer increases sharply for people who smoke and drink alcohol. For another example, exposure to the insulating material asbestos, combined with smoking, adds up to a deadly hazard.

Smokers know that they are risking lung cancer, but many are sure it won't happen to them. Others believe that if they contract it, x-ray tests can catch it in time to save their lives. Unfortunately, by the time a cancerous spot in the lung is only a millimeter across—just large enough to be seen on an X-ray—it may already be too late to cure it.

Key Points *Smoking cigarettes is linked with health hazards such as bronchitis, emphysema, COLD, cancer of the lungs, and other cancers. Drinking alcohol greatly increases the smoker's cancer risk.*

The Heart and Circulatory System

Smoking is as damaging to the heart and circulatory system as it is to the lungs.

M**INI** G**LOSSARY**

chronic obstructive lung disease (COLD): a term for several diseases that interfere with breathing. Asthma, bronchitis, and emphysema are examples of COLD.

379

first antismoking ordinance. **(15 min., Interdisciplinary)**

Activity 2.10
Nonsmoking Movement Timeline. Have a small group of students trace the history of the nonsmoking rights movement in the U.S. They could create a timeline to highlight various dates such as 1987 when Waterfield, MN passed the

Activity 2.11
Advertisement Analysis. Ask students to collect printed ads for tobacco products including smokeless tobacco. These ads should then be attached to index cards and passed around the room. As students look at the ads, they should score each ad on a scale of 1 to 5 with 5

being "very appealing to adolescents" and 1 being "not appealing to adolescents." Select all ads that had an average score of four or better and discuss the techniques used in these ads that are particularly appealing to teens. Be sure to examine the pictures for subtle messages such as those implying masculinity, femininity, popularity, maturity, and other supposed benefits of smoking. **(30 min., Critical Thinking)**

Teacher Support Notes

① **Epinephrine:** These first two bulleted items—faster heart rate and increased blood pressure—are a result of the fact that nicotine stimulates epinephrine secretion. This is part of the stress response, which students learned about in Chapter Four.

② **Research on Smoking in Cardiovascular Disease:** For enrichment, you may want to tell students that researchers are still debating whether quitting smoking does in fact reduce the risk of cardiovascular disease for people who have smoked. The original study that indicated a reduced risk for smokers was done by Gary D. Friedman, M.D. and others of the Permanente Medical Group. Subsequent researchers have criticized their findings, stating the design of their study was flawed. It may be that quitters are simply a different type of people to start with and that they already have a lower risk. More research is needed before a firm conclusion can be drawn.

📖 Fast Facts
More than 50,000,000 Americans smoke cigarettes.

380

A health professional can easily tell a nonsmoker from a smoker, based on the performance of the lungs and heart.

It causes about one-fifth of all deaths from heart disease and stroke. Smoking burdens the heart in five ways at the same time:

- Nicotine speeds up the heart rate. This increases the heart's work load, so the smoker's heart requires extra oxygen.
- Nicotine also raises the blood pressure. The heart has to push blood around the body against this pressure. This, too, increases the heart's work load and the need for oxygen.   ①
- Smoking reduces the amount of oxygen the blood can carry. When the smoker inhales, the blood gets a dose of **carbon monoxide** from the smoke. The carbon monoxide takes the place of oxygen in the red blood cells. This reduces the red blood cells' ability to transport oxygen. As a result, the heart muscle receives less oxygen than it needs.   ②
- Nicotine also triggers the formation of

blood clots. When clots lodge in arteries that feed the heart muscle, they kill parts of that muscle—heart attacks. When they lodge in arteries that feed the brain, they kill parts of the brain—strokes.
- Smoking drastically reduces the blood flow in the heart's own arteries, another cause of heart attack.

To sum up, two major ingredients of cigarettes—tars and nicotine—damage the body's two major life-support systems. Tars reduce the lungs' ability to *supply* oxygen. Nicotine increases the heart's *need* for oxygen.

Key Points ▶ *Smoking burdens the heart and circulatory system in several ways. Smoking reduces the body's supply of oxygen, but increases the heart's need for it. Smoking is strongly linked with heart disease.*

Activity 2.12

Writing Warnings. Assign students to write their own Surgeon General's warnings to be put on cigarettes and smokeless tobacco products. Remind students that some young people start to smoke as early as seven or eight. Their messages should be aimed at kids age 12 or younger. Writing their own warnings should help students gain insight and a better understanding of the dangers associated with using tobacco products. **(10–15 min.; Extend, Enrich)**

Activity 2.13

Creating Antismoking Ads. In this activity, groups of three or four students will be asked to design ads to convince people **not** to smoke. They might highlight some of the diseases associated with smoking or some of the unflattering aspects of smoking such as yellow teeth, bad breath, smelly hair, stained fingers, or burned clothing. They should select ad techniques similar to those used by tobacco companies such as "join the crowd," "look mature," etc. Some of the ads produced might be displayed around the school to promote a smoke-free environment. **(30 min., Cooperative Learning)**

(continued on next page)

Other Effects of Smoking

Smoking damages other organs besides the lungs and the heart. In fact, it harms every organ. Smoking:

- Shuts down circulation in the small vessels, causing cold hands and feet. In some cases, this results in a disease that requires surgical removal of limbs.
- Causes wrinkling of the skin, especially of the face. (Smokers in their 40s may look as if they are in their 60s.)
- Increases risks of **ulcers** (and makes dying from ulcers more likely).
- Increases tolerance to drugs, making larger doses needed for illness and pain (and can make vaccinations ineffective).
- Greatly increases risks of heart attack and stroke in women who take oral contraceptives (see Figure 15–4).
- In pregnant women, limits the oxygen supply to the fetus (resulting in smaller babies, premature births, miscarriages, a doubled risk of birth defects, impaired development in children up to age 11, and early death of infants).
- Causes women to become infertile; causes early menopause and increased bone loss.
- Reduces oxygen supply to the brain, impairing memory.
- Thickens mucus, increasing the risk of chronic and painful infection of the **sinuses** (this can spread to the brain and spinal cord—a life-threatening condition).
- Interferes with the immune response, making colds, flu, and other infections likely.
- Prevents normal sleep (quitters sleep better within three nights of quitting).
- Exposes the chest to radiation (smoking one and a half packs of cigarettes a day for one year is equal in radiation to having 300 chest X rays).

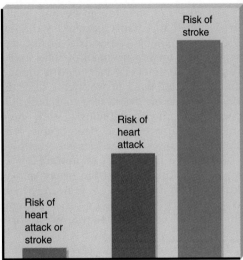

Figure 15–4 Smoking and Oral Contraceptives. A woman who smokes and takes birth control pills is 10 times as likely to suffer a heart attack and 20 times as likely to have a stroke as a woman who does neither.

- Makes it likely that men will produce abnormal sperm (this can result in birth defects).
- Causes hearing loss (this worsens over time).
- Encourages gum disease.
- Is associated with an increased risk of leukemia (cancer of the blood-producing organs).

① — Mɪɴɪ Gʟᴏssᴀʀʏ —

carbon monoxide: a deadly gas; a gas formed during the burning of tobacco.
ulcers: open sores in the lining of the digestive system.
sinuses (SIGN-us-es): spaces in the bones of the skull.

Teacher Support Notes

① **Smoking and Influenza:** Researchers have made a connection between smoking and the flu (influenza). One report showed that during an outbreak of flu in a medical unit in Israel, young men who smoked contracted the disease more frequently than did nonsmokers. About half the nonsmokers contracted flu while a little more than 2/3 of the smokers contracted it. The smokers also tended to get sicker. Some of them required more bed rest or were absent from work for a longer time. As a result of these observations, researchers predicted that nearly 20 percent of all the influenza and over 25 percent of all the severe influenza in this instance could have been avoided had the people not smoked.

Activity 2.14

Learning to Say No. Many adolescents have minimal refusal skills. To help students refuse tobacco, have them role-play the following situations. They should try to develop a refusal for smoking in each scene. Have the class help the non-smoker by suggesting lines he/she might say to refuse smoking.

A. Three male teens are riding in a car. The driver, who is older, lights up a cigarette and offers one to the student on the passenger side who reluctantly accepts. The student in the back seat does not want to smoke but the boys in the front pressure him to "be a man and light up."

B. A group of girls are in a school washroom. Two girls are smoking and a third enters. When they offer her a cigarette, she shakes her head no and they all begin to laugh and tease her. **(45 min.; Extend, Enrich)**

EVALUATE
▶ **S**ECTION II

Activity 2.15
Pop Quiz
How can smoking affect:

Teacher Support Notes

① **Handout—Smoking Facts:** In your supplementary material you will find a handout entitled "Smoking Facts" that gives students seven short, hard-hitting facts about the dangers of smoking.

② **How Smoking Shortens Life:** Here are more statistics on how smoking shortens life. In one study of 100,000 insurance policy holders, smokers' death rates were doubled at every age for all people. Based on this study, a healthy, nonsmoking 32-year-old man can expect to live to almost 79 years of age, but a man of 32 who smokes to less than 72 years. Some have argued that people who smoke are more prone to take risks and that their riskier lifestyle is what kills them rather than their smoking habit. In this study, however, after the deaths by accidents and violence were discarded, the gap in mortality rates between smokers and nonsmokers widens from 2.5 to 1 to 2.8 to 1.

✏ Fast Facts

Americans spend approximately $42 billion a year for tobacco products.

---

382   UNIT 4 Drug Use and Abuse

The effects of smoking go beyond health to personal appearance. Besides wrinkling the skin, smoking causes bad breath and yellows the teeth. The smell of stale smoke clings to the smoker's hair, clothes, home, and car. Therefore, people who find the smell unpleasant want to avoid both the person and the surroundings. Many non-smokers refuse even to date people who smoke.

Then there is the cost. At upwards of $2 a pack, smoking can cost the heavy smoker from $1,000 to $2,000 a year. A person who collected that amount in a personal fund instead could visit Hawaii every three years.

Finally, there is the danger of fire. Fires started by dropped cigarettes cause some 2,000 deaths and 4,000 injuries a year. Altogether, smoking is the single greatest cause of preventable death in the United States today. ①

Low-tar, low-nicotine cigarettes are no better than the regular kind just described. Smokers who switch to them often smoke more cigarettes, smoke to a shorter butt, puff more often, or inhale more deeply. Such smokers face the same risks as smokers of regular cigarettes.

Pipe smoking also carries high risks. Pipe smokers who do not inhale tend to have lower rates of lung and heart diseases than do cigarette smokers. However, they are likely to develop cancer of the lips and tongue. Pipe smoke is higher in tar than cigarette smoke, so those who inhale may face a higher risk of lung cancer than they would from cigarettes.

Quitting smoking is clearly the best way to avoid the ills caused by tobacco use. The sooner, the better, too. The risks of heart attacks in both men and women fall rapidly to the range of nonsmokers' risks within a few years. The risk of dying from lung cancer falls steadily in people who quit smoking. Ten years after quitting, the risk is

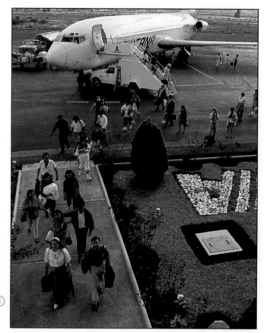

You can save enough money quitting smoking to vacation in Hawaii.

② about half of that for smokers. In short, people who quit smoking live longer than those who continue to smoke.

Still, reducing the number or the strength of the cigarettes smoked is better than doing nothing. The less a person smokes, the smaller the risks. Every cigarette counts.

It must be clear by now what a high price people pay for smoking. Still, the tobacco companies intentionally promote their products to young people, as described in the Consumer Awareness section, "Teen Idols Used to Sell Cigarettes."

▶ **Key Points**   *Smoking harms every organ of the body. It is the single greatest cause of preventable death in the United States today. Pregnant women's smoking harms fetuses and endangers the lives of newborns. Smoking damages appearance and attractiveness, and is expensive.*

1. Lungs? (makes mucus abnormally thick, slows action of cilia)
2. Heart and circulatory system? (Nicotine speeds up heart rate, raises blood pressure, and triggers formation of blood clots; smoking reduces the amount of oxygen the blood can carry and reduces the blood flow in the heart's own arteries.)
3. Physical appearance? (causes wrinkles, yellow teeth, bad breath)
4. An unborn fetus? (can cause smaller

and premature babies, miscarriages, birth defects, impaired development in children, and early death of infants)
(20 min.; Reteach, Reinforce)

CLOSE
SECTION II

Activity 2.16
Pictures of a Smoker. Have students draw a picture of a smoker. They

are to show and label as many affected body parts as they can. This will show comprehension of the material learned in Section II. **(20 min.; Reteach; Reinforce)**

CONSUMER AWARENESS

Teen Idols Used to Sell Cigarettes ①

A feature photograph of teen idols Jason Priestly and Luke Perry (stars of the television show *Beverly Hills 90210*) appeared recently in a major magazine. In the photo Priestly is shown holding a cigarette in his hand and dangling a carefully posed pack of cigarettes from the pocket of his jeans—readers can easily recognize the brand. A watchdog group has published a complaint about an "intentional promotional placement by Philip Morris" (a cigarette company).* The complaint centers on the promotion of cigarettes to teens.

The problem is that companies often sneak paid commercials into movies and magazines that interest teens today. They do this in ways that unsuspecting people don't recognize. For example, many movies ② display brand names on products in ways that viewers are sure to notice. The companies that make the products pay the movie producers huge sums to display them. The companies target their audiences carefully. Teenagers are often targets of such promotions, and while some products such as soft drinks or sports equipment are not harmful, others such as alcohol and cigarettes are dangerous.

In the photo mentioned above, Priestly and Perry are surrounded by teenaged girls wearing bathing suits. What could distort teen self-images more effectively?

The audience for "90210" is 69 percent female teenage viewers, and here they are shown admiring Priestly who is directly promoting cigarette smoking to them.

Cigarette companies are aggressively promoting their products to young people in ways like this. Disturbingly, their strategies seem to be working. Over 3000 American teenagers become regular smokers *each day*. Although the cigarette companies will say that smoking is an "adult habit" and that Priestly is in his middle twenties, the photo is obviously targeting a much younger audience by using the idols and images that appeal to teens.

CRITICAL THINKING

1. *Do you think that people who see product labels in movie scenes or magazine photos realize that they are viewing paid advertisements from manufacturing companies?*
2. *How do you think people react to the products they see used or held by stars they admire? How is this reaction different from the reaction to regular advertisements?*
3. *If you can recall seeing products advertised in this manner, describe how the product was displayed in the scene or photo and tell what effect this had on you.*

*A Cigarette Company's Blatant Pitch to Teens, *Priorities*, Summer 1992, p. 35.

Teacher Support Notes

① **Handout—Analyzing Advertisements for Tobacco:** Guidelines for analyzing tobacco ads are included in a handout in your supplementary material.
② **Answers to Critical Thinking:** Answers to these questions will vary.

❝ **Thoughts on Health** ❞

A custom loathsome to the eye, hateful to the nose, harmful to the brain, dangerous to the lungs, and in the black stinking fume thereof nearest resembling the horrible Stygian smoke of the pit that is bottomless.
– **King James I of England**

In this section students will learn about:
1. The risks involved with passive smoking.

Activity 3.1
Role-Playing. Ask two students to role-play. One is a smoker lighting up a cigarette in a car. The other is a non-smoker who does not want the car to smell like smoke. How does each justify his or her feelings to the other? Ask for volunteers to analyze the arguments. **(30 min., Critical Thinking)**

TEACH
SECTION III
(Guided and Independent Practice)
Activity 3.2
Nonsmoker's Survival Guide.

Form groups of three to four students to write an article entitled "Survivor's Guide to Living Around Smokers." Each group is to come up with ten tips for protecting health in an environment of smokers. Tips might relate to survival in smoke-filled washrooms, homes, job places, cars, etc. Combine all the tips and turn in the article to the school newspaper for possible publication. **(20 min., Cooperative Learning)**

Section II Review
Answers
1. **a.** carcinogens; **b.** bronchi **c.** tars **d.** carbon monoxide **e.** ulcers
2. See the last paragraph on page 377 for the complete answer.
3. nose, lips, mouth, tongue, lung, throat, esophagus, bladder, pancreatic, kidney
4. limits the oxygen supply to the fetus, resulting in smaller babies, premature births, miscarriages, a doubled risk of birth defects and impaired development in children up to age 11, and early death of infants
5. premature wrinkling of skin, bad breath, yellow teeth, stale smell of smoke on hair and clothing
6. Answers will vary.

✍ Fast Facts
People who cut back on the number of cigarettes they smoke should not think that they are necessarily reducing the amount of danger to their systems. When smokers puff on fewer cigarettes, they typically start inhaling more smoke from each cigarette. In one study, smokers reduced the number of cigarettes they smoked each day from 37 to 5. Their exposure to tar and nicotine declined only 50%.

384

384 UNIT 4 Drug Use and Abuse

SECTION II REVIEW

Answer the following questions on a sheet of paper.
Learning the Vocabulary
The vocabulary terms in this section are: *tars, carcinogens, emphysema, bronchi, mucus, cilia, bronchitis, chronic obstructive lung disease, carbon monoxide, ulcers,* and *sinuses.*
1. Match the following phrases with the terms:
   a. cancer-causing agents
   b. two main airways in the lungs
   c. harmful chemicals in burning tobacco
   d. gas formed during burning of tobacco
   e. open sores in the lining of the digestive system

Learning the Facts
2. Explain what happens to the lungs of a person with emphysema.
3. List the cancers that are more likely to occur in smokers than in nonsmokers.
4. In what ways can smoking affect the unborn child of a pregnant woman?
5. List the effects of smoking on personal appearance.

Making Life Choices
6. Reread this section. What ethnic group has the highest chance of developing lung cancer? Why do you think this is so? The number of women smoking is on the rise. What is the most common type of cancer in women today? Why has this change occurred in the last few years?

SECTION III

Passive Smoking

The smoke that reaches smokers is a little different from the smoke that reaches those in the room with them. The **mainstream smoke** from a cigarette is the smoke that passes through the cigarette and then enters the smoker's lungs. The **sidestream smoke** is the smoke that enters the air from the burning tip of the cigarette.

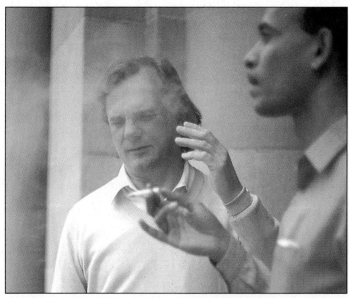

People who can't stand smoke find it hard to be around smokers.

EVALUATE
SECTION III

Activity 3.3
Essay. Have students pick one of the following questions and write a well-supported essay answer to that question without using their books.
1. What health hazards are presented by passive smoking?

2. What can you do as a nonsmoker to avoid passive smoke? **(Reteach, Reinforce)**

CLOSE
SECTION III

Activity 3.4
Letters to Future Spouses. Assign students to write a letter to a future spouse who smokes. Have them

explain why they would not marry unless the potential spouse stops smoking. Encourage students to explain how smoking causes health risks for both of you, as well as creates other undesirable effects. **(30 min.)**

Does inhaling sidestream smoke (passive smoking), cause lung cancer? Many experts now say yes. Families and co-workers of people who smoke run an increased risk of dying of lung cancer. You may choose not to smoke. However, if you live or work with a smoker, you are a smoker, too—a passive smoker.

Passive smoking raises not only cancer risks, but also the risks of heart disease. Nonsmokers who live with smokers suffer damage to their hearts. For example, passive smokers cannot exercise as well as nonsmokers, probably because smoke reduces blood flow to their hearts. Passive smoking also raises heart attack risks.

Living or working with a smoker creates other hazards, too. Passive smoking worsens allergic symptoms, **asthma**, and sinus conditions. It irritates the eyes, especially if a person is wearing contact lenses. It causes headaches, dizziness, and nausea. In babies and children, it doubles the risk of lung infections, causes permanent lung damage, and brings on asthma attacks. If a pregnant woman lives with a smoker during her pregnancy, her infant faces many of the same risks as the infant born to a smoking mother.

There is no question about it: other people's smoking is bad for nonsmokers. In fact, 53,000 deaths a year are linked to passive smoking. This makes passive smoking the third leading preventable cause of death in the United States, behind active smoking and alcohol drinking.

The harm to passive smokers comes from sidestream smoke, which contains over 40 known carcinogens, as well as other compounds. One of its gases is carbon monoxide. In a closed room with smokers, a nonsmoker may suffer from the same lack of oxygen in the blood as was described for the smoker. Figure 15–5 shows that a person exposed to a smoky room may inhale more carbon monoxide than is considered safe. (A hazard of sitting in a traffic jam, as

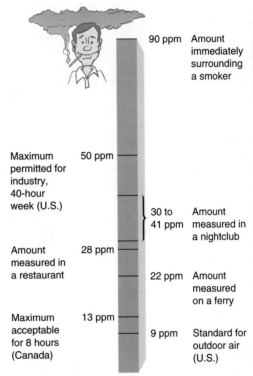

	90 ppm — Amount immediately surrounding a smoker
Maximum permitted for industry, 40-hour week (U.S.) — 50 ppm	
	30 to 41 ppm — Amount measured in a nightclub
Amount measured in a restaurant — 28 ppm	
	22 ppm — Amount measured on a ferry
Maximum acceptable for 8 hours (Canada) — 13 ppm	
	9 ppm — Standard for outdoor air (U.S.)

② **Figure 15–5** Carbon Monoxide Sources Compared. Spending one hour in a smoke-filled room presents the nonsmoker with as much carbon monoxide as smoking one cigarette would. The abbreviation *ppm* refers to parts per million—units of carbon monoxide per million units of air.

①

MINI GLOSSARY

mainstream smoke: the smoke that flows through the cigarette and into the lungs when a smoker inhales.

sidestream smoke: the smoke that escapes into the air from the burning tip of a cigarette (and may then be inhaled by the smoker or by someone else).

asthma: difficulty breathing, with wheezing sounds from the chest caused by air rushing through narrowed air passages.

Teacher Support Notes

① **Handout—International Smoking:** Your supplementary material contains a handout that will give students some examples of how people of other nations are responding to the increasing evidence regarding the harmful effects of smoking.

② **Overhead—Carbon Monoxide:** Your supplementary material contains an overhead of this illustration. Students may be a bit confused with the *ppm* abbreviation. Explain that if they had any quantity of air, a scientist examining that air could divide it up into a million parts. The numbers in the illustration represent how many of those million parts would be carbon monoxide. It's not important that they understand what all those other parts are, but rather that they compare the numbers shown in the illustration to see that "90" parts is the amount immediately surrounding a smoker. This is much higher than desired.

FOCUS
SECTION IV

In this section students will learn about the:
1. Problems associated with smokeless tobacco and nicotine addiction.
2. Double messages of advertisements, which cause many to overlook warnings.

Activity 4.1
Effects of Smokeless Tobacco.
Ask some volunteers to explain what effects smokeless tobacco had on them the first time they tried it. List these effects on the board. Explain that nicotine caused all these unpleasant feelings.

Activity 4.2
Panel Discussion. Tell students they have been asked to serve on a panel of experts that will devise a plan to discourage the use of smokeless tobacco in the general public as well as among teens. What incentives and deterrents can they think of to discourage its use? **(25 min.; Extend, Enrich)**

TEACH
SECTION IV
(Guided and Independent Practice)

Fast Facts
The risks of lung cancer are 30% higher for spouses of smokers than spouses of non-smokers.

Teacher Support Notes

① **Smoker's vs. Non-smoker's Rights:** Most students will probably support the types of restrictions that are described in this paragraph. Ask if anyone believes that these restrictions have infringed upon the smoker's rights. What case can these people make for allowing the smokers to smoke when and where they want?

Section III Review

Answers
1. Answers will vary.
2. worsens allergic conditions, irritates eyes, causes headaches, dizziness, and nausea
3. raises the risks of cancer and heart disease. In babies it doubles the risk of lung infections, causes permanent lung damage, and brings on asthma attacks.
4. 53,000
5. Answers will vary.

386

---

you probably know, is the high concentration of carbon monoxide in the air from the exhaust pipes of the jammed cars. As you also know, a person who breathes these fumes in a closed car dies within minutes.) Carbon monoxide has no smell, so you cannot tell if it is present. One sign of exposure, though, is yawning.

Many nonsmokers rightly demand that smoking not be allowed in areas they share. Thanks to the efforts of nonsmokers' rights associations, most restaurants now have nonsmoking areas, and some ban smoking altogether. Motels provide nonsmokers' rooms, and a federal law bans smoking on most airline flights. Almost every state bans smoking in public transportation, hospitals, elevators, schools, and libraries.

If you object to people's smoking near you, you can practice being assertive. Without being insulting to the smoker, simply say, "Please don't smoke. It bothers me."

> **Key Points** *Passive smoking raises the risks of cancer, heart disease, and many other hazards. Passive smoking is the third leading cause of preventable death in the United States.*

SECTION III REVIEW

Answer the following questions on a sheet of paper.
Learning the Vocabulary
The vocabulary terms in this section are: *mainstream smoke, sidestream smoke,* and *asthma.*
1. Write a sentence using each term.

Learning the Facts
2. How does passive smoking affect allergic and sinus conditions?
3. What are the health problems associated with passive smoking?
4. How many deaths a year are linked to passive smoking?

Making Life Choices
5. Reread the Consumer Awareness section on page 383. If you could, how would you have television portray the real images of

smokers? Describe the portrait of a smoker you'd put on television. Why do you suppose this hasn't been done before? What does this tell you about the media and the tobacco industry?

SECTION IV

Smokeless Tobacco

① Some people use **smokeless tobacco** products—snuff or chewing tobacco. People dip snuff by holding a pinch of moist, shredded tobacco between the gum and cheek, where it gradually releases its nicotine. Chewing tobacco is chewed, and then held in the cheek in a wad or **quid** like snuff. This stimulates the release of saliva. This saliva becomes contaminated with tobacco and must be spit out, not swallowed.

The use of smokeless tobacco by high school athletes is on the rise. Although the habit carries health risks, as many as one out of three high school athletes has tried or used smokeless tobacco. Smokeless tobacco products produce the same addiction as smoked products, because they also deliver the drug nicotine.

The tobacco industry tries to get people hooked on smokeless tobacco. A typical advertisement suggests: "Use this sparingly at first, because it will irritate the gums. After a few weeks, the irritation will lessen. Start slowly, and increase use over time, because it takes time to get used to strong products and large doses." The person who is alert to double messages will see that this one says the product is dangerous, but to go ahead and use it anyway.

Smokeless tobacco use is linked to many health problems, from minor mouth sores to cancer. Snuff dipping is linked with cancerous tumors in the nasal cavity, cheek,

EVALUATE
SECTION IV

Activity 4.3
Posters. Ask each student to make a poster illustrating the dangers of smokeless tobacco. Have them create a large warning label that should be placed on all packages and cans.

CLOSE
SECTION IV

Activity 4.4
Essays. Ask students to write an essay explaining how they would answer their ten-year-old brother who asked them to buy him some snuff. What would they tell him about the effects of smokeless tobacco?

FOCUS
SECTION V

In this section students will learn strategies for:
1. Quitting nicotine-related habits.
2. Helping someone else quit.

Activity 5.1

(continued on next page)

---

gum, and throat. Tobacco chewing holds a *greater* risk of mouth and throat cancers than does tobacco smoking. One of baseball's legends, Babe Ruth, was a heavy user of snuff and chewing tobacco. He died of throat cancer at the age of 53.

The dentist who examines a person's mouth for signs of oral cancer looks for **leukoplakia**. These are whitish or greyish patches that form in the mouths of tobacco chewers, and they tend to become cancerous. They develop where the quid is held.

Other drawbacks to tobacco chewing and snuff dipping include bad breath, brown teeth, and blunted senses of smell and taste. Tobacco chewing also damages the gums, wears away the tooth surfaces, and eats away the jawbones. This makes it likely that users will lose their teeth in later life.

> **Key Points** ▶ *Smokeless tobacco contains nicotine and so is addictive. Its use carries risks of mouth sores; cancerous tumors of the mouth, nasal cavity, cheek, gum, and throat; bad breath; and brown teeth.*

SECTION IV REVIEW

Answer the following questions on a sheet of paper.

Learning the Vocabulary
The vocabulary terms in this section are *smokeless tobacco, quid,* and *leukoplakia.*
1. Write a sentence using each term.

Learning the Facts
2. List the health problems associated with smokeless tobacco.
3. What are the dental problems that occur with the use of smokeless tobacco?

Making Life Choices
4. The tobacco industry gets young teenagers hooked on smokeless tobacco by showing professional athletes using these products. Teenagers look up to these athletes. How can you help prevent fellow teens from getting started? How can health advocates compete against professional athletes pushing smokeless tobacco?

SECTION V

The Decision to Quit

A smoker who couldn't quit asked a successful quitter how to do it. The quitter replied, "I just got my inner self and my outer self together. When they had agreed that we should quit, we did. It was easy."

Over 30 million people in the United States have quit using tobacco in the last 20 years or so. Many teenagers are deciding not to start. Of people who still smoke, nine out of ten would like to stop but say they "can't." Still, people do decide to quit. The next section is addressed to smokers, but it applies to the users of smokeless tobacco as well.

How People Quit Smoking

A newspaper columnist invited his smoking readers to explain why they continued to smoke. He expected a flood of angry letters scolding him for his strong antismoking messages. Instead, most letters read like this one:

"Don't refer to what we do as smoking—refer to it as nicotine addiction. Nobody really likes smoking all that much. It's the nicotine that we get hooked on. I am trying to quit. It is truly the most difficult thing I've ever experi-

---

MINI GLOSSARY

smokeless tobacco: tobacco used for snuff or chewing rather than for smoking.
quid: a small portion of any form of smokeless tobacco.
leukoplakia (loo-koh-PLAKE-ee-uh): whitish or greyish patches that develop in the mouths of tobacco users and that may lead to cancer.

Teacher Support Notes

Section IV Review
Answers
1. Answers will vary.
2. minor mouth sores; cancerous tumors in nasal cavity, cheek, gum, throat; a greater risk of cancer of mouth and throat
3. bad breath, brown teeth, damage to gums, wearing away of tooth surfaces, eating away jawbones
4. Answers will vary.

✏ **Fast Facts**

In 1989 the state of Oregon began requiring that death certificates note whether or not tobacco use was a contributing cause in the death. In the deaths recorded in Oregon in 1989, one in four were related to tobacco.

Reasons for Quitting. Have students help you generate two lists on the board. One list is reasons to smoke. The other list is reasons to stop smoking. This will get students to realize that there are many more reasons to stop smoking than to start or continue to smoke or use smokeless tobacco. **(10 min.)**

TEACH
SECTION V
(Guided and Independent Practice)

Activity 5.2
Habit-Free Weekend. Ask students to stop (for a weekend) a habit or addiction that they have. Some examples would be biting nails, eating candy, or chewing gum. On Monday, have students give a short oral report explaining how they did. Ask if it was as easy as they had originally thought. Explain that a chemical addiction would be tougher to give up because of the physical and psychological addiction. **(30–45 min.; Enrich, Extend)**

Activity 5.3
Product Investigations. Have students visit a store to investigate products

66 Thoughts on Health 99

Cigarettes are killers that travel in packs.
– Marie S. Ott

Teacher Support Notes

① **Withdrawal:** Ask students if they have ever been around a friend, acquaintance, or relative who has tried to quit smoking. What effects did this experience have on that person? Was the person able to endure the effort, or did he or she eventually give in and resume smoking? Has that person tried again to quit?

Fast Facts

In 1915 fewer than 20 billion cigarettes were smoked in the United States. By the late 1980s the number of cigarettes smoked had escalated to almost 600 billion a year, 30 times the 1915 rate. During that same period the U.S. population increased from about 100 million people to just over 225 million, an increase of only 2-1/4 times the 1915 population. In the early part of the century lung cancer was a rare disease.

388

388 UNIT 4 Drug Use and Abuse

enced—and I haven't had an uneventful life. If I give in to the addiction, I know I'll die with a cigarette in my hand."

In other words, people continue smoking because they are hooked. Whenever they try to quit, they face withdrawal: irritability, restlessness, anxiety, and of course, a craving for nicotine. It takes several weeks or a month of abstinence for withdrawal symptoms to fade. The Health Strategies section on this page, "Giving Up Smoking," provides some tips for the quitter. ①

Successful quitters believe they can succeed. They know they can resist the urge to smoke. With each success, they gain more confidence and resist more easily.

Smokers must remind themselves again and again of the health benefits—both immediate and long-term—of quitting. Smoking cuts life short by about 18 years. The truth is, there just are not many 85-year-old smokers. They died many years before.

One of the nice things about being able to breathe is that you can smell things.

Smokers trying to quit find it useful to find out what they like most about smoking. This chapter's Life Choice Inventory enables people to find out what about smoking is most important to them—stimulation, handling the cigarette, relaxation, or others. Then, when they try to quit, they can meet those needs in other ways. The Life Choice Inventory offers suggestions for each type of smoker.

After discovering what they enjoy most about smoking, it helps for smokers to make a list of activities that will take the place of smoking. For example, smoking may be the way some people relax. To replace this function, such people must find new ways to relax. A long, hot bath or some light stretching may help release tension (see Chapter 4 for more on relaxation, and Chapter 10 for stretching exercises). Other types of smokers should find other activities to replace smoking's functions.

There are two ways to quit—tapering off or quitting all at once (cold turkey). A way to taper off is to start smoking each day an hour later than the day before. Another is to take up a fitness activity that will squeeze out the smoking. For example, many people take up jogging and notice that smoking limits their performance. This may give them the motivation to quit smoking.

HEALTH
STRATEGIES

Giving Up Smoking

To give up smoking, smokers must:

1. Ask themselves whether they really want to quit.
2. Believe in their ability to succeed.
3. Review the health benefits of quitting smoking.
4. Expect to be challenged.
5. Plan their strategy.
6. Find new ways to relax.
7. Make a list of alternative activities.
8. Commit themselves.
9. Seek support.
10. Tune in to the immediate rewards.

that help people stop smoking. Have students write a report that includes prices, method each product uses, and how long the process will take. Ask students to look for information about success rates and money-back guarantees. Have students present a summary of all the methods found in a short oral report. This will inform students about some of the products on the market to help people fight nicotine addiction. **(45 min., Interdisciplinary)**

Activity 5.4
Creating New Products. Assign students to create their own methods or products to help people stop smoking. Have them explain how it should work, how they would market it, how much it would cost, and how they would advertise it. Ask students to present their products or methods to the class in the form of a poster or video as they would advertise them. **(1 hr.; Extend, Enrich)**

Activity 5.5
Smokeout Day Projects. Assign students to work together on a project to help promote the Great American Smokeout Day. Explain that groups could make videos, posters, fliers, bookmarks, bookcovers, buttons, or stickers. Their primary goal is to come up with an original slogan or saying promoting the day set aside for people to not smoke. Have groups pre-

(continued on next page)

LIFE CHOICE INVENTORY

Why Do You Smoke? ①

Here are some statements people make to describe what they get out of smoking cigarettes. On the scoring handout or on a piece of paper, the smoker should record the number (1, 2, 3, 4, or 5) that describes how often he or she feels this way (see below). Important: ANSWER EVERY QUESTION. (If you don't smoke, this quiz may help you understand a friend or acquaintance who does.)
5 = Always   4 = Frequently   3 = Occasionally   2 = Seldom   1 = Never

Stimulation
A. I smoke cigarettes to keep myself from slowing down.
B. I smoke cigarettes to stimulate myself, to perk myself up.
C. I smoke cigarettes to give myself a lift.

Handling
D. Handling a cigarette is part of the enjoyment of smoking.
E. Part of the enjoyment of smoking a cigarette comes from the steps I take to light up.
F. When I smoke a cigarette part of the enjoyment is watching the smoke as I exhale it.

Pleasure/Relaxation
G. Smoking cigarettes is pleasant and relaxing.
H. I find cigarettes pleasurable.
I. I want a cigarette most when I am comfortable and relaxed.

Crutch/Tension Reduction
J. I light up a cigarette when I feel angry about something.
K. When I feel upset, I light up a cigarette.
L. When I feel blue, I smoke cigarettes.

Craving/Psychological Dependence
M. When I have run out of cigarettes, I find it almost unbearable until I can get more.
N. When I'm not smoking, I am very much aware of it.
O. I crave a cigarette when I haven't smoked for a while.

Habit
P. I smoke cigarettes without being aware of it.
Q. I light up a cigarette without realizing I still have one burning in the ashtray.
R. I sometimes find a cigarette in my mouth and don't remember putting it there.

SCORING

1. On your paper add up your scores as follows:
   Stimulation score = A + B + C.
   Handling score = D + E + F.
   Pleasure/relaxation score = G + H + I.
   Crutch/tension reduction score = J + K + L.
   Craving/psychological dependence score = M + N + O.
   Habit score = P + Q + R.
   The highest scores indicate which aspects of smoking will be hardest for you to give up.

2. Substitute these activities for any needs previously satisfied by smoking:
   • *Stimulation.* Brisk walking, other exercise, dancing.
   • *Handling.* Toy with a pen or pencil. Draw. Play with a coin, a smooth stone, or plastic straws.

(Continued on next page)

Teacher Support Notes

① **Life Choice Inventory:** Students who are nonsmokers can benefit from doing the Life Choice Inventory and answering the questions as if they did smoke. This could help them understand a friend or acquaintance who smokes. You could also have these students identify a friend or a relative who does smoke and have students administer the inventory to that person. The students could ask the questions orally and record the responses. They could then read to the person the strategies suggested in the scoring section.

✎ Fast Facts

According to the Office of Smoking & Health, Federal Centers for Disease Control, 41.2% of white high school students, 32% of Hispanic students, and 16.8% of African-American students smoke or use other tobacco products.

sent their ideas to the rest of the class.
(20 min., Cooperative Learning)

Activity 5.6
    Role-Playing. Assign students to
pair up and role-play in front of the class.
One is a smoker, the other is a friend try-

ing to get the smoker to quit. Discuss reasons the friend should quit smoking. How do they encourage quitting? What methods do they suggest to help the smoker? **(45 min.; Reteach, Reinforce)**

Activity 5.7
    Adopt-A-Smoker. Suggest that students try to find a smoker who wants to quit, preferably a student that many of them know or a volunteer from the class.

Have the entire class adopt this smoker to help him or her quit. The class members could each devise a way to help. For example:
1. Contact the smoker's brothers and sisters to help at home.
2. Make chewy snacks to substitute for cigarettes.
3. Escort the student to classes to avoid areas in the school where smoking may occur.

Teacher Support Notes

① **Cold Turkey Tips:** If there are any smokers in your class who are about to try quitting cold turkey, here are some additional tips you can give them. They should:
• Promise themselves they will not smoke at all for a week. More than a week is too much to handle.
• Inform everyone close to them. This puts their reputations at stake.
• Get a friend to quit with them.
• Ask for special consideration at first in case they're irritable.
• Keep busy—very busy—in whatever way they can.
• If they do smoke, they shouldn't stop with just one. They should smoke a whole pack in rapid succession to make themselves sick.
• When they crave a smoke, they should breathe deeply and pantomime the smoking process.
• When they feel like reaching for a cigarette, reach for the radio or the telephone instead—talk with someone, find substitute activities.
• Take up some form of physical activity. This will get their hearts and lungs in shape again. Great pleasure comes from the rapid recovery of breathing.

390

Why Do You Smoke? (continued)

• *Pleasure/relaxation.* Substitute chewing gum, healthful snacks or beverages, social or physical activities.
• *Crutch/tension reduction.* Choose physical activity, healthful snacks or beverages, chewing gum, or social activities.
• *Craving/psychological dependence.* Isolate yourself completely from cigarettes until the craving is gone— or use a patch or nicotine gum as described in the chapter. Giving up cigarettes may be so hard and cause

so much discomfort that once you do quit, you will be strongly motivated to resist the temptation to go back to smoking. You'll know that if you do start smoking again, you will have to go through the same agony to quit again.
• *Habit.* Try to break your habit patterns. Become aware of each cigarette you smoke. Ask yourself, "Do I really want this cigarette?" You may be surprised at how many you do not want.

While tapering off works well for some people, most are more successful quitting cold turkey. This is because the hard part is over more quickly. Two weeks after quitting, people who quit cold turkey have fewer and less intense cravings for cigarettes than those who cut back gradually.

At first, quitters are keenly aware of the craving to smoke. They constantly fight the temptation to light up again. Tuning in to the pleasures of *not* smoking raises the odds in favor of success. Quitters list small and big pleasures:

• I can breathe deep breaths of clean air.
• I'm free from having to carry cigarettes and matches wherever I go.
• My behavior is not a threat to anyone's health. I can look my friends and family members in the eye.

①

• Food tastes delicious, and I can smell flowers.
• My clothes and hair smell fresh, not like smoke.
• I can walk easily without getting out of breath.
• I can talk on the phone without panicking if my cigarettes are out of reach.
• There are no dirty ashtrays around me.
• I don't burn holes in my clothes.
• I have more money to spend on other things.
• That attractive nonsmoker who sits next to me in class has started showing an interest in me.

No matter why people decide to quit, what makes them stick with it is that after only two or three days, they feel better physically, as well as emotionally.

4. Meet the student to engage in exercise.

5. Provide things for the student to "handle" in place of a cigarette such as wooden puzzles or rubber bands.

6. Create posters of the negative aspects of smoking to put in the student's room at home or in his or her locker.

7. Call student in the evening to check on progress or be available if the student needs to call someone to avoid smoking

a cigarette.

8. Help the student make a list of reasons he or she want to quit and post copies on notebooks, locker, etc.

9. Provide gum so the smoker is never without it.

10. Provide fruit juice instead of soft drinks and coffee.

11. Make the smoker's lunch.

12. Devise rewards for every day without smoking.

13. Talk to the smoker's friends and get them to help by not smoking in the smoker's presence.

Be sure all are patient and not judgmental in dealing with the smoker. If the smoker slips, forgive and go back on the program. The smoker should keep a log of progress.

Each student could then write what they did on an index card and have the smoker

(continued on next page)

Some people can't make it alone, or don't choose to. Classes are offered by Smokenders, the American Cancer Society, the American Lung Association, and the American Heart Association. A class can help to identify a smoker's style and tailor a quitting plan to each person's needs.

Some smokers are afraid that if they quit, they will gain weight. Some people actually lose weight. However, most quitters do gain—usually about 4 to 5 pounds, but sometimes more—for two reasons. Smoking is an oral behavior, and some quitters turn to another oral behavior to take its place—eating. People can prevent weight gain, however, by drinking fluids, snacking on crunchy vegetables, and taking up physical activity. ①

Even smokers who do gain a few pounds say it's worth it to give up cigarettes. Later, as ex-smokers, they take the weight off. Others have done it; you can too. Chapter 9 in this book tells how.

Nicotine-containing gum and nicotine patches are aids available to smokers as stepping-stones to freedom from smoking. Both the gum and the patches are available by prescription. The gum delivers the same amount of nicotine as two or three cigarettes. The user must stop smoking and chew the gum instead. The patch adheres to the skin and delivers nicotine to the bloodstream.

The gum and the patch help quitters, first, to lose all the habits of smoking: handling the cigarettes, puffing on them, and so forth. After that (the theory goes), it becomes much easier to taper off the use of the gum or the patch, since nicotine addiction is the only problem left.

Key Points ▶ *The smoker must make a firm decision to quit. Many programs and strategies can help a smoker to quit. Quitting is not easy, but the rewards of a smoke-free life are worth the work.*

How to Help the Smoker Quit

What if you are a concerned bystander who wants to help a smoker quit? First, you must realize that smokers can quit only when they are ready. Your job, then, is to help them get ready. You cannot force them to quit.

The key to helping is "tough love"—a term borrowed from alcoholism treatment. The idea is this. If you really care about a person, you will not keep quiet about a dangerous habit. Assert yourself. Confront the person. At the same time, show that you care. Make it clear that you reject the behavior, not the person. Talk about the risks of the behavior. Offer research news you hear about the effects of smoking and the benefits of quitting. Focus on issues that matter to the person. Tell a friend at school, for example, that smoking hurts sports performance and that it is unattractive.

Do not be surprised, though, if the smoker cannot "hear" what you are saying. The person may be committed to smoking, at least at present. The person knows about, but ignores, health warnings: "Yes, I know." If the person continues to smoke, then protect your own health. Insist, "Don't smoke around me." Someday your comments, along with others, may tip the scale in favor of health, and the person will quit. ②

THERE AIN'T NO FUTURE IN THIS!

LUNG 100's BUSTER

Many people are quitting smoking successfully.

✎ **Fast Facts**

Assume that the average smoker takes ten drags on a cigarette. If that person smokes one pack of cigarettes a day, he or she will take 200 hits of the addictive drug each day.

Teacher Support Notes

① **Fluids:** Tell students that liquids such as water, sparkling water, iced tea, and low-calorie fruit juices will help fill them up, and help rid their bodies of toxins from smoking. The sweetness will please their recovering awareness of sweet taste.

② **How to Help:** To reinforce their reading in this section, you may want to ask students to do the following writing assignment. Have them write a paragraph to finish this statement, "I will do my part to reduce senseless behavior, smoking, and the use of smokeless tobacco, which causes life-threatening illness and death, by. . . ."

write whether it helped and why, on the back of the card. Cards could then be collected and used as quit tips for the next class that adopts a smoker. Be sure students continue to contact and reinforce the former smoker for the entire semester. **(Extend, Enrich)**

EVALUATE
SECTION V

Activity 5.8
Essay. Have students pick one of the following questions and write a well-supported essay answer without using their books:
1. Why must a person want to quit smoking before you can help?

2. What can a person do to replace the act and mannerisms of smoking?
3. Why should a person quit smoking?
4. How can a nonsmoker help a smoker quit smoking?
(20 min.; Reteach, Reinforce)

CLOSE
SECTION V

Activity 5.9

Teacher Support Notes

① **Replacement Activities for Smoking:** Ask students which activities in the illustration they think would be the most effective replacements for smoking for them personally. Also ask why the artist left the last box empty. (to make the point that doing nothing is better than smoking) Ask students if they have any additional ideas. You may want to give extra credit for panels that they could create similar to the ones in the illustration to represent alternatives to smoking.

---

392   UNIT 4 Drug Use and Abuse

Smoke-free ways to relax.   ①

Employers can help by banning smoking on the job. This may seem unfair to smokers, but it is fair to nonsmokers, it protects their health, and it is legal. Studies show that smokers take more breaks and are absent from work more often than nonsmokers.

Some magazines, films, and other media can help by not advertising tobacco. This

Letter to a Friend. In order to show that students have mastered the information in Section V, have them write a letter to a friend or relative who smokes. Have them include why the person should stop smoking, and what products can help him or her stop. Students should explain that they disapprove of the habit, not the person, and that they would support any attempts to quit. This will give students a chance to use all the information learned from this section. **(30–45 min.; Reteach, Reinforce)**

RETEACH/BONUS

Here are some additional activities for the various sections of this chapter. You may want to use these activities to reteach certain concepts, or you may choose them as alternatives to earlier activities. Some could also be used in conjunction with the Straight Talk Feature beginning on the next page.

Business Interviews. Assign students to question an owner of a business that is smoke free. Encourage them to find out the reason the business is smoke free and if the owner ran into opposition from smoking clients or employees. Have

(continued on next page)

Gum containing nicotine helps some smokers quit.

takes courage, because advertising is so profitable. Even children can help, by asking parents who smoke to stop.

Many are working toward the goal of a smoke-free society by the year 2000. Some communities have passed no-smoking laws. The number of people still smoking and the number of young people just starting are beginning to fall. The only group that opposes this trend is, of course, the tobacco industry. ①

The tobacco industry does what any industry must do to be successful: make profits and find new markets for its products. Unfortunately, however, to do these things, tobacco companies must start more people using tobacco. This destroys health, so much of the normal business activity of the tobacco industry is viewed as **unethical** by many people. The Straight Talk in this chapter focuses on the tobacco industry's use of double messages to promote itself at the cost of the world's health.

Key Points ▶ *If you want to help smokers quit, remember that smokers can quit only when they are ready. Express your concern. Offer information. If they are not willing to quit, protect yourself by insisting that they do not smoke around you.*

SECTION V REVIEW

Answer the following questions on a sheet of paper.

Learning the Vocabulary
The vocabulary term in this section is *unethical.*
1. Write a sentence using the vocabulary word.

Learning the Facts
2. Describe the withdrawal symptoms people experience when they quit smoking.
3. Name the different strategies described in this section to help a person quit smoking.
4. List seven pleasures quitters gain when they stop smoking.

Making Life Choices
5. Two devices are on the market to help you quit smoking: nicotine gum and the patch. Learn from a pharmacist or physician how each of these works and explain.

Answers to Fact or Fiction

Here are the answers to the questions at the start of the chapter.

1. False. The main reason for continuing to smoke is addiction to nicotine. **2.** True. **3.** True. **4.** False. Nicotine is a highly addictive drug. **5.** True. **6.** True. **7.** True. **8.** False. The risks of cancer of the mouth and throat are greater for people using smokeless tobacco products than for smokers.

MINI GLOSSARY

unethical: against the rules of right and wrong; not in line with accepted moral standards.

Teacher Support Notes

① **Smoke-Free Society:** Ask students if they think it's possible to have a smoke-free society. Ask them to give reasons why they think this would or would not be possible.

Section V Review

Answers

1. Answers will vary.
2. irritability, restlessness, anxiety, craving for nicotine
3. Refer to the Health Strategies on page 388 for possible answers.
4. Refer to the bulleted points on page 390 (not Why Do You Smoke?) for possible answers.
5. Answers will vary.

✉ Where to Write

Nonsmokers Rights Associations
344 Bloor Street, West, Suite 308
Toronto, Ontario
M5S3A7

they seen any benefits from being smoke free? Ask students to present a short summary to the class. **(Extend, Enrich)**

A Smoke-Free Home? Assign students to research how much money and how many machines it would take to filter smoke from the air in an entire house. Emphasize that filters would be needed for each room where people smoked. Also, filters would be needed in each car where smoking might take place. Have students turn in their reports and explain where they would buy their filters and how much it would cost to live smoke free with a smoker. **(45 min., Advanced)**

Role-Playing. Have four students role-play a situation in which they are dining in a restaurant and there are two tables side by side with two persons at each table. One person is smoking, and it is bothering those at the other table. Have students demonstrate assertive but not aggressive ways to solve the situation. Do this role-play twice. The first time the restaurant does not have smoking regulations; and the second, they are sitting in a nonsmoking section. A fifth student might

---

Teacher Support Notes

① **Handout—Public Health Objectives:**
Your supplementary material contains the objectives for the nation regarding tobacco as stated by the U.S. Department of Health and Human Services. You may want to distribute this handout as you conclude the main part of this chapter.

② **Targeting Young People:** The tobacco companies say that young people are not the target audience for their products. If this is true, the students should not be very familiar with their products. You can test this in class by asking students to brainstorm cigarette brand names. Don't use a brand name more than once. For example, if someone says *Winstons*, then *Winston Lights* or *Winston 100's* are not allowed. Write all the brand names on the blackboard. How many were named? This should prove the point that teens are being reached by tobacco advertising.

🖊 Fast Facts

Cigarette manufacturers spend $3.5 *billion* annually on advertising and promotion.

STRAIGHT

TALK

① # Tobacco Advertising and Ethics

Should tobacco companies be free to advertise products that are both addictive and deadly? The tobacco companies, of course, say yes. Many medical and health groups, however, are urging the federal government to ban all advertising of tobacco products.

How does each side state its case?

The tobacco companies argue that to ban tobacco advertising would be against the Constitution's First Amendment, which grants freedom of the press. (This is a basic freedom, in the democratic way of life.) These companies say that all viewpoints should be expressed. Consumers, they say, can judge for themselves what is harmful.

Tobacco opponents argue that the government should not allow advertising of harmful products. Such ads are deceiving, and consumers cannot, they say, judge wisely.

The tobacco industry argues back, claiming that such bans are typical of a totalitarian state, not of a democracy. (In a totalitarian state, the state bans views it does not want its citizens to hear.)

Can the tobacco companies really demand freedom of the press for

their advertisements? After all, their products harm people.

Yes, they can, because freedom of the press protects the right to print opinions, and even misinformation. It ② prohibits only the printing of slander—that is, false information about a person that injures the person or damages the person's reputation.

Tobacco advertising is not slander. It simply says that people will like the product. Tobacco ads make no health or safety claims. They do deceive people into thinking that tobacco use is safe by showing healthy, glamorous actors with cigarettes in their hands. However, to deceive is not a crime. The law says, "Let the buyer beware." It is up to consumers to guard against deception. The tobacco company, Philip Morris, argues in favor of allowing tobacco ads, saying: "Advertising does not make smokers start smoking." Philip Morris says any ban on advertising is a threat to the

most basic right of Americans to exchange ideas.

Do tobacco advertisements work?

Each day many people start to smoke. As a result, the tobacco companies are thriving. They are even thought of as respectable businesses, because they donate some of their tremendous profits to hospitals, universities, churches, and charities. Tobacco companies are struggling to improve their reputations but they still produce and sell products that harm people's health.

Do tobacco companies admit that their products are harmful?

No, and in fact, companies still gear their advertisements toward young people to encourage them to smoke. As always, this endangers youngsters' future health. However, it favors the interest of the $30-billion-

(Continued on next page)

be added to act as the server.

Research on Local Laws. Select one student to research the laws in your state, city, and county regarding non-smoking sections and places where people may smoke. Have them share their findings with the rest of the class. **(Extend, Enrich)**

Cultural Differences. Ask students who have traveled in other countries or who have parents who are from other countries to discuss the prevalence of smoking and any smoking "rules" in these countries. **(Multicultural)**

STRAIGHT TALK   *(Continued)*

a-year tobacco industry, which grows on nicotine addiction. In short, tobacco companies get away with murder.

Wow. One minute you're talking about advertising and the next, you're talking about killing people. Are people accusing tobacco companies of killing their loved ones?

Powerful groups such as Doctors Ought to Care (DOC), the American Public Health Association, and the American Council on Science and Health argue that there is now firm scientific proof that cigarette smoking causes diseases that are often fatal. A question that is central to the issue is, "Are tobacco companies liable for deaths caused by their products?" This question has already been put to the test in court, and the tobacco industry has lost a case.

Is it possible to prove that smoking has caused a lung cancer death?

Not in individual cases, no. As you saw in the chapter, smoking greatly increases the number of deaths from many kinds of diseases. Clearly, it does cause individual deaths. But some nonsmokers die of these same diseases, too. You

can't tell whether a particular death was caused by smoking. The person might have died of the disease anyway.

So how can tobacco's opponents keep the tobacco companies from "committing murder," as you say?

The group called Doctors Ought to Care (DOC) is working on that. DOC is trying to convince lawmakers that smoking does cause deaths. Each time a smoker dies of lung cancer, coronary artery disease, emphysema, or any other tobacco-related illness, the health care provider sends a black-bordered announcement of the death to the client's senator or representative. The announcement states that tobacco smoking is the major avoidable cause of the disease that caused the person's death.

By making its point that smoking does cause deaths, DOC hopes to convince lawmakers to consider a ban—or at least restrictions— on tobacco advertising. A similar effort conducted in England led to restrictions on tobacco advertising.

Do newspapers and magazines have to publish tobacco ads?

No, they don't. In fact, many magazines no longer accept tobacco advertisements. This is hard for magazines to do, because money from tobacco ads can be a major source of income for magazines.

Can the courts decide whether the tobacco companies really have the right to print ads that glamorize cigarette smoking?

The courts are working on that question. One view says that if someone writes something, and you read it, and it leads you to take action, and that *action* harms your health, the law should punish the writer. Where the harm is to the pocketbook, except in cases of slander, the courts have always held the position "Let the buyer beware." That position assumes that buyers are adults, supposedly capable of protecting themselves. However, tobacco ads are often aimed at children who are too young to know how to protect themselves. In addition, the harm is not only to financial well-being, but to health and life. The next few years should see some interesting new thoughts on this question.

Where to Write

American Lung Association
1740 Broadway
New York, NY 10019

Where to Write

Tobacco Institute
Suite 841
1845 I Street
Washington, DC 20006

Vocabulary
1. Answers will vary.
2. Mainstream smoke is the smoke that goes straight from the cigarette into the smoker's lungs, while sidestream smoke is the smoke that escapes from the burning end of a cigarette that is inhaled by the smoker and others.
3. **a.** asthma **b.** unethical **c.** sinuses
4. **a.** emphysema
b. bronchitis **c.** ulcers
5. **a.** Mucus **b.** tars
c. Leukoplakia **d.** quid

Recall
Section I
1. slowed heart rate, lowered blood pressure, nausea, headache, irritability, restlessness, anxiety, drowsiness, inability to concentrate, and a craving for another dose
Section II
2. Anywhere from one-fourth to one and one-half pounds of sticky tar collect in the lungs each year, causing emphysema and diseases of the lung.
3. bronchitis, emphysema, chronic obstructive lung disease, lung cancer
4. Lungs are filled with carcinogens, which are cancer causing. The tar makes the coat of mucus thick and slows down the action of the cilia. Each puff on a cigarette paralyzes the cilia and numbs the throat so the smoker experiences relief from irritation. Bronchitis usually develops in all smokers after about ten years. Emphysema takes longer to develop.
5. speeds up the heart rate, raises the blood pressure, reduces the amount of oxygen the blood can carry, triggers the formation of blood clots, reduces the blood flow in the heart's own arteries
6. smaller babies, premature births, miscarriages, a doubled

CHAPTER REVIEW

LEARNING THE VOCABULARY

nicotine	bronchitis	sidestream smoke
tars	chronic obstructive lung disease	asthma
carcinogens	carbon monoxide	smokeless tobacco
emphysema	ulcers	quid
bronchi	sinuses	leukoplakia
mucus	mainstream smoke	unethical
cilia		

Answer the following questions on a separate sheet of paper.

1. Write a paragraph using at least ten vocabulary terms. Underline each of the terms that you use.
2. Explain the difference between mainstream smoke and sidestream smoke.
3. *Matching*—Match each of the following phrases with the appropriate vocabulary term from the list above:
   a. difficulty breathing, with wheezing sounds from the chest
   b. against the rules of right and wrong
   c. spaces in the bones of the skull
4. *Word Scramble*—Use the clues from the phrases below to help you unscramble the words:

   a. **phmmseeay** _____ flexible air sacs that have burst
   b. **oiibchtnrs** _____ thickened mucus, and deep, harsh coughing
   c. **rulesc** _____ open sores in the lining of the digestive system
5. a. _____ is a slippery secretion produced by cells of the body's lining.
   b. Burning _____ release many carcinogens.
   c. _____ are whitish or grayish patches in the mouth that may lead to cancers.
   d. A small portion of smokeless tobacco is referred to as a _____.

RECALLING IMPORTANT FACTS AND IDEAS

1. List the withdrawal symptoms people experience as a dose of nicotine wears off.
2. Explain what tar does to the respiratory tract.
3. Name at least four respiratory problems associated with smoking.
4. Describe why smokers are more susceptible to respiratory infections than nonsmokers.
5. List the effects nicotine has on the heart and circulatory system.
6. In what ways can smoking affect the unborn child of a pregnant woman?
7. What can carbon monoxide do to a passive smoker?
8. Describe the steps that are being taken to protect nonsmokers from sidestream smoke.
9. What are the dangers to oral health of using smokeless tobacco?
10. Describe why using smokeless tobacco is not preferable to smoking, for health's sake.
11. How can quitting smoking improve a person's health?
12. Explain why smokers sometimes gain weight when they quit smoking.
13. List the different programs available for smokers who want to quit.
14. Explain how you can influence your peers not to smoke.

risk of birth defects and impaired development in children up to age 11, early death of infants

Section III

7. A nonsmoker may suffer from the same lack of oxygen in the blood as is typical for a smoker.

8. Most restaurants have nonsmoking areas, and some ban smoking altogether; motels provide nonsmokers' rooms; federal ban on smoking on most airline flights; states ban smoking in public transportation, hospitals, elevators, schools, and libraries.

Section IV

9. mouth sores, mouth and throat cancers, leukoplakia, bad breath, wearing away of tooth surfaces, damage to gums

10. Answers will vary; could include: smokeless tobacco still contains nicotine, can cause cancers of the mouth and throat, causes brown teeth and bad breath like smoking, etc.

Section V

11. Answers will vary; could include: live longer, take deep breaths, walk easily without getting out of breath

12. Smoking is an oral behavior, and some quitters turn to another oral behavior such as eating to take its place. Drinking fluids, snacking on crunchy vegetables, and taking up a physical activity can help prevent weight gain.

13. Classes are offered by Smokenders, the American Cancer Society, the American Lung Association, and the American Heart Association.

14. Answers will vary; could include: by confronting the person, but showing that you care at the same time; informing them of the health risks of smoking; commenting that their smoke is harming you; by commenting that you do not think it is cool to smoke, and in fact, it is even unattractive.

CRITICAL THINKING

1. Reread the Straight Talk entitled "Tobacco Advertising and Ethics" on page 394. Some individuals have filed suit against the tobacco industry because family members have died due to smoking. What are arguments for each side of the controversy? Which side would you support and why?

2. Laws have been passed to prohibit smoking on all domestic airplanes. In what other places do you feel it is important to prohibit smoking? What can you do to help prohibit smoking in those places? What action can you take? Why will you take this action?

ACTIVITIES

1. Draw a picture of the human body and label the health problems that are associated with smoking. What parts of the body are most affected and why?

2. Smoking causes emphysema. In doing this experiment, you will feel like a person who has emphysema. You need a straw to perform this experiment. Plug your nose and put the straw in your mouth and breathe through it. Now jog in place for two minutes. Plug your nose and breathe through the straw again. Does breathing through the straw make you feel uncomfortable? In what ways are you uncomfortable? What have you learned about emphysema in doing this experiment?

3. List at least ten statements that might influence you or your friends to smoke. Change them to statements that would influence you not to smoke.

4. Form small groups in your class and go to the elementary school and give a presentation on not smoking. How could you persuade these young kids not to smoke? What strategies would work best with these kids? Suggestions: lectures, puppet shows, plays, admired role models.

5. Find someone you know who smokes. Make charts showing what times of day the person smokes. Use the information to try to help the person quit. Convince the person to replace smoking behaviors with other positive health behaviors. Give rewards for positive progress and demand penalties if the person demonstrates negative smoking behavior.

6. Write to your local chapter of the American Heart Association, Lung Association, or Cancer Society for information about ways to quit smoking. Share the information with the rest of your class.

7. Go to the library and look up ways companies market their cigarettes in our country and other countries. Compare and contrast the ways that cigarettes are marketed in several countries.

8. Make a collage of different smoking advertisements found in magazines. Change the advertisements to persuade people not to smoke. Put these collages up around the school.

MAKING DECISIONS ABOUT HEALTH

1. Your mother has been a heavy smoker all her life. The health effects are obvious to you, but not to her. She's short of breath and can walk only a few steps without wheezing. She suffers from frequent colds and her physician has warned her that she's risking severe heart trouble if she continues to smoke. Now the physician has told your family that her life is in imminent danger, "She must stop smoking or else I can't be responsible for her health care anymore." Still, she refuses to quit. "I'd rather smoke and die happy," she says "than live without my habit." What do you do and why?

CHAPTER 16 PLANNER

OVERVIEW

Chapter 16 is 20 pages long and is divided into the four sections listed to the right. The major learning outcomes are also listed to the right. This chapter introduces students to microbes and focuses on the transmission of those that cause infectious diseases. The importance of the public health system in the control of infectious diseases is stressed. Also explained fully is the defense against infectious diseases provided by the body's immune system. Students are provided with some health strategies they can use to minimize their risks of infection.

MAKING LIFE CHOICES RESOURCES

A variety of activities, handouts, quizzes, and tests to accompany this chapter are available in the *Making Life Choices* supplementary material. You may pick and choose from those materials as appropriate for your amount of class time and the ability levels of your students. Some of the resources you might want to consider using are:

Overheads
• How Viruses Multiply and Cause Infection
• How Infections Spread

Handouts
• The First Vaccine
• Researching Infectious Diseases
• Immunization Schedule
• U.S. Public Health Service Objectives for the Nation

Teacher Information Sheet
• How Fever Works

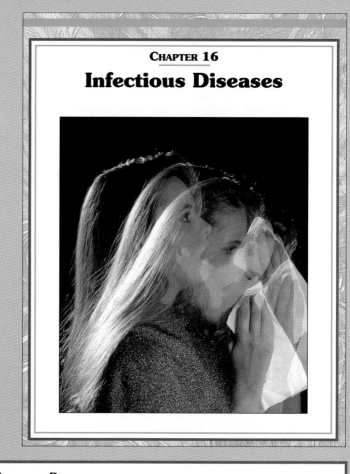

CHAPTER 16
Infectious Diseases

CHAPTER PROJECT

Have students write to a pharmaceutical firm for information on preparation of vaccines, storage of vaccines, shelf life, and how they are distributed in the United States. Compile the results in class.

Activity To Introduce Chapter

Ask students how many of them have had chicken pox. Explain that chicken pox is caused by a virus and that most people get this disease only once. Ask the students why someone might never get chicken pox. Then tell students that some people do get this infectious disease twice. Why might this happen? (shingles occurring in later life) Ask students at what age they think most people become infected. Why do they suppose people tend to get the disease at that age?

Ask students what the term *incubation* means and explain that for chicken pox it is 12 to 19 days. Review some symptoms. Explain that treatments might include an anti-itching lotion. Health care providers might also suggest the infected person's nails be cut. Discuss why this might be necessary.

OUTCOMES

After reading and studying this chapter, you will be able to:

✓ Identify the microbes, how they develop, and common diseases they cause.

✓ Describe the public health system's defenses against infectious diseases.

✓ Describe how the body defends itself against infectious diseases.

✓ Describe the course of an illness.

✓ Outline actions a person can take to avoid infectious diseases.

✓ Identify types, symptoms, and treatments of food poisoning.

✓ Discuss the transmission, symptoms, detection, and treatment of mononucleosis.

CONTENTS

I. Meet the Microbes

II. Public Defenses against Infectious Diseases

III. The Body's Defenses and Infectious Diseases

IV. Taking Action

Straight Talk: *Mononucleosis—The Kissing Disease*

FACT OR FICTION

What do you think? *Are the following statements true or false? If you think they are false, then say what is true.*

1. It would be a great service to humankind if we could wipe out all microbes.

2. A healthy body is host to millions of microbes.

3. Soap and water washing is an effective way to remove bacteria from the skin.

4. A hospital is a place where people can easily pick up infectious diseases.

5. Antibiotics are among the few medicines effective against viruses.

6. Fevers are dangerous, especially when people have infections.

7. Food poisoning can be fatal.
(Answers on page 414)

■ **Reminder:** Knowing how to study can increase your knowledge, improve your grades, *and* cut down on your study time. See the *Studying Health* section at the front of your text for some suggestions to help you study this chapter.

NOT ENOUGH TIME?*

This chapter could be covered in four or five days if students read the entire chapter, do a number of the suggested activities in the teacher's edition, and complete a number of the handouts from the resource material. If you have only two days to cover this chapter, the following are some suggestions to help you make sure that you cover the main objectives.

TIME	SUGGESTIONS
Day 1	Assign Sections I and II prior to class. Also assign the "Life Choice Inventory" on page 413 and the "Fact or Fiction." During class have the students do Activitity 1.1 and Activity 1.3 in Section I, and Activity 2.1 in Section II.
Day 2	On day 2, assign Section III, including the "Consumer Awareness" on page 412 and the "Straight Talk" at the end of the chapter. During class do Activities 3.2, 3.3, and 3.8 in Section III.

*Please refer to the 18-week daily lesson plans in the supplementary material for additional suggestions.

Answers to "Fact or Fiction"

Here are the answers to the questions at the start of the chapter.
1. False. Many microbes are harmless and provide services needed for life. **2.** True. **3.** True. **4.** True. **5.** False. Antibiotics are useful against bacteria but useless against viruses. **6.** False. Low fevers are usually not harmful and are part of the body's defense against infection. **7.** True.

SUGGESTED RESOURCES

Student Readings
1. Benenson, Abram, S. ed. *Control of Communicable Diseases in Man.* Washington, DC: American Public Health Association, 1985.
2. Hansen, G. R. *Common Medicines*, 2nd ed. Salt Lake City, 1987.

Teacher Readings
1. Purtilo, David T. *A Survey of Human Diseases.* Menlo Park, CA: Addison-Wesley, 1978.
Videos
1. *Allergies, Nothing to Sneeze At.* Opportunities for Learning, Inc., P.O. Box 8103, Mansfield, OH 44901-8103.

In this section students will learn the:
1. General classes of microbes that cause infectious diseases.
2. Modes of transmission of microbes.

Activity 1.1
Water Samples. Place several microscopes around the classroom with samples of water taken from local creeks or ponds. A concave slide can be used. Next to the microscope, place a glass container with a larger sample of the same water. Attach a 3 × 5 card that reads: "What do you see?" Explain to the students that the water under the microscope is the same as that in the glass container. Discuss the differences in what they see. **(10 min.)**

Activity 1.2
Pathogen Transmission. Design a bulletin board that will demonstrate ways pathogens can be transmitted. Divide the bulletin board into four sections with the following headings: *Direct Contact, Droplets, Animals, Objects.* Ask the students for examples of each topic. Ask students to bring in pictures from magazines and newspapers demonstrating each method of transmission. As students

Teacher Support Notes

① **Microbes and Pathogens:** Make sure students know the difference between microbes and pathogens. Do all pathogens cause disease? (yes) Do all microbes cause disease? (no) Are all microbes pathogens? (no) Are all pathogens microbes? (yes)

② **Endogenous Bacteria:** For enrichment you might want to tell students that the normally harmless bacteria that live on the skin, in the digestive tract, and elsewhere in the human body are called *endogenous* bacteria. Some normally harmless, endogenous bacteria can become pathogenic, given the opportunity. These bacteria are often called *opportunists* because they take advantage of opportunities that come their way.

③ **Aerobes vs. Anaerobes:** For further enrichment, explain that all bacteria can be divided into two general categories: *aerobes* and *anaerobes*. The aerobes require oxygen to grow; the anaerobes require an oxygen-free environment to grow. There are exceptions—some bacteria can function in both environments.

400   UNIT 5   Disease Prevention

You are surrounded by millions of **microbes**—living things too small for the human eye to see without the help of a microscope. They are all around you—on the surfaces you touch, in the air you breathe, on the forkfuls of food that you lift to your mouth, and on the surfaces of your body. Most are harmless. Many even perform valuable services, such as decomposing wastes to reusable nutrients. Others, however, can cause **infectious diseases**. These microbes are known as **pathogens**. This chapter focuses on the pathogens and offers strategies you can use to protect yourself against infections.

SECTION I

Meet the Microbes

The **bacteria** and the **viruses** are two types of microbes. Some bacteria can be beneficial. For example, those normally found in the human digestive tract protect *against* some diseases and help digest food. If a person's immune system becomes weakened, though, even these normally helpful bacteria may cause illness. As for viruses, they specialize in causing illness. They have no known beneficial functions.

You are surrounded; microbes are all around you.

Bacteria and viruses cause many different diseases. The next two sections discuss a few of the more common disease-causing bacteria and viruses.

In addition to bacteria and viruses, **fungi**, **protozoa**, **worms**, and other **parasites** also cause illness. These are all general classes, within which exist both innocent and harmful varieties.

Bacteria

Many bacteria grow and multiply best in environments like the human body: warm, dark, moist, and nutrient-rich. Bacteria thrive inside deep puncture wounds, where medicines applied to the surface cannot reach. Normally, ordinary soap makes bacteria slippery so that they are easy to wash away with water. A puncture wound, however, requires medical attention.

A type of bacterium especially likely to invade a puncture is the one that causes **tetanus**, a disease that is serious and often fatal, even when the person receives medical help. Tetanus bacteria produce a poison that causes uncontrollable muscle contractions. When the muscles that work the lungs and heart become involved, tetanus kills the person. Tetanus shots provide immunity against the tetanus poison.

Many people die worldwide from **tuberculosis**, a bacterial infection of the lungs. Deaths from tuberculosis declined for years in the United States until recently. However, the number of cases is on the rise again. People who have AIDS (see Chapter 17) often develop tuberculosis. The early symptoms of tuberculosis include fever, tiredness, night sweats, and weight loss. Chest pains and shortness of breath develop as the disease destroys the lungs.

More and more people are also victims of **Lyme disease**. The bacteria responsible for Lyme disease are passed to people by ticks that live on wild deer. The disease usually

TEACH
SECTION I
(Guided and Independent Practice)

Activity 1.3
Good vs. Bad Microbes. Ask students if they agree with the statement that all microbes are bad. Ask if any student can think of an example of a good microbe and what valuable service it performs. **(5 min.; Extend, Enrich)**

Activity 1.4
Tree Houses. Discuss the following situation with the class. Two brothers are planning to build a tree house in a wooded area near their home. Ask the students what situations could arise that would expose the brothers to infectious diseases and how the boys might protect themselves. **(10 min., Critical Thinking)**

Activity 1.5
Bacteria vs. Viruses. Ask students to write a one-page essay on how bacteria differ from viruses. **(5 min., Interdisciplinary)**

---

begins with a red dot on the skin. Weeks to months later, Lyme disease causes flulike symptoms such as severe headache, neck pain, and stiff joints.

People who live near forests or meadows or who often walk or hike into them should take extra precautions against tick bites. Wearing high socks, wearing long pants, and using tick repellent (especially on the ankles, legs, and groin area) are effective measures. Early treatment involves intensive antibiotic therapy.

> **Key Points** *Pathogenic (disease-bearing) bacteria multiply in moist, dark, warm, nutrient-rich body tissues. Tetanus, tuberculosis, and Lyme disease are all caused by bacteria.*

Viruses

Viruses differ significantly from bacteria. Viruses are much smaller than bacteria. While bacteria are cells, viruses are not. Viruses are mainly just bits of genetic material that can invade living cells—even bacterial cells. By using the cells' equipment, viruses reproduce themselves with astonishing speed. In the living cell, viruses take over the cell's genetic machinery and force it to serve their purposes—to reproduce more viruses. The multitudes of new viruses then move on to infect other cells. ②

Vaccinations offer protection against infectious diseases.

Viruses harm living cells, so they cause diseases. Most people suffer through at least one **cold** each year, and some people come down with **flu** (short for **influenza**). Most times, people can rightly blame viruses for causing these miseries.

MINI GLOSSARY

microbes: tiny organisms, such as bacteria, yeasts, and viruses, that are too small to be seen with the naked eye; also called microorganisms.

infectious diseases: diseases caused, and transmitted from person to person, by microorganisms or their toxins; also called *communicable,* or *contagious diseases,* or simply *infections.*

pathogens: microbes that cause diseases.

bacteria (singular, **bacterium**): microscopic, single-celled organisms of varying shapes and sizes, some capable of causing disease.

viruses: organisms that contain only genetic material and protein coats, and that are totally dependent on the cells they infect.

fungi: living things that absorb and use nutrients of organisms they invade. Fungi that cause illnesses include *yeasts* and *molds.*

protozoa (PRO-toh-ZOH-ah): tiny, animal-like cells, some of which can cause illnesses.

worms: visible parasites that burrow into the blood supplies of victims.

parasites: living things that depend for nourishment on the bodies of others that they inhabit.

tetanus: a disease caused by a toxin produced by bacteria deep within a wound.

tuberculosis: a bacterial infection of the lungs.

Lyme disease: a bacterial infection spread by tiny deer ticks.

cold: an upper respiratory tract infection.

flu: short for **influenza** (in-flew-EN-za), a highly contagious respiratory infection caused by any of a variety of viruses.

Fast Facts
In 1918 and 1919 an influenza pandemic killed 20 million people worldwide.

Teacher Support Notes

① **Describing Viruses:** Tell students that viruses depend entirely on the living tissue of other organisms. Outside of the living cells they have no way of reproducing. They do not eat, they do not breathe, they do not grow or mature. Each virus has a body that is the ultimate in simplicity. It is made up of only a bit of genetic material that can direct a cell to reproduce the virus and a protein case to carry that material.

② **Overhead—How Viruses Multiply:** Your supplementary material contains an overhead entitled "How Viruses Multiply and Cause Infection," which shows how a virus attacks a cell and multiplies itself.

Activity 1.6

Pop Quiz. Write the A–I descriptions on the board, then have the students number their papers 1–9. Read the terms aloud and have students write the letter of the correct description on their papers.

(H) 1. microbes

(I) 2. tetanus
(E) 3. infectious disease
(C) 4. chicken pox
(A) 5. virus
(G) 6. bacteria
(F) 7. Lyme Disease
(D) 8. head lice
(B) 9. fungi

A. invades a cell and uses it to reproduce
B. athlete's foot
C. caused by a virus, itchy blisters
D. parasitic insect, burrows into hair
E. a contagious disease
F. bacteria carried by a deer tick

G. grows in dark, moist area, single-celled
H. too small to see with the naked eye
I. associated with puncture wounds

Teacher Support Notes

① **Yeasts:** Ask students how these are different from the molds as explained in the Mini Glossary. (Yeasts are one-celled fungi; molds have many cells.)

② **Parasitic Worms:** The most common worms are flatworms, tapeworms, roundworms, pinworms, and hookworms. They thrive by inflicting bites on their hosts to obtain blood. One of the most prominent is the roundworm that causes trichinosis.

Section I Review

Answers

1. Answers will vary.
2. Bacteria are actually single-celled organisms, while a virus is only genetic material and is totally dependent on the cells it infects. Some bacteria can be helpful to the body, while viruses have no known benefits.
3. bacteria, viruses, fungi, protozoa, and worms
4. tetanus
5. a red dot on the skin, severe headache, neck pain, and stiff joints following a week to months later
6. Answers will vary; could include: too much stress, caffeine addiction, mental depression, sleep deprivation, and boredom.
7. Answers will vary.

402

Viruses cause diseases by invading cells.

Once flu and cold symptoms are gone, the virus causing the illness is usually gone from the body, too. Other viruses, though, can remain in the body for life. In later years, long after the symptoms of the initial illness are gone, these viruses can cause disease once again. An example is **shingles**, a painful skin condition in adults that is caused by renewed activity of the same virus that brought them **chicken pox** as children. An adult with shingles can pass the virus to others, who will get chicken pox if they have not previously had it.

Another illness possibly caused by a virus, **chronic fatigue syndrome**, makes its presence known only through a severe, never-ending tiredness that disrupts normal life completely. People who feel worn out shouldn't jump to the conclusion that they suffer from this illness, though. Some more common causes of fatigue are too much stress, caffeine addiction, mental depression, sleep deprivation, and boredom. These and other causes of fatigue are more easily treated than the syndrome.

 Viruses are not cells. Viruses cause diseases by invading cells and forcing them to reproduce viruses. Some remain in the body for life.

Other Pathogens

In addition to bacteria and viruses, pathogens include the fungi—both **yeasts**

① and **molds**. Fungi cause an amazing variety of illnesses, from **athlete's foot** to dangerous and incurable lung infections. Next in the pathogen lineup come protozoa, single-celled creatures that cause diarrhea and other ills. As for worms and other parasites, ② the most dangerous of these are fairly rare in the United States. Some worms and parasites, such as **pinworms** and **head lice**, are common and easily cured.

Key Points *Fungi (yeasts and molds), protozoa, worms, and other parasites cause a variety of diseases.*

SECTION I   REVIEW

Answer the following questions on a sheet of paper.

Learning the Vocabulary
The vocabulary terms in this section are *microbes, infectious diseases, pathogens, bacteria, viruses, fungi, protozoa, worms, parasites, tetanus, tuberculosis, Lyme disease, cold, flu, shingles, chicken pox, chronic fatigue syndrome, yeasts, molds, athlete's foot, pinworms,* and *head lice.*
1. Write a paragraph using at least ten vocabulary terms. Underline the terms you use.

Learning the Facts
2. What is the difference between viruses and bacteria?
3. List five types of microbes.
4. Which type of bacterium commonly invades puncture wounds?
5. What are the symptoms of Lyme disease?
6. List three common causes of fatigue.

Making Life Choices
7. Young children get a greater number of infections than adults. List as many reasons as you can think of why children are more susceptible to pathogens. How many times have you contracted an infectious disease this year? As a teenager, have you found that you are more or less susceptible to pathogens than when you were a young child? Why do you suppose that this is so?

Activity 1.7

Pathogen Identification. Ask volunteers to close their books and name the different types of pathogens identified in Section I and some common infectious diseases they cause. You might give some bonus points for those who can do this. **(Review, Reteach)**

FOCUS
SECTION II

In this section students will learn the:
1. Defenses against infectious diseases offered by the public health system.

Activity 2.1

School Provisions. Ask the students to list ways the school district attempts to provide protection against infectious diseases. Encourage students to include help provided by custodial crews, cafeteria staff, bus drivers, teachers, school nurses, and administrators. If available, distribute the school district's immunization requirements. Discuss their lists in class. **(15 min.)**

SECTION II

Public Defenses against Infectious Diseases

With so many pathogens bombarding everyone every day, why aren't people ill from infection most of the time? Actually, they would be, except that people have defenses. Public health systems provide one defense. People's own barriers and immune systems provide another.

To understand how diseases are prevented, it helps to know how they spread. One way to view the spread of disease is as a cycle: an infected person (the host) contaminates the air or food or objects near another who breathes the air or eats the food or handles the objects and transfers the pathogen to his or her body. Chances are that, once inside, the pathogen will grow and multiply in the body of the new host, causing disease.

An example might help to illustrate the cycle. Not long ago, students at a certain high school were coming down with the dangerous liver disease **hepatitis** in record numbers. Health officials hurried to test the school's water, its cafeteria food, and adult employees for a carrier of the hepatitis virus. They had no luck. Finally, someone noticed that all the sick students had something else in common—they all liked to stop at the same neighborhood bakery for glazed treats. (A glaze is the sweet coating that covers some doughnuts and other baked goods.) Have you guessed how the students contracted hepatitis? A baker at the shop was suffering from an active case of hepatitis, but thought it was only flu. Through unsanitary food handling practices used at the bakery, he had contaminated the glaze that coated most of the sweet items in the shop. Because glaze is not cooked and is kept for use from day to day, the virus lurking there survived to infect many. Once the host had been identified, the cycle of infection was broken and the threat of new cases vanished.

Public sanitation measures provide some protection against infections. Government agencies chlorinate public water supplies and treat sewage to kill pathogens that could otherwise contaminate drinking water. Where sanitation is poor, sick people

MINI GLOSSARY

shingles: a painful skin condition caused by the reemergence of the chicken pox virus in later life.

chicken pox: a usually mild, easily transmitted viral disease causing fever, weakness, and itchy blisters.

chronic fatigue syndrome: unexplained repeated bouts of extreme fatigue that bed rest does not cure and that last at least six months; caused by a virus.

yeasts: one-celled fungi, some of which cause diseases.

molds: many-celled fungi, some of which cause diseases.

athlete's foot: a fungal infection of the feet, usually transmitted through contact with floors.

pinworms: small, visible, white parasitic worms that commonly infect the intestines of young children.

head lice: tiny, but visible, white parasitic insects that burrow into the skin or hairy body areas.

hepatitis: a liver disease caused by any of several types of viruses transmitted by infected needles (drug use, tattoos, blood transfusions), by eating raw seafood from contaminated water, and by any contact (including sexual contact) with body secretions from infected people.

Teacher Support Notes

① **Overhead—How Infections Spread:** Your supplementary material contains an overhead that illustrates the process described in this paragraph. For enrichment you may want to give students some additional terminology. For example, one factor needed to spread an infection is a *reservoir of infection*, which is the source of the infectious disease agent. Another factor is a *portal of exit*, which is a means for the pathogen to escape the reservoir. A third factor is a means for the pathogen to reach the host. Nonliving transmitters are called *fomites*. A living thing that transmits an infection is called a *vector*. Another factor that's necessary is a *portal of entry*, which is a means for the pathogen to enter the host body.

Activity 2.2
Life Changes. Ask students to discuss which changes in the way people live today have helped bring about the decline of many infectious diseases. **(15 min., Critical Thinking)**

Activity 2.3
Posters. Have the students develop a list of suggestions to persuade people to receive immunizations and booster shots. Have the students use these lists to create posters supporting and encouraging immunizations. **(30 min.)**

Activity 2.4
Flu Vaccines. Flu vaccines are offered to the public yearly. Discuss with the students what is in the vaccine, how it works, and if it guarantees immunity. If it doesn't guarantee immunity, why do people get vaccinated? **(5 min., Critical Thinking)**

Activity 2.5
Research Paper. Have students choose an infectious disease not discussed in detail in this chapter and write a report about it. They should include infor-

---

Teacher Support Notes

① **Teen Views Follow-Up Questions:** The following are some questions you may want to use to encourage discussion of the ideas expressed by the students in the Teen Views feature:

a. How many students get flu shots? Do they seem to help?

b. Do some students seem to catch more colds than others? Why?

c. Among the reasons given by the students in the feature as to why people might catch colds more frequently are not wearing warm clothes, not keeping dry, being around people who are infected, not getting enough sleep, being overly stressed, not eating right, and not washing at appropriate times. Do students think any of these reasons are more of a factor than the others? If so, which ones?

404

---

404 UNIT 5 Disease Prevention

TEEN VIEWS

Do you seem to catch more than your share of colds and flu? ①

Yes, most people tend to catch colds or the flu because they don't wear warm clothes when the weather is bad and don't keep dry when it rains or snows. Being around a group of people who are infected with the cold virus doesn't help either. Most people can try and avoid the flu by getting a flu shot. I seem to catch a cold more often than the flu. I am also an asthmatic, and it is very important that I take care of my body. A lot of times I don't always do that, and then I pay the consequences. **Wendy D. Milligan, 16, Great Falls High School, MT**

Colds are the most easily spread viruses around and it just happens that I catch them all of the time. I always seem to be blowing my nose and feeling fatigued. I don't get as much sleep as my body needs. I only get about seven hours of sleep each night when I really need about nine hours. I stress myself out and my immune system weakens. Finally, I am allergic to dust and pollen which make me sneeze and sniffle. The first two reasons I can control, and need to, so that colds will stay away from me. **Kevin R. Krick, 17, Orange Park High School, FL**

I try to take good care of my health. By doing things like eating well, sleeping enough, and being emotionally strong, I can maintain a resistance to fight colds and flu. **Liz McClelland, 15, Duluth East High School, MN**

No. I rarely catch a cold and if I do it's not very bad. I wash my hands after I use the restroom, when I work outside, and before I eat except before lunch. I feel good about myself, I'm in good shape, and I don't want to get sick. **Carol Ann Miller, 15, Westside High School, NE**

---

pass on diseases such as **cholera** through untreated water. People who travel to countries with poor public health systems must take precautions against infections that may be common to a particular area. Travelers should avoid raw fruits, vegetables, meats, and seafood. In addition, they should boil local water for at least five minutes before using it.

In public pools and other shared facilities, **disinfectants** are applied to surfaces to kill microbes before they can spread. Even simple bathing and washing each day with soap and water washes many bacteria away and protects against some infections. In case of a cut or other wound, **antiseptics** prevent bacterial growth on the skin.

Public health programs often control viral diseases by destroying animal and insect carriers of viruses, and by immunizing people. For example, **rabies** is often spread to people through bites or scratches from infected animals. To protect people from rabies, health departments require that household pets be immunized and that infected animals be destroyed.

mation about type of pathogen, transmission, a description of the stages of the disease, the usual duration of the disease, and treatments. **(Extend, Enrich)**

Activity 2.6
Newspaper Reporting. Have students locate a recent newspaper or magazine article that discusses some of the controversy about immunizations and write a one-page summary and reaction. They

should include a copy of the article with the date and source. **(Extend, Enrich)**

Activity 2.7
Historical Research. Have students research one infectious disease in terms of how it spread through the world and affected history. **(Extend, Enrich)**

Activity 2.8
Have students visit or call the local Red

Cross and find out the types of emergency measures they recommend for preventing infectious epidemics after a disaster. Students may report their findings orally.

EVALUATE
SECTION II

Activity 2.9
Pop Quiz.

(continued on next page)

Some illnesses in people can also be prevented by immunization. This involves injecting a **vaccine**—a drug made from the pathogen or from a poison it produces, which trains the body's immune system to recognize the active disease agent when it invades. Just as an airplane pilot in training practices on a flight simulator before trying out a real plane, the body practices on the vaccine as a sort of pathogen simulator. If the real invader arrives, the practiced reaction is so fast that the disease never has a chance to develop.

The status of infectious diseases is constantly changing. At present, the U.S. Public Health Service is working hardest to control the following infectious diseases: tuberculosis; hepatitis; **pneumonia; polio (poliomyelitis); measles; rubella; mumps;** AIDS; and **hospital infections,** which may include any of these or others. Many people are admitted to hospitals because of infectious diseases. The diseases spread easily to others, causing much preventable illness and expense.

While public health systems can control diseases, they can seldom completely eliminate a disease. One disease, **smallpox,** may be an exception. For all others, though, control is the best outcome to hope for. Even **bubonic plague,** spread by rats in ancient days, has not been wiped out completely.

The "controlled" diseases are simply that—they are under control. Their causes are alive and with us today, waiting in the wings for public health systems to break down, or for drugs to lose their effectiveness. These diseases could easily become uncontrollable today if conditions became right once again.

> **Key Points** *Public health measures control many infectious diseases. Chlorination of water, treatment of sewage, immunization of people and animals, and destruction of carriers are all measures used to control diseases.*

MINI GLOSSARY

cholera (KAH-ler-uh): a dangerous bacterial infection causing violent muscle cramps, severe vomiting and diarrhea, severe water loss, and death.

disinfectants: chemicals that kill microbes on surfaces. Bleach is a disinfectant.

antiseptics: agents that prevent the growth of microorganisms on body surfaces and on wounds.

rabies: a viral disease of the central nervous system that causes paralysis and death.

vaccine: a drug made from altered microbes or their poisons injected or given by mouth to produce immunity.

pneumonia: a disease caused by a virus or bacterium that infects the lungs, with high fever, severe cough, and pain in the chest; especially dangerous to the very old or young.

polio (poliomyelitis): a viral infection that produces mild respiratory or digestive symptoms in most cases but that may produce permanent paralysis or death; preventable by immunization.

measles: a highly contagious viral disease characterized by rash, high fever, sensitivity to light, and cough and cold symptoms; preventable by immunization.

rubella: a viral disease that resembles measles but that lasts only a few days and does not cause serious complications, except in pregnancy; preventable by immunization.

mumps: a highly contagious viral disease that causes swelling of the salivary glands and, occasionally, of the testicles; preventable by immunization.

hospital infections: infectious illnesses acquired during hospitalization.

smallpox: a severe viral infection with skin eruptions; once often fatal, it is now under control, thanks to immunizations.

bubonic plague: a bacterial infection causing swollen lymph glands and pneumonia, frequently fatal.

66 Thoughts on Health 99

Meditating over a disease, I never think of finding a remedy for it but instead, a means of preventing it.
– Louis Pasteur

Teacher Support Notes

① **Handout—The First Vaccine:** Your supplementary material contains a handout that briefly describes smallpox and the development of the smallpox vaccine.

② **Hospital Infections:** An infection acquired in a hospital is called a *nosocomial* (no-soh-COH-me-ul) *infection.* Patients may be infected by health care personnel, other clients, or visitors. People in hospitals who contract infections unrelated to their original conditions greatly extend their hospital stays and expenses.

③ **Mini Glossary Definitions:** Refer students to the definitions in the Glossary in the back of the book, where some terms are defined more fully.

SECTION II REVIEW

Answer the following questions on a sheet of paper

Learning the Vocabulary

The vocabulary terms in this section are *hepatitis, cholera, disinfectants, antiseptics, rabies, vaccine, pneumonia, polio, measles, rubella, mumps, hospital infections, smallpox,* and *bubonic plague.*

1. The intestinal disease _____ can be contracted from infected water, milk, or foods.
2. To prevent the spread of infectious agents, you can spread _____ on surfaces and use _____ on your skin.
3. Immunization can prevent some illnesses in people and involves injecting a _____.
4. The disease _____, which is spread by rats, is still on the loose in the world.

Learning the Facts

5. Why are public water supplies chlorinated?
6. How do public health programs control viral diseases?
7. List five infectious diseases that the United States Public Health Service is working hard to control.

Making Life Choices

8. In recent years, some groups have challenged the right of government to make laws requiring immunizations of children for entry into school. If you were given the task of justifying the need for these laws, what would you say? Why do you think so many parents fail to have their children immunized? What could be done to encourage people to be vaccinated?

SECTION III

The Body's Defenses and Infectious Diseases

The body has many barriers against infectious diseases. When a disease does get past the first barriers, the body can often still fight it off.

Barriers to Diseases

One way the body controls pathogens is to bar their entry into the tissues by way of barriers such as skin and membranes. The skin is beautifully designed to protect the body. The skin produces salty, acidic sweat secretions (most microbes don't like salt or acid). It also has one-way pores that let things out but won't let microbes in.

The membranes that line the body chambers are also barriers to pathogens. The membranes have even more defenses than the skin. These include a layer of mucus that traps microbes, cilia (beating, hairlike structures) that sweep them out, and cells and chemicals of the immune system that destroy them. These internal membranes fend off great numbers of pathogens every day. Together with the skin, they are the body's first line of defense against diseases.

If a pathogen passes through the body's outer membranes, the immune system takes over fully. Usually, the immune system can destroy invaders in time to prevent diseases. If you are healthy now, thank your immune system for serving as your personal bodyguard, fighting off invaders every day.

It is hard to say just where in the body the immune system is located, because parts of the system are everywhere (see Chapter 6). An important part of the system is the bone marrow, which grows white blood cells called **lymphocytes**. Another part of the system is the **thymus gland**, which incubates some of the lymphocytes and changes them into **T cells** (T for *thymus*). The T cells then have the ability to recognize enemies. Other lymphocytes become **B cells**.* B cells

---

*B is for *bursa*, an organ in the chicken in which B cells were first observed.

In this section students will learn about the:

1. Defenses against infectious diseases offered by the human body.

Activity 3.1
Resistance Tips. Ask the students to create a list of ten tips for building resistance to disease and tell why these tips could work. **(10 min., Critical Thinking)**

TEACH
SECTION III
(Guided and Independent Practice)

Activity 3.2
Immune System Role-Play. Select students to role-play the immune system and how it reacts when a pathogen gets into the body. Select students to play the role of T cells, B cells, antibodies, lymphocytes, and a pathogen. When the

pathogen comes into the class, show the actions the immune system would take. **(15 min.; Reteach, Reinforce)**

Activity 3.3
Fevers. Ask the students to explain why it might be a bad idea to try to reduce a slight fever during an infection. Discuss how a fever fights disease. **(5 min.; Reteach, Reinforce)**

(continued on next page)

make **antibodies**, large molecules that serve as ammunition to kill invaders. The invaders are known as **antigens** (see Figure 16–1). ①

1. Body is challenged by foreign invaders (antigens).

2. Immune system cells record shape of invaders.

3. Cells use this memory record to make antibodies.

4. Later, antibodies destroy foreign invaders.

5. Memory remains to make antibodies faster the next time this foreign invader attacks.

Figure 16–1 Antigens and Antibodies

The lymphocytes travel in body fluids. During an infection, they are drawn to the lymph nodes, and make them swell. You can feel the small, lima-bean shaped lymph nodes in your throat swell up when you are getting a cold.

Another type of swelling is produced by the action of **histamine**, a chemical produced by some lymphocytes. Histamine inflames the site of attack and attracts defenders to it. During a cold, your nasal passages swell and become inflamed from histamine's action. In allergy, histamine's effects are unwanted, because they bring no benefits—only discomfort. The drugs called antihistamines work by reversing histamine's effects; relieving the symptoms of unwanted swelling and inflammation from allergy.

The strike force of T and B cells works as a unit. If one of the T cells spots an enemy it recognizes, it sends out an alert (a chemical message). B cells respond to the alert by making antibodies that destroy the invader.

When T cells have identified an enemy and B cells have fired antibodies at it and killed it, still other lymphocytes (we'll call

MINI GLOSSARY

lymphocytes (LIM-fo-sites): white blood cells, active in immunity.
thymus gland: an organ of the immune system.
T cells: lymphocytes that can recognize invaders that cause illness.
B cells: lymphocytes that make antibodies.
antibodies: large protein molecules produced to fight infective or foreign tissue.
antigens: foreign substances in the body, such as viruses or bacteria, that stimulate the immune system to produce antibodies.
histamine (HIST-uh-meen): a chemical of the immune response that produces inflammation (swelling and irritation) of tissue.

Activity 3.4

Infectious Disease Research.
Working in pairs, the students are to select an infectious disease and trace the course of that disease through the five periods. Research time will be needed to obtain the proper incubation period, the correct symptoms, any medical treatment, and total recovery period. The final product can be an oral presentation, a poster, or a written report.

Activity 3.5

Case Study. Have students write a fictional case study of a person with an infectious disease. They should include information about each stage of the illness. **(Reteach, Reinforce)**

Activity 3.6

Fighting Pathogens. On poster board have students illustrate the way the body fights invasion by pathogens. **(Reteach, Reinforce)**

Activity 3.7

Stages of Disease. Have students write a description of the stages of an infectious disease through the eyes of a specific pathogen. Be sure they identify

408

FIGURE 16-2

The Course of a Disease ①

Period	Events
1. Incubation	The period after invasion of pathogens, when they multiply in the body. The person may be unaware of the infection at this stage and may infect others without knowing it. The immune system may begin to detect the invaders. The immune system often wipes out the pathogens in this stage and stops the disease. If the immune system fails in this task, the disease progresses to the next phase.
2. Prodrome	The onset of symptoms, such as fever, sneezing, and coughing. These are the same for many diseases. In this stage, the disease is easily transmitted. The immune system is stepping up its fight.
3. Clinical	The period of symptoms known to be caused by the disease. The immune system is in full battle. (Medical treatments could possibly shorten this and succeeding stages.)
4. Decline	The period when the immune system has almost won the fight against the infection, and symptoms are going away. Memory cells form.
5. Convalescence (con-va-LESS-ence)	The period when the body repairs damage and returns to normal. The pathogen may or may not remain in the body. If it does, the person may remain a carrier of the disease, able to infect others even if no symptoms are evident.

them scavenger cells) capture and devour the dead invader. In the background are still other cells (memory cells) that "remember" the invader so that the system can quickly destroy it, should it show up again.

As you might suspect, all of this death and destruction could be hazardous if it got out of hand, so the body has developed a shutoff system to control it. The immune response is shut down and other cells become active as the battle comes to an end. When the action is over, only some antibodies and memory cells remain, but they carry the history of what has happened. Memory cells live on for many years. They are responsible for the immunity that follows many infections or immunizations.

You may wonder why people can't develop immunity to colds, flu, or cold sores. Why do people get these illnesses over and over again? Why don't the memory cells do their job? Actually, it is likely that the symptoms of sickness we call "a cold" represent many *different* colds, each caused by a different pathogen. Also, some flu viruses can hide from the immune cells just well enough to keep the cells from recognizing them when they reinfect the person. The reason why a person who gets cold sores (fever blisters) will have repeated outbreaks is that the virus takes up residence in the nerves of the face and hides there. When the virus becomes active again, the immune system doesn't fully recognize the old enemy fast enough to prevent an outbreak.

EVALUATE
SECTION III

Activity 3.8
Pop Quiz.
1. Histamines are drugs used to relieve the irritation of mucous membranes. (F)
2. An important part of the immune sys-tem is the bone marrow, which produces lymphocytes. (T)
3. The onset of the symptoms of a dis-ease is called the *convalescence* period. (F)
4. Memory cells are responsible for the immunity that follows an infection. (T)
5. Fevers can assist the immune system by destroying pathogens that cannot sur-vive at higher body temperatures. (T)

CLOSE
SECTION III

Activity 3.9
Oral Review. Have students close their books and name the five stages in the course of a disease and give a brief description of each.

Key Points *The body defends itself against infections. Skin and membranes offer a barrier to microbes. The immune system fights infections that make it past this barrier.*

Recognizing the Course of an Illness

Occasionally, pathogens break through the body's defenses and produce illness. Not all diseases develop the same way, but many do. A person who recognizes the early phases of an infection can take action right away. The five phases are described in Figure 16–2 on the opposite page.

The **prodrome** symptoms listed in Figure 16–2 are ones you might have with any of a number of infections, many of them minor. One warning: if any of the pro-drome symptoms listed in Figure 11–8 in Chapter 11 are present, do not delay seek-ing help. These symptoms can mean the disease is serious.

A person who has developed a bacterial infection can assist the immune system's defenses by taking antibiotics—drugs that prevent bacterial growth. With bacterial numbers in check, the immune system can overpower and eliminate the pathogenic bacteria. Each type of antibiotic is useful only against certain kinds of bacteria, how-ever. Therefore, it takes a trained health care provider to select the right one and to get the dosage right.

Antibiotics are useless against viruses, be-cause antibiotics work by preventing cell growth, and viruses are not cells. The im-mune system has to work by itself to wipe out the virus. All that can be done for most viral infections is to relieve symptoms until the disease runs its course.

If you develop a fever, think twice before you reach for fever-relief medicine. Fever has long been feared because it often devel-ops with dangerous diseases. However, fever itself may actually assist the immune

Fever Guidelines

Oral temperatures over 104° F: seek medical attention.

Oral temperatures between 100°-104° F: control with acetaminophen or ibuprofen (give aspirin only to people over 19 years of age to prevent Reye's syndrome; see Chapter 12).

Oral temperatures 100° F and less: do not treat. (If fever persists, see a health care provider.)

Figure 16–3 Fever Guidelines

system in its fight against infection. For ex-ample, cold viruses thrive and multiply at temperatures between 86 and 95 degrees Fahrenheit, but die off at higher tempera-tures. Fever also helps to activate the im-mune system. Figure 16–3 above provides fever guidelines.

Key Points *Many illnesses follow a predictable course. Antibiotics act against bacterial diseases, but are useless against viruses. A mild fever can help the immune system fight an infection.*

MINI GLOSSARY

prodrome: the onset of general symptoms common to many diseases, such as fever, sneezing, and coughing.

Teacher Support Notes

① **Antibiotics:** Because antibiotics are overused in the United States, antibiot-ic-resistant bacteria are becoming a greater threat to health. For example, suppose a person is taking an antibiotic for a particular condition. This person has a large population of nor-mally harmless bacteria in the digestive tract. While the antibiotic is killing the desired bacteria, it also wipes out many of these intestinal bacteria. The most sensitive bacteria stop multiplying, but those that are resistant to the drug survive and multiply. Thus, a population of drug-resistant bacteria suc-ceeds the original population. These bacteria do not harm at the moment, but their drug resistance sets the stage for potential problems.

② **Teacher Informa-tion Sheet:** Your supple-mentary material contains background information entitled "How Fever Works."

In this section students will learn:
1. Ways people can protect themselves from infectious disease.
2. How food poisoning can be prevented.

Activity 4.1
Immunization Records. From a local pediatrician or from a public health office, obtain an immunization chart. Distribute copies of the chart to each student and discuss when shots should be given, how long they are good for, and if booster shots are necessary.

As an assignment, have students take the chart home to record the dates of all the vaccines they have received since birth. (Assign number 4 under "Activities" on page 417.) If parent(s) cannot locate a record of immunization, the student may want to get the information from the school's health office.

The following day discuss the students' immunization records. What did they discover? Were any booster shots due? Ask the students if they can think of any additional vaccines that might be needed if they were to travel to an underdeveloped country. (A local pediatrician or public health worker may be willing to speak

Section III Review
Answers
1. T cells, B cells
2. histamine
3. prodrome
4. The skin produces salty acidic sweat and has one-way pores to let things out, but not in. The mucus and cilia in membranes trap microbes and sweep them out. These internal membranes fight off great numbers of pathogens each day. They are the body's first line of defense against disease.
5. The T cells recognize enemies.
6. During an infection, the lymphocytes are drawn to the lymph nodes and make them swell.
7. The histamine inflames the site of attack and attracts defenders to it. During a cold, the nasal passages swell from the histamine.
8. incubation, prodrome, clinical, decline, convalescence; if you can recognize the early phases of an infection, you can take action right away
9. Answers will vary.

> **❝ Thoughts on Health ❞**
>
> *Sickness is felt, but health not at all.*
> – *Proverb*

SECTION III   REVIEW

Answer the following questions on a sheet of paper.

Learning the Vocabulary
The vocabulary terms in this section are *lymphocytes, thymus gland, T cells, B cells, antibodies, antigens, histamine,* and *prodrome.*
1. When a disease attacks the body, cells known as _____ recognize the invaders and cells known as _____ produce antibodies to fight the disease.
2. Antihistamines work by reversing _____'s effects: they relieve irritation of mucous membranes.
3. The stage of a disease when the symptoms are appearing is the _____.

Learning the Facts
4. Why are your skin and internal membranes important in defending you against infections?
5. How does the body's immune system know when a disease agent has attacked the body?
6. Why does your throat sometimes swell up when you are getting a cold?
7. How does inflammation help you to fight off a cold?
8. Identify the steps in the course of a disease. Why is it useful to know them?

Making Life Choices
9. The body's immune system is speedy and accurate in its responses to infection. In view of how "smart" the body is, what do you think of someone who hurries to take drugs every time a minor health problem sets in? When is it wise to take drugs and when is it not wise? How can you be sure to do the right thing in each case?

SECTION IV

Taking Action

One of the most important steps a person can take to avoid infectious diseases is to keep immunizations up to date. (Chapter 11 provides a schedule of recommended

Sneezes contain millions of microbes.

immunizations.) What more can people do to prevent infections? Keep your resistance up by taking care of your immune system. It works best when given a balanced diet. Related to diet is alcohol intake. Alcohol and many other drugs are directly toxic to the immune system, weakening resistance.

Regular physical activity supports the immune system. If you don't exercise, start.

Stress also makes illness likely. You may have noticed that when you are worried or nervous about something, your throat tends to get sore. This is a warning that before long, unless you manage the stress better, the pathogens you encounter can make you ill.

The principles of self-protection against colds and other infections are summarized in the Health Strategies section on the next page, "How to Avoid Infections." To see how well you protect yourself, refer to the Life Choice Inventory.

Airborne Infections

You can often avoid viral and other infections by remembering that for pathogens to cause disease, they must be transferred from a person or an object to you. Millions of pathogens are sprayed into the air by uncovered sneezes and coughs.

Imagine that the viruses or bacteria are a quart of red paint that has been sprayed all

TEACH

SECTION IV
(Guided and Independent Practice)

Activity 4.2
Statement Analysis. Ask the students if they agree with the following statements:

"If food tastes fine and smells fine, it is OK to eat," and "It's OK to drink water from a stream if it is clear." Discuss their opinions. **(10 min., Critical Thinking)**

Activity 4.3
Reducing Risks. In each of the following situations, ask the students to identify how the individual could reduce the risks of getting an infection and why the suggested behavior would reduce risk:

1. Rhonda has to work tonight and does not know how she is going to write the paper that is due tomorrow. She is very worried and may have to pull an all-nighter.

2. Ellen is sick a lot. When she goes to the doctor, he notices that she chews her fingernails.

3. John is always tired. He comes home every day, watches TV, and eats his

(continued on next page)

HEALTH STRATEGIES

How to Avoid Infections

1. Take measures against bacterial growth, both on your body and in your surroundings—maintain a cool, well-lit, dry, clean environment.
2. To remove bacteria from skin, use soap and water. To kill bacteria, use antiseptics on skin and disinfectants on surfaces and objects.
3. Obtain medical treatment for deep wounds.
4. Stay current with immunizations to develop necessary immunity before infection sets in.
5. Avoid unnecessary contact with people who are ill.
6. Do not share objects with people who are ill.
7. Wash your hands often throughout the day, especially before eating.
8. Keep away from people who are coughing or sneezing into the air.
9. Select a diet that supports immune system health, such as was described in Chapter 8.
10. Do not drink alcoholic beverages.
11. Exercise regularly.
12. Do not use tobacco.
13. Control stress.
14. Get adequate rest.

over your classroom, and is still wet. What would happen if you touched the surfaces and then touched your mouth, eyes, or nose? You would have red paint on your face. This is how bacteria and viruses invade your body. In public places, stay a good distance away from anyone who is carelessly sneezing or coughing into the air,

and touch no "red" surfaces. Wash yourself, including your hair, and even your clothes, if you think you've been sprayed. Comfort sick people with soothing words from across the room instead of with hugs or kisses. This advice holds for cold and flu viruses and for many other microbes as well. This chapter's Consumer Awareness section explains how to tell whether your sniffle is a cold or the flu, and what to do about either one.

Key Points ▶ *To minimize their risks of infection, people can keep immunizations up to date, maintain distance when others are ill, and keep their immune systems strong.*

Food Poisoning

If you had awakened this morning with abdominal cramps, a headache, vomiting, diarrhea, and a fever, would you have suspected yesterday's meatball sandwich as the cause? Maybe you should have. At least one-third of people living in the United States are treated for food poisoning each year. It may be that almost everyone experiences a touch of some type of food poisoning in a year's time. However, most people mistakenly pass the incidents off as "stomach flu." The truth is that while some viruses do cause intestinal distress, food poisoning is a much more likely cause.

Pathogens growing in foods can make people sick in two ways: by infecting them or by poisoning them. In the first case, a pathogen such as the ***Salmonella*** bacterium

MINI GLOSSARY

Salmonella: a common foodborne pathogen causing digestive system infections in many people each year.

Teacher Support Notes

① **Avoiding Infections:** Have students rate themselves on each of these 14 strategies. For each one, would they rate their behavior as Excellent, Fair, or Poor? What is the one strategy that they could implement that would most improve their resistance to disease? As another way for students to assess their behavior, have them do the Life Choice Inventory on page 413.

favorite snack food—potato chips.
(10 min., Critical Thinking)

Activity 4.4
Causes of Death. On the chalk board write the following:

Leading Causes of Death in the U.S. in 1900
1. Pneumonia and Flu
2. Tuberculosis
3. Inflammation of the DigestiveTract

Leading Causes of Death in the U.S. Today
1. Heart Disease
2. Cancer
3. Stroke

Compare the three leading causes of death in the United States today and those in the 1900s. Discuss what advances have occurred to cause such a

change in the first list. What impact has lifestyle had on today's list? (You may want to refer students back to the beginning of Chapter 1 where this topic is covered in more detail.) **(10 min.; Extend, Enrich)**

Activity 4.5
Sanitation Aids. Explain to the students that the best way to fight pathogens is by practicing sanitation. Ask them to

---

✉ **Where to Write**

National Health Information Clearinghouse
P.O. Box 1133
Washington, DC 20013

Teacher Support Notes

① Critical Thinking Answers:

1. They throw money away if they spend it on antibiotics that do them no good. Another drawback to using antibiotics to fight what is probably a virus is that the body can develop antibiotic-resistant cells that can cause the person harm later.

2. Answers will vary. Students will hopefully see a middle ground with regard to this question. Many people do overreact to symptoms, thus increasing their medical bills needlessly when the body could take care of the disease.

✍ Fast Facts
The chances are one in three that a chicken sold in a supermarket is infected with salmonella.

---

412 UNIT 5 Disease Prevention

CONSUMER AWARENESS — Is It a Cold or Is It Flu?

Almost everyone suffers from an **upper respiratory infection** at least once each year. A person whose eyes begin to water, nose starts to run, or throat gets scratchy thinks of little else but obtaining relief from these symptoms. When this happens to you, the most important step is to decide what you have, so that you can use effective treatments. After all, what feels like the start of a cold may turn out to be something worse—even **infectious mononucleosis** or pneumonia.

Influenza, or flu, is almost always caused by a virus. Thus antibiotics bring no relief. Flu usually spreads as an **epidemic** in the spring or fall of the year. It sweeps through a population, and nearly everyone in the area suffers at least a mild attack. Flu symptoms develop one or more days after exposure to the virus. The early symptoms are identical to some of those of a cold: possible fever and chills, runny nose, sneezing, and nasal congestion. Unlike colds, though, flu brings a sudden muscle weakness and aches and pains in the arms, legs, and back. A dry, hacking cough, which produces no mucus but which may cause chest pain, is another telling sign of flu. Some people report suffering psychological depression from the flu, lasting up to a week beyond full recovery from the other symptoms.

Flu strains bear the names of the locations where they are thought to have originated—Hong Kong flu, Russian flu, Asian flu, and so on. Flu shots taken in the fall can provide immunity to some of them. However, flu shots go out of date

each year as new strains of virus develop.

Colds can be viral or bacterial. Symptoms that characterize a cold are a sore throat; watery eyes; hoarseness; and a thick, greenish yellow nasal discharge. Some people believe that exposure to drafts or having wet feet is a sure way to bring on a cold. In reality, exposure to viruses, not wet feet or drafts, will bring on a cold.

Sometimes, though, a cold or flu turns out to be dangerous. You should definitely see a health care provider immediately if any of the following symptoms occur:

- A cold or flu that is accompanied by headache or facial pain (indicating sinus infection).
- A deep, "honking" cough; wheezing; or shortness of breath (indicating bronchitis or pneumonia).
- High fever (above 104 degrees Fahrenheit).
- Pain in the ears.

A lung infection, left untreated, robbed the "Muppet" puppeteer Jim Henson of his life. Colds and flu are usually harmless and cannot be medicated away, even with antibiotics. Some, though, are not so ordinary. The right treatment can be lifesaving.

① CRITICAL THINKING

1. Why do you think it is important to know that flu and most colds are caused by viruses?
2. Some people see a physician for every sniffle, "just in case." Do you agree or disagree with this course of action? Why?

EVALUATE

SECTION IV

Activity 4.6
Pop Quiz.
1. It's important to keep _____ up to date. (immunizations)
2. Millions of pathogens are sprayed into the air by an uncovered _____. (sneeze)
3. Keep _____ from people who are ill. (away or back)
4. Regular _____ supports the immune system and makes you look good, too! (exercise)
5. _____ can make you ill unless you learn to manage it. (Stress)
6. Abdominal cramps, vomiting, and diarrhea are signs of _____ _____. (food poisoning)
7. Toss out cans of food that _____ out on top. (bulge)
8. Keep _____ food _____. (hot, hot)
9. Keep _____ food _____. (cold, cold)
10. Eat only foods that have been prepared on a _____ _____. (clean surface)
(5 min.)

(continued on next page)

LIFE CHOICE INVENTORY

How Well Do You Protect Yourself against Infectious Diseases?

A no answer to any of the following questions indicates a way to improve defenses against infection.

1. Do you keep your environment cool, clean, dry, and well lit?
2. Do you wash your hands several times during the day and before mealtimes?
3. Are your immunizations up to date?
4. Do you heed the advice of public health departments during times when people should receive special immunizations?
5. Do you avoid sharing food, beverages, utensils, towels, and other objects with people who have symptoms of contagious infections, such as colds, cold sores (fever blisters), flu, or others?
6. Do you, whenever possible, place yourself at a distance from people who are coughing or sneezing into the air?
7. Is your diet balanced and adequate—the kind of diet your immune system needs?
8. Do you abstain from drinking alcohol?
9. Are you including exercise in your daily routine?
10. Do you make time for rest and fun?
11. Is stress under control in your life?
12. Do you abstain from using tobacco?
13. If you do get sick, do you follow the full course of treatment to prevent a relapse?

can infect the digestive tract, causing the symptoms just mentioned. In people weakened by illness or in the very old or very young, *Salmonella* infections can be fatal.

Pathogens also cause illnesses by giving off poisons into food as the numbers of pathogens grow. For example, a person unfortunate enough to eat canned food contaminated with the poison **botulin toxin** faces severe, usually fatal nervous system damage unless medical treatment is prompt. Symptoms of **botulism** come on fast, many times while the person is still at the table. If you or someone you're with experiences double vision, muscle weakness, or difficulty swallowing or breathing after eating canned food, get medical help right away.

Some people have come to accept a yearly bout or two of intestinal illness. In truth, though, most of these illnesses can be pre-

MINI GLOSSARY

botulin toxin: a potent poison produced by bacteria in sealed cans, plastic packs, or jars of food.

botulism: the often fatal condition of poisoning with the botulin toxin.

upper respiratory infection: an infection of the membranes of the nasal cavities, sinuses, throat, and trachea, but not involving the lungs.

infectious mononucleosis (MON-oh-new-klee-OH-sis): a viral infection involving mononucleotes, a type of white blood cell. The symptoms vary from mild, coldlike symptoms to high fevers, swollen glands, and spleen and liver involvement; also called *mono*.

epidemic (EP-ih-DEM-ick): an infection that spreads rapidly through a population, affecting many people at the same time.

Fast Facts

According to a United Nations report, pneumonia is the biggest killer of children in the world, resulting in 3.6 million deaths annually. Most of these cases are preventable with a five-day course of antibiotics that costs only 25 cents.

Where to Write

Center for Health Promotion and Education
Center for Disease Control
1600 Clifton Road
Bldg. 3, Rm. 33A
Atlanta, GA 30333

Activity 4.7
Relieving Stress. Divide the students into groups of three or four and have them develop a list of healthy ways to relieve stress. Have each group read its list to the class. **(10 min.; Reteach, Reinforce)**

Activity 4.8
Vaccine Research. Have a student(s) write to a pharmaceutical firm for information on the preparation of vaccines, storage of vaccines, and how they are distributed in the United States. Discuss the findings with the class. **(Extend, Enrich)**

Activity 4.9
Review Questions. Students should be able to answer the following questions:
1. What are some ways to prevent infections?
2. What are the symptoms of food

Teacher Support Notes

① **Handout—U.S. Public Health Service Objectives:** A handout in your supplementary material gives the U.S. Public Health Service objectives from the U.S. Department of Health and Human Services for immunization and infectious diseases.

Section IV Review
Answers
1. upper respiratory infection
2. epidemic
3. Infectious mononucleosis
4. Salmonella is an actual bacteria that causes digestive system infections, while botulin toxin is the poison produced by bacteria in sealed cans, plastic packs, or jars of food.
5. Answers will vary. Refer to the Health Strategies on page 411 for possible answers.
6. sore throat; watery eyes; hoarseness; thick, greenish-yellow nasal discharge
7. Answers will vary; could include: a cold or flu accompanied by headache or facial pain; deep "honking" cough, wheezing or shortness of breath; high fever above 104 degrees Fahrenheit; and pain in the ears.
8. Answers will vary.

414

---

vented. To protect yourself, insist that the food you eat be prepared according to three simple rules: keep hot food hot, keep cold food cold, and keep the kitchen clean.

Rule #1. Keep hot food hot, because microbes die at temperatures above about 140 degrees Fahrenheit—piping, steaming hot. Refuse hot dishes such as meatballs, cream soups, casseroles, and other foods that have been allowed to stand at room temperature or that feel just warm. Spoiled food often tastes fine, because the pathogens or toxins may have no taste or smell. However, they will still make you sick. And certainly, if the food smells or tastes bad, throw it out.

Rule #2. Keep cold food cold, because microbes divide and produce poisons very slowly at temperatures below 40 degrees Fahrenheit. Refuse cold dishes that have been allowed to stand at room temperature for 2 hours or more. Macaroni salad; cold meats; egg, ham, or chicken salads; and many others should be served refrigerator-cold.

Rule #3. Eat only foods that have been prepared and served on clean surfaces by clean hands. Avoid foods served with utensils that previously held raw meats or that are dirty from other uses.

One last rule: toss out any cans of food that bulge out on top or that appear to be leaking. Even a taste of such food can cause deadly botulism, and the risk of this illness far outweighs whatever pleasure you might find in the food. If you follow these rules, you may have to skip a meal once in a while, but you can make up for it later. At least, aside from feeling hungry, you will be fine.

Key Points *Food poisoning is a likely cause of intestinal distress. Pathogens growing in foods can make people sick by infecting them or by poisoning them. To protect yourself from food poisoning, keep hot food hot, keep cold food cold, and keep the kitchen clean.*

SECTION IV REVIEW

Answer the following questions on a sheet of paper

Learning the Vocabulary
The vocabulary terms in this section are *Salmonella, upper respiratory infection, infectious mononucleosis, epidemic,* and *botulin toxin.*
1. At least once a year almost everyone suffers from an _____ which affects the nasal cavity, sinuses, throat, and trachea.
2. An _____ is an infection that spreads rapidly through a population affecting many people at the same time.
3. _____ is a viral infection involving mononucleocytes.
4. What is a difference between *Salmonella* and botulin toxin?

Learning the Facts
5. List four steps a person can take to avoid infectious diseases.
6. What are some common cold symptoms?
7. List three symptoms that would require a visit to a health care provider.

Making Life Choices
8. Take the Life Choice Inventory on page 413 to determine how well you protect yourself against infectious diseases. Identify those habits you need to change. What other health practices can you add to the list that would prevent the spread of infection?

①

Answers to Fact or Fiction

Here are the answers to the questions at the start of the chapter.

1. False. Many microbes are harmless and provide services needed for life. **2.** True. **3.** True. **4.** True. **5.** False. Antibiotics are useful against bacteria but useless against viruses. **6.** False. Fevers are part of the body's defense against infection and low fevers are not dangerous. **7.** True.

3. What are some ways to protect your-self from food poisoning?
(Reteach, Reinforce)

microbes were first discovered.

Additional projects could be assigned to research individuals who were pioneers in the fight against disease.
(10–15 min.)

RETEACH/BONUS

Past Beliefs. Ask students to discuss some past beliefs concerning the causes of diseases prior to the time

STRAIGHT TALK

Mononucleosis— The Kissing Disease

Beginning at about age 15, teenagers are likely to come down with infectious mononucleosis, or "mono." Recovery from this viral attack is usually complete, and complications are rare. However, the illness can make some people feel sicker than ever before.

Why do they call mono the kissing disease?

The name "kissing disease" is related to a theory about activities of the age group most likely to get the disease—15- to 30-year-olds. People in this age range are most active in courting, and therefore in kissing, the theory goes, and mono is thought to be spread through oral contact.

Interestingly, mono sometimes sweeps through a school population as an epidemic, indicating one of two things: that mono spreads by modes other than kissing or that students in some school populations are extraordinarily fond of all of their classmates. People who are married for many years hardly ever get mono, because they are only kissing each other. This makes them less likely to pick up infections.

What are the symptoms?

Mono is difficult to diagnose from symptoms alone, because it can imitate so many other conditions. One person may be infected and develop only a mild sniffle. Another may experience weakness, a severe sore throat, fever, swollen glands, an enlarged spleen, and an infected liver with symptoms like those of the dangerous liver infection hepatitis. Mono may come on slowly or quickly. Once the first attack subsides, it can come on again with even more ferocity.

How can physicians tell whether someone has mono?

A blood test that takes just minutes can accurately diagnose mono. The test studies the white blood cells known as mononucleocytes, from which the disease gets

its name. This test is the only way to distinguish mono from many other infections ranging from colds to hepatitis.

How dangerous is mono?

Luckily, few people suffer serious side effects from a bout of mono. The spleen may become sensitive and, very rarely, may rupture, requiring surgery. This is why people diagnosed with mono are advised to take it easy. Athletes with mono are told to warm the bench instead of playing hard at a sport that may injure the spleen.

After a person recovers from mono, can it come back?

The immune system develops immunity to mono after one bout. That one course of the illness can last as long as a few months. After full recovery, mono will not strike the same person again.

✍ Fast Facts

In its "State of the World's Children 1993" report, UNICEF found that two-thirds of the 12.9 million child deaths each year are caused by only three diseases—pneumonia, diarrheal disease, and measles—all of which are either preventable or curable. In the early '80s, diarrheal disease was the biggest killer of the world's children, claiming almost 4 million young lives each year. Now there are one million fewer deaths each year associated with dysentery and other intestinal ailments.

Vocabulary

1. a. athlete's foot
b. hepatitis **c.** fungi
d. T cells **e.** head lice
f. worms **g.** flu
h. B cells
2. a. Yeasts are one-celled fungi, while molds are many-celled fungi.

b. Rubella only resembles measles, lasting a few days and causing no serious complications for the sufferer, except in pregnancy. Measles causes rash, high fever, sensitivity to light, cough, and cold symptoms for the sufferer.
3. a. pathogens **b.** rabies
c. Tuberculosis **d.** Infectious diseases

4. a. Lymphocytes **b.** Lyme disease **c.** tetanus **d.** Pneumonia

Recall

Section I
1. warm, dark, moist, and nutrient-rich
2. Answers will vary; could include: wearing high socks, wearing long pants, using tick

repellent (especially on the ankles, legs, and groin area).
3. Answers will vary; could include: colds, flu, chicken pox, shingles, and chronic fatigue syndrome.
Section II
4. An infected person contaminates the air, food, or objects near another who breathes the air or eats the food or handles

---

CHAPTER REVIEW

L EARNING THE VOCABULARY

microbes	yeasts	smallpox
infectious diseases	molds	bubonic plague
pathogens	athlete's foot	lymphocytes
bacteria	pinworms	thymus gland
viruses	head lice	T cells
fungi	hepatitis	B cells
protozoa	cholera	antibodies
worms	disinfectants	antigens
parasites	antiseptics	histamine
tetanus	rabies	prodrome
tuberculosis	vaccine	*Salmonella*
Lyme disease	pneumonia	botulin toxin
cold	polio	botulism
flu (influenza)	measles	upper respiratory infection
shingles	rubella	infectious mononucleosis
chicken pox	mumps	epidemic
chronic fatigue syndrome	hospital infections	

Answer the following questions on a separate sheet of paper.

1. **Matching**—*Match each of the following phrases with the appropriate vocabulary term from the list above:*
   a. a fungal infection of the feet
   b. a disease of the liver caused by several types of viruses transmitted by infected needles
   c. living things that absorb and use nutrients of organisms they invade
   d. lymphocytes that can recognize invaders that cause illness
   e. tiny but visible parasitic insects that burrow into the skin or hairy body areas
   f. visible parasites that burrow into the blood supplies of victims
   g. a viral respiratory infection that can become epidemic
   h. lymphocytes that make antibodies.
2. a. What is the difference between yeasts and molds?
   b. What is the difference between measles and rubella?
3. **Word Scramble**—*Use the clues from the*

phrases below to help you unscramble the vocabulary words from the list above:
   a. **theapogns** Microbes that cause diseases are called _____.
   b. **seibar** Mammals transmit _____ by biting.
   c. **serclutbusoi** _____ is a bacterial disease of the lungs.
   d. **fentioiusc seaeisds** _____ _____ are diseases caused by and transmitted from person to person by microorganisms or their toxins.
4. a. _____ are white blood cells active in immunity. They include both T cells and B cells.
   b. The bacterial infection that is spread by deer ticks is called _____.
   c. A disease caused by a toxin produced by bacteria deep within a wound is called _____.
   d. _____ is a condition caused by an infection of the lungs with high fever, severe cough, and pain in the chest.

the objects and transfers the infection to his/her body.

Section III

5. bars entry by way of skin and membranes and the immune system

6. If the T cells spot an enemy they tell the B cells so that the B cells can produce antibodies to destroy it.

7. To "remember" the invader so that the system can quickly destroy it, should it show up again. They are responsible for the immunity that follows many infections or immunizations.

8. clinical

9. Antibiotics work by preventing cell growth, and viruses are not cells.

10. Cold viruses die off at temperatures above 95 degrees Fahrenheit and fever helps to activate the immune system.

Section IV

11. Answers will vary; could include: weakens—alcohol, many other drugs, and stress. Answers will vary; could include: strengthens—exercise and balanced diet.

12. Wash yourself, including your hair, and even your clothes, if you think you've been sprayed with a cough or sneeze. Do not comfort ill people with hugs and kisses.

13. Answers will vary; could include: abdominal cramps, headache, vomiting, diarrhea, and fever.

14. keep hot food hot; keep cold food cold; eat only foods that have been prepared and served on clean surfaces by clean hands

RECALLING IMPORTANT FACTS AND IDEAS

1. In what type of environment do bacteria grow and multiply best?
2. Name some precautions you can take against tick bites.
3. Name three diseases caused by viruses.
4. Describe how infections spread.
5. How does the body defend itself against pathogens?
6. How do T and B cells work together to destroy disease-causing invaders?
7. What is the role of the memory cells?
8. During which phase of infection is the immune system in full battle?
9. Why aren't antibiotics effective against viruses?
10. How does a fever assist the immune system?
11. Name one thing that weakens the body's resistance and one thing that strengthens resistance.
12. How can you avoid contracting airborne infections?
13. What are some symptoms of *Salmonella* poisoning?
14. Name three rules that should be followed when preparing food.

CRITICAL THINKING

1. In 1979 the U. S. Surgeon General stated that "the health of the people has never been better." Taking into account recent changes in the infectious disease pattern, what kind of statement do you think the Surgeon General might have made in 1989? What statement do you think will be made in 1999? Justify your answers.

ACTIVITIES

1. Find a newspaper or magazine article less than one year old that discusses some aspect of infectious diseases. Write a one-page summary and reaction to the article. Include a copy of the article with the date and source.
2. Interview a local public health official to obtain the following information: how the local public health unit keeps track of local incidences of infectious diseases, what infections are most common in your area, and what reports must be made to higher levels of government. Identify the name of the person interviewed and the agency the person works for.
3. Choose a developing country and find out which infectious diseases are common in that country. Discuss what is being done to control the diseases.
4. Call your doctor's office and ask someone to send you an official written record of the immunizations you received. Find out when you are due to receive your next booster doses and ask if you should be vaccinated against any other diseases. Turn in a copy of your immunization record, booster doses, and dates.
5. On the left half of a poster board, make a collage of advertisements for cold remedies. On the right half, collage your own non-drug alternatives for treating a cold.
6. Identify some of the community programs in your area that are aimed at preventing disease. List the name, address, and phone number of each program and the services they provide to help reduce the spread of infectious disease.
7. Choose a foreign country you would like to visit and find out what health precautions are necessary to travel to that country. What vaccines are necessary and why?

MAKING DECISIONS ABOUT HEALTH

1. There is a big dance at school tonight and you are really looking forward to going. Unfortunately you have had a headache all day, your throat is feeling a little bit sore, and you have the chills. Would you take an aspirin substitute and go to the dance or would you stay home and rest? What is likely to happen as a result of your decision?

417

CHAPTER 17 PLANNER

OVERVIEW

Chapter 17 is 28 pages long and divided into the three sections listed at the right. Major learning outcomes are also listed to the right. This chapter introduces students to some of the most common STDs, including AIDS. It provides information on the transmission, causes, symptoms, complications, treatments, and preventative actions for each disease. The chapter also stresses the importance of individual choices regarding abstinence, sexual behavior, and drug usage, in avoidance of STDs. The importance of good communication between partners about sexual values, possible infection, and limits for sexual contact, is discussed.

MAKING LIFE CHOICES RESOURCES

A variety of activities, handouts, quizzes, and tests to accompany this chapter are available in the *Making Life Choices* supplementary material. You may pick and choose from those materials as appropriate for your amount of class time and the ability levels of your students. Some of the resources you might want to consider using are:

Handouts
• U.S. Health Service Objectives
• HIV Behavior Diagrams

CHAPTER PROJECT

This chapter project is one that could be done by the entire class or small groups within the class. Instruct students to create a play or skit that provides information about STDs through a story format. The purpose of this play/skit is to encourage the audience to take every possible precaution to avoid contracting an STD. It may also include information on the complications and dangers of STDs.

Variations might be to have each group do its play/skit on a different STD, or have the entire class create a play/skit about AIDS. Students may be encouraged to create scenery, props, music, or rap. The play/skit could be performed live for the class or videotaped and shown to the class at a later date. (The length of the play/skit would be determined by the amount of time you have for this activity.)

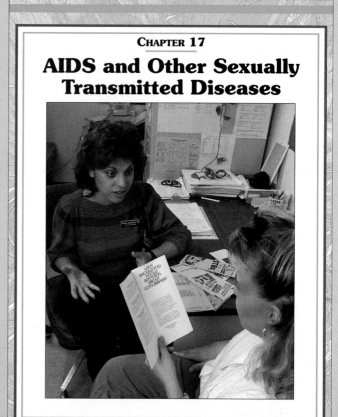

CHAPTER 17

AIDS and Other Sexually Transmitted Diseases

SUGGESTED RESOURCES

Student Readings
1. *Does AIDS Hurt?* ETR Associates. PO Box 1830, Santa Cruz, CA 95061-1830.
2. Daugirdas, John. *Sexually Transmitted Disease.* Hinsdale, IL: MedText, Inc.
3. Brandt, A. *No Magic Bullet.* New York: Oxford University Press, 1987.

Teacher Readings
1. Shilts, Randy. *And the Band Played On: Politics, People, and the AIDS Epidemic.* New York: St. Martins Press, 1987.
2. *American Red Cross Program on HIV/AIDS.* This is a complete curriculum on teaching HIV/AIDS with accompanying videos, flip charts and transparency masters.

Activity To Introduce Chapter

Since the topic of this chapter is sometimes difficult for students to discuss in a mature fashion, begin with a "pretest" to help students separate fact from fiction on STDs. This is a safe way for students to uncover their own false beliefs without revealing them to classmates. Use the "Fact or Fiction" feature as the pretest. The "Fact or Fiction" feature might also be used by students at the end of this chapter to check their

Teacher Resources

1. Centers for Disease Control National AIDS Information Clearinghouse, PO Box 6003, Rockville, MD 20850.

understanding and prepare them for the final test on the chapter. An extension of this activity might be to have students give the "Fact or Fiction" statements to others, such as family members and other students outside the health class to determine the most common errors believed by these groups of people.

NOT ENOUGH TIME?*

You could easily spend six to seven days on this chapter, depending on the number of activities you assign. The following are suggestions to help make sure you cover the key topics if you only have four days for this chapter.

TIME	SUGGESTIONS
1 Day	Assign Section I to be read at home before class. On the day of this lesson, begin with Activity 1.1 to get students' interest. In low-ability classes, have students do Activity 1.2 prior to taking the quiz suggested in the Activity to Introduce Chapter. Have students take the quiz during class. Let them grade their own papers to avoid embarrassment about wrong answers. Then do Activity 1.3 using cooperative learning to speed up the process of going over various STDs.
2 Days	Presentations planned the previous day in Activity 1.3 should be given, limiting each group to three minutes. Do Activity 1.2 to introduce students to some of the vocabulary words in this section.
3 Days	Assign for today Sections II and III to be completed prior to class. Begin discussion of AIDS with a few students' responses to Activity 2.1. After ten minutes of discussion, use the Straight Talk to explain how AIDS attacks the body. Have the cards prepared for Activity 2.3, on transmission, and hand out to the class. Complete this activity and tell students there will be a brief quiz at the beginning of class tomorrow to see if they understand AIDS. (Activity 2.5) You may assign Activity 2.6 to reteach the material.
4 Days	Begin with the quiz in Activity 2.5. Then do Activity 3.1. Return to the story in Activity 1.1 and complete Activity 3.2. Select either Activity 3.3 or 3.4 depending on the needs of your students. Activity 3.6 or 3.7 may be assigned as homework to evaluate this section.

Please refer to the 18-week daily lesson plans in the supplementary material for additional suggestions.

Answers to "Fact or Fiction"

Answers to "Fact or Fiction" can be found on page 440.

In this section students will learn:
1. The symptoms, treatments, complications, and prevention measures for seven STDs.
2. The effects of STDs on fertility, pregnancy, and the unborn child.
3. About other infections of the genital and urinary tract that are not sexually transmitted.

Activity 1.1

Giving Advice. Present students with a fictitious story about two adolescents who have been dating each other for four months. The girl, Tina, has never had sexual intercourse with anyone before, but she does not know the sexual history of her boyfriend, James. As they have grown closer emotionally, they have also grown closer physically, and Tina thinks they will soon be making a decision about intercourse. Tell the students to imagine that Tina has come to them for advice. She wants to hear the pros and cons of becoming sexually active, and she is especially concerned about STDs. They are to list three items of advice they would give Tina.

Students may write their advice on

Teacher Support Notes

① **Pathogens:** If you did not do Chapter 16, you will need to explain the meaning of pathogen. You could refer students back to the explanation on page 400.

② **Abstinence:** Abstinence (refraining from sexual intercourse) is emphasized at every opportunity throughout the text and is discussed at length in Chapter 20. It will also be discussed thoroughly later in this chapter. Review the definition here for slower students.

③ **Discharge:** Some students may not know what is meant by the term *discharge*. You could tell them that it is a thick, fluid material that oozes from the body—in this case the penis. You could compare it to the phlegm that they blow from their noses. Phlegm is a symptom of their colds, as discharges are often symptoms of a sexually transmitted disease.

④ **Regular Check-Ups:** Emphasize the point that regular check-ups are important because symptoms of an STD are not always visible. They will read repeatedly of STDs that do not announce themselves. The complications caused by these illnesses can only be avoided if health care providers know they're there.

The pathogens that cause **sexually transmitted diseases (STDs)** can all be transferred from person to person by way of sexual contact. That is, a person who has sexual relations with someone else who is infected can come down with one or more of these diseases. Once in the body, STDs cause symptoms ranging from rashes and bumps to blindness and death.

Some of the common STDs are caused by bacteria. These are curable, because antibiotic drugs can help the body kill off bacterial infections. Others are caused by viruses and so remain incurable, because antibiotics are useless against viruses.

The most threatening of the incurable STDs, by far, is **acquired immune deficiency syndrome (AIDS)**. As the last section of this chapter shows, however, one defense is 100 percent effective against the sexual transmission of AIDS and all other STDs, curable or not. That defense is abstinence from sexual intercourse.

This discussion refers to many parts of the reproductive tract and other parts of the body. For pictures and explanations of these body parts, you may want to review Chapter 6. Looking ahead to the first few sections of Chapter 21 will provide you with additional information on the reproductive organs.

You may also wish to review the information in Chapter 16 on infectious diseases. Understanding the general principles of infection will help you understand how STDs develop and how they are treated.

SECTION I

Common Sexually Transmitted Diseases

STDs are so common among some groups of people that they rival the common cold in frequency. So many varieties of STDs exist in the world that space limits this section to mentioning only the most common ones. Figure 17–1 on pages 422 and 423 briefly describes the common STDs. The next few sections are arranged to present the most widespread STDs first, and to provide some details about their symptoms, harmful effects, and available treatments.

Some people hold false ideas about how to prevent STDs. They believe that simple measures such as washing the reproductive organs after intercourse or taking birth control pills can prevent STDs. These ideas are false. You will see by the end of this chapter that STD prevention requires knowledge, thought, and effort—not guesswork—to be effective.

Chlamydia

An STD that threatens the health of millions of people in the United States, but often causes no symptoms to warn them, is **chlamydia**. Men with this bacterial infection may feel a little burning when urinating or notice some mucuslike white discharge from the penis. Some may feel pain in the testicles. A few others may develop greatly enlarged lymph glands in the groin or may become infertile from a longstanding infection. Many men, however, have no symptoms at all.

Women with this infection may have some discharge from the vagina. Many, though, have no symptoms. A few have burning pain when urinating, pain in the lower abdomen, fever, bleeding or pain with sexual intercourse, or irregular menstrual periods.

With or without symptoms, chlamydia can progress to injure the reproductive organs. This is one reason why regular physi-

TEACH
SECTION I
(Guided and Independent Practice)

Activity 1.2
Vocabulary Ranking. Before assigning the reading in this section, put the following words on the board: *pathogen, symptom, antibiotics, discharge, infertile, bacteria, virus, lymph glands, sterility, cervix, genitals, absti-*nence, condom, vaginal, fetus.

Ask students to copy each word, and rank it according to the following scale:

0—I don't know what it means.

1—I've heard the term, but I'm not sure I can explain it.

2—I am fairly certain I understand this term well enough to explain it to someone else.

(continued on next page)

---

cal examinations that include STD tests are recommended for sexually active people. Many STDs can be silently progressing without symptoms to alert the person of their presence.

In advanced cases, chlamydia spreads to the deeper pelvic structures of women—a dangerous condition known as **pelvic inflammatory disease (PID)**. More than any other condition, PID has the ability to cause sterility in women. Men, too, may become sterile when chlamydia spreads to the testicles.

Because most people have no symptoms, they seek no treatment and allow the disease to do its damage unopposed. Without routine testing, sexually active people may unknowingly suffer damage from chlamydia and, equally unknowingly, spread it to others.

When chlamydia damages a woman's reproductive tract, she becomes likely to suffer an extremely dangerous and potentially fatal condition—**ectopic pregnancy**. In this condition, scar tissue blocks one or both fallopian tubes, the passages through which fertilized eggs must travel to enter the uterus. The embryo cannot implant and grow normally in the uterus. Instead, it grows in one of the tubes, and eventually ruptures the tube. Ectopic pregnancy is shown in Figure 17–2 on page 424.

Even in a normal pregnancy, chlamydia causes trouble. During birth, the bacteria can infect the lungs or eyes of the newborn baby, causing pneumonia or blindness. Health care providers can prevent these tragedies by treating infected pregnant women with antibiotics before delivery.

Although chlamydia is treatable with antibiotics, only a health care provider should make the choice of which drug to use. Self-prescribed treatments are dangerous and ineffective (see the Consumer Awareness feature, "Tricks Used to Sell STD Treatments," later in this chapter).

Key Points *The common STD chlamydia can damage the reproductive organs, often without any symptoms to warn the person. Untreated chlamydia infections can lead to ectopic pregnancies or infections of newborns during birth. Antibiotics effectively treat chlamydia infections.*

Gonorrhea

As with chlamydia, some people infected with **gonorrhea** do not feel any symptoms. Also as with chlamydia, the damage from the bacteria that cause gonorrhea can advance silently, bringing permanent damage to many organs of the body. This makes periodic testing for gonorrhea especially important for sexually active people.

MINI GLOSSARY

sexually transmitted diseases (STDs): diseases that are transmitted by way of direct sexual contact. An older name was *venereal diseases.*

acquired immune deficiency syndrome (AIDS): a fatal, transmissible viral disease of the immune system that creates a severe immune deficiency, and that leaves people defenseless against infections and cancer.

chlamydia (cla-MID-ee-uh): an infection of the reproductive tract, with or without symptoms; a frequent cause of ectopic pregnancy or failure to become pregnant.

pelvic inflammatory disease (PID): an infection of the fallopian tubes and pelvic cavity in women, causing ectopic pregnancy and pregnancy failures.

ectopic pregnancy: a pregnancy that develops in one of the fallopian tubes or elsewhere outside the uterus; a dangerous condition.

gonorrhea (gon-oh-REE-uh): a bacterial STD that often advances without symptoms to spread through the body, causing problems in many organs.

After they have ranked each word, ask for anyone who ranked any term a "2," and write the student's name after the word. Then ask those who ranked the words a "2" to explain them to the rest of the class. Explain any terms that were not ranked a "2." Students write the definitions and use this vocabulary list to help them read the section. **(15 min., Special Needs)**

Activity 1.3

Group Research. Divide the class into eight groups. Each group will be assigned one STD to research. Each group will be given class time to prepare a 3–5 minute talk on its assigned disease. They should be encouraged to create visual aids such as transparencies (drawn by students and made by you), posters, models, or chalk drawings. Each group must include information on cause, symptoms, treatment, complications, and prevention. Each group must also make a set of flash cards that teach about this disease. Cards should contain a question on one side and the answer on the other, such as: "What are three symptoms of chlamydia?" Answer, "burning during urination, a discharge, and abdominal pain."

Teacher Support Notes

① **STD Chart:** This chart contains a great deal of information about the common STDs. Its primary value will be as a reference to students as they work through the chapter. Students should be aware that the different categories of information have been condensed and that they can learn much more about the different factors for each disease in the text explanations and descriptions.

② **Preventing STDs:** Among the other things you'll want to do with this chart is focus students' attention on the preventive measures given for the different STDs. A conscious attempt was made by the authors to emphasize the abstinence message. While different specific measures are given for the different diseases, abstinence is mentioned first for each one.

FIGURE 17-1

Common Sexually Transmitted Diseases ①

Disease Name

	AIDS	Chlamydia	Genital Herpes	Genital Warts
Symptoms	Swollen lymph glands, diarrhea, pneumonia, weight loss, other infections, night sweats	In men, usually mild burning on urination. In women, vaginal discharge, abdominal pain, or no symptoms	Painful, blister-like sores on or near penis, anus, vagina, cervix, or mouth	Dry, wartlike growths on or near penis, anus, cervix or vagina
Treatment or cure	Treatment aimed at relieving symptoms; no cure	Antibiotics for both partners simultaneously	No cure; prescription medication may lessen severity and frequency of outbreaks	No cure; controlled by removal of growths or abnormal cervical cells
Potential complications	Immune system failure, severe illness leading to death, usually in six months to two years; infection of infants leading to death	In women, pelvic inflammatory disease (PID) with abdominal pain, fever, excessive menstrual bleeding, ectopic pregnancies, infertility. In men, dangerously enlarged lymph glands of the groin or infection of the testicles leading to sterilization. Infection during birth can cause blindness or illness in newborn	Recurrence; herpes eye infection, infection of newborn during childbirth	Recurrence; cervical cancer; penile cancer; possible obstruction of cervix, vagina, anus
Prevention measures ②	Abstinence from sexual intercourse and from use of intravenous drugs; mutual sexual monogamy with uninfected partner; some protection provided by condoms	Abstinence from sexual intercourse; mutual monogamy with an uninfected partner; some protection provided by condoms	Abstinence from sexual intercourse; mutual monogamy with uninfected partner; some protection provided by condoms only if sores are absent from groin and thighs	Abstinence from sexual intercourse; mutual monogamy with uninfected partner; some protection provided by condoms

These cards may be used by the class to help them study for the test on this section or the entire chapter, and you should retain them once completed by each group. **(20 min., Cooperative Learning)**

Activity 1.4
Herpes Discussion. Have students explain: **1.** Why it could sometimes be difficult for a woman to tell if a herpes infection has become active and has

formed blisters. **2.** Why this is important if she decides to engage in sexual contact with someone. **3.** Is there any way a man might protect himself from exposure? **(5 min., Critical Thinking)**

Activity 1.5
Pap Test Report. Have a student research and report on the development and use of the Pap test for cervical cancer. Some hospital labs may be able to

supply slides of normal and abnormal Pap tests, so students can see the difference between normal cervical cells and malignant cells. **(5 min. for report; Extend, Enrich)**

Activity 1.6
Canker vs. Chancre. Write two words on the board: "canker" and "chancre." Ask students to explain the differ-

(continued on next page)

Gonorrhea	Pubic Lice	Syphilis	Trichomoniasis
Possibly no symptoms; vaginal/penile discharge; in males, painful urination, tender lymph nodes, testicular/abdominal pain, fever; in females, painful menstruation or urination, bleeding after intercourse	Itching; lice in pubic hair; eggs, possibly visible, clinging to hair strands	Primary (3 weeks after exposure): chancre on penis, vagina, rectum, anus, cervix. Secondary (6 weeks after primary): rash on feet and hands; flu-like symptoms, including anorexia, fever, sore throat, nausea, headache. Tertiary (10 to 20 years later): severe nerve damage	Possibly no symptoms in men; in women, frothy, thin, greenish discharge; genital itching and pain
Antibiotics for both partners simultaneously	Prescription or over-the-counter shampoo, lotion, or cream used by both partners simultaneously	Antibiotics for both partners simultaneously	Antibiotics for both partners simultaneously
Sterility, skin problems, PID, arthritis, infection of heart lining, infection of eyes of newborns	Skin irritation	Brain damage; heart disease; spinal cord damage; blindness; infection of fetus, causing death or severe retardation	Bladder and urethra infections
Abstinence from sexual intercourse; mutual monogamy with uninfected partner; some protection provided by condoms	Abstinence from sexual intercourse; mutual monogamy with uninfected partner; not sharing towels or bedclothes with others; good personal hygiene; no protection provided by condoms	Abstinence from sexual intercourse; mutual monogamy with uninfected partner; some protection provided by condoms	Abstinence from sexual intercourse; mutual monogamy with uninfected partner; some protection provided by condoms

Teacher Support Notes

① **Curable vs. Incurable:** Once students have studied the chart, you might have them list the STDs that are curable on one side of a paper and those that are not on the other. Discuss the following questions: What do the curable diseases have in common? What do the incurable ones have in common? (The curable diseases are caused by bacteria or parasites and respond to antibiotics, but the incurable ones are caused by viruses—AIDS, herpes, genital warts—for which we do not have cures.)

ence between these words. Canker sores, which appear in the mouth for unknown reasons, have no relation to syphilis. Canker sores are painful while chancres from syphilis are not. **(3 min., Special Needs)**

Activity 1.7
"The Great Imitator." Ask students to explain why syphilis might be called "The Great Imitator." (because the symptoms of syphilis, in its three stages, mimic many other disorders) Have students brainstorm some other diseases a syphilis victim might believe he or she has contracted. The symptoms come and go, leading victims to believe the disease has gone away. Sometimes the victim may

not make a connection between the symptoms and a sexual contact that took place months ago. **(10 min.; Extend, Enrich)**

Activity 1.8
Premarital Testing. Have students debate whether or not a blood test for syphilis should continue to be required before a couple can obtain a marriage license. Do students feel there are any

---

✐ Fast Facts

In one study of 144 couples in which one partner had herpes and the other didn't, 14 (10%) transmitted herpes even though the couples knew about the infection and tried to avoid passing it.

Teacher Support Notes

① **Physical Exams:**
Once again it's recommended that you emphasize the importance of physical exams because a person can have the disease and not be aware of it. The symptoms mentioned here for women are not apparent in most cases. As students read the rest of this section on gonorrhea, they should see the importance of detecting the disease in its early stages.

✉ Where to Write

Centers for Disease Control
Center for Health Promotion and Education
1600 Clifton Rd., Bldg. 3, Room 33A
Atlanta, GA 30333

424

424 UNIT 5 Disease Prevention

Normal pregnancy

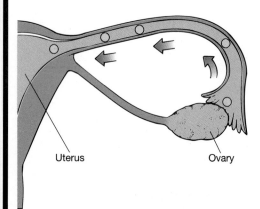

Uterus
Ovary

Normally, a fertilized egg travels freely through the fallopian tube and lodges and develops in the uterus.

Ectopic pregnancy

Scar tissue   Fertilized egg

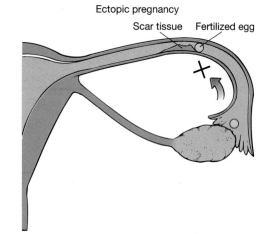

In PID, scar tissue partly blocks the tube leading to the uterus so that although tiny sperm can swim up the tube, the large fertilized egg is trapped and lodges to begin developing in the tube.

Figure 17–2 Ectopic Pregnancy

Men are most likely to have warning symptoms with gonorrhea infections—a thick, pale yellow discharge from the penis and a burning feeling when urinating. Women who have symptoms may notice a yellow-green vaginal discharge and pain when urinating. However, most women have no symptoms at all. ①

If left untreated, the gonorrhea bacteria can spread all over the body. They can attack the joints, leading to arthritis; attack the skin, leading to sores and other problems; attack the heart, weakening it; and attack the reproductive system, leading to sterility in both men and women. Gonorrhea can cause PID in women and can infect infants' eyes at birth, causing blindness. To protect babies born in the United States against blindness from gonorrhea, public health laws require that a gonorrhea-killing antibacterial agent be used in every infant's

eyes within minutes after birth. Erythromycin ointment has replaced silver nitrate as the treatment of choice.

In people who seek treatment for gonorrhea infection, antibiotics effectively cure most cases. However, a few cases of the disease each year are reported to resist cure by the drugs. For these cases, combinations of drugs or special antibiotics have been developed to wipe out the infection before it can seriously damage the person.

While the infection is curable, no treatment known can restore health to an organ damaged by gonorrhea. The longer a person has the infection, the higher the risks to health.

Key Points ▶ *Gonorrhea is a bacterial STD that attacks many organs of the body when left untreated. Antibiotic drugs are usually effective in treating it, but a few resistant cases are reported each year.*

other tests couples should be required to take? Would this infringe on a person's rights? **(15 min., Critical Thinking)**

Activity 1.9
   Uncertainties. Ask students: What would you do if you thought you had contracted an STD, but were uncertain? Will asking for a routine physical exam from your doctor guarantee that you will be tested for STDs? (No. These tests are only

ordered when the patient makes the physician aware of the possibility of infection, or if the physician happens to notice a symptom.) **(10 min.; Reteach, Reinforce)**

Activity 1.10
   Symptoms List. Have students write a list of all the possible symptoms of all the STDs in this section. Have a contest to see which student can list the most in a given time period during class.

(10 min.; Reteach, Reinforce)

Activity 1.11
   Diagnosis and Treatment. Provide students with a list of clinics, hospitals, and public health facilities in your area that provide diagnosis and treatment of STDs. If possible, obtain information concerning the cost of various diagnostic tests, and the cost of treatment. Be aware

(continued on next page)

CONSUMER AWARENESS

Tricks Used to Sell STD Treatments

STDs can be embarrassing. Some people who suspect they may have an STD may feel so embarrassed that they seek treatment on their own, outside the medical community. Drug pushers make large profits selling antibiotics. However, the chances of being cured from taking street drugs are very small. More likely, the attempt will delay needed medical attention, allowing the disease time to progress and to damage the body. ①

Especially for STDs such as genital herpes, genital warts, and AIDS—for which no real medical cures exist—tricksters with fake "cures" are everywhere. The desire for privacy is understandable. Reaching for any hope of cure is also natural.

Still, only health care professionals have access to reliable treatments. People should not let shame or fear keep them from seeking the best possible medical help. Health care providers do not waste time pointing fingers at people who are sick. They are more likely to congratulate them for seeking help.

CRITICAL THINKING

1. *Why are pills sold on the street as antibiotics not likely to cure even a bacterial STD?*
2. *How does a drug from a physician compare to one obtained from a pusher?*
3. *Why would a person with an STD for which there is no cure be especially vulnerable to the lies of quacks?*

Genital Herpes

Another common STD, **genital herpes**, is caused by a virus, not by bacteria. Thus it cannot be cured once it sets in. The disease is different from those discussed so far in another way, too—it is not known to cause internal organ damage. Testing for herpes is expensive and is not usually recommended as part of a routine STD screening. ②

The virus causes clumps of painful blisters to appear on the skin (see Figure 17–3, on page 428). The blisters last for as short a time as a few days or for as long as several months. The blisters can occur in several areas of the body:

- On the penis.
- In and around the vaginal area.
- In the mouth or on the lips.
- On the thighs or abdomen.
- Around or in the anus.

The sores cause pain, burning, or itching. They closely resemble those of a related condition—cold sores or fever blisters on the mouth. The mouth infection is most often caused by the herpes simplex I virus, while the genital infection is usually caused by the herpes simplex II virus. The two

MINI GLOSSARY

genital herpes (HER-peez): a common, incurable STD caused by a virus that produces blisters. The symptoms clear up on their own, but the virus remains to cause future outbreaks.

of any laws that govern diagnosis and treatment of STDs in minors, and if parental permission is required. **(5 min.)**

Activity 1.12
Chlamydia and the Newborn.
Explain to students that a mucus membrane exists over the eyes and in the respiratory system, just as one exists in the birth canal. Although the bacteria cannot enter the body through the skin (unless, of course, the skin is cut or scratched), it can survive in the mucus membrane. Finally, tell the students that the Chlamydia infection of the eyes is prevented by the use of erythromycin. Ask them why they think erythromycin is applied in all newborn babies' eyes, even if there is no reason to suspect that the mother has Chlamydia. (5 min.)

Activity 1.13
Outcomes of Untreated STDs.
Discuss the possible outcomes of having an untreated STD. Each row of students should work together to prepare a brief list of negative outcomes for someone who has an untreated case of:
1. Gonorrhea/Chlamydia
2. Syphilis
3. Trichomoniasis
4. Pubic lice

Teacher Support Notes

① **Teen Views Follow-Up Questions:** Here are some questions to help promote class discussion of the Teen Views comments.
a. Do students agree with Shaterra Marshall's view that education will help stop the epidemic?
b. Should parents be doing more to inform their children, as Jennie Miller says?
c. Patrice Saunders says it is up to those people involved in sexual intercourse and the sharing of needles to stop the AIDS epidemic; it is not up to society. Do students agree or disagree?
d. How do students feel about Tasha Perkins's answer in which she states that "society should be promoting abstinence instead of the use of condoms?" How many of your students agree? How many disagree?
e. Sara Walt believes many people are "scared" to talk about AIDS. What do students think can be done to help rid society of the fear?
f. From what source(s) have students received the most information about AIDS? From what source(s) do students believe they *should* receive the most information about AIDS?

426 UNIT 5 Disease Prevention

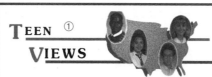

TEEN ①
VIEWS

What more should society be doing to stop the AIDS epidemic?

Our society should put more money into the schools to help teach younger kids about the disease and the responsibility they have to stop the spread of HIV. We need to get rid of the ignorance and the fear. AIDS is forever. **Shaterra Marshall, 17, Wilson High School, CA**

Parents and guardians need to talk to their kids about the dangers of unprotected sex and of contaminated drug needles. **Jennie Miller, 15, Duluth East High School, MN**

Our society gives off such confusing, mixed messages that it's hard to know what's right. The most effective way to combat AIDS is abstinence. No matter how long you preach and educate about abstinence, however, you have to consider the fact that teenagers today are having unprotected sex. It's important that teenagers recognize their right to say no and their right to choose abstinence, but safe-sex education is the key to preventing the spread of AIDS. **Erin Michelle Gielow, 15, Thousand Oaks High School, CA**

It's not up to our society to stop the AIDS epidemic. It's up to the people who are involved in sexual intercourse or the sharing of needles. My main concern is about the drug users. What is being done to help stop the sharing of needles? **Patrice Saunders, 17, Poughkeepsie High School, NY**

Our society should be promoting abstinence instead of the use of condoms in order to stop the AIDS epidemic. The only way to be positive that you won't get AIDS is to not have sex. **Tasha Perkins, 14, South Carroll High School, MD**

A lot more. MTV provides more information than news stations, newspapers, and even school. I believe this fact alone shows that the group of society to which I belong is frighteningly ignorant. **Brendon Burchard, 15, Great Falls High School, MT**

Awareness. A lot of people don't know how you can get it or what it really is. If a parent is against their kid learning about it, most likely they are scared. We've got to stop being scared. **Sarah Walt, 16, Newberg High School, OR**

We should continue to give out information on AIDS, and more people that have AIDS should come out to share with us, so maybe people will get the picture that AIDS is closer to home than most people think. **Ali Ribeiro, 14, Westside High School, NE**

Everyone is able to contract AIDS. It doesn't matter how old you are, what color or race. We are all in this together. Society also has to realize that not all kids are going to practice abstinence. They have to tell the kids what precautions they should take. **Laura Lee Love, 16, Great Falls High School, MT**

The most common saying about AIDS when it is brought up is "That will never happen to me" or "I can't get AIDS." It can happen to you. **Amanda Helton, 15, Carter High School, TN**

Drops placed in a baby's eyes at birth can help protect the eyes against STD infection.

viruses can take each other's places, though, causing the same sorts of sores in either location.

A person need not have obvious sores to transmit the virus. A woman may have internal blisters and not be aware of them. She then can unknowingly transmit the virus to others. It also may be possible for men without active sores to transmit the virus by way of semen. Typically, though, the virus is passed to others by active blisters. After blisters have completely healed, the risk of passing the virus to someone else drops dramatically, but not completely to zero.

With the first outbreak, a person may feel ill with fever, headache, muscle aches, painful urination, and swollen glands. Thereafter, the virus hides in nerve fibers, where it is safe from attack by the body's immune system. Later, the virus can become active again, and again cause sores. Some people experience only one episode in a lifetime.

Others suffer outbreaks many times a year for 10 to 15 years or even longer.

Among the more rare, serious effects of herpes are dangerous eye infections that can result from touching the eyes after touching the blisters. Also, the newborn baby of a woman with herpes is at extreme risk if blisters have been present during the baby's birth. Herpes infections in newborns can cause blindness, severe mental retardation, and even death. Women with active blisters at the time of labor must give birth by surgical methods to eliminate the risk of infecting the newborn.

While not curable, herpes is treatable with an oral antiviral drug that reduces the frequency, duration, and severity of outbreaks. A prescription cream applied to the blisters may shorten an outbreak. However, questions about the cream's effectiveness have not been fully answered.

Key Points ① *Herpes is an incurable viral STD that can cause repeated outbreaks of painful blisters. Herpes can infect newborns causing severe mental retardation, blindness, and death.*

Genital Warts

② Among the STDs, **genital warts** is the only one known to cause cancer—cancer of the cervix in women. Over 50 forms of the genital warts virus are known to exist. In addition to causing cancer, the virus can also cause harmless warty growths on the genitals that resemble in appearance the warts people get on their hands.

Like the herpes virus, the virus of genital warts does not respond to drugs. Once in

MINI GLOSSARY

genital warts: a viral STD that causes wartlike growths on the infected areas, sometimes called *condyloma* (con-di-LOW-ma). The viruses that cause genital warts can also cause cervical cancer in women.

to multiply out of control. Similarly, the birth control pill can change the climate of the vagina, favoring the growth of yeast. Explain that frequent douching is not recommended because it may also encourage an increase in yeast organisms. **(10 min.; Extend, Enrich)**

Activity 1.16
Diagrams. Provide a diagram of the reproductive and urinary systems, so that students can see the route UTIs can take to reach the kidneys. **(5 min., Special Needs)**

Activity 1.17
Jock Itch. Ask students to explain why the term "jock itch" is used to describe ringworm of the thigh and groin.

Ask: Can girls also get this disorder? What about nonathletes? What "climate" is necessary for this fungus to thrive? **(10 min., Critical Thinking)**

Activity 1.18
Effects of Clothing. Ask students to describe the type of underwear that might increase the chances of the wearer developing a yeast infection or jock itch, and the type that would discourage the growth

Teacher Support Notes

① **Pap Test:** This might be a good time to have students discuss the mental conflict between acknowledging the need to take a preventive measure vs. the embarrassment or censure that might result from allowing other people to know that the person has done something they probably shouldn't have. Have students reread this section on genital warts. Then ask them to name the greatest fear associated with the warts virus. (cervical cancer) How many times would a person have to have sexual relations to contract the virus? (one) What could be the result if a person contracts cervical cancer and does nothing to stop the spread of the cancer? (death) Ask what the benefit of identifying the cancer can be. (If the cancer is detected early, it can usually be cured.) Ask students if they think that every female who has had premarital sex also chooses to have regular Pap tests. If not, why not? How would students choose? Could they convince a friend to have the test? How might the friend defend the choice not to have the test?

428 UNIT 5 Disease Prevention

Figure 17–3 Herpes Blisters, Genital Warts, and Syphilis Chancre

the body, the infection remains for life. Treatment consists of removal of the growths or abnormal cervical tissue by surgery; by freezing; or for external growths, by applying a prescription medication (*not* the liquid available for regular warts). Even after treatment, the virus remains in the body, and the warts tend to grow back. Only special laboratory procedures can detect the existence of the virus.

The story of the discovery of the link between the warts virus and cervical cancer shows that scientists are often called upon to think like detectives. A few years ago, researchers knew only that some form of viral STD was linked to cervical cancer in women. They at first thought the herpes virus was the culprit. Then a story became known of a man who had the unfortunate experience of marrying five times, only to have each wife die of the same disease—cervical cancer. After studying the history of this man and his wives, researchers concluded that he carried the warts virus, and that each wife had become infected with it. Acting on this information, many more researchers completed experiments that later proved that the genital warts virus did actually cause cervical cancer. Genital warts infection is now named as the leading cause of death from cervical cancer world-

wide. The virus may be responsible for an epidemic of cervical cancer in the United States. The virus may also be linked with cancer of the penis in men, but this is rare.

Many sexually active people have the virus, but most never know it. Only 10 percent of people who carry it ever develop the warts that reveal the virus's presence in the body. A woman may discover her infection when a routine **Pap test** detects abnormal cervical cells.

The warts virus may reside on the skin of the genitals, invisible and symptomless, or may be present in semen of infected people. People who have had sexual intercourse with more than one partner are at greatest risk for carrying the virus. Even young women who have had no more than one sex partner, however, may have become infected with this common virus. Thus these women should have Pap tests taken on schedule, without fail, to detect abnormal cervical cells. Without detection and treatment, the abnormal cells may turn cancerous and endanger the lives of these women.

Key Points ▶ *Genital warts are caused by a virus that also is a major cause of cervical cancer worldwide. The virus is most often present without growths and is thought to infect many sexually active people.*

Syphilis

In the years before the discovery of antibiotics, many people suffered for years from the brain damage and other symptoms of advanced **syphilis** before they died of its effects. Some of the people suspected of having had or having died of syphilis include Al Capone, Julius Caesar, Cleopatra, Napoléon Bonaparte, Catherine the Great, Peter the Great, Henry VIII, Mary Tudor, John Keats, Franz Schubert, Oscar Wilde, Vincent van Gogh, Ludwig van Beethoven, and Adolf Hitler. For complete cure of a syphilis infection today, a person who is diagnosed with this bacterial infection needs only a physician's prescription and a trip to the corner drugstore. Syphilis remains a major public health problem, however, despite its high cure rate. ①

Syphilis announces its presence within a few weeks after infection with a hard, painless sore called a **chancre** that disappears in a few weeks on its own. This sore can help people recognize and treat syphilis before spreading it to others. Some women, however, may not notice the chancre, especially if it occurs deep within their internal tissues. Figure 17–3 shows what a chancre looks like. It also shows how different in appearance it is from the sores of genital herpes and the growths of genital warts.

If a person infected with syphilis allows the chancre stage to pass by without treatment, the sore will heal, but the infection moves on to the next stage. The next stage of syphilis brings swollen glands, a skin rash, hair loss, or flu-like symptoms. These symptoms may seem ordinary to the sufferer and may not cause sufficient alarm for the person to seek help. If the person fails to seek medical help at this stage, these symptoms, too, clear up by themselves in a few weeks. Untreated, the disease progresses to its **latent** stage, a period of symptomless advancement of the disease.

The latent stage of syphilis is long—as long as 10 to 20 years. During this stage the infected person feels well but can transmit the disease to others. With few outward clinical signs, the infection begins to silently attack the internal organs.

In the final stage of syphilis, the infection destroys whole organs. The results are permanent: blindness, deafness, brain damage, skin damage, and heart disease. Without treatment, death is likely. Even in the final stage, a syphilis infection can still be cured and its progression stopped. However, by that time, permanent organ damage has already been done. To escape the worst of syphilis, then, early diagnosis and treatment are critical.

Possibly the saddest effects of syphilis are those on the **fetus** of a pregnant woman with the infection. Syphilis easily enters the bloodstream of the fetus. Unless the woman is treated early in her pregnancy, her fetus is sure to be infected. Syphilis may kill the fetus or cause severe brain damage. Many severely retarded inmates of mental hospitals, who are 20, 40, 60, and even 80 years

MINI **G**LOSSARY

Pap test: a test for cancer of the cervix (the lower part of the uterus). A few cells are removed painlessly and examined in a laboratory.

syphilis: a bacterial STD that, if untreated, advances from a sore (chancre) to flu-like symptoms, then through a long symptomless period, and later to a final stage of irreversible brain and nerve damage, ending in death.

chancre (SHANG-ker): a hard, painless sore; chancres develop early in syphilis infections.

latent: temporarily unseen or inactive.

fetus: a developing human being before birth (See Chapter 21).

Activity 1.20
Graphic Representations. Place students in eight groups. Assign each group one STD for which it is to prepare a graphic representation. This should be a drawing on 8-1/2 × 11-inch paper that presents the most important facts about

this disease in graphic form. For example, to express the idea that a disease can cause sterility, a baby might be drawn in a circle with a diagonal line through it. To graphically represent symptoms, students might draw a body with a rash, a chancre, and a damaged brain. Less creative students might simply list symptoms in an artistic way. Each drawing should have the disease name at the top.

These graphic representations might

then be duplicated for each student to use as a way of reviewing. **(30 min., Cooperative Learning)**

Activity 1.21
Brochures. Ask the girls in the class to write a paragraph as if they were writing a brochure to be handed out to women in the doctor's office. This brochure is to be on yeast infections or UTI in women, and should include a dis-

---

Teacher Support Notes

① **Acquiring Trichomoniasis:** You might want to inform students that trichomoniasis can be acquired by borrowing a bathing suit or damp towel.

🖎 Fast Facts

According to the World Health Organization, 120 million dollars were spent worldwide in 1991 on safer-sex education, condoms, and other AIDS prevention measures in developing countries. The organization recommended that this amount be increased to at least 2.5 billion dollars. The organization further reported that only 6% of the total AIDS prevention dollars and 11% of the treatment dollars have gone to developing countries.

✉ Where to Write

Office of Disease Prevention and Health Promotion
300 7th Street, SW
Room 613
Washington, DC
20201

---

430 UNIT 5 Disease Prevention

old today, are there because they were infected with syphilis before they were born.

> **Key Points** ▶ *Syphilis is a dangerous bacterial STD. Although the infection is easily cured by antibiotics, its early symptoms may go unrecognized. This permits the disease to progress silently to cause irreversible organ damage and death. Syphilis attacks the fetus of an infected woman, causing severe mental retardation and other effects.*

Trichomoniasis

The STD **trichomoniasis** is caused by a parasite. Most often, trichomoniasis is acquired by sexual activity. On rare occasions, it has been acquired by trading wet clothes or towels with an infected person. In women, this infection causes an unpleasant-smelling, foamy, yellow-green or grey discharge; abdominal pain; pain when urinating; or itching in the genital area. Most men have no symptoms. A few have a watery discharge or burning when urinating. Men often unknowingly transmit the disease to their partners. Antibiotics are an effective treatment.

> **Key Points** ▶ *Trichomoniasis is caused by a parasite and is treated effectively with antibiotics.*

Multiple STDs

A person who has one STD may very well have others. This is of special concern, because one STD may mask another, more dangerous one. Syphilis, for example, is a serious second infection. Its early symptom, the chancre, easily hides in, say, a cluster of herpes blisters. If the herpes alone is diagnosed, the syphilis will go untreated and will silently spread through the body. A person who contracts any STD should see a health care provider and request a test for syphilis—and, possibly, for several other STDs. All of the STDs listed in Figure 17–1 presented earlier in the chapter are likely second infections, even **pubic lice**. The symptoms listed in Figure 17–4 on the opposite page mean that medical help is needed right away.

> **Key Points** ▶ *STDs often occur together. Anyone who contracts one STD should be tested for others.*

In mature relationships, partners can talk freely about STD prevention—a reason to postpone sexual intercourse until a relationship matures.

FIGURE 17-4

Common Symptoms of STDs

These symptoms mean that medical help is needed right away:

- Unusual discharge from vagina, penis, or rectum.
- Pain or burning while urinating.
- Pain in the abdomen (women), testicles (men), or buttocks and legs.
- Blisters, open sores, warts, rashes, or swelling in the genital area or sex organs.
- Flu-like symptoms: fever, headache, diarrhea, aching muscles, swollen glands.

Getting Help and Protecting Others

Anyone who suspects the presence of an STD should get help. Among possible sources of help are parents, school health services, public health departments, community STD clinics, or the offices of private physicians. Most organizations keep information about individuals, such as names, confidential. (They may report the incidence of the diseases for tracking purposes.) Treatments may be free of charge in some clinics.

Anyone diagnosed with an STD must notify any sexual partners. Otherwise, the partners may end up passing the disease back and forth several times. They may suffer needless harm, and they may pass the disease to someone else.

The best way to notify a partner about an STD is simply to do it as directly as possible—in person or on the phone, when only that person is listening. A letter is a bad idea because letters have a way of getting opened by other people or lost in the mail. In the conversation, the person who has been diagnosed should tell the partner:

- That a positive STD diagnosis has been made and that the partner (or former partner) should be checked, too, even if no symptoms have appeared.
- That the partner should immediately inform anyone else with whom he or she has had sexual contact.

① Above all, it is essential to tell sexual partners about the infection.

Key Points *A person with a diagnosis of an STD should be treated immediately and inform others who may have the infection.*

Other Infections

The STDs just described are usually transmitted by sexual contact. Other infections of the genital and urinary organs that are *not* transmitted by sexual contact are also common. Like STDs they should be treated right away to maintain the health of the reproductive or urinary tract organs.

② Most girls and women suffer from vaginal yeast infections at some time in life. A **yeast infection**, or **candidiasis**, is caused by a yeast that normally lives in the vagina. This yeast usually causes no problem but may multiply out of control to cause intense itching, burning, irritation, and swelling of

MINI GLOSSARY

trichomoniasis (trick-oh-mo-NEYE-uh-sis): an STD caused by a parasite that can cause bladder and urethral infections.

pubic lice: an STD caused by tiny parasites that breed in pubic hair and cause intense itching.

yeast infection or **candidiasis** (can-did-EYE-a-sis): an infection caused by a yeast that multiplies out of control in the vagina; not a sexually transmitted disease.

FOCUS
SECTION II

In this section students will learn the:
1. Way HIV invades and attacks the body.
2. Methods of transmission of AIDS.

Activity 2.1
HIV Discussion. Students are asked

to imagine that a new student is being added to their class. This student is known to be HIV positive. (Others in the class may be HIV positive, but not know it.) Have the class discuss the following questions either in groups or as an entire class.
1. Should the family of this student inform the school about his or her HIV status?
2. Should the school inform the parents of other students of this student's HIV sta-

tus, and should the student's identity be revealed?
3. What rights of privacy does the student have in regard to others knowing his or her medical condition?
4. How would you react to the inclusion of this student in your class? How would you treat him or her?

It would be best not to draw any conclusions on these questions until after the class has completed Section II. Then the

---

Section I Review
Answers

1. **a.** genital herpes **b.** latent **c.** sexually transmitted diseases (STDs)
2. curable: chlamydia, gonorrhea, pubic lice, syphilis, trichomoniasis; incurable: AIDS, genital herpes, genital warts.
3. During birth, the bacteria can infect the lungs or eyes of the newborn, causing pneumonia or blindness.
4. Gonorrhea bacteria attack the joints, causing arthritis; attack the skin, leading to sores; attack the heart, weakening it; attack the reproductive system, leading to sterility; cause PID in women; cause blindness in babies born to women with gonorrhea.
5. on the penis, in and around the vaginal area, in the mouth or on the lips, on the thighs or abdomen, around or in the anus
6. notify any sexual partner
7. Answers will vary.

---

432 UNIT 5 Disease Prevention

the outer genitals and a whitish, lumpy vaginal discharge. A woman who is pregnant, takes birth control pills, has diabetes, takes antibiotics, or uses douches is especially likely to develop candidiasis.

Over-the-counter antifungal creams relieve symptoms and help cure yeast infections. For prevention, wearing loose-fitting cotton—not nylon—underwear or panty hose with cotton panels is best. Should yeast infections occur frequently, or not respond to treatment, a woman should see a physician.

Another common complaint occurs when bacteria invade the urinary tract, causing **urinary tract infections (UTIs)**. The urethra (the tube through which urine leaves the body) leads to the bladder and makes a convenient route for invading bacteria.

Most UTIs cause frequent, urgent, and painful urination. Some people notice a dull, aching pain above the pubic bone or blood in the urine.

UTIs are easily treated with antibiotics. If left untreated, however, infection of the bladder may progress to a possibly fatal infection of the kidneys. People who get UTIs often may be able to reduce the frequency by drinking extra fluids; urinating frequently; and for women, wiping from front to back after urination or bowel movements.

Ringworm of the inner thigh and groin, nicknamed **jock itch**, causes intense itching. It is caused by a fungal infection. This condition is common among athletes who sweat heavily and whose clothes stay wet for long periods. Over-the-counter medications usually clear it up. Other preventive measures include staying dry, not sharing towels with others, and not allowing clothing to touch the floor.

> **Key Points** ➤ *Yeast infections and urinary tract infections are infections of the genitals and urinary organs that are not sexually transmitted. These can sometimes be prevented by routine self care. They are easily treated.*

SECTION I REVIEW

Answer the following questions on a sheet of paper.

Learning the Vocabulary

The vocabulary terms in this section are *sexually transmitted diseases (STDs), acquired immune deficiency syndrome (AIDS), chlamydia, pelvic inflammatory disease (PID), ectopic pregnancy, gonorrhea, genital herpes, genital warts, Pap test, syphilis, chancre, latent, fetus, trichomoniasis, pubic lice, yeast infection, candidiasis, urinary tract infections (UTIs),* and *jock itch.*

1. Match each of the following phrases with the appropriate term.
   a. a common, incurable STD caused by a virus that produces blisters
   b. temporarily inactive
   c. diseases that can be transmitted by direct sexual contact

Learning the Facts

2. Which STDs are curable? Incurable?
3. Describe the health problems of a newborn baby whose mother has chlamydia.
4. Describe the physical problems that occur in people who are not treated for gonorrhea.
5. List and identify the areas of the body on which genital herpes blisters occur.
6. What should people do if they are diagnosed with STDs?

Making Life Choices

7. Reread the "Common Sexually Transmitted Diseases" chart in Figure 17–1 on pages 422–423. How serious do you consider the risks associated with STDs as compared with the risks from smoking, drug or alcohol abuse, or other risky behavior?

432

students may want to rethink their answers. A simplified version of this activity is found on page 445 of the student text. This activity is recommended for classroom discussion; the activity on page 445 works better as an end-of-chapter writing assignment. **(15 min., Critical Thinking)**

TEACH
SECTION II
(Guided and Independent Practice)

Activity 2.2
HIV Behavior Diagrams. Explaining how HIV behaves in the body to low-ability students can be difficult. Your supplementary material contains an activity that includes four diagrams that will help low-ability students see how HIV affects

the immune system and the results that occur. The diagrams graphically compare germs to a fire, white cells (T cells) to a fire alarm, antibodies to water, and so on. **(20 min., Special Needs)**

Activity 2.3
Risk Continuum. On index cards, print in large letters ways that AIDS could be spread from one person to another

(continued on next page)

SECTION II

Acquired Immune Deficiency Syndrome (AIDS)

"Abstinence is the only sure way to protect oneself from acquiring STDs."

—Former U.S. Surgeon General Koop

A disease of enormous concern worldwide is acquired immune deficiency syndrome (AIDS). First observed in the late 1970s, AIDS has spread rapidly to more than 100 countries and every inhabited continent of the globe. Health care authorities are working hard to stop AIDS from becoming an even bigger problem.

Experts predict that AIDS will soon be one of the leading causes of death, especially of younger people, in the United States. Today, the virus that causes AIDS is spreading rapidly among high school students. Many teenagers are considered to be at high risk for contracting **HIV** (the virus that causes AIDS). Within the last few years, the number of teens who test positive for the AIDS virus has doubled and even, in some areas, tripled.

People who think that they are too young to get AIDS, not the right type to get it, or are somehow excused from getting it are its most likely next victims. It used to be true that only certain kinds of people got AIDS, but no longer. Today, the only people who are completely safe from AIDS are those who make themselves safe.

①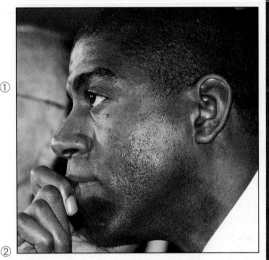

The announcement by basketball star Ervin "Magic" Johnson that he was HIV positive helped to focus national attention on the AIDS crisis.

The Progression of AIDS

AIDS is unique among infectious diseases in that the immune system cannot fight it off. Once in the body, the AIDS virus (HIV) relentlessly attacks the immune system itself, disabling its defenses. This leaves the body open to many infections. People in the late stages of AIDS develop rare forms of cancer and a wide variety of infectious diseases rarely seen in people with functioning immune systems.

MINI GLOSSARY

urinary tract infections (UTIs): bacterial infections of the urethra that can travel to the bladder and kidneys; not a sexually transmitted disease.

jock itch: a fungal infection of the groin and inner thigh; not a sexually transmitted disease.

HIV: an abbreviation for *human immunodeficiency virus,* the virus that causes AIDS.

Teacher Support Notes

① **HIV Positive Quotes:** Quotes such as this one can be found in recent publications dealing with AIDS. You might want to assign students, either individually or in groups, to find their own quotes.

② **AIDS Definition:** You may want to break down the AIDS acronym. *Acquired* means something that is obtained; *immune* and *deficiency* are words that students have learned earlier; *syndrome* means a group of signs or symptoms that, collectively, indicate a disease or disorder or other abnormal condition.

③ **Most Likely Victims:** Ask students what this sentence means: Why are the people who think they are not going to get it the most likely to get it?

④ **The Immune System:** You may want to refer students back to the discussion and illustration of the immune system in Chapter 6.

(one idea on each card). Also, print ways AIDS is not spread. Figure 17–6 would be a good beginning, but you may also want to include other behaviors students incorrectly believe to be means of transmission, such as eating in a restaurant that has an employee who is HIV positive, or dry kissing. Prepare enough cards so that every student has one. Draw a long line on the chalkboard. At one end write "High Risk" and at the other "No Risk." Have each individual student read what is on his/her card, come up and place it in the chalk tray at the point he/she believes it falls on the continuum between a high-risk behavior and a no-risk behavior, in regard to transmission of HIV. Make no comments on the placement of the cards until all are placed. Then students may discuss which cards they feel should be moved to more accurately reflect the risk of each activity. You may interject information when students do not seem to have a clear idea of the risk. Once the cards are more properly placed, it will be clear that AIDS is spread in only four fluids: blood, semen, vaginal fluids, and breast fluids. In addition, a mother can infect her unborn baby during pregnancy.

Teacher Support Notes

① **Progression of Disease:** Ask students what STD they read about earlier in this chapter that resembles AIDS. (syphilis) How *is* AIDS similar to syphilis? (People often do not experience symptoms right away or are not aware of the symptoms. People can remain in good health for many years after contracting the disease. Toward the end, serious damage is done to the body, and death occurs.) What are the differences? (AIDS is caused by a virus while syphilis is caused by bacteria. There is a cure for syphilis now; there is no cure for AIDS. While the duration of the disease varies a great deal for both diseases, AIDS does seem to bring on death sooner than syphilis.)

② **Search for Cures:** As an enrichment you may want to give students an example of ongoing AIDS research. Flossie Wong-Staal, a prominent researcher at the University of California, San Diego, is trying a "molecular knife" that disables the HIV virus by slicing up its genetic code. Introduced into a test-tube culture of AIDS-infected blood cells, it slowed the spread of the virus 70–90%.

Being infected with HIV is not the same as having the disease AIDS, because infected people may not experience AIDS symptoms right away. Some people who become infected with HIV sicken and die within six months. Others may remain in good health and without symptoms for six to ten years. Ultimately, though, the infection moves into its deadly stage—the disease AIDS. After symptoms marking the beginning of AIDS develop, most victims die within two years, and the rest within five years. ①

The virus attacks the white blood cells of the immune system—specifically, T cells. The virus destroys the T cells and disables their essential function of signaling B cells to produce antibodies (see Chapter 16). The T cells are not only unable to help fight off HIV, but are also ineffective against other microorganisms and cancer cells. With the immune system so weakened, infections of all kinds thrive unchecked.

The first symptoms of AIDS are usually vague. Fatigue, appetite loss, weight loss, persistent vaginal yeast infections, and nagging cough are typical. As the disease progresses, it causes persistent swollen lymph nodes, skin rashes, fever, and diarrhea. It often causes fungal infections of the mouth. HIV also robs the body of precious lean tissues needed to fight diseases. Infections may make the weight losses worse, but the losses may begin years before other symptoms of AIDS show up. Some people in Africa, noticing the weight loss, named AIDS "slim."

HIV makes its way to the brain and nervous system, causing severe mental disorders. Mental symptoms include mood swings, apathy, withdrawal, agitation, depression, hallucinations, delusions, anxiety, and memory loss. When HIV invades the nervous system, it affects the muscles, too, causing leg weakness, poor coordination, and unsteady walking.

Finally, AIDS progresses to the stage of failure of immunity. At this stage, victims often suffer a rare form of pneumonia, a rare skin cancer called **Kaposi's sarcoma**, tuberculosis, and many other diseases. These AIDS-related infections and cancers resist treatment and steadily worsen. Many people with AIDS do not die of AIDS itself. They die of other diseases against which they have become defenseless.

A person diagnosed with AIDS must accept many heavy losses. First the person must accept the diagnosis. Then follow the losses of health, employment, finances, sexual activity, and some social support. People who develop AIDS can expect to lose physical strength, mental sharpness, control of life activities, self-esteem, and in the end, life itself.

Upon receiving the diagnosis, some victims become emotionally and psychologically disabled, even to the point of becoming suicidal or homicidal (wanting to kill themselves or others). Others, though, react with courage. One young woman who believes she must have contracted HIV as a teenager has committed the rest of her life to traveling and speaking to teen groups about AIDS. Basketball star Magic Johnson has become a powerful voice for groups trying to stop the spread of HIV. Many others work in quieter ways—they join local education efforts, they support those who have been newly diagnosed, they work in AIDS food banks, or they answer calls for a helping hotline. They may be facing losses, but even so, their self-esteem stays high as they find new, meaningful roles.

To date, no one has recovered from AIDS. With treatments of drugs, radiation, and surgery, some people with AIDS are living a few years longer than others before them. Still, none are recovering.

② Researchers have made progress in their search for AIDS therapies. An important step was discovering that an anticancer

Abstinence, accurate information, and medical tests are three important defenses against AIDS.

drug (zidovudine, formerly called azidothymidine, or AZT) slows down the progress of AIDS. A vaccine to prevent HIV infection is slow in coming. This is because vaccines work by stimulating the immune system, which HIV destroys. Many anti-AIDS drugs are being hurried through testing procedures to make even unproved drugs available to those with no other hope. People with AIDS understandably want to try any drug—proven or not—that offers even the smallest chance of comfort or cure.

Key Points *The progression of AIDS begins when a person acquires HIV. The person often remains free of symptoms for years before developing AIDS. People with AIDS most often die from diseases that advance as the immune system fails.*

Transmission of the AIDS Virus

People who feel and look healthy can be infected with HIV and can transmit it to others. HIV carriers are probably most contagious when AIDS has set in. However, they can pass the virus to others before they develop any signs of illness, during the incubation stage. Teenagers who are infected with HIV rarely have symptoms of AIDS because the disease stage hasn't had time to develop.

Most people with HIV acquired their infections by way of sexual intercourse. These people can then pass the virus on to others by way of blood, semen from the penis, fluids of the vagina, or other body fluids. Figure 17–5 on the next page shows how rapidly AIDS is spreading. The number of those who are infected with HIV is thought to be ten times greater than the number of people with AIDS.

Steady sex partners of people with AIDS are taking the greatest risks of contracting HIV. However, it may take just one contact with an infected person to acquire the virus. This means a single sexual encounter can infect a formerly healthy person with HIV.

Passionate, open-mouthed kissing may also transmit HIV, but no proven cases have been reported yet. Authorities warn that passionate kissing should not be considered safe, though. Just a few years ago, no proven cases of AIDS from ordinary vaginal sex had been reported "yet," but now vagi-

M INI G LOSSARY

Kaposi's (cap-OH-zeez) **sarcoma:** a normally rare skin cancer causing a purplish discoloration of the skin, seen commonly among people with AIDS.

Activity 2.5
  Pop Quiz.
1. Only homosexuals need to be concerned about getting AIDS. (F)
2. A person is declared to have AIDS as soon as the virus enters the body. (F)
3. A person can feel and look healthy but

still be infected with HIV, and be capable of spreading the disease. (T)
4. Mosquitoes can spread AIDS. (F)
5. The more sexual partners a person has, the greater the risk of contracting AIDS. (T)

CLOSE
SECTION II

Activity 2.6

Statement Cards. Instruct students to write three true statements describing the progress of AIDS (HIV) in the body, and three true statements describing how AIDS is spread. Statements could be written on cards and then exchanged at random. If students receive statements that do not seem correct, they should raise their hands and read them out loud. The class will then decide if the statements are true or false. Collect the cards to eval-

Teacher Support Notes

① Clean Needles:
Experts estimate that one-third of the nation's AIDS cases originated from IV drug use. Specifically, 71% of all females with AIDS are linked directly or indirectly to IV drug use. In a two-year study done in New Haven, Connecticut, it was demonstrated that a needle exchange program dramatically slows the rate of infection without encouraging new IV drug use. In the New Haven study, more than 90% of the needles confiscated and exchanged for clean needles were contaminated with the AIDS virus.

② Qualifying Transmission: Students should realize that each of the sentences here and throughout this section on AIDS have been carefully qualified because researchers cannot be 100% sure about transmission of the AIDS virus. Ask students to reread the sentences and then tell you what they know for sure about the transmission of the HIV virus. Did they read carefully enough to notice the verb *appears*? If not, use this experience to stress the importance of careful reading. The information is changing constantly.

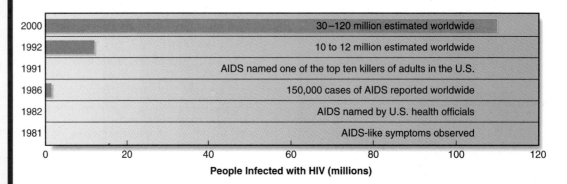

2000	30–120 million estimated worldwide
1992	10 to 12 million estimated worldwide
1991	AIDS named one of the top ten killers of adults in the U.S.
1986	150,000 cases of AIDS reported worldwide
1982	AIDS named by U.S. health officials
1981	AIDS-like symptoms observed

People Infected with HIV (millions)

Figure 17–5 AIDS Time Line

nal intercourse is known as a major route of infection. Only traces of whole cells are needed to convey the virus from person to person. Semen commonly carries HIV, but so can blood—the amount you see sometimes when brushing your teeth, for example. Intense kissing can easily cause lips to bleed. Passing this tiny amount of blood to a partner through kissing could possibly pass on the virus as well.

The sharing of needles among people who practice **intravenous (IV) drug abuse** is the second most common path by which HIV travels from person to person. So little blood is needed to pass the virus that even being scratched by an infected needle can transmit AIDS. Unsterilized needles used for any purpose are dangerous, including the needles of acupuncture, tattooing, ear piercing, and electrolysis (the removal of hair by electricity using a needle).

Another way people have acquired HIV infections is by way of blood or blood products used in medical treatments. Those who received blood up until 1985 were unknowingly risking being infected with the virus, because blood products were not screened as they are today. Thanks to advances in screening techniques and treatments, today's blood supply is much safer

than in the past. People have also contracted AIDS from organ transplants when the organ donors carried HIV.

HIV can be transmitted to infants in three additional ways. Women who have AIDS or who carry the virus can infect their offspring during pregnancy, during birth, or by way of breastfeeding.

HIV appears *not* to be transmitted by casual contacts such as sharing meals, shaking hands, coughing, or sneezing. Nor does it seem to be transmitted by mosquitoes or other insects, by saunas, by pools, or by food handled by HIV carriers. HIV is also not transmitted to people who donate blood using sterilized needles; by vaccinations using sterilized needles; or by contact with unbroken, healthy skin. HIV does not appear to be transmitted by touching shared objects, such as toilet seats. Intimate sexual activity or contact with blood—not casual contact—transmits HIV. Figure 17–6 reviews ways HIV is transmitted and ways that it is not transmitted.

Key Points ▸ *AIDS is a fatal disease caused by infection with a virus, HIV. HIV is readily transmitted by way of sexual contact or exchange of blood. HIV does not appear to be transmitted through casual contact.*

uate student understanding at the end of this section. This activity is also valuable for low-ability students because the students do not read their own statements, thus avoiding embarrassment when a statement is incorrect. **(30 min.; Reteach, Reinforce, Special Needs)**

FOCUS

SECTION III

In this section students will learn:
1. Behaviors that will eliminate the risk of acquiring an STD.
2. Behaviors that will reduce but not definitely eliminate the risk of acquiring an STD.

Activity 3.1
An Avoidable Disease? Write the following statement on the board: "AIDS is a disease you don't have to get." Ask

students to comment on this statement. Do they agree that AIDS is an avoidable disease? If so, how does one avoid it? Students may be able to determine that the major ways to avoid AIDS are abstinence, mutual monogamy with an uninfected person, and avoidance of IV drugs. **(10 min., Critical Thinking)**

FIGURE 17-6

Ways HIV Is Transmitted and Ways It Is Not Transmitted

HIV is known to be transmitted by:

- Any form of sexual intercourse with an infected partner
- Sharing infected needles
- Ear piercing with an infected needle
- Acupuncture using an infected needle
- Tattooing using an infected needle
- Removal of hair by electrolysis using an infected needle
- Infected blood transfusions
- Infected organ transplants
- Pregnancy, childbirth, or breastfeeding by an infected mother (virus transmitted to infant)

HIV is *not* known to be transmitted by:

- Casual contact
- Mosquitoes
- Eating food
- Blood donation
- Vaccines using sterilized needles
- Contact with unbroken, healthy skin
- Touching shared objects, including towels
- Wearing clothes of an HIV infected person
- Using a toilet used previously by an HIV infected person
- Hugging an HIV infected person
- Swimming with an HIV infected person

SECTION II REVIEW

Answer the following questions on a sheet of paper.
Learning the Vocabulary
The vocabulary terms in this section are *HIV, Kaposi's sarcoma,* and *intravenous (IV) drug abuse.*
1. Matching: Match each phrase with the appropriate vocabulary term from above.
   a. the virus that causes AIDS
   b. a normally rare skin cancer causing a purplish discoloration of the skin

Learning the Facts
2. What is the difference between HIV and AIDS?
3. Who is safe from AIDS?
4. What does the AIDS virus do, after it gets into the body?
5. What are the physical symptoms of AIDS?
6. What is the treatment for AIDS?

Making Life Choices
7. Look at Figure 17–6. Which items did you already know? Have you heard of other ways AIDS is transmitted or not transmitted? How can we correct misconceptions?

SECTION III

Strategies against Sexual Transmission of AIDS and Other STDs

The rest of this chapter gives details about how people must adjust their sex lives to protect themselves from contracting AIDS and other STDs. First, it describes those practices that *eliminate* the risk of acquiring a disease through sexual behaviors. These behaviors promise that people who

MINI GLOSSARY

intravenous (IV) drug abuse: the practice of using needles to inject drugs of abuse into the veins. (The word *intravenous* means "into a vein.")

Section II Review
Answers
1. a. HIV **b.** Kaposi's sarcoma
2. HIV is only the virus that causes AIDS, while AIDS is the actual disease that causes the immune system to be defenseless against infections and cancers.
3. No one is completely safe. However, those who choose to abstain from sexual intercourse and intravenous drug use have eliminated the most frequent of transmission routes.
4. attacks the immune system, disabling its defenses
5. See page 434, paragraphs 3–5 for a complete listing of symptoms.
6. drugs (AZT), radiation, surgery
7. Answers will vary.

Activity 3.2

Role-Playing. At the beginning of this chapter, in Activity 1.1, a story was presented about Tina, who was concerned about the sexual history of her boyfriend prior to agreeing to have sex with him. To expand on this story, ask if two students would be willing to role-play a conversation between Tina and her boyfriend. The purpose of the conversation is for Tina to learn about the sexual history of her boyfriend, so that she can decide whether he might be HIV positive. Once she determines that he could be HIV positive, she must then convince him to be tested. Perhaps more than one pair of students could role-play this situation so that the class could see different ways of beginning a conversation on this difficult topic. For variety, reverse the situation so that the male is concerned about Tina's sexual history, and wants to convince her to be tested. Notice whether students vary their approaches when the roles are reversed. **(20 min., Critical Thinking)**

Activity 3.3

Refusal Skills. Since refusal skills

Teacher Support Notes

① **Mutually Monogamous:** This a term that will sound difficult to students and is one with which they probably are unfamiliar. *Monogamous* is defined in the Mini Glossary. Ask them to define *mutually*. (having to do with both parties; same for both people involved) They should see that it's not enough for one person to be monogamous; both must be.

✍ Fast Facts

According to a University of Southern California study, the more sexual partners an HIV-infected man has had, the less likely he is to try to notify them of the risk.

follow them consistently will not contract an STD through sexual contact. Total commitment to **abstinence** or to a mutually **monogamous** relationship with an uninfected partner are the only strategies that eliminate the risk of STD entirely. Then **safer-sex strategies** are described—behaviors that will reduce STD risk but that cannot promise complete protection. The Health Strategies feature on this page, "Avoiding Contracting Sexually Transmitted Diseases," summarizes these guidelines. ①

Eliminating the Risk of STDs

Only two strategies, if practiced consistently, reduce the risk of sexually acquired infections to zero. Keep in mind, though, that AIDS and other infections of the blood can be passed by nonsexual means. The strategies you are about to study prevent *sexual* transmission only. Beyond these, remember to never let anyone stick you with a needle, to pierce your ears, to give you a tattoo, to remove hair, and so forth, unless you are certain that the needle has been steam heat sterilized for 15 minutes or more, or is a disposable needle that has never been used.

H EALTH
S TRATEGIES

Avoiding Contracting Sexually Transmitted Diseases

*People can **completely** protect themselves from contracting STDs by:*

1. Practicing sexual abstinence.
2. Having a mutually monogamous sexual relationship with an uninfected partner.

*People can **reduce** their STD risks by:*

1. Avoiding contact with partner's body fluids.
2. Using latex condoms with spermicides throughout every sexual act to keep body fluids from being exchanged.
3. Refusing alcohol or other drugs.
4. Avoiding high-risk behaviors, and avoiding relations with others who engage in high-risk behaviors.

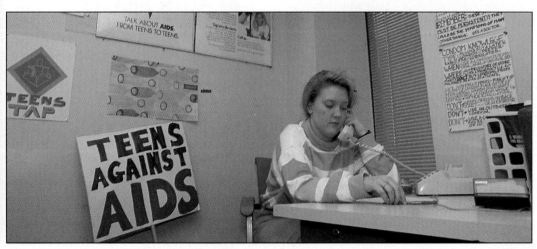

are a big part of practicing abstinence, have two students role-play a situation in which the boy is trying to convince the girl to have sex with him, and the girl believes in abstinence. In this role-play situation, ask a *male* student to take the part of the girl and a *female* student to take the part of the boy. It will be interesting for the class to witness the various "lines" males use to convince the girl, and the various ways the girl can use to refuse his sexual advances without "putting him down." **(15–45 min.)**

Activity 3.4
"**Safe Sex?**" Write the words "safe sex" on the board and ask students whether they believe there is such a thing as safe sex. The topic of condom failure should be brought out in this conversation. Students should be made aware of the fact that condoms can leak or break.

Consider whether instruction on proper condom usage is appropriate for students. If so, this would be a good time for this information to be presented. However, students should conclude that even when properly used, condoms can fail, so there is really no such thing as safe sex, unless both partners have tested negative for STDs. **(10–30 min., Critical Thinking)**

(continued on next page)

The most effective way to protect against STDs is not to have sexual relations with other people (abstinence). Abstinence from sexual activities and drug use is the most effective strategy for preventing STDs.

Limiting sexual relations to one uninfected partner only, who is also monogamous, also provides protection from STDs. Safety here depends on knowing the partner's infection status and on knowing that the partner is monogamous.

The problem is, though, that people can have many STDs, including AIDS, without even knowing it. Before using the strategy of mutual monogamy, partners must determine two things:
• The prospective partner's infection status.
• The prospective partner's sexual faithfulness.
Until the partner's infection status is known, it is not safe to have sex.

It's OK to ask about a potential partner's sexual history. Unfortunately, though, people do not like to reveal their sexual pasts, and so they may be tempted to lie. A physician reported that he had asked an AIDS-infected client whether he had told his sex partner of the AIDS infection. The client responded, "No, Doctor, it would have broken the mood." ①

Even if a prospective partner is truthful, the person may be unaware of a current infection. People can be infected even though they feel well and look healthy. You cannot tell by looking who is infected and who is not. Asking about STDs may not even be enough. Medical testing, especially for AIDS, is not unreasonable. Both partners must be willing to be tested.

A caution about AIDS testing—it seems that in some cases, the blood of people who are infected may register as negative for the virus, especially during the early stages. That is, if a person was infected just last week, last month, or several months ago, then there is some chance that the person might test negative for the virus today. This is just one more reason why abstinence from sexual intercourse is a good idea.

Key Points ▶ *Abstinence or mutual monogamy with an uninfected partner are the only safe sexual practices.*

Reducing the Risk of STDs

Some strategies can reduce—but not eliminate—risks of acquiring an STD. With these strategies, the goal is to avoid any exchange of body fluids. Condoms made of latex material (not natural skin) and treated with a spermicide, if properly used, is effective in reducing the risks of STDs. A condom may provide an effective barrier to body fluids, and the spermicide may kill some bacterial cells and weaken some viruses. Before choosing condoms for protection, though, people should be aware that some types are more reliable than others and that all types require special care after purchase.

How effective are condoms in preventing STDs such as AIDS? Researchers are uncertain since few reliable studies have been done. In these limited studies, however, the failure rates in preventing HIV transmission have ranged from 0% to 17% depending on how consistently and effectively the condoms have been used. Of course, even a 1% failure rate can be fatal in AIDS cases.

MINI GLOSSARY

abstinence: refraining completely from sexual relations with other people; also called *celibacy* (SELL-ih-ba-see).
monogamous: having sexual relations with one partner only, excluding all others. These relationships are usually long-term relationships.
safer-sex strategies: behavior guidelines to reduce STD risk, but that do not reduce the risk to zero.
spermicide: the compound nonoxynol-9, intended for birth control, that also kills or weakens some STD organisms.

Teacher Support Notes

① **Truthful Claims:** Have students discuss whether or not they think that most people would be honest in these situations. If they were in a situation like this, would they be honest?

✎ Fast Facts

According to the National Association of State Boards of Education, in 1991, 29 states required sex education in public schools. Eighteen of these states required that abstinence be stressed. Three states required the discussion of condoms.

Activity 3.5

Cultural Attitudes. Have students discuss the attitudes various cultures have toward extramarital sex using the following questions: Are the standards each sets for males and females the same? How are people who "break the rules" treated or "punished" in each culture? Do some cultures have "double standards?" Do some races have a higher incidence of AIDS than others? How do these statistics relate to the culture's "rules" about sexual behavior for teens? Are the most restrictive cultures the ones with the lowest incidence of AIDS? Why or why not? **(30 min.; Multicultural, Critical Thinking)**

Activity 3.6

Risks and Strategies. Have students divide a piece of paper into three columns. At the top of the first column instruct them to write "No risk of STDs." At the top of the second column write "Reduced risk of STDs." For the third col-

Teacher Support Notes

① **Handout—U.S. Health Service Objectives:** In the supplementary material you will find a handout that lists the objectives established by the U.S. Department of Health and Human Services for HIV infections, sexually transmitted diseases, and related aspects of these conditions. You may want to distribute the handout at the conclusion of the chapter.

Section III Review

Answers

1. a. monogamous
b. abstinence
c. spermicide
2. abstinence; mutually monogamous sexual relationship with an uninfected partner
3. the prospective partner's infection status, and the prospective partner's sexual faithfulness
4. latex
5. Answers will vary. Avoiding alcohol and drugs helps you to make wise decisions and avoid having sex against your better judgment.

Chapter 14 made clear that alcohol robs a person of judgment. Other mind-altering drugs do, too. All of the strategies against STDs require judgment and will, and these are the first two mental qualities to be affected by alcohol. Many teens report that they experienced unplanned sexual involvement after or while drinking. They later regretted these encounters. Therefore, a decision to avoid alcohol will support your effort to remain free of STDs.

Lastly, be aware of groups at high risk for STDs. Avoid sexual involvement with:

- Intravenous drug users.
- Anyone who has had previous sexual partners and who has not, since then, been tested for STDs.

Key Points *The best way people can prevent the spread of STDs is by practicing abstinence. Another preventative measure that will reduce the risks of STDs is by using latex condoms with spermicide (from 0 to 17% failure rate depending on how they are used). Alcohol and other mind-altering drugs rob people of judgment.* ①

SECTION III REVIEW

Answer the following questions on a sheet of paper.

Learning the Vocabulary

The vocabulary terms in this section are *abstinence, monogamous, safer-sex strategies,* and *spermicide.*

1. Use the clues given to help you unscramble the words.
   a. **aooougmmns** _____ having sexual relations with one partner only, excluding all others.
   b. **aeeibcnnts** _____ refraining completely from sexual relations with other people
   c. **eeiicdmprs** _____ a compound that kills sperm and may weaken some STD organisms

Learning the Facts

2. What are the two ways to eliminate the risk of STDs?
3. Describe what two things must be determined before mutual monogamy is effective.
4. What type of condom is most effective against STDs?

Making Life Choices

5. Reread the Health Strategies feature, "Avoiding Contracting Sexually Transmitted Diseases," on page 438. How can you be completely protected from STDs? Explain how avoiding alcohol and other drugs may reduce the risks of STDs.

Answers to Fact or Fiction

Here are the answers to the questions at the start of the chapter.

1. False. Bathing or washing the reproductive organs after sexual intercourse is not enough to prevent sexually transmitted diseases. **2.** False. Birth control pills do not protect a woman against any form of sexually transmitted disease. **3.** False. Sexually transmitted diseases often progress with no outward symptoms. An example is chlamydia. **4.** False. If you develop an STD, the considerate thing to do is to inform your partner. This protects you from reinfection, protects the health of your partner, and protects others. **5.** False. Asking potential partners about past sexual experiences does not ensure that you will learn the truth about whether they are free of STDs. **6.** False. Condoms may provide an effective barrier to body fluids, but they sometimes fail to protect against STDs.

umn write "Strategies against STDs." Have students list items they can recall from this section that belong in each column. For example: *No risk*—abstinence, mutually monogamous relationship; *Reduced Risk*—use condoms, limit sexual contacts, communicate values; *Strategies*—avoid mind-altering drugs when with your date, discuss sexual values with your partner, avoid use of needles, avoid exchanging body fluids with anyone who uses needles. **(15 min.)**

CLOSE
SECTION III

Activity 3.7
Avoiding AIDS and STDs. Return to Activity 3.1 and the statement "AIDS is a disease you don't have to get." Have each student write a paragraph detailing what they plan to do to avoid AIDS and other STDs. **(15 min.; Reteach, Reinforce)**

RETEACH/BONUS

Story Questions. Read to students a story about two students who have been going together for many months and have recently begun having a sexual relationship: "Alex has developed a burning

(continued on next page)

STRAIGHT TALK

AIDS Risks and Routine Health Care

AIDS has changed people's attitudes about health care, including those of health care providers themselves. Several reports exist of health care workers who became infected with HIV while administering routine care to AIDS patients. In most of these cases, the workers accidentally stuck themselves with hypodermic needles that were contaminated with the AIDS virus. Lately, a few reports have surfaced of the opposite occurrence—patients have become HIV positive by way of receiving routine health care from infected health care providers. ①

How often do health care workers contract AIDS because of the work they do?

Very rarely. In fact, only a handful of such cases exists. Most health care workers are well trained to prevent the spread of all dangerous diseases. They take every precaution to protect themselves and their patients. Only when health workers become tired, careless, or hurried—do accidents happen.

What about someone like me? I am interested in health care as a profession. Maybe I should change my mind.

That would be a shame. Millions of people have highly rewarding careers in the health care field and remain free of any sort of contagious disease.
Do consider the risks of acquiring a disease before you

make a decision, but keep the risks in perspective. The chance of dying from almost any other cause is enormous compared to the chance of dying from AIDS acquired by offering routine health care. This is true even if you choose to specialize in treatment of AIDS patients. After all, no one knows better than a health care professional how to stop the spread of disease. Teamed with a healthy self-concern, this knowledge keeps the vast majority of health care workers safe from AIDS, hepatitis viruses, pneumonia bacteria, and all the other disease-causing organisms that surround them daily.

What about the opposite case? For example, can I get AIDS from my dentist?

That can happen. In a widely publicized case in Florida, Kimberly Bergalis, a young woman, contracted AIDS

during routine dental surgery. While suffering enormous pain from the disease, she acted to make her case known. With help from her family and friends, she traveled to speak with the nation's leaders, urging them to take action to protect other unsuspecting clients from contracting AIDS during routine medical procedures. Kimberly was one of six patients thought to have been infected by one HIV-positive dentist.

What did Kimberly want the nation's leaders to do?

Kimberly and her family hoped to convince lawmakers to pass laws requiring every health care worker to be tested for HIV, and to make the results of those tests known to their patients.

What did the lawmakers do?

(Continued on next page)

sensation when he urinates and a yellow discharge from his penis. He recognized the signs of an STD. He has gone to a clinic, and has been diagnosed and treated for an STD. Now he is trying to decide what to do about telling his sexual partner. Alex believed his sexual partner had

never had a sexual relationship before this one. Now he isn't sure he was told the truth. To make matters worse, at a party a week ago, Alex had too much to drink, and messed around with someone else, because his partner couldn't go to the party with him. Although they did not have intercourse, Alex is worried that he could have contracted the STD at the party." After reading the story, ask students what STD they think Alex has. Do

they think Alex has an obligation to tell his sexual partner about the infection? If so, have them write a conversation between Alex and his sexual partner designed to inform the partner. If not, ask them to predict what the consequences of not informing his partner might be, for both of them. Discuss their answers. **(40 min. if done entirely in class, 20 min. if they write outside class)**

STRAIGHT TALK   *(Continued)*

The leaders did not enact laws, but they did provide voluntary guidelines. The guidelines state that all health care workers performing procedures likely to pass the virus, such as surgery and tooth extractions, should first be tested for HIV. A worker who tests positive is advised not to perform surgery, or at least to notify clients before the surgery.

These guidelines are not laws. However, each state may decide to use them to set down its own laws. Without laws and enforcement, workers suffer no penalty if they choose not to follow the guidelines. This leaves it up to health care clients to protect themselves.

How can clients protect themselves without knowing whether the health care provider is HIV positive?

One way is to simply ask whether your health care provider has been tested, and whether the test was positive. Another way is to stay alert. Notice whether your health care provider uses routine precautions such as these:

- Uses a new set of gloves for each client.
- Disinfects instruments (including handles) between clients.
- Wears gowns, masks, and

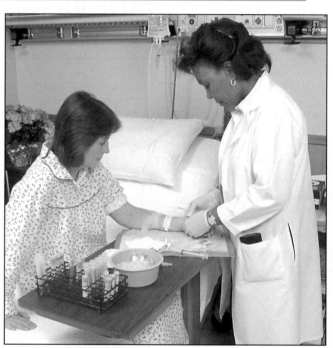

Health professionals who use precautions can protect themselves and their clients from AIDS.

other protective gear whenever blood or other body fluids are present.

The overwhelming majority of health care providers follow all these precautions and more. But one did not, and five of his clients were infected with HIV.* Watch carefully: if equipment looks used, if gloves are lacking, or if you feel suspicious, leave at once. Then report the health care provider to your parents, to the school nurse, or to the

person's professional association.

That's scary. Would I be better off not seeing a dentist?

Without doubt, you would be making a mistake to let fear of AIDS or anything else prevent your receiving routine dental care. Your odds of contracting AIDS from a health care

*In 1991, Kimberly Bergalis died of AIDS.

(Continued on next page)

Role Playing. Students may find it helpful to role-play a couple in which one person (usually male) has been informed that he has an STD, and he is about to tell his sexual partner that the partner should be tested. Encourage students to be direct. **(10 min.)**

Avoiding High-Risk Behaviors. Have students create posters or a newspaper feature article that influences others to avoid the high-risk behaviors of IV drug use and sexual activity. This might be done as a contest with bonus points awarded to the winning students. Winning posters might be displayed around the school and winning articles published in the school paper.

STRAIGHT TALK   *(Continued)*

professional are infinitely small. The cases you read about earlier in this section are the only known cases of patients being infected by a dentist. Without regular dental care, though, you can count on developing some other condition—gum disease, for example.

Other steps to reduce your risks of AIDS are worth taking. Here are the ways to avoid acquiring or transmitting the AIDS virus:

- Be alert during procedures using needles or other tools that puncture the skin. Insist that they be new or sterilized before use.
- Never share needles with anyone for any purpose. (If you abuse drugs, and especially if you inject them, get help for the drug problem quickly.)

- Women with HIV who have given birth to HIV-negative infants should not breastfeed them. (HIV is passed through breast milk.)
- Practice sexual abstinence, or, less effectively, follow the precautions concerning sexual activities presented in this chapter.

✍ Fast Facts

In 1992 in New York City, AIDS was the leading cause of death among children, ages one to four, and among women, ages 25 to 39.

✍ Fast Facts

A survey conducted in 1992 revealed that up to 31% of heterosexuals in the United States put themselves at some level of risk for contracting AIDS, usually by having multiple sex partners or unprotected sex with someone who is either HIV positive, a blood transfusion recipient, an intravenous drug user, or engaged in some other high-risk behavior. Only 17% of those with multiple sex partners said they used condoms all the time.

Vocabulary

1. Answers will vary.
2. **a.** fetus **b.** pelvic inflammatory disease (PID) **c.** intravenous (IV) drug use
3. **a.** Pap test **b.** ectopic pregnancy **c.** pubic lice **d.** genital warts **e.** Safer-sex strategies
4. **a.** gonorrhea **b.** chlamydia **c.** syphilis

Recall

Section I

1. chlamydia

2. A gonorrhea-killing anti-bacterial agent called erythromycin is applied to every infant's eyes within minutes after birth.
3. A woman may have internal blisters and not be aware of them.
4. feeling ill with fever, headache, muscle aches, painful urination, swollen glands
5. cancer of the cervix
6. removal of the growths or abnormal cervical tissue by surgery; by freezing; by applying prescription medication to external growths
7. detection of abnormal cervical cells
8. The chancre stage begins with the presence of a hard, painless sore that disappears in a few weeks on its own.

The next stage brings swollen glands, skin rash, hair loss, flulike symptoms that clear up by themselves in a few weeks.

The latent stage is the symptomless advancement of the disease.

The final stage infects

CHAPTER REVIEW

LEARNING THE VOCABULARY

sexually transmitted diseases (STDs)	Pap test	jock itch
acquired immune deficiency syndrome (AIDS)	syphilis	HIV
	chancre	Kaposi's sarcoma
chlamydia	latent	intravenous (IV) drug abuse
pelvic inflammatory disease (PID)	fetus	abstinence
ectopic pregnancy	trichomoniasis	monogamous
gonorrhea	pubic lice	safer-sex strategies
genital herpes	yeast infection	spermicide
genital warts	candidiasis	
	urinary tract infections (UTIs)	

Answer the following questions on a separate sheet of paper.

1. Write a paragraph using at least ten vocabulary terms or phrases. Underline each term or phrase that you use.
2. **Matching**—Match each of the following phrases with the appropriate vocabulary term from the list above:
   a. a developing human being before birth
   b. an infection of the fallopian tubes and pelvic cavity in women
   c. the practice of using needles to inject drugs of abuse into the veins
3. a. A _____ is a test for cancer of the cervix.
   b. An _____ is a pregnancy that has begun to develop in one of the fallopian tubes or elsewhere outside the uterus.
   c. An STD caused by tiny parasites that breed in pubic hair and cause intense itching is called _____.
   d. A viral STD that causes wartlike growths on the infected areas is called _____.
   e. _____ are behavior guidelines to reduce STD risk.
4. **Word Scramble**—Use the clues from the phrases below to help you unscramble the vocabulary terms from the list above:
   a. **aeooghnrr** _____ a bacterial STD that often advances without symptoms to spread through the body
   b. **aaiycdhlm** _____ an infection of the reproductive tract
   c. **iiyhlpss** _____ a bacterial STD that, if untreated, advances from a sore to flu-like symptoms and, years later, to severe nerve damage.

RECALLING IMPORTANT FACTS AND IDEAS

1. Which STD threatens the health of millions of people in the United States?
2. Explain what the United States does to protect babies' eyes against gonorrhea.
3. Why is it easier for women than for men to transmit the herpes virus?
4. List and identify symptoms of the first outbreak of genital herpes.
5. What can genital warts cause in women?
6. Describe the treatment for genital warts.
7. What is the purpose of a Pap test?
8. List and identify the stages of syphilis and the symptoms of each stage.
9. What could happen to the fetus of a woman with syphilis?
10. List the signs of a trichomoniasis infection in women.
11. Which women are especially likely to develop candidiasis?

organs causing blindness, deafness, brain damage, skin damage, and heart disease leading
to death.
9. possible death or very
severe mental retardation
10. unpleasant-smelling,
yellow-green or grey discharge;
abdominal pain; pain when urinating; itching in the genital
area

11. women who are pregnant,
using birth control pills, have
diabetes, take antibiotics, or
use douches
Section II
12. 30–120 million estimated
worldwide
13. mood swings, apathy, withdrawal, agitation, depression,
hallucinations, delusions, anxiety, memory loss

14. sexual intercourse; by the
transmission of blood, semen,
fluids of the vagina or other
body fluids; possibly through
open-mouthed, passionate
kissing; sharing of needles
among intravenous drug users;
unsterilized needles used for
acupuncture, tattooing, ear
piercing, and electrolysis
15. during pregnancy, during

birth, by way of breast-
feeding
16. casual contact; mosquitoes; eating food; blood
donation; vaccines using
sterilized needles; contact
with unbroken, healthy
skin; touching shared
objects
Section III
17. intravenous drug
users; anyone who has
had previous sexual part-
ners and who has not,
since then, been tested for
STDs

---

12. Approximately how many cases of AIDS are
predicted by the year 2000?
13. What are the mental symptoms of AIDS?
14. Describe the ways in which the AIDS virus is
transmitted in adults.
15. Name the three additional ways that the AIDS

virus is transmitted to infants.
16. List and identify ways in which HIV is not
transmitted.
17. It is especially important to avoid becoming
sexually active with certain groups of people.
What groups are they?

CRITICAL THINKING

1. Reread the Straight Talk section on page 441,
"AIDS Risks and Routine Health Care." Whose
fault do you think it was that Kimberly Bergalis
died in 1991? Was it the dentist's fault? The
government's? Kimberly's? How can we
prevent other needless deaths like Kimberly's?
What would you have done differently to
prevent Kimberly's infection if you had been
Kimberly? What would you have done

differently if you had been the dentist?
2. Do you think a school should let the public
know if someone with AIDS is going to the
school? What would you do if you found out
someone with AIDS was in your class? Explain
how you would react to being lab partners
with an AIDS individual. Would you tell your
parents about this? How would they react?

ACTIVITIES

1. Make a list of organizations in your area that
treat sexually transmitted diseases. Include
phone numbers and addresses for each.
2. Write an editorial for your school newspaper
on innocent victims of AIDS, like Kimberly
Bergalis. Discuss in the article what the public
can do to prevent more such cases.
3. Visit several local dentists' offices and ask
questions about their equipment, especially
their hand pieces, and how they sterilize them.
Make a comparison showing which dentists
take the most precautions and which dentists
take the fewest precautions. Rate each of the
dentists on safety after your trips.
4. Make a collage of all the famous people you
know that have died from the AIDS virus.
Display these around the school.

5. Cut out at least five articles from magazines
and newspapers about AIDS research. Write
a one-page report on your findings.
6. Have a class debate on Magic Johnson. Do
you think such an athlete should play
basketball in the NBA? Who is at risk if he
plays? Would you play against him?
7. Take a class survey on how you feel about
AIDS patients in hospitals. Do you think they
should all be in an isolated area? If you were
a nurse or a doctor, would you treat AIDS
patients? Why, or why not?
8. Ask your parents a series of questions on the
transmission and prevention of AIDS. Are their
answers similar to the ones in this chapter? If
not, ask them to call the AIDS hotline and get
more information on this deadly disease.

MAKING DECISIONS ABOUT HEALTH

1. Two seniors, Billy and Tess, have been going
steady for two years. Tess is a virgin. Billy has
had sexual relationships with three other girls.
Lately, Billy has had painful urination, tender
lymph nodes, and abdominal pain. He is afraid
to tell Tess, because he wants to have a

sexual relationship with her. If Billy tells Tess,
is he sure to lose her? If he doesn't tell her,
might he give her a sexually transmitted
disease? What would you do if you were Billy?
What would you do if you were Tess?

CHAPTER 18 PLANNER

OVERVIEW

Chapter 18 is 22 pages long and is divided into the three sections listed to the right. Major learning outcomes of the chapter are also listed to the right. Briefly, this chapter introduces students to the concept of relating lifestyle habits to the development or prevention of disease, particularly cardiovascular disease. It stresses the importance of knowing the risk factors of lifestyle diseases such as CVD and stroke, as well as the alternatives for reducing such risks.

MAKING LIFE CHOICES SUPPLEMENTARY MATERIAL

A variety of activities, handouts, quizzes, and tests to accompany this chapter are available in the *Making Life Choices* supplementary material. You may pick and choose from those materials as appropriate for your amount of class time and the ability levels of your students. Some of the resources you might want to consider using are:

Overheads
• The Heart's Major Arteries
• An Overview of the Cardiovascular System
• Two Kinds of Pressure in the Capillaries
• The Formation of Plaques in Atherosclerosis
• A Thrombus and an Embolus
• The Effect of Stroke Location
• Comparing HDL and LDL

Handouts
• Cutting Down on Salt
• Fat Percentages of Common Foods
• Comparing Fats
• U.S. Public Health Service Objectives for the Nation

Teacher Information Sheets
• Heart Disease and Influenza
• Intervention Studies
• Hypertension

Answers to "Fact or Fiction"

Answers to the Fact or Fiction can be found on page 464.

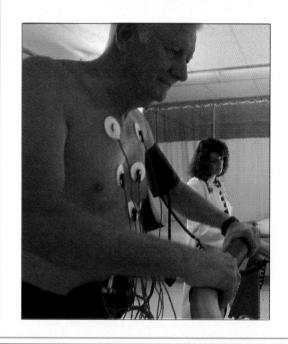

CHAPTER 18

Heart and Artery Disease

CHAPTER PROJECT

As a class, develop 10–15 questions students will use to interview someone in their communities or families who has had a heart attack, a stroke, or some type of heart surgery. The interview questions should address lifestyle habits relating to risk factors (smoking, exercise, etc.) Some questions should relate to lifestyle changes they have made, if any; changes they still need to make; regrets, if any; and disabling results they may have endured. Conclude with discussion, students' reactions, and any impact the interviews had on students.

Activity To Introduce Chapter

Have students assume each of the following body positions and perform each of the activities for five minutes, recording their heart rates after each one: sitting; resting supine; resting supine, feet elevated; standing at attention; walking very slowly; and running in place. Have students record their 30-second heart rates and multiply each rate by 2 for their minute rates. Have them answer the following questions:
1. Which position has the lowest pulse rate?
2. Which position has the highest pulse rate?
3. What can you infer about pulse rate and exercise?

OUTCOMES

After reading and studying this chapter, you will be able to:

✓ Identify the parts of the circulatory system and their functions.
✓ Describe the major diseases of the cardiovascular system and some medical treatments for each.
✓ List the warning signs of heart attack and stroke.
✓ Identify the risk factors for cardiovascular disease.
✓ Explain how to reduce the risks of cardiovascular disease.

✓ Explain the link between emotional health and cardiovascular disease.

CONTENTS

I. The Circulatory System
II. Cardiovascular Disease
III. Reducing Risks of CVD

    Straight Talk: *Emotions and the Heart*

FACT OR FICTION

What do you think? Are the following statements true or false? If you think they are false, then say what is true.

1. Everyone is developing heart disease, even teenagers.
2. The heart muscle receives all the nutrients and oxygen it needs from the blood in its chambers.
3. The sound of the heartbeat can tell much about the health of the heart.
4. For a person who has suffered a heart attack, it is too late for

lifestyle changes to be of any help.
5. You can tell whether your blood pressure is high by the way you feel.
6. The most important dietary measure a person can take to avoid heart disease is to eat more margarine.

(Answers on page 464)

■ **Reminder:** Knowing how to study can increase your knowledge, improve your grades, *and* cut down on your study time. See the *Studying Health* section at the front of your text for some suggestions to help you study this chapter.

SUGGESTED RESOURCES

Student Readings
1. American Heart Association. *1988 Heart Facts.* Dallas: American Heart Association, 1989.

Teacher Readings
1. Kaplan, N.M. *Prevent Your Heart Attack.* New York: Pinnacle Books, 1987.

Videos

1. *Health Habits for Healthy Life.* 1981, Filmfair Communications, 10900 Ventura Blvd., P.O. Box 1728, Studio City, CA 91604.

Software
1. *Health Problem Series: Heart Disease.* Opportunities for Learning, Inc., 800-243-7116.

NOT ENOUGH TIME?*

You could easily spend six days teaching this chapter (three days in each section). However, if you have only two or three days to devote to this chapter, the following are some suggestions to help you make sure that you cover the key topics if you have limited time.

TIME	SUGGESTIONS
2 Days	Day 1—Assign Section II prior to class. Open class with Section II Activities 2.1, 2.2, and 2.3. Next, do Activity 2.6. Do the Close Activity 2.9, and end by evaluating with the pop quiz, Activity 2.8. Assign Section III for homework.
	Day 2—Begin class with Section III Activity 3.1. Follow this with Activities 3.4, 3.5, and 3.8, Section III. Have Activity 3.12, Section III, set up to be going on in the back of the classroom while the class continues. Evaluate by asking students to respond to the three statements in Activity 3.14, Section III. For extra credit points assign Activities 3.3 and 3.6, Section III.
3 Days	Day 1—Assign Section I prior to class. Begin class with Activity 1.1, Section I to raise interest level. Next, do Section I, Activity 1.2 for extra credit. Conclude the class with writing the paragraph (Section I, Activity 1.4). Assign Section II for homework.
	Day 2—Same as day 1 in the 2 Day plan.
	Day 3—Same as day 2 in the 2 Day plan.

Please refer to the 18-week daily lesson plans in the supplementary material for additional suggestions.

4. Why does raising your feet or standing elevate the pulse rate?
5. How can the pulse rate be lowered in all the body positions?
6. Why is lowering the pulse rate good for the heart muscle? In addition to this activity, contact your local chapter of the American Heart Association for directions on how to conduct the Harvard Step Test. Students will be able to determine their Cardiopulmonary Classification from their results of this test.

In this section students will learn that the:

1. Circulatory system provides each body cell with all it needs to live.
2. Heart, blood vessels, blood, and lymph play important roles in keeping cells alive and well.

Activity 1.1

Heart Sounds. Have students listen with a stethoscope to their own heartbeats and a partner's heartbeat to identify the "lub-dub," two-step rhythm. Ask which chambers create the lub sound and which create the dub sound. Discuss the real

source of the sound. (the closing of the valves) Ask how you murmur when you talk. (mouth slightly open) Discuss how this is related to a heart murmur. **(10–15 min.; Extend, Enrich)**

Activity 1.2

Heart Diagram. Ask a student to begin this activity by drawing a diagram of the heart on the board. Ask other students, one at a time, to add, correct, or

---

📖 Fast Facts

Heart disease can be prevented. Mortality from heart attacks has decreased by 44% over the past thirty years. The death rate due to heart disease has decreased by 14%.

Teacher Support Notes

① Cardiovascular: Because cardiovascular and other words with the root *cardio* are commonly encountered in our society, you may want to break the word up so that students will be more likely to remember it and similar words. Tell them that cardio comes from the Greek word *kardia*, which means heart. Vascular is from the Latin word *vasculum*, meaning small vessel. Thus, vascular refers to the blood vessels or a system of blood vessels.

📖 Fast Facts

The first heart attack in the United States was not reported in the American medical literature until 1912.

Teenagers often believe (wrongly) that they have little to fear from heart disease. They think that older people—people their grandparents' and parents' ages, not teenagers—have heart disease. To a point, their beliefs are valid. Indeed, few young people suffer with advanced heart disease. But the danger in this reasoning is that heart disease starts young—very young.

Disease of the heart and blood vessels—**cardiovascular disease (CVD)**—develops slowly over a lifetime. Of the three kinds of blood vessels—the **arteries**, **capillaries**, and **veins**—the disease is most noticeable in the arteries. Therefore, properly speaking, we should be referring to *heart and artery* disease. ①

In this country, almost everyone has some degree of heart and artery disease. Even children only four or five years old have early traces, which steadily worsen through the years. Autopsies on soldiers as young as 18 have shown that their arteries were already clogged with fat.

Disabling disease is not inevitable, though. Experts believe that, in many cases, the choices young people make have everything to do with how fast their heart and artery disease progresses and whether or not it reaches the danger point by middle age. You can take action now to promote the health of your own circulatory system before heart and artery diseases take their toll on your health.

SECTION I

The Circulatory System

The system of the body that performs the task of providing cells with all that they need to live is the circulatory system—the heart and blood vessels (see Chapter 6). Also called the **cardiovascular system**, it pumps the equivalent of 4,000 gallons of **blood** around the body each day, driving this blood with over 85,000 heartbeats.

The heart, at the center of the circulatory system, is almost all muscle. Four hollow **chambers** inside collect blood and then pump it out again into tough, elastic arteries. The heart can be compared with an import-export business. Just as an importer receives and distributes goods, the heart receives and distributes blood. Two of the heart's four chambers function as receiving areas and two, as shipping areas. The receiving chambers, the **atria**, pool the blood as it arrives from the body. The shipping chambers, the **ventricles**, contract powerfully to send the blood on its way again.

The heart does not benefit from the blood within its chambers. That blood does not nourish or cleanse the heart's tissues. The heart relies on its own network of vessels—the **coronary arteries**—for nourishment. The coronary arteries branch into capillaries that weave all over the heart's outer surface and feed it with nutrients and oxygen (see Figure 18–1). This fact becomes important to understanding how the heart is affected by disease of the arteries.

You have probably listened to your own or someone else's heartbeat and noticed its two-step rhythm, sometimes called *lub-dub*. The first beat ("lub") is the sound made when the atria contract to send the blood they have pooled to the ventricles below them. The second beat ("dub") is the sound made when the powerful ventricles contract to send the blood on its way to the lungs and the body. (The atria relax and pool more blood during the "dub.")

You may be wondering why the contraction of the heart muscle should make any sound at all. In reality, it does not. The sound comes from the slapping shut of the heart's **valves**—flaps of tissue located at the delete from the picture, and label all of the structures as the diagram progresses. Minimal labeling should include: left atrium, right atrium, left ventricle, right ventricle, aorta, inferior and superior vena cava, septum, pulmonary artery, pulmonary vein, and valve locations. Arrows should be used to indicate the path of the flow of blood into, through, and out of the heart, to the lungs, back to the heart, and out to the body. Two chalk colors could

be used for the arrows, heart chambers, and blood vessels to differentiate oxygenated and deoxygenated blood flow. Check each correct item as they go so that those are not eliminated. Refer students to Figure 18–1 below and Figure 6–7 on page 146 in Chapter 6 to make final additions or deletions. If students are not knowledgeable enough to keep this activity moving along, you may wish to have them use Figures 18–1 and 6–7 as

a guide at the beginning of this activity. **(15–20 min., Cooperative Learning)**

Activity 1.3
Functions of the Lymph System.
Ask students the following questions:
1. Do cells produce waste materials that must be carried away? (yes) **2.** What carries away waste materials in sinks? (water) **3.** What would happen if water

(continued on next page)

Right Coronary Artery   Left Coronary Artery

Figure 18–1 The Heart's Major Arteries. The coronary arteries feed the heart muscle itself. The heart derives no nourishment from the blood inside its chambers.

entrances and exits of the chambers. The heart's valves are illustrated in Figure 6–7 on page 146, in Chapter 6. (You may wish to turn back there to review the circulatory system as you read this chapter.) Normally, the valves allow blood to flow in only one direction on its way through the heart. If the valves are damaged or unusually shaped, however, some blood will flow backward. This changes the heartbeat sound (a **heart**

murmur). Heart murmurs usually do not indicate trouble. Sometimes, though, they can mean that the heart requires medical attention. A heart examination includes a physician's listening to the heartbeat and,

MINI GLOSSARY

cardiovascular disease (CVD): a general term for all diseases of the heart and blood vessels.
arteries: blood vessels that carry blood from the heart to the tissues.
capillaries: the smallest blood vessels, which connect the smallest arteries with the smallest veins. Substances normally trapped in thick-walled arteries and veins can easily pass through the delicate walls of the capillaries.
veins: blood vessels that carry used blood from the tissues back to the heart.
cardiovascular system: the system of structures that circulates blood and lymph throughout the body. (Also called the *circulatory system*).
blood: the thick, red fluid that flows through the body's blood vessels and transports gases, nutrients, wastes, and other important substances around the body. Blood also plays roles in body temperature regulation.
chambers: rooms; in the heart, large, hollow areas that receive incoming blood from the lungs and tissues and ship it out again.
atria (singular, atrium): the two upper chambers of the heart—the receiving areas that pool incoming blood.
ventricles: the two lower chambers of the heart—the shipping areas that send blood on its way to the lungs or the tissues.
coronary arteries: the two arteries that supply blood to the heart muscle.
valves: flaps of tissue that open and close to allow the flow of blood in one direction only. The heart's valves are located at the entrances and exits of its chambers.
heart murmur: a heart sound that reflects damaged or abnormal heart valves.

Teacher Support Notes

① **Overhead—The Heart's Major Arteries:** Your supplementary material contains an overhead of this illustration.
② **Coronary Arteries:** Ask students how the coronary arteries differ from other arteries. (They supply blood to the heart muscle itself, not to other parts of the body.) Tell students that *coronary*, like cardio, is a term that has to do with the heart.

Fast Facts

Each year 1-1/4 million Americans suffer heart attacks. Almost 40% occur between November and February. Doctors say that cold weather stimulates the body to produce a group of chemicals, including adrenaline, that causes the heart to beat faster, the blood to clot more easily, and the blood vessels leading to the heart to constrict.

did not flow freely to do this? (a clog would develop) Give some examples of wastes and what would happen if they were allowed to build up. Ask the students to relate this to the function of lymph. **(5–10 min., Critical Thinking)**

Activity 1.4
Short Essay. Have students write a paragraph about the circulatory system using the terms in this section. They may include several words in one sentence. **(15 min.; Reteach, Reinforce)**

Activity 1.5
Vocabulary Jeopardy. Create a jeopardy game using the fifteen vocabulary words in this section. Call out a word. The students must give a question related to the word. **(45 min.; Reteach, Reinforce)**

Teacher Support Notes

① **Overhead—Cardiovascular System:** Your supplementary material contains an overhead that provides an overview of the cardiovascular system. You may want to use the overhead as you have students read this section.

② **Overhead—Pressure in the Capillaries:** An overhead in your supplementary material illustrates both the pressure produced by the heart in pumping the blood through the arteries and the osmotic pressure that draws fluid back into the veins.

Section I Review

Answers

1. cardiovascular system
2. Valves
3. coronary arteries
4. Arteries carry blood from the heart to the tissues, while veins carry used blood from the tissues to the heart.
5. 4,000
6. The coronary arteries branch into the capillaries that weave all over the heart's outer surface and feed it.
7. The sound comes from the slapping shut of the heart's valves—flaps of tissue at the entrances and exits of the chambers.
8. Answers will vary.

450

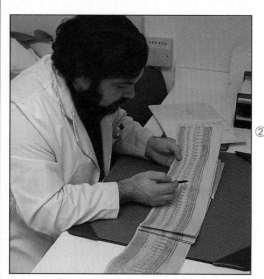

A record of the heart's electrical activity reveals much about its health.

possibly, an **electrocardiogram**. An electrocardiogram is a record of the electrical activity of the heart.

The blood vessels are perfectly built to do their jobs of nourishing and cleansing the tissues. The arteries' thick walls are built to withstand the pressure of the blood surging from the ventricles. As the arteries branch out, they become smaller in diameter and more numerous. They end in networks of capillaries—webs of tiny, thin-walled vessels too small to see. No part of the blood can cross the thick artery walls. However, the thin capillary walls allow some of the blood's clear fluid (**lymph**)—with nutrients, oxygen, and other chemicals such as hormones—to be forced out of the bloodstream into the tissues. The fluid that is drawn back into the blood carries with it wastes from the tissues. The capillaries that carry waste-laden blood then merge with others to form greater vessels, the veins. These transport this used blood to the lungs for renewal. Figure 6–7 in Chapter 6 on page 146 illustrates this route.

So, to repeat, as the blood moves through a capillary net, much of its fluid—with its cargo of nutrients and oxygen—is strained out. The fluids flow around the cells of the tissues, providing them with nutrients and oxygen and collecting their wastes. The used fluids seep back into the bloodstream to be carried away for cleaning and renewal. In this way, the tissues are nourished and cleansed.

Disease in any part of the circulatory system affects many of the body's tissues, of course, because the blood nourishes all the tissues. Any disease that affects the heart muscle or other working parts of the heart is called **heart disease**. The term *cardiovascular disease* refers to diseases of all parts of the cardiovascular system, including both the heart and blood vessels. The onset of these diseases can be postponed or prevented by changes in people's lifestyles. Therefore, these diseases can often be controlled by individuals.

> **Key Points** *The cardiovascular system consists of the heart and the blood vessels. This system serves as the tissues' supply line for both nutrients and oxygen and as their waste disposal system.*

SECTION I REVIEW

Answer the following questions on a sheet of paper.

Learning the Vocabulary

The vocabulary terms in this section are *cardiovascular disease, arteries, capillaries, veins, cardiovascular system (circulatory system), blood, chambers, atria, ventricles, coronary arteries, valves, heart murmur, electrocardiogram, lymph,* and *heart disease.*

1. The system of structures that circulates blood and lymph throughout the body is called the _____.
2. _____ are flaps that allow the body's fluids to flow in one direction only.
3. The _____ are the arteries that supply blood to the heart muscle.

FOCUS

In this section the students will learn the:
1. Frequency of CVD in the U.S. today.
2. Relationship between atherosclerosis and CVD.
3. Warning signs of heart attack and stroke, and medical treatments for these

diseases.

Activity 2.1
Ranking Causes of Death. List the following causes of death on the board: heart disease, cancer, accidents, suicide, and AIDS. Ask students to consider the list and pick the one they think most people die of every year in the U.S. Count the number of students choosing each and record it on the board next to their

choices. Stress that heart disease is the number-one killer. Are they surprised? **(5 min., Critical Thinking)**

Activity 2.2
Don't Become a Statistic. Ask your students to stand next to their seats. Count off the students, one through four. Ask all the fours to sit down. Tell them that one in every four people living in the

(continued on next page)

---

4. What are the differences between veins and arteries?

Learning the Facts
5. The equivalent of how many gallons of blood are pumped around the body each day?
6. How does the heart obtain the nutrients and oxygen it needs?
7. Where does the heartbeat sound come from—that is, what makes the sound?

Making Life Choices
8. Lifestyle choices students make today affect their potential for developing cardiovascular disease. Why do people always think that cardiovascular disease won't happen to them? How does this thinking cause people to make poor health choices and not change unhealthy behaviors?

SECTION II

Cardiovascular Disease

Cardiovascular disease (CVD) is the number-one killer of adults. Many people become sick and die of CVD long before they reach retirement age. One in every four people living in the United States is ill with some form of this disease. Most others are in some stage of developing it. Fortunately, however, everyone can take steps to reduce the risks of developing CVD.

Atherosclerosis and Blood Clotting

The disease **atherosclerosis**, or hardening of the arteries, is the most common form of CVD. It begins with an accumulation of mounds of soft fat along the inner walls of all the arteries of the body. Such mounds gradually enlarge and harden with mineral deposits to form **plaques**, which make the passageway through the arteries

① narrower than normal (see Figure 18–2 on the next page). As mentioned, the heart muscle depends on blood flow through its own arteries for nourishment and oxygen. In atherosclerosis, the arteries that supply the heart begin to narrow and harden, depriving the heart of its health and strength. Arteries that feed other organs and tissues narrow and harden, too, impairing the health of the organs and tissues they serve.

Atherosclerosis not only weakens the heart, but leads to high blood pressure, too. Normally, as blood pushed by heartbeats surges through the arteries, the arteries expand to allow blood to pass and then contract again. Arteries hardened by plaques cannot expand, so the pulses of blood must squeeze through them. This causes pressure to build up, because the blood backs up at the narrowed areas while the heart strains to push it through. This high blood pressure in the arteries, or hypertension, is a major contributor to CVD.

Hypertension damages the artery walls and can even cause them to go into spasms, further blocking blood flow. Also, as pressure

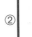

MINI GLOSSARY

electrocardiogram: a record of the electrical activity of the heart that, if abnormal, may indicate heart disease.
lymph: the clear fluid that bathes each cell and transfers needed substances and wastes back and forth between the blood and the cells. Lymph also plays a role in immunity.
heart disease: any disease of the heart muscle or other working parts of the heart.
② **atherosclerosis** (ATH-uh-roh-scler-OH-sis): the most common form of CVD; a disease characterized by plaques along the inner walls of the arteries.
plaques (PLACKS): mounds of fat, mixed with minerals, that build up along artery walls in atherosclerosis.

Fast Facts
Women under 45 are 1/10 as likely to have heart attacks as men under the age of 45.

Teacher Support Notes

① **Hardening of the Arteries:** Have students reread this passage making sure that they understand how hardening of the arteries can harm the individual in two very different ways. (Hardening of the coronary arteries weakens the heart; hardening of the other arteries damages the organs and tissues throughout the rest of the body.)

② **Atherosclerosis:** This word will be a difficult one to pronounce for most students. Have them practice aloud with each other.

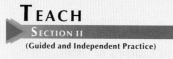

U.S. is ill from some form of CVD. Point out that those who are now sitting represent people with CVD. Ask them how it makes them feel. Would they like to be able to do something about becoming a statistic? **(3–5 min., Critical Thinking)**

Activity 2.3

Aneurysms. Obtain several long, skinny balloons that are small and which will blow up in one area upon initial inflation. (This usually works best with very cheap or poor-quality balloons.) Use one to demonstrate an aneurysm. Have stu-

dents look at Figure 18–3. Give them five minutes to review the chapter information on aneurysms and be able to: **1.** Explain how or why an aneurysm develops. **2.** Give a cause for an aneurysm developing. **3.** Tell what can result from an aneurysm. Ask for volunteer answers and award extra credit. **(10 min.; Reteach, Reinforce)**

Activity 2.4

Teacher Support Notes

① **Overhead— Plaques:** Your supplementary material contains an overhead of these drawings, which you may want to use as you discuss this illustration.

② **Detecting Heart Disease:** As enrichment you may want to remind students that the heart is a muscle. Explain that as it tries to respond to the extra strain of high blood pressure, it becomes larger and stronger, especially in its left ventricle. More and more research indicates that an enlarged left ventricle reflects advancing heart and artery disease. This heart abnormality can be detected by a test that compares the mass of the left ventricle to the other portions of the heart. This comparison produces a score known as the *left ventricle mass index.*

✎ Fast Facts

According to the American Heart Association, short people are more likely to suffer heart attacks than tall people. The risk of heart attack goes down three percentage points for every inch of height.

452   UNIT 5 Disease Prevention

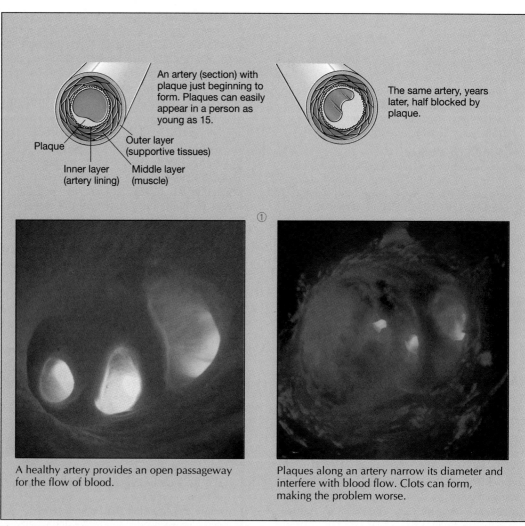

A healthy artery provides an open passageway for the flow of blood.

Plaques along an artery narrow its diameter and interfere with blood flow. Clots can form, making the problem worse.

Figure 18–2 The Formation of Plaques in Atherosclerosis

builds up in an artery, the arterial wall may become weakened and balloon out, forming an **aneurysm**. An aneurysm can burst. When this happens in a small artery, it leads to death of the tissue surrounding it. In a major artery such as the **aorta**, a ruptured aneurysm leads quickly to massive bleeding (hemorrhage) and death. Figure 18–3 illustrates an aneurysm and a hemorrhage.

Abnormal blood clotting is another threat caused by atherosclerosis. Under normal conditions, clots form and dissolve in the blood all the time. Small, cell-like bodies in the blood, known as **platelets**, cause clots to form whenever they detect injuries. This normal function protects the body against blood losses by plugging minor wounds. Clots also form accidentally inside the blood

Contributing Factors. This activity can be done in groups of two to four or individually. Bring in pieces of plastic tubing or lawn hoses of varying thicknesses, quality, and diameter. Have the students flex them, examine them, etc. Discuss which will last the longest and why, and show how the flow of fluid varies with the diameter. After students have examined the hoses and a short discussion period is finished, ask students to respond to the following questions in writing: **1.** In which pieces of hose or tubing is the pressure the highest? **2.** Which blood vessels in their bodies would correspond to these pieces? **3.** In which pieces of hose or tubing is the pressure the lowest? **4.** Which blood vessels in their bodies would correspond to those pieces? **5.** What contributes to increasing the pressure in any of the pieces of hose? What contributes to decreasing the pressure in any of the pieces of hose? Relate each of the contributing factors to its corresponding effect on the blood vessels. Discuss several factors for Question 5. Answers will vary but some possibilities include: increased pressure around the outside of the vessels, as with edema or water retention; buildup of material inside the vessels, as with cholesterol or plaque; decreased flexibility of the vessels, as

(continued on next page)

An aneurysm   A hemorrhage

Figure 18–3 An Aneurysm and a Hemorrhage

vessels when the platelets encounter rough spots such as plaques. Normally, they soon dissolve again. In atherosclerosis, however, platelets encounter many plaques and begin the clotting process more often than normal. Clots thus tend to accumulate.

Atherosclerosis can cause blockage of an artery in any of three ways:

1. The plaques themselves can enlarge enough to block the flow of blood.
2. A blood clot may form, stick to a plaque, and gradually grow until it cuts off the blood supply like a plug (a **thrombus**). In the arteries of the heart, such a blockage is called a **coronary thrombosis** (a type of **heart attack**). In a vessel that feeds the brain, the blockage is called a **cerebral thrombosis** (a type of **stroke**).
3. A clot may also break loose, become a *traveling* clot (an **embolus**), and circulate until it reaches an artery too small to allow its passage. The sudden blockage of the vessel is an **embolism**.

When an artery is blocked, the tissue normally supplied by the blocked vessel may suddenly die. Tissue death can occur gradually, too, resulting in organ damage.

The development of atherosclerosis reaches a **critical phase** when more than half of the inner surfaces of the arteries are covered with plaques. Once in the critical phase, a person faces a high risk of heart attacks or strokes.

> **Key Points** ▶ *Atherosclerosis is the formation of plaques in the arteries. It worsens hypertension and makes blood clots likely. Atherosclerosis can cause blockage of arteries that feed critical organs, such as the heart or brain.*

Heart Attack

Heart attacks are the most common of the life-threatening events brought on by atherosclerosis. A heart attack occurs when blood flow to the heart becomes so restricted that some of the heart's muscle tissue

MINI GLOSSARY

aneurysm (AN-your-ism): the ballooning out of an artery wall at a point where it has grown weak.

aorta (ay-OR-tah): the largest artery in the body; it conducts freshly oxygenated blood from the heart to the tissues.

platelets: tiny, disk-shaped bodies in the blood, important in blood clot formation.

thrombus: a stationary clot. When it has grown enough to close off a blood vessel, this dangerous event is a *thrombosis.*

coronary thrombosis: the closing off of a vessel that feeds the heart muscle by a stationary clot, or *thrombus.*

heart attack: the event in which vessels that feed the heart muscle become blocked, causing tissue death.

cerebral thrombosis: the closing off of a vessel that feeds the brain by a stationary clot, or *thrombus.*

stroke: the shutting off of the blood flow to the brain by plaques, a clot, or hemorrhage.

embolus (EM-bow-luss): a clot that breaks loose and travels through the bloodstream. When it causes sudden closure of a blood vessel, this dangerous event is an *embolism.*

embolism: the sudden closure of a blood vessel by a traveling blood clot, or *embolus.*

critical phase: in atherosclerosis, the stage when plaques cover more than half of the inner surfaces of the arteries.

Teacher Support Notes

① Prostaglandins: Hormones that control the action of the platelets are *prostaglandins.* An imbalance among these hormones can contribute to the formation of clots. A person who has suffered a minor stroke may feel that the problem is being dismissed lightly when the doctor prescribes only aspirin. Aspirin, however, modifies the prostaglandins and so can suppress the platelets' clotting action.

② Overhead—Thrombus vs. Embolus: An overhead in your supplementary material illustrates the difference between a thrombus and an embolus.

🖉 Fast Facts

Men who wake up feeling exhausted rather than rested may be at risk for a heart attack. Scientists suspect that waking up exhausted might be a warning sign of heart disease or depression, which often precedes a heart attack.

453

with hardening of the arteries. **(30 min., Critical Thinking)**

Activity 2.5
   Blood Vessel Models. Create a blood vessel with a loosely rolled piece of poster board. Line the inside with a cloth that has a nap or rough surface. Obtain as many ping-pong balls as possible. Attach a small square of Velcro to each ball. Allow the students to demonstrate blood clots (a thrombus and an embolus) by rolling balls inside the tube. Ask students to identify which configurations of the ping-pong balls represent a thrombus, thrombosis, an embolus, and embolism. This may be done in groups of two to four students, one group at a time or simulta-neously if you have been able to con-struct more than one blood vessel model. (Extra credit could be given to students who volunteer to construct blood vessels at the beginning of this unit.) This activity could be used as a demonstration by the teacher or one or two students. **(10–15 min.; Reteach, Reinforce)**

Activity 2.6
   The Silent Killer. Ask students to

Teacher Support Notes

① **Teen Views Follow-Up Questions:** The fol-lowing are some questions you may want to use to encourage discussion of the ideas expressed by the students in the Teen Views feature:
a. Ask students how they would respond to Ryan Engle's first sentence. (While answers will vary, students should mention what they have read in this chapter about everyone having heart disease and how making healthy life-style choices can delay the disease.)
b. Do students agree with Ryan Engle, that they have more important things to worry about than heart disease?
c. Do students think they are immortal? If not, what do they think Shew An Ho means in saying teens think themselves immortal?
d. Do students believe that teens pay less atten-tion to their diets than they should? Do they eat healthier now than they did when they began this course?
e. Do students believe they can make a signifi-cant difference in how long they can live without feel-ing the effects of heart dis-ease by altering their current lifestyle decisions?

454

---

454   UNIT 5 Disease Prevention

TEEN **V**IEWS

Should teenagers be concerned with heart disease? ①

I don't think that teenagers need to be concerned with heart disease. I don't know all that much about the dis-ease or its causes. I think that the teenagers of today already have a lot to worry about. With the problems of AIDS, the ozone layer, and much more, we already have enough to think about without worrying about a disease that doesn't affect us until we are older. **Ryan Engle, 16, East High School, MN**

Teenagers today concern themselves not with what they eat, but their self-image. If teenagers are more conscious of what they con-sume, it will decrease the risk of heart disease in the years ahead. The conse-quences of eating meals from fast food restaurants, high cholesterol foods, and sugary snacks will sneak up from behind them and catch them off-guard. Teens have an idea of immortality—that no real harm will happen to them. **Shew An Ho, 15, Carter High School, TN**

Yes. Anybody, regardless of age, can have heart disease. Teenagers to-day aren't as aware of healthy eating habits as they should be. We eat whatever we want, whenever we want it. Don't get me wrong, I'm not saying that teenagers should have a strict diet to follow, but we should be more aware of and responsible for what we put into our bodies. **Bobbett Plummer, 16, Poughkeepsie High School, NY**

Heart disease isn't something that is going to really affect you as a teenager but what you do as a teenager, could affect this problem in adult-hood. When you're a teenag-er, you really don't think about this and do not watch what you eat, nor do you exercise on a regular basis. If teenagers would take action now and plan for the future, we could prevent this prob-lem. **Philip Haynes, 17, New-man High School, GA**

---

dies for lack of oxygen. When heart muscle tissue dies, it is replaced by scar tissue that cannot do the heart's pumping work. The remaining muscle tissue must work harder to make up for the loss.

   Another problem of reduced oxygen to the heart is pain. When the oxygen supply to the heart is reduced, the heart may still be able to meet the needs of a physically inactive person, but a sudden exertion or emotional upset can bring on a pain in the chest, called **angina**. Angina is not always a symptom of a heart attack, but it can be. A person experiencing angina may deny that a heart attack is occurring and blame the symptoms on "indigestion." Many heart attack victims might have been saved had they only taken their pain seriously. If you or someone nearby suffers any of the heart attack symptoms listed in Figure 18–4, get medical help fast. Chapter 24 offers first aid procedures for heart attack victims.

   Often, a person has no pain before a first heart attack occurs and so may not be write down the statement "High blood pressure is called the silent killer because . . ." and ask them to complete the statement. Ask for volunteers to read their statements and award extra credit points for the best ones. Then review what numbers indicate blood pressure is high. **(10 min., Critical Thinking)**

Activity 2.7
   Current Articles. Collect newspaper

and magazine articles about heart transplants and artificial hearts. Ask students to read and share something special about their articles. Time needed will vary according to the length of the articles. If possible, collect articles as similar as possible in length. **(10–15 min. for reading and 5–10 min. discussion; Extend, Enrich)**

EVALUATE
SECTION II

Activity 2.8
Pop Quiz.
1. CVD is the number-one killer of adults in the U.S. today. (T)
2. Hardening of the arteries is the main cause of heart attack. (T)

(continued on next page)

FIGURE 18-4

Warning Signs of Heart Attack and Stroke

The warning signs of heart attack:
Even though not every heart attack is announced by clear-cut symptoms, you should get help immediately if you or someone you are with:

1. Feels uncomfortable pressure, fullness, squeezing, or pain in the center of the chest lasting for more than two minutes.
2. Experiences pain that spreads to the shoulders, neck, or arms.
3. Becomes dizzy, faints, sweats for no apparent reason, or has nausea or shortness of breath—especially when other symptoms are present.

The warning signs of stroke:
Report to a physician immediately any of the following:

1. Sudden, temporary weakness or numbness in any part of one side of the body.
2. Temporary loss of speech or of understanding of speech.
3. Dizziness, unsteadiness, or unexplained falls.
4. Temporary dimness or loss of vision, particularly in one eye.

Even if damaged, the heart keeps pumping.

Medical Treatments for Heart Attack Victims

Heart attacks do not always end in death or disability. Many times a person who suffers a minor heart attack can recover fully. One drug given within a few hours after the onset of a heart attack triggers the clot-dissolving action of the blood and thus stops a heart attack in its tracks, preventing much tissue damage. Other drugs may be used to strengthen and stabilize the heartbeat. A **pacemaker** is an implanted device that provides electrical stimulation for a failing heartbeat.

A common surgery for a failing heart is **coronary artery bypass surgery**. This involves replacing the blocked coronary arteries with sections of the person's own veins or with synthetic tubing. In another form of surgery, instruments inserted into the arter-

warned of the coming attack. Even medical tests designed to predict future heart attacks often fail to do so. Many heart attack deaths are sudden and unexpected.

> **Key Points** *A heart attack occurs when blood flow to the heart becomes so restricted that part of the heart muscle dies for lack of oxygen. Symptoms often include pain; they demand prompt attention.*

MINI GLOSSARY

angina (an-JYE-nuh or ANN-juh-nuh): pain in the heart region caused by lack of oxygen.
pacemaker: a device that delivers electrical impulses to the heart to regulate the heartbeat.
coronary artery bypass surgery: surgery to provide an alternate route for blood to reach heart tissue, bypassing a blocked coronary artery.

EVALUATE
(Continued)

3. Slurred speech is a warning sign for heart attack. (F)
4. A pacemaker keeps the heart beating by tiny electric shocks. (T)
5. A lifetime of exercise is not effective in preventing heart disease or heart attacks. (F)

6. Angina coats the inner walls of the arteries, restricting blood flow. (F)
7. An embolus is a traveling blood clot. (T)
8. Most people are in some stage of developing heart disease. (T)
9. We do not know the causes of high blood pressure. (F)
(5 min.; Reteach, Reinforce)

CLOSE
SECTION II

Activity 2.9
Identifying Symptoms. Make up different scenarios of people with symptoms of varying degrees of heart disease and/or stroke. Ask the students to identify the situation as heart attack, heart disease, or stroke. You may read these or

---

Teacher Support Notes

① **Stroke:** Stroke was defined earlier in the chapter. Ask students to define it here. (the shutting off of blood flow to the brain by plaques, a clot, or hemorrhage)

② **Small Stroke:** As background information you may want to know that health care providers refer to the small strokes as *transient ischemic attack (TIA)*.

③ **Overhead—Stroke Location:** In your supplementary material you will find an overhead of illustration 18–5, which you may want to use during coverage of this section in class.

④ **Opposite Side:** Make sure students see that damage to one side of the brain affects the opposite side of the body. Point out the use of color, which matches the opposite sides of the brain and body in this illustration.

🖎 Fast Facts

Strokes kill approximately 150,000 Americans each year. They are the third leading cause of death, 90% of the survivors have permanent impairments. More than seven billion dollars are spent each year to care for our two million stroke survivors.

456

---

456   UNIT 5 Disease Prevention

ies flatten, scrape, or vaporize the plaques and so widen the passageways.

Sometimes the heart is so badly damaged ② that it cannot recover its ability to pump enough blood to meet the needs of body tissues. In such cases, the person's life can often be saved by a **heart transplant**. Transplants are not a sure cure, and are a last resort for several reasons. A person who needs a new heart may have to wait years for one to become available. Even after a transplant, rejection of the new heart by the body's immune system is a constant threat. ③

The heart acts as a pump. Scientists are working to develop mechanical pumps to do the work of the living heart. An **artificial heart** would have the advantage that the human immune system would not recognize it as foreign and so would not reject it. Even the most progressive medical techniques are only temporary repairs, though. ④ Nothing has been found that will cure atherosclerosis. Blockages recur, and people may require repeated treatments. Because medicine isn't perfect, people with heart trouble may be lured into the hands of quacks and receive treatments that are frauds.

Lifestyle factors such as proper diet and physical activity have proved helpful in preventing or postponing CVD, and in hastening recovery from heart attacks. Medical advances are exciting, but in the end, everyday health habits may well turn out to be most reliable for preventing—and even sometimes reversing—heart disease.

> **Key Points** Heart attacks do not always end in death or disability. Treatments of heart attacks and heart disease range from clot-dissolving drugs to heart transplants.

Stroke

Strokes occur in the same way as heart attacks do—by the blocking of arteries—but the arteries are located in the brain. Strokes are not as common as heart attacks. How- ①

ever, they still claim many of the lives lost to atherosclerosis each year. Sometimes a person will suffer a small stroke—a warning that a blockage is forming. A minor stroke may have no lasting effect except to startle a person into taking action to reverse damaging habits.

When a major stroke occurs, a part of the brain is starved for blood and dies. This dead tissue interferes with the person's mental and physical functioning. The location of the damage determines the nature of the impairment, as shown in Figure 18–5.

Victims of severe strokes are robbed of their former abilities. They must start from

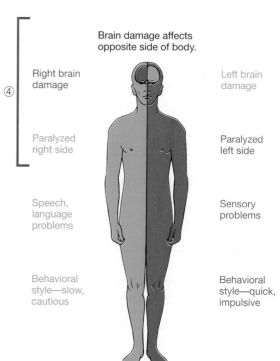

Brain damage affects opposite side of body.

Right brain damage

Left brain damage

Paralyzed right side

Paralyzed left side

Speech, language problems

Sensory problems

Behavioral style—slow, cautious

Behavioral style—quick, impulsive

Figure 18–5 The Effect of Stroke Location. Damage on one side of the brain affects the opposite side of the body.

have students act them out. Your supplementary material contains different scenarios to use for this activity. **(5 min.; Reteach, Reinforce)**

FOCUS
SECTION III

In this section students will learn that:
1. CVD and many of today's diseases develop slowly over a lifetime.

2. These diseases are directly linked to lifestyle habits and often to each other.
3. Improving personal choices can enhance life's quality and longevity.

Activity 3.1
Lifestyle. Ask students to define *lifestyle*. Discuss their definitions. Reach a class consensus on an appropriate definition. Have students list as many specifics as they can think of that are involved in a lifestyle. Ask them if they think some diseases may be primarily lifestyle diseases. Have them give examples of what these diseases might be and discuss their opinions and reasons. You may want to refer them back to the beginning of Chapter 1. **(10 min., Critical Thinking)**

(continued on next page)

---

scratch to relearn even simple personal hygiene or how to walk. Most stroke victims can recover some functioning, but recovery is always an exhausting test of will for the victim, medical professionals and family.

Strokes can also arise from the bursting of aneurysms (hemorrhages) in the small vessels of the brain. Like heart attacks, strokes require immediate medical attention. Act quickly, should any of the warning signs of stroke occur.

Key Points *Strokes are blockages or hemorrhages in the vessels that feed the brain. Strokes often result from atherosclerosis and can impair a person's functioning.*

SECTION II REVIEW

Answer the following questions on a sheet of paper.
Learning the Vocabulary
The vocabulary terms in this section are *atherosclerosis, plaques, aneurysm, aorta, platelets, thrombus, coronary thrombosis, heart attack, cerebral thrombosis, stroke, embolus, embolism, critical phase, angina, pacemaker, coronary artery bypass surgery, heart transplant,* and *artificial heart.*
1. What is the difference between an embolus and a thrombus?
2. Small, cell-like bodies in the blood that are important in clot formation are known as _____.
3. In a vessel that feeds the brain, blockage of the vessel by a stationary clot is called a _____.

Learning the Facts
4. What has happened to the arteries of someone diagnosed with atherosclerosis?
5. What occurs when someone has a heart attack?
6. List the three warning signs of a heart attack.

Making Life Choices
7. What would you do if someone in your family appeared to be having a heart attack but denied it and insisted on continuing with whatever he or she was doing?

SECTION III

Reducing Risks of CVD

CVD and other diseases we face today are not caused by the microbes that caused most diseases in the past, but by habits of lifestyle. These lifestyle diseases do not come on suddenly, but develop over years. Even so, when people find out they have CVD, they may be as surprised as if they had just come down with the measles. Yet many of their own personal choices—repeated day after day, year after year—may have made the disease almost a certainty.

Risk Factors

The many **risk factors** linked to CVD are listed in Figure 18–6 on the next page. Some of the risk factors are powerful predictors of CVD. If you are young and have none of them, the odds of your developing CVD in the next six years may be less than 1 in 100. If you are older and have all the major factors, the chance may rise to close to 1 in 2.

The Life Choice Inventory shows one way of calculating your risk score. This system isn't perfect. A few people with many risk factors live long lives without disease. A few people with only a few or none die young of CVD. On the average, though, the more risk factors in a person's life, the greater that person's risk of disease.

MINI GLOSSARY

heart transplant: the surgical replacement of a diseased heart with a healthy one.
artificial heart: a pump designed to fit into the human chest cavity and perform the heart's function of pumping blood around the body.
risk factors: factors linked with a disease by association but not yet proved to be causes.

Teacher Support Notes

① **Teacher Information Sheet—Heart Disease and Influenza:** Your supplementary material contains information regarding the possible connection between heart disease and influenza.

Section II Review

Answers
1. A thrombus is a stationary clot, while an embolus is a clot that breaks loose and travels through the bloodstream.
2. platelets
3. cerebral thrombosis
4. See page 451, column 2, for complete answer.
5. Some of the heart's muscle tissue dies for lack of oxygen when blood flow to the heart is restricted.
6. Refer to Figure 18–4 on page 455 for answers.
7. Answers will vary.

Activity 3.2
  Risk Factors. Ask students to define *risk* and discuss their answers. Reach a class consensus on an appropriate definition. Have each student write an example of a risky activity to support the definition. Now ask students to offer definitions for *risk factor*. Discuss risk factor, then for the

activity students wrote about, have them list as many things as they can that are risk factors involved in that activity. Finally, ask students to identify those risk factors on their lists that can be eliminated, modified, or reduced, etc. **(10 min., Critical Thinking)**

TEACH
SECTION III
(Guided and Independent Practice)

Activity 3.3
  Factor Analysis. Have students look at the risk factors for heart and artery disease in Figure 18–6. On paper have students respond to each one as C for controllable or N for noncontrollable. **(5 min.; Reteach, Reinforce)**

Activity 3.4
  Disease Contributors. Make flash cards of five lifestyle diseases (heart,

---

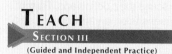

Fast Facts

In a study in England, subjects who were sedentary started doing aerobic exercises for 30 minutes, three or four times a week. Without using any drugs their systolic blood pressure dropped an average of 5 mm, and their diastolic blood pressure went down about 8 mm.

Teacher Support Notes

① **Teacher Information Sheet—Intervention Studies:** An information sheet in your supplementary material entitled "Intervention Studies" explains the process scientists go through to prove or disprove risk factors. You may find this information to be interesting background.

② **Smoking and Heart Disease:** To make sure students did not miss any of the several ways in which smoking damages the heart, ask them to name as many ways as they can. (raises blood pressure, increases heart rate, increases the heart muscle's need for oxygen, starves the heart and other tissues for oxygen, and makes the formation of clots likely)

458 UNIT 5 Disease Prevention

FIGURE 18-6

Risk Factors for Heart and Artery Disease

- Heredity (history of CVD prior to age 55 in family members).
- Gender (being male).
- Smoking.
- Hypertension.
- High blood cholesterol, high LDL, and/or low HDL (see page 462).
- Glucose intolerance (diabetes).
- Lack of exercise.
- Obesity (30 percent or more overweight).
- Stress.

  Many diseases—not just heart and artery disease—share the same risk factors (see Figure 18–7 on page 461). Many diseases also act as risk factors of other diseases. This means that if you scored high on risk factors for heart and artery disease, you also may have an increased risk of developing hypertension, obesity, diabetes, and certain cancers. The Health Strategies section on this page, "Reducing the Risk of CVD," briefly describes actions you can take to counter each of the risk factors for CVD.
  Of all the risk factors, heredity and gender are unchangeable, but can alert you to the need for extra diligence in controlling *other* risk factors. The four factors that respond best to lifestyle changes and that have emerged as major predictors of risk of CVD are smoking, hypertension, high blood cholesterol, and diabetes.

Key Points *Major risk factors for heart disease are heredity, gender, smoking, hypertension, high blood cholesterol, and diabetes. Lack of exercise, obesity, and stress also play roles. People can reduce their risks by controlling their risk factors.*

HEALTH
STRATEGIES

Reducing the Risk of CVD

To reduce the risk of CVD:

1. Learn about your heredity, and use the information. Control the lifestyle factors that may affect you.
2. Don't smoke. If you do smoke, stop.
3. Keep your blood pressure below 125/80 if you are a teenage girl; 130/80 if you are a teenage boy.
4. Keep your blood cholesterol within the normal range (below 170 milligrams per deciliter for teenagers).
5. If you have diabetes, keep your blood sugar under control.
6. Exercise vigorously for at least 20 minutes three or more times weekly.
7. Maintain appropriate body weight.
8. Control stress. Learn to relax.

Source: Adapted from R. E. Olson, How to reduce your risk of coronary heart disease (CHD), *Priorities,* Spring 1990, p. 21.

Smoking

  When tobacco smoke enters the lungs, it delivers to the blood a load of nicotine, a stimulant that triggers the stress response. This raises the blood pressure, increases the heart rate, and greatly increases the heart's need for oxygen. At the same time, carbon monoxide from the smoke is mistaken for oxygen and picked up by the blood. Carbon monoxide provides no oxygen to tissues. It simply rides in the blood, starving the tissues of oxygen. Not only that, but nicotine directly damages blood platelets, making clot formation likely.

diabetes, cancer, high blood pressure, emphysema) and five cards of communicable diseases (colds, chicken pox, flu, mono, and meningitis). Mix up the cards, and hold them up one at a time. First ask students to tell whether the disease is a communicable disease or not. Then ask which lifestyle habits might contribute to the development of each. Discuss the similarities and differences. Discuss the fact that all diseases can be contributed to in some way by lifestyle and/or personal habits. **(10 min., Critical Thinking)**

Activity 3.5
Self-Risk Analysis. Assign the Life Choice Inventory, "How Healthy is Your Heart?" below. Each student should read the inventory and score themselves to determine their risk of heart attack. Point out that at their age they should have a score from zero to nine—very remote.

(5 min.; Reteach, Reinforce)

Activity 3.6
Lifestyle Choices. Ask students to identify the risk factors that contributed to a less than perfect score for them on the Life Choice Inventory discussed in Activity 3.5. On paper, the students should put their names, the risk factors they identi-

(continued on next page)

LIFE CHOICE INVENTORY

How Healthy is Your Heart?

Every disease has risk factors. Those for heart disease are among the best known. The better you know the nature of the risks you face, the better you can decide what preventive measures may be appropriate for you. To determine your risk of heart disease, pick the item in each category that most nearly describes you. Then score as directed.

1. *Gender.* If you are: Female, 0 points; Male, 4 points.
2. *Family heart disease history.* (Consider just heart attacks and strokes as heart disease here.) If you have:
   No relatives with heart disease, 1 point.
   One relative with heart disease over 60 years, 2 points.
   Two relatives with heart disease over 60 years, 3 points.
   One relative with heart disease under 60 years, 4 points.
   Two relatives with heart disease under 60 years, 6 points.
3. *Smoking.* If you smoke:
   Not at all, 0 points; A cigar or pipe, 1 point.
   10 cigarettes or fewer per day, 3 points.
   11 to 30 cigarettes per day, 4 points.
   30 or more cigarettes per day, 6 points.
4. *Blood pressure.* If you are a teenager and your diastolic blood pressure (the lower of the two numbers on a blood pressure reading) is: ①
   Less than 80, 0 points.
   80 to 84, 1 point.
   85 to 89, 2 points.
   90 to 94, 4 points.
   95 or more, 5 points.
   (If you don't know your blood pressure, give yourself 5 points.)
5. *Blood cholesterol.* (If you don't know your cholesterol level, guess at the amount of fat in your diet.) If you have: ②
   Cholesterol below 170 or almost no fat in diet, 0 points.

Cholesterol 170 to 185 or a low-fat diet, 1 point.
Cholesterol 186 to 199 or a moderately low-fat diet, 2 points.
Cholesterol 200 to 239 or a typical American diet, 4 points.
Cholesterol 240 to 300 or a high-fat diet, 5 points.
Cholesterol over 300, 6 points.
6. *Diabetes.* If you have:
   No relatives with diabetes, 0 points.
   One relative with diabetes, 2 points.
   Two relatives with diabetes, 3 points.
   Diabetes in yourself beginning before age 20, 6 points.
7. *Exercise.* If you engage in:
   Strenuous exercise both at work and at leisure, 0 points.
   Moderate exercise both at work and at leisure, 1 point.
   Sedentary work and intense leisure-time activity, 2 points.
   Sedentary work and moderate leisure-time activity, 3 points.
   Sedentary work and light leisure-time activity, 4 points.
   Little or no activity, 6 points.
8. *Body weight.* (Use the weight you selected for yourself in the Life Choice Inventory of Chapter 9.) If you are:
   5 or more pounds below appropriate weight, 0 points.
   Up to 5 pounds above appropriate weight, 1 point.

(Continued on next page)

Teacher Support Notes

① **Adult Blood Pressure:** Students may have their parents take the inventory. If so, the corresponding blood pressure values for adults are: less than 85 equals 0 points; 85–89 equals 1; 90–104 equals 2; 105–114 equals 4; and 115 or more equals 5.

② **Adult Blood Cholesterol Values:** Corresponding cholesterol values for adults are: below 180 equals 0 points; 180–199 equals 1; 200–219 equals 2; 220–239 equals 4; 240–300 equals 5; and over 300 equals 6.

✍ **Fast Facts**

Approximately 500,000 Americans will die from coronary heart disease this year, which is approximately one person per minute.

fied, and state one lifestyle choice they would be willing to change or improve, to better their scores. Give the students a 5 × 7 card on which they can print their names and the statement: "I am willing to _____ to improve the quality and longevity of my life as well as reduce my risk for

developing heart disease." **(10 min.; Extend, Enrich)**

Activity 3.7
Warning Signs. Display these posters from the Heart Challenges packet: (A Heart Challenges packet may be obtained from your American Heart Association free of charge) **1.** *Don't Learn These Warning Signs The Hard Way* **2.** *Ignore These Signals And You May*

Not Live To Regret It. Ask a student to read a warning sign or signal of heart attack or stroke and explain what may be happening to cause that symptom or warning sign. **(15–20 min., Critical Thinking)**

Activity 3.8
Controllable Factors. Display the poster *The Real Facts of Life* from the Heart Challenges packet. Use the poster

---

Teacher Support Notes

① **Teacher Information Sheets—Hypertension:** In your supplementary material you will find two background information sheets on hypertension. One focuses on the relationship between hypertension and sodium; the other discusses recent research regarding the treatment of moderate hypertension.

② **Self-Test for Hypertension:** You may want to warn students against the use of self-test machines, which people can use themselves in their homes or in a pharmacy. Readings from these machines are usually not accurate. You may also want to emphasize to students that hypertension produces its harmful effects without a single symptom. You can't rely upon your body to warn you. You must find out your own blood pressure to tell whether or not you have hypertension.

③ **Handout—Cutting Down on Salt:** In your supplementary material you will find a handout entitled "Cutting Down on Salt." This handout gives the students several suggestions on how they might go about cutting down on their salt intake.

460

How Healthy is Your Heart? (continued)

6 to 19 pounds above appropriate weight, 2 points.
20 to 39 pounds above appropriate weight, 3 points.
40 to 60 pounds above appropriate weight, 4 points.
More than 60 pounds above appropriate weight, 6 points.
9. *Stress.* If you are:
Almost always relaxed, 0 points.
Sometimes tense or depressed, 1 point.
Frequently tense or depressed, 2 points.

Almost always tense, 4 points.
Constantly anxious/depressed, 5 points.

Scoring

Add the points for the nine answers. Your current risk of heart attack is:
0 to 9: Very remote.
10 to 19: Below average.
20 to 29: Average; consider lowering your score.
30 to 39: High; reduce your score.
40 to 50: Danger—reduce your score!

No combination of factors could better set the stage for heart attacks. The action needed to reduce the risk of CVD from smoking is obvious. Don't smoke. If you do, plan to stop. Even people who have smoked for years can reduce their risks by quitting.

Key Points ➤ *Smoking damages the heart. To reduce risks of CVD, don't smoke.*

Hypertension

A certain blood pressure is vital to the trading of materials between tissues and the bloodstream. The pressure of the blood against the capillary walls is what pushes fluids out into the tissues.

The term *hypertension* refers to excess pressure of the blood in the arteries. Hypertension has a link to heredity; it runs in families. People who are middle-aged or elderly, black, obese, heavy drinkers, users of oral contraceptives, or suffering from kidney disease or diabetes often develop hypertension.

The most effective single step you can take to protect yourself from CVD is to know whether your blood pressure is high or not. A health care professional can give you an accurate blood pressure reading.

When blood pressure is measured, two numbers are important: the pressure during contraction of the ventricles of the heart and the pressure during relaxation of the ventricles. The first number is the **systolic pressure** (during the "dub" of the heartbeat). The second number is the **diastolic pressure** (during the "lub"). Figure 18–8 on page 462 shows what a blood pressure reading means.

Hypertension can usually be controlled by medication or by means of lifestyle strategies. Limiting salty, fatty foods while choosing more nutrient-rich, high-fiber, low-fat foods; losing weight; exercising aerobically; and reducing stress may help lower blood pressure. In severe hypertension, or when other factors increase CVD risks, drugs that lower blood pressure can be a lifesaving treatment.

In some cases, control of hypertension is a matter of reducing body fatness. In addition to diet, regular aerobic activity seems to point out controllable risk factors versus those that can't be controlled. Ask a student volunteer to make a comment on one and another student to suggest a guideline for reducing its risk. **(10 min., Critical Thinking)**

Activity 3.9
Parents' Risk Inventory. For extra credit, have students take their books home and ask their parents to score

themselves on the Life Choice Inventory to determine their current risk of heart attack. Tell students to ask parents to make a pledge as students did in Activity 3.6. **(2–3 min. for instructions; Extend, Enrich)**

Activity 3.10
Food Diary. Before beginning this chapter, ask students to keep a food diary for a week. Make an overhead of *The*

Mystery of Cholesterol from the Heart Challenges packet. Using the information about cholesterol, ask students to add up their intake on a daily basis to see if the total is below 300 mg a day. Ask them to identify what they could and would substitute to bring that level below 300 mg. Point out cholesterol only comes from animal fats. Discuss the fact that saturated fats also increase cholesterol levels.

(continued on next page)

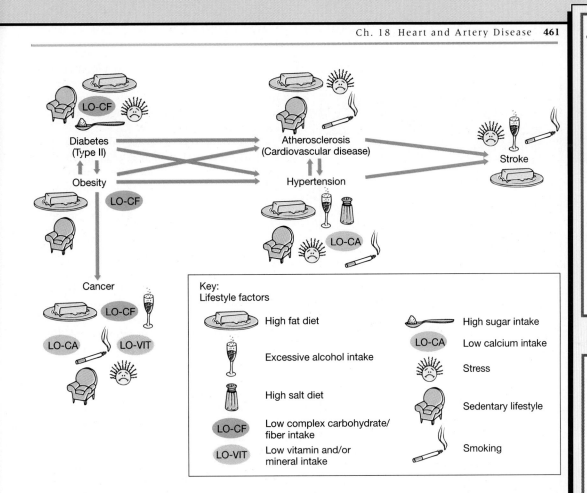

Figure 18–7 Lifestyle Risk Factors and Degenerative Diseases. Arrows show relationships between diseases. An arrow between two diseases shows that one is a risk factor for the other. The risk moves in the direction of the arrow—the disease at the arrow's point is more likely to develop in someone who suffers from the disease at the arrow's origin. The characters around each disease name show lifestyle factors thought to contribute to the development of each disease.

to help keep blood pressure in the normal range. In many people, physical activity can be as effective as drugs in lowering blood pressure.

Key Points ▶ *Hypertension is high blood pressure. Atherosclerosis can lead to hypertension, and hypertension worsens atherosclerosis. To fight hypertension, first know your blood pressure. If it is high, take steps to control it.*

M INI G LOSSARY

systolic (sis-TOL-ic) **pressure:** the blood pressure during that part of the heartbeat when the heart's ventricles are contracted and the blood is being pushed out into the arteries.

diastolic (DYE-as-tol-ic) **pressure:** the blood pressure during that part of the heartbeat when the heart's ventricles are relaxing.

Teach
(Continued)

(15 min., Extend, Enrich)

Activity 3.11

Obesity. From the Heart Challenges packet entitled *Obesity—an Important Risk Factor*, do mini lesson #7, practice card 7.3. **(10–15 min., Critical Thinking)**

Activity 3.12

Students' Blood Pressures. Take students' blood pressures or have the school nurse visit the class and take their blood pressures. Have the nurse explain systolic and diastolic pressures. Ask the nurse to give them the normal range for blood pressure. Be sure to discuss that one reading out of the normal range could easily occur and that it is not necessarily an indication of hypertension. Ask stu-

dents what might produce a high reading just one time. Ideally, the school nurse can set up in the back of the classroom and students can go back to get their blood pressures taken while the class progresses with other activities. **(5–10 min. for explanation; Extend, Enrich)**

Activity 3.13

Saturated or Unsaturated? Ask students to list and examine ten food

---

Teacher Support Notes

① **Test for Cholesterol Level:** This test for high blood cholesterol levels is called the *blood lipid profile*.

② **Overhead—Comparing HDL and LDL:** Your supplementary material contains an overhead transparency that compares HDL and LDL. This overhead will help you make the point to students that the more HDL the body has in comparison to LDL, the less risk there is of heart attack.

462　UNIT 5　Disease Prevention

FIGURE 18-8

How to Interpret Your Blood Pressure

When the blood pressure is taken, two measures are recorded: the systolic pressure first, and the diastolic pressure second (example: 120/80). High blood pressure is defined differently for different purposes. For teenage boys, a systolic reading over 130 or a diastolic reading over 80 generally indicates a too-high blood pressure. For teenage girls, a systolic reading over 125 or a diastolic reading over 80 generally indicates a too-high blood pressure.[a]

$\dfrac{120}{80}$ { This is the systolic pressure.

{ This is the diastolic pressure, the most sensitive indicator of hypertension.

Source: Task Force on Blood Pressure Control in Children, Report of the Second Task Force on Blood Pressure Control in Children—1987, *Pediatrics* 79 (1987): 1–25.

[a]Heavier or taller adolescents have higher blood pressures than smaller individuals of the same age. Therefore, a health care provider should assess the meaning of a teen's blood pressure reading.

Elevated Blood Cholesterol

Like hypertension, high blood cholesterol is a symptomless risk factor for cardiovascular disease. High blood cholesterol is much talked about but little understood. Cholesterol is a type of fat (see Chapter 7). It is found in foods and is also made and destroyed in the body.

Blood cholesterol may be high in some people who are born with the tendency to make it too fast or destroy it too slowly. Other people have high blood cholesterol for lifestyle reasons: they eat too much fat, exercise too little, are obese, or all of these.

① A blood test can tell you your blood cholesterol level, and Figure 18–9 shows how to interpret it. Cholesterol levels are important for everyone, from the youngest toddler to older adults.

Cholesterol, being a fat, does not mix well in the blood, which is watery. However, proteins mix so well with watery substances that they can carry fats along with them in the blood. To ship cholesterol and other fats from place to place in the body by way of the bloodstream, the liver first wraps the cholesterol and fat with protein in packages called **lipoproteins**.

② Two kinds of lipoproteins carry cholesterol (as well as other fats) around the body. These are **low-density lipoproteins (LDLs)** and **high-density lipoproteins (HDLs)**. The LDLs carry cholesterol from the liver (where it is made) to the tissues, which use it to make hormones, to build cell membranes, and to make vitamin D. These are all beneficial uses of cholesterol. However, harm from cholesterol may also occur. When the tissues have all the cholesterol they need, LDLs tend to deposit excess cholesterol along the artery linings, forming plaques. HDLs, on the other hand, work to gather up excess cholesterol from the artery linings and carry it back to the liver to be disposed of.

Whatever a person does that raises the LDL concentration in the blood raises that person's risks of developing CVD. In contrast, raised HDL levels are associated with a lowered risk of CVD. The thing to remember about the blood level of HDL is "the higher, the better."

Several factors affect the blood cholesterol level. Some of the factors you can control, and some you can't. First, being female helps. Women have higher HDL levels than men. Second, nonsmokers have higher HDL levels than smokers. Maintaining appropriate body weight is helpful. Diet and physical activity also affect blood choleslabels brought from home or available in your classroom. (Fill a box with food labels that you've brought from your home.) The students should read the ingredients and information available and decide whether the foods belong in the saturated or unsaturated fat categories. Have students mark them as mostly saturated, mostly unsaturated, all saturated, or all unsaturated. Point out key words to look for such as hydrogenated, cocoa butter, coconut, or palm oil. **(20 min.; Extend, Enrich)**

EVALUATE
▶ SECTION III

Activity 3.14
Pop Quiz.
1. Explain the following statement in relation to the health of your heart: "Moderation in all things."
2. Why is it sometimes hard to make healthful choices?
3. Explain that to remain healthy does not mean you must live a dull life and say good-bye to all pleasures. **(15 min.; Reteach, Reinforce)**

CLOSE
▶ SECTION III

Activity 3.15

(continued on next page)

FIGURE 18-9

Cholesterol Values for Teenagers

Total Cholesterol (mg/dl)ᵃ

Acceptable	less than 170
Borderline	170 to 199
High	200 or higher

Source: American Academy of Pediatrics, Report of the Expert Panel on Blood Cholesterol Levels in Children and Adolescents, *Pediatrics* (supplement) 89 (1992): 545–554.

ᵃBlood cholesterol is measured in milligrams per deciliter of blood.

---

terol. Regular aerobic activity seems to lower LDL and raise HDL in the blood. The role of diet is complex, but the complexities are worth learning and applying. The next section shows you why.

Key Points ▶ *Elevated blood cholesterol predicts CVD. Two types of blood cholesterol are important in CVD: LDL and HDL. LDLs are harmful, because they carry cholesterol to the tissues and can deposit cholesterol in artery walls, worsening atherosclerosis. HDLs are beneficial, because they carry cholesterol away from the arteries for disposal. Exercise raises HDL and lowers LDL levels.*

Diet and Cholesterol

People are often confused about the role of diet in connection with high blood cholesterol. They think that cholesterol in foods raises blood cholesterol. It does, but regular dietary fat—especially saturated fat—raises it much more. The most important key to lowering blood cholesterol seems to be to eat as little total fat as possible while still eating a balanced diet. The fat you do eat should be mostly the unsaturated type. (Chapter 7 gave guidelines to choosing low-fat foods.)

Fish oils are new among dietary defenses against heart disease. The fatty acids in fish oil alter the blood's chemistry so as to favor the dissolving of blood clots over the making of them. One or two fish meals a week are all it takes to gain this benefit.

Dietary fiber also offers protection against heart disease. High-fiber foods move quickly through the digestive tract, and carry cholesterol with them. Diets high in fiber are typically low in fat and cholesterol anyway—another fiber advantage. Some people's elevated blood cholesterol does not respond to changes in lifestyle. Such people may need cholesterol-lowering drugs.

Key Points ▶ *High blood cholesterol carries an elevated risk of CVD. The body normally makes and uses cholesterol. Many factors affect blood cholesterol.*

Diabetes

Earlier in the chapter, Figure 18–7 showed that certain diseases act as risk factors for other diseases. The disease **diabetes** is a risk factor for atherosclerosis, obesity and hypertension, along with all the ills associated with them. One out of every four people

---

MINI GLOSSARY

lipoproteins (LIP-oh-PRO-teens): protein and fat clusters that transport fats in the blood.
low-density lipoproteins (LDLs): lipoproteins that carry fat and cholesterol from the liver, where they are made, to the tissues where they are used. LDLs also deposit cholesterol in arteries, forming plaques.
high-density lipoproteins (HDLs): lipoproteins that carry fat and cholesterol away from the tissues (and from plaques) back to the liver for breakdown and removal from the body.
diabetes: a disease that causes a dangerous buildup of the blood sugar glucose in the body; if left untreated, diabetes damages many tissues and organs including the heart and eyes, and can lead to heart disease and blindness.

Fast Facts

One study of 2,000 male heart patients found that just two fish meals weekly reduced the rate of recurrent heart attacks by 30%.

Teacher Support Notes

① **Handout—Dietary Fat and Cholesterol:** Have students do the activity in your supplementary material entitled "Fat Percentages of Common Foods."
② **Handout—Comparing Fats:** A handout in your supplementary material compares saturated and unsaturated fat characteristics.

Fast Facts

Eating two carrots a day might lower your cholesterol by 10 to 20 percent. Carrots contain pectin, which binds with bile acids to reduce blood cholesterol.

463

The heart prefers fiber to saturated fat.

in the United States has diabetes in the family. Diabetes ranks among the ten leading causes of death. It is a major cause of blindness, kidney failure, leg amputations, and birth defects.

People with diabetes need to manage their diets carefully. They must eat healthy, balanced, high-fiber meals; control their weight; and avoid sweets, such as candy and ice cream. Some need drugs to stimulate their secretion of insulin. Some need to take insulin itself. All may benefit from programs of regular physical activity.

Key Points *Diabetes is a risk factor for atherosclerosis and obesity. Diabetes is among the ten leading causes of death. People with diabetes need to eat healthy, balanced high-fiber meals and to avoid sweets. Physical activity is also beneficial.*

SECTION III REVIEW

Answer the following questions on a sheet of paper.
Learning the Vocabulary
The vocabulary terms in this section are *risk factors, systolic pressure, diastolic pressure, lipoproteins, low-density lipoproteins, high-density lipoproteins,* and *diabetes.*
1. Write a sentence using each vocabulary term.
2. Protein and fat clusters that transport fats in the blood are called _____.
3. What is the difference between systolic and diastolic blood pressure?

Learning the Facts
4. List four risk factors for heart and artery disease.
5. What are the only two risk factors that are unchangeable?
6. How can high blood pressure usually be controlled?

Making Life Choices
7. Take the Life Choice Inventory on page 459. What was your score? Were you pleased with your score? Why, or why not? In what areas did you do especially well? In what areas did you score poorly? What specific changes do you need to make to reduce your risks of heart disease? Be aware that changes in your health habits are effective only if you consistently practice them.

early afternoon and at its lowest in the morning. (T)

6. The human heart weighs about 1/200 of the total body weight. (T)

7. The human heart beats about four billion times during an average lifetime. (T)

8. Each heartbeat lasts about 8/10 of a second. (T)

9. The heart beats over 85,000 times a day. (T)

10. In one minute the heart pumps from 8 to 10 pints of blood. (T)

Ask students to identify which statements are examples of the heart's incredible ability to perform its functions. (1, 3, 7, 8, 9, and 10) Ask students to figure the approximate weight of their own hearts based on their own weights and statement 6. **(10–15 min.; Extend, Enrich)**

Changes In Heart Rates. Obtain an electrocardiograph printout paper (or several if possible) from a local doctor or hospital to show students. Borrow a walk-around heart monitor to wear in class (or have a different student in each class wear it) to show changes in heart rate with different activities, such as talking, resting, and walking. Discuss the effect of body activity on the heart as shown on the printout. **(10 min.; Extend, Enrich)**

STRAIGHT TALK

Emotions and the Heart

Emotional health, while often linked to CVD, is much less clearly involved than the risk factors mentioned in this chapter. Still, people with many social ties seem to develop less heart disease than people with few or none. Married men have been shown to have less heart disease than single men, and owners of pets (even pet fish!) may have lower blood pressure than others.

I've always heard that some people are "type A," and that they are more prone to heart disease. What does type A mean?

The theory of type A and type B personalities tries to explain heart disease in terms of people's feelings and behaviors. According to this theory, the type A person finds it hard to cope with leisure time and likes to be constantly busy doing things. Type B people are able to rest when tired and rarely push themselves. Early scientific work separated type A from type B people and then watched them over a period of years. The reports seemed to show that type A people had more than twice the rate of CVD as the type B people. As years of studies passed, though, new findings began to conflict with the early evidence. Today, the type A/type B theory has been all but discounted by scientists. Most people, however, still regard it as true.

Do you mean that type A people don't suffer from CVD more often than type B people?

Actually, type A and type B personalities may not even exist. They may, but research about them can also be taken to mean that *anyone* could fit the description of type A, given the right circumstances.

The more responsibility people have and the less control they have over decisions that affect their lives, the higher the CVD risk. Perhaps a person with any personality type would become "type A" under such conditions and suffer increased risks of CVD.

Do emotions relate to CVD in any way, then?

Researchers may still use the term "Type A" to describe people with the tendency to be chronically hostile, angry, and distrustful. Much more solid evidence is needed, however, before this tendency can be called a risk factor of CVD.

One of the keys to CVD prevention may lie in control of the stress response. In fact, you have probably noticed a relationship between the blood and the brain. When people get mad, they may turn red in the face. The blood vessels of the neck and temples enlarge and stand out under the skin.

The connection between stress, anger, and CVD makes some sense. The stress hormones are the same ones that raise the blood pressure. Of course, high blood pressure leads to CVD.

People (at least some people) can learn to lower their blood pressure by practicing meditation, prayer, or other relaxation techniques. Similarly, plain old affection and love can affect the heart and arteries. No doubt the mystery of CVD—like all the great human mysteries—involves the mind and spirit, as well as the body.

Answers

Vocabulary

1. **a.** artificial heart
b. electrocardiogram
c. pacemaker **d.** capillaries **e.** embolism
2. **a.** Low-density lipoproteins carry fat and cholesterol from the liver to the tissues, while high-density lipoproteins carry fat and cholesterol away from the tissues back to the liver.
b. Atherosclerosis is caused by the accumulation of plaques on the inner walls of the arteries.
c. Atria receive the incoming blood into the heart, while the ventricles send blood out of the heart.

d. A heart attack is when the vessels that feed the heart muscle become blocked, while a stroke is when the vessels leading to the brain become blocked.
3. **a.** blood **b.** risk factors
c. heart attack **d.** angina
e. heart murmur **f.** chambers
g. cardiovascular disease
4. **a.** critical phase, plaques

b. Heart disease **c.** coronary artery bypass surgery **d.** aorta

Recall
Section I
1. arteries, veins, capillaries
2. 85,000 times
Section II
3. atherosclerosis
4. the ballooning out of an artery wall at a point where it has been weakened by

deterioration
5. Answers will vary; could include: the plaques can enlarge enough to block the flow of blood; a blood clot may form, stick to a plaque, and grow until it cuts off the blood supply like a plug; and a clot may break loose and circulate until it reaches an artery too small to allow its passage.

CHAPTER REVIEW

LEARNING THE VOCABULARY

cardiovascular disease	heart disease	angina
arteries	atherosclerosis	pacemaker
capillaries	plaques	coronary artery bypass surgery
veins	aneurysm	heart transplant
cardiovascular system	aorta	artificial heart
blood	platelets	risk factors
chambers	thrombus	systolic pressure
atria	coronary thrombosis	diastolic pressure
ventricles	heart attack	lipoproteins
coronary arteries	cerebral thrombosis	low-density lipoproteins (LDLs)
valves	stroke	high-density lipoproteins (HDLs)
heart murmur	embolus	diabetes
electrocardiogram	embolism	
lymph	critical phase	

Answer the following questions on a separate sheet of paper.

1. **Word Scramble**—*Use the clues from the phrases below to help you unscramble the vocabulary terms from the list above:*
   a. **laritacifi terha** A pump designed to fit into the human chest cavity and perform the heart's function is called an _____ _____.
   b. **criaetogrlderacom** An _____ is a record of the electrical activity of the heart.
   c. **rekamepac** A _____ is a device that delivers electrical impulses to the heart to regulate the heartbeat.
   d. **selarpciali** Tiny blood vessels that form a net and weave in and around in tissues are called _____.
   e. **melobmsi** An _____ is the sudden closure of a blood vessel by a travelling blood clot.
2. a. What is the difference between low-density lipoproteins and high-density lipoproteins?
   b. What is the relationship between atherosclerosis and plaques?
   c. What is the difference between atria and ventricles?
   d. What is the difference between a heart attack and a stroke?

3. **Matching**—*Match each of the following phrases with the appropriate vocabulary term from the list above:*
   a. a thick red fluid that flows through the body's blood vessels
   b. factors that are linked with a disease by association but are not yet proved to be causes
   c. the event in which vessels that feed the heart muscle become blocked
   d. pain in the heart region caused by a lack of oxygen
   e. a heart sound that reflects damaged or abnormal heart valves
   f. large hollow areas in the heart
   g. a general term for all diseases of the heart and blood vessels
4. a. The development of atherosclerosis reaches a _____ when more than half of the arteries are covered with _____.
   b. _____ is any disease of the heart muscle or other working part of the heart.
   c. Surgery to provide an alternate route for blood to reach the heart tissue is known as _____.
   d. The large main artery that conducts blood from the heart to the body's smaller arteries is the _____.

6. Answers will vary; could include: sudden, temporary weakness or numbness in any part of one side of the body; temporary loss of speech or of understanding of speech; dizziness, unsteadiness, or unexplained falls; and temporary dimness or loss of vision, particularly in one eye.

7. Drugs can trigger the clot-dissolving action of the blood and stop a heart attack in its tracks, and strengthen and stabilize the heartbeat.

Section III

8. Answers will vary; could include: learn about your heredity, and use the information and control the lifestyle factors that may affect you; don't smoke; keep your blood pressure below 130/80 if you are a teenager; keep your blood cholesterol within the normal range; if you have diabetes, keep your blood sugar under control; exercise vigorously for at least 20 minutes three or more times weekly; maintain appropriate body weight; control stress; and learn to relax.

9. medication; limiting salty, fatty foods while choosing more nutrient-rich, high-fiber, low-fat foods; losing weight; exercising aerobically; reducing stress

10. 80

11. through a blood test

12. less than 170

13. High-fiber foods move quickly through the digestive tract, and carry cholesterol with them.

14. One out of every four people in the United States has diabetes in the family.

Straight Talk

15. The stress hormones are the same ones that raise the blood pressure, and, of course, high blood pressure leads to CVD.

RECALLING IMPORTANT FACTS AND IDEAS

1. What are three types of blood vessels?
2. Approximately how many times a day does the heart beat?
3. What is the most common form of CVD?
4. What is an aneurysm?
5. List two ways atherosclerosis can cause blockage of an artery.
6. Name three warning signs of a stroke.
7. What can drugs do to help a person who has had a heart attack?
8. Name four health strategies for reducing the risk of CVD.
9. What steps can be taken to help lower blood pressure?
10. A teenager's blood pressure is generally considered too high when the diastolic pressure exceeds what number?
11. How is elevated blood cholesterol detected?
12. What is an acceptable blood cholesteral value for a teenager?
13. How does dietary fiber offer protection against heart disease?
14. How common is diabetes?
15. Explain the connection between stress and CVD.

CRITICAL THINKING

1. During the last century, the American way of life became synonymous with the "good life," a life filled with abundant food, the best in medical treatment, and technological progress. Discuss how biological, psychological, sociological, and cultural factors have played a role in the development of CVD as the leading cause of death in America today.

ACTIVITIES

1. Develop two case histories. In one describe someone at risk for CVD and in the other describe someone with hardly any risk for heart disease.
2. Keep a diary of all the lifestyle risk factors for heart disease to which you are exposed for a full week. Develop a list of ways to avoid these risk factors.
3. Investigate a culture that has a low incidence of heart disease. Research the diet, lifestyle, and exercise habits of the people.
4. Choose a character from a television show you frequently watch. Develop a list of the healthy or unhealthy behaviors the character exhibits. Be sure to give the name of the program and the character you choose.
5. Make a full day's menus of foods that are low in saturated fats and salt. Describe the foods you would select for each of the three meals that would promote heart health.
6. Visit your local ambulance corps and interview a paramedic. Find out what is done for heart patients while they are in transit to the hospital. Tape record the interview or write a short report.
7. Go to the library and locate information that identifies the death rates for CVD over the past ten years. Draw a graph of the death rates over this period and describe the patterns you notice.

MAKING DECISIONS ABOUT HEALTH

1. Lately, your grandfather has been experiencing sharp chest pains and has felt as though he couldn't breathe when playing actively with his grandchildren. What might your grandfather be experiencing, and what should he do about it?

467

CHAPTER 19 PLANNER

OVERVIEW

Chapter 19 is 20 pages long and is divided into the four sections listed to the right. Major learning outcomes are also listed to the right. Briefly, this chapter introduces the students to cancer. It stresses the importance of the individual's lifestyle choices in reducing the chances of developing certain kinds of cancers. This chapter also gives a brief overview of: how cancer develops, controllable risk factors, screening and early detection, cancer treatments, and how to live with cancer. It also includes some "hands-on" information in regards to suggestions on what you can do when someone close to you has cancer. The last section of the chapter deals with the human side of cancer and stresses how love, support, and communication are necessary for everyone concerned in the struggle against this disease.

MAKING LIFE CHOICES RESOURCES

A variety of activities, handouts, quizzes, and tests to accompany this chapter are available in the *Making Life Choices* supplementary material. You may pick and choose from those materials as appropriate for your amount of class time and the ability levels of your students. Some of the resources you might want to consider using are:

Overheads
• Initiators and Promoters
• Cancer Cure by Surgery

Handouts
• Factors Beyond People's Control
• Medical Tests
• U.S. Health Service Objectives

Teacher Information Sheets
• Causes of Cancer
• Relationships with People Who Have Cancer

Answers to "Fact or Fiction"

1. True. 2. False. Tanning booths or sunlamps are no safer than sunbathing, as far as cancer risks are concerned. 3. False. While people with fair complexions who burn easily are at greater risk, everyone needs to use sunscreen to prevent skin cancer from sun exposure. 4. True.

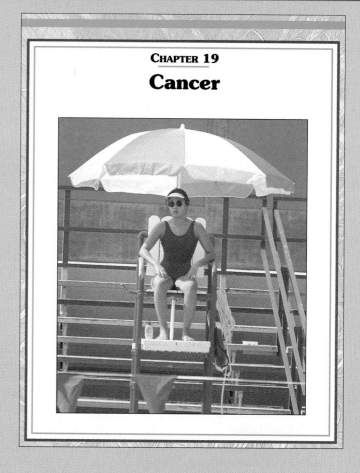

CHAPTER 19
Cancer

Activity To Introduce Chapter

Have the students write down all of their behaviors and those of their parents that they feel might contribute to the possibility of cancer developing someday. The answers could vary: "I smoke two packs of cigarettes a day." "My parents have smoked all their lives." "I don't ever use a sunscreen, and I burn often." "I use smokeless tobacco." "I don't eat right." Now have them imagine what life would be like without these habits or behaviors. Have them write the benefits they would receive if they or their parents no longer engaged in these behaviors. How would their lives change? Would they feel better? How would their lives change physically? Financially? Mentally? Have a class discussion on their answers. Some might include: "I'd save a lot of money if I didn't smoke." "I wouldn't have as many wrinkles, freckles, or sunburns if I used sunscreen."

OUTCOMES

After reading and studying this chapter, you will be able to:

✓ **Identify the four classes of cancer.**
✓ **Explain how cancer develops.**
✓ **Discuss the risk factors of cancer.**
✓ **Describe the methods of detection and treatment for cancer.**
✓ **Discuss the implications of living with cancer.**
✓ **Describe the links between nutrition and cancer prevention.**

CONTENTS

I. **How Cancer Develops**
II. **Risk Factors That People Can Control**
III. **Early Detection and Treatment**
IV. **Living with Cancer**

Straight Talk: *Nutrition and Cancer Prevention*

FACT OR FICTION

What do you think? Are the following statements true or false? If you think they are false, then say what is true.

1. You can prevent most cancers by choosing healthful ways to live.
2. People who would like to tan without risking skin cancer can do so in tanning booths or with lamps.
3. People with darkly pigmented skin are naturally protected against skin cancer and so do not need sunscreen products.
4. The detection of many common cancers requires routine tests and self-examinations.

(Answers on page 483)

■ **Reminder:** Knowing how to study can increase your knowledge, improve your grades, *and* cut down on your study time. See the *Studying Health* section at the front of your text for some suggestions to help you study this chapter.

CHAPTER PROJECT

Divide the students into groups. Assign each group a different number of packs of cigarettes smoked per day. They may or may not use calculators in this activity at your discretion. Use the average cost of cigarettes per pack in your area. (Example: $2.00 a pack)

Group 1—One pack a day for 20 years.
Group 2—One-and-a-half packs a day for 15 years.
Group 3—Three packs a day for 30 years.
Group 4—One-and-a-half packs a day for five years.
Group 5—Two packs a day for 18 years.

Have them answer these questions:
1. At $2.00 a pack how much money goes up in smoke in one year?
2. How much in the number of years given to your group?
3. How much does it cost for you to smoke each week?
4. How much goes up in smoke each month?
5. If you saved the money you would have spent in the allotted times—list some things you could have bought and paid for in cash.

NOT ENOUGH TIME?*

You could easily spend five or six days teaching this chapter if the students read this entire chapter, do a fair number of activities suggested in the teacher's edition, and complete a sampling of the resource material accompanying this text. In addition you may want to show some videos. It is likely, however, that you may have only one or two days to cover this chapter.

TIME	SUGGESTIONS
1 Day	Assign Sections I and II prior to class. Go over the definition of cancer and how cancer develops. Do Activities 1.1 and 1.2 in Section I, and Activity 2.1 in Section II.
2 Days	Assign Sections III and IV prior to class. During class on day 2, have students complete Activity 3.2 in Section III and Activity 4.1 in Section IV.

*Please refer to the 18-week daily lesson plans in the supplementary material for additional suggestions.

SUGGESTED RESOURCES

Student Readings
1. *Cancer Facts and Figures—1988.* New York: American Cancer Society, 1989.
2. Schulz, Charles M. *Why, Charlie Brown, Why?*
3. Gunther, John. *Death Be Not Proud.*

Teacher Readings
1. Beattie, Edward J. Jr. and Cowan, Stuart D. *Toward the Conquest of Cancer.* New York: Crown Publishers, 1980.
2. Fine, Judylaine. *Afraid to Ask: A Book for Families to Share About Cancer.*

Films
1. *Something Very Special* (about breast self-exams). American Cancer Society.
2. *Self-Examination of the Testes.* American Cancer Society.

Videos
1. *Taking Control* (about healthy lifestyles, reducing cancer risk). American Cancer Society, 1986.
2. *Smokeless Tobacco.* American Cancer Society, 1984.
3. *Why, Charlie Brown, Why?* An animated feature about children with cancer. United Feature Syndicate, Inc., 1990.

Software
1. *Health Problem Series: Cancer.* Opportunities for Learning, Inc., 800-243-7116.

In this section students will learn:
1. To define cancer and differentiate between benign and malignant tumors.
2. The stages in the development of cancer and the meaning of the word *metastasized*.

Activity 1.1

Know the Disease. Put the following quote by Cervantes on the board and leave it up for the rest of the chapter: "The beginning of health is to know the disease." Have a class discussion using these questions: What do you know about cancer? What is your reaction when you hear the word cancer? Emphasis should be on "knowing cancer" and that each student has lifestyle choices to make that

may determine whether or not he/she contracts cancer. Some additional discussion questions are: Since cancer is the second leading cause of death in the United States, what are you going to do to prevent cancer from robbing you of your life? Are you going to ignore the facts and hope it will go away, or are you going to do what Cervantes said and begin "to know the disease?" **(15–20 min., Critical Thinking)**

🖋 Fast Facts

Cancer affects one out of every four people in the United States today.

Teacher Support Notes

① **Teacher Information Sheet—Causes of Cancer:** Your supplementary material contains information on two possible contributors to the development of cancer.

② **Classes of Cancer:** To help students learn the following types of cancer, write *lymph*, *leuk*, *carcin*, and *sarc* on the board in one column and in another column write *immune*, *blood*, *glands*, and *connective tissues*. In between the two columns write oma and emia. Put a plus sign to the left of oma and emia and an equal sign after them. Have students make the proper connections.

③ **Overhead—Initiators and Promoters:** Your supplementary material contains an overhead of Figure 19–1, for use at this point.

✉ Where to Write

American Cancer Society
90 Park Avenue
New York, NY 10016

---

470   UNIT 5 Disease Prevention

Years ago, the future for someone diagnosed as having **cancer** was bleak. Today, millions of people are fighting battles against cancer and winning. Still, preventing cancer is far easier than curing it. Most cancers result from conditions in people's lives, many of which they can control themselves. For example, the number-one cancer in both men and women is now lung cancer, which is closely linked to smoking. Lung cancer is seen only rarely in people who don't smoke. ①

Over a hundred diseases are called cancer. Each has its own name and symptoms, depending on its type and location in the body. Some cancers are named for the body tissues in which they arise, with the suffix *-oma* (meaning **tumor** or other **malignancy**) added on. For example, cancer of the pigmented cells of the skin, the melanocytes, is called **melanoma**. A tumor of the bone marrow is a **myeloma**—*myelos* means "marrow." Other cancers are named in other ways.

Generally, all cancers can be assigned to one of four classes, depending on tissue type: ②

- Cancers of the immune system organs are **lymphomas**. ③
- Cancers of blood-forming organs are **leukemias**.
- Cancers of the glands and body linings—such as the skin, the lining of the digestive tract or lungs, or other linings—are **carcinomas**.

- Cancers of connective tissue, including bones, ligaments, and muscles, are **sarcomas**.

SECTION I

How Cancer Develops

Cancer begins with a change in a normal cell. After the change, the cell begins reproducing itself out of control. The steps in the development of many cancers are thought to be:

1. Exposure to a carcinogen (an **initiator**).
2. Entry of the initiator into a cell.
3. Change of the cell's genetic material. The change may be a **mutation**.
4. Possible speeding up of cancer formation by a **promoter**.
5. Out-of-control multiplication of the cells.
6. Tumor or other malignancy formation.

Initiators and promoters work together, an effect shown in Figure 19–1. Alcohol and tobacco work this way in the development of cancers of the mouth, throat, and esophagus. Normally, these cancers are rare. In a person who smokes two packs of cigarettes a day, the risk of developing them is one and a half times greater than for the

Initiator only

A few tumors develop.

Promoter only

No tumors develop.

Initiator plus promoter

Many tumors develop.

Figure 19–1 Cancer Initiators and Promoters. Initiators and promoters work together to produce many more tumors than initiators alone.

TEACH
SECTION I
(Guided and Independent Practice)

Activity 1.2
Memory Game. Play the memory game. The first person reads the first step in how cancer develops on page 470, and says it aloud: "Exposure to a carcinogen." The second person says the second one: "Entry of the initiator into a cell," then says the first step and the second step. The third person reads the third step: "Change of the cell's genetic material. The change may be a mutation," and then the first and second, and then repeats the third step, and so on. The more students hear the six steps, the better able they are to remember them. This activity also involves the whole class. Research says that students retain information when they hear it a minimum of seven times. Also point out that this activity shows that everyone can learn if they know how to study. **(30 min.; Reteach, Reinforce)**

Activity 1.3
Carcinogens. Have the students make a list of all substances or materials that they know to be carcinogenic or cancer causing. Their list can be general or broken down into particular substances.

(continued on next page)

Two factors that work together as carcinogens: tobacco and alcohol.

nonsmoker. Should that smoker also drink two alcoholic drinks each day, the risk would become 15 times greater. Alcohol alone does not increase the risk of these particular cancers, but it promotes them, once they have started. Tobacco smoke probably acts in both ways: it initiates cancers and promotes them, too. ①

All of the changes that lead to cancer happen inside an individual's cells, so cancer itself is not contagious—that is, it cannot be passed from person to person. Once started inside the body, cancer can grow and damage any tissue, from the solid bone to the fluid blood.

Normally, cells divide only when new cells are needed. A cancerous cell, though, does not respond to the command to stop dividing. It divides continuously. The result may be a lump of tissue (a tumor).

Sometimes a tumor may be harmless, or **benign**. It does not spread. Rather, it is a well-defined, solid mass contained in an external membrane. A benign tumor poses no threat and can simply be removed. ②

Cancerous tumors, on the other hand, are malignant. They present a threat to health. As a cancerous tumor gains in size, it competes with normal tissues around it for nutrients, oxygen, and space. With time, the cancer interrupts the normal functions ③

of the tissues or organs into which it grows. In cancer of the large intestine, for example, the tumor may block the passage of

MINI GLOSSARY

cancer: a disease in which abnormal cells multiply out of control, spread into surrounding tissues and other body parts, and disrupt normal functioning of one or more organs.

tumor: an abnormal mass of tissue that can live and reproduce itself, but performs no service to the body.

malignancy: a dangerous cancerous growth that sheds cells into body fluids and spreads to new locations to start new cancer colonies. (The word *malignant* means "growing worse.")

melanoma: an especially dangerous cancer of the pigmented cells of the skin, related to sun exposure in people with light-colored skin.

myeloma: a cancer originating in the cells of the bone marrow.

lymphomas (limf-OH-mahs): cancers that arise in organs of the immune system.

leukemias (loo-KEE-me-ahs): cancers that arise in the blood cell–making tissues.

carcinomas (car-sin-OH-mahs): cancers that arise in the skin, body chamber linings, or glands.

sarcomas (sar-KOH-mahs): cancers that arise in the connective tissue cells, including bones, ligaments, and muscles.

initiator: a carcinogen, an agent required to start the formation of cancer.

mutation (myoo-TAY-shun): a change in a cell's genetic material. Once the genetic material has changed, the change is inherited by the offspring of that cell.

promoter: a substance that assists in the development of malignant tumors, but does not initiate them on its own.

benign (be-NINE): noncancerous; not harmful; a description of a tumor that is not able to spread from one area to another.

Teacher Support Notes

① **Cigarettes:** You may want to refer students back to Chapter 15 and the discussion of the many chemicals in addition to nicotine that are found in cigarettes. Some of these chemicals probably act more as initiators, while others act more as promoters of cancer.

② **Benign vs. Malignant:** It might be helpful to write *benign* and *malignant* on the board together and point out to the students that they are opposite in meaning. Tumors can be either malignant or benign. If they are benign they are not cancerous.

③ **Malignant Tumors:** As background information you may want to know that the processes that transform normal cells into malignant ones are unknown. But the cells' genetic material is believed to be involved. Oncogene, a portion of the cancer cell's genetic material, is suspected of playing a key role in the transformation process.

Have students put a "C" beside the carcinogens that can be controlled by an individual's lifestyle choice and an "NC" by carcinogens over which we have little or "no control." Have a class discussion on the lists themselves, specific breakdowns, and lifestyle choices affecting the

intake of or exposure to carcinogens.
(15 min., Critical Thinking)

EVALUATE
SECTION I

Activity 1.4
Pop Quiz. Have students match the terms with the description.
1. carcinogen (c)
2. initiator (e)

3. mutation (f)
4. promoter (d)
5. benign (b)
6. malignant (g)
7. metastasized (h)
8. tumor (a)
9. melanoma (j)
10. myeloma (i)
a. a lump of tissue
b. noncancerous tumor
c. a substance causing a cell to change

Teacher Support Notes

① **Teen Views Follow-up Questions:** Following are some questions you may want to use to encourage discussion of the ideas expressed by the students in the Teen Views feature:
a. Do students think that people who have a habit such as smoking block the potential negative consequences out of their minds?
b. Do students think that there is a relationship between smoking and maturity? If so, how would they explain this relationship?
c. If any students smoke, do they think that smoking relieves stress?
d. Do students agree or disagree with John-Henry Anderson who seems to say that smoking is "sexy?"
e. Nicholos Gould thinks that the busier a person is the harder it is to quit smoking. Do students agree with this?
f. Do students agree that it's more difficult not to smoke if their group of friends smoke? What can be done to counteract this problem?

📢 Fast Facts

According to the World Health Organization, five million people die each year from cancer.

472 UNIT 5 Disease Prevention

TEEN **V**IEWS

Why do people smoke, knowing it causes cancer? ①

Many people smoke because their friends or family do. Once they've started, most likely they can't quit. They get addicted and don't want to stop. Teenagers don't fully realize the dangers or they think they can stop before they get lung cancer. **Kelly Harmer, 14, South Carroll High School, MD**

Most people you see smoking are the ones who are addicted. They *think* that they need to smoke in order to get rid of their problems or relieve themselves from stress. It's not that they can't quit, cause they can. They just want to believe that smoking is their only answer and escape. Knowing that you can get lung cancer and die from it doesn't matter to them when they're smoking—they just push it out of their minds until it's too late. **Laura Pearson, 17, Duluth East High School, MN**

For people who already smoke, it is extremely difficult to break the habit be-

cause of the nicotine addiction. It is possible to do, but you must dedicate time to it and for many working people who have a busy schedule, it is hard to do. Many teens do it to fit in with the specific crowd that they hang out with. It is really difficult not to smoke if you are with your friends and they all smoke. Teens have a tendency not to look ahead in life and see that this habit will eventually lead to lung trouble. There is the feeling "It can't happen to me," and with this in people's heads, they smoke out of spite. **Nicholos Gould, 17, Poughkeepsie High School, NY**

I think that people smoke because of peer pressure. Kids today feel a drastic need to be popular so they will do anything, even things that cause death, to be popular. What they don't understand is that people will respect them more if they stand up for their beliefs. If everybody made their actions consistent with their beliefs, the world would be a smoke-free habitat. **Kevin Bylund, 14, Westside High School, NE**

Few people start smoking with the intention of making it a habit. Most start when they are young, for ridiculous reasons, then become addicted. When a person becomes addicted to something, the risks involved become obsolete. For most smokers, their cigarettes take priority over a lot of things, often their health. Smokers often justify or rationalize their smoking habit so they don't have to take full responsibility for doing something they know is harmful to them. Some might not think about the long-term effects smoking has—others just might not care. **Autumn Spencer, 17, Orange Park High School, FL**

Smoking is a way to be a "rebel" and aggravate your parents. It's "sexy" to smoke, but there is nothing "sexy" about bad breath and smelly clothes. Women might smoke in order to lose weight by not eating. Finally, if all their friends are doing it, why not go along with the flow? **John-Henry Anderson, 16, Great Falls High School, MT**

into a cancer-causing gene
d. a substance that assists in the development of malignant tumors
e. an agent required to start the formation of cancer
f. a change in a cell's genetic material
g. cancerous tumor
h. to have migrated from one part of the body to another
i. a cancer originating in the cells of the bone marrow
j. dangerous cancer of the pigmented cells of the skin
(15 min.)

CLOSE
SECTION I

Activity 1.5
Review Questions. Before going on to the next lesson, students should be able to answer these questions: **1.** What is the difference between a cancerous tumor and a benign tumor? **2.** What are some common carcinogens? **3.** What is the difference between a promoter and an initiator? **4.** What are the four classes of cancers? **5.** What are the steps in the development of cancer? Discuss the answers to these questions in class.
(15–20 min.; Reteach, Reinforce)

the intestinal contents. In cancer of the brain, the growing tumor threatens thought processes and control of the body.

In addition to invading surrounding tissues, cancer cells break loose from the original site and ride the rivers of body fluids to colonize new areas. When a cancer is just beginning, it sheds only a few cells. As it enlarges, however, more and more of these wild cells escape and start new growths in other body parts. At this point, the cancer is said to have **metastasized**. Cancer causes death when it interrupts the functioning of vital organs, such as the blood-building organs, lungs, or brain.

The immune system is on the watch for escaped cancer cells. The system works to stop these dangerous travelers before they lodge in body tissue, but it can catch only a certain number of cancer cells at any one time. When the immune defenses fail, cancer treatment is needed. The success of treatment often depends on whether or not it gets under way before the cancer has metastasized.

After the initiating event, some cancers take as long as 20 years to develop. By the time a health care provider detects a cancer, the initiator and promoters that caused it are long gone. This is why it is hard to know what the original causes of cancer are.

Key Points › *Cancers are classified according to the types of tissue they affect. Cancer develops in stages. It is dangerous in that it can interrupt the functioning of vital organs.*

___ **SECTION I** ___ **REVIEW** ___

Answer the following questions on a sheet of paper.
Learning the Vocabulary
The vocabulary terms in this section are *cancer, tumor, malignancy, melanoma, myeloma, lymphomas, leukemias, carcinomas, sarcomas, initiator, mutation, promoter, benign,* and *metastasized.*

1. What is the difference between melanoma and myeloma?
2. What is the difference between carcinomas and sarcomas?
3. A _____ assists in the development of a malignant tumor.
4. An abnormal mass of tissue that can live and reproduce but performs no service to the body is called a _____.

Learning the Facts
5. What are the four classes of cancer?
6. How does a cancer cell differ from a normal cell?
7. What type of tumor does not spread and is usually removed with no threat?
8. When does cancer cause death?
9. How does the immune system help fight cancer?
10. Why is it difficult to determine what the original causes of cancer are?

Making Life Choices
11. The American Cancer Society believes that one of the biggest problems health workers must overcome is the ignorance and fear that prevent people from seeking medical attention early enough. One technique the American Cancer Society has used to help solve this problem is to seek out famous people to appear in public service announcements. Do you feel this is an effective technique? Why or why not? What measures would you suggest to make as many people as possible aware of the necessity of prompt medical attention? What method do you believe would be most likely to sway you and why?

MINI GLOSSARY

metastasized (meh-TASS-tuh-sized): when speaking of cancer cells, a term that means the cancer cells have migrated from one part of the body to another, and started new growths just like the original tumor.

Section I Review
Answers
1. Melanoma is cancer of the skin, myeloma is cancer of the bone marrow.
2. Carcinomas are cancers that arise in the skin, body chamber linings, or glands. Sarcomas are cancers that arise in the connective tissue cells.
3. promoter
4. tumor
5. lymphomas, leukemias, carcinomas, sarcomas
6. Cancerous cells do not stop dividing after they receive the command to stop.
7. benign
8. when it interrupts the functioning of vital organs
9. by trying to stop dangerous travelers before they lodge in the body tissue
10. Some cancers take 20 years to develop.
11. Answers will vary.

In this section students will learn the:
1. Environmental risk factors for cancer, which people can control.
2. Ways to evaluate and to reduce their risks of getting cancer.

Activity 2.1

Initiating Changes. Have students take the Life Choice Inventory on page 475. Then have them look at all the "no" answers and discuss what can be done to change those "no" answers to "yes" or "sometimes." Students should pick out two "no" answers and write a way in which they could change their lifestyles in order to reduce their chances of contracting cancer. Have them write two behavior changes that they will honestly try to do to

reduce their risks. Lead a class discussion on how to change certain patterns of behavior. **(25 min., Critical Thinking)**

Activity 2.2
Precautions. On a piece of 8-1/2 × 11-in. paper have each student write the answer to this question: What are some

---

Teacher Support Notes

① **Handout—Factors Beyond People's Control:** Your supplementary material contains a handout that gives information on the causes of cancer that are beyond people's control.

② **Tobacco and Cancer:** You may want to refer students back to Chapter 15, which has additional information on cancers whose risks are increased by smoking. You may also want to remind students that people who use smokeless tobacco are at risk for cancer.

③ **Overexposure to the Sun:** Ask students if they think people spend too much time in the sun. If so, why? Answers may include that suntans are attractive to many people. Sunlight may actually help clear up some cases of acne and to brighten moods. Some exposure to the sun is important to the making of vitamin D.

S ECTION II

Risk Factors That People Can Control

Risks of cancer fall into three categories. Some risks, you can control totally—the ones that have to do with your own behavior. Some risks, you can control partially—for example, the risks posed by environmental pollutants. You can learn about these and minimize your exposure to them.

Some risks, you cannot control at all. For example, if a major disaster should occur in your area and expose everyone to a carcinogen, that would be a risk you couldn't control. You also cannot control your gender, your genetic inheritance, and your age, and these affect your risks of cancer. This section focuses on the risks you can control—your smoking behavior, your exposures to radiation, and your choices of diet and exercise. This chapter's Life Choice Inventory can help you evaluate your cancer risks regarding the known controllable factors.

Tobacco

Almost everyone knows of the link between smoking and cancer, and with good reason. The evidence for the link is firm. Eighty percent of hospitalized lung cancer victims are smokers. In any community of the world, an increase in smoking is followed by a jump in numbers of lung cancer cases. When researchers spread chemicals from tobacco smoke on a patch of living skin, cancer develops at the site.

About a third of all cancer deaths are linked to tobacco use. Not only lung cancer, but also cancers throughout the body, fol-

low smoking. Cancer of the larynx (voice box), mouth, esophagus, urinary bladder, kidney, pancreas, and many other organs have all been linked to tobacco use.

Key Points ▶ *Tobacco use is a preventable cause of cancers of the larynx, mouth, esophagus, bladder, kidney, and pancreas, as well as of the lungs.*

Radiation

Overexposure to the sun's ultraviolet (UV) rays causes most cases of skin cancer. Today, more and more of these rays are hitting the earth's surface as pollution from human activity destroys the atmospheric shield (the ozone layer) that used to filter them out. Chapter 25 tells more about this effect.

Skin cancers come in several varieties. A major distinction is between the fast-spreading, lethal skin cancer known as melanoma and other, less-threatening surface cancers of the skin. Only one blistering sunburn, if received during the teen years, may be enough to double a person's risk of melanoma. In contrast, working or playing in the sun daily makes people likely to develop the more easily treated forms of skin cancer. This means that people who let themselves in for occasional large doses of sun are taking the greatest risks of contracting the most serious type of skin cancer. Such people include indoor workers on summer vacation in the South and pale-skinned, weekend sunbathers. Figure 19–2 on page 476 shows the different forms of skin cancer.

While no one is immune to the sun's damaging effects, skin color can help predict who is most at risk for cancer. The pigment **melanin** in dark-skinned people protects against UV damage. The protection is limited, however. People with dark skin can still get cancer. The amounts of melanin in all but the lightest-colored skin increase with sun exposure. The resulting

precautions that can be taken to avoid dangerous overexposure to the sun? Have a class discussion. Make a master list of their answers on the chalkboard or on an overhead transparency. Answers should include:
1. Use of a waterproof sunscreen. The higher the SPF (sun protection factor), the better.
2. Protect the lips with a sunscreen lip balm.

3. Enjoy the sun for short periods on many occasions rather than staying out in the sun all day.
4. Take along a big hat.
5. Wear sunglasses that are marked as blocking out UV rays.
(30 min., Critical Thinking)

Activity 2.3
Dietary Factors. Have a class discussion on the four dietary factors that

are strongly linked to high cancer risks: high meat intake, high fat intake, low vegetable intake, low grain intake.

In the discussion, stress ways that students can cut down on meat without giving it up and how to cut down on fat intake. Discuss fiber and how to increase vegetable intake in their diets as painlessly as possible. **(25 min.; Reteach, Reinforce)**

LIFE CHOICE

INVENTORY

How Well Do You Protect Yourself against Cancer?

You cannot eliminate all cancer risks from your life. You can, however, take steps to reduce them. Questions answered No indicate ways you can improve.

1. Are you a nonsmoker? Do you avoid using tobacco in any form? Do you request that those around you not smoke?
2. Are you careful not to sunburn? Do you avoid tanning salons? Do you wear sunglasses that block out ultraviolet rays when outdoors? Do you obtain regular eye exams?
3. Do you question the necessity of x-ray examinations?
4. Have you had your home tested for radon and taken any necessary steps to prevent exposure?
5. Do you read and follow instructions on the labels of chemicals that you use in

the home, in the garden, or on the job?
6. Do you choose a variety of foods from a balanced diet that supply adequate fiber, vitamin A, and vitamin C, without too much fat? Do you eat vegetables from the cabbage family often?
7. Do you keep your weight within the normal range for your height?
8. Do you limit your intakes of cured and smoked meats?
9. Do you abstain from drinking alcohol?
10. Do you exercise regularly?
11. Do you perform breast or testicular self-examination regularly?
12. Do you, or will you, seek employment with low occupational hazards?

---

tan is the body's defense against the dangerous rays—but not against the cancers they cause.

Should a would-be tanner tan indoors, then? No. All sunlamps and tanning booths bombard the skin with UV radiation. Can-

cer risks from sunlamps and booths are just as high as those from sunbathing.

People can take precautions to avoid dangerous overexposure to the sun. Sunscreen ① products block ultraviolet radiation and prevent burning, and so are a wise investment. The higher a product's sun protection factor

Use sunscreen and take along a big hat.

 MINI GLOSSARY

melanin (MELL-eh-nin): the protective skin pigment responsible for the tan, brown, or black color of human skin; produced in abundance upon exposure to ultraviolet radiation.

Activity 2.4
Pop Quiz.
1. There is no proven link between the use of tobacco and cancer. (F)
2. Cancer risks from sunlamps and booths are just as high as those from sunbathing. (T)
3. Most cases of skin cancer are caused by overexposure to the sun's ultraviolet rays. (T)
4. The name of the fast-growing lethal skin cancer is melanoma. (T)
5. The mixture of vitamins that occurs in fruits and vegetables may help block the progress of certain cancers. (T)
(15 min.)

Activity 2.5
Review Questions. Before going on to the next lesson, students should be able to answer these questions:
1. How can you cut down on the amount of exposure to radiation (UV rays) from the sun?

Teacher Support Notes

① **Tanning Pills:** You may want to warn students against the use of tanning pills. These products have not been approved by the FDA and have caused death in at least one previously healthy young woman.

② **Electricity:** You may want to tell students that another potentially risky form of radiation is that from electricity such as high voltage power lines and electrical appliances. Most standard home appliances are probably safe with the exception of electric blankets. Use an electric blanket only to warm the bed and then unplug it. Video display terminals and TVs emit radiation also.

🔊 Fast Facts

Two Swedish studies published in 1992 provide some evidence linking electricity and cancer. In a study of all people living within 328 yards of a high tension line, it was found that children in this area had a higher risk than others of contracting leukemia. A second study linked on-the-job exposure to electromagnetic fields to leukemia in workers.

476

Basal cell carcinoma.

Squamous cell carcinoma.

Malignant melanoma.

Figure 19–2 Forms of Skin Cancer. Report skin spots that resemble any of these three to a physician immediately.
Source: Courtesy of The Skin Cancer Foundation, New York, New York.

(SPF), the more protection it provides (but brand names don't matter at all).

All people—even people with dark skin—should use waterproof sunscreens of at least SPF 15 during sunny or warm weather. To be protected, a person wearing a bathing suit needs to use a full ounce of product spread on the skin with each application. Enjoy the sun for short times rather than on all-day trips. Take along a big hat. And be aware that ultraviolet rays penetrate clouds, so burns are likely even on cool, cloudy days.

People are exposed to more radiation than just from sunlight. A great deal of background radiation bombards us from the cosmos, from the soil, and from the air and water. Human-made radiation comes from medical and dental X rays and from aboveground nuclear weapons testing anywhere on earth. X-ray examinations are often required for proper medical care. However, wise clients inform their health care providers that they wish to avoid X rays when possible.

You can also be exposed to radiation from a gas, **radon**, that forms naturally in the ground and escapes through cracks and vents. This can present a risk of cancer to people whose homes are built over ground where radon is escaping. People in radon-rich areas should have their homes tested, and if radon is present, arrange for ventilation so that harmful levels of the gas will not accumulate.

> **Key Points** *Sun overexposure ages the skin and promotes skin cancer. Sunscreen filters the harmful rays and lowers cancer risks. Radiation from too many X rays or from radon can increase cancer risks.*

Diet and Exercise

Four dietary factors link strongly with high cancer risks: high meat intakes, high fat intakes, low vegetable intakes, and low grain intakes. Vegetarian diets probably protect against certain types of cancers, especially colon cancer. Meats that have been cured, smoked, charbroiled, or burned contain carcinogens. Fat in foods probably promotes the development of cancer. The fibers in vegetables and grains help to protect against cancer of the large intestine,

These foods contain nutrients and nonnutrients that are protective against cancer.

probably by trapping carcinogens in the digestive tract and carrying them out of the body. People wonder if food additives might cause cancer, or if supplements might prevent it. The answers to these questions are in this chapter's Straight Talk.

Physical activity works along with diet in cancer prevention. Physically active people enjoy a reduced risk of cancer, especially colon cancer. People who fail to work out regularly suffer more cancers of this type. This effect may be related to constipation—a problem common in sedentary people but rare in exercisers. The stools contain carcinogenic material, and the longer they stay in the colon, the more the chance of their changing the cells of the colon's lining. Exercise strengthens the muscles used to move the bowels and massages the intestines to help move their contents along. With regular bowel movements, the contents of the stools spend little time in contact with the colon lining.

Key Points *A diet low in fat, and meat and high in grains, fruits, and vegetables may minimize the risks of certain cancers.*

SECTION II REVIEW

Answer the following questions on a sheet of paper.

Learning the Vocabulary
The vocabulary terms in this section are *melanin* and *radon*.

1. Write a sentence using each vocabulary term.

Learning the Facts
2. What percentage of lung cancer victims are smokers?
3. What causes most skin cancer?
4. Name the four dietary factors that link strongly with high cancer risks.

Making Life Choices
5. Determine how well you protect yourself against cancer by taking the Life Choice Inventory on page 475. Do you feel you are doing enough to protect yourself against cancer? Why or why not? List the steps you need to take to reduce your risk of cancer.

SECTION III

Early Detection and Treatment

The treatment of cancer involves sophisticated equipment, powerful drugs, and specialized medical staff. The detection of common cancers, however, requires mostly routine tests and self-examinations. The sooner a cancer is detected, the better the chances for a complete cure.

Cancer Detection

Figure 19–3 on the next page lists cancers, such as **Hodgkin's disease** and oth-

① MINI GLOSSARY

radon (RAY-don): a gas that arises from the earth where radioactive materials are present.
Hodgkin's disease: a lymphoma that attacks people in early life and is treatable with radiation therapy.

self-exams and being aware of the eight warning signs as they apply to changes in their bodies. Discuss how self-esteem, fear, ignorance, and responsibility help determine our ability to take responsibility for making wise choices such as doing self-exams and thereby detecting cancer

early and enhancing chances of survival. **(40 min., Critical Thinking)**

TEACH
▶ **S**ECTION **III**
(Guided and Independent Practice)

Activity 3.2
CAUTIONS. Write the word C-A-U-T-I-O-N-S vertically on the board or on an overhead. After each letter write the warning sign starting with that letter. (See

the text page below.)
Leave space between the first letter and the second letter of the word so that you can cover the warning signs with a piece of paper and slide it down as you talk about each one for review. Give a brief overview of the warning signs. Then go over them one by one. Call on a student to give you the first warning sign, then move the paper down so the first warning sign can be seen and ask for the

Teacher Support Notes

① **Studying Figure 19–3:** After students have been assigned to read Figure 19–3, have them close their books and then see how much of the information from the figure they can generate. Begin by having them list the six types of cancers most often causing death in people ages 15–34. Then see how many symptoms they can remember for each disease. Finally, write the text descriptions of survival on the board and see if they can match those to the proper types of cancer.

✍ Fast Facts

Melanoma is the second leading cause of death for American men ages 15–35. According to a researcher at the New York University Medical Center, the following six factors increase the likelihood that a person will contract melanoma: red or blond hair; marked freckling of the back; three or more blistering sunburns as a teenager; more than three years with an outdoor summer job as a teenager; a family history of skin cancer; and actinic keratoses, a scaly skin condition caused by sun damage.

478

478 UNIT 5 Disease Prevention

_____ **F**IGURE **19-3** _____ ①

Cancers Most Often Causing Deaths in People Ages 15 to 34

Disease	Early Smptoms	Survival with Early Diagnosis and Prompt Treatment[a]
Brain and nervous system cancer	Personality changes; bizarre behavior; headaches; dizziness; balance and walking disturbances; vision changes; nausea, vomiting, or seizures	Poor to good
Breast cancer	Unusual lump; thickening in, change in contour in, dimple in, or discharge from, the nipple	Good (about 50 percent)
Hodgkin's disease	Swelling of lymph nodes in neck, armpits, or groin; susceptibility to infection	Good (54 percent)
Leukemia	Acts like infection, with fever, lethargy, and other flulike symptoms; may also include bone pain, tendency to bruise or bleed easily, and enlargement of lymph nodes	Poor to good (up to 50 percent), depending on the type of leukemia
Skin cancer	Unusual discoloration, swellings, sores, or lumps; change in color or appearance of a wart or mole; tenderness, itching, or bleeding from a lump or mole	Excellent (up to 90 percent)
Testicular cancer	Small, hard, painless lump; sudden accumulation of fluid in the scrotum; pain or discomfort in the region between the scrotum and anus	Good to excellent (66 to 86 percent)

[a]The survival rates are estimates based on five years of disease-free survival. For all cancers, survival rates drop dramatically after metastasis.

---

ers, that most often cause deaths among young people. It also describes the symptoms associated with each. Any of the symptoms listed should be checked by a health care provider immediately.

Often, cancer gives some warning to the person who is developing it. Cancer can develop without symptoms, but it is wise to heed all the messages your body sends you, particularly the following warnings:

- **C**hange in bowel or bladder habits, such as diarrhea or constipation.
- **A** sore that does not heal.

- **U**nusual bleeding or discharge.
- **T**hickening or lump that suddenly appears anywhere in the body.
- **I**ndigestion or difficulty swallowing.
- **O**bvious change in a wart or mole.
- **N**agging cough or hoarseness.
- **S**udden weight loss.

To remember this list, recall that the first letters in the warning signs spell the word *CAUTIONS*. Having one of these symptoms does not necessarily mean that you have cancer. A cold or eating too much might second one. The student continues until an incorrect answer is given. When one is missed, call on someone else to start with number one again and to go through all eight warning signs. (45–50 min.; Reteach, Reinforce)

Activity 3.3

Helpful Phone Numbers. Have the students imagine the following: You have just been told that you have had a change in a mole and that it has become cancerous. The doctor gives you some advice but you would like more information and perhaps a second opinion.

Divide the class into groups of five to eight. Give each group a phone book. Have them look up the numbers they could call to get more information about their conditions. They may also use their textbooks. Give them approximately ten minutes. Ask each group for the names and numbers they found. On an overhead transparency write the names and the numbers they give you. (45–50 min.; Extend, Enrich)

Activity 3.4

Side Effects. Have the students list side effects that people develop as a result of cancer treatments. Have a class discussion on the side effects. Stress that

(continued on next page)

Researchers are finding a relationship between exercise and a reduced risk for some types of cancer.

bring about some of them, for example. Just remember that when symptoms last for more than a week, or when they occur more than once, they require the attention of a health care provider.

Self-examinations are particularly useful for the early detection of cancer. The instructions for performing the breast self-examination were illustrated in Chapter 11. A medical professional who sees a person only once a year or so may not notice small changes that would be obvious to a person familiar with his or her own body.

Of course, a professional can detect a lump in places not easily examined at home. Laboratory tests are important, too. The most accurate test for early breast cancer is the **mammogram** (an x-ray examination). Because mammograms involve radiation, which itself can cause cancer, they are used sparingly.

Other tests that 18-year-olds should have include, for young women, a Pap test, a pelvic examination, and a breast examination (by a physician). Young men 18 years old should have a testicle and prostate examination (by a physician). Both genders need examinations of the thyroid, lymph nodes, mouth and throat, and skin. For every advantage in early detection of can-

② cer, these tests (and others) should continue on schedule throughout life.

Unfortunately, some healthy young women seek to "improve" their breasts through implant surgery. They should know that silicone breast implants can interfere with mammograms, hiding cancers until they've reached a life-threatening stage. Also, silicone may leak from faulty implants, or implant coverings may disintegrate, and the chemicals released may elevate cancer risks.

③ Detection tests are important, but even more important is to discover how to prevent cancer's occurrence. No disease has ever been cured out of existence. As is now the case with smallpox and polio, widespread success can be claimed only when the disease is prevented from occurring. Still, the technology for curing cancer remains important to individuals who have developed the disease.

Key Points *Self-examinations of the breasts, testicles, and skin can help to protect against cancer. Other tests conducted by health care* ① *providers are also useful.*

Cancer Treatment

As soon as cancer is diagnosed, a person should seek treatment—not just any treatment, but the treatment most likely to be successful. This means finding medical experts, not quacks. Because cancer is scary, people may become irrational and seek help that promises miracles and delivers nothing but heartache. This chapter's Consumer Awareness section describes how cancer frauds are peddled.

MINI GLOSSARY

mammogram: x-ray examination of the breast, a screening test for cancer.

---

today health care professionals make every effort to keep the patient as comfortable as possible during treatment. There are drugs that prevent or reduce the nausea. Also, pain and diarrhea are treated. The only side effects that some cancer patients have to adjust to are loss of hair and fatigue. **(20 min.; Extend, Enrich)**

EVALUATE
SECTION III

Activity 3.5
Pop Quiz.
1. The earlier the diagnosis of symptomless cancer, the greater the chance of complete recovery. (T)

2. Education is the first step in protecting yourself against cancer. (T)
3. The mammogram is not really the most accurate test for the early detection of breast cancer. (F)
4. Self-examination of the breasts, testicles, and skin can help protect against cancer. (T)
5. Women should have a Pap test. (T)
6. Cancer treatments destroy cells in two ways: by removal of malignant tissue and

---

✍ Fast Facts

Experts estimate that today 60% to 70% of all women with early breast cancer still undergo mastectomy. Only 30% to 40% are treated with the equally effective option of lumpectomy, followed by radiation. That's less than half of those who would be considered good candidates.

Teacher Support Notes

① **Answers to Critical Thinking:**
1. Their fear overwhelms their ability to reason; They become so afraid of dying that they will try anything.
2. They think they have nothing to lose. They may also be persuaded that health care providers are not really concerned about them and that the people who claim to have cures are really the ones who want to help them.
3. profit

✉ Where to Write

Leukemia Society of America, Inc.
733 3rd Avenue
New York, NY 10017

CONSUMER AWARENESS
Deception of the Desperate

Not all cancer treatments called "cures" are effective. Frauds in health are always cruel. Those aimed at cancer victims are especially so, because they prey on people who are already suffering. Laetrile is a cancer-cure hoax. Another such hoax is immuno-augmentative therapy, or IAT. This one involves traveling to foreign countries for dangerous blood transfusions that not only fail to fight cancer, but also spread AIDS and hepatitis to the already sick victims. Countless other vitamin, mineral, and drug "therapies" offered to cancer victims are scams.

Sometimes people report that a phony cancer cure worked. Famous quack-buster Victor Herbert has listed five possible reasons for this.

- The person never had cancer.
- The cancer was cured by conventional therapy, but the quack took the credit.
- The cancer is still silently progressing, but the person *thinks* that it has been cured.
- The person has died of cancer, but is reported as cured.

- The person's cancer went away by itself, and the quack took the credit.

The sellers of bogus treatments capitalize on people's fear of cancer and scare them into believing that medical doctors frown on their methods for dishonest reasons. "The doctors don't care if you die," they say. "They just want your money first." Loving life, wanting to trust someone, wanting to hope that a cure is possible, victims of cancer easily fall prey to this sort of deception, as do relatives and friends who are willing to try anything to help their loved ones get well.

① **CRITICAL THINKING**

1. Why do people's fears of cancer make them easy targets for quacks?
2. Why do you think someone with cancer might take chances by trying unproven therapies?
3. What motivates quacks to sell fake cancer cures?

Being diagnosed as having cancer can be a frightening experience, but people should try to put their fears aside. Fear can interfere with the body's healing response, and hope can help with cure. Hope is possible, because tremendous numbers of treatments end in success, thanks to advances in cancer treatment research. For more information about cancer, people can call a cancer hotline number.*

Cancer treatments destroy cancers in two ways: by removal of the malignant tissue from the body and by destruction of cancer cells within the body. If the cancer has metastasized, surgical removal or destruction of a tumor may not eliminate all the

*The National Cancer Institute's information service number is 1-800-4CANCER. The American Cancer Society's number is 1-800-ACS-2345.

7. The cure rate for most cancers remains about the same even though metastasis has occurred. (F)

8. Chemotherapy involves using drugs to seek out and destroy cancer cells in the body. (T)

9. Radiation and chemotherapy kill only cancer tissue and not normal tissue. (F)

10. A person who gets cancer today has a reason to be hopeful about the possibili-ties for a cure. (T)

(15 min.)

CLOSE

SECTION III

Activity 3.6

Review Questions. Before going on to the next lesson, students should be able to answer these questions:

1. What are the eight warning signs of cancer?

2. What are some "protective factors" and "preventable risk factors" against cancer?

3. What body organs can be self-examined for early detection of cancer?

4. Name the basic types of cancer treatments.

5. List some of the major side effects of chemotherapy or radiation.

(continued on next page)

---

cancer cells. Cancer *cure* comes when every cancer cell is either removed from the body or wiped out by treatments.

Many cancers are treatable through surgery alone. Removal of a tumor can stop the cancer growth at a site, especially if the cancer is still small. The cure rate drops off, however, as the tumor invades surrounding tissues and metastasizes to other body parts. For example, the large intestine may contain precancerous growths called **polyps**. Removal of polyps protects against cancer. If the polyp begins to invade just a few millimeters into the tissue, however, its surgical removal no longer guarantees complete freedom from cancer at that site.

A small tumor on the skin or other external membrane can sometimes be destroyed by freezing with liquid nitrogen. Such a procedure is often performed in the physician's office and causes little inconvenience or pain.

A treatment for cancer, sometimes used together with surgery, is **radiation therapy**. Medical professionals use several methods to kill tumors with radiation. A beam may be focused on the area known to be cancerous. Radioactive materials may be implanted in the tumor or, in some cases, injected into the bloodstream (when it is known that they will be absorbed only by the tumor). Under bombardment from the radioactivity, the fast-growing cells of the cancer become disrupted and die off. Unfortunately, when a beam of radiation is used, some cancer cells may lie outside the beam area and remain unaffected. Also, some healthy tissue that lies within the beam area is destroyed. The problem cannot be solved by exposing the whole body to radiation, because the body cannot tolerate so much radiation.

In addition to surgery and radiation, a third approach is chemical treatments of cancer, called **chemotherapy**. These offer a major advantage when a tumor has metastasized. Once in the body, the drugs seek out and destroy the escaped cancer cells, as well as tumors in all locations. More than 40 drugs are now used against cancer in different ways—to cure, to inhibit cancer growth, to relieve pain, and to allow the person to lead a more normal life. Often, radiation and chemotherapy are used together.

Both radiation and anticancer drugs that kill cancer tissue also kill normal tissues, although more slowly. Rapidly-dividing cells in the body are affected the most. The cells of the digestive tract, for example, normally divide rapidly, so treatments produce diarrhea, nausea, and vomiting. Other side effects are skin damage, hair loss, and fatigue. New blood cells also arise from a rapidly dividing tissue, so people being treated for cancer may develop blood problems.

Described here are only a few treatments for cancer. Many more have proved effective. More still are under development. A person who gets cancer has reason to be hopeful about possibilities for a cure.

 Key Points *Cancer treatments aim to remove cancerous tissue and to destroy cancer cells. Common treatments include surgery, radiation therapy, and chemotherapy.*

MINI GLOSSARY

polyps: tumors that grow on a stem, resembling mushrooms. Polyps bleed easily, and some have the tendency to become malignant.

radiation therapy: the application of cell-destroying radiation to kill cancerous tissues.

chemotherapy: the administration of drugs that harm the cancer cells, but that do not harm the client, or at least do not harm the client as much as the disease does.

Fast Facts

A two-year study monitored women with a high risk for developing breast cancer. Those who received 15% of their calories from fat showed less than three times the damage to the DNA in their cells than those whose diets were 30% fat. This is important because lab tests on animals have linked DNA damage to breast tumors.

Teacher Support Notes

① **Overhead—Cancer Cure by Surgery:** Your supplementary material contains an overhead that illustrates the progression of cancer and the likelihood of an effective cure by surgery at the different stages of the cancer's progression. This overhead should help students see the importance of early detection.

CLOSE
(Continued)

6. List the two ways cancer treatments destroy cancer cells. Discuss the answers to these questions in class. **(25 min.; Reteach, Reinforce)**

FOCUS
SECTION IV

In this section students will learn that:
1. Being diagnosed with cancer involves not only a physical battle but also an emotional battle.
2. Cancer affects not only the person with cancer, but also friends and family.

Activity 4.1
Emotions. Lead a class discussion dealing with the emotions that people with cancer will probably experience as well as the emotions that will be felt by the family and friends of the person affected. Emotions might include anger, fear, envy, and sadness. Discuss each emotion and give an example of situations in which that emotion might be displayed when cancer is involved. (Save the list for later

---

Section III Review
Answers

1. mammogram
2. Chemotherapy
3. polyps
4. 1-800-4CANCER
5. by removal of the malignant tissue from the body and by destruction of cancer cells within the body
6. Some cancer cells may lie outside the beam area and remain unaffected, while some healthy tissue that lies within the beam area is destroyed.
7. surgery, radiation therapy, and chemotherapy
8. Answers will vary.

Teacher Support Notes

① **Teacher Information Sheet—Relationships with People Who Have Cancer:**
Your supplementary material contains background information entitled "Relationships with People Who Have Cancer" that consists of guidelines recommended by the American Cancer Society for talking to people who have learned they have cancer. You may be able to use some of the examples included with the information in your discussion of this topic in class.

SECTION III REVIEW

Answer the following questions on a sheet of paper.

Learning the Vocabulary
The vocabulary terms in this section are *Hodgkins's disease, mammogram, polyps, radiation therapy,* and *chemotherapy.*

1. A _____ is an x-ray examination of the breast.
2. _____ is the administration of drugs that seek out and destroy escaped cancer cells as well as tumors in all locations.
3. Tumors that grow on a stem, bleed easily, and tend to become malignant are called _____.

Learning the Facts
4. What is the national cancer hotline phone number?
5. What are the two ways cancer treatments destroy cancer?
6. What is the disadvantage of using radiation therapy?
7. Name three common treatments for cancer.

Making Life Choices
8. Cancer patients often reach a stage in which all appears futile. At this point some people feel it is justified to try every possible treatment that has even the most remote chance of effecting a cure. Do you feel this is an appropriate action? Why or why not? What do you think you would do if faced with this situation?

SECTION IV

Living with Cancer

In the battle against a seemingly inhuman tissue, physicians tend to focus on machines, drugs, and techniques. The tissue, though, is within a living, feeling human being. Treatments often invade the person's life in intimate ways. People diagnosed with cancer must struggle to retain wellness in those areas that remain open, and mean-

---

HEALTH STRATEGIES

① Helping a Friend with Cancer

To help a loved one with cancer:

1. **Be there.** Don't avoid your friend, who needs your presence now more than ever before.
2. **Touch the person.** A hug or other physical gesture oftentimes can say more than words.
3. **Let the person talk.** Don't avoid the word *cancer.* Ask if your friend wants to talk about the illness. If so, expect negative emotions, and accept them.
4. **Make specific offers of help.** Ask if you can mow the grass, help with schoolwork, go shopping, fix a snack, baby-sit, or do any other task that needs to be done—and then do it.
5. **Help the friend's family.** They are suffering, too. Tell family members you can stay with your friend for a few hours while they run errands or care for personal needs that may have been neglected.
6. **Recognize limitations.** Involve your friend in as many of your normal activities as possible, but remember that people with cancer tire easily. Don't be offended if your friend cancels an outing or cuts a visit short because of pain or fatigue.
7. **Be positive.** No matter what the future holds, everyone with cancer needs laughter, hope, and talk of plans for tomorrow.

Source: Adapted with permission from the *University of Texas Lifetime Health Letter*, Houston, January 1990, p. 2.

TEACH
SECTION IV
(Guided and Independent Practice)
Activity 4.2

Correlation of Emotions and Stages. Refer to the list of emotions you wrote in Activity 4.1. List the emotions on an overhead transparency or on the board. Have a class discussion by asking

the students when the person affected, friends, or family might feel these emotions. Use the time frame: from the first time the person is told that he or she has cancer to the person's cure or death from the disease. Here you may want to introduce some supplemental material on the five stages of grief. Explain that each stage of grief will highlight an emotion and that once acceptance is achieved the person, family, and friends can begin to effectively

fight the disease. The stages of grief are discussed in the Straight Talk feature in Chapter 22. **(25 min.; Extend, Enrich)**

EVALUATE
SECTION IV
Activity 4.3

Pop Quiz. The Review Questions in the Close activity can provide material for a pop quiz at this point.

---

while deal with the disease. They have fears to cope with. They may need to move emotionally through the stages of grief before they can take part in their own treatments and recoveries.

Some people find ways to face the crisis with courage. They are spurred into action, not despair. They cultivate a sense of humor in the midst of fear. Such people maintain strong family bonds and bonds of friendship throughout the illness. They also have an invaluable asset to recovery—the will to live.

Dealing with Pain

Drugs can help lessen the pain of cancer. Often, though, drugs alone are not enough to produce pain-free living. A form of positive self-talk, known as **positive imaging**, or **guided imaging**, may be useful for people struggling with pain. A therapist who teaches positive imaging may tell the person to relax with eyes closed and picture the pain as a mad dog. Then the person imagines reaching out to the dog, trying to coax it into stopping its snarling and growling, and gradually taming it to the point where it begins to wag its tail.

The dog represents the pain. The client begins to relax when confronted with it, and soon learns that it is possible to deal with it. The pain then becomes less of an enemy. Cancer clients who used positive imaging have been shown in some experiments to live longer than those who did not. The effect is probably related to the placebo effect, discussed in the Straight Talk of Chapter 4. The Health Strategies section on the previous page, "Helping a Friend with Cancer," offers ways you can help a friend or loved one with cancer.

Key Points *Dealing with a diagnosis of cancer takes courage. Dealing with pain takes effort. Positive imaging can be useful to those struggling with pain.*

SECTION IV REVIEW

Answer the following questions on a sheet of paper.
Learning the Vocabulary
The vocabulary term in this section is *positive imaging (guided imaging).*
1. Write a one-sentence description of positive imaging.

Learning the Facts
2. What are some of the struggles faced by those with cancer?
3. List three strategies for helping a friend with cancer.

Making Life Choices
4. Look over the Health Strategies feature, "Helping A Friend with Cancer," on page 482. Imagine that you are fighting your own battle with cancer. What strategies would you add to the list for people who are close to you to follow? Now imagine someone close to you has cancer. Which suggestions on the list would you find easy to follow?

Answers to Fact or Fiction

Here are the answers to the questions at the start of the chapter.

1. True. **2.** False. Tanning booths or sunlamps are no safer than sunbathing, as far as cancer risks are concerned. **3.** False. While people with fair complexions who burn easily are at greater risk, everyone needs to use sunscreen to prevent skin cancer from sun exposure. **4.** True.

MINI GLOSSARY

positive imaging (guided imaging): a technique used to help achieve the relaxation response. The person imagines achieving positive outcomes to present challenges.

Teacher Support Notes

① **Handout—U.S. Health Service Objectives:** Your supplementary material contains a handout that lists the U.S. Public Health Service objectives for the nation as established by the U.S. Department of Health and Human Services for cancer. You may want to distribute this handout as students conclude reading this chapter.

Section IV Review
Answers
1. Answers will vary.
2. They must retain wellness in those areas that remain open, cope with fears, and move emotionally through stages of grief before taking part in their own treatments.
3. Answers will vary; could include: be there, touch the person, let the person talk, make specific offers of help, help the friend's family, recognize limitations, and be positive.
4. Answers will vary.

CLOSE
SECTION IV

Activity 4.4
Review Questions. Before going on to the next lesson, students should be able to answer these questions:
1. What is positive imaging?
2. How does positive imaging help control the pain associated with cancer?

3. What can you do to help if you find out a friend or family member has cancer?
4. What are three things needed by cancer patients and their families to help them cope and learn to live with cancer?
5. The cancer battle is fought on two levels. What are they? **(25 min.; Reteach, Reinforce)**

RETEACH/BONUS

Life Situations. Put these two life situations on the board or a prepared overhead. Have the students write answers to the questions at the end of each life situation. After they have finished, have a class discussion.
Life Situation #1—You are a 14-year-

✍ Fast Facts

In 1970 the chances of an American woman developing breast cancer were 1 in 16. In 1990 the chances were 1 in 10 according to the American Cancer Society.

Teacher Support Notes

① Unknown Links:
Researchers have not established strong links between foods and cancer in the way that they have with tobacco. To make this point, tell them that Japanese people living in Japan develop more stomach and less colon cancer than people in the United States. However, when Japanese people come to the U.S., their children develop both stomach and colon cancer at a rate like that of U.S. citizens. Japan and the U.S. are both industrial countries. Something in the environment must be causing the changed cancer patterns. The change in diets is an obvious candidate.

☎ Where to Call

National Cancer Institute
1-800-638-6694

484   UNIT 5   Disease Prevention

STRAIGHT TALK

Nutrition and Cancer Prevention

The links between diet and cancer are not as certain as the links of cancer with other risk factors. ①
People who eat a certain way cannot be assured of freedom from cancer. However, they can reduce their risks. A warning: Popular books and magazines make many claims regarding diet and cancer. They know people will buy publications that promise control over cancer, and not all their claims are well founded.

How do foods relate to cancer development and prevention?

Foods are made of chemicals. These include the nutrients, of course (carbohydrate, fat, protein, and the vitamins and minerals). Thousands of other chemicals can also be found in foods, such as the deep red pigment of beets, the aromatic chemical in bananas, and the "hot" chemical of peppers. Every one of these chemicals may affect cancer development.

As just one example, roasted turkey contains a proven carcinogen, but to receive enough of it to initiate cancer, you'd have to eat 2 tons of turkey. The body easily destroys the amount of the carcinogen in your Thanksgiving dinner. Almost every meal contains such chemicals, but the body has the ability to handle them.

Do additives cause cancer?

Food additives have little to do with cancer. The law

forbids the addition to food of any substance that has ever been shown to cause cancer.

I've seen labels warning that saccharin causes cancer in laboratory animals. Is saccharin safe?

Saccharin has been in use for over 100 years as a sweetener, but was almost banned when evidence showed that extremely high doses caused bladder tumors in rats. The effect is limited to rats, though. Saccharin-containing foods must bear the warning label you mentioned, but most researchers still believe saccharin to be safe for people.

I feel better about additives, but isn't it still best to choose fresh foods over processed foods?

Yes, fresh foods are best for nutrition. However, do scrub fruits and vegetables to remove pesticide residues

before eating them. Fresh foods may even help protect against cancer, if they are low in fat. In contrast, processed foods are inferior. Most have lost nutrients, and are high in fat and calories. Dietary fat and calories probably promote cancer.

Would cutting down on fat lessen people's chances of developing cancer?

Yes, in theory. However, this idea has arisen mostly from work with experimental animals, not people. Scientifically, findings about rats cannot be assumed true about people. (And of course, researchers cannot start cancers in people and then feed them to study the effects of diet.) Still, people's cancer rates go up as a population's fat intake rises. Reducing the fat intake of the average adult by about half seems wise.

One other concern about fat and meats: carcinogens

(Continued on next page)

old male high school student. While taking a shower you feel a lump on your neck. It feels hard but it is not painful. You do not want to worry your parents so you are hesitant to tell them. However, you are concerned about the lump. How would you deal with this problem?

Life Situation #2—You are a 14-year-old female high school student. Your mother tells you that your grandmother died of breast cancer and that she is going yearly for a mammogram. What can you deduce from this new information? What are your concerns? What action would you take in view of the information you have just been given? **(15 min., Critical Thinking)**

Essay. Put this statement on the board or an overhead: "People who are suffering often make the best teachers and set a good example for each of us."

Have the students write a one-page essay telling what this statement means to them. Ask the questions: **1.** What do suffering people show us? **2.** Why does a suffering person make a good teacher? **3.** What do you have to do in order to learn from someone who is suffering? **4.** When you watch someone fight cancer, what effect can this have on your view of the value of life? **(25 min., Critical Thinking,)**

STRAIGHT TALK *(Continued)*

form whenever fats or meats are burned, charred, or smoked. Limit intake of smoked or charbroiled meats to one or two servings a week. ①

Are some breakfast cereals protective against cancer?

Cereals and other high-fiber foods have at least some evidence in their favor, although it is not as strong as the evidence concerning fat. Still, the fiber of fruits and vegetables may help to protect against some cancers. On the other hand, it could be something other than fiber in vegetables that is protective. ②

Do researchers know what that "something" in vegetables might be?

Vitamin C is a likely candidate. People with digestive tract cancers report eating few vegetables in general, and fewer vitamin C-containing vegetables. Especially, **cruciferous vegetables**—cabbage, broccoli, brussels sprouts, are important, as are those that are rich in **beta-carotene**, the plant form of vitamin A. Carotene may interfere with the earliest cancerous changes in cells. The best vegetables to supply carotene are the bright orange and yellow ones, along with leafy green vegetables.

FIGURE 19-4

Cruciferous Vegetables and Carotene-Rich Fruits and Vegetables

Cruciferous Vegetables	Carotene-Rich Fruits and Vegetables
Broccoli	Apricots, Cantaloupe
Brussels sprouts	Asparagus
Cabbage (all varieties)	Broccoli, Carrots
Cauliflower	Green onions
Greens (collards, mustards, turnips)	Greens (all varieties)
Kale	Lettuce (dark green)
Kohlrabi	Mangoes, Papayas
Rutabagas	Oriental cabbages
Turnip roots	Parsley, Spinach
	Squash (hard, winter)
	Sweet potatoes

Can I just take a supplement to be sure I get enough vitamins? Preparing fresh vegetables is a bother.

No one knows if supplements are effective against cancer in the same way foods are. For one thing, vegetables contain many types of fiber as well as vitamins. For another thing, vegetables contain other chemicals, such as the one that gives cruciferous vegetables their cabbage-like taste. These chemicals may turn out to be important in preventing some kinds of cancer.

The best way to get all the nutrients and non-nutrients that may be protective against cancer is to eat a wide variety of fresh foods; limit fats; choose foods with fiber; and choose fresh vegetables often, especially the ones listed in Figure 19–4. One other suggestion: Vary your choices. Don't let your diet become monotonous. Whenever you switch from food to food, you are diluting whatever is in one food with what is in the others.

Mini Glossary

cruciferous vegetables: vegetables of the cabbage family.
beta-carotene: an orange pigment in plants that can be changed to vitamin A in the body.

Teacher Support Notes

① **Fat and Cancer.** You may want to tell students that it may be certain forms of fat that are related to increased cancer rates. Some findings point to linoleic acid, the essential omega-6 fatty acid of vegetable oils. Polyunsaturated fats are more often associated with tumor growth than are saturated fats. In laboratory experiments with animals, fat does not initiate the cancers, but after exposure from a known carcinogen, a high-fat diet does make more cancers develop.

② **Vegetarians and Cancer:** For enrichment, you may want to tell students that vegetarians have lower mortality rates from cancer than the rest of the population, even when cancers related to smoking and alcohol are removed from the comparisons. These findings match up with general findings that high vegetable and grain intakes correlate with low cancer rates.

CHAPTER REVIEW
Answers

Vocabulary
1. **a.** Lymphomas
b. positive imaging
2. **a.** Metastasized
b. Sarcomas
c. leukemias **d.** mutation
e. malignancy
3. **a.** melanin **b.** benign
c. myeloma **d.** cancer
e. cruciferous vegetables **f.** carcinomas

Recall
Section I
1. lung cancer
2. exposure to a carcinogen, entry of the initiator into the cell, change of the cell's genetic material, possible speeding up of cancer formation by a promoter, out-of-control multi-plication of the cells, tumor or other malignancy formation
3. Tobacco is the initiator of mouth, throat, and esophagus cancers, while alcohol is the promoter of these cancers once they have started. Smoking makes these cancers one-and-a-half times more likely, but coupled with alcohol they become 15 times greater.

Section II
4. Answers will vary; could include: smoking behavior, exposure to sun's ultraviolet rays, and choosing proper diet and exercise.
5. lung, larynx, mouth, esophagus, urinary bladder, kidney, pancreas
6. less-threatening surface cancers of the skin

CHAPTER REVIEW

LEARNING THE VOCABULARY

cancer	initiator	polyps
tumor	mutation	radiation therapy
malignancy	promoter	chemotherapy
melanoma	benign	positive imaging (guided imaging)
myeloma	metastasized	cruciferous vegetables
lymphomas	melanin	beta carotene
leukemias	radon	
carcinomas	Hodgkin's disease	
sarcomas	mammogram	

Answer the following questions on a separate sheet of paper.

1. a. _____ are cancers that arise in the immune system.
   b. A technique called _____ is used to help achieve a relaxation response.

2. *Word Scramble*—Use the clues from the phrases below to help you unscramble the vocabulary terms from the list above:
   a. **tizetemasasd** _____ means that cancer cells have migrated from one part of the body to another.
   b. **marascos** _____ are cancers that arise in connective tissue cells such as bones, ligaments, and muscles.
   c. **saimekuel** Cancers that arise in the blood cell-making tissues are known as _____.
   d. **itutmaon** A _____ is a change in a cell's genetic material.

   e. **ynalgimanc** A dangerous cancerous growth that sheds cells into body fluids and spreads to new locations to start new cancer colonies is called a _____.

3. *Matching*—Match each of the following phrases with the appropriate vocabulary term from the list above:
   a. a brown pigment in human skin
   b. noncancerous
   c. a cancer originating in the cells of the bone marrow
   d. a disease in which abnormal cells multiply out of control, and spread into surrounding tissues and other body parts
   e. broccoli, brussels sprouts, cauliflower, and cabbages
   f. cancers that arise in the skin, body chamber linings, or glands

RECALLING IMPORTANT FACTS AND IDEAS

1. What is the number one type of cancer in both men and women?
2. List six steps in the development of cancers.
3. How do alcohol and tobacco work together to promote cancer?
4. Name two cancer-causing factors people can control.
5. What types of cancers are most common in smokers?
6. What is the most common type of skin cancer?

7. Why is indoor tanning considered dangerous?
8. What precautions should people take to avoid dangerous overexposure to the sun?
9. Where does man-made radiation come from?
10. What types of meats contain carcinogens?
11. Why do sedentary people tend to suffer from colon cancer?
12. What are the early symptoms of leukemia?
13. When is a person considered to be cured of cancer?

486

7. Sunlamps and tanning booths bombard the skin with UV radiation, making the cancer risks as high as those from sunbathing.
8. sunscreen with at least 15 SPF, hats
9. medical and dental X rays, above-ground nuclear weapons testing anywhere on the earth
10. meats that have been cured, smoked, charbroiled, or burned
11. Sedentary people often suffer from constipation. The stools may contain carcinogenic material, and the longer they stay in the colon, the more the chance of their changing the cells of the colon's lining.
Section III
12. Acts like an infection, with fever, lethargy, and other flulike symptoms; may also include bone pain, tendency to bruise or bleed easily, and enlargement of lymph nodes.
13. when every cancer cell is either removed from the body or wiped out by treatments
Straight Talk
14. asparagus, broccoli, carrots, green onions, greens, lettuce (dark green), oriental cabbages, parsley, spinach, squash (hard, winter), sweet potatoes
15. eat a wide variety of fresh foods; limit fats; choose foods with fiber, and choose fresh vegetables often, especially cruciferous and carotene-rich ones

14. What types of vegetables are the best sources of carotene?

15. What is the best way to get all the nutrients and nonnutrients that may be protective against cancer?

CRITICAL THINKING

1. Attitudes about cancer have undergone changes over the years. In recent years a number of famous people, including former President Reagan and first lady Nancy Reagan have been treated for cancer. Many of these cases have received much attention in the media. Do you think this has had a positive effect on the public's attitude toward cancer? Why or why not? What could be the drawbacks of so much public attention?

2. Many public places now ban smoking in common areas. Do you think the health benefits justify this restriction? Why or why not? Do you feel that these laws infringe on the rights of the individual? Why or why not? What other restrictions would you place on smoking?

ACTIVITIES

1. Interview someone from the American Cancer Society to obtain the following information: current cancer research topics, hopes for a cancer cure, most recent treatments, and the kind of service the American Cancer Society offers to cancer patients and their families. Include the name and title of the person you interviewed. Hand in a written report of your findings or an audio tape of your interview.

2. Design an educational pamphlet aimed at high school students to inform them about cancer.

3. Keep a log for five days of all the lifestyle and environmental risk factors for cancer to which you are exposed. For each risk factor listed, identify how you could reduce your risk.

4. Create a poster board chart with the following columns: type of cancer, high-risk groups, warning signs. Choose five different types of cancer and fill in the columns with the appropriate information for each.

5. Contact a local hospice organization and make arrangements to interview a nurse, doctor, or volunteer who works there. Write a one-page report that summarizes the person's experiences with cancer at the facility.

6. Write a short report on the measures used to protect workers in a high-risk industry such as asbestos removal or nuclear power plant operation. You can obtain information from newspaper and magazine articles or from someone that works in the industry.

7. Make a poster of your own illustrations to depict common myths that are associated with getting cancer.

8. Choose one of the following cancer screening or treatment methods: thermography, immunotherapy, or CT scan. Research the method you have chosen and write a brief report on it.

MAKING DECISIONS ABOUT HEALTH

1. Your friend's mother has just come from seeing a doctor who informed her that she has a lump in her breast that may be malignant. The doctor has recommended biopsy surgery in two days and requests that she sign a consent form prior to surgery that would allow him to perform an immediate mastectomy (breast removal operation), should the tumor be malignant. What do you think she should do? What factors should she take into consideration when deciding whether to follow the doctor's recommendation? How can she make sure she receives the best care possible without increasing her risk?

CHAPTER 20 PLANNER

OVERVIEW

Chapter 20 is 24 pages long and is divided into the three sections listed at the right. Major learning outcomes are also listed to the right. The chapter deals primarily with the issue of relationships. Section I allows the students to explore the differences between mature love and infatuation. Section II helps the students identify what to look for in a potential partner for a relationship. Students will discuss issues in dating, abstinence, and sexual pressures. The important elements for a successful partnership, as well as the stages in the development of a healthy relationship, are highlighted. Section III gives the students guidelines for dealing with conflict in a constructive manner. In the "Straight Talk," some very frank facts are given concerning date rape.

MAKING LIFE CHOICES RESOURCES

A variety of activities, handouts, quizzes, and tests to accompany this chapter are available in the *Making Life Choices* supplementary material. You may pick and choose from those materials as appropriate for your amount of class time and the ability levels of your students. Some of the resources you might want to consider using are:

Handouts
• What Is Your Capacity for Intimacy?
• Myths and Truths About Healthy Relationships
• Attributes I Consider Important in a Prospective Partner
• Writing a Marriage Contract

Teacher Information Sheet
• Relationship Compatibility

Answers to "Fact or Fiction"

See page 506 for answers to the "Fact or Fiction" questions.

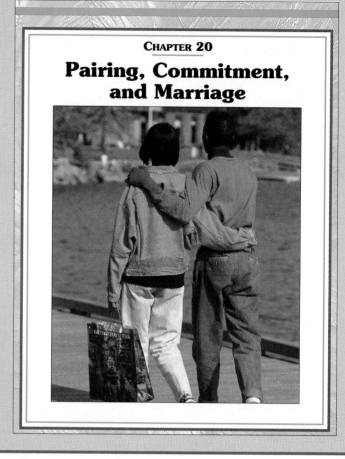

CHAPTER 20
Pairing, Commitment, and Marriage

CLASS PROJECT

Divide the class into the following subgroups:
• Two couples plan their weddings, including *all* costs.
• Two couples arrange their divorces, including costs and division of property according to your state's rules.
• Two couples are to be expecting a baby and develop all costs and activities involved in preparing for the baby. They must visit a maternity ward and birthing class.

Activity To Introduce Chapter

It is important to establish an environment that allows the students to ask questions and state their opinions. This activity will set the tone for open, frank discussions of the sensitive issues covered in this chapter. For this activity, use the Fact or Fiction questions. You may want to add the following questions:
1. Jealousy is never a part of mature love relationships.
2. Beginning a relationship with someone who is on the rebound is asking for trouble.
3. If two seniors have been in a close relationship for a year, continuing abstinence will ruin the relationship.
4. If a girl is dressed seductively, she's just "asking for it" if

---

• Two couples are moving from an apartment and are buying a house. They must show the differences in costs and savings, and research what is involved in buying a house. They must go to an open house and interview a realtor.

The couples will report their findings to the class. This can be expanded to the point of having a "fake wedding" take place in class!

---

she gets raped.

Ask students to answer the questions honestly, then discuss in class as many as time permits. As you discuss each question, ask how many said *True* and how many said *False*. Then ask students to volunteer their reasons for their answers. Do not say that any of the answers are right or wrong—leave each question open-ended. When you are finished, tell the students that these topics will be covered in this chapter and that they should check their answers again at the end of the chapter to see if their opinions have changed.

NOT ENOUGH TIME?*

It would be easy to spend two weeks discussing relationships and marriage and it would be recommended that you try to spend several days on this unit. However, it's more likely that you'll have only a few days to spend on this chapter. The following is a suggestion for a three-day unit.

TIME	SUGGESTIONS
1 Day	Assign Sections I and II prior to beginning the unit. On day 1 do Activity 1.1 to initiate a discussion on relationships. Follow this up with Activity 2.7. Have a prepared handout with all the information from this activity ready to give the students at the end of class. They are to review it for the next day.
2 Days	On day 2 begin with Activity 2.4. Then begin a discussion on the major points of Section II. The discussion should cover the important factors necessary for a successful relationship. Assign Section III to be read for the following day.
3 Days	On day 3 have a guest speaker come in to talk about violence in relationships and date rape. Be sure the person is prepared to give facts and guidelines for prevention. Or, have a marriage counselor come in to discuss major issues causing divorce and how to increase the chances for a successful marriage.

Please refer to the 18-week daily lesson plans in the supplementary material for additional suggestions.

SUGGESTED RESOURCES

Student Readings

1. Gordon, Sol. *Why Love Is Not Enough.* Boston: Bob Adams, Inc., 1988.
2. Harley, Willard F., Jr. *His Needs, Her Needs, Building an Affair-proof Marriage.* Old Tappan, NJ: Revell, 1986.

Teacher Readings

1. *He Says, She Says: Closing the Communications Gap Between the Sexes.* New York: G.P. Putnam Sons, 1992.
2. Knox, David. *Choices in Relationships.* St. Paul: West Publishing Co., 1985.
3. Cherlin, Andrew J. *Marriage, Divorce, Remarriage.* Cambridge: Harvard University Press, 1992.

In this section the students will learn the:

1. Difference between infatuation and mature love.
2. Role of psychological intimacy in a relationship.

Activity 1.1

Opinion Circle. You need a sponge ball for this activity. Before class begins, put five to seven statements on the board. You may develop your own or choose from the following:

1. "Love at first sight" can really happen.
2. For a relationship to last, there must be physical intimacy.
3. Teenagers don't really know how to be in a mature, loving relationship that can lead to commitment and marriage.
4. The most important qualities necessary in a healthy relationship are _____.
5. A person who is in a relationship with a chemically dependent person should _____.
6. In order to love someone else, you must love yourself first.
7. There are more advantages than disadvantages to sexual abstinence in a relationship.

Teacher Support Notes

① **Importance of Relationships:** Ask students if they agree with the statement that people who do not have close relationships will suffer poor mental and physical health more often than people who have such relationships. Without naming names, can they think of examples that support their opinions one way or the other?

✎ Fast Facts

In a study published in *Working Mother*, 53% of the wives surveyed said that their husbands were their best friends. This study is one of the first times that a majority of wives have said this. On the other hand, husbands have named their wives as best friends in studies since the 1960s.

All people need close relationships with others. It is important to share even simple daily life events with someone else. It is important to talk about problems and to voice and hear others' opinions. People who live without such relationships more often suffer poor mental and physical health than do people who maintain these relationships. ①

Loving, close relationships with family and friends are extremely important. It is not necessary, however, to have an exclusive, couples-type **love** relationship with a special person. Such relationships can be fulfilling, but much of a young person's self-growth and healthy development can be better achieved without such a relationship. Only when a person can focus energy inward can that person accept, improve, love, and nurture the self. Some relationships that are not loving, or that are abusive, can even destroy emotional health and interfere with personal growth.

People spend much time and effort looking for love relationships. This is as it should be, since love relationships can enhance or detract from life and emotional health. A force so powerful in life is worth exploring. This chapter looks at relationships from dating through commitment. It explores both the rewards and the problems of the relationships of couples.

LYNDON WAS INFATUATED WITH THE FAMOUS FEMALE HOCKEY PLAYER, PATTY "THE HACKER" BOODROU...

Infatuation is an excited state, and thrives on illusion.

alone. Take a look at Figure 20–1 to find some clues.

It is natural to feel infatuation at times, especially in the teen years, when the feelings of attraction are brand new. Infatuation can be part of learning about love. Some relationships that begin as infatuation later develop into love. However, relationships built solely on infatuation usually do not work out well. They usually end when the fantasies on which they are built fade away.

Unlike infatuation, **mature love** is a strong affection for, and an enduring, deep attachment to, a person whose character the partner knows well. The person accepts and tolerates the partner's negative qualities. Mature love involves a *decision* to be

SECTION I

Infatuation or Mature Love?

The first step in learning how to have a strong, close love relationship is learning what one is. "Am I really in love, or is this just **infatuation**?" If you have ever asked yourself this question, you're not

Love is an honest state and thrives on clear vision.

Have the class sit in a circle, then give the following directions:

1. This is an activity based on listening to each other's opinions.
2. Only the person holding the ball can speak. Once that person is done, the ball is passed to someone whose hand is raised.
3. Whoever goes first chooses the first topic to either answer or agree/disagree with it. Stay on that topic until all who want to speak on that topic have had a chance. *Then* someone can change the topic.
4. There is no such thing as a wrong opinion. Everyone is entitled to his or her opinion. When someone disagrees with it, he/she is *not* attacking the person, just the opinion.
5. Once we've covered the topics, you have the right to create a new topic with the teacher's approval.

After the activity, it is important to discuss the purpose: 1. It promotes great listening skills. 2. It allows us to speak our opinions and hear both similar and different opinions. 3. It helps us reaffirm or change our opinions on various topics. 4. It introduces several topics covered in this chapter. **(20 min. to full class period, Critical Thinking)**

Infatuation	Mature Love
Usually occurs at beginning of relationship	Develops gradually through learning about person
Sexual attraction is central	Sexual attraction is present but warm affection/friendship is central
Characterized by urgency, intensity, sexual desire, and anxiety	Characterized by calmness, peacefulness, empathy, support, and tolerance of partner
Driven by excitement of being involved with a person whose character is not fully known	Driven by deep attachment; based on extensive knowledge of both positive and negative qualities
Extreme absorption in another	Wanting to be together without obsession
Insecurity, distrust, lack confidence; feel threatened	Security, trust, confidence, unthreatened feeling
Nagging doubts and unanswered questions, partner remains unexamined so as not to spoil the dream	Thorough knowledge of partner exists; mature acceptance of imperfections
Based on fantasy	Based on reality
Consuming, often exhausting	Energizing in a healthy way
Low self-esteem (looking to partner for validation and affirmation of self-worth)	High self-esteem (each person has sense of self-worth with or without partner)
Each needs the other to feel complete	Relationship enhances the self, but person can feel complete without relationship
Discomfort with individual differences	Individuality accepted
Each often tears down or criticizes the other	Each brings out best in partner; relationship is nurturing
Partners need to rush things, like sex or marriage; sense of urgency so as not to lose partner	Partners are patient, no need to rush the events of relationship, sense of security, no fear of losing partner
One is threatened by other's individual growth	Each encourages other's growth
Relationship not enduring, because it lacks firm foundation	Relationship is enduring, sustaining—based on strong foundation of friendship

Figure 20–1 Is It Love or Just Infatuation?

MINI GLOSSARY

love: affection, attachment, devotion.
infatuation: the state of being completely carried away by unreasoning passion or attraction; addictive love.
mature love: a strong affection for, and an enduring, deep attachment to, a person whose character the partner knows well.
intimacy: being very close and familiar, as in relationships involving private and personal sharing.

devoted to a person. It also requires psychological **intimacy**. This is *not* the same thing as sexual intimacy, as you will see.

Intimacy is probably the most important part of a love relationship. Intimacy builds slowly as two people become familiar with, and close to, each other. Two intimate people reveal, a little at a time, the parts of

Teacher Support Notes

① **Infatuation vs. Mature Love:** After students have studied this figure, have them close their books. Ask a student to state one of the characteristics, either from mature love or infatuation, without designating it as one or the other. Then ask for volunteers to tell whether that characteristic is one of mature love or infatuation and to give the corresponding characteristic for the other category. For example, a student says "based on reality." The volunteer would say that this is a characteristic of mature love and that the corresponding characteristic of infatuation is "based on fantasy." Continue the exercise until all of the characteristics have been identified.

Activity 1.2

Mature Love. Ask the students to quietly review the list of qualities for mature love in the book. As they look at each quality, they are to ask themselves if that quality has been part of their relationships. Ask them to ask themselves why

not. Stress that each person deserves the best in a relationship. What will they settle for in a relationship? **(15 min., Critical Thinking)**

Activity 1.3

Psychological Intimacy. Ask the students to think about the word *intimacy*. Then ask them how many immediately thought of something physical. State that although physical intimacy can be a part

of a lasting relationship, *psychological intimacy* is more important. Then ask them to describe aloud psychological intimacy. Once they have described it, ask if they agree that it is more important than physical intimacy. Stress the correlation between psychological intimacy and best friends. **(15 min.; Extend, Enrich)**

Teacher Support Notes

① **Handout—Capacity for Intimacy:** Your supplementary material contains the student activity entitled "What is Your Capacity for Intimacy?" This activity sheet will help students evaluate whether or not they are able and willing to be psychologically intimate. You may want to distribute the activity after students have completed Section I.

Section I Review

Answers

1. **a.** mature love **b.** love **c.** intimacy **d.** infatuation
2. They usually end when the fantasies on which they are built fade away.
3. Answers may vary; could include: it builds trust as two people share both the bad and good things of themselves that they do not share with others; it causes people to be able to be open and trusting with each other; intimacy provides the basis for a relationship to develop naturally.
4. Physical, or sexual, intimacy can be available right away, while psychological intimacy takes time to grow.
5. Answers will vary.

492

---

492   UNIT 6   The Life Cycle

Learning to love begins with early fantasies.

themselves that they keep hidden from others. They share both the parts they are proud of, and those they are ashamed of. Both people are open and trusting with each other.

Before people can become intimate, both must feel that, even with their faults honestly displayed, they are worthy of love. That is, they must have high self-esteem and feel good about themselves.

Intimacy takes time to develop. There is no such thing as "instant intimacy." You can have instant hot chocolate or fast food, but not instant intimacy. Intimacy develops slowly.

The idea that some things must develop slowly seems foreign to people in our fast-paced society. So most times, they rush relationships. They may make the mistake of

trying to substitute physical, sexual intimacy, which can be available right away, for psychological intimacy, which takes time to grow. This doesn't work. Time, along with open sharing, permits a relationship to develop in its natural stages, as described in the next section.

> **Key Points** ① *Infatuation is an all-consuming desire for a partner. It is based on fantasy and is often mistaken for love. Mature love is a strong attachment to someone a person knows very well. It is based on psychological intimacy.*

SECTION I   REVIEW

Answer the following questions on a sheet of paper.

Learning the Vocabulary

The vocabulary terms in this section are *love, infatuation, mature love,* and *intimacy.*

1. Match each of the following phrases with the appropriate term.
   a. a strong affection for and an enduring deep attachment to a person
   b. affection, attachment, devotion
   c. being very close and familiar in a relationship
   d. the state of being carried away by unreasoning passion or attraction; addictive love

Learning the Facts

2. What is the problem with relationships built solely on infatuation?
3. Explain why intimacy is so important in a love relationship.
4. Describe the difference between physical intimacy and psychological intimacy.

Making Life Choices

5. After studying Figure 20–1, "Is It Love or Just Infatuation?", do you think most of your relationships are mature love or infatuation? Why do you think your relationships are this way? Do you think you should change your relationships? If so, how? Explain why it is difficult at your present age to experience mature love.

EVALUATE
SECTION I

Activity 1.4
Pop Quiz. Ask the students to write definitions of the following terms: *intimacy, mature love, infatuation.*

CLOSE
SECTION I

Activity 1.5
Relationship Essay. Ask each student to write an essay describing his/her perfect relationship. It may be one they have now or one they dream of having. They must include the qualities *they* deem are high priorities and also what they expect each person to bring into this ideal relationship. **(20 min., Critical Thinking)**

FOCUS
SECTION II

In this section the students will learn the:
1. Stages of a love relationship.

(continued on next page)

SECTION II

How to Develop a Healthy Relationship

No two relationships are exactly alike or develop in just the same way. However, healthy relationships have some things in common. First, each partner in a relationship must have a positive self-image. Once you feel strong and sure of yourself, you are better able to know what to look for in a partner.

Second, you should be aware, always, that love develops in stages, such as those listed in Figure 20–2. Love cannot be rushed. Once you find an appropriate partner, do not give in to the temptation to try

Love relationships usually follow these stages in their development.

Stage 1: Attraction
Something about the person catches your attention. You are attracted to each other.

Stage 2: Casual friendship
You and a person who interests you enjoy activities together. For example, you both may enjoy movies or ball games, and plan those activities together. During this stage, you explore each other's characteristics. Each is on "best behavior," so commitments are not appropriate yet.

Stage 3: Close friendship
As you spend more time together, you learn about each other's feelings and values. You begin to discover each other's emotional and spiritual tendencies. At this stage, the relationship may progress or retreat.

Stage 4: Intimate friendship
The friends reveal their faults. They let down their masks of best behavior, and reality sets in. By this time each trusts the other's acceptance, because the true self of each—complete with faults—has been seen by the other. The couple may decide to "go steady," or may relax back to being close friends.

Stage 5: Mature love
In this stage all of the initial hurdles are past. Each partner continues developing socially, intellectually, emotionally, and spiritually. The degree of closeness of mature love makes conflict likely, but the partners learn to resolve conflict in healthy ways. (The Health Strategies box "Constructive Conflicts," presented later, describes healthy ways of resolving conflicts.)

Figure 20–2 The Stages of a Love Relationship   ①

2. Ways to identify people who might be "available for love."
3. Advantages and disadvantages of dating and going steady.
4. Advantages of sexual abstinence.
5. Consequences of early sexual involvement.

6. Facts involved in external and internal sexual pressure.
7. Skills involved in developing a healthy, committed relationship.
8. Qualities necessary for a successful marriage.

Activity 2.1
Relationship Stages. Develop a small bulletin board with five building blocks designed like Figure 20–2. Put

numbers 1 through 5 on the top of the blocks (one number per block). On the sides, place the key words of that stage of a love relationship, but then cover them. *After* the students have been assigned this chapter to read, ask them to name *and* describe each stage. Start with block "1." Once a few have given answers, take off the covering. Discuss. Then do the next stage. Once all stages are uncovered, ask if they agree that these

---

Teacher Support Notes

① **Teacher Information Sheet—Relationship Compatibility:** In your supplementary material you will find a detailed explanation of the Meyers–Briggs Type Indicator and how the four basic temperaments used in this assessment relate to compatibility and relationships. You may find this information interesting and useful prior to discussing compatibility with students.

② **Checking for Compatibility:** Before they read this passage, ask students to list factors that should be considered in evaluating compatibility. How do their lists compare with the factors listed here? Which of these factors would they add to their own lists? Why?

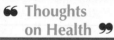
Thoughts on Health

There are people who would have never fallen in love if they had never heard of love.
–Francois de La Rochefoucauld

494

---

to "hurry things along" by skipping the early phases of development. These early times provide the foundation of a strong relationship later on. Be patient.

Key Points *Healthy intimate relationships grow in stages that shouldn't be rushed.*

What to Look for in a Partner   ①

In thinking about a person who interests you, make sure that the person has time and energy available for love. Such people:

- Are not involved in other love relationships.
- Are well over heartaches; have not just recently broken up with someone else.
- Are open to being in a relationship with you.
- Are free of chemical or psychological addictions. (People with addictions to alcohol or other drugs, people who gamble, or people with eating disorders cannot function well in love relationships.)
- Have time to devote to a relationship.
- Have high self-esteem.
- Are close to you geographically—they live in your city or state.

In addition, the person must be compatible with you in terms of social values and beliefs. To evaluate these factors, see if you can honestly answer yes to the following questions: ②

- *Does the person have several close friends?* A person who has learned to keep and enjoy close friendships can put this talent to work in a love relationship.
- *If the relationship folded, would you still want that person as a friend?* Without friendship, the relationship may crumble during times of conflict.
- *Are you happy with the way the person treats other people?* Watch how the person deals with school employees, waitresses, maids, sales clerks, parking-lot attendants,

telephone operators, and close friends. If you wouldn't want to be on the receiving end of that behavior, don't get involved. You may be an exception during courtship, but you won't be later on.

You can be friends with people who lack these qualities, but beware of deeper relationships until these problems are resolved.

Also, be sure that *you* are available for a relationship. For example, suppose you baby-sit, study, work at an after-school job, hold offices in clubs, and volunteer in the community. You may be too busy at the moment to give a relationship the time and energy it needs to grow.

Key Points *Some people are available for relationships, but others are not. Choose carefully.*

Dating

Single people of all ages like to **date**—that is, to enjoy leisure activities with other people to get to know them better. In the later half of the teen years, dating takes on more importance, while peer groups lose some of their appeal. Teens can be said to move from cliques to couples, as peer groups loosen their grip and couples begin to pair off.

While dating may be fun, it is not entirely free of stress. A couple's first date, for example, may lead to thoughts of self-doubt and worry that the person may not like you. Those are normal thoughts and feelings. Don't let them discourage you from dating. The person who practices assertive behavior and maintains high self-esteem stands to gain much from dating others. Most dates are fun—or at least not disastrous. And those who date learn how to communicate with many different types of people.

An especially useful form of dating is a double date in which two couples go to-are equally important steps in the development of a solid relationship. Stress how often people skip these stages because they are in a hurry to create and have an intimate relationship, and that it is because these stages are skipped that the relationship fails. **(15–20 min.; Reteach, Reinforce, Special Needs)**

Activity 2.2
Love Puzzle. On another part of the bulletin board have a large circle drawn with eight puzzle pieces sketched in. (Have a copy of this eight-piece puzzle made and cut into eight pieces.) Above the circle write, "Who's Available for Love?"

On the eight pieces you have cut out, list the qualities necessary for someone to be available. (page 494) Put them *all* into question form and add the following as #8: "Is the person compatible with you in social values and beliefs?" There should be one question per puzzle piece.

Begin the lesson by reminding students to keep an open mind about their past, present, and future relationships. Ask for eight volunteers who are comfortable explaining who/what makes a good potential partner in a relationship. Shuffle the puzzle pieces and hand them out. Ask students to take turns tacking them on the

(continued on next page)

TEEN VIEWS

What's the hardest part of dating? ①

Finding the person who best compliments my personality. I look for fun-loving people who want to have a good time without risking their health or happiness. I also look for people who possess confidence and self-pride. It is much easier to date someone if you have developed a friendship with them first. Many people put up facades to gain acceptance. You have to see through these walls and find the true person behind them. **Kelley Cloutier, 17, Orange Park High School, FL**

Being pushed or pressured into sex. The longer you date someone, the harder it gets to resist. Sometimes, the guy expects it, and that's not right. With sex comes more mental, social, and emotional problems. **Kristi Aylor, 17, Robert E. Lee High School, TX**

The hardest part is when you have to meet the family. The father is the hardest to deal with. He's going to talk with you and ask you all sorts of questions about whether or not you have a job or if you're still in school. **Render Godfrey, 17, Newman High School, GA**

Trying to impress my date, while at the same time trying not to give him the wrong impression. **Andrea Bell, 15, Westside High School, NE**

Meeting expectations from your friends, your girlfriend, and your parents. Your friends put pressure on you to "score" when you go out with your girlfriend. Your girlfriend puts pressure on you to act like a gentleman and be fun. Your parents put pressure on you to wait until you're an adult to have a sexual relationship. **Terrence Williams, 16, Poughkeepsie High School, NY**

gether. This creates a casual and safe environment in which to check out people whom you do not know well. A sad fact is that many rapes each year occur in dating situations (see this chapter's Straight Talk). Double dating provides safety and reduces stress. With four people talking and having fun, it's not hard to feel at ease.

People of both sexes may feel uncertain about the "proper" way to date. Who should ask the other out? Who should phone? Who should pay? In years past, the rules of dating were rigid. Today, though, these rules are more relaxed. The best approach may be one that fits in with the values both people developed at home.

It is natural to feel nervous when going out with someone for the first time. However, try to remember that even if this date doesn't go well, there will be many others in the future. The best way to ensure that a date will go well is to be open to the possibility that you will be forming a friendship, not a lifelong relationship. Pos-

MINI GLOSSARY

date: a social event designed to allow people to get to know one another. A double date (two couples) is a safe arrangement for early dates with people you do not know well.

Teacher Support Notes

① **Teen Views Follow-up Questions:** Following are some questions you may want to use to encourage discussion of the ideas expressed by the students in the Teen Views feature:

a. Is it more common to date someone with whom you've already established a friendship or someone you do not know as well? Why?

b. Do students believe that most people do put up a facade, as Kelley Cloutier does, when they first date someone new? How long before they are able to be "themselves?"

c. Do students agree that the longer two people date, the harder it is to resist the sexual pressure? Is it always the male, rather than the female, who exerts this pressure?

d. Do students agree with Terrence Williams, that, for the most part, dating involves a great deal of pressure? Is the enjoyment of dating worth the pressure they must endure?

board and reading and explaining that part to the class. Once all eight are put up, ask the whole class for examples of when one of these was not there and the relationship failed. (Example: I went out with someone who was on the rebound and I ended up being his/her stepping stone. His/Her next relationship *after* me worked!)

Reminder: No names should ever be given when discussing experiences.

In closing, put up the three final questions (italicized questions on 494) around the circle—stressing the importance of each. Finally, remind the students that these questions *all* apply to themselves in determining if they are ready for a relationship. **(Full class period, Critical Thinking)**

TEACH
SECTION II
(Guided and Independent Practice)

Activity 2.3
Questionnaires. Divide the class, boys on one side, girls on the other. Hand out a questionnaire (sample at the end of this activity) explaining that they are to fill

---

Fast Facts

In a *Chicago Sun Times* poll, 80% of American men said they would marry the same women if they had to make the decision again. Only 50% of the women said they would marry the same men.

Teacher Support Notes

① **Handout—Healthy Relationships:** For enrichment, your supplementary material contains a handout for students entitled "Myths and Truths About Healthy Relationships."

② **Meeting New People:** Ask students for suggestions to add to this list of ways to meet new people. After you have a complete list, ask them to rate the strategies from most likely to be effective to least likely. Which strategies do most students think will be most effective?

66 Thoughts on Health 99

Love does not consist in gazing at each other but in looking together in the same direction.
– Antoine de Saint-Exupéry

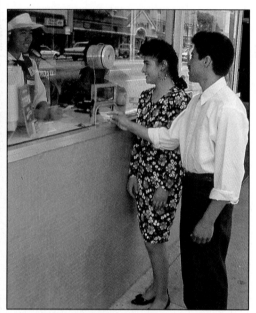

Dating is a good way to start getting to know somebody.

sibly the best way of learning how to date is not through dating at all, but through attending social gatherings in group settings. Check the Health Strategies section on this page, "Meeting New People," for some ideas on expanding your possibilities.

Some who have dated for a while decide to go steady or become a couple with a favorite date. Going steady has some advantages, such as relief from the stress of dating new people and freedom from the worry of not having a date for important occasions. However, it brings many disadvantages as well. While young people who go steady may feel secure, they may also feel tied down. They lose the opportunity to date a variety of others. They also may focus on the growth of the steady relationship instead of on their own growth. If preserving the pair becomes more important than the emotional health of the individu-

als, this can lead to diminished self-esteem.

Another disadvantage of going steady is sexual pressure. This topic will be discussed at length later in this chapter. Sexual pressure may be especially strong when two people who are attractive to one another spend all their spare time together.

Another pressure may come into play: false feelings of responsibility for another person's sexual pressures. Many times teens

---

HEALTH **S**TRATEGIES

Meeting New People

These suggestions are just a few out of dozens you can use to meet new people. Once you start thinking along these lines, you'll come up with many more ideas of your own.

1. Join a youth group (try religious and service clubs or a school activity).
2. Take up a hobby, such as dancing or collecting baseball cards. Attend meetings with others who share the same interest.
3. Create a group around a common theme—for example, a foreign language group or a comedy video group.
4. Learn to play a sport after school. Play on, or watch, local teams. Be a fan.
5. Volunteer time in an organization you believe in, such as the American Cancer Society or Habitat for Humanity.
6. Learn to play a musical instrument, and join a school or community band or orchestra.
7. Get physically fit and attend to nutrition and sleep needs. High-level wellness gives you the energy you need for leisure activities.

these out honestly *without* putting their names on the sheets. They may put a code name on the top if they wish. Once they are finished, collect the boys' sheets and give them to the girls and vice versa. Explain that the purpose of this activity is to see the point of view of the opposite gender and to have the opportunity to ask each other questions about likes, dislikes, expectations, etc. Once both sides have had a chance to read the sheets, the teacher, as moderator, begins the discussion by

asking who has a comment or question about something on the sheets. Once that issue has been discussed, the other side brings up a point, and so on. Near the end of class begin to summarize by asking each side: **1.** What surprised them? **2.** What bothered them? **3.** What have they learned? **(One class period or more!)**

 Sample Questionnaire
1. One thing that puzzles me about

guys/girls is _____.
2. One trait I find attractive in a guy/girl is _____.
3. One trait that turns me off in a guy/girl is _____.
4. If only guys/girls would _____.
5. If I could ask guys/girls one question, it would be _____.
6. What I fear the most in a relationship is _____.

(continued on next page)

---

will fear that if they refuse **sexual intercourse**, their partners will go with someone else. In fact, it may be that the partner would agree to **abstinence** from sexual intercourse, and take pride in that choice. If not, this probably indicates a serious flaw in the relationship where the values of the partners would appear to conflict.

①

> **Key Points** *Possibly the best way of learning how to date is not through dating at all, but through attending social gatherings in a group setting. Going steady has some advantages and disadvantages.*

Advantages of Sexual Abstinence

Some high school students say that it seems as if everyone around them has become sexually active. The reality is, that only some teens become sexually active before leaving high school. Those who do become involved sexually often find that it can interrupt the normal growth of a relationship. Immature partners may focus on sexual activity but neglect their intellectual, emotional, social, and spiritual growth.

Sexual activity can cloud a person's judgment. A relationship that is unhealthy or abrasive, but meets sexual needs, can be more difficult to end than a friendship gone bad. Becoming sexually involved is a way of declaring to the world your choice of a mate. Should a relationship end, the loss can bring public criticism, as well as distress.

Early sexual involvement can also cause distrust. If a partner becomes sexually involved easily, doubts arise about the person's values and ability to be faithful. Self-control is a necessary quality, if a person is to move his or her life in the desired direction.

Teenage sexual activity is a concern not just for teens, but for everyone in our society. Sexual intercourse poses risks. Teens who are sexually active often suffer sexually transmitted diseases and have become a

fast-growing risk group for infection with the AIDS virus.

A famous research group, the Alan Guttmacher Institute, reports, "Each year one-quarter of the sexually active women between 15 and 19 seek treatment for a sexually transmitted disease." This figure includes only those who seek treatment. Many more suffer infections and fail to be treated. The only sure way to prevent sexually transmitted diseases is to abstain from sexual activity.

Teen pregnancy is another national tragedy. The effects on the lives of both the girl and the boy can be enormous. Here are some of the frequent and serious problems resulting from teen pregnancies:

- Interruption of education.
- Early marriages with a high likelihood of divorce.
- Continuing legal responsibility to support a child.
- High risks of poverty.
- Low infant survival rates.
- Overall tendencies toward higher numbers of births.

② The costs to society in terms of lost education, lost earning power, and increased need for support of the individuals is staggering.

MINI GLOSSARY

sexual intercourse: the reproductive act between the sexes. The term *intercourse* means communication of any kind—talking, for example. Sexual intercourse between human beings is termed *coitus* (CO-ih-tus). Between animals it is termed *copulation* (cop-you-LAY-shun).

abstinence: refraining from sexual intercourse (or other behavior, such as smoking or drinking).

Teacher Support Notes

① **Conflicting Values:** Ask students if they agree with the basic idea stated here, that one partner's insistence on having sexual relations indicates a serious flaw in the relationship. Do students agree, or do they think that the two people could be perfectly matched for each other in every way and have only this one basic difference? In other words, could this one difference of opinion separate two people who otherwise might become lifelong partners?

② **Society's Cost:** For class discussion, ask students if people should take society into consideration when they're making decisions about whether or not to engage in sexual intercourse. If a person won't abstain for one's own good, is it possible the person might abstain for the good of society? Should unmarried teen parents be required to repay in some way the cost that the pregnancy has created?

7. When I think of a healthy relationship, I imagine _____.
8. The most important quality I want in a relationship is _____.

Activity 2.4
Advantage/Disadvantage Circles.

Draw two *large* circles on the board. In the middle of one, put the word *abstinence*. In the middle of the other, put the words *sexual intercourse*. Ask volunteers to go up to the circles and write in the circles either advantages or disadvantages of each one. Allow them to continue until all who want to participate have done so. Then begin with the circle on sexual intercourse and read aloud all the statements. Ask students if they'd like to add any.

Then either add or stress the major disadvantage points such as: **1.** The spread of diseases; **2.** Pregnancy; **3.** Can ruin reputation; **4.** Can ruin relationship.

Now go to the abstinence circle and repeat the process. Stress that if a person says *no* and the other person *stays* in the relationship, the relationship probably has a solid foundation. **(20 min.; Extend, Enrich)**

---

66 Thoughts on Health 99

First love is only a little foolishness and a lot of curiosity.
–George Bernard Shaw

Teacher Support Notes

① **Abstinence and Intimate Relationships:**
Ask if engaging in abstinence would promote a healthy intimate relationship rather than detract from it. Would this always be the case or would it vary from one relationship to another? Would any students argue against the proposition that postponing sexual intercourse will in *all* cases promote a longer lasting, healthier, more intimate relationship?

② **Sexual Activity:** Ask students to write on a slip of paper what they believe is the percentage of students at your school who engage in sexual intercourse before they graduate. Write the results on the board showing the range of the responses and the most frequent responses. Then ask students what information they used in making their estimates. How reliable is this information?

Again, abstinence from sexual intercourse is the only guarantee against teen pregnancy.

Few teenagers are mature enough to develop lasting and committed sexual relationships. For teens, as for many others, sexual abstinence can create a feeling of freedom. Abstinence allows teens to grow and develop without interruption by diseases or pregnancy. Abstinence also allows time for the growth of a healthy intimate relationship. Thus, for reasons of both emotional and physical health, abstinence is becoming more popular than ever before in this century. ①

> **Key Points** *Abstinence is necessary for a new relationship to grow in a healthy way. Early sexual involvement can prevent personal growth of the partners and carries serious risks to health and life goals.*

How to Cope with Sexual Pressures

You often hear people talk about the "pressures" to have sexual intercourse. They ② focus on peer pressure, pressures from images of sexiness in the movies, in popular music, and on TV, or the pressure from a partner who wants to have intercourse. Another source of pressure comes in the form of product advertisements (see the Consumer Awareness box in this chapter). All of these **external pressures** can be difficult to deal with.

Even more difficult to deal with are pressures that come from inside. Human beings have a natural, biological drive to reproduce. This normal drive builds up **internal pressures** that can be hard to deal with. During the teen years these pressures can be especially intense and can be equally strong in people of both sexes.

People with healthy self-esteem don't allow others to bully or convince them to do things they do not wish to do. All of the ideas on resisting peer pressure first presented in the Straight Talk of Chapter 3 apply here.

A psychologically intimate relationship is most fulfilling.

Activity 2.5

Walls of Indecision. This activity will need advanced preparation by students. Ask one guy and one girl to volunteer to be, in a role-play, boyfriend and girlfriend in a six-month relationship. Divide the class equally into four groups with the following tasks:

Group 1: This group will develop internal pressures as to why the two should have sex. The members of this group will be the couple's internal voices saying why they should do it. They will argue with Group 2.

Group 2: This group will develop internal pressures to *not* have sex. They will be the behavior control voices of the couple—their consciences. They will argue with Group 1.

Group 3: This group will develop the external pressures that might influence the two to have sex. They may bring in media props. They will argue with Group 4.

Group 4: This group will develop a defense against external pressures for sex. They will analyze the motives of the media and use reasonings as to why the two should *not* be influenced by others. They will argue with Group 3.

Day 1 (Friday): The groups are formed and given their tasks and directions. They may research in class using their

(continued on next page)

The real problem of abstaining from sexual intercourse is not the battle with the wills of other people. Instead, it is the battle between a person's conscious will and the person's own biological drives. This is the meaning of the phrase *will power*—the power of exerting your own will over any other force, even that of your own basic drives.

The internal drive to have sexual relations is a fact of life for almost all sexually mature people. Teens may find the drive especially hard to handle, because it is new to them. They may even confuse feelings of the sex drive and those of love. People often want to express sexual feelings, especially when they fall in love.

The challenge to couples who are not yet mature and committed is to find ways of expressing love and sexual feelings so that both people benefit. Any activity that makes the other person feel loved, and that takes some extra thought or effort on the part of the giver, is satisfying for both. Think of how you felt the last time a friend gave you a hug, gave you a small gift, did you a favor, or confided in you. The good feelings those gestures brought were a genuine form of love. You can express your love in all sorts of caring ways without having sexual intercourse.

To express sexual feelings in appropriate ways, it is necessary to decide *in advance* what course of action is right for you. People who approach a situation without a clearly determined plan may find themselves tempted to "throw caution to the wind," just for the thrill of a moment. People who tend to seek out excitement—**thrill seekers**—must fight especially hard against these temptations.

To cope with strong sexual desires, it helps to channel the sexual energy into other activities. Instead of using will power to oppose the sexual drive, use it to shift gears to another activity. Dancing, sports, walking, or other activities requiring movement can release sexual energy. Some people feel that writing, speaking, singing, painting, or other expressive activities can also serve this purpose.

When a situation threatens to get out of control, some find it helpful to say mentally to themselves the word *STOP—Stop, Think, Other* activities, *Plan* to abide by your vow of abstinence (see Figure 20–3 on the next page). That way, they never have to look back and say, "I don't know why. It just happened." Sexual intimacy is too important to just let happen. Remember STOP, to give yourself time to think.

> **Key Points** *Pressure to have sexual intercourse arises both internally and externally. Internal pressures are hard to deal with. Doing so requires a preplanned strategy and will power.*

Breaking Up and How to Cope

More often than not, the relationships formed in early life break up. This is true for many reasons. Immature people may hide their true selves at first, only to discover that they cannot keep up a false act for long. Both partners end up resenting each other for being less than perfect in real life. It also happens that partners who are sincere but young may change and outgrow certain relationships. Most times, breakups

---

MINI GLOSSARY

external pressures: regarding sexual feelings, messages from society, peers, and others that pressure people to have sexual intercourse.

internal pressures: regarding sexual feelings, a person's internal biological urges toward having sexual intercourse.

thrill seekers: people who are especially likely to take chances in exchange for momentary excitement.

Teacher Support Notes

① **Willpower:** Ask students for examples of situations in which they used their willpower to overcome a drive for food, water, shelter, or safety, that for one reason or another, they did not want to give in to at that time. Do they apply this same willpower to their sexual drives?

② **Breakups of Early Relationships:** Ask students to poll older brothers and sisters to determine whether or not most high school romances matured into marriages and other long-term commitments, or have most of those relationships been dissolved? Have each student report back to class with the number of relationships identified and the number that have been maintained for a minimum of three years after high school.

textbooks or go to the library. You might bring in magazines to help with the research. Students will have the weekend to prepare. Each person in each group must have something to say. While the groups are working, you need to prepare the two role-players, explaining that they

are both wondering whether or not to "take the step." On Monday their thoughts will be spoken out loud as they walk through the "walls of indecision."

Day 2 (Monday): Groups 1 and 2 face each other, and Groups 3 and 4 face each other. The groups leave enough space for the couple to walk through. You should have prepared ahead an actual stop sign such as the one shown in Fig. 20–3. Instruct the couple to slowly walk through

the "walls of indecision" as each person gets a chance to speak "his/her case." The couple is to listen carefully to the "walls." When they finally get to the end, the teacher holds up the sign, STOP! The teacher asks the class to listen to the couple now as the teacher asks them: What was the most convincing argument they heard from the voices? What sticks in their minds? What decision is each leaning toward? Then ask the whole class,

---

66 Thoughts on Health 99

The sound of a kiss is not so loud as a cannon, but its echo lasts a great deal longer.
– **Oliver Wendell Holmes**

Teacher Support Notes

① **The STOP Method:** Ask students if they believe this strategy could help people maintain their abstinence from sexual intercourse. Ask them to develop one or two questions each that they would use in the think stage. Write all the questions on the board. If students are not sure what type of questions apply here, tell them they're looking for questions that would help them remember what's most important to them—questions that would help them see that what they're about to do may be something that they would regret later. You may also want students to develop a list of activities that they could have at hand to take the place of the sexual activity.

S—Stop. Stop the activity that threatens to get out of control. This first step may be difficult but is critical for remaining in control.

T—Think. Analyze what is happening. Does your present behavior agree with your values? Would your parents approve? Develop in advance a list of questions meaningful to you.

O—Other activities. If your behavior feels out of control—if it conflicts with your values— direct the energy of the moment into other activities (going out for ice cream or to a movie, for example).

P—Plan. Make the next time easier by planning how to remain in charge. Decide not to plan dates that involve too much time alone (for example, plan to double date or date in public places). Commit to using this method every time you begin to feel out of control.

Figure 20–3 The STOP Method for Maintaining Sexual Abstinence   ①

are best for both partners, although it may not feel that way at the moment.

While no one really dies of a broken heart, the pain, depression, and stress that can follow breaking up may make people physically ill. Stress weakens the immune system and so can make illness likely. The breakup of a special love relationship can be difficult to cope with. You feel lonely, rejected, and depressed. What do you do?

One thing you can do is to prepare to experience grief—whether for the loss of the loved one, or for loss of the fantasy of love. The Straight Talk section at the end of Chapter 22 presents the stages of grief to expect. Give yourself the time you need to grieve fully. It is natural and normal to feel intense loneliness and pain. However, those feelings fade with time. A Health Strategies section in Chapter 5, "Coping with Mild De-

"Whose decision and pressure is it really in the end?" *Each individual's.* Each person has the physical ability to say NO or YES. NO ONE, NOTHING makes them say it. Have everyone sit right where they are and then point to the stop sign. Go over each letter and what it stands for, stressing that each person must be absolutely sure before making such an important decision. This STOP method can help people deal with the internal and external pressures so that in the end the decision is made entirely by the individual. **(2 full days, Critical Thinking)**

Activity 2.6
Breaking Up. Role-play breaking up. Stress to each person the importance of taking ownership of his/her part in the breakup and how to have this happen with their heads held high. Stress that threats ("I'll kill myself if you leave me")

should not be given in to; that anger and accusation only push the person farther away; that promising to change for the person strips an individual of his/her pride, identity, and self-esteem. By accepting the breakup and admitting you felt it coming, you can be a part of ending it rather than having it done *to* you. Then ask if these two can be friends right away. The answer is usually NO—not for a

(continued on next page)

CONSUMER AWARENESS

Love and Sex in Advertisements

Most people want to be part of special love relationships. Advertisers use this desire for love to help sell their products. They try to make consumers think that certain products can make people more attractive, sexier, more self-confident, and therefore more likely to be loved. A certain brand of toothpaste claims, "Want love? Get our brand!" A chewing gum commercial shows two sets of physically beautiful twins getting to know one another over sticks of gum. A breath mint is sold as "social insurance." The ads say that you never know when you'll meet someone special, so why take a chance on having less-than-sweet breath?

Some advertisers even go beyond using the need for love. They capitalize on people's sexual feelings by using subconscious sexual suggestions to make using their products seem sexy. For example, a close

look at an image of a bottle in an ad for a certain brand of liquor reveals a shadowy figure of a nude woman within the bottle. The image is just clear enough for the subconscious mind to detect it, but not so clear as to be obvious.

Buying a product may be easier than working to improve self-esteem. However, the only way to become truly more attractive involves work—the work of developing self-esteem to a highly polished level.

① CRITICAL THINKING

1. *Name some characteristics of people who are influenced by advertisements that promise increased attractiveness. Why do you think people with these characteristics are most likely to be influenced?*

pression," offers tips that can help with the feelings of loss from a breakup.

A mistake a person may make during this painful time is to quickly seek a new partner. The temptation to do so may be strong, but resist it. You may not have vision clear enough to judge a new partner. Give yourself six months to a year to heal.

People in grief often need affection. Activities and friends can fill the void. When you feel like your old self again, you may be ready for a new relationship.

Key Points *When coping with a breakup, expect to feel grief. Avoid seeking a new partner too soon.*

Commitment

Anyone choosing to have a long-term **monogamous** relationship must do something extraordinary—make a **commitment**

MINI GLOSSARY

monogamous (mon-AH-ga-mus): a term describing relationships, especially marriage, in which the partners are sexually intimate with each other, but with no one else. These relationships are usually long-term relationships.
commitment: a decision to embark on a long-term monogamous relationship with another person, without a guaranteed outcome.

Teacher Support Notes

① **Answers to Critical Thinking:** Answers will vary, but students should see that one of the most important characteristics is low self-esteem. Other characteristics are a high value on social acceptance, inability to see through false claims, and a tendency to look for short-cuts and easy solutions to problems.

② **Being Patient:** Tell students that the unresolved grief from the past relationship will interfere with the ability to form a new one. Getting involved "on the rebound" will likely result in the breakup of the new relationship, thus creating *two* relationships to grieve about. Also, self-esteem is usually low at the time after a breakup, even for an emotionally healthy person. When self-esteem is low, people will likely be attracted to and attract new partners with low self-esteem to match.

501

while—they need to respect each other's right to grieve over the loss. Making contact with each other can only confuse the situation. **(20 min.; Extend, Enrich)**

Activity 2.7
Relationship Categories. Put

these four categories across the top of the board (or newsprint): *Infatuation, In Like, Dependency, In Love.* Divide the class into four groups, each with equal numbers of boys and girls. Ask the groups to brainstorm the qualities or symptoms for each category of relationships. (They will probably laugh at and question the "In Like.") Once the groups are finished, go over each category by allowing a spokesperson from each group

to take turns giving *one* symptom or quality. As one group speaks, check the other three groups to see if they agree. Be sure you have your own prepared lists of qualities that you want the students to know. Derive your "Infatuation" and "In Love" lists from the chapter. Some characteristics for "In Like" are: buddies, no strings attached, convenient, better than nothing, casual sex may or may not be involved, no excitement, no commitment, no future,

---

❝ Thoughts on Health ❞

True love is like ghosts, which everyone talks about and few have seen.
–Francois de La Rochefoucauld

Teacher Support Notes

① **Self-Sufficiency:** Students may have a difficult time seeing how important it is to devote attention to the self in order to develop a healthy relationship with someone else. Ask them if they can think of reasons why the more self-esteem and self-sufficiency a person exhibits, the stronger that person's relationships will be with others. (Some reasons are that the person will be more able to compromise; the person will be more open and direct and not have to pretend or cover up feelings and ideas; and the person will tend to have fewer feelings of insecurity, doubt, and jealousy about the partner—all of which can lead to problems in a relationship.)

---

502 UNIT 6 The Life Cycle

to another person. A commitment is a promise to make a long-term choice, in the face of many possible options, with the knowledge that all will not always go well. Some think that commitment is the highest form of maturity in relationships.

Choosing a life partner is a tricky business. Many people choose wrongly. Developing a long-term, intimate bond that truly satisfies both partners involves much more than simply loving each other, the wish to do so, or stating that such a bond exists.

What *does* hold a partnership together? Psychologist Carl Rogers put it this way: "We each commit ourselves to working together on the changing process of our present relationship, because that relationship is currently enriching our love and our life and we wish it to grow." Every word in

this statement is significant. Figure 20–4 shows what the words mean.

To this list of elements of partnership we would add *independence.* The person who finds ways to meet many of his or her own needs *outside* the paired relationship will be most successful at pairing. Recall the needs described in Maslow's scheme (Chapter 3). You cannot ask your partner to provide total security—whether emotional, financial, or physical. You must stand on your own feet and provide your own security. You, yourself, are the only person you will never lose. Understanding and practicing self-sufficiency is a major factor in maintaining healthy, lasting relationships.

Key Points ▶ *Love requires each partner to commit and work together, to accept change in the current relationship, and to be enriched by it.*

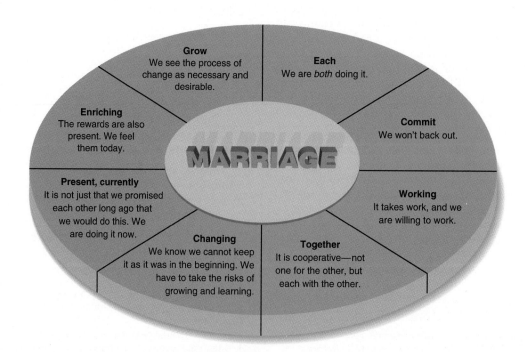

Figure 20–4 Elements of Partnership According to Rogers

a relationship where the romance has ended but neither wants to hurt the other, "fun to be around, so why not?"

Some characteristics for "dependency" are: "I need him/her for my own identity, security;" "No one else would want me so I'd better stick with him/her even if he/she does hit me;" "He/she *makes* me happy, he/she *makes* my life worth living." In a dependent relationship, jealousy is generally very high because both people have very low self-esteem and are very insecure. Thus, there are many rules in this relationship as to who can talk to whom and where each is allowed to go. Aggressive people tend to enter dependent relationships with passive people. Fighting and making up by having sex dominate the relationship, with very little conversation or fun with other couples. The two people dominate each other's lives.

You should stress that if the students see themselves in a relationship other than a love relationship, then it's up to them to decide if the relationship needs to *end* or *change*. They must have an open mind as to the realities of their relationships. **(one full period, Cooperative Learning)**

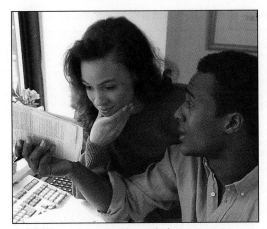

In a real marriage, people work things out.

Marriage

Did you ever wonder what happened to Cinderella and the Prince after they married? Did they really live happily ever after? The idea that **marriage** will magically make people happy is probably the most destructive idea that partners can have. Marriage is never the *end* of the story, as in fairy tales. It is the beginning.

The highest form of commitment between two people in our society is marriage, a relationship based on these ideas:

- The relationship is permanent, or at least permanence is something the partners will work for.
- The partners will be most important to one another. No other relationship with another person will take a higher place.

Before they marry, people would do well to look honestly at what they expect. One way to do this is to answer together the questions in this chapter's Life Choice Inventory. Clearly, it is essential to find out what a potential partner means when the word *marriage* comes up. The Health Strategies section on this page, "Developing a Healthy Intimate Relationship," sums up

---

> **HEALTH STRATEGIES**

Developing a Healthy Intimate Relationship

To establish a healthy intimate relationship:

1. Learn the difference between a healthy intimate relationship and infatuation.
2. Build your self-esteem.
3. Make sure your partner has time and energy for love. Make sure you do too.
4. Give yourself time to get to know new people socially, intellectually, emotionally, and spiritually.
5. Spend some of your free time alone with your partner and some with other friends. Maintain your identity.
6. Let the sexual involvement follow commitment in the relationship. Marriage is the highest form of commitment.
7. Know the meaning of commitment.
8. Explore your expectations of marriage.
9. Learn to work through conflict in healthy ways.

---

this chapter's points about developing healthy relationships. The next section gives tips on weathering disagreements within the relationship.

① **Key Points** Marriage is the highest form of commitment in our society.

② **MINI GLOSSARY**

marriage: the institution that joins a man and a woman by contract for the purpose of creating and maintaining a family.

Teacher Support Notes

① **Handout—Prospective Partner Attributes:** At this point you may want to distribute the activity in your supplementary material that asks students to describe the characteristics they consider important, first in a dating situation and then in a marriage partner.

② **Handout—Marriage Contract:** Your supplementary material contains an activity that calls for students to write a marriage contract. If you choose to use this activity, it is suggested that you use it as a follow-up to the Life Choice Inventory.

Activity 2.8

Key Words. Put a list of key words and terms on the board. Point to one and ask students what they remember from the reading and activities. Go over each one as a review. Some of the words and terms you could use are: *infatuation, mature*

love, dependent relationships, in like, intimacy, people available for relationships, abstinence, early sexual involvement, sexual pressures, breaking up, long-term commitment (marriage). **(20 min.)**

CLOSE
► SECTION II

Activity 2.9

Philosophical Chairs. Do an Agree/Disagree activity using statements on marriage. Read the statement. Students move to one side if they agree, and the other side if they disagree, then give their responses. People can switch sides if they wish. Some statements you might use are:

1. Marriage is the highest form of commitment in our society.

2. Living together before marriage can help prevent divorce by helping the couple

---

Teacher Support Notes

① **Will the Marriage Work?** Although most of your students are far from being ready to consider marriage seriously, they will probably enjoy speculating on their answers to the questions included here. Working their way through the inventory should also help them develop a better understanding of what a committed, long-term relationship is and how it differs from infatuation. An obvious category that was deleted from this inventory as it was adapted for high school students, is sexuality. Depending on the age and maturity level of your students, you may or may not want to give them the following questions about sexuality:

1. How often will each of us want to have sexual intercourse?

2. Would each person be willing to have intercourse if the other wants to do so? Can each express desire freely to the other?

3. Is nudity acceptable around the house?

4. Is it important to either partner how the other dresses?

5. Is it acceptable to each of us if the other flirts?

6. How much affection is appropriate in public?

LIFE CHOICE
INVENTORY

Will the Marriage Work? ①

Will the marriage work? Differences of opinion will pepper an otherwise bland relationship with challenges—but these differences can also destroy the relationship. It helps to know ahead of time where the major differences will be. The more of these questions the two people agree on, the more likely the marriage will work.

Money

1. Should both partners work? Should one stop working after children come?
2. Should we keep all our money in a shared bank account? If so, who should pay the bills?
3. What should the limits be on the use of credit cards?
4. Who decides on big purchases?
5. Should we follow a written budget?
6. If one of us wants to do something more rewarding personally than financially, will that be all right?
7. If one of our careers requires a move, will the other consider moving?
8. How much of our income should we save, invest, and spend on insurance?
9. Who will own the home, car, and other property? One of us? Both of us?

Children

1. Do we want to have children? How many? When?
2. Should children's needs be put before one of our needs?
3. How much money shall we save for, or spend on, the children's needs?
4. Who should discipline the children, when, and how?

In-Laws

1. How close is each of us to our families? Will it be important to see them frequently?

2. Is each of us willing to be advised by the other's parents?
3. Can we or should we accept financial help from our families? How much, for what, and from which family?

Religious Traditions

1. Are our religious beliefs similar? If not, can we each accept the other's beliefs?
2. Does either of us feel strongly that the other must attend religious services?
3. Should children be raised with particular religious beliefs?
4. Should religious practices be part of every day's routine? How will religious holidays be spent?
5. How much money, energy, or time should we spend on religious and charitable organizations?

Miscellaneous

1. Is profanity acceptable? Under what conditions?
2. Is alcohol drinking acceptable? If so, how much drinking? Will drinking in front of children be OK?
3. Is smoking acceptable? When and where?
4. Should both of us go to bed at the same time? Who should get up first?
5. Who should do the shopping? Who should choose major purchases, such as houses and automobiles?
6. Should each of us be willing to tell the other everything we think, feel, and do?

decide if they are right for each other.
3. Independence is a crucial element in marriage or any monogamous relationship.
4. Long-term, healthy relationships eventually become content and enjoyable when they stop growing and changing.
5. Relationships involve work and sacrifice.
6. If a person cheats on his or her partner, the relationship should end.
7. One partner should put his/her career

on hold to raise the children.
Wrap up this activity by reviewing the Elements of Partnership in Figure 20–4.
(20–40 min., Critical Thinking)

SECTION III

In this section the students will learn:
1. The difference between constructive and destructive conflicts.

2. Ten strategies used in constructive conflicts.

Activity 3.1
   Handling Conflict. Put the following statement from the text on the board: *"How partners handle conflicts can determine whether the relationship grows or dies."* Then ask the students if conflict is normal. If they agree that it is, put the

(continued on next page)

SECTION II REVIEW

Answer the following questions on a sheet of paper.
Learning the Vocabulary
The vocabulary terms for this section are *date, sexual intercourse, abstinence, external pressures, internal pressures, thrill seekers, monogamous, commitment,* and *marriage.*
Fill in the blank with the correct answer.
1. _____ between human beings is termed *coitus.*
2. _____ is a term describing relationships, especially marriage, in which the partners are sexually intimate with each other but with no one else.
3. Refraining from sexual intercourse is called _____.
4. _____ are messages from society, peers, and others that pressure people to have sexual intercourse.

Learning the Facts
5. What two things do healthy relationships have in common?
6. List one advantage and one disadvantage of going steady.
7. Describe the pressures teenagers face to have sexual intercourse.
8. What is the most destructive idea people have about marriage?

Making Life Choices
9. Your friend, Sally, is thinking about dropping out of high school to get married. What advice would you give Sally? Why would you give her that advice? Would your advice be different if Sally were a guy named Jim?

SECTION III

Working through Conflict

Partners may think that anger and conflict have no place in a "happy," committed relationship and so may try to hide their negative feelings. In reality, every human

relationship has conflicts. How partners handle those conflicts can determine whether the relationship grows or dies.

Destructive things happen when people fail to address their feelings of anger. These people may find other, unhealthy outlets for their anger, such as drinking alcohol, abusing drugs, overeating, or gambling. They may tell friends about their anger instead of telling the one who needs to know—the partner. They may become depressed or develop other psychological problems.

Some people believe (falsely) that hitting or other physical aggression can help to "clear the air." Actually, partners withdraw in response to such events. Assertion, not aggression, is the path to clear air (see Chapter 2). Equally useless tactics are leaving when a conflict starts, refusing to talk, not taking the other person seriously ("He's just had a hard day"), or not giving the other person time to respond. Saving up hurts is useless. They come spilling out in a confusing mess at some later date.

People can handle differences constructively. The Health Strategies box on the next page, "Constructive Conflicts," tells how.

Key Points ▶ *Work through conflict by clearly defining and addressing each problem while honoring the other person.*

SECTION III REVIEW

Answer the following questions on a sheet of paper.
Learning the Facts
1. What happens when people fail to address their feelings of anger?
2. Explain why physical aggression doesn't clear the air.
3. List and identify at least four constructive ways to deal with conflicts.

Making Life Choices
4. Give an example of a conflict you have experienced in a relationship or a friendship. How did you handle the situation? How would you handle it now?

Section II Review

Answers
1. Sexual intercourse
2. Monogamous
3. abstinence
4. External pressures
5. Each partner has a positive self-image and is aware that love develops in stages.
6. Answers will vary. See page 496 for possible answers.
7. External pressures: peer pressure; pressures from images of sexiness in the movies, in popular music, and on TV; pressure from a partner who wants to have intercourse; pressure from product advertisement.
   Internal pressures: the natural biological drive to reproduce.
8. the idea that marriage will magically make people happy
9. Answers will vary.

Note: Answers for Section III Review can be found on the following page.

---

conflict constructively. After a brief discussion, review the ten ideas (from the text) listed. **(20 min., Critical Thinking)**

with typical statements such as, "What's the matter?"—"Nothing." "You *always* do this to me!"; "We never talk." Create an explosion between the two in which they argue over *everything* that has bothered one of them. At the height of it (name-calling and statements they'll regret later), freeze the role-play and ask the class if this is typical in relationships. (Hopefully, it was.) Ask if it was healthy or unhealthy and why. **(10 min., Critical Thinking)**

word *destructive* on one side of the board under the quote and *constructive* on the other side. Ask the students to give examples of handling conflict destructively. Be sure *all* examples from the text are used and discussed.

Then ask for examples of handling

TEACH
SECTION III
(Guided and Independent Practice)

Activity 3.2
Role-Play. Before class, ask two students, male and female, to role-play an argument in class. Help them practice

---

Section III Review
Answers

1. Answers will vary; could include: find unhealthy outlets for anger, such as drinking alcohol or abusing drugs; may tell friends about their anger instead of telling the partner; may become depressed or develop other psychological problems; and believe that physical aggression can help to "clear the air."
2. Partners withdraw in response to such events.
3. Answers will vary. Refer to the Health Strategies on this page for possible answers.
4. Answers will vary.

Teacher Support Notes

① **Constructive Conflicts:** Have students evaluate their use of the strategies listed below. They need not do this for a romantic type of relationship. They could use a relationship with a friend, a sibling, a parent, or other relative. Have them identify two or three conflicts that have occurred in one of these relationships. They should write a brief statement describing the conflict and then write yes or no for each of the strategies listed—yes, if they use the strategy; no, if they do not use it. Discuss.

HEALTH **S**TRATEGIES

Constructive Conflicts ①

When you find yourself in conflict with another person:

- Be honest. Say what you mean and what you feel.
- Use only "I" statements ("I don't like it when . . .") rather than "you" statements ("Why don't you . . ." or "You make me . . ." or "You are a . . .").
- Reflect—repeat your partner's complaint in your own words, to be sure you understand—and wait for agreement.
- Ask, don't guess. You don't really know what is on your partner's mind until you ask.
- Choose a good time and place for working out issues. Some people agree on formal "gripe hours."
- Solve only one issue at a time. Other issues demand their own gripe sessions.
- Be sure that the issue at hand is the real issue and that some deeper, more personal problem is not hiding behind the complaint. For example, a complaint about a partner's choice of entertainment may really be about an unfairly divided burden of paying for it.
- Ask for specific changes that will lead to an end to the conflict. Ask for only one or two changes, and only when necessary.
- Be open to change yourself.
- Don't try to win. If there's a winner, there's a loser. Both people should win—in terms of closeness, intimacy, and self-esteem.

Answers to Fact or Fiction

Here are the answers to the questions at the start of the chapter.

1. False. People may be intimate psychologically as well as sexually.
2. False. You can tell when love is real because it develops slowly through the conscious choices of both partners.
3. True. **4.** True. **5.** False. In healthy, intimate relationships, sex is an expression of the intellectual, social, emotional, and spiritual closeness that couples share. **6.** False. To cope with a breakup, it is best to give yourself six months to a year to heal and build up support. **7.** False. Couples in healthy, intimate relationships maintain separate interests, as well as shared ones. **8.** False. To make a marriage work, couples need love and mutual agreements on some of life's basic issues.

EVALUATE
SECTION III

Activity 3.3
Pop Quiz. Prepare quiz questions on 3 × 5 cards ahead of time using the Section Review questions and the Chapter Review questions for this section. Divide the class into two equal teams. The team that wins the game gets ten bonus points

on the Chapter Test. **(20 min. to full period)**

CLOSE
SECTION III

Activity 3.4
Instant Replay. Have students recreate the scene from Activity 3.2. Instead of having the situation evolve into an argument, have the students use con-

structive methods to work through the conflict. **(15 min., Critical Thinking)**

RETEACH/BONUS

Healthy vs. Unhealthy Relationships. Draw a large circle on the board and divide it into eight equal sections. Put any girl's name in the middle. (preferably

(continued on next page)

STRAIGHT TALK

Date Rape

Rape is a serious crime that occurs all too frequently. One of every four women will suffer a rape in her lifetime. Most people know about stranger rape—a woman who is in a public place or in her own home is sexually assaulted by an unknown attacker. No less dangerous, and much more common, is rape by an attacker who is known to the victim. She may even be dating him. This kind of rape is date rape (also called acquaintance rape*).*

Isn't stranger rape completely different from date rape?

No, both are crimes of violence. The only difference between rape by an unknown attacker and date rape is that in the latter type, the attacker and victim know each other. In both instances, the attacker forces sex on the victim. Any forced sexual activity is a crime.

I know that women and girls are raped, but can boys be raped?

Ten percent of all rape victims are male. Any form of forced invasion of any body part by another person in any way is rape.

How serious is rape?

Legally, rape is considered very serious, deserving jail penalties and fines. Rape is also serious physically. The rapist may be armed and may

kill or injure the victim. The rapist may carry sexually transmitted diseases—even AIDS—and inflict them on the victim. The attack itself may be painful and physically damaging, and the victim may require medical treatment. A female victim also faces the threat of pregnancy as a result of the attack.

Beyond the physical threats, rape is a serious threat to the victim's mental health. Rage, terror, and emotional pain that can last for years are all common in victims of such personal violations. A writer for *Time* ① once put it this way: "When the body is violated, the spirit is maimed. How long will it take, once the wounds have healed, before it is possible to share a walk on a beach, a drive home from work, or an evening's conversation without always listening for a quiet alarm to start ringing deep in the back of the memory of a terrible crime?"

Are date rapes really rape?

Yes, but they are hard to prove in court. Consider how a date rape report reads, after the fact. Two people got together socially for an evening, and they went to a private place. Then they had sexual intercourse. One of them says that intercourse was forced. The other claims it wasn't. The problem is that no one else was there. Only the two people involved know what really happened. Cases end up being one person's word against another's.

How big a problem is date rape nationally?

Date rape is the most common form of rape in our society. Compared with the incidence of rape in many other countries, the United States has a high rape frequency. Evidently, something about the way we live makes date rape likely.

(Continued on next page)

📝 **Fast Facts**

Thirty-three percent of the victims of violent crime are under the age of 20.

Teacher Support Notes

① **Male Victims:** You may want to tell students that when men are raped, other men are usually, but not always, the attackers. You might also want to point out that while men are not the victims in most rapes, men are indirectly affected because their wives, sisters, girlfriends, and mothers—people they love—are the victims.

📝 **Fast Facts**

In 1970, 67% of American women said that men were basically kind, gentle, and thoughtful. In 1990, the percentage of women who believe this had dropped to 51% according to a Roper Organization poll.

not one that you have in class) Label the sections of the circle according to the different aspects of a teen's life *before* a boyfriend enters the picture: Family, Friends, School, Job, Religion, Hobbies, Sports/Clubs, Private Time. Design with the class the "typical girl" by writing descriptions into the appropriate sections. First do the *healthy* lifestyle: works ten hours a week, is in soccer and ski club, has three to five good friends, takes little sister shopping and to the movies, goes to church once a week, has a B average in school, writes to a pen pal, rides horses, and takes piano lessons.

Now _____ (boy's name) enters the picture. Show how an *unhealthy* relationship begins by erasing Friends and putting in his name. Erase the examples in the other sections and put in his name, explaining *how* he interferes with that part. (Example: She's never home anymore or does anything with her sister; she doesn't take extra hours at work, and he drives her to and from work; her grades are falling as she spends time with _____ instead of her homework.

So, _____ and _____ end up having sex. Then _____ decides he's bored with

Teacher Support Notes

① **Coy Behavior:** Ask students what *coy* means. (The dictionary defines it as cute playfulness, pretending to be shy, reluctance to make a commitment. Students may use words such as *tease* or *flirt*.) Ask students to give examples. Perhaps some students would volunteer to role-play coy behavior. Discuss what messages are conveyed. Are they the intended messages?

📖 Fast Facts

A woman with an annual income of less than $3,000 is six times as likely to report being raped as is a woman with an income of more than $15,000 according to a researcher at the University of Arizona.

STRAIGHT TALK   *(Continued)*

The social costs of rape are enormous. Not only do victims suffer all the outcomes already mentioned, but courts, jails, and law enforcement systems are straining with the burden of rape prevention and its punishments.

Has research discovered why date rape is common here?

Not for certain, but one theory blames the media. Movies, television, music videos, and romance novels written in this country often suggest that women want to be raped. They plant the idea that when a woman says no, she will change her mind and say yes if a man overpowers her. This idea is completely false. No normal person wants to be raped, and *no* means *no*.

Another problem in our society that may lead to rape is the way girls and boys are taught to think about sex. Girls learn early to be indirect about sex, to dress and look sexy, but not to have sexual intercourse. As women, they may say no verbally, but their clothes or body language may seem to say yes. This is no excuse for rape, but it can confuse some men. Some men think that when a woman says no, she really means yes—that she is just being coy. Most boys are ① ever even reported. Some

taught to be aggressive—to go for what they want without restraint. As men, they may use physical power to force sexual intercourse.

If a girl is dressed in a tight miniskirt, a cutoff top, lots of makeup, and high-heeled shoes, isn't she asking for it?

No one ever asks for rape. A girl dressed as you describe may be "asking for" attention or admiration, or she may be totally unaware of the effect of her appearance on others. The law protects a woman's right to choose clothing for herself, so long as she is decently covered. No amount of makeup nor shortness of skirt is an invitation to rape.

What if a guy gets so "turned on" that he can't stop himself?

Rape is an act of violence, not of passion. In fact, the only role of sex in rape is as a weapon. Rapists want to humiliate their victims. They are usually unstable, aggressive men who hold strong feelings of anger—not desire—toward women. They take this anger out on their victims.

Are most rapists caught?

Sadly, it is likely that fewer than 10 percent of rapes are ever even reported. Some

rape victims do not report the crimes because they fear the police will treat them badly. Others do not report attacks because they feel embarrassed, as though they somehow brought the attack on. Even if a case goes to court, the victim undergoes still more trauma by attacks on her character from the opposing attorneys. If more rapes were reported, more rapists would be convicted. It takes courage, but reporting rapes is important. Even if the victim does not want to press charges against the rapist, the rape should be reported. That way, the statements will be on record in case the victim decides to prosecute later.

I heard someone say that a woman who gets mad at a man might just say he raped her to get even. Does that happen?

It may, but these false stories usually come to light during a trial. In fact, the whole purpose of a trial is to establish the truth about what happened. False reporting of rape is a crime in itself and is treated harshly by the justice system.

(Continued on next page)

her. She's not interesting anymore. There's nothing to talk about; there's only complaining. Erase his name from all the circle parts and ask the class where _____'s (the girl's) identity is now. She has nothing in her life to fall back on. She gave up everything for _____ and now that he is gone, she's lost.

Now draw another circle next to this one with the same divisions. Label the old circle *Unhealthy* (it's now empty); label the other *Healthy*. Ask the students how a healthy relationship would look. The relationship should intertwine with the lifestyle sections but should never take away anything from a person's life. *Small* amounts of time are taken from each section for the new relationship, but she is still growing in all parts of her life.

(He *sometimes* does things with her family and friends and sometimes he *doesn't*; he *sometimes* takes her to work and she asks for time off for only *very special* occasions, etc.) *If* the relationship ends, she still has a life to fall back on and still feels good about herself. She will grieve the loss, but there will be support. **(20–30 min.; Extend, Enrich)**

STRAIGHT TALK (Continued)

How can a woman protect herself from becoming a victim of rape?

First of all, just keep it in mind as a possibility. Figure 20–5, "Preventing Acquaintance Rape," sums up other precautions you should take.

As for precautions against stranger rape, there's a Health Strategies box in Chapter 23, "Rape Prevention Tips," that offers suggestions. Finally, reread the section of this chapter called "What to Look for in a Partner."

① Rape is a serious crime that causes emotional trauma. The best protection is prevention. Should rape occur, report it, and seek medical treatment immediately.

FIGURE 20-5

Preventing Acquaintance Rape

Be aware that people you know can hurt you. To prevent acquaintance rape:

1. Get to know any potential date well as a friend before going anywhere alone with him.
2. Never accept a ride home from a social function with someone you've just met.
3. If you are interested in dating a person, go out with him in a group, and be on the lookout for warning signs. These are warning signs that suggest a risk of rape—the person:

   - Abuses you verbally (insults you, ignores you, or blows up at you).
   - Tries to boss you around by telling you who your friends should be or how to dress.

   - Talks as if he hates or dislikes women.
   - Gets jealous for no reason.
   - Tries to get you to drink alcohol, take drugs, or go someplace alone with him.
   - Acts physically cruel to you, other people, or animals.
   - Acts aggressively toward you when you don't want him to (sits too close, touches you, blocks your way with his body).
   - Has a fascination with weapons.

4. Do not let anyone you don't trust get you alone in a room or building.
5. If you fear someone, tell an adult in a position of authority about your fears. If that person refuses to help you, find another. Don't take no for an answer.

Fast Facts

More than half the victims of date rape on college campuses had been drinking when assaulted, as had been three-fourths of their attackers, according to research done by a University of Arizona psychiatrist.

Teacher Support Notes

① **Statutory Rape:** Tell students that *statutory* refers to statutes, or laws, which say that it is illegal to have sexual relations with a girl under the age of 16 or 18, depending on the state. Statutory rape laws are based on the idea that young girls are not mature enough to make a decision about whether they should have sex and that a male who has sex with a girl this age is taking advantage of the girl's immaturity. This type of rape differs from other rapes in that there is no violence—the girl consents to the sexual activity.

Answers

Vocabulary

1. **a.** internal pressures
b. sexual intercourse
c. external pressures
d. thrill seekers
2. **a.** commitment
b. Mature love **c.** date
3. **a.** Monogamous
b. marriage **c.** abstinence **d.** intimacy

Recall

Section I

1. poor mental and physical health
2. Refer to Figure 20–1 on page 491 for possible answers.
3. Refer to Figure 20–1 on page 491 for possible answers.

Section II

4. The stages are attraction, casual friendship, close friendship, intimate friendship, and mature love. Refer to Figure 20–2 on page 493 for complete definitions of each stage.
5. Look for people who are not involved in other love relationships; are well over heartaches, have not just recently broken up with someone else; are

open to being in a relationship with you; are free of chemical or psychological addictions (people with addictions cannot function well in love relationships); have time to devote to a relationship; have high self-esteem; and are close to you geographically.
6. social values and beliefs
7. the person who practices

assertive behavior and maintains high self-esteem
8. by creating a casual and safe environment in which to check out people whom you do not know well
9. join a youth group; take up a hobby and attend meetings with others who share the same interest; create a group around a common theme;

learn to play a sport after school, play on, or watch, local teams; volunteer time in an organization you believe in; learn to play a musical instrument and join a school or community band or orchestra; get physically fit and attend to nutrition and sleep needs
10. Answers may vary; could include: it can interrupt the nor-

---

CHAPTER REVIEW

LEARNING THE VOCABULARY

love
infatuation
mature love
intimacy
date

sexual intercourse
abstinence
external pressures
internal pressures

thrill seekers
monogamous
commitment
marriage

Answer the following questions on a separate sheet of paper.

1. **Matching**—*Match each of the following phrases with the appropriate vocabulary term from the list above:*
   a. a person's internal biological drive that urges the person toward having sexual intercourse
   b. the reproductive act between the sexes
   c. messages from society, peers, and others that pressure people to have sexual intercourse
   d. people who are likely to take chances in exchange for momentary excitement
2. a. A _____ is a decision to embark on a long-term monogamous relationship with another person, without a guaranteed outcome.
   b. _____ is a strong affection

   for and an enduring deep attachment to a person whose character is well known.
   c. A social event designed to allow people to get to know one another is called a _____.

3. **Word Scramble**—*Use the clues from the phrases below to help you unscramble each term:*
   a. **aooougmmns** _____ partners are sexually intimate with each other, but with no one else.
   b. **aaeigmrr** _____ Institution that joins a man and a woman by contract.
   c. **aeeibcnnst** _____ Refraining from sexual intercourse.
   d. **aiicmnty** _____ Relationships involving private and personal sharing.

RECALLING IMPORTANT FACTS AND IDEAS

1. People who live without relationships are likely to suffer what?
2. List signs of infatuation.
3. List signs of mature love.
4. List and define the stages of a love relationship.
5. Identify and describe characteristics to look for in a potential partner.
6. In what areas should partners be compatible with each other?
7. Describe the sort of person who can gain the most from dating.
8. How is double dating especially useful when you just begin to date someone new?
9. List ways to meet new people.
10. What problems are associated with sexual activity in a high school relationship?

11. What risks are associated with teenage sexual activity?
12. It is said that abstinence gives freedom to the people in a relationship. What sorts of freedom does abstinence give?
13. Identify the pressures associated with sexual intercourse.
14. Give examples of activities that can make people feel loved without having sexual intercourse.
15. List activities that can release sexual energy.
16. In what ways do people become physically ill following break-ups?
17. How long must a person take to heal after a relationship has failed?
18. What is the highest form of maturity in a relationship?

mal growth of a relationship; neglect intellectual, emotional, social, and spiritual growth; can cloud a person's judgment; loss of relationship can bring public criticism, as well as distress; and can cause distrust.

11. sexually transmitted diseases, including AIDS; teen pregnancies

12. It gives the freedom to grow and develop without interruption by diseases or pregnancy.

Abstinence also allows time for the growth of a healthy intimate relationship.

13. peer pressure; pressures from images of sexiness in the movies, in popular music, and on TV; or the pressure from a

partner who wants to have intercourse; the biological drive to reproduce

14. Answers may vary; could include: a hug, giving a small gift, doing a favor, confiding in others, sending a card or note of encouragement.

15. dancing, sports, walking or other activities requiring movement, writing, speaking,

singing, painting, or other expressive activities

16. The pain, depression, and stress that can follow breaking up may make people physically ill. Stress weakens the immune system, making illness more likely.

17. six months to a year

18. commitment

19. Refer to the Health Strategies on page 503 for possible answers.

Straight Talk

20. date rape

21. abuses you verbally; tries to boss you around by telling you who your friends should be or how to dress; talks as if he hates or dislikes women; gets jealous for no reason; tries to get you to drink alcohol, take drugs, or go someplace alone with him; acts physically cruel to you, other people, or animals; acts aggressively toward you when you don't want him to (sits too close, touches you, blocks your way with his body); has a fascination with weapons

---

19. Describe how to establish a healthy intimate relationship.

20. What is the most common form of rape in our society?

21. List the warning signs that suggest a risk of acquaintance rape.

CRITICAL THINKING

1. The Life Choice Inventory in this chapter deals with whether your marriage will work. Do you think couples who are going to marry should take this inventory? If so, why? If not, why not? How do you think this inventory would help the success rate of marriages? Do you think a couple about to be married should agree on a certain number of the questions before getting married? If so, how many? Why? If not, why not?

2. Acquaintance or date rape is a growing problem in society today. Reread the Straight Talk on page 507. Why are men getting mixed signals from women? How are the media at fault? What are we being taught about sexual behaviors and how does that lead to date rape? Discuss how education can help stop this serious violent crime.

ACTIVITIES

1. Complete the following sentence on a piece of paper: Love is . . . . Write all of the class members' answers on the board and compare the many ways love is defined. Discuss your response with the rest of your class.

2. Cut out the personal advertisements in the paper. Discuss why you think this is a good way to meet people or why you think it is a bad way to meet people. List the pro's and con's to share with your class.

3. Design your own dating service for high school. How would you pair students up? What would you call your service? What days and times would you work?

4. Write an editorial for your school newspaper on date rape. Be sure to include how to prevent date rape in your paper.

5. Interview two happily married couples: one couple that has been married at least 30 years

and another couple that has been married under five years. Ask them what the keys are to their happy marriages. Are their lists similar? What conclusions can you draw about happy marriages?

6. Describe the characteristics you consider important, first in a dating situation, then in a marriage partner. Use attributes like looks, personality traits, educational background, age, religious beliefs, ethnic group or race, values (political, ethical), and interests. Are your lists for dates different from your lists for marriage? If so, how and why are they different?

7. Go to your local law enforcement agency and write down the number of rape cases that were reported in your community for the year. Are the numbers surprising to you? Report this to the rest of your class.

MAKING DECISIONS ABOUT HEALTH

1. You haven't had a date in a long time. You think to yourself that you must be the loneliest person on earth tonight. You feel jealous when you hear about your friends' relationships. They aren't all perfect, but at least they provide some companionship. There must be something wrong with you; you're just not the likable

type. You're facing another night of watching television alone in your room. How might you build up your self-esteem at a time like this? What changes in your attitude might you make and how? What constructive actions could you take to ease your loneliness?

CHAPTER 21 PLANNER

OVERVIEW

This chapter is 33 pages long and divided into the seven sections listed to the right. The major learning outcomes are also listed to the right. In this chapter students will learn about the reproductive system and its functions, stages of pregnancy, fetal development, the birth process, birth defects, and other associated problems. Students will also study the positive and negative aspects of parenting and will learn how to identify abuse.

MAKING LIFE CHOICES RESOURCES

A variety of activities, handouts, quizzes, and tests to accompany this chapter are available in the *Making Life Choices* supplementary material. You may pick and choose from those materials as appropriate for your amount of class time and the ability levels of your students. Some of the resources you might want to consider using are:

Overheads
- Sperm Production
- Menstrual Cycle
- Fertilization
- Cell Division
- Stages of Development
- The Placenta
- Comparison of Nutrient Needs
- The Stages of Childbirth

Handouts
- Reproductive System Labeling
- Tests During Pregnancy
- Effects of Potentially Harmful Substances on the Fetus
- The Parenting Process
- Breast Milk vs. Formula
- General Guidelines for Parenting
- U.S. Public Health Service Objectives

Teacher Information Sheets
- Critical Periods
- Body Changes
- Nutrients During Pregnancy
- PKU
- Bonding

CHAPTER 21

From Conception through Parenting

CHAPTER PROJECT

Before you begin the chapter, have each student write an essay entitled, "As a Parent I Will Be . . . " Make sure students *do not* write their names on the papers. Shuffle the papers and distribute them. Have the papers read aloud. You may read them to be more assured of confidentiality. The class may wish to vote on the best future parent in the class. (This could become a new superlative for the school annual.) After completing the chapter, have students write the same essay again. As these essays are read to the class, have students note differences between the first set of essays and the second set.

Activity To Introduce Chapter

Have each student bring in one of their baby pictures. Display them on a bulletin board, numbered individually. Have a contest to see who can correctly identify the greatest number of their classmates. Each student should number a paper according to the number of pictures, then write the name of a classmate to identify each picture. **(40 min.)**

OUTCOMES

After reading and studying this chapter, you will be able to:

✓ Discuss the responsibilities associated with having children.
✓ Describe the phases of the menstrual cycle and how conception occurs.
✓ Describe the signs of pregnancy and the tests used to confirm it.
✓ Describe the development of the fertilized egg from conception to birth.
✓ Discuss why early prenatal care and a healthy lifestyle are important to the development of the unborn baby.
✓ Identify birth defects and other problems that may occur during pregnancy.
✓ Describe the birth process.
✓ Discuss the responsibilities of being a parent.

CONTENTS

I. Deciding to Bear or Adopt Children
II. Reproduction
III. Pregnancy
IV. Fetal Development
V. Birth Defects and Other Problems
VI. Childbirth
VII. The Elements of Parenting

    Straight Talk: *Drinking during Pregnancy*

FACT OR FICTION

What do you think? *Are the following statements true or false? If you think they are false, then say what is true.*

1. The lifestyle choices a couple makes in the weeks *before* pregnancy can affect their future child's development.
2. A missed menstrual period is a sure sign of pregnancy.
3. A woman can have a miscarriage (spontaneous abortion) without being aware of it.
4. Pregnant women should not be physically active.
5. A woman who is pregnant should "eat for two."
6. Probably the single most important task in parenting is to help the child develop positive self-esteem.

(Answers on page 539)

■ **Reminder:** Knowing how to study can increase your knowledge, improve your grades, *and* cut down on your study time. See the *Studying Health* section at the front of your text for some suggestions to help you study this chapter.

SUGGESTED RESOURCES

Student Readings
1. *Facts about Premature Birth* (pamphlet). National Institute of Child Health and Human Development. Washington, DC: Government Printing Office, 1985.
2. *The Health Benefits of Smoking Cessation: A Report of the Surgeon General, 1990.* U.S. Department of Health and Human Services, Public Health Service. Washington, DC: Government Printing Office, 1990.

Teacher Readings
1. Rosso, P., "Placental Growth, Development, and Function in Relation to Maternal Nutrition." *Federation Proceedings.* 39 (1980): 250–254.

Videos
1. *Eating for Two: Prenatal Nutrition for a Healthy Baby.* Cambridge Educational, 800-468-4227.
2. *Pregnancy: Mom and the Unborn Baby.* Cambridge Educational, 800-468-4227.
3. *Ten Ways to Be a Better Parent.* (25 min.) Cambridge Educational, 800-468-4227.

Software
1. *Positive Parenting.* Opportunities for Learning, Inc., 800-243-7116.

NOT ENOUGH TIME?*

You could easily spend four or five days teaching this chapter if students read the entire chapter, do a fair number of the suggested activities in the teacher's edition, and a complete sampling of the handouts from the resource material accompanying this text. It is likely, however, that you will have only two or three days to devote to this chapter. Following are some suggestions to help you make sure that you cover the key topics if you have limited time.

TIME	SUGGESTIONS
1 Day	Assign Sections I and II, the "Life Choice Inventory" and "Fact or Fiction," prior to class. During class have students do Activity 1.2 in Section I and Activity 2.1 in Section II.
2 Days	On day 2 assign Sections III, IV, and V prior to class. During class have the students complete Activity 3.1 in Section III, Activity 4.3 in Section IV, and Activity 5.6 in Section V.
3 Days	On day 3 assign Sections VI and VII prior to class. During class have students complete Activity 6.3 in Section VI and Activity 7.4 in Section VII.

*Please refer to the 18-week daily lesson plans in the supplementary material for additional suggestions.

Answers to "Fact or Fiction"

1. True. **2.** False. Nonpregnant women may miss periods because of other factors, and pregnant women may have a menstrual period. **3.** True. **4.** False. Physical activity during pregnancy may reduce discomfort and help to ensure a quick recovery from childbirth. **5.** False. A pregnant woman should not "eat for two," or she will gain unneeded fat. **6.** True.

In this section the student will learn:
1. To analyze the advantages and disadvantages of being a parent.
2. How adoption compares to bearing children.

Activity 1.1

Personal Sharing. Ask if anyone in the class is adopted or knows someone who is adopted. Ask if they would share some of their personal feelings about being adopted. If no one can personally share, ask the class to imagine what it might be like to have been adopted. Make a list on the board as they share. **(10–15 min.)**

TEACH
SECTION I
(Guided and Independent Practice)

Activity 1.2

Parenting Discussion Groups. Divide the class into small discussion groups. Tell the class they are going to analyze the issues of parenting vs. non-parenting, and adopting vs. bearing your own children. Have them select a leader,

Teacher Support Notes

① **Becoming Parents:** Make sure students understand this key point—the younger they are when they have children, the more the children will change their lives. Ask them to express the meaning of these two sentences in their own words to make sure they understand. Can they think of reasons why this would be so? (Some possible answers: Older people are often more financially secure and, therefore, better able to handle the demanding financial obligations; children limit parents' lifestyle options, and since younger people are still experimenting with the kind of lifestyle they want to pursue, children will have more impact on younger people who are still exploring their options.)

66 Thoughts on Health 99

The first half of our lives is ruined by our parents and the second half by our children.
– Clarence Darrow

514

When people become parents, they change their lives forever. The younger the people, the more impact children will have on their future. In this chapter you will learn about the reproductive process and some basic elements of parenting. ①

For parents who are ready to accept the responsibility, babies are a joy.

SECTION I

Deciding to Bear or Adopt Children

The decision whether or not to have a child is affected by personal beliefs, needs, and wishes. For example, people may base their decisions on childhood memories or romantic fantasies of what families are like. People need to love and to be loved, and they may wish to participate in the human chain of life. Outside pressures—such as a spouse's needs, or parents' or friends' expectations—can also affect these decisions. Finally, people may simply wish to experience being parents. Most decisions, however, are based on this single question: How would it affect my life if I had a child to raise? After all, children are "forever"—even more so than marriage partners.

The decision to have a child is sometimes based on fantasies.

To get an idea how "forever" children are, you can try the following exercise. Pretend an egg is a baby, and that you are its parent. Don't put it down. Carry it from place to place, even while shopping or showering. Bathe it every day. Keep an eye on it at all times. Sleep with it close by. Set your alarm for 2 A.M., and check the egg. Never let it out of your sight unless you can get another person to agree to tend to it as you are doing. Try this for one week, and you will get some sense of what it would be like to care for a child. Multiply the week by 52 for a year, and then by 20 for the duration of active parenthood. If you find this exercise difficult, remember that rearing a child is more difficult still. An egg requires neither food nor discipline. It does not cry, soil diapers, or get sick. This chapter's Life Choice Inventory offers further insight into how you may be affected by your choice to become a parent.

Some mature people are ready to parent. For them, one possible route to parenthood is to adopt. People may choose adoption because they want to offer a home to a homeless child or because they have been unable to bear a child themselves.

Adoption is not quick. It requires persistence, patience, and the willingness to work recorder, and spokesperson in each group. The leader is responsible for guiding the discussion, following the directions, and staying on task. The recorder is responsible for the group's written work. The spokesperson will share the group's consensus with the entire class. Instruct the recorder to label a piece of paper "Parenting vs. Nonparenting." Under each heading create two columns: label these "Advantages" and "Disadvantages."

Do a second paper with the heading "Adoption vs. Bearing Children," following the same directions. On the reverse side have them record final decisions and rationales. Tell the groups to list as many items as they can under the advantages and disadvantages for each of the issues. Then discuss which option they feel is the best choice and why. **(40 min., Cooperative Learning)**

EVALUATE
SECTION 1

Activity 1.3
Persuasive Writing. Have the students do a persuasive paper on one of the following topics: adoption, becoming a parent, choosing not to bear children, or why teens should not have children. **(40–60 min.)**

Ch. 21 From Conception through Parenting 515

LIFE CHOICE INVENTORY

Are You Ready to Have a Child? ①

The answers to these questions will help you grasp the impact on life of bearing a child.

1. How will having a child affect your schooling or career? It is hard to work full-time and be a full-time parent, too.
2. Someone has to be aware of the child's whereabouts and needs, 24 hours a day, for 18 or so years. During the hours that you can't do it, who will?
3. If your partner is unable to carry the responsibility of parenthood, how will you carry it by yourself?
4. How will having a child affect your relationships with others? Will your partner be willing to share your attention, energy, and love with a baby?
5. Where will you be able to get help (for example, baby-sitters or relatives) when you need to get away? You cannot raise a child without help.
6. Will you be willing to give up much of your free time to devote yourself to the needs of a child? Will your partner? Children limit your freedom to play.
7. Are you willing and able to pay for proper prenatal and newborn care?

Pregnant women, new babies, and new mothers have needs that are costly. Can you meet these needs?

8. Are you willing and able to invest your money for years in the well-being of your child? The cost of raising a child to adulthood varies. On the average, however, the cost in the early 1990s was about $100,000.
9. How well would you be able to adjust to raising a less-than-perfect child? Parents always run a small risk of having a handicapped child.
10. Are you willing to make a new baby the center of attention? The new family member will grab the spotlight, and you may feel neglected.
11. Have you vented anger and frustration on pets or children in the past? If so, wait to have children until you receive help in learning to redirect hostility— important in stopping the pattern of child abuse.

with an agency. Such agencies may seem to "sit in judgment," but they take seriously their job of matching parents and children. They do ask questions about people's private lives, but only so that they can be sure the match is a good one.

Babies with medical problems are usually the easiest to adopt, as are children of certain other countries. Foster parenthood offers an opportunity to care for older children ②

with special needs. Foster children need homes but may not be able to stay permanently. Opening a home—and life—to them is especially challenging and rewarding.

Key Points ▸ *The decision to become parents is often affected by romantic ideas and pressures from others. Those considering parenting must realistically assess how a child would change their lives. Adoption is one route to parenting.*

Teacher Support Notes

① **Is the Time Right?** Even if you have younger students, this Life Choice Inventory could prove valuable. Having to think about answers to these questions will further impress upon students the tremendous change in their lives that would occur should they have children.

② **Foster Children:** Tell students that *to foster* means to give parental care to; to nurture. Adoption is permanent, whereas foster care is temporary.

✏ Fast Facts

Some Hawaiians still practice the ancient custom of *hanai*, in which couples having several infants give infants to couples unable to have children. Hanai takes place openly among family and friends, unlike our modern adoption procedures.

515

Activity 1.4

Review List. Instruct the students to list all the advantages and disadvantages they have learned for each of the following: adoption, teen parenting, being a parent, and choosing not to bear children. Have them compare their lists and dis-

cuss any different items. **(60 min.; Reteach, Reinforce)**

FOCUS
SECTION II

In this section the student will learn:
1. The steps of the menstrual cycle and how it relates to the reproductive process.
2. How conception and fertilization take place.

Activity 2.1

Reproductive System Labeling. Give the students drawings of the male and female reproductive systems contained in your supplementary material. Have students label each part in the systems with the correct term. Have the students record the function of each part on the back of the paper, identifying each as they go. As part of this activity you may wish to include a handout containing the

Section I Review

Answers

1. spouse's needs, parents' or friends' expectations
2. to offer a home to a homeless child or because they cannot conceive or bear a child
3. those with medical problems and children of certain other countries
4. Answers will vary.

Teacher Support Notes

① **Overhead—Sperm Production:** In the supplementary material you will find an overhead showing how the male body produces sperm. As students look at the overhead, tell them that the brain's pituitary gland starts the process of sperm production by releasing two hormones— FSH (follicle-stimulating hormones) and LH (luteinizing hormone). These pituitary compounds stimulate sperm production and release. The testicles respond by producing the hormone *testosterone*. Testosterone is essential for the continuous production of sperm cells.
② **Overhead—Menstrual Cycle:** In your supplementary material you will also find an overhead showing the events that occur during menstruation.

___SECTION I___   ___REVIEW___

Answer the following questions on a sheet of paper.

Learning the Facts
1. What outside pressures do people encounter while deciding whether or not to have a child?
2. Why might people choose adoption?
3. Which children are the easiest to adopt?

Making Life Choices
4. Reread the Life Choice Inventory on page 515 and answer the questions. Do you feel you are ready for parenthood? Why or why not? Do you want to have children? If so, when? What do you want to accomplish before you begin a family? How was this inventory helpful?

SECTION II

Reproduction

The beginning of a whole new human being takes place in a single moment. That event is **conception.** Because many complex events lead up to conception, let's review the male and female reproductive systems before proceeding with an explanation of how conception occurs.

Reviewing Reproduction

You have probably already studied the male and female reproductive systems in this course and in earlier health and biology courses. To review some of the changes that take place in your body as the reproductive system develops, you may want to reread the Physical Maturation section in Chapter 3. You may also want to reexamine the sections on the reproductive systems in Chapter 6. Following your review, read the next section in this chapter, which

describes an extremely important chain of events—the **menstrual cycle**—that directly affects conception.

Key Points *Earlier chapters in this text will help you review the reproductive process before more careful study of pregnancy and parenting.*

The Menstrual Cycle

Among the many ways in which men and women differ is the way they each produce reproductive cells—the **sperm** and the **ova.** In the male body, a constant flow of the hormone testosterone stimulates sperm cells to mature in a steady flow. Sperm mature daily. In the female system, though, only one (or sometimes two or three) ova ripen and are released each month. This cyclic ripening depends on hormonal changes that occur in a monthly rhythm—the menstrual cycle.

Once each month, or every 28 days on the average, the uterus prepares itself to host a pregnancy. The cycle begins with the building up of the uterine lining with soft tissue and a rich blood supply. Sometime after this, often about mid-cycle, the ripened ovum bursts from the ovary. This is **ovulation.**

The ovum is gently swept into the tubes leading to the uterus. What happens next depends on whether or not sperm cells are present in the reproductive tract—whether or not a man and woman have had sexual intercourse. If the egg encounters sperm cells, it may become fertilized, and if fertilized, it may embed itself in the prepared uterine lining, beginning a pregnancy.

The other possibility is that the egg is not fertilized or that it does not embed in the uterine lining. In this case, it passes out of the body unnoticed. With no pregnancy, the uterine lining weakens in the two weeks following ovulation, and is eventually shed. This shedding of the uterine lining parts and definitions of their functions in a matching format (also included in your supplementary material). The student would then need to match the part with the function. **(30 min.; Reteach, Reinforce)**

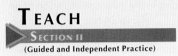

TEACH

SECTION II
(Guided and Independent Practice)

Activity 2.2
Menstruation Projects. Divide the

class into small groups. Assign each group one of the following projects to complete and present to the class:
   Menstruation Time Line
   Have this group prepare a time line to illustrate the menstrual cycle in the life of a female. Have them mark the common age level for the onset of menstruation and label with common occurrences that accompany the onset. Have them record some common problems that may occur

along the continuum; for instance, the problems that can arise in women who smoke and use oral contraceptives after age 35. They could also mark pregnancy symptoms and complications during the average years of childbearing. They should mark the common age of menopause and label the common signs.
   Teenage Cycle Graph
   Assign this group the task of interviewing

(continued on next page)

Figure 21–1 The Menstrual Cycle. The cycle begins with bleeding. The lining of the uterus then begins to thicken to become ready to support pregnancy. If no pregnancy occurs, the lining weakens and is shed in menstrual bleeding to start the cycle over.

is menstruation. Following menstruation, the whole cycle begins anew in preparation for a future pregnancy. The cycle is summarized in Figure 21–1.

In menstruation, a few tablespoons of blood and fragments of the uterine lining flow from the vagina. Menstruation lasts four to five days on average. These few days of menstrual flow are only the outward sign of the amazing events that have taken place in the body in the earlier four weeks.

Menstruation normally varies from time to time. It may be a little late or early, with lighter or heavier flows, or it may last for more or fewer days than expected. Also normal during menstruation are contractions of the muscular uterus—menstrual cramps.

If cramping is uncomfortable, treatment with the over-the-counter drug ibuprofen is usually effective in relieving it. Should

① cramping become severe or menstrual irregularities become extreme, a health care provider should check for problems.

Key Points   *The menstrual cycle involves a cyclic shifting of hormones that promote a monthly ripening of an ovum and the preparation of the lining of the uterus for pregnancy. If pregnancy does not occur, the lining is shed in menstruation.*

MINI GLOSSARY

conception: the union of an ovum and a sperm that starts a new individual.
menstrual cycle: the cyclic ripening of an ovum and the preparation of the uterus for pregnancy; also called the *ovulatory cycle.*
sperm: the male cells of reproduction.
ova (singular, **ovum**): the female cells of reproduction. Ova are also called *eggs.*
ovulation: the ripening and release of an ovum.

a set number of teenage girls and recording responses to the following questions: At what age did you begin menstruating? How many days is your average period? How many days are average between periods? Have you ever missed a period? Instruct them to create a graph or chart to illustrate their findings. **(1 class period for presentations, Cooperative Learning)**

EVALUATE
SECTION II

Activity 2.3
Pop Quiz. 1. The single moment an ovum and sperm meet to create a new life is called _____. (conception)

2. The average menstrual cycle is _____ days. (28)
3. Which reproductive organ produces the menstrual flow by shedding its lining? _____ (uterus)
4. How long is the average life span of an ovum? _____ (12 to 24 hrs.)
5. Conception occurs in what part of the female reproductive system? _____ (fallopian tubes)

Teacher Support Notes

① **Overhead—Fertilization:** In your supplementary material you will find an overhead transparency of Figure 21–2.
② **Conception:** To check comprehension, ask students how long the egg can live? (12–24 hours) How long can sperm live? (up to three days) Can intercourse a few days before ovulation produce pregnancy? (yes) Can intercourse two days after ovulation produce pregnancy? (No, the egg would no longer be alive.)
③ **Rhythm Method:** The *rhythm method* is explained in Part B of your special sexuality unit.

✎ **Fast Facts**

A study conducted in the early 1980s showed that one-third of the girls and women polled in the survey did not know what was happening to them when they got their first menstrual periods.

Conception

What follows is a description of conception. Imagine a family—wife, husband, and baby-to-be. Inside the woman's body, an ovum, tinier than the period at the end of this sentence, has grown ready for **fertilization.** The man has produced millions of even tinier, microscopic sperm cells, as he has done every day since puberty.

Now the man and woman have had sexual intercourse. Sperm swim up the vagina, propelled by their long, whipping tails. The ovum powerfully attracts them to its surface. One sperm finally enters the ovum, triggering an instant change in the ovum's surface so that no more sperm can penetrate (see Figure 21–2). The genetic material of the two cells unite within the fertilized ovum. The ovum plants itself in the uterine wall (**implantation**) and begins to develop. About 60 percent of all fertilized ova either fail to implant or dislodge later, to be lost from the body.

For conception to occur, sexual intercourse must take place within a certain time limit. An ovum lives for just 12 to 24 hours, and living sperm must arrive during this brief life span if they are to fertilize the ovum. Sperm can live for up to three days within the female reproductive tract, so if they get there first, they can wait. Intercourse within a few days before ovulation can easily lead to conception.

A couple who wants to conceive can use the **fertility awareness method.** This method is related to the rhythm method used to prevent pregnancy. It is used to help a woman determine the time of ovulation. The couple can then time sexual intercourse so as to make sure sperm are available at the right time to fertilize the ovum. Drug stores sell at-home urine-testing kits that show a woman when she is ovulating.

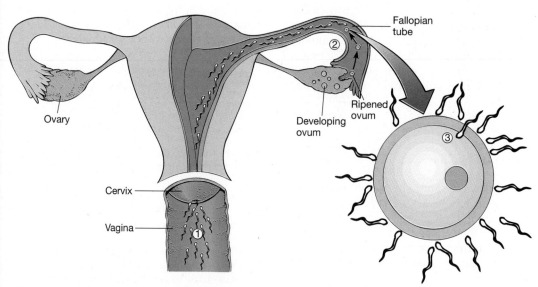

Figure 21–2 Fertilization. Sperm from the penis (1) begin the journey toward a ripened ovum, released earlier from the ovary (2). The sperm work together to weaken the ovum's outer layer, but only one sperm can enter (3). (Both sperm and ovum have been greatly enlarged for this illustration.)

CLOSE
SECTION II

Activity 2.4
Question Cards. Give students 3 ×
5-inch cards as they enter the room.
When everyone is seated, tell them they
are to write on their cards any questions
they have about reproduction, childbirth,
heredity, etc. You will read these and be

prepared with answers during the next
class period. Don't have them put their
names on the cards. They will feel more
at ease to ask a question if they are not
identifiable. **(5 min.)**

FOCUS
SECTION III

In this section the student will learn the
value of:

1. Preparing for pregnancy.
2. Pregnancy tests.

Activity 3.1
Lifestyle Do's and Don'ts. Before
students read this section, have them
brainstorm a list of do's and don'ts for
males and females prior to childbearing.
Their lists should include any lifestyle
behaviors that could possibly benefit or
harm their future children. **(20 min.)**

Key Points *In conception, an ovum and sperm
unite to form a fertilized ovum. The
fertilized ovum may then implant itself in the wall of
the uterus and start a pregnancy. Couples can increase
their chances for pregnancy by using the fertility
awareness method.*

SECTION II REVIEW

Answer the following questions on a sheet of paper.
Learning the Vocabulary
The vocabulary terms for this section are
*conception, menstrual cycle, sperm, ova, ovum,
ovulation, fertilization, implantation,* and *fertility
awareness method.*
1. Match each of the following phrases with
   the appropriate term from above.
   a. male cells of reproduction
   b. ripening and release of an ovum
   c. joining of an ovum and a sperm

Learning the Facts
2. Describe how men and women produce
   reproductive cells.
3. What happens to the egg after one sperm
   penetrates it?
4. How long do sperm live in the female
   reproductive tract?

Making Life Choices
5. The menstrual cycle is an important part of
   reproduction. At what age do you think
   young girls should be educated about
   menstruation? Why do you think it is
   important for a girl to understand
   menstruation? Why is it important for guys
   to understand the process of menstruation?

**Both parents can prepare in advance for
a healthy pregnancy.**

that person is in an excellent position to
make choices that will give the baby-to-be
every possible advantage.

Concerns before Pregnancy

During the three months prior to conception, the ovum of the mother and the
sperm of the father go through a maturing
process that includes cell division. Anything
that prevents or disrupts cell division can
damage those new cells at a tender stage. A
newly recognized fact is that the man's
health habits before conception, as well as
the woman's, are important. For at least
three months before pregnancy, *both* parents
should be free from drugs of all kinds—
over-the-counter medications; prescription
medications (with the physician's OK); and
mind-altering drugs, including alcohol.
① Both prospective parents should be well
nourished. Nutrition affects the ova and
sperm, and good nutrition supports the hormone balance needed for conception. Before

SECTION III

Pregnancy

Preparation for a healthy pregnancy begins far in advance. When someone decides, "Yes, I'm ready to have a baby now,"

MINI GLOSSARY

fertilization: the joining of an ovum and a
  sperm.
implantation: the lodging of a fertilized ovum
  in the wall of the uterus.
fertility awareness method: a method of
  charting ovulation. It involves tracking
  menstrual periods, body temperature, and
  types of cervical mucus.

Teacher Support Notes

① Drug-Free Parents.
Ask students if they knew
that the condition of *both*
parents could affect the
baby. Did they know that
the use of drugs by the
parents *prior* to conception
could affect the baby?

Section II Review

Answers
1. **a.** sperm **b.** ovulation
c. conception
2. *men:* The hormone
testosterone stimulates
sperm cells to mature
daily; *women:* only one (or
sometimes two or three)
ovum ripens in the ovaries
and is released. This cyclic
ripening depends on hor-
monal changes that occur
in a monthly rhythm.
3. an instant change in the
ovum's surface so that no
more sperm can penetrate
4. up to three days
5. Answers will vary.

poster; Extend, Enrich)

Poster Campaign. Have class members prepare posters (to be displayed in the school) for a "Prepare Now for Future Children" campaign. The posters should specify do's and don'ts for lifestyle habits. **(1 hour to prepare**

✍ Fast Facts

According to research at the Boston University School of Medicine, women should not use hot tubs or saunas during the first three months of their pregnancies. Intense heat increases the odds of a baby developing spinal cord defects such as spina bifida. Using a hot tub or sauna just twice during the first trimester of a pregnancy triples the risk.

Section III Review

Answers

1. be free from drugs of all kinds and be well nourished
2. by choosing a poor diet in order to lose weight or by snacking on candies, high-fat snacks, and soda pop
3. missed menstrual period, bluish cast in the woman's cervix and outer genital area, full and tender breasts, darkening of nipples
4. Answers will vary.

---

pregnancy, a diet that follows the advice of Chapters 7 and 8 would well cover the nutrient needs of the future parents.

When a woman whose nutrition has been poor becomes pregnant, she may not have stored the nutrients she needs to produce a healthy baby. Women may be poorly nourished for other reasons. A woman who chooses a poor diet in order to lose weight or who snacks on candies, high-fat snacks, and soda pop may not have full nutrient stores. She may not know how to choose a good diet or she may not have enough money to buy nourishing food (help for these problems is available to those who seek it). If pregnancy is in her future, she should develop healthy eating habits now. She should also be physically active. Then, once pregnancy is confirmed, she can continue eating and exercising as she did before, and her baby-to-be is likely to be healthy.

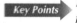 *Health habits of both parents prior to pregnancy affect the probable health of the baby-to-be.*

Pregnancy Tests

Long before any tests are taken, a woman may suspect that she is pregnant. A typical sign is a missed menstrual period. However, periods are missed for many reasons, and one or two periods can also occur during early pregnancy. For these reasons, missed periods are not an accurate indicator

Only an accurate test can resolve immense suspense.

"We're pregnant!"

of pregnancy. More reliable are subtle color changes in the woman's cervix and outer genital area, which darken with a bluish cast. Another sign is that the breasts may become tender and full, and the nipples may darken.

A chemical test can confirm that a woman is pregnant. All such tests rely on detecting one of the many hormones present during pregnancy. Home pregnancy test kits are available and are widely used. However, the instructions for using them may not be clear, or the results may be hard to figure out. The tests performed by a medical lab are more accurate.

Key Points *Indicators of pregnancy include missed menstrual periods and changes in the woman's body. Chemical tests detect one of the hormones of pregnancy.*

SECTION III   REVIEW

Answer the following questions on a sheet of paper.

Learning the Facts
1. What health habits should both parents be maintaining if they think they may be within three months of starting a pregnancy?
2. Describe how women are most likely to be poorly nourished in our society.
3. List the visible signs of pregnancy in a woman's body.

Making Life Choices
4. Pregnancy tests are expensive. Many women use over-the-counter pregnancy test

EVALUATE
SECTION III

Activity 3.3
Project Assessment. Assign a grade to the poster. (Activity 3.2) Criteria for grading:
1. extensiveness of information
2. correctness of content
3. creativity

4. use of color and materials
5. attractiveness

CLOSE
SECTION III

Activity 3.4
Impromptu Speeches. Have each student briefly summarize, in an impromptu speech, the characteristics of a healthy prechildbearing lifestyle, and the best pregnancy tests available (in their opinions). Give a two-minute limit. **(1 hr.)**

FOCUS
SECTION IV

In this section the student will learn:
1. The stages of pregnancy from conception to birth.

(continued on next page)

---

kits. What are some of the problems of using these kits? Do you think they are effective in diagnosing a pregnancy? Would you use a pregnancy kit? Why or why not?

SECTION IV

Fetal Development

A day after fertilization, the fertilized egg—even while it is still traveling toward the uterus through the fallopian tube—

From fertilization through week two: zygote.

From week three through week eight: embryo.

From week nine through the end of pregnancy (usually the 40th week): fetus. From eight weeks to birth, the fetus grows 20 times longer and 50 times heavier.

A newborn infant.

Figure 21–3 Stages of Fetal Development ②

③ begins to divide. If the first two new cells become detached at this stage, two babies—identical twins—will begin to develop. (In contrast, if two eggs have been released and fertilized at the same time, the two babies will be fraternal twins, not identical twins.)

① In each stage of **gestation** thereafter, the developing future infant is given a name—first **zygote,** next **embryo,** and finally **fetus.** Figure 21–3 displays each stage.

The Zygote

The fertilized egg, upon its first division, becomes a zygote. After the zygote becomes implanted in the uterine wall, cell division goes on and on. Each new set of cells divides again to create a ball of many smaller cells. These cells sort themselves into three layers that eventually form the various body systems.

From the zygote's outermost layer of cells, the nervous system and skin begin to develop. From the middle layer, the muscles and internal organ systems form. From the innermost layer, the glands and linings of the digestive, respiratory, and urinary tract systems form.

MINI GLOSSARY

gestation (jes-TAY-shun): the period from conception to birth. For human beings, normal gestation lasts from 38 to 42 weeks.

zygote: the product of the union of ovum and sperm, so termed for two weeks after conception. (After that, it is called an *embryo.*)

embryo (EM-bree-oh): the developing infant during the third through eighth week after conception.

fetus (FEET-us): the developing infant from the ninth week after conception until birth.

Teacher Support Notes

① ***Fetal:*** Some students may not realize that *fetal* is an adjective form of *fetus,* which students first encountered in Chapter 17.

② **Overhead—Stages of Development:** In your supplementary material you will find an overhead of Figure 21–3.

③ **Overhead—Cell Division:** Your supplementary material contains an overhead demonstrating simple cell division as it usually occurs. You may want to use this overhead as you explain to students how identical twins and fraternal twins are created.

2. Proper nutritional guidelines for pregnant women.
3. Factors that identify high- and low-risk pregnancies.

Activity 4.1
Experiencing Pregnancy. The

Empathy Belly is a 33 lb. garment that enables the wearer to experience more than 20 pregnancy symptoms. The Empathy Belly comes with an instructional video on its use. The Empathy Belly is distributed by Birthway, Inc., 14804 N.E. 75th St., Redmond, WA 98052, 1-800-882-3559. If, however, your school does not have the resources available to purchase the Empathy Belly, see Activity 8 on page 544. **(30 min.)**

Activity 4.2
Pregnancy Stages. Divide the class into groups of two or three. Assign each group one of the nine months of pregnancy. Have them design a segment of a large bulletin board of the "happenings" during their assigned month of pregnan-

Teacher Support Notes

① **Overhead—The Placenta:** Your supplementary material contains an overhead of Figure 21–4.

② **Placenta Functions:** For enrichment you may want to tell students that among the functions of the placenta is the preparation of the mother's breasts for lactation (the making of milk). The placenta also shields the fetus from its mother's immune system, which would otherwise perceive the fetus's blood as foreign and would attack it. The placenta serves as a biochemical barrier; it allows dissolved substances to pass to the fetus, but blocks blood corpuscles and large molecules. If you want to give the students more specific information about the hormones involved, you could tell them that the placenta also serves as an endocrine gland, producing large amounts of progesterone and estrogen, the hormones that maintain pregnancy.

✍ Fast Facts

24% of pregnant American women receive no prenatal care during the first three months of pregnancy.

522

---

522   UNIT 6 The Life Cycle

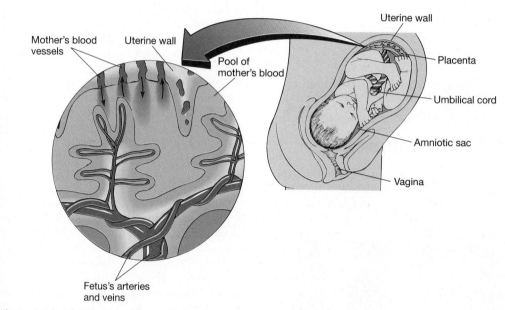

Mother's blood vessels — Uterine wall — Pool of mother's blood

Uterine wall — Placenta — Umbilical cord — Amniotic sac — Vagina

Fetus's arteries and veins

Figure 21–4 The Placenta ①

Key Points ▶ *In the first stage of development, the zygote becomes a three-layered ball of cells. Each layer forms different organ systems of the body.*

The Placenta and Other Structures

After implantation, a whole new organ—the **placenta**—grows within the uterus, shown in Figure 21–4. Two other new structures form. One is the **amniotic sac,** a sort of fluid-filled balloon that houses the developing fetus. The other is the **umbilical cord,** a ropelike structure stretching from the fetus's "belly button" to the placenta. The umbilical cord contains blood vessels that conduct the fetus's blood to and from the placenta.

The placenta is a sort of pillow of tissue in which fetal and maternal blood flow side by side; the two bloods never mix. The mother's blood delivers nutrients and oxygen to the fetus's blood across the walls of the vessels. Fetal waste products are also

carried away by the mother's blood, to be excreted by the mother.

The placenta is a highly active organ. It gathers up hormones, nutrients of all descriptions, large proteins such as antibodies, and other needed items and pumps them into the fetal bloodstream. The placenta ② also releases hormones that maintain pregnancy into the maternal blood.

The placenta must develop normally if the future infant is to grow properly. Should the placenta break down, the fetus would be left with no source of nutrients or oxygen. One reason why nutrition before pregnancy is so important is that the placenta is built largely from nutrient stores already in the mother's body at the start of pregnancy.

Key Points ▶ *The placenta provides nutrients, other materials, oxygen, and waste disposal for the developing fetus. The placenta maintains pregnancy by producing hormones. Proper placental development is essential to a successful pregnancy.*

cy. Encourage students to use charts, pictures, or drawings to illustrate that stage of pregnancy. When they have completed their sections, the bulletin board will be a large visual of the stages of pregnancy. **(30 min. to plan, one class to create; Extend, Enrich)**

Activity 4.3
Pregnancy Terms. Prepare a list of terms dealing with pregnancy. The list should include terms found in this section of the text and could also include all or some of the following: *identical twins, fraternal twins,* and *gamete.* Make a copy of the list for each student. Highlight a different term on each sheet. Tell the students to study the term highlighted on their lists and prepare to teach the class about that term. As each student teaches, the rest of the class should take notes on their lists of terms. At the conclusion of the teach-ing, every student will then have a completed vocabulary sheet of pregnancy terms, with information defining those terms taught to them by their classmates. **(one class period to present; Reteach, Reinforce)**

Activity 4.4
Reproductive Bingo. Make bingo cards using all the terms in this section,

(continued on next page)

The Embryo

An embryo goes through many astonishing changes. The number of cells in the embryo doubles approximately every 24 hours. In comparison, this rate slows to only one doubling during the final ten weeks of pregnancy. The embryo's size changes very little. However, the events taking place are of enormous importance.

At eight weeks, the embryo is only a little more than an inch long, but it already has a complete central nervous system, a beating heart, a complete digestive system, well-defined fingers and toes, and the beginnings of facial features. Anything that disrupts the embryo's rapid development alters the structure of the body permanently.

> **Key Points** *The embryo develops rapidly, forming the early stages of all the major organ systems of the body.*

The Fetus

The tasks of the fetus are to gain in size and weight. Each organ grows to maturity with its own timing. Each organ has certain **critical periods** during its growth—critical in the sense that the events taking place during those times can occur only then and not later.

Outside events can affect an organ's critical period. If, during the critical period, cell division is limited by some factor, that organ will be damaged. Forever after, the damaged organ will not function as well as it might have otherwise. Later recovery is impossible. Thus, exposure to a harmful chemical, a nutrient deficiency, or other injury during one stage of development might affect the heart. During another stage, it might affect the developing limbs.

The brain and central nervous system are first to reach maturity in the developing fetus. During its critical period, the fetal

① brain increases by 100,000 cells *a minute.* Problems during this time can limit brain development permanently. Mental functioning throughout life can be subnormal. Pregnancy, then, is clearly a time for a woman to take special care of her health.

> **Key Points** *The organ systems that started developing earlier grow and develop to make the fetus ready for birth. Each organ has a critical period of rapid growth during which it is especially likely to be injured by negative external factors.*

Spontaneous Abortion

Not all fertilized eggs develop to become infants. About 10 percent fail to implant in the uterus and are shed without anyone's ever knowing they were there. Of those that do implant, about half are shed in **spontaneous abortion,** or **miscarriage.** Spontaneous abortion is a natural and expected part of fertility. Many times it prevents imperfect embryos from becoming full-term infants.

② —— MINI GLOSSARY ——

placenta (plah-SEN-tah): an organ that develops during pregnancy; it permits exchange of materials between maternal and fetal blood.

amniotic (am-nee-OTT-ic) **sac:** the "bag of waters" in the uterus, in which the fetus floats.

umbilical (um-BIL-ih-cul) **cord:** the ropelike structure through which the fetus's veins and arteries extend to and from the placenta.

critical periods: periods during development when a body organ is especially sensitive to harmful factors. A critical period is usually a period of rapid cell division.

spontaneous abortion; or miscarriage: the expelling of a zygote, embryo, or fetus from the uterus, not induced by medical means.

Teacher Support Notes

① **Overhead—Growth and Stages of Development:** In your supplementary material you will find an overhead that represents the actual sizes of the developing embryo and fetus during the first months of growth following fertilization. This overhead will help students (many of whom will be confused by the many different names given to the baby at various stages of its development) learn and remember the different phases of growth.

② **Teacher Information Sheet—Critical Periods:** In the supplementary material you will find a list of specific examples of the effects of malnutrition during the critical periods of fetal development.

📢 Fast Facts

The weight of the typical fetus will increase from less than one gram (less than 4/100 of an ounce) to about 3,500 grams (7-1/2 pounds).

with one term in each square. Make the cards so that you have different terms in each space, much like real bingo cards. Don't make all cards the same or every student can bingo at the same time. You need a set of cards with the function or description of each term on the cards. Distribute the cards, one to each student.

Students also need something to use as markers: beans, paper, etc. Draw one card at a time, and read it aloud. The students listen, think of which term you are describing, and look to see if that term is on their cards. If it is, they use a marker to cover that square. Once a student has markers in a row, column, or diagonally they should shout, "bingo." You may check them by having them uncover squares one at a time and tell you the

term. You check to see if the description for that term is in the stack of those you have called. You can give a prize or grade points as rewards for winners. **(30 min.; Reteach, Reinforce)**

Activity 4.5
Student Interview. Instruct the students to interview a woman who is currently pregnant or a mother. If both options are available have them interview

---

Teacher Support Notes

① **Teacher Information Sheet—Body Changes:** In the supplementary material you will find background information on body changes associated with pregnancy.
② **Morning Sickness:** Many students may overlook this point about when morning sickness can occur. Ask students when it occurs. (any time of the day or night)

524

---

524   UNIT 6   The Life Cycle

Most spontaneous abortions take place early, with no more sign than a heavy menstrual flow. The woman's hormones change, and she may feel depressed but not even know why.

A spontaneous abortion late (after three months) in pregnancy resembles a birth and presents greater hazards. An infection may start in the uterus and spread throughout the body unless caught and treated early. A woman who experiences a late spontaneous abortion may feel grief as intense as if a child had died.

> **Key Points**   *Spontaneous abortion is the loss of a zygote, embryo, or fetus from the uterus. It is a natural event in normal fertile women.*

The Woman's Experience

While the great changes of pregnancy take place in her body, a pregnant woman's life seems to go on much as before, at least outwardly. However, she experiences it differently. Here's an imaginary story to help you understand what the mother-to-be is feeling.

In one family, the mother-to-be, Gina, doesn't want to go out after work anymore. Her pregnancy barely shows, yet she always feels tired. Pablo, the young father-to-be, wonders if she is overreacting. (Pablo is used as an example here of Gina's chief support person. People other than the father may fill this role.)

Pablo doesn't realize that the changes he can see are trivial compared with the dramatic events taking place inside Gina's body. She is producing more blood. Her uterus and its supporting muscles are increasing in size and strength. Her joints are becoming more flexible in preparation for childbirth, and her breasts are growing and changing in preparation for **lactation.** The hormones creating all these changes may also affect Gina's brain and change her mood. She may be having problems with constipation, shortness of breath, frequent urination,

backaches, or **morning sickness.**

② The nausea of "morning" sickness actually comes at any time of the day or night. It may be a healthy sign, because it results from the many hormones needed to support pregnancy. Sometimes, nibbling on crackers before getting out of bed or snacking on small meals throughout the day helps to relieve it.

Gina needs to be fit now, just as she did before. Physical activity may reduce some of her discomforts and help to ensure a quick recovery from childbirth later on. Most types of physical activity are approved, as long as the abdomen is protected against injury. Gina should progress slowly in an exercise routine if she is just starting ① one. If she was physically active before pregnancy, she can continue as before, so long as she is comfortable in doing so.

Relaxing for two.

As pregnancy stretches the skin over a woman's abdomen, buttocks, and breasts, the skin's lower layers may begin to painlessly separate, forming scars. The tendency to develop these "stretch marks" runs in families. Perhaps the most a woman can do to control them is to keep her weight gain within the recommended limits. Magic lotions don't work, as this chapter's Consumer Awareness explains.

the mother. In this interview the student should ask: "What is pregnancy like? What different feelings and emotions did you experience? Did you have any specific complications? Were there any physical deterrents to normal daily activities? What special exercises and/or nutrition plans did you follow? How often did you visit your health care provider? What special tests did he/she do, and at what stages of the pregnancy?" The students should then write a case study of that woman's pregnancy and present it in class. **(one class period for presentations; Extend, Enrich)**

Activity 4.6

Notebook. Have each student create a notebook of illustrations of the stages of pregnancy. The illustrations should be hand drawn. Have the students label each drawing to properly explain their illustrations. They should include a drawing for each month and brief explanations of the major developments that occur in that month. The students should design an attractive cover for their notebooks and title them. Notebooks should be organized in the correct order of the stages of fetal development. **(Reteach, Reinforce, Special Needs)**

(continued on next page)

CONSUMER AWARENESS

Misleading Labels

Stretch marks are permanent. No real preventive measures or cures for them exist, although they can be minimized by gaining no more than the weight required. Spreading a product on the skin won't prevent the damage, even if the product contains vitamin E or other nutrients.

A label may not legally claim that a product prevents stretch marks, but may suggest it by using a name like Mother's Lotion. Perhaps the best sales gimmick is a price low enough so that even though a woman may be suspicious, she'll buy it just in case it might help a little. Even at a low price, the manufacturer can make millions if enough women try the product.

Many con games work this way. Identify them by their key components: no effective treatment (a call to your pharmacist or health care provider can tell you that much), a label that suggests more than it says, and a low price.

① CRITICAL THINKING

1. *Why must manufacturers not claim that a product will cure stretch marks?*
2. *Why is it profitable for them to suggest the product might do so?*
3. *Which other products can you think of that are marketed in this way?*

During pregnancy, as at other times, a woman needs to deal skillfully with stress. Studies suggest that stress can cause changes in the nerve cells of embryos. Pregnant women should practice the relaxation techniques described earlier, in Chapter 4.

Some final advice to Pablo: Treat Gina with respect for the changes she must handle. Give her extra love and understanding. And Gina, keep Pablo informed as to how you feel. Encourage him to share his feelings, too. Communication between the partners during this time will lay a strong foundation for the shared parenthood ahead.

Key Points ▶ *External changes during pregnancy are minor, compared with the internal changes. Many discomforts can be relieved through physical activity. Pregnant women should relax.*

② Nutrition during Pregnancy

An earlier part of this chapter pointed out that malnutrition *before* pregnancy can affect the health of a future fetus. Malnutrition *during* pregnancy not only can reduce the infant's number of brain cells but also can impair every other body organ and system.

MINI GLOSSARY

lactation: the production of milk by the mammary glands of the breasts for the purpose of feeding babies.
morning sickness: the nausea (upset stomach) a pregnant woman may suffer at any time of the day; thought to be related to the hormones that maintain pregnancy.

525

Nutrition Plan. Have each student or pair of students design a minimum of a one-week menu that is nutritionally sound for a pregnant woman. Specify for which month of pregnancy the week should be, or allow the students to choose which month they wish. They should include complete breakfast, lunch, and dinner menus, plus snacks, and at what time of day they would be eaten. They should provide some explanation of why these foods were chosen. They should also provide information regarding any special dietary requirements their imaginary pregnant women might have. Tell the students to be creative, but realistic, as they create this menu and this imaginary woman it is for. If students personally know someone who is pregnant at the time, allow them to design a menu for that person. **(1 hr.; Extend, Enrich)**

EVALUATE
► SECTION IV

Activity 4.8
Definition Bee. Prepare a list of terms used during this section, including

---

66 Thoughts on Health 99

The commonest fallacy among women is that simply having children makes one a mother—which is as absurd as believing that having a piano makes one a musician.
– Sydney Harris

Teacher Support Notes

① **Teacher Information Sheet—Nutrients During Pregnancy:** Your supplementary material contains background information on the importance of four nutrients during pregnancy. These four nutrients are calcium, fluoride, zinc, and iron.

② **Calories vs. Nutrients:** Check students' retention of what they learned about calories and nutrients in Chapter 7. Ask them what a calorie is (measure of food's energy). What are nutrients? (compounds in food that the body requires for proper growth, maintenance, and functioning) Do they remember what percentage of their diets should come from each of the three energy-producing nutrients? (30% from fat, 60% from carbohydrates, 10% from protein)

---

526 UNIT 6 The Life Cycle

Prenatal care and expert advice support healthy pregnancies.

Nutrient needs during pregnancy are greater than at any other time of life. When the baby is born, its body will contain bones, muscles, blood, and other tissues made from nutrients the mother eats. For a pregnant teenage girl, nutrient needs are extraordinary. This is because the food she eats must supply the nutrients not only to support her growing baby but also her own growth. A diet that includes a variety of foods is the best source of all the needed nutrients.

All pregnant women need professional advice on supplements. Experts recommend iron supplements for all pregnant women. ①

Some may need other nutrients. Only a trained health care provider can recommend a set of supplements that will be right for any one woman. Self-chosen supplements may not meet the pregnant woman's needs or may even be toxic (poisonous).

A woman's nutrient needs increase tremendously in pregnancy, but her energy needs increase just a little. A pregnant woman should not "eat for two." If she does, she will gain unneeded fat and give birth to a fat baby. She needs foods with high nutrient levels but low calorie levels—nutrient-dense foods. That means she needs a diet about the same as the one recommended in Chapter 8, but with one more serving of milk and vegetables daily, and one more daily serving of meat or meat alternates. ②

Most women should gain about 25 to 35 pounds—mostly of lean tissue—during pregnancy. This weight gain supports normal growth of the placenta, the uterus, the breasts, and a 7½-pound baby, as well as an increased blood and fluid volume. Figure 21–5 shows an example of how a weight gain of 31 pounds is distributed. Pregnant teens should strive for gains at the upper

Eating for a healthy baby.

_____**F**IGURE 21-5_____

Example Weight Gain during Pregnancy

Development	Weight Gain (Pounds)
Infant at birth	7½
Placenta	1
Mother's added blood	4
Mother's added fluid	4
Growth of uterus	2½
Growth of breasts	3
Fluid to surround infant	2
Mother's fat stores	7
Total	31

their descriptions or definitions; or, use the bingo cards from Activity 4.4. Tell the students to number a piece of paper according to how many terms you have prepared. Call out a term and have the students write the proper definition or description of the term; or, read a description or definition and have the students write down which term was described. Randomly mix the type of questioning. This could be done as a "bee" test, as well. Instead of having the students record answers on their own papers, have them divide into two teams and have each team number off beginning with one. Then call out the questions as before. Begin with number 1 on one team. If the student who is number 1 responds correctly, the team earns a point, if not, move to number 1 on the other team. They either earn the point or you move back to number 2 on the first team, and so on. No points are taken away, only added for correct responses. They must answer on their own; no one on their teams may help them. When you are finished, you can have a certain letter grade for a number of correct responses. You may wish to set a minimum for a C, more to answer for a B, and the members of the winning team all get an A. This is a good test procedure for positive reinforce-

(continued on next page)

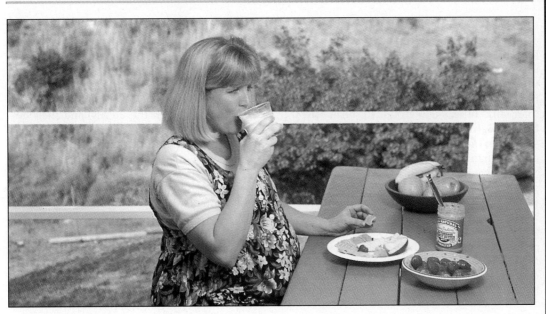

Nutritious foods help grow a healthy baby.

end of the range, because some of the weight gained is that of their own maturing bodies. Obese women should gain less— about 15 pounds—and not of fat, but of lean tissue built from nutrient-dense foods.

> **Key Points** *Nutrition in pregnancy is critical to health. The pregnant teenager needs nutrients to support both her growth and the pregnancy. Pregnant women need advice from their health care providers on supplements. A weight gain of 25 pounds or more is advised.*

High-Risk Pregnancies

Most babies are born healthy, but some are not. Some pregnancies are riskier to the life and health of the mother and fetus than are others. Figure 21–6 lists factors that identify a **high-risk pregnancy.** Many of the factors that threaten pregnancy are easy to control once they are discovered. This is why early **prenatal care** is so important.

Prenatal care supplied by health care providers is important to the health of pregnant women. Prenatal care affords the opportunity to test for risk factors throughout pregnancy. Many clues to abnormalities are present in samples of maternal blood or urine.

A pregnant teen is considered at special risk. As already mentioned, the demands of pregnancy compete with those of her own growth. Furthermore, pregnant teens have more complications during pregnancy than do older women. A pregnant teen is likely to become anemic (because of low iron

Mini Glossary

high-risk pregnancy: a pregnancy more likely than others to have problems, such as premature delivery or a low birthweight. Many factors contribute to pregnancy risks.

prenatal care: medical and health care provided during pregnancy.

Teacher Support Notes

① **Prenatal:** Although prenatal care is defined, you may want to examine the word *prenatal* more carefully. Tell students that *natal* is an adjective describing birth. Prenatal describes events that take place *before* birth. Natal comes from the Latin word *nasci*, which means to be born.

✎ Fast Facts

Mortality among infants weighing less than 5-1/2 pounds at birth is 17 times greater than among infants with birth weights above 5-1/2 pounds.

527

ment. Have no failures if everyone at least puts forth an effort. **(60 min., Special Needs)**

Activity 4.9
Pop Quiz.
1. Explain the conceptual difference between identical and fraternal twins. (identical develop from one egg and sperm that join and split; fraternal develop from two separate eggs and sperm)
2. Name the new organ that develops after implantation to house the embryo. (placenta)
3. What is the common name of a spontaneous abortion? (miscarriage)
4. What is the name given to the production of milk used to feed the infant by the mammary glands? (lactation)
5. How many pounds should most women gain during pregnancy? (25 to 35 lbs.)

CLOSE
SECTION IV

Activity 4.10
Creative Writing. Have the students do a creative writing assignment, imagin-

---

Teacher Support Notes

① **Prematurity:** The normal gestation period for human beings is 40 weeks. It is difficult, however, to obtain accurate and objective data on the exact length of gestation; therefore, the birth weight of 5.5 pounds or less has been accepted in the medical community as the clinical criterion of prematurity, regardless of the period of gestation. As further background, you may be interested to know that other measures suggested for prematurity are crown–heel length (47 cm or less), crown–rump length (32 cm or less), and the ratio of the thorax circumference to the head circumference (less than 93%).

② **Factors Affecting Pregnancy:** This figure contains nine major risk factors during pregnancy. Students should be required to learn these risk factors. Have them study the figure, close their books, and be able to list each factor with a brief explanation.

---

stores combined with rapid growth and lack of medical care) and to experience prolonged labor (because of the mother's physical immaturity). Perhaps the greatest risk, though, is death of the teenage mother's infant. Teenage mothers are more likely than any other age group to bear **low-birthweight** infants. Low-birthweight infants are more likely to die during early infancy than infants of normal birthweight.

Many women with high-risk pregnancies give birth to low-birthweight babies. An infant's birthweight is a predictor of the baby's future health. Low-birthweight infants (those who weigh 5½ pounds or less at birth) often face illness and early death. Many die before their first birthday. They may be too weak to suck to obtain milk or to cry to win attention. Therefore, their conditions often worsen.

Low birthweight can arise from two causes. One is early birth. When the infant is born early, it is called a **premature** infant (born before the 37th week). Such babies are the right size for the number of days they have spent in the uterus, and their development is normal. They may be small, but they catch up if given proper care. The other cause of low birthweight is growth failure in the uterus. Babies who are small for this reason are called **small for date.** These infants do not catch up as well.

> **Key Points** *Any of a number of factors can increase the risk level of a pregnancy. One common outcome of a high-risk pregnancy is a low-birthweight baby, who is less likely to survive than is a baby of normal weight.*

FIGURE 21-6

Factors Affecting Pregnancy Outcome ②

Factor	Effect on Risk[a]
Maternal weight	Too low weight and too high weight increase risk.
Maternal malnutrition	Nutrient deficiencies and overdoses increase risk. Food fads increase risks of malnutrition.
Socioeconomic status	Poverty, lack of family support, and lack of education increase risk.
Lifestyle habits	Smoking, drug, and alcohol use and abuse increase risk.
Age	The youngest and oldest mothers have the greatest risk.
Pregnancies	
Number	The more previous pregnancies, the greater the risk.
Timing	The shorter the time between pregnancies, the greater the risk.
Outcomes	Previous problems predict risk.
Multiple births	Twins or triplets increase risk.
Maternal blood pressure	High blood pressure increases risk.
Sexually transmitted diseases	Many such infections, including AIDS, can attack the fetus and greatly increase risk.
Chronic diseases	Diabetes, heart, and kidney disease, certain genetic disorders, and others increase risk.

[a]Among the risks associated with these factors are low birthweight, mental retardation, and a collapsed umbilical cord.

FOCUS

SECTION V

In this section the student will learn about:
1. Common congenital abnormalities and birth defects.
2. Tests to detect possible problems or abnormalities with the fetus.
3. The adverse effects of drug use before

pregnancy on a child's development.

Activity 5.1
  Brainstorming. Ask the class to tell of any birth defects or abnormalities they can think of. List these on the board. The students should make their own lists at the same time at their desks. Ask them to share where they heard about these, and what they know about them. **(15 min.)**

SECTION IV REVIEW

Answer the following questions on a sheet of paper.

Learning the Vocabulary

The vocabulary terms for this section are *gestation, zygote, embryo, fetus, placenta, amniotic sac, umbilical cord, critical periods, spontaneous abortion or miscarriage, lactation, morning sickness, high-risk pregnancy, prenatal care, low birthweight, premature,* and *small for date.*

Fill in each blank with the correct answer.

1. The product of the union of the ovum and sperm for two weeks after conception is called the _____.
2. The _____ is the "bag of waters" in the uterus, in which the fetus floats.
3. The production of milk by the mammary glands of the breasts for the purpose of feeding babies is called _____.
4. A _____ baby is a baby born before the end of the normal nine months.

Learning the Facts

5. What does the mother's blood deliver to the fetus?
6. Describe an embryo at eight weeks.
7. Describe what is taking place inside Gina's body when she is pregnant.
8. Why is a pregnant teen at special risk?

Making Life Choices

9. Reread the Consumer Awareness section entitled "Misleading Labels" on page 525. Why do you suppose so many women try these products? What does this tell you about our society?

SECTION V

Birth Defects and Other Problems

Although most infants are born normal, some have **congenital** abnormalities—*congenital* meaning "from birth." Some of

these conditions are diseases. Others involve abnormally formed body parts, and these are known as **birth defects.** Congenital abnormalities can arise from many causes. Two of them, genetic inheritance and exposure to harmful chemicals or radiation before or during the development of the fetus, are discussed here. Others include accidents during childbirth, severe nutrient imbalances, and exposure to excessive heat, to name a few.

Certain abnormalities run in families. A **genetic counselor** can advise a family on the odds of bearing a child with a congenital abnormality and help them choose whether to bear or adopt children.

Inherited Problems

A risk associated with pregnancies of older-age parents is bearing a child with **Down's syndrome.** Down's syndrome is an inherited condition that causes the child to be born with many physical abnormali-

---

MINI GLOSSARY

low birthweight: a birthweight of 5½ pounds (2,500 grams) or less, used as a predictor of poor health in the newborn infant. Normal birthweight for a full-term baby is 6½ pounds or more.

premature: born before the end of the normal nine-month term of pregnancy.

small for date: a term used to describe an infant underdeveloped for its age, often because of malnutrition of the mother.

congenital (con-JEN-ih-tal): present from birth.

birth defects: physical abnormalities present from birth.

genetic counselor: an advisor who predicts and advises on the likelihood that congenital defects will occur in a family.

Down's syndrome: an inherited condition of physical deformities and mental retardation.

Section IV Review

Answers

1. zygote
2. amniotic sac
3. lactation
4. premature
5. nutrients and oxygen
6. only a little more than an inch long, but already has a complete central nervous system, a beating heart, a complete digestive system, well-defined fingers and toes, and beginnings of facial features
7. See the last paragraph in the first column on page 524.
8. The demands of pregnancy compete with those of her own growth. A pregnant teen is likely to become anemic and to experience prolonged labor. A pregnant teen is more likely to bear a low birthweight infant, which is more likely to die during early infancy than an infant of normal birth weight.
9. Answers will vary.

Activity 5.2

Reports. Assign each student one of the defects or problems the class brainstormed in Activity 5.1. Have students read and study the topic, and be prepared to report to the class all they can find out about that defect. Allow the students to do oral presentations several days later. **(one class period for presentations; Extend, Enrich)**

Activity 5.3

Tour. Arrange a tour of the local hospital's labor and delivery area. Arrange to have the tour conducted by a doctor or health care professional who can point out specific care areas for babies born with defects or abnormalities. Allow the students to ask questions and receive answers from the tour guide. Have the students take notes during this tour and write a summary of the main points they learned concerning birth disorders and problems. **(Extend, Enrich)**

Activity 5.4

Teacher Support Notes

① **Teacher Information Sheet—PKU:** Your supplementary material includes background information on PKU.

② **Inherited Problems:** As enrichment tell students about the *Rh factor*. Blood tests performed early in pregnancy establish whether or not a woman's blood contains the Rh factor. If a woman with Rh-negative blood conceives a child with Rh-positive blood (inherited from the father), her body may detect the Rh factor's presence in the fetus and develop antibodies against it.

③ **Handout—Tests During Pregnancy:** Your supplementary material contains a handout listing some of the more common tests that health care providers use during pregnancy to detect potential problems.

④ **Handout—Effects of Harmful Substances:** For enrichment you may want to distribute the handout in your supplementary material entitled "Effects of Potentially Harmful Substances on the Fetus."

---

ties and mental retardation. The condition starts at fertilization, when an error in the transfer of genetic material occurs. The error is then repeated and passed on to every cell of the child's body.

Many other inherited conditions affect offspring. For example, **PKU (phenylketonuria)** is the inherited inability of the cells to handle one of the amino acids (parts of protein). Brain damage causing severe mental retardation can result if PKU goes untreated. At birth, every baby born in the United States is tested for PKU by the medical attendant so that PKU babies may be given a special diet right away to prevent brain damage. ①

Many inherited problems can be prevented or controlled with special diets or drugs. ② Thanks to appropriate prenatal care and tests such as **amniocentesis**, the overwhelming majority of babies are born normal. ③

Many drugs and other environmental factors can harm developing infants.

> **Key Points** ▶ *Congenital abnormalities are inborn conditions that last throughout life. Down's syndrome and PKU are examples.*

Harmful Chemicals and Other Factors

Chemicals, radiation, and many other factors cause birth defects. Such factors may damage developing organs directly, or they may act by limiting the supply of oxygen or nutrients to the fetus. Many attack the genetic material of the dividing cells. When the genetic material in a cell of a developing embryo or fetus is damaged, the damage multiplies with every division. The final, completed organ of which those cells are a part remains abnormal throughout life.

Many drugs, including alcohol (see this chapter's Straight Talk), are known to damage developing fetuses. Most drugs of abuse also harm developing fetuses. Their effects are still under study. Some of the known ones are listed in Figure 21–7. ④

Other harmful environmental factors include contaminants, radiation, diseases such as **rubella**, and compounds in spoiled foods. Even large doses of some nutrients can be harmful in pregnancy—especially large doses of vitamins A, B_6, C, and D; the mineral, iodine; and other minerals.

Pregnant women should not smoke. Smoking limits the delivery of oxygen and nutrients to the growing fetus. The more a mother smokes, the smaller her baby will be. The pregnant woman who smokes risks retarded development of her infant and complications at birth. The effects can last throughout childhood. In addition, **sudden infant death syndrome (SIDS)**—the sudden, unexplained death of an infant—may be linked to a woman's cigarette smoking during pregnancy. SIDS may even be linked to smoking by others in the household—the sidestream smoke discussed in Chapter

---

FIGURE 21-7

Some Negative Effects of Drugs of Abuse on Pregnancy

Drug	Effect
Amphetamines	Suspected nervous system damage; behavior abnormalities
Barbiturates	Newborn drug withdrawal lasting up to six months
Cocaine	Uncontrolled jerking motions; paralysis; abnormal behaviors; permanent mental and physical damage
Marijuana	Short-term irritability at birth
Opiates (including heroin)	Drug withdrawal in the newborn; permanent learning disability (attention deficit disorder)

Hazards from environmental contaminants are severe. The problem of environmental contamination is enormous, and it affects everyone. Thus it is given an entire chapter (Chapter 25) of this book. A woman who fears that she may have been exposed to an environmental danger should call a hotline to find out what to do. Even ordinary household chemicals, such as insecticides or cleaning fluids, should be used with extreme care.

Like chemicals, radiation of certain kinds can harm cells. Radiation passes through cells and disrupts their genetic material. One way a fetus might be exposed to such radiation is through X rays. If X rays become necessary, the woman who knows or suspects that she is pregnant should inform all medical personnel.

The harmful agents discussed here are only a few of thousands that we are exposed to every day. However, the odds of being affected by them are small. The body can tolerate small doses and repairs damage

15. Finally, the surgeon general has warned that maternal cigarette smoking causes death in otherwise healthy fetuses and newborns.

Some claim that pregnant women should give up coffee, tea, and colas because of the caffeine they contain. However, the caffeine in a cola or two is well within safe limits. When people give too much attention to relatively safe practices, they tend to forget what is really important. There would be little point in a woman's giving up colas and continuing to smoke two packs of cigarettes a day. The Health Strategies feature on the next page, "How to Keep a Pregnancy Safe," sums up the risk factors most important to avoid during pregnancy.

MINI GLOSSARY

PKU (phenylketonuria): a congenital disease causing severe brain damage with mental retardation if left untreated; now detected and treated at birth.

amniocentesis (am-nee-oh-cen-TEE-sis): a test of fetal cells drawn by needle through the woman's abdomen.

rubella: an infectious disease, especially dangerous to pregnant women because it can cause malformations in fetuses.

sudden infant death syndrome (SIDS): the unexpected and unexplained death of an apparently well infant; the most common cause of death of infants between the second week and the end of the first year of life; also called *crib death*.

Activity 5.6

Disorder Charts. Have the students construct charts listing inherited problems, problems not genetic in nature, and problems due to chemical effects. Assign each student one of the topic areas. Students are to find at least one specific dis-

order associated with that type of cause and prepare an informational chart regarding that disorder. Display the chart in the classroom. Allow time for students to view the charts and record notes on every disorder charted. **(Extend, Enrich)**

FOCUS
SECTION VI

In this section the student will learn

about the:
1. Events and procedures of childbirth.
2. Different types of birth.

Activity 6.1

Video. Show a childbirth film. Local prenatal clinics, health departments, and childbirth class instructors at local hospitals have these readily available. There are many to choose from. Have the students take notes during the film and write

---

Teacher Support Notes

① **Smoking:** You may want to give your students some further information about the negative effects of smoking. For example, just two cigarettes smoked in succession reduce the chest breathing movements of the fetus. You may also want to tell them that studies even suggest that smoking during pregnancy increases the risk of childhood cancer.

② **Term:** Some students may not know the word *term* as it's used here. Tell them that health care providers use the word to mean the time in which a pregnancy of normal length ends. They say that the mother had her baby at "full term" or that she carried her baby "to term."

Section V Review

Answers
1. Answers will vary.
2. genetic inheritance; exposure to harmful chemicals or radiation before or during the development of the fetus; accidents during childbirth; severe nutrient imbalances; exposure to excessive heat
3. Smoking limits the delivery of oxygen and nutrients to the growing fetus, resulting in retarded development and complications at birth.
4. Answers will vary.

HEALTH STRATEGIES

How to Keep a Pregnancy Safe

1. Avoid drugs, smoking, and alcohol.
2. Exercise moderation in other things, such as physical activity and caffeine use.
3. Avoid environmental toxins.
4. Skip unnecessary X rays.

①

quickly, especially when it is well nourished. Parents who have nourished themselves well, who have avoided drugs and alcohol, who have obtained medical care, and who have been reasonably careful around chemicals and other harmful factors can look forward with happy anticipation to the next step of parenting—childbirth.

Key Points *Pregnant women should avoid drugs, including alcohol and tobacco. They should use care around chemicals and harmful agents.*

SECTION V REVIEW

Answer the following questions on a sheet of paper.

Learning the Vocabulary
The vocabulary terms for this section are *congenital, birth defects, genetic counselor, Down's syndrome, PKU (phenylketonuria), amniocentesis, rubella,* and *sudden infant death syndrome (SIDS).*
1. Outline an article about birth defects. Use each term above in your outline.

Learning the Facts
2. Identify some causes from which abnormalities can arise.
3. Why shouldn't pregnant women smoke?

Making Life Choices
4. What can you do to encourage parents to keep pregnancies safe?

SECTION VI

Childbirth

If you could look into a pregnant woman's uterus just before birth, you might notice that the fetus seems to be breathing. It is practicing, readying its fully formed lungs for the endless succession of breaths that will support life for some 70 or more years to come. The fetus wakes up, smiles, kicks, rolls over, stretches, sleeps, and dreams. It may suck its thumb, and its tiny hands may grasp the umbilical cord. The pregnant woman is well aware of these activities. When the fetus kicks, she knows it. It is she who is kicked. When the fetus hiccups, its mother feels tiny, rhythmic movements.

As the time for birth nears, conditions become cramped in the fetus's tiny quarters. Its head then turns downward and fits snugly into the mother's pelvis, an event called **lightening.** The mother feels relief from the pressure on her cramped stomach, heart, and lungs. She can breathe and eat more easily.

② Near term, the mother may perceive mild contractions of her uterus and think that labor has begun. Termed **false labor** by some, mild contractions are common throughout later pregnancy. A more descriptive name might be "warm-up contractions," because they indicate that the muscular uterus is practicing for the hard work of the birth that will follow. Labor bears an appropriate name. It is the hardest of all physical efforts, and once it has begun, the woman cannot rest until it is finished.

Labor begins as the woman's hormones cause the muscles of her uterus to contract powerfully and rhythmically. Thereafter, labor proceeds by stages. In the first one, the **dilation stage,** the cervix dilates until the baby's head can pass through it. In this a brief explanation of the childbirth procedure.

TEACH
SECTION VI
(Guided and Independent Practice)

Activity 6.2

Birth Simulation. Demonstrate regular and breech birth processes by placing a small doll inside a sock. As you push the doll through the sock from toe to top opening, explain the process. Turn the doll around to show the breech birth. **(10 min.; Reteach, Reinforce)**

Activity 6.3

Demonstration. Using charts and models of childbirth, which can be purchased or borrowed from health agencies, describe the steps of the birth process. Be sure to name specific body parts that are involved. **(20 min.; Reteach, Reinforce)**

EVALUATE
SECTION VI

Activity 6.4

Birth Process Review. Without the benefit of notes, models, or drawings, have the students list the steps of childbirth in the correct order, and give brief explanations of each step. **(20 min.)**

(continued on next page)

The birth of a baby marks the start of a new life for the whole family.

stage, the contractions become more and more powerful and closer and closer together. Then a transition occurs, bringing on the still more powerful contractions of the **expulsion stage.** In this stage, the baby's head starts to emerge from the birth canal (**crowning**), the amniotic sac breaks (if it has not broken already), and the baby is born. Sometimes the birth attendant (physician or midwife) makes a small cut, an **episiotomy,** in the vaginal wall to prevent tearing of tissue during birth. The final stage of labor, the **placental stage,** consists of several final contractions that expel the placenta, or **afterbirth.**

Nearly all babies dive into the world head-first. Rarely, a **breech birth** occurs. In a breech birth, the feet or hind end is born first, the head last. About half of these few cases pose no extra problems. In some cases, the attendant may decide to call for a surgical birth, or **cesarean section.** The physician then cuts through the mother's abdomen and lifts the baby and placenta out. A baby who is too large to pass safely through the mother's pelvis may also be delivered by cesarean section. If other prob-

 MINI GLOSSARY

lightening: the sensation a pregnant woman experiences when the fetus settles into the birth position.

false labor: warm-up contractions that many women experience before the birth process.

dilation stage: the stage of childbirth during which the cervix is opening.

expulsion stage: the stage of childbirth during which the uterine contractions push the infant through the birth canal.

crowning: the moment in which the top (crown) of the baby's head is first seen.

episiotomy (eh-PEEZ-ee-OT-oh-me): a surgical cut made in the vagina during childbirth when the vagina cannot stretch enough without tearing to allow the baby to pass.

placental stage: the final stage of childbirth in which the placenta is expelled.

afterbirth: the placenta and membranes expelled after the birth of the child.

breech birth: a birth in which the infant is born in a position other than the normal head-first position.

cesarean (si-ZAIR-ee-un) **section:** surgical childbirth, in which the infant is taken through a cut in the woman's abdomen.

66 Thoughts on Health 99

A suburban mother's role is to deliver children obstetrically once, and by car for ever after.

– Peter de Vries

Teacher Support Notes

① **Overhead—The Stages of Childbirth:** Your supplementary material contains an overhead showing the stages of childbirth.

② **Cesarean Section:** For enrichment tell students that the term *cesarean birth* originated, according to tradition, when Julius Caesar was cut out from his mother's womb immediately after her death. The first reported cesarean section performed on a living woman occurred in the 17th century when a butcher cut open his wife's uterus to save her and their child.

534

EVALUATE (Continued)

Activity 6.5

Pop Quiz. Write the terms on the board. Have students match the terms and descriptions as you read the descriptions. Match the following:

1. episiotomy (d)
2. afterbirth (b)
3. breech birth (e)
4. exhaustion (c)
5. breastfeeding (a)

a. something that can aid in weight loss for a new mother
b. the placenta following childbirth
c. cause of postpartum depression
d. cutting the vaginal opening
e. feet or hind end first at birth

CLOSE

SECTION VI

Activity 6.6

Birth Process Drawings. Have the students create a series of drawings to illustrate the birth process. Encourage them to label the body parts and record information about each step in the procedure to describe the process completely. **(40–60**

Teacher Support Notes

① **Handout—The Parenting Process:** The supplementary material includes an activity entitled "The Parenting Process."

Section VI Review

Answers

1. a. false labor **b.** episiotomy **c.** postpartum depression
2. For answers, see the first paragraph in column two on page 532.
3. *dilation stage*—the cervix dilates until the baby's head can pass through it; *expulsion stage*—the baby's head starts to emerge from the birth canal, amniotic sac breaks, and the baby is born; *placental stage*—several final contractions that expel the placenta
4. a breech birth, a baby who is too large to pass safely through the mother's pelvis, signs that the baby is being stressed, the mother is bleeding excessively
5. Answers will vary.

Fast Facts

Cesarean births account for 20.3% of all births. More than 800,000 women a year have C-sections, which is almost a 400% increase over the past 20 years.

lems arise during labor—such as signs that the baby is being stressed, or the mother is bleeding excessively—a cesarean birth may be chosen as the safest way to deliver the child. Cesarean sections are relatively safe for both mothers and babies. However, recovery for mothers involves more healing and takes longer.

With the birth of her infant, the mother normally loses all the weight of the fetus, the placenta, and the associated fluids. She is left with the body fat she gained during pregnancy. Breastfeeding can draw on these fat stores and help the woman lose weight. Without breastfeeding, many women lose these pounds within a few weeks or months, but it may take more effort to do so.

Some women feel depressed after giving birth, feel like crying, or are unable to sleep. Such discomforts may result from the sharp changes in hormone levels that occur after birth or from simple exhaustion caused by the baby, who doesn't yet sleep for long stretches. New fathers, too, sometimes experience this **postpartum depression,** or "the blues." Spending a few weeks quietly alone with family sometimes helps to ease the adjustments.

The time after childbirth brings changes for everyone in the household. Not only is there a new baby to care for; there are new roles to play. Suddenly, a woman is a mother, a man is a father. All these changes seemingly happen overnight, and everyone may be a bit uncertain in playing the parts at first. Slowly, a new routine sets in. The new ways become as comfortable as the old ones were. But what routine is best? Now that you have children, what do you do with them?

Key Points ▶ *Childbirth progresses in stages. It may be preceded by false labor. Some women experience depression after giving birth.*

SECTION VI REVIEW

Answer the following questions on a sheet of paper.

Learning the Vocabulary

The vocabulary terms for this section are *lightening, false labor, dilation stage, expulsion stage, crowning, episiotomy, placental stage, afterbirth, breech birth, cesarean section,* and *postpartum depression.*

1. Match each of the following phrases with the appropriate term from above.
   a. warm-up contractions that many women experience before the birth process
   b. a surgical cut made during childbirth when the vagina cannot stretch enough without tearing to allow the baby to pass
   c. the emotional depression a new mother or father experiences after the birth of an infant

Learning the Facts

2. What activities does the fetus do before birth?
3. Describe the stages of labor.
4. Present the reasons why a cesarean section may be necessary.

Making Life Choices

5. Beau and Molly are having their first child and are quite concerned. The doctor thinks the baby is too big to be delivered vaginally. The doctor suggests a cesarean section. What should Beau and Molly do? How will this affect future children? What would you do if you were in the same situation?

SECTION VII

The Elements of Parenting

① Parenting is a skill that can be learned. While it is true that almost everyone has had a model to follow—that of their own parents—most people would do well to learn more about the needs of children. Doing

FOCUS
SECTION VII

In this section the student will learn to:
1. Debate the issues of breastfeeding vs. formula feeding.
2. Identify positive parenting strategies.
3. Develop personal plans for being positive parents.

Activity 7.1
Positive Parenting Skills. Have every student list as many positive parenting skills and negative parenting skills as they can (two-minute limit). Compare numbers of items listed to determine a "winner." Have the winner begin sharing from his or her list and others add skills that have not yet been noted. **(20 min.)**

TEACH
SECTION VII
(Guided and Independent Practice)

Activity 7.2
Parent Interviews. Have each student interview a parent. You can have students prepare their own sets of questions or you could give them the "Parenting Process" handout, which has

(continued on next page)

Breast milk and infant formula are nourishing foods for growing babies.

what comes naturally may not always be best for the child. One of the first parenting decisions a couple is called upon to make is how to feed their newborn.

Breastfeeding or Formula Feeding? ① ①

In most cases, a woman can choose freely between feeding breast milk or formula, knowing that both will support growth of the infant equally well. However, if the infant is premature, if the family has little economic support, or if other factors act to the baby's disadvantage, then breastfeeding is the best choice, especially at first. This is because the earliest form of breast milk, **colostrum,** protects the infant against dis-

eases. Glands in the mother's breasts transfer immunity factors such as antibodies from the mother's blood to the colostrum. Later breast milk contains immunity factors too, but the milk of the first few months is richest in them.

Some women should not breastfeed their babies. If a woman takes drugs, they will

---

MINI GLOSSARY

postpartum depression: the emotional depression a new mother or father experiences after the birth of an infant.
colostrum (co-LAHS-trum)**:** a milklike substance rich in antibodies; the breast milk made during the first few days after birth.

Teacher Support Notes

① **Handout—Breast Milk vs. Formula:** For enrichment, distribute the handout entitled "Breast Milk vs. Formula."
② **Breastfeeding Advantages:** For enrichment you may want to give students some additional information about breastfeeding. For example, it benefits the mother by stimulating a reflex that causes uterine contractions, thus promoting the return of the uterus to its normal size. It also draws energy from the few pounds of fat that the mother's body stored to support lactation. It benefits the infant because this milk's unique nutrient composition supports optimal infant growth. For example, breast milk promotes the absorption of iron and zinc and stimulates the development of the infant's digestive tract. Breastfeeding also promotes bonding, which stimulates healthy emotional growth in the infant.

prepared questions. They need questions to determine such things as: age they became a parent, age they think is best for parenting, why they feel that way, problems they may have encountered as a parent, age-specific behaviors they have encountered, discipline and motiva-

tional strategies they have found to be effective and those that were not effective, and specific characteristics and techniques they feel are necessary for positive parenting. The students should then conduct the interviews, using the questionnaires they have designed. Have students write a report of their findings, including their personal observations, some advantages and disadvantages of parenting, and when they feel is the best

time in life for parenting. Students should also summarize the responsibilities of parenting in all stages of a child's life. **(40 min.; Extend, Enrich)**

Activity 7.3

Debate. Have the students, under your direction, discuss the advantages and disadvantages of breastfeeding and formula feeding. Then divide the class into four groups: one *for* breastfeeding,

Teacher Support Notes

① **Teen Views Follow-up Questions:** The following questions will help you promote classroom discussion of the issue raised in the Teen Views feature:

a. Do students think that Jessie Loskarn's parents are unusual? Why?

b. Rebeka Estrada implies that teens may realize more than adults how important it is to raise children in healthy and loving environments. Do students agree with her?

c. Do students agree with Nicole Bernier that it is wrong for young parents to leave the responsibility of raising their children to *their* parents? How much help from the parents is acceptable?

d. How important are a college education and a high salary to raising children? How do these factors compare in importance to "what's inside and what you can share with the child," as stated by Sarah Friedman?

e. Are any of the students' siblings teen parents? Would they share what they know of their siblings' experiences?

f. Do students think that it's harder to raise a child today than it was in previous years? Why? In what ways would it be easier to raise a child today?

TEEN VIEWS — Can teenagers be good parents? ①

My mom was 18 and my dad was 21 when I was born, and they're great parents. A lot depends on how willing the teenagers are to give up their free time. **Jesse Loskarn, 14, South Carroll High School, MD**

Teens can become good parents with the help of their own strong, good, supportive parents. Teens know how important it is to raise children in a healthy and loving environment. **Rebeka Estrada, 15, Hilltop High School, CA**

Most teenagers are not emotionally ready to handle a baby. Also, both teenagers have to get a job to support themselves, and when they do that, they usually have to quit school and ruin any chance of a future. **Brandon Jones, 15, Carter High School, TN**

It's highly unlikely. Most teenagers are rather unpredictable. If two dependable teenagers are getting a good, steady income and have no major plans for the future, a child might become a possibility. **Spring Verstraete, 14, South Carroll High School, MD**

I've seen this happen—a

teenager has a child and leaves the responsibility to a parent. The teenager still wants to do the things other teens are doing. It's not right though. If the teenager makes the decision to have sex, then it's her or his responsibility to raise the child properly. **Nicole Bernier, 15, Great Falls High School, MT**

Teenagers have just as good a chance to be good parents as adults. I don't think age makes any difference at all. There are plenty of adults who are horrible parents, and there are horrible teenage parents, too. If I were to have a child now, I know I'd definitely be a better parent than mine were to me. It's not based on how many years of college you've been through, or what your annual salary is. It's what's inside and what you can share with the child like values, morals, and experiences. **Sarah Friedman, 16, Wilson High School, CA**

My oldest sister was a teenager mother. She chose to keep her son; no way did any of us like the idea of giving him up; we all loved him to pieces. I have seen her struggle. She finished

school and graduated, but it's been very hard. It's very important for every child to have two parents. **Danielle Fick, 15, Fargo South High School, ND**

No. Teenagers are still growing up and just beginning to take responsibilities for the things they do. Having a child is a bigger responsibility. There is so much a baby or child needs that sometimes we as teenagers may not fulfill their needs. We need to have a chance to grow up. Most teenagers are not ready and they end up pregnant because of carelessness. It's even harder now to bring up a child in today's world with all the violence and racism. **Angelica Castillo, 16, Robert E. Lee High School, TX**

Teenagers can be wonderful parents. There are places you can go to be a better parent. I say "good luck" to those who are young and have children. I think with effort and affection anyone can become a good parent. **Christine Dueis, 15, Fargo South High School, ND** one *against* breastfeeding, one *for* formula feeding, and one *against* formula feeding. Have the groups study their issues and be prepared to debate their opposing groups. Allow time in class for the debates. **(one or two class periods for debates; Extend, Enrich)**

Activity 7.4
Child Development Groups.
Divide the class into groups and assign each group one year of child development. One group takes birth to one year, one takes one to two years, and so on, as far as you deem necessary to assign all groups a different stage. Have the groups decide on and prepare a chart of positive parenting skills for that stage of development. Encourage the class to consult some outside medical professionals and parents, and to do research to gather additional information. Have them relate the specific parenting skills to certain developmental characteristics that occur at that age. Refer them to Chapter 3. Have the groups pass their completed charts to other groups. They should analyze and critique each other's charts until each group has had a chance to view each chart. **(1 hr. to view charts, Cooperative Learning)**

(continued on next page)

---

usually be secreted in her breast milk. Drug addicts, including alcohol abusers, are capable of taking such high doses that their infants will become addicted through the breast milk. Thus women addicted to drugs should not breastfeed. (Most prescription drugs, however, do not reach nursing infants in large enough quantities to harm them.) Also, women who test positive for the AIDS virus should not breastfeed uninfected babies, because the virus can be passed to the infant through breast milk.

> **Key Points** *Breastfeeding offers some unique advantages to most babies, but formula supports growth as well as breast milk. Some women should not breastfeed because of drug abuse or infection.*

Meeting Children's Needs

Parenting is not a one-way process. It is not just adult people acting on little ones. Children contribute to it, too. Children participate in their own development from early on, making conscious choices and taking advantage of opportunities presented to them. Their own choices, to a great extent, determine the adults they will become.

A parent's job is to support a child's developmental needs. These include physical, emotional, and social needs.

Parents must, above all, meet their children's physical needs. From infancy until they are financially able to stand alone, children need food, clothing, play activities, school equipment, the company of other children, transportation to wherever these resources are, and health care. Parenting manuals offer details on these topics.

Every child needs healthy food and physical activity throughout growth. The role of food is easily explained. Infants and children need nutrients, from which they build their bodies. But it has been shown that food, even nutritious food, without love is not enough. Given touching and attention,

NO!

Children participate in their own development from early on.

children grow better than they would otherwise. Also, physical activity is important. Children don't get enough exercise just by being children. In fact, the children of today are less fit, fatter, and more disease-prone than at any time in the past. Young children need physical activity. It is up to adults to give them opportunities for it.

As for a child's emotional and social needs, look at Erickson's scheme of the development of children in Chapter 3, which is also a statement of the tasks for parents. Parents are supposed to help their children develop trust, autonomy, initiative, and industry. In other words, parents are supposed to nurture and shape the person who will someday be an adult.

Probably the single most important task for the parent is to instill in the child a strong sense of self-esteem. As earlier chapters showed, the feeling that "I am OK, I am worthwhile" helps an individual to be effective in every area of life. These include relationships with others, work, play, and contributions to the larger society. Also vital is to place limits on behavior—in other words, **discipline.** Having reasonable limits makes children feel safe and secure.

MINI GLOSSARY

discipline: the shaping of behavior by way of rewards and/or punishments.

537

Activity 7.5

Parenting Pamphlets. Have the groups from the previous activity assemble the parenting skills from their research and classmates' evaluations into a parenting skills pamphlet. Have each group type a concise list. Assign jobs within each group for publication of this pamphlet. (designing a cover, assembling, printing, editing, and circulating) The class should culminate this activity by publishing and circulating their parenting skills pamphlets. **(Extend, Enrich)**

E**VALUATE**
SECTION VII

Activity 7.6
Pop Quiz.
1. Name one advantage and one disadvantage of breastfeeding and formula feeding. (Answers will vary.)
2. Name and describe at least three types of abuse parents can inflict upon their children. (Answers will vary.)
3. Identify at least six positive parenting skills and explain what makes them positive. (Answers will vary.)

✍ Fast Facts

Every two minutes someone abuses a child. Every two hours a child dies from abuse.

☎ Where to Call

Beech-Nut Nutrition Hot Line, 1-800-523-6633. Gerber Products Co., 1-800-443-7237. Dieticians and nutritionists will answer questions about what to feed babies.

✍ Fast Facts

Youngsters from broken families are four times more likely to divorce than children of married couples who stay together according to the Center for Adult Children of Divorce in South Lake Tahoe, CA.

538 UNIT 6 The Life Cycle

Children thrive on love and play.

Many people have grown up in less-than-ideal family circumstances. In the worst cases, parents whose own childhoods included physical, sexual, or psychological **child abuse** tend to become abusive themselves. This behavior becomes especially likely whenever their own needs are not met. Chapter 5 provided details about dysfunctional families—the kind in which child abuse takes place.

Child abuse is illegal, of course. You can help prevent it. If you ever encounter a suspected case of sexual or other abuse of a child, believe the child. The majority of children's reports of such situations are truthful. Seek expert help, support, and counseling for the child and for the abuser. You can report child abuse without giving your name. Check the "Abuse Registry" in the front of your phone book for a toll-free number or look back to Chapter 5.

Some common threads draw together all the theories of child development. Children are not miniature adults. That is, they think and reason in ways unique to children. Children develop in known stages. Each child proceeds through those stages at his or her own pace, depending partly on the child's own genetic tendencies and partly on the environment furnished by adults.

> **Key Points** *Parents must provide for their children's physical, emotional, and social needs. Perhaps the most important aspect of parenting is to foster children's self-esteem. Child abuse is illegal.*

SECTION VII REVIEW

Answer the following questions on a sheet of paper.
Learning the Vocabulary
The vocabulary terms in this section are *colostrum, discipline,* and *child abuse.*
Fill in each blank with the correct answer.
1. _____ is a substance produced by the breasts before they begin producing milk.

office, and how learning good parenting skills can help prevent some types of abuse. **(Extend, Enrich)**

RETEACH/BONUS

Here are some additional activities for the various sections of this chapter. You may want to use these activities to reteach certain concepts, or you may choose them

as alternatives to earlier activities. Some could also be used in conjunction with the Straight Talk feature on the next page.

Research. Assign each student a lifestyle habit that can be harmful to a pregnancy. Instruct students to research the effects that habit can have on children. Specify that they should name disorders or complications that could come

(continued on next page)

Activity 7.7
Guest Speaker. Invite a guest speaker from parenting classes, the sheriff's office, or social services to talk to the class about abuse cases. The speaker can include topics such as causes, intervention by the county or local sheriff's

---

2. Verbal, psychological, physical, or sexual assault on a child is called _____.
3. _____ is the shaping of behavior by way of rewards and/or punishments.

Learning the Facts
4. Why is breastfeeding a baby in the first few months after birth important to the baby's health?
5. What is the single most important task for the parent?
6. How can you prevent child abuse?

Making Life Choices
7. Your best friend Brianna has been psychologically abused all her life. After reading this section, what action would you take to help your friend? Why would you take that action? Would you have taken the same action if you had been abused? Why or why not?

Answers to Fact or Fiction

Here are the answers to the questions at the start of the chapter.

1. True. **2.** False. Nonpregnant women may miss periods because of other factors, and a pregnant woman may have a menstrual period. **3.** True. **4.** False. Physical activity during pregnancy may reduce discomfort and help to ensure a quick recovery from childbirth. **5.** False. A pregnant woman should not "eat for two," or she will gain unneeded fat. **6.** True.

MINI GLOSSARY

child abuse: verbal, psychological, physical, or sexual assault on a child.

✉ Where to Write

Maternity Center Association
48 E. 92nd St.
NY, NY 10029

Section VII Review
Answers
1. Colostrum
2. child abuse
3. Discipline
4. Glands in the mother's breasts transfer immunity factors such as antibodies from the mother's blood to colostrum, the earliest form of breast milk. These immunity factors are then transferred to the baby.
5. to instill in the child a strong sense of self-esteem
6. If you should confront a suspected case of child abuse, believe the child, and seek expert help, support, and counseling for the abuser.
7. Answers will vary.

from the lifestyle habits of one or both parents. They may wish to include information they can secure from interviewing a doctor, nurse, medical person, or a parent who has had experiences with certain complications due to their own personal habits prior to childbearing. Have the stu-

dent write a report using his/her research and present the report to the class.

Abuse Determinations. Type five or six scenarios of abusive situations, such as rape, child beating, peer violence, parental neglect, sexual molestation of a child by an acquaintance or relative, etc. These could be imaginary or come from local news reports. Prepare a four-column worksheet entitled "Identify

the Abuse." Label the columns: "What kind of abuse is this?" "Who is being abused?" "Who is the abuser?" "What needs to be done to stop this abuse?" Give a short lecture on the types of abuse: neglect, sexual, verbal, emotional, mental, economic, physical, molestation, exploitation, etc. Then give the scenarios and worksheets to small groups. Have them discuss the situation and answer the questions. Have the groups share

---

❝ Thoughts on Health ❞

Men are what their mothers made them.
– Emerson

Teacher Support Notes

① **Lasting Effects:** Point out to students that perhaps the most important and tragic aspect of these symptoms is that damage that is evident at birth remains forever. Children with FAS never fully recover.

② **Mental Retardation:** You may want to tell students that of the leading causes of mental retardation, FAS is the only one that is totally preventable. The surgeon general has issued a statement that pregnant women should drink absolutely no alcohol. Containers of beer, wine, or liquor now must carry the warning: *Women should not drink alcoholic beverages during pregnancy because of the risk of birth defects.*

✍ Fast Facts

Approximately 10,000 babies die from preventable causes each year in the United States according to an interim president of the Children's Defense Fund.

---

540 UNIT 6 The Life Cycle

STRAIGHT TALK

Drinking during Pregnancy

Drinking alcohol during pregnancy can cause fetal alcohol syndrome (FAS). The fetal brain is delicate, and its normal development depends on a steady supply of glucose and oxygen. Alcohol reduces the blood flow to the fetal brain and so reduces the brain's supplies of these vital substances. In addition, alcohol itself crosses the placenta freely and directly damages the brain.

About 1 in every 750 children born in the United States is a victim of FAS. Three times as many babies are not diagnosed with FAS, but are born with minor damage from alcohol that cannot be seen until later. The mothers of these children drank, but not enough to cause the visible, obvious effects of FAS.

What are the symptoms of fetal alcohol syndrome?

At its most severe, **FAS** involves:

- Retarded physical growth, both before and after birth.
- Damage to the brain and nerves, with mental retardation, poor coordination, and hyperactivity.
- Abnormalities of the face and skull.
- Many major birth defects (defects in major organ systems—heart, ears, genitals, and urinary system).

In cases of less severe damage (**subclinical FAS**), the symptoms are subtle—hidden under a normal-looking exterior. Parents of such babies may not suspect any defects, yet they may exist. They can be disastrous: learning disabilities, abnormal

① behaviors, walking problems, other coordination problems, and more.

How much alcohol does a woman have to drink to cause FAS?

② Clearly, 3 ounces of alcohol (the amount of alcohol in six beers or six hard-liquor drinks) a day is too much. However, as few as two drinks a day can cause the damage of fetal alcohol syndrome. The most severe damage is likely to be done in the first month, even before the woman is sure she is pregnant. Even if the woman stops drinking immediately after she learns that she is pregnant, it may be too late to prevent all the damage. Women who drink two drinks a day are also more likely to have spontaneous abortions (miscarriages), perhaps because alcohol poisons the fetus. In one

study, women who drank as little as two drinks *a week* were found to have more miscarriages than nondrinkers. Thus, in some cases, it appears that very small amounts of alcohol can endanger fetuses.

What about the timing? Why is the first month so crucial?

Oxygen is critical to the development of the fetus's central nervous system. A sudden dose of alcohol can halt the delivery of oxygen through the umbilical cord. During the first month of pregnancy, even a few minutes of alcohol exposure and oxygen lack can cause major damage to the rapidly growing brain.

The effects of FAS are severe and lifelong. A person

(Continued on next page)

Parenting Classes. Check for meetings of parenting classes in your area. Many school systems, hospitals, and health departments sponsor these. With permission from the leader, require your students to attend a meeting and write a brief report on that visit. Have your students attend parenting classes to distribute and discuss their "parenting pamphlet" made in class. You might also require the students to do some volunteer work in parenting skills projects sponsored by the health department, social services, mental health department, or the school system. **(Extend, Enrich)**

STRAIGHT TALK *(Continued)*

who was exposed to alcohol before birth may respond differently to alcohol in adulthood. That person may also respond differently to some drugs. Learning disabilities also last a lifetime. They are caused by even low levels of alcohol intake. Not every learning disability is caused by alcohol in pregnancy, but no doubt some are. Some experiments even show ill effects from alcohol consumed *before* pregnancy occurred. The *Journal of the American Medical Association* advises women to stop drinking as soon as they *plan* to become pregnant.

It is important to know, though, that if a woman has drunk heavily during the first two-thirds of her pregnancy, she can still prevent some damage by stopping heavy drinking during the last third.

Do any authorities say that a few drinks during pregnancy are not harmful? No drinking at all seems extreme.

The answer is no. The authorities are all on one

side—against drinking. On the other side, there was one opinion, but it has been changed. The American Council on Science and Health (ACSH) expressed the view, at first, that adult women who drank only a little during pregnancy should not be made to feel guilty. Recently, though, the ACSH has changed that opinion. It now says this:

> Probably an occasional glass of beer or wine is tolerable in pregnancy . . . provided that one drink

does not lead to another. Total prohibition of drinking is an unacceptable rule for many people. Nevertheless, we believe that many pregnant women will prefer to give up drinking for the duration of pregnancy.

Is that the position of this book?

Yes, it is. It is a personal choice, but if we had it to make, we would choose the healthy baby.

Mini Glossary

FAS (fetal alcohol syndrome): a cluster of birth defects, including permanent mental and physical retardation and facial abnormalities, seen in children born to mothers who abuse alcohol during pregnancy.

subclinical FAS: a subtle version of FAS, with hidden defects including learning disabilities, behavioral abnormalities, and motor impairments.

①

Teacher Support Notes

① **Handout—U.S. Public Health Service Objectives:** In your supplementary material you will find a handout that lists the U.S. Public Health Service objectives for the nation in the areas of maternal and infant health. You may want to distribute this handout to your students.

📖 Fast Facts

According to a study by British doctors, a baby's weight is an indication of its health in middle age. The study showed that male babies weighing 5.5 pounds or less at birth, or under 18 lbs. when they were one year old, were at higher risk for heart disease than those who weighed 9.5 pounds when born, or more than 26 lbs. by their first birthday.

CHAPTER REVIEW
Answers

Vocabulary
1. **a.** embryo **b.** implantation **c.** morning sickness **d.** Down's syndrome **e.** breech
2. **a.** Gestation **b.** umbilical cord **c.** Low birthweight **d.** PKU (phenylketonuria) **e.** Crowning
3. **a.** colostrum **b.** afterbirth **c.** lightening **d.** conception

Recall
Section II
1. it may embed itself in the prepared uterine lining, beginning a pregnancy
2. it shrinks in the two weeks following ovulation and is eventually shed
3. 4 to 5 days on the average
4. sexual intercourse while an ovum is present in the woman's body
5. 12 to 24 hours
Section III
6. Nutrition affects the ova and sperm, and good nutrition supports the hormone balance needed for conception.
Section IV
7. nutrients and oxygen
8. The fetus would be left with no source of nutrients or oxygen.
9. the brain and central nervous system
10. imperfect embryos from becoming full-term infants
11. most types of physical activity, as long as the abdomen is protected
12. the number of the infant's brain cells can be reduced and every other body organ and

CHAPTER REVIEW

LEARNING THE VOCABULARY

conception	spontaneous abortion or miscarriage	lightening
menstrual cycle	lactation	false labor
sperm	morning sickness	dilation stage
ova	high-risk pregnancy	explusion stage
ovum	prenatal care	crowning
ovulation	low birthweight	episiotomy
fertilization	premature	placental stage
implantation	small for date	afterbirth
fertility awareness method	congenital	breech birth
gestation	birth defects	cesarean section
zygote	genetic counselor	postpartum depression
embryo	Down's syndrome	colostrum
fetus	PKU (phenylketonuria)	discipline
placenta	amniocentesis	child abuse
amniotic sac	rubella	FAS
umbilical cord	sudden infant death syndrome	subclinical FAS
critical periods	(SIDS)	

Answer the following questions on a separate sheet of paper.

1. *Matching*—*Match each of the following phrases with the appropriate vocabulary term from the list above:*
   a. the developing infant during the second through the eighth week after conception
   b. lodging of a fertilized ovum in the wall of the uterus
   c. the nausea a pregnant woman may suffer at any time of the day
   d. an inherited condition of physical deformities and mental retardation
   e. a birth in which the infant is born in a position other than the normal head-first position

2. a. _____ is the period from conception to birth.
   b. The rope-like structure through which the fetus's veins and arteries reach the placenta is called the _____.
   c. _____ is a birthweight of 5-1/2 pounds or less, used as a predictor of poor

   health in the newborn infant.
   d. A congenital disease causing severe brain damage with mental retardation if left untreated is called _____.
   e. _____ is the moment during childbirth in which the top of the baby's head is first seen.

3. *Word Scramble*—*Use the clues from the phrases below to help you unscramble the vocabulary terms from the list above:*
   a. **oouclmrst** _____ milk-like substance rich in antibodies, made in the mother's breasts during the first few days after birth
   b. **aeibfhrrtt** _____ the placenta and membranes expelled after the birth of the child
   c. **eiigglnnht** _____ the sensation a pregnant woman experiences when the fetus settles into the birth position
   d. **eiooccnnpt** _____ union of an ovum and a sperm that starts a new individual

system can be impaired
13. 25–35 pounds
Section V
14. Answers will vary; could include: chemicals, radiation, smoking, alcohol, drugs, environmental contaminants, compounds in spoiled foods, large doses of Vitamins A, B6, C, and D, the mineral iodine, and the German measles virus.

Section VI
15. makes an incision through the mother's abdomen and lifts the baby and placenta out
16. It is the hardest of all physical efforts, and the woman cannot rest until it is finished.
Section VII
17. if a woman takes drugs, abuses alcohol, or tests positive for the AIDS virus

18. food, clothing, play activities, school equipment, the company of other children, transportation to wherever these resources are, and health care
Straight Talk
19. retarded physical growth, before and after birth; damage to the brain and nerves, with mental retardation,

poor coordination, and hyperactivity; abnormalities of the face and skull; many major birth defects (defects in the major organ systems—heart, ears, genitals, and urinary system)
20. Oxygen is critical to the development of the fetus' central nervous system, which occurs during the first month of development. Even a few minutes of alcohol exposure and oxygen lack at this crucial time can cause major damage to the rapidly growing brain.

RECALLING IMPORTANT FACTS AND IDEAS

1. What happens to the egg in the woman's body after it is fertilized?
2. Explain what happens to the uterine lining when the egg is not fertilized.
3. How long does menstruation last?
4. What must happen for conception to occur?
5. How long does the female's ovum live?
6. Why is it important for parents to be well nourished before they start a pregnancy?
7. What does the placenta pump into the fetal bloodstream?
8. Explain what happens to the fetus if the placenta breaks down.
9. Which body systems reach maturity first in the developing fetus?
10. What does spontaneous abortion or miscarriage often prevent?
11. What kind of physical activity is best for a pregnant woman?
12. Describe the effects of malnutrition during pregnancy.
13. What is the recommended weight gain for a pregnant woman?
14. What are some harmful factors known to damage developing fetuses?
15. Describe what the doctor does when a woman has a cesarean section.
16. Why do people say that labor bears an appropriate name?
17. Under what conditions should women not breastfeed their babies?
18. In what ways must parents provide for their children's physical needs?
19. Describe the symptoms of fetal alcohol syndrome.
20. Explain why the first month of pregnancy is so critical to the development of the fetus.

CRITICAL THINKING

1. Reread the Straight Talk on page 540 entitled "Drinking during Pregnancy." Notice how critical the first month of pregnancy is. Note that most women do not even know they are pregnant in the first month. What can be done to help women who drink alcohol when they might be pregnant? Why do you think so many babies are born with fetal alcohol syndrome? How can we educate women about this problem? What can we do to help the infants born with fetal alcohol syndrome?

ACTIVITIES

1. Call an adoption agency and ask them how long it would take to adopt a baby. Ask about babies from all ethnic groups. Which babies are the quickest to be adopted and why? Which babies take the longest to be adopted?
2. Being a parent is not easy. Pretend an egg is a baby and that you are a parent. Take care of that egg for one week. The egg must go everywhere you go. You must set the alarm at 2:00 A.M. every night to check on the egg (it might need you). Keep a journal of your experiences about being a parent.
3. Interview your parents about your birth. What type of birth was it? Was your father present for your birth? Describe how the labor process was for your mother.

MAKING DECISIONS ABOUT HEALTH

1. Autumn and Jason have been having unprotected sexual intercourse. They try to time it so that they avoid the "dangerous" time of the month, but neither is certain of exactly when that time is. So far, Autumn hasn't gotten pregnant, and they continue using no contraception.

   a. What is your opinion of the way Jason and Autumn are dealing with their situation? Why do you feel as you do?
   b. What do you think the outcome of this situation might eventually be and why?

543

The Law and Sexuality

An unfortunate reality in our society is the all-too-frequent occurrence of sexual crimes. It may help you to know about the types of sexual crimes that occur and the penalties that result.

Following are descriptions of five general categories of sexual crimes: rape, sexual abuse of children, prostitution, deviate sexual behavior, and harassment. These descriptions provide an overview of the laws as they exist currently in the United States as a whole. As with all laws, the laws related to sexuality may vary from state to state. For specific laws in your state, contact your state's Attorney General's office.

Rape

Throughout history rape has been defined as an illegal act in which a man forces a woman to have sexual intercourse against her will. In most states today the definition of rape has been broadened to include a wide range of sexual assaults, which apply to both men and women. Rape is a felony, which means it is a serious crime, punishable by at least one year in prison.

Sexual Abuse of Children

Many different sex crimes are committed against children. Statutory rape is a rape committed against a female who is not legally old enough to agree to have sexual intercourse. In this type of rape consent is not an issue—if the female is underage, it is rape whether she consents or not. The legal age varies from state to state (for example: Connecticut, 16; Wisconsin, 17; Texas, 17) and even within the same state, depending on circumstances and the degree of the felony.

Other types of sexual crimes against children include abduction or enticement; child pornography, which is the exploitation of children in sexual ways for financial gain; and incest (sexual relations between people who are closely related), which is a crime usually committed against children. All forceful or violent sexual attacks against children are, of course, illegal.

Prostitution

Prostitution is the act of engaging in sexual relations in exchange for money or something of value. A person can also be convicted of prostitution if he or she offers to engage in a sexual act for money or requests money for performing a sexual act. Prostitution is illegal in all states except Nevada.

Deviate Sexual Behavior

Until 1961 all states outlawed sex between members of the same sex. Since that time, however, many states have made such acts legal for consenting adults, in private. (Both heterosexual and homosexual acts committed in public are crimes.) About half the states still have laws such as the Texas law that says "A person commits an offense if he engages in deviate sexual behavior with another individual of the same sex." (21.06)

Sexual Harassment

Sexual harassment cases have received increased attention in recent years and many cities and states have written laws to prohibit this type of conduct. Sexual harassment involves unwelcomed sexual advances or requests for sexual favors. These advances and requests may be combined with undesirable verbal or physical conduct of a sexual nature.

SPECIAL UNIT

Sexual Behavior and Pregnancy Prevention

Sexuality affects life in many ways. Sexual love between partners often plays an important role in maintaining a couple's bond to each other. In addition, sexual intercourse may lead to pregnancy, a happy event in the lives of many couples who are ready to bear and raise children together.

Sexuality and pregnancy can also be disastrous for those not yet prepared to support children. Knowing how, and choosing, to prevent pregnancy until the time is right can prevent lifelong regrets.

CONTENTS

A1

PART A PLANNER

OVERVIEW

Part A is 16 pages long and divided into the three sections listed at the right. Major learning outcomes are also listed to the right. Part A begins by making a distinction between sex and sexuality and explaining the differences and the much broader meaning of these terms than they probably realized. Part A also introduces students to sexual activities, sexual myths, and sexual orientation. Students have the opportunity to explore their own attitudes and feelings as they study these topics.

MAKING LIFE CHOICES RESOURCES

A variety of activities, handouts, quizzes, and tests to accompany this chapter are available in the *Making Life Choices* supplementary material. You may pick and choose from those materials as appropriate for your amount of class time and the ability levels of your students. Some of the resources you might want to consider using are:

Overheads
• Genes and Chromosomes
• Male Organs
• Female Organs
• Male Reproductive System
• Female Reproductive System

Handouts
• Attitudes About Sexuality
• Myths and Truths About Masturbation
• Effects of Drugs on Sexual Functioning
• Teen Pregnancy, STDs, and AIDS Statistics

Part A
Sexual Behavior

SUGGESTED RESOURCES

Student Readings
1. McCoy, Kathy, Ph.D., and Wibbelsman, Charles, M.D. *The New Teenage Body Book*. New York: The Putnam Publishing Group.
2. Bell, Ruth. *Changing Bodies, Changing Lives*. New York: Vintage Books, 1988.
3. Alyson, Sasha, ed. *Young, Gay, and Proud*. Boston, MA: Alyson Publications, Inc., 1985.

Teacher Readings
1. McCammon, Knox, and Schact, *Choices in Sexuality*, Minneapolis/St.Paul: West Publishing, 1993.

2. Gordon, S. "Sexuality Education in the 1990s." *Health Education*. (January/February, 1990):4–5.
3. *Understanding Sexuality—Making Healthy Choices*. St. Paul, MN: Health Start, 1988. Comprehensive sexuality unit for senior high students.

Software
1. *Ask Me: Sexual Information for Adolescents*. Body changes, birth control, sexual intercourse, pregnancy, and STDs are covered. Opportunities for Learning, Inc., 800-243-7116.

OUTCOMES

After reading and studying Part A, you will be able to:

✓ **Identify the stages of the sexual response.**

✓ **List and describe examples of sexual myths.**

✓ **Describe various sexual orientations.**

CONTENTS

I. Sexual Activity
II. Sexual Myths
III. Sexual Orientations

Straight Talk: *Condoms and STDs*

FACT OR FICTION

What do you think? Are the following statements true or false? If you think they are false, then say what is true.

1. The term *sexuality* refers to sexual activity—primarily sexual intercourse.
2. Activities such as touching, hugging, and kissing can be emotionally satisfying, as well as physically satisfying.
3. At puberty, hormones produced by the body create a drive for reproduction.
4. The most important sex organs—

the organs that control sexual behavior—are the penis and the clitoris.
5. Men with the largest penises are the best lovers.
6. Aphrodisiacs are not really able to enhance or restore people's sexual desires and abilities.
7. Homosexuals are all alike in terms of their lifestyles.

(Answers on page A13)

■ **Reminder:** Knowing how to study can increase your knowledge, improve your grades, *and* cut down on your study time. See the *Studying Health* section at the front of your text for some suggestions to help you study Part A.

NOT ENOUGH TIME?*

It is likely that you will have only one or two days to devote to this chapter. Following are some suggestions to help you make sure that you cover the key topics if you have limited time.

TIME	SUGGESTIONS
1 Day	Assign Sections I–III prior to class. During class have students complete Activities 1.5 and 1.11 in Section I.
2 Days	On day 2, during class, assign Activity 2.4 in Section II and Activity 3.2 in Section III. Use Evaluate activities as time permits.

*Please refer to the 18-week daily lesson plans in the supplementary material for additional suggestions.

CHAPTER PROJECT

Have each student interview a parent, grandparent, or friend about the dating customs when they were the student's age. As a class, develop a list of interview questions to be used. Share these interviews as oral reports or make a class book of interviews. This is a good long-term project and can be effective in strengthening school/community ties.

Answers to "Fact or Fiction"

1. False. Sexuality is a part of a person's total personality from birth to death, with or without sexual activity. **2.** True. **3.** True. **4.** False. The brain, not the penis and clitoris, is the most important sex organ. **5.** False. The brain controls the sexual response. Therefore, what a woman *thinks* about a man is at least as important as any physical aspect of intercourse. **6.** True. **7.** False. If you tried to identify "the" homosexual lifestyle, you could not do it.

Activity To Introduce Chapter

Activity 1.1 in Section I is an excellent kick-off activity for the entire unit. Another possibility for an introductory activity is for the students to brainstorm, as a class (or in small groups), 101 ways to show love without having sex.

In this section students will learn:
1. The meaning and purpose of *sex* and *sexuality*.
2. Typical reactions to early sexual feelings.
3. The four phases of sexual response.

Activity 1.1
Information Sources. Have students list every place from which they get sexual information. Have them rank the list in two ways: from most to least reliable and from most to least accessible. The list might include: friends, magazines, parents, teachers, books, TV, movies, church, etc. Compare the students' lists and their rankings.

Activity 1.2
Desirable Attributes. In small, gender-segregated groups, have students list the attributes they most desire in a person they might date. After allowing time for the lists to develop, post the lists on the wall or copy them onto the board. Lead a discussion about the similarities and differences. Commonly, the boys' lists will contain more physical attributes and the girls' lists will contain more personality

Teacher Support Notes

① **Sex and Sexuality:**
If students do not see the difference between these two terms, refer them to the definitions in the Mini Glossary. You could also tell them that *sexuality* is broader and more complex than *sex*. Sexuality involves not only sex, but also what we do sexually and who we are sexually.

② **Overhead—Genes and Chromosomes:**
The supplementary material contains an overhead that illustrates the way in which completely new and unique individuals are created. Terms such as sperm, ovum, and zygote were introduced in Chapter 21.

③ **Purpose(s) of Sex:**
After reading this page, ask students to describe in their own words the purpose of sex. (It guarantees that living things will reproduce and that they will mix to create new combinations.) Ask students if they think the accomplishments that result from sex are positive. In answering, you may want to tell them to consider what the world would be like without sex. What would it be like if living things could be reproduced, but did not create different combinations? Would the world be a better or worse place to live?

A4

A4 Special Unit Sexual Behavior and Pregnancy Prevention

What is **sex** for? And what is **sexuality** all about? Sex and sexuality are such interesting subjects, and so personally important, that people seldom back off far enough to look at them from a scientific point of view. It's worth a minute to think about this, though—for sex is much more than just something embarrassing that people hesitate to talk about. As for sexuality, it is much more than a characteristic people find exciting, scary, and hard to manage. Sex and sexuality play important roles in all of nature.

Sex plays two major roles in nature. First, it ensures that living things reproduce their kind—that pine trees produce more pine trees; that eagles produce more eagles; and that human beings produce more human beings. Second, sex ensures that the hereditary materials individuals carry (the genes) are repeatedly shuffled and dealt out in different combinations in every new individual.

Here's how this shuffling works. You have, in the cells of your body, genes from your mother and genes from your father, for every characteristic that makes you you. Your genes govern surface traits such as your eye color, skin color, and hair color; and also deep-down traits such as your musical ability (or lack of it), your friendliness or competitiveness, and everything else about you. The potential to develop these traits was passed on to you at the moment when you were conceived. Half of them came from your father and half from your mother, and the mixture determined what sort of person you turned out to be. Of course your life experiences affect how you turn out, too, but the limits on what you can become are set by your genes.

If it comes time for you to take part in creating a new individual, you will pass half of these traits on—but they won't be your mother's half, or your father's half. They

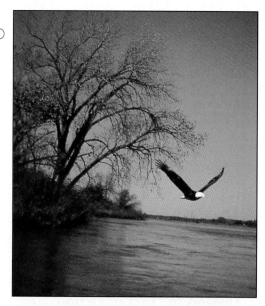

Most living things, including eagles and trees, reproduce their kind using sexual reproduction.

will be a mixture. You may pass on the potential to develop your mother's brown eyes and love of learning, and your father's strong hands and sense of rhythm. Your partner will also pass on a mixed set of traits, some from each parent. The child you produce will end up with a new combination never before seen in a human being. The child may, for example, have brown eyes from your mother, a sense of rhythm from your father, special mathematics ability from your partner's mother, and skill at sports from your partner's father.

Every new child is a brand-new individual, carrying a combination of traits never tried before, thanks to sexual reproduction. Sex, in short, provides a way to mix inherited traits into new combinations in every generation. Each living thing, whether it is a pine tree, an eagle, or a human being, has a unique chance to try a new way of living and thriving in an ever-changing world.

traits. Ask students what they would add to or subtract from the lists if they represented the persons they planned to marry. (15 min.)

TEACH

SECTION I
(Guided and Independent Practice)

Activity 1.3
Comparing Species: Have students pick one type of animal, research that animal's sexual behavior, and prepare a presentation for the class. You may want to have students work in groups. Each presentation should include one or two graphics (poster, overhead, video, slides, etc.) and should conclude with a comparison of at least one aspect of that animal's sexuality with human sexuality. If possible, coordinate this activity with the students' biology teachers. **(preparation 1–2 wks, presentations 3–5 minutes; Interdisciplinary)**

Activity 1.4
Ranking Photos. Cut out a large variety of magazine photos of attractive, well-dressed men and women. Try to get as wide a variety of looks as possible. Have students rank the photos from most attractive to least attractive. See if boys as a group and girls as a group can guess

(continued on next page)

When parents attempt to explain sex to their children, people sometimes joke about it and say that they had a talk about "the birds and the bees." Actually, though, it is no joke. Sexual reproduction—the mixing and recombining of genetic traits—has made it possible for birds and bees, as well as ourselves, to survive to this day in time.

For sex to work, every individual must reduce its genetic material by half and then have the opportunity to get together with another individual and combine halves. That is exactly what takes place when sexual reproduction occurs. The male contributes half of his genes in a sperm, the female contributes half of hers in an egg. The sperm and egg combine, and a new individual begins to develop. (The same process does occur in eagles, by the way, and it is only slightly different in pine trees. In pine trees, it is pollen, not sperm, that carry genes from one individual to another. This discussion will stay, however, with human beings.)

Every type of living thing survives on earth only so long as it can reproduce. For that reason, the sex drive is very strong—it must be to ensure that reproduction will take place. That is why each person's sexuality has such an influence on the person's life. The famous attraction between the sexes is a deep-down, basic, instinctual attraction that leads to the continuation of life. It also motivates the expression of one of the highest forms of human emotional and spiritual development—love.

Sexuality is a part of a person's total personality from birth to death, with or without sexual activity. The way you walk, think, and feel, and the ways you talk to and touch others, all are affected by your sexuality. Sexuality affects the young, the old, the handicapped, all races, all sizes—all people.

Your sexuality is greatly influenced by the way you feel about yourself. This

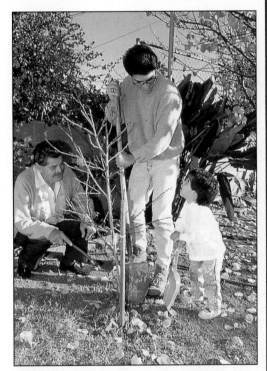

Reproduction creates new generations and future hopes.

① means that your level of self-esteem is a good measure of your sexuality. Your thoughts, feelings, values, and self-concept are all part of your sexuality.

In this text you have already learned a great deal about human sexuality. In Chapter 3 you learned about the sexual maturation called puberty that takes place during your teen years. In that chapter you also

MINI GLOSSARY

sex: a general term used to mean both gender and sexual intercourse.
sexuality: the quality of being sexual. Sexuality is part of the total person: physical, emotional, social, intellectual, and spiritual. Sexuality is part of who people are.

Teacher Support Notes

① **Sex Drive:** For enrichment you may wish to give students some additional information about the sex drive. For example, you could tell them that experts disagree as to whether or not human sexual behavior is primarily physiological or psychological. Sexual arousal may be produced by direct stimulation of the body's *erogenous zones*, including the genitals, mouth, breasts, ears, and to a lesser degree, the surface of the entire body. More than physical contact is required, however. Most would agree that sexual desire can exist separately from physical sexual stimulation, and it is the psychological component that motivates sexual behavior. Physical factors also play a role, however. In males, strength of the sex drive is related to the amount of hormones, primarily testosterone, secreted by the testes. For example, when the supply of testosterone dramatically increases at puberty, the sex drive also increases.

the order the other group will choose. Discuss the fact that different people have different opinions about what constitutes an attractive person. **(15 min., Critical Thinking)**

Activity 1.5
Safe Dating. Have students brainstorm a variety of activities a dating couple can engage in which do not allow the opportunity for sexual intercourse but do allow the opportunity for affection. Discuss the concept of dangerous dates, dates which are more likely to lead to intercourse. (drive-in as opposed to walk-in movie) **(15 min., Critical Thinking)**

Activity 1.6
Standards of Attractiveness. Show students as many photos as you are able to gather of people throughout history. Be sure the people in the photos are considered (by historical standards) attractive. Old school yearbook photos can add humor to this activity. Discuss how standards for attractiveness change as society changes. Ask the students what they believe influences our society's

---

A 1992 Center for Disease Control study found that 54% of students in grades 9 to 12, and 70% of seniors, had had sex.

Teacher Support Notes

① **Handout—Sexuality Assessment:** Your supplementary material contains a four-page questionnaire entitled "Attitudes About Sexuality," which will help students determine their own thoughts and feelings about sexuality.
② **First Sexual Arousal:** If students ask when sexual arousal first occurs, you could tell them that sexual researcher Alfred Kinsey observed instances of orgasm in boys as young as five months old and girls as young as four months. Kinsey also found that 50% of males and 25% of females report having engaged in preadolescent sex play.
③ **Handout—Masturbation:** Your supplementary material contains a handout entitled "Myths and Truths About Masturbation."

A6 Special Unit Sexual Behavior and Pregnancy Prevention

learned about gender roles and gender identity. In Chapter 20 you learned about love relationships and the many sexual pressures that accompany those relationships and that exist in today's society. In Chapter 21 you learned about conception and pregnancy.

In this part of the text you will learn about sexual behaviors, ranging from a person's first physical sexual feelings to sexual intercourse. You will also learn about sexual myths and problems. Finally, you will learn about sexual orientations. ①

SECTION I

Sexual Activity

As you know from reading Chapter 20, people who have developed a healthy intimate relationship frequently decide to commit to each other. The highest form of commitment between two people is marriage. Sex can add fulfillment to marriage.

Touching, hugging, and kissing are pleasurable activities physically. These activities may also satisfy emotional needs, and therefore, can be emotionally fulfilling. It is normal and natural in a committed relationship for these activities to sometimes lead to sexual intercourse. Let's now look at how sexual feelings and desires develop and the sexual activities that result.

The First Sexual Feelings

For most people their first sexual relationship is with themselves. At an early age ② boys and girls begin to flirt with themselves in the mirror, enjoying their own attractiveness. They also enjoy physical sensations, such as rubbing lotions onto the skin, sunbathing, and swimming. These are the natural healthy beginnings of sexual feel- ③ ings and activities.

Sexual attraction motivates the expression of love.

When young people reach puberty, the hormones produced by their bodies set up a drive for reproduction. This drive can become intense at times. People may need to release it.

One way the body provides for this release is through **wet dreams**. Almost all adolescent boys, and many girls, experience such dreams from time to time. The **orgasm** that occurs during a wet dream is the body's normal reflex for releasing sexual tension.

Eventually children's natural playfulness and curiosity lead them to explore their genitals. This may lead to **masturbation**, an activity that may continue in adulthood.

Many people are opposed to masturbation. They believe it is wrong and harmful. In the past, people were even told that masturbation caused pimples, warts, excessive hair growth, and many other terrible things.

opinion of beauty. **(15 min.; Extend, Enrich)**

Activity 1.7
  Customs Comparisons. Have students do some research and then write a paper in which they compare the sexual and dating customs of the past to what they see as current sexual and dating customs. They could choose to go back 25, 50, 100, or 200 years. Have them

include their own opinions of how the differences have hurt or improved society. They should also comment on how sexual myths have influenced both past and current dating customs.

Activity 1.8
  Posters. Have students design posters with safe date suggestions. When appropriate, display posters on campus. **(30 min.; Reteach, Reinforce)**

Activity 1.9
  Jigsaw Statistics. Provide students with the handout "Teen Pregnancy, STD, and AIDS Statistics" from the resource material. Have students learn this information in jigsaw style. (Jigsaw—students are put in home groups. Members of home groups separate and form learning groups with members of other home groups to study the statistics they have

(continued on next page)

Of course these beliefs are all myths—none of them are true.

It is fairly common for adolescent boys and girls to be troubled and confused about their desires to masturbate. They may feel guilty and ashamed because it's something they feel they must hide. They may feel that their parents and adults do not approve.

Most medical experts believe, however, that masturbation can be helpful in many situations. Masturbation can be useful, partly because it does not involve other people. For young people, and for people without partners, it provides a way to release sexual tension without risking pregnancy or diseases. By releasing sexual tension it can also help people avoid sexual relationships that they would later regret. In addition, masturbation gives people in immature relationships the time they need to develop mature love together before engaging in sexual intercourse.

> **Key Points** ▶ *In a sense, most people's first sexual relationships are with themselves.*
> *Natural playfulness often leads to masturbation, which is a way to satisfy a biological drive without involving other people.*

Sexual Intercourse

Sexual intercourse is, in a physical sense, a simple act. It is also complex, though, because the two people who engage in it bring to it their moods, ideas, self-concepts, feelings about their relationship, and everything else that makes them unique. This section is about the physical events of sexual intercourse.

Sexual stimulation results in **erection** (stiffening) of the penis in males. Fluid moves down the man's urethra, neutralizing the acid left there by urine and creating a safe environment for sperm. Females experience **engorgement** (swelling) of the clitoris and surrounding tissues, and a tip-

ping upward of the uterus. Lubricating fluids begin to flow within the vagina.

During the man's erection, a drop or so of fluid leaves the penis. This fluid may contain live sperm that can begin a pregnancy. Sperm can easily travel, even from the outside of the vagina, into the uterus. To prevent pregnancy, this early drop of fluid, along with any semen, must be prevented from touching the vagina.

The act of intercourse itself occurs when a man and a woman position their bodies so that the woman's vagina receives the man's penis. Sexual intercourse proceeds with a rhythmic movement of the bodies and usually ends with the man's orgasm and **ejaculation**. The woman's orgasm can occur prior to, along with, or after the man's.

> **Key Points** ▶ *Sexual stimulation leads to male erection and female engorgement, with fluid being secreted from both the penis and the vagina. Sexual intercourse occurs when the penis and vagina unite.*

 MINI GLOSSARY

wet dreams: dreams during which orgasm occurs; a normal release for the sexual drive; in boys, these are also called *nocturnal emissions*.

orgasm: a series of muscular contractions of the sex organs that release tension and end in relaxation; it typically occurs after a period of sexual stimulation.

masturbation: stimulating one's own genitals, usually until orgasm occurs.

erection: the state of a normally soft tissue when it fills with blood and becomes firm. Both the penis and clitoris can become erect.

engorgement: swelling; with reference to the sexual response, the sex organs' filling with blood preparatory to orgasm.

ejaculation: the expelling of semen from the penis, brought about by the involuntary muscular contractions of orgasm.

---

been assigned. Students return to the home group and teach other members of the home group what they have learned.) **(30 min., Cooperative Learning)**

Activity 1.10
Alternatives. Have students work in groups to develop lists of nonsexual ways

sexual tension can be released. Combine their lists to create a class list. Discuss the list with the class. You might want to post the list in the classroom. **(Cooperative Learning, Critical Thinking)**

EVALUATE
SECTION I

Activity 1.11
Pop Quiz.
1. What is considered to be the highest form of commitment between two people? (marriage)
2. What drive, in the body, is produced by hormones during puberty? (the drive for reproduction)
3. With whom are most people's first sexual experiences? (themselves)
4. What is the master sex organ? (the

Teacher Support Notes

① **Male and Female Orgasms:** Experts disagree as to whether or not ejaculation accompanies female orgasm. The female orgasm usually lasts longer than the male orgasm. It's also the case that after orgasm, about 15% of all women return to the plateau phase and may have another orgasm before resolution. Whereas, after the male orgasm there is a short *refractory period* during which a second orgasm is typically not possible.

Section I Review
Answers
1. a. engorgement
b. resolution **c.** wet dreams
2. eye, skin, and hair color; musical ability (or lack of it), friendliness, competitiveness, and everything else about you
3. a drive for reproduction
4. It can be helpful in many situations because it does not involve other people, releases sexual tension without threat of pregnancy or disease, and helps to avoid immature sexual relations.
5. clitoris, vagina, penis
6. excitement, plateau, orgasm, and resolution
7. tilts forward
8. Answers will vary.

A8

The Stages of the Sexual Response

The mystery of the sexual response lies in the human brain. The brain—not the penis or clitoris—is the master sex organ. The brain is the commander of the events described in the next few paragraphs. Among the organs that respond to the brain's instructions are the clitoris and vagina, and the penis.

The four phases of the sexual response for both partners are **excitement, plateau,** orgasm (already described), and **resolution.** Each phase may differ from person to person and may vary in the same person from time to time.

The excitement phase may begin even before physical contact occurs—people are said to be "in the mood" for sexual contact. A loving couple may kiss and then touch one another in ways that stimulate both. This activity, frequently called **foreplay,** leads to erection in the male and engorgement in the female. During this time, the couple can enjoy the emotions of tenderness, love, and gratitude, as well as feelings of sexual pleasure.

If sexual stimulation continues, the partners move into the plateau phase. In this phase the lower third of the vagina constricts, the uterus tilts forward, and the penis enlarges further. The clitoris withdraws under its foreskin as it becomes more sensitive, but still responds through this protective layer of skin.

With more stimulation, orgasm occurs. Orgasm is a reflex—an involuntary response that follows stimulation of the genitals. In women, orgasm involves involuntary rhythmic contractions of the uterus, the outer portion of the vagina, and the surrounding muscles. In men, it involves ejaculation of semen through rhythmic contractions of the penile muscles. Orgasm lasts just a few seconds. ①

In the resolution stage following orgasm, the physical changes of arousal reverse. Tensed muscles relax. Congested blood vessels and swollen tissues return to normal.

Key Points ▸ *The four stages of the sexual response are excitement, plateau, orgasm, and resolution. The sexual response is experienced in the reproductive organs but is controlled by the brain.*

SECTION I   REVIEW

Answer the following questions on a sheet of paper.
Learning the Vocabulary
The vocabulary terms in this section are *sex, sexuality, wet dreams, orgasm, masturbation, erection, engorgement, ejaculation, excitement, plateau, resolution,* and *foreplay.*
1. Match each of the following phrases with the appropriate term.
   a. swelling; with reference to the sexual response, the sex organs' filling with blood preparatory to orgasm
   b. in sexual intercourse, the stage of relaxation that follows orgasm
   c. dreams during which orgasm occurs

Learning the Facts
2. Which traits are genes responsible for?
3. When young people reach puberty, what effects do the hormones produced by their bodies bring about?
4. What do medical experts believe about masturbation?
5. What organs respond to the brain's instructions during the sexual response?
6. What are the four phases of the sexual response?
7. What happens to the uterus in the plateau phase?

Making Life Choices
8. Many people view masturbation as being wrong and harmful. What are your beliefs about masturbation? How did you acquire these beliefs?

brain)
5. What are the stages of sexual response? (excitement, plateau, orgasm, and resolution)

CLOSE

Activity 1.12
  Debates. Have students engage in a series of debates on the following topics:

1. Sexual tension can be controlled. Agree or disagree.
2. The mind, not feelings, should control sexual activity. Agree or disagree.
3. Dating activities do not influence sexual activity. Agree or disagree.
(1 class period for debates, Critical Thinking)

FOCUS
SECTION II

In this section students will learn:
1. Some sexual myths.
2. How self-esteem relates to sexuality.

Activity 2.1
  Myths. Lead a discussion to define

(continued on next page)

SECTION II

Sexual Myths

People hold many false ideas about sexuality. Probably the most widely held and destructive myths concern body measurements. One myth says that a man with a large penis makes the best lover. This is false from two points of view. First, most women experience most sexual stimulation in the clitoris, an external organ. A longer penis, therefore, is not more stimulating to a woman. Second, the brain controls the sexual response. Therefore, what a woman *thinks* about a man is at least as important as any physical aspect of intercourse.

A related myth is that a woman with large breasts is more sexual than a woman with small breasts. Actually, women's breasts are equally sensitive to stimulation, regardless of size. Also, a woman's responsive, caring, considerate, and romantic attitude—not her breast size—is most effective in arousing her partner.

A particularly destructive idea is that once a person has had sexual intercourse, that person is committed to having intercourse again. In reality, a person who is no longer a **virgin** can choose abstinence just as a virgin can. The person has every right to do so. Fear of pregnancy or diseases can also come into play at any time. The person may change moral or religious beliefs, or may simply decide to wait for the right person to come along. For many different reasons, saying no is always an option.

Some people try to pressure others into having intercourse by claiming ill effects from sexual arousal. Is it unhealthy to become sexually aroused and then not proceed to orgasm? No, it isn't harmful, although it may be frustrating. Sometimes it is even useful. For example, if a couple is

In a truly intimate relationship, closeness and caring are as important as sexual attractiveness.

MINI GLOSSARY

excitement: as used to describe a stage of sexual intercourse, the early stage.
plateau: literally, a high, flat place. In sexual intercourse, the plateau phase is the period of intense physical pleasure preceding orgasm.
resolution: in sexual intercourse, the stage of relaxation that follows orgasm.
foreplay: activity in which each partner gives pleasure to the other prior to intercourse.
virgin: a term applied to people before their first occasion of sexual intercourse.

Teacher Support Notes

① **Chemical Attraction:** The common expression to represent sexual attraction, that there is "chemistry" between two people, may turn out to be true. Sexual response may be more related to biochemistry than to external physical attributes. Science has discovered that human beings, like many other species, produce odor chemicals, called *pheromones*, that are recognized by others. Pheromones produce a sensation of recognition, not of true smell. For example, pheromones are produced on the skin surrounding a woman's nipples, which helps infants to readily recognize their mothers' breasts. Adults of both genders produce pheromones around the mouth, which are exchanged during kissing. Human bonding may be reinforced by the exchange of these chemicals, leading to a special recognition of the other.

FOCUS
(Continued)

the word *myth*. List on the board common myths, not necessarily related to sex. Discuss why myths occur and if they are ever dangerous, such as myths saying you cannot get pregnant the first time you have sex, and beer is not as addicting as whiskey. **(15 min.)**

TEACH
SECTION II
(Guided and Independent Practice)

Activity 2.2
Telephone. Play the game "Telephone." The students sit in a large circle. A message is whispered to one person who whispers it to the person on his or her left. This continues until the message has gone around the circle. The last per-

son says the message out loud, and it is compared to the original message. Discuss how facts can become distorted by repetition. Relate this to the development of myths. **(15 min.)**

Activity 2.3
Myth Busters. Have students make "Myth Buster" books. Each student writes three to seven myths about sex along with the truth in a small booklet. Appropri-

Teacher Support Notes

① **Answers to Critical Thinking:**
1. They don't work and many are dangerous.
2. Worries and anxieties that distract the person, fear of pregnancy or STDs, and physical fatigue are factors.
3. Communicate with a partner so that the partner knows what the problems are and try to remedy them individually or together. Seek counseling help if necessary.

② **Sexual Dysfunction:** For enrichment tell students that in men, a sexual dysfunction may manifest itself in the inability to achieve and maintain an erection. In women, the most common complaints are lack of sexual excitement and lack of orgasm during intercourse. The causes of such complaints are varied: physical abnormalities, problems in the love relationship, lack of communication between the lovers, and others. Often the person is worried about some other part of the relationship, which prevents the enjoyment of sex, and the worries must be dealt with before the sex can return to normal. Most people experience at least some difficulty in enjoying sex at some time during their lives.

A10   Special Unit Sexual Behavior and Pregnancy Prevention

CONSUMER AWARENESS

Pills and Potions

The idea of a potion to increase sexual desire—an **aphrodisiac**—has always intrigued people. In a fairy tale, a sprinkling of magic powder can make a princess suddenly notice an overlooked suitor. In real life, no secret compound, no exotic ingredient, and no food or nutrient can enhance or restore sexual desire. So-called aphrodisiacs do not work, and they may be dangerous. Many are strong stimulants, hormones, or depressants. According to the Food and Drug Administration, all claims for aphrodisiacs are false, misleading, or unsupported by scientific evidence. Chances are that if the sexual response fails, the body is signaling a need for attention. Some causes of reduced sexual

response include use of alcohol, drugs, or tobacco; excess worry or depression; or lack of communication between partners. Thought, time, and energy can often solve such problems. However, money spent on products cannot do so.

① CRITICAL THINKING

1. *Aphrodisiacs come in all forms, from the dangerous drug called "Spanish fly" to ground-up horns of the endangered rhinoceros. Why are none of these available in drugstores?*
2. *If a person should fail to respond to a loved partner sexually, what are some factors that might be influencing the response?*
3. *What should the person do about them?*

experiencing **sexual dysfunction**—an inability to perform sexual activities—a counselor may advise that they try to excite one another but avoid orgasm. This can work to intensify their desire for each other and solve their problem.

To have good sexual technique, must a person have had many sex partners? Actually, each individual has needs that differ from those of others. It is easy to learn bad habits from other people that must be unlearned later. In monogamous, committed relationships, people have a lifetime to explore and provide for their partners' likes and dislikes. That is the true key to satisfying sexual relations.

Some people believe that people of certain physical types, considered attractive by

society, are the most sexual people. Although social custom may define certain people as pleasing to look at, it is self-esteem, not physical makeup, that determines sexuality. The people with the healthiest sexuality are those with the highest self-esteem. People considered physically attractive may turn out to have high self-esteem, but you can't tell by appearances. A healthy sexuality cannot be established by wearing the latest fashions or an expensive brand of cologne. The person with a strong internal self who values others is best able to mature into a sexually healthy person.

The last sexual myth of this section concerns the idea that a product might increase sexual appetite. The Consumer Awareness section shows that this idea is simple minded.

A10

ate illustrations may be included. (30 min.; Reteach, Reinforce)

Activity 2.4

"NO" Responses. Have students brainstorm effective responses to sexually coercive phrases, such as:
1. You would if you loved me.
2. Everyone is doing it.
3. I'll only put "it" in for a minute.
4. Don't worry, nothing will happen.

5. Are you a baby or something?
6. Guys are supposed to be experienced.
7. I'll get sick from this erection if I don't have sex.
8. Sex is natural for a girl and guy.
9. We've been together so long, it (sex) is the next step.
10. It will make our relationship stronger.
(20 min., Critical Thinking)

Activity 2.5

Role-Play. Have students role-play the coercive phrases and responses they developed in the preceding activity. Allow them to practice in small groups and then ask for volunteers to perform their phrases and responses in front of the class. **(30 min.; Extend, Enrich)**

Activity 2.6

Nice Friends. Have students

(continued on next page)

A parent is often the best person to ask, when questions about sex arise.

Key Points *People hold many false ideas about sexuality. It is self-esteem, not physical makeup, that determines sexuality.* ①

SECTION II   REVIEW

Answer the following questions on a sheet of paper.

Learning the Vocabulary
The vocabulary terms in this section are *virgin, aphrodisiac,* and *sexual dysfunction.*
1. Write a sentence using each of the vocabulary terms.

Learning the Facts
2. What is always an option regarding sexual intercourse?
3. Why do people sometimes say that it is harmful to be sexually aroused and not have sexual intercourse?

4. What is the true key to satisfying sexual relations?

Making Life Choices
5. There are many myths about sexual intercourse and sexuality in general. How can education change these myths? How would you go about changing these myths?

MINI GLOSSARY

aphrodisiac (af-roh-DEEZ-ee-ack): a substance reputed to excite sexual desire. Actually, no known substance does this, but many claim to do so.
sexual dysfunction: impaired responses of sexual excitement or orgasm due to psychological, interpersonal, physical, environmental, or cultural causes; formerly called *impotence* in men and *frigidity* in women.

Teacher Support Notes

① **Handout—Effects of Drugs on Sexual Functioning:** Your supplementary material contains a handout showing how several drugs affect sexual functioning.

Section II Review

Answers
1. Answers will vary.
2. saying no (abstinence)
3. It is a technique used to pressure a person into having intercourse by saying it is unhealthy.
4. having a lifetime to explore and provide for a partner's likes and dislikes
5. Answers will vary.

🔬 Fast Facts

Percentage of men saying that a woman's face is her most attractive feature—27%; percentage of women saying that a man's face is his most attractive feature—55%.

A11

describe the nicest person they know and write all the reasons that person is nice; or, have them describe the nicest character they see on TV and list all the reasons that character is nice. Have the students describe the physical features of a sexy person of the same gender as the nice

person. Discuss which person is preferable as a friend. Ask if their feelings are influenced by who might see them with this friend. Are there times when looks count more than personality? When and why? **(20 min., Critical Thinking)**

EVALUATE
SECTION II

Activity 2.7

CLOSE
SECTION II

Activity 2.8
Vocabulary Dice. Write 12 words relating to this section and the first section

Teacher Support Notes

① **Homosexuality:** You may want to expand upon the definition of homosexuality. For example, Kinsey preferred to do away with the concepts of heterosexual and homosexual *identities*. For him only heterosexual and homosexual *behaviors* existed. This was a result of his research, which found that many people have both homosexual and heterosexual responses or feelings. He reported in the early '50s that 50% of the men and 28% of the women in his studies had same-sex sexual experiences; 38% of the men and 13% of the women had orgasm in these experiences. Furthermore, he discovered that sexual preferences could change over a person's lifetime. This research led him to believe that it was erroneous to classify people as either heterosexual or homosexual.

📢 Fast Facts

92% of gay males and 81% of lesbian women interviewed have at one time or another suffered verbal abuse because of their sexual orientation.

A12

SECTION III

Sexual Orientations

Most people are sexually attracted to members of the opposite sex. These people are **heterosexual**. Some people, however, are attracted to members of the same sex. These people are **homosexual**. ——①

In the United States, many people have strong feelings, both positive and negative, about homosexuality. Religious teachings often speak against it. Because homosexual men were among the first groups to suffer high risks of the fatal disease AIDS, people may even fear homosexuality. In fact, the irrational fear of homosexuals has a name: **homophobia**. In some societies and in some groups of our society, however, ho-

Like all people, homosexual people need to feel useful to society. These people are signing the AIDS quilt.

mosexuality is seen as an accepted difference in some people's sexual orientation.

Evidence about the origins of homosexuality is just now being gathered. Physical brain differences between homosexual and heterosexual men have been observed. Whether these differences are responsible for homosexuality, however, has not been proved. Hormones may also play a role in the development of normal sexuality, especially in early human development.

Whether people are born homosexual or whether the orientation develops from environmental influences is not known. In any case, homosexuality is no longer considered an emotional illness to be "cured" by therapy.

As for AIDS, it is no longer limited to homosexual people. However, some of their sexual practices may expose homosexual men to a particularly high risk of contracting the AIDS virus. Homosexual women, on the other hand, have a lower risk than heterosexual women of contracting AIDS sexually. (Heterosexual people, especially teens, now are increasingly at risk, as you know if you read the section on AIDS in Chapter 17.)

Along with other false ideas, many stereotypes surround homosexuality. One such stereotype is that homosexual people are all alike in terms of their lifestyles. If you tried to identify "the" homosexual lifestyle, however, you could not do it. Homosexual people may be uncommitted or monogamous, secretive or open. They may be lawyers, dentists, grocers, accountants, sales clerks, or anything else.

Everyone needs to feel accepted by a community. Homosexual people are not different from others in this regard. Homosexuals sometimes form communities to provide the identity and support they need.

People can also be **bisexual**, a term that refers to experiencing sexual desires for members of both sexes. Some other people

(to review those terms) on the board. Have student volunteers roll dice and define the word that corresponds to the number they rolled. As the game progresses, words must be used correctly in a sentence, spelled, or used as the base of a question you develop. Here is a sample word list:
1. sexuality, **2.** wet dreams, **3.** masturbate, **4.** erection, **5.** myth, **6.** foreplay, **7.** virgin, **8.** sex, **9.** dysfunction, **10.** aphrodisiac, **11.** sexual orientation, **12.** orgasm.
(20 min.; Reteach, Reinforce)

FOCUS

> SECTION III

In this section students will learn:
1. The meaning of sexual orientation.
2. To evaluate their own feelings about homosexuality.

Activity 3.1
Anonymous Answers. Have students write anonymous answers to the following questions. Should homosexuals be allowed to: Adopt children? Join the military? Teach? Become members of the clergy? Serve as police officers? Marry? Then discuss how the enforcement of these laws would affect heterosexuals. Chart the class answers to all questions

(continued on next page)

---

are **asexual**, meaning that they do not feel sexual desire for people of either gender. Bisexuality is not the same as feeling warm toward members of both sexes and expressing affection for them by hugging, kissing, or patting on the back. Most people's expressions of such feelings do not imply bisexuality. In early adolescence, it is common for young heterosexual males to share early sexual experiences with same-sex peers. This does not indicate homosexuality or bisexuality.

> **Key Points** *People may be heterosexual, homosexual, bisexual, or asexual. Regardless of sexual orientation, people need to belong to a community.*

SECTION III REVIEW

Answer the following questions on a separate sheet of paper.

Learning the Vocabulary
The vocabulary terms in this section are *homosexual, heterosexual, homophobia, bisexual,* and *asexual.*
1. Word Scramble: Use the clues given to help you unscramble the words.
   a. **aiooobhhmp** _____ an irrational fear and hatred of homosexuals
   b. **aeoouhlmsx** _____ feeling sexual desire for persons of the same gender
   c. **aeeeouhlrstx** _____ feeling sexual desire for persons of the other gender

Learning the Facts
2. What factors may play a role in the development of sexuality?
3. Is it possible to identify "the" homosexual lifestyle? Why or why not?
4. What contributions has the disease AIDS made to the fear known as homophobia?

Making Life Choices
5. Reread the Consumer Awareness on page A10 of this section. In real life are there such compounds as those mentioned? Why do you think people believe that there are aphrodisiacs? Do you believe in aphrodisiacs?

Answers to Fact or Fiction

Here are the answers to the questions at the start of Part A.

1. False. Sexuality is part of a person's total personality from birth to death, with or without sexual activity.
2. True. **3.** True. **4.** False. The brain, not the penis and clitoris, is the most important sex organ. **5.** False. The brain controls the sexual response. Therefore, what a woman *thinks* about a man is at least as important as any physical aspect of intercourse. **6.** True. **7.** False. If you tried to identify "the" homosexual lifestyle, you could not do it.

MINI GLOSSARY

heterosexual: feeling sexual desire for persons of the other gender.
homosexual: feeling sexual desire for persons of the same sex, popularly called *gay* or, in women, *lesbian.*
homophobia: an irrational fear and hatred of homosexuals, usually based on the fear of becoming a homosexual.
bisexual: being sexually oriented to members of both sexes.
asexual: having no sexual inclinations.

Section III Review
Answers
1. a. homophobia
b. homosexual
c. heterosexual
2. hormones, brain differences
3. No, homosexuals may be uncommitted or monogamous, secretive or open. They come from all walks of life.
4. It is associated with gay men because they were the first to have the disease, causing more fear of homosexuals.
5. Answers will vary.

Fast Facts

Time/CNN polls done in 1978 and again in 1992 showed that American adults' attitudes about homosexuality had changed little in 15 years. In response to the question "Are homosexual relationships between consenting adults morally wrong?" 53% said yes in '78, 54% in '92.

and display results. At the end of Section III have students once again answer these questions. Discuss any changes. **(30 min.)**

Activity 3.2

Character Analysis. Get magazine photos of attractive and unattractive men, women, boys, girls, and adults of all ages. Write a general biography for each photo. Include good and bad personality traits, education, family, age, and a name. Have

students choose:
1. Who they would hire to be an employee.
2. Who they would like to date.
3. Who they would like for a friend.
4. Who they would like to work for.
5. Who they would like as a teacher.

Discuss students' choices and reasons. After they have chosen, tell them the sexual orientation for each photo. Be sure to have gays, lesbians, bisexuals, asexuals,

---

Teacher Support Notes

① **Condoms and STDs:** You may want to assign this Straight Talk to students as they complete Chapter 17. This Straight Talk was placed here, in the optional Special Unit, because many school districts do not discuss condoms in their health classes.

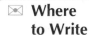

✉ Where to Write

Sex Information and Education Council of the U.S.
Publications Office
1855 Broadway
New York, New York 10023

☎ Where to Call

Sex Information Hotline (Los Angeles)
1-213-653-1123
Community Sex Information, Inc.
(New York)
1-212-982-0052

STRAIGHT TALK — Condoms and STDs ①

Abstinence, and restricting sexual activity to contact only with a mutually monogamous partner, are the only ways to be 100% sure of preventing STDs. Beyond these methods, experts say that using condoms provides the best protection against AIDS and other STD infections. However, even those experts say that condoms are not perfect for the task. Condoms may be good, but the question "How good?" is important.

I've seen all sorts of medical pamphlets that say to use condoms to protect against AIDS. Are you telling me that condoms don't protect people?

Condoms, without a doubt, are the best available device for protection. They prevent untold numbers of cases of STDs, including AIDS, each year. Some types of condoms are definitely better than others. However, it is important to be aware that no condom can guarantee safety.

Which type is best?

Latex condoms with spermicide applied to them are the most effective. The type made of natural skin or lambskin are the least effective. These have pores, as all skin does. The pores are large enough to permit bacteria and viruses to pass through them. Latex condoms have no pores, and

therefore provide a barrier against microbes.

Latex condoms with spermicide do protect against STDs, then?

Yes, but even latex condoms do not provide perfect protection. One way to look at the effectiveness of condoms is to study populations that use them. While most people who use condoms will be protected against STDs most of the time, a certain number of individuals who use condoms (and use them correctly) still become infected with STDs. Condoms sometimes fail when used for birth control. Just as they may fail to prevent pregnancy occasionally, they also sometimes fail to prevent STDs.

I know condoms sometimes fail for birth control. But they work most of the time, right?

Yes, they do prevent pregnancy most of the time. But consider this—a pregnancy from condom failure may be dramatic in its negative economic, scholastic, and emotional impact on young people, but it is rarely fatal. On the other hand, a case of AIDS from condom failure is invariably fatal. Some sexual partners of people with AIDS have become infected with HIV because they relied on condoms for protection.

Are you saying that condoms are not worth using?

Condoms are better than nothing, but abstinence is better still. Barring abstinence, condoms are the best protection now available against all forms of STDs. They protect far more often than they fail. But in addition to condoms, common sense is

(Continued on next page)

and heterosexuals. Ask the students if they would choose differently. **(20 min., Critical Thinking)**

EVALUATE
SECTION III

Activity 3.3
What Have You Learned? Have students write two things they have learned in Section III. On the same paper,

have them write any questions they might still have after studying the material. Be sure to get answers for any questions asked. **(15 min.; Reteach, Reinforce)**

CLOSE
SECTION III

Activity 3.4
Guest Speaker. Invite a psychologist to come to class to discuss the topic

of homosexuality. Before the speaker's visit, have students write out questions they would like the speaker to answer. Be sure to read the questions yourself to screen out any that may be inappropriate. A local college or university that offers human sexuality courses would be a source for obtaining a qualified speaker. **(Extend, Enrich)**

STRAIGHT TALK   *(Continued)*

required. Do not have sexual relations—even using condoms—with people likely to be carrying HIV. Take the precautions and use the strategies suggested in Chapter 17. Stay aware that condoms fail. Don't be lulled into trusting condoms completely. They are not completely trustworthy.

Why do condoms fail?

One reason is that people make mistakes in using them. Instructions on correct use of condoms appear in the next chapter.

What are the other reasons why condoms fail?

Condoms can be defective. They age and break down. They slip off if the fit isn't right. They burst, tear, and leak. They can be damaged while still in the package. Ninety-five percent of the time, condoms are in good condition and perform as they were intended. The other 5 percent of the time, however, they are defective, fail, and expose the partners to each other's secretions during intercourse. Even a condom that does not break may allow secretions to leak over the top. If STD-causing organisms are in a person's secretions, they can infect that person's partner.

Don't companies that make condoms test them before selling them?

Testing of each condom before sale is not practical. Manufacturers do spot-check batches of condoms and report the results of these tests to the government watchdog agency the Food and Drug Administration. If any batches prove defective, they are recalled from sale. Defective batches still slip through. However, by far the ① major causes of condom failure lie with the users, not with the condoms themselves. People simply do not know how to select, store, and use their latex condoms.

I want to know whether some latex condoms are better than others.

Absolutely. Most varieties purchased from vending machines are of notoriously low quality, and may be old and brittle. Condoms from drugstores have an expiration date printed on the package, usually abbreviated *EXP*. Beyond that date, using the condoms is risky. Also, the package should say that the condoms can prevent diseases. Some condoms are just novelties and are useless for disease prevention. Also, look for the words *latex* and *nonoxynol-9*.

My friend carries condoms around all the time. Is that a good idea?

It is not a bad one, especially if the person is sexually active. But condoms require careful handling and storage. Otherwise, they may break down.

Tell me about how to handle and store them.

Heat and light break condoms down. Thus they should be stored in a dark, cool place, such as a closet or drawer. Glove compartments of cars get too hot. Wallets, purses, and pockets offer little protection from keys, pens, and other sharp objects.

Opening condom packages also requires special care. Use fingers to tear the package open. Don't use teeth, fingernails, scissors, or other sharp objects that may damage the condom. Once the package is open, inspect the condom. If the material sticks to itself or is gummy or brittle, discard it.

Remember that condoms— even perfect ones—are only a second line of defense. A person's first and best defenses are abstinence from sexual intercourse or mutual monogamy with an uninfected partner.

Teacher Support Notes

① Effectiveness Rates: Part B of this Special Unit explains the difference between laboratory and user effectiveness for contraceptives and gives effectiveness rates for both. You may want to refer students to the explanation of the two different rates and the rates for condoms. These rates have to do with the prevention of pregnancy but you could still use them to emphasize the point that effectiveness drops from laboratory to user because people make mistakes. This principle holds with the prevention of STDs, as well as pregnancy.

✉ Where to Write

American Association of Sex Educators and Counselors
815 15th Street, N.W.
Washington, DC
20005

Answers

Vocabulary

1. a. Ejaculation is the expelling of semen from the penis, brought about by the involuntary muscular contractions of orgasm. Excitement is the early stage of sexual inter- course. **b.** Plateau is the period of intense physical pleasure preceding orgasm, while orgasm is a series of muscular contractions of the sex organs that release tension and end in relaxation.
2. a. excitement **b.** aphrodisiac **c.** sexuality
3. a. Sex **b.** foreplay **c.** sexual dysfunction

4. a. ejaculation **b.** masturbation **c.** bisexual
5. Answers will vary.

Recall
Section I

1. It ensures that all living things reproduce their kind. It also ensures that the hereditary material individuals carry is repeatedly shuffled and dealt out in different combinations.
2. your self-esteem, thoughts, feelings, values, and self-concept
3. marriage
4. Because the two people who engage in it bring to it their moods, ideas, self-concepts, feelings about their relationship, and everything else that makes them unique.

PART REVIEW

LEARNING THE VOCABULARY

sex	ejaculation	sexual dysfunction
sexuality	excitement	heterosexual
wet dreams	plateau	homosexual
orgasm	resolution	homophobia
masturbation	foreplay	bisexual
erection	virgin	asexual
engorgement	aphrodisiac	

Answer the following questions on a sheet of paper.

1. Explain the differences between
   a. excitement and ejaculation
   b. plateau and orgasm
2. **Matching**—*Match each of the following phrases with the appropriate vocabulary term from the list above:*
   a. as used to describe a stage of sexual intercourse, the early stage
   b. a substance reputed (falsely) to excite sexual desire
   c. the quality of being sexual, part of the total person
3. a. _____ is a term used to mean both gender and sexual intercourse.
   b. An activity which gives each partner pleasure before intercourse is called _____.

c. A problem formerly referred to as impotence in men or frigidity in women is now called _____.
4. **Word Scramble**—*Use the clues from the phrases below to help you unscramble the terms:*
   a. **aaeioucjlnt** _____the expelling of semen from the penis
   b. **aaioubmnrstt** _____stimulating one's own genitals, usually until orgasm occurs
   c. **aeiublsx** _____being sexually oriented to members of both sexes
5. Write a paragraph using at least ten of the vocabulary terms. Underline each vocabulary term that you use.

RECALLING IMPORTANT FACTS AND IDEAS

1. What two major roles does sex play in nature?
2. What factors have influenced your sexuality?
3. What is the highest form of commitment?
4. Why is sexual intercourse considered a complex act?

5. What is the master sex organ?
6. Describe two myths concerning sexuality.
7. What determines sexuality?
8. Name at least two false statements about homosexuality.

CRITICAL THINKING

1. Reread the Straight Talk on page A14, "Condoms and STDs." Can condoms guarantee safety against AIDS? List ways that condoms fail. Why are latex condoms better to use than other types? Where should condoms be stored? What can happen if they are not stored correctly?
2. Jayne and Julie are homosexuals. They have

been living together for seven years. They have had a monogamous relationship all that time. They plan to spend the rest of their lives with each other. They want to adopt a baby. What do you think about a homosexual couple's adopting a baby? Do you think Jayne and Julie should be permitted to adopt? Why or why not?

5. the brain
Section II
6. Answers will vary; could include: a man with a large penis makes a better lover, a woman's breast size makes her more sexual, and the idea that certain products can increase sexual appetite.
Section III
7. It is self-esteem, not physi-

cal make-up that determines sexuality. The people with the healthiest sexuality are those with the highest self-esteem.
8. Answers will vary; could include: homosexuals are all alike, AIDS is only a homosexual disease.

A CTIVITIES

1. Aphrodisiacs are growing in popularity. Make posters showing various aphrodisiacs and claims for each. Write a statement to prove these claims are not true. Post these around your school.
2. Put together a booklet with the following phone numbers: an AIDS hot line, a local planned parenthood organization, a teen talk number, a crisis pregnancy center, and a gay hot line number. Make these available for everyone at your school to use.

3. Interview your parents or grandparents about dating customs when they were your age. Develop a list of questions with the members of your class. What are the similarities? What are the differences? Share these interviews as oral reports.

M AKING DECISIONS ABOUT HEALTH

1. You have been in a relationship for several weeks, and the question of sexual intimacy has been raised. You are sexually inexperienced, and even though you care for the other person and feel a sexual attraction, you have been taught that sex before marriage is wrong. You feel confused, because part of you wants a sexual relationship, but the other part fears

that sexual intimacy will lead to loss of respect or rejection. What will you do at this point?
2. Would you prefer to marry someone who is a virgin or someone who is sexually experienced? What would be the advantages and disadvantages of marrying a virgin as compared to marrying a person who is sexually experienced?

✉ **Where to Write**

Sex Information and Education Council of the U.S.
Publications Office
1855 Broadway
New York, NY 10023

PART B PLANNER

OVERVIEW

Part B, "Preventing Pregnancy," is 31 pages long and divided into the six sections listed to the right. Major learning outcomes are also listed to the right. This chapter examines the important choice students make between abstinence and becoming sexually active. It looks at all the contraceptives available, explains how they work, and evaluates their effectiveness. Decisions that must be made if a teenager becomes pregnant are also explored.

MAKING LIFE CHOICES RESOURCES

A variety of activities, handouts, quizzes, and tests to accompany this chapter are available in the *Making Life Choices* supplementary material. You may pick and choose from those materials as appropriate for your amount of class time and the ability levels of your students. Some of the resources you might want to consider using are:

Overheads
- Implants and Oral Contraceptives
- IUD
- Diaphragm
- Condoms
- Vasectomy
- Tubal Ligation

Handouts
- Community Resources
- Abstinence vs. Sexual Intercourse
- Conflicting Views on Abortion
- Public Health Service Objectives
- Sample Welfare Expenses
- Pregnancy Scenarios

Teacher Information Sheets
- Family Planning
- *Depo-Provera*
- Abortion
- Choices Diagram

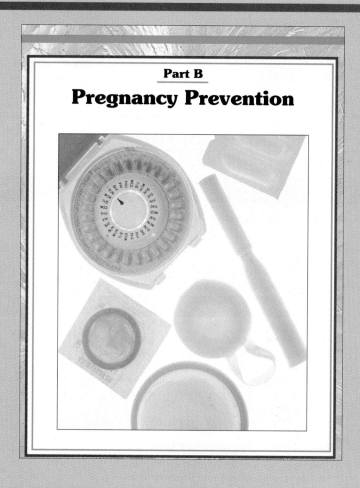

Part B
Pregnancy Prevention

CHAPTER PROJECT

Divide the class into groups of three for this class project. Tell students that on a given day each group will present for the class how one method of contraception works. They must do the research and develop any props they might need. The presentation should be three to five minutes long. There will, however, be an interesting twist in the presentations. All of the chairs will be pushed back against the walls and a large uterus with fallopian tubes and ovaries will be outlined on the floor in rope or yarn. Students will walk through these outlines. The teacher can provide a softball with white crepe paper streamers attached to represent the sperm and a large balloon or small beachball to represent the egg. Students are encouraged to design and construct the contraceptive device they will be explaining out of paper, cardboard, cloth, foil, plastic, etc. The design will be used in conjunction with the floor diagram. Grade students on their creativity and the accuracy of their presentations.

OUTCOMES

After reading and studying this chapter, you will be able to:

✓ Discuss the risks of using contraceptives.
✓ List all of the contraceptive methods and state the effectiveness rate of each.
✓ Identify which methods of contraception also help prevent sexually transmitted diseases.
✓ Explain how to use each method of contraception.
✓ Identify the methods not recommended for contraception.
✓ Identify the two methods of sterilization and describe how they work.
✓ List the options available to women who have unwanted/unplanned pregnancies.

CONTENTS

I. The Power of Pregnancy
II. Choosing Contraception
III. The Standard Contraceptive Methods
IV. Methods Not Recommended for Contraception
V. Sterilization
VI. Contraceptive Failure
   Straight Talk: *Why People Don't Use Contraceptives*

FACT OR FICTION

What do you think? Are the following statements true or false? If you think they are false, then say what is true.

1. Most people have trouble getting pregnant.
2. People who are sexually active, but who do not use contraceptives, are acting as if they wish to have a child.
3. People who first obtain all the facts can find the perfect contraceptive method.
4. Condoms can be as effective as oral contraceptives in preventing pregnancy.
5. Withdrawal is an effective method of preventing pregnancy.
6. If sexually active couples who do not wish to have a child would begin using contraception now, the majority of abortions would be prevented.

(Answers on page B24)

Reminder: Knowing how to study can increase your knowledge, improve your grades, *and* cut down on your study time. See the *Studying Health* section at the front of your text for some suggestions to help you study this chapter.

Answers to "Fact or Fiction"

1. False. For healthy, sexually active heterosexual couples, pregnancy occurs easily. **2.** True. **3.** False. No contraceptive method is perfect. To obtain the advantages of one method, a person must be willing to put up with its disadvantages. **4.** True. **5.** False. Withdrawal fails to prevent pregnancy in most users. **6.** True.

Activity To Introduce Chapter

Don't tell students you will be discussing abstinence, just start with this activity.

Ask students to give examples of attributes the ideal contraceptive would have. Students will come up with qualities such as: either sex could use it, prevents STDs, 100% effective, free, readily available, biodegradable, no side effects, easy to use, etc. Write all of their responses on the board. Once the list has been completed, ask students if any one method can do all of these things. The students' immediate response is usually a firm "NO!" Ask them to think again, and quite quickly they realize abstinence is the answer. Discuss. **(15 or 20 min.)**

NOT ENOUGH TIME?*

Since one million teens become pregnant each year, this is not a section that can be covered briefly. However, a few shortcuts could be made. Assign the chapter to be read prior to class.

TIME	SUGGESTIONS
Days 1 & 2	Section I should be covered completely since it lays the groundwork for the rest of the chapter. It also stresses the importance of delaying pregnancy until a person is ready for the responsibilities raising a child entails.
Day 3	Section II. Do Activity 2.1 and Activity 2.2. Also include Activity 3.1 in Section III.
Days 4 & 5	Discuss the different contraceptives, their effectiveness, and how they work. Choose activities from the section that best fill the students' needs for understanding.
Day 6	Discuss birth control that does not work. Do Activity 4.1 in Section IV. Do Activities 6.2 and 6.4 in Section VI.

*Please refer to the 18-week daily lesson plans in the supplementary material for additional suggestions.

SUGGESTED RESOURCES

Student Readings
1. McCoy, Kathy, Ph.D., and Wibbelsman, Charles, M.D. *The New Teenage Body Book.* New York: The Putnam Publishing Group.
2. Morowitz, Harold and Trefil, James. *The Facts of Life.* Oxford University Press.

Teacher Readings
The magazine listed below is a quarterly that contains current sex education material and activities for the classroom.
1. *The Family Life Educator.* Published by ETR Associates, P.O. Box 1830, Santa Cruz, California 95061-1830.
2. McIlhaney, Joe S. Jr., M.D. *Safe Sex.* Grand Rapids, MI: Baker Book House, 1992.

Videos
1. *Taking Charge: Teens Speak Out About Sexuality and Birth Control.* Fanlight Productions, 47 Halifax Street, Boston, MA 02130.

FOCUS
SECTION I

In this section students will learn that:
1. Pregnancy is the rule, not the exception, for sexually active people using no contraception.
2. Unplanned pregnancies change teenagers' lives permanently and may keep them from achieving their goals.

Activity 1.1
Planning Ahead. Ask students how much planning goes into choosing and being accepted at a college. Have the class brainstorm a list of things that must be done. Now have students generate a list of things that would have to be planned before a couple became parents. Inquire why people might put so much thought into college plans but have sex and never consider the outcome of their

actions. **(20–25 min., Critical Thinking)**

TEACH
SECTION I
(Guided and Independent Practice)
Activity 1.2
Child Support Costs. Find out what a minimum child support payment is in your state. Have students use that number to calculate the father's total payment. (18 years) Discuss the students' reac-

Teacher Support Notes

① **Teacher Information Sheet—Family Planning:** Your supplementary material contains background information from the U.S. Public Health Service summarizing some accomplishments and problems in family planning.

② **Pregnancy as Disaster:** Ask students to speculate on what would happen to them if they or a person with whom they were having a relationship became pregnant. How would their lives change? Would the changes be disastrous, as the text suggests? Have them list as many specific ways as possible in which pregnancy would be a disaster.

③ **Contraception vs. Birth Control:** Ask students to look at the definition of contraception in the Mini Glossary on the opposite page. Then ask them to explain the difference between the terms *contraception* and *birth control.* Contraception is any method used to prevent conception. Birth control is any method of preventing birth. Birth control, therefore, is a broader term and includes such things as abortion, which is not included as part of contraception.

B2   Special Unit Sexual Behavior and Pregnancy Prevention

Sexual intercourse, which you read about in Part A of this unit, can lead to pregnancy. For married couples who are ready to bear and raise children together, pregnancy is a happy event. It can strengthen the couple's relationship, enhance their spiritual beliefs, and promote their personal growth. For couples who are not yet ready to raise and support children, however, pregnancy can be a disaster.

In this part of the text you will learn how people can prevent pregnancy until the time is right. What you learn here could possibly prevent a lifetime of regrets.

Of course the only guarantee that a pregnancy will not occur is total abstinence from sexual intercourse. People who are sexually active, however, and who choose one of the standard birth control methods discussed in the following pages can be pretty sure of preventing pregnancy. While none of these methods offer abstinence's 100% effectiveness, sexually active couples can count on these methods to prevent pregnancy in most cases.

SECTION I

The Power of Pregnancy

Some people think that pregnancy is difficult to achieve. For healthy, sexually active, heterosexual couples, though, pregnancy occurs easily. Most people have no trouble starting a pregnancy. Ninety percent of sexually active couples who do nothing to prevent becoming pregnant become pregnant within one year. As Figure B–1 shows, pregnancy is the rule—not the exception—for sexually active people using no **contraception.**

The power of pregnancy to affect people's lives is dramatic. Unwed teenage mothers and fathers are deeply affected. For the girl, an unplanned pregnancy may alter most of the rest of her life story. She may become isolated from her peers during her pregnancy. If she returns to school afterwards, her schoolmates will have moved on without her. Former boyfriends may now avoid her.

Unless the couple gives the baby up for adoption, both his and her freedom to go on to further education and hoped-for careers can be lost permanently. The father of the child is legally responsible for the child's financial support for the next 18 years. An unwed teenage mother is likely to end up with more children than her peers will ever have. Busy from that time on with providing for their children, both parents are forced to neglect their own personal growth.

Ten percent of all teenage girls and their partners face unwanted pregnancies each year. In the past, girls were often left to face the burden alone. State laws are rapidly changing, however, and more and more fathers are being held legally responsible. Most states punish nonsupportive parents harshly.

In addition, physical risks always occur with adolescent pregnancies. The health of both mother and infant may suffer. You learned about the physical risks of pregnancy in Chapter 21.

The power of pregnancy affects other people in less obvious and less dramatic ways. The fear of pregnancy can damage relationships. Many couples worry and may disagree about contraception. They must make hard choices. Surprise pregnancies are common, and a person who has had one or more may come to fear sexual activity itself, rather than enjoy it. When unwanted pregnancies occur, careers may end, relationships may crumble, and even spiritual beliefs may be challenged.

tions. **(10–15 min.; Reteach, Reinforce)**

EVALUATE
SECTION I

Activity 1.3
Pros and Cons. Have students list all of the positive things about having a baby while unmarried and still in high school. Have them list the things that would be difficult. Ask the class why 95%

of teens who give birth keep their babies instead of giving them up for adoption. **(25 min., Critical Thinking)**

CLOSE
SECTION I

Activity 1.4
Future Plans. Have the students imagine two high school couples. Both couples have college and career plans

before they marry and have families. One couple is having regular, unprotected sex. The other couple has decided to postpone sex until marriage. Ask, "Given what you know, what is likely to be the future outcome for each couple?" **(15 min.)**

Among ten sexually active couples using no contraception,

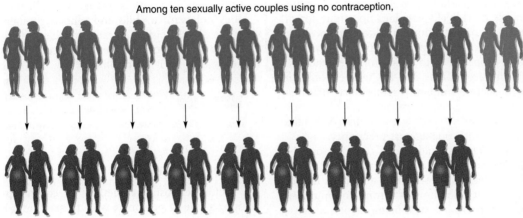

Nine become pregnant within one year.

Figure B–1 The Odds of Pregnancy Are High.

Key Points   *For a sexually active couple using no contraceptives, the odds of conceiving are high. Unplanned pregnancies can change people's lives, especially the lives of teenagers.*

___ SECTION I ___ REVIEW

Answer the following questions on a separate sheet of paper.
Learning the Vocabulary
The vocabulary term in this section is *contraception.*
1. Write a sentence using the vocabulary term.

Learning the Facts
2. What percentage of teenage girls and their partners face unwanted pregnancies each year?
3. How long is the father of a child legally responsible for financial support?
4. List problems that occur with unwanted pregnancies.

Making Life Choices
5. Your best friend Cheryl has come to you with a problem. She is pregnant, and the father of the baby, Jim, does not want her to have the baby. You and Cheryl are seniors

and will graduate in four months. What will you advise Cheryl to do? What is the best solution to her problem, knowing her partner Jim wants no part in raising a baby? Would you do the same thing if you were in this situation?

SECTION II

Choosing Contraception

②   Not all people see contraception in the same way. Some people's religious beliefs forbid its use. Other people would like

___ MINI GLOSSARY

contraception: any method of preventing conception. The term *birth control* is often used to mean the same thing, but technically, birth control includes abortion.

In this section students will learn that:
1. Whether or not a person uses contraception is a personal choice.
2. Professional help may be needed to decide which contraceptive is best.

Activity 2.1

Reliable Contraceptives. Have students imagine that a couple is going to engage in sex for the first time. In small groups ask students to brainstorm what will determine whether or not the couple will use a reliable contraceptive. Each group can report back one or two of their ideas. **(15–20 min., Cooperative Learning)**

Activity 2.2
Sources Available. Twenty-five percent of high school students don't know where or how to get contraceptives. Ask, "How could someone get birth control advice or contraceptives in our community?" List the sources known to students

Teacher Support Notes

① **Textbook Position:** Make sure students realize that the fact that they are studying this information does not mean that they are being advised to use contraception. The text has stressed, from page one, the need for each person to make his or her own choices and that the purpose of the text is to provide information to help people make wiser, more informed choices. This text has also presented a strong case for abstinence in several chapters prior to this one.

② **Wanting a Child:** Make sure students read and reread this sentence: **"People now having sexual intercourse but using no means of contraception are acting as if they wish to have a child."** It is a strong statement of the importance of abstinence and/or the use of contraception. You may want to refer students back to Chapter 21, which described the ways in which a baby changes the parents' lives.

③ **Handout—Community Resources:** An activity in your supplementary material provides guidelines to help students locate and organize information regarding counseling services available in their communities.

B4

B4 Special Unit Sexual Behavior and Pregnancy Prevention

everyone worldwide who is sexually active to use it. This chapter does not argue for or against contraception. It takes the position that the choice is personal and presents the facts people need to make informed choices. ①

Contraception is not for women only. It is a shared human responsibility that accompanies sexual intercourse. No one should ever assume that a partner will take care of protecting against pregnancy.

The couple should discuss the topic openly. Being concerned about contraception shows that a person is concerned about his or her partner. It also shows a strong commitment to the partner's well-being. Open discussions about contraception not only help the couple find a suitable method, but also tend to bring them closer together and strengthen their relationship.

People now having sexual intercourse, but using no means of contraception, are acting as if they wish to have a child. Deciding to have a child is not a decision that should be made casually. It demands much thinking through, as Chapter 21 made clear. ② ③

Honest talk about contraception leads to both wise planning and closeness.

Until that decision is made, anyone who does not want a child and who is sexually active should either abstain from sexual intercourse or choose a method of contraception—and use it every time. ①

Key Points *Whether or not to use contraception is a personal choice to be made by each sexually active person who does not want to have a child.*

Where to Get Help

Before choosing a method of contraception, a young person is wise to seek advice from a parent. Expert advice from a physician, physician's assistant, or nurse practitioner is also helpful. The professional will check for health problems, provide education, and, if one is needed, write a prescription. Student health centers, county health departments, and family planning centers often have reliable printed information sheets. Many provide other contraceptive services at a reasonable cost. Special-help clinics are sometimes available to teenagers.

Religious organizations may also provide counseling services. They may address topics of sexuality, pregnancy, and other issues, as well as contraception.

If you choose to seek outside help, make an advance appointment. Remember that such agencies are made up of individuals, and not every counselor is the right one for every person. If you should feel uncomfortable with one counselor, ask to see someone else. If you don't get the information you are seeking from one type of center, go to another.

Remember, too, that no contraceptive method is perfect. With the advantages a method presents, disadvantages are also a certainty. People must be willing to compromise. You should also remember that two contraceptive agents—latex condoms with the spermicide nonoxynol-9, and female condoms with the same spermicide on the board. Add ones they may not think of. Discuss the advantages and disadvantages of getting contraceptives or advice from each source. **(15–20 min.; Extend, Enrich)**

Activity 2.3

Misleading Results: Using page B18 have students compare laboratory effectiveness to user effectiveness. Ask students which effectiveness rates fell the most dramatically in real use. Which rate do students think is quoted by the manufacturer of the contraceptive product? How many students think this is misleading the consumer? Discuss. **(20–25 min.; Extend, Enrich)**

EVALUATE
SECTION II

Activity 2.4

(continued on next page)

Pop Quiz.

1. What is it called when a person chooses not to become sexually active? (abstinence)

2. Where is reliable contraceptive advice available? (doctors, clinics, Planned Parenthood, school nurse, etc.)

3. What does STD stand for? (sexually transmitted disease)

4. What is the difference between labora-

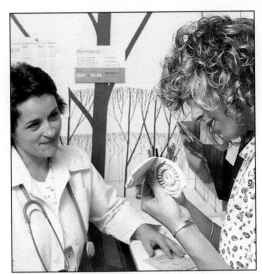

Before choosing a method of contraception, seek accurate information.

applied—provide the best protection against some sexually transmitted diseases (STDs).

> **Key Points** *No contraceptive method is perfect. Many people need professional help to find the one that will be best for them.*

Two Kinds of Effectiveness

One of the most important aspects of a contraceptive method to consider is its **effectiveness**. For example, you may hear an expert say that the effectiveness of a contraceptive method is 98.5 percent. Later, you may hear another trusted source say it is only 92 percent effective. Both may be right. The two numbers are different because they are obtained by two different types of scientific studies.

The first expert just mentioned is quoting studies that answer the question, How well does this method work in 100 *couples who use it perfectly* for one year? These studies are run in laboratories that permit no mis-

takes. When this contraceptive method is used perfectly, then its **laboratory effectiveness** is 98.5 percent.

The second expert is quoting studies of what happens in real life. These studies answer the question, How many *typical users* out of 100 become pregnant while using the contraceptive method for one year? The **user effectiveness** is 92 percent. In real life, 8 women out of 100 become pregnant, because in real life people make mistakes. This chapter lists both kinds of effectiveness ratings whenever possible. Giving only one might be misleading.

> **Key Points** *The effectiveness rating of a contraceptive method depends on how it was studied. Laboratory studies measure effectiveness when the method is used perfectly, but real users make mistakes.*

Side Effects

① The side effects of contraceptive methods can also be misleading. Some lists of side effects are long and sound threatening. Keep in mind, though, that a drug company has to report every side effect, even if it occurs in only one of a million users. Before you start to worry about the dangers of contraception, remember that carrying and delivering a baby pose risks that are far greater than those of using any contraceptive method except one (the Pill, for a

 MINI GLOSSARY

effectiveness: how well a contraceptive method or device prevents pregnancy, expressed as a percentage. The **laboratory effectiveness** is the percentage of women protected from pregnancy in a year's time under ideal laboratory conditions. The **user effectiveness** is the percentage of typical women users who are protected.

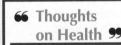 **Where to Write**

American Institute of Family Relations
5287 Sunset Blvd.
Los Angeles, California 90027

Teacher Support Notes

① **Side Effects:** Side effects were first introduced and defined in Chapter 12. You may want to refer students back to that discussion or ask them to define the term without looking back. (effects other than the intended effects of a drug or procedure)

❝ Thoughts on Health ❞

The management of fertility is one of the most important functions of adulthood.
– Germaine Greer

B5

tory effectiveness and user effective-ness? (used perfectly vs. the way normal people use the contraceptives)

5. When considering contraceptive side effects, what is the only method of birth control that poses more risk than carrying and delivering a baby? (The Pill, for a

woman who smokes, is a greater risk.)

CLOSE
SECTION II

Activity 2.5
Cultural Differences. Tell students one million teenagers become pregnant each year. That is ten percent of all teenage girls and their partners. Other countries that are similar to the U.S. in

standard of living and education don't have the high pregnancy rates we do. Only 1 in 30 Swedish teens and fewer than 1 in 20 English, Canadian, or French teens becomes pregnant. Ask students why they think this happens. **(30–40 min., Multicultural)**

FOCUS
SECTION III

Teacher Support Notes

① **Comparing Numbers:** Ask the following questions to check that students are able to read and understand the information provided in this figure.
a. Are any pregnancy prevention methods as safe as or safer than canoeing? (yes) If so which ones? (IUDs, diaphragms, condoms, spermicides, fertility awareness methods, and sterilization of men)
b. Of the pregnancy prevention methods listed, which is the most dangerous? (smoker using birth control pills)

Section II Review

Answers
1. user effectiveness
2. laboratory effectiveness
3. effectiveness
4. helps the couple find a suitable method and tends to draw them closer together, strengthening the relationship
5. parent, physician, physician's assistant, student health centers, county health departments, family planning centers, religious organizations
6. must report every side effect, even if it has affected only one in a million users
7. 1 in 1,000; 1 in 14,300; Remaining answers will vary.

B6

B6   Special Unit Sexual Behavior and Pregnancy Prevention

woman who smokes). In fact, driving down the street is much more likely to injure your health. Figure B–2 compares some other risks with those of contraception.

> **Key Points** Contraceptive methods carry risks, but most are far lower than the risks of carrying a pregnancy to term.

SECTION II   **R**EVIEW

Answer the following questions on a sheet of paper.
Learning the Vocabulary
The vocabulary terms in this section are *effectiveness, laboratory effectiveness,* and *user effectiveness.*
Fill in the blank with the correct term.
1. The _____ of a contraceptive method is a measure of the percentage of *typical* women users who are protected from pregnancy in a year's time.
2. The _____ is the percentage of women protected from pregnancy in a year's time if they use a contraceptive method *perfectly.*
3. How well a contraceptive method or device prevents pregnancy is, in general, called its _____.

Learning the Facts
4. What happens in a relationship in which the couple openly communicate about contraception?
5. Where can a young person go to get advice about contraceptives?
6. What must drug companies do about the side effects of products they sell?

Making Life Choices
7. Look at Figure B–2, "Risks of Contraception in Perspective." What are the risks of dying within one year for a person riding a motorcycle? For a person going through pregnancy? For a person using contraception? Are you surprised at the results? What does this tell you about the risk of death from contraceptives? Does this affect your beliefs about the wisdom or foolishness of using contraceptives? Why or why not?

FIGURE B-2

Risks of Contraception in Perspective ①

Activity	Chance of Death in a Year
For all men and women:	
Motorcycling	1 in 1,000
Automobile driving	1 in 6,000
Powerboating	1 in 6,000
Rock climbing	1 in 7,500
Playing football	1 in 25,000
Canoeing	1 in 100,000
For women aged 15 to 44 years:	
Using tampons	1 in 350,000
Having sexual intercourse (risk of death from pelvic inflammatory disease)	1 in 50,000
Preventing pregnancy:	
Using birth control pills	
Nonsmoker	1 in 63,000
Smoker	1 in 16,000
Using intrauterine devices (IUDs)	1 in 100,000
Using diaphragms, condoms, or spermicides	None
Using fertility awareness methods	None
Undergoing sterilization:	
Women	1 in 67,000
Men	1 in 300,000
Continuing pregnancy	1 in 14,300
Terminating pregnancy:	
Illegal abortion	1 in 3,000
Legal abortion	
Before 9 wks.	1 in 500,000
Between 9 and 12 wks.	1 in 67,000
Between 13 and 15 wks.	1 in 23,000
After 15 weeks	1 in 8,700

Source: R. A. Hatcher and coauthors, *Contraceptive Technology (1990–1992)*: 146. Used with permission.

1. The advantages of abstinence and how it compares to the standard methods of contraception.
2. To name and describe standard methods of contraception.
3. To compare both laboratory and user effectiveness rates for different contraceptive methods.
4. To describe side effects of different contraceptive methods.

Activity 3.1
Abstinence. Explain to students that abstinence means different things to different people. Give examples of expressions of affection: holding hands, hugging, dry mouth kissing, french kissing, above the waist petting, below the waist petting, etc. Hand an index card to each student and have students write expressions of affection between a couple that, in their opinion, can be considered abstinent. Tell students

not to put their names on the cards and that the cards will be collected, shuffled, and read. Give students five minutes to write their responses. Read the students' responses to the class. Discuss. Ask if a person is more likely to eventually have intercourse if that person is engaging in heavy petting, rather than limiting behavior to hugging and platonic kissing. Also ask why different people define abstinence differently. **(20 min.; Extend, Enrich)**

SECTION III

The Standard Contraceptive Methods

As you read about each contraceptive method, you may notice that some are given more space than others. This is not because they are better methods, but because they are more complex in their actions. Effectiveness and safety are the main factors to consider for each one.

Abstinence

The safest, most effective method to consider is abstinence. These days, young people from New York to California, from the Midwest to the southern states—in fact, teens from all over the United States—are choosing abstinence more often than ever before. Part of the reason is to avoid pregnancy. Also, teens are more aware these days of the threats they face from AIDS, herpes, and other sexually transmitted diseases.

When used correctly, abstinence is the most effective contraceptive—100 percent effective, in fact. To use abstinence correctly, though, a couple must remember that a pregnancy can begin if even a single drop of fluid from the penis is deposited near the opening of a woman's vagina. Sperm from this fluid can swim into the vagina and up through the uterus to find a waiting ovum. Therefore, to be 100 percent effective in preventing pregnancy, abstinence must include preventing any contact at all between the man's penis and the woman's vagina.

Another enormous benefit of abstinence is its 100 percent effectiveness against sexually transmitted diseases—effectiveness far above that of the latex condom, the next best choice for disease prevention. Again,

HEALTH STRATEGIES

Avoiding Pregnancy

People can <u>completely</u> *protect themselves from pregnancy by:*

1. Practicing sexual abstinence

People can <u>reduce</u> *their risks of becoming pregnant by using:*

1. Oral contraceptives
2. Hormone implants and injections
3. Intrauterine devices (IUDs)
4. Vaginal spermicides
5. Diaphragms
6. Vaginal contraceptive sponges
7. Cervical caps
8. Male condoms
9. Female condoms
10. The rhythm method
11. Sterilization

proper use of the method is essential. Diseases can be transmitted by any contact between penis and vagina.

① The decision to abstain from sexual intercourse can take courage and willpower in the face of internal and external pressures to look sexy and act sexy. Most people who succeed, however, say it is worth the effort. They say they can best focus on their own growth and pursue their own goals without the demands of a sexually intimate relationship. Finally, when they become ready to make a lifelong commitment, they have grown in character and self-esteem and are well able to become partners. At that point, another method of contraception may be needed. The Health Strategies section on this page contrasts abstinence with other ways to avoid pregnancy or to reduce the risk of becoming pregnant.

❝ Thoughts on Health ❞

We all worry about the population explosion, but we don't worry about it at the right time.
– Art Hoppe

Teacher Support Notes

① **Handout—Abstinence vs. Sexual Intercourse:** Your supplementary material contains a questionnaire designed to help students decide whether or not they are really ready for sexual intercourse. It may be effective in persuading students who are considering sexual intercourse to decide against it. It consists of ten questions followed by comments. Depending upon the age and maturity level of your students, you may or may not want to use this activity.

Activity 3.2

History of the Pill. Give students the history of "the Pill."

In 1934, progesterone was isolated in the laboratory. Researchers knew from previous experiments that ovulation did not happen in animals when proges-terone levels were at their highest. The reason for this was that progesterone would create the illusion of a false pregnancy and, of course, no ovulation occurs during pregnancy. This was proven when it was given to animals and it did inhibit ovulation.

In 1954, Carl Djerassi was successful in synthesizing progesterone. The man-made hormone was more potent than naturally occurring progesterones, so it could be used in very small amounts.

Three other researchers, Gregory Pincus (often called the "father of the Pill"), J. Rock, and C.R. Garcia were doing research to develop a more effective contraceptive. They tested hundreds of different compounds on animals until they found what would work best.

In 1956 the trio tested their new contraceptive on women in Puerto Rico. It was so effective that within a short time, "the

Teacher Support Notes

① **Oral Contraceptives:** Some students may not realize this category of contraceptives is called *oral* contraceptives because it refers to the mouth. Tell students that oral contraceptives are those that are taken orally, through the mouth.

② **Ovulation:** You may want to refer students back to the Chapter 21 discussion of ovulation before they read the following explanation of how oral contraceptives work.

③ **Progestin:** Tell students that taking pills is not the only way to introduce progestins into the body. Some contraception devices release the drugs directly into the uterus or vagina. Women can also receive a shot of progestins that lasts for three months. Among devices that release progestin are IUDs and vaginal rings. The shot, called *Depo-Provera*, was approved by the FDA in late 1992 and was first available in the U.S. in January of 1993.

✎ Fast Facts

20% of unwed teenage mothers become pregnant again within a year of giving birth.

> **Key Points** ▶ *Abstinence is the only contraceptive method that is 100 percent effective against both pregnancy and sexually transmitted diseases.*

Oral Contraceptives

Many women choose **oral contraceptives**, popularly known as "the Pill." The Pill is the most popular nonsurgical method of contraception. One type of oral contraceptive, the **combination pill**, uses synthetic versions of the female reproductive hormones **estrogen** and **progesterone** to prevent pregnancy (The laboratory-made progesterone is called **progestin**). Another type of pill, the **minipill**, contains only progestin. Figure B–3 shows some packets of typical pills. Each packet contains a month's supply.

The estrogen present in combination pills prevents pregnancy by stopping ovulation. Pills vary in the amounts of hormone they contain. Most packets of pills deliver hormones for 21 days of the menstrual cycle, and then provide seven inactive pills to help the woman stay on schedule during menstruation. A woman may still ovulate during her first month on such pills. Therefore, she should use a backup method of contraception during this time.

The minipill, as mentioned, contains no estrogen—only progestin. Unlike combination pills, which suppress ovulation, the minipill mostly affects the uterus itself. The progestin in the minipill thickens the mucus surrounding the uterine opening (cervix), so that sperm cannot penetrate. Progestin may also deactivate sperm cells. Progestin also interrupts the normal preparation of the uterine lining so that a fertilized egg may not implant.

Pill users may have difficulty remembering to take the pills. The effectiveness of the Pill, as with any type of contraception, depends on regular and correct use. If a woman forgets to take her pill for a day or more, she

FIGURE B-3
Oral Contraceptives

Oral contraceptive effectiveness:
  Combination pills, laboratory rating = 99.5 percent.
  Combination pills, user effectiveness = 98 percent.
  Minipill, laboratory rating = 99 percent.
  Minipill, user effectiveness = 95 percent.

should take the missed pill as soon as she remembers it, get back on her pill schedule, and use a backup method of contraception for the remainder of that pill cycle.

The side effects of oral contraceptives range from common, bothersome symptoms to rare, life-threatening conditions. The *number* of side effects is high, but remember that most side effects are rare. Among the more common, less serious side effects are tenderness of the breasts, emotional depression or fatigue, nausea or vomiting, skin conditions, weight gain or loss, stopping of menstruation, unexpected vaginal bleeding, and a tendency to develop vaginal yeast infections. More rare are high levels of sugar and fat in the blood, an impaired sex drive, headaches, and fluid retention. Among the most rare and serious side effects are diseases of the heart, kidney, liver, or gallbladder; stroke; benign tumors of the uterus;

Pill" became popular worldwide. Ask students what the development of the pill has meant to people everywhere.

What impact has it had on the earth's environment? **(15 min., Multicultural)**

Activity 3.3
Parental Advice. Put students in groups of three or four. Have students imagine they are parents of teenage children. Both of their children, a boy age 17 and a girl age 15, are dating regularly. What advice would they give their children about sex and contraceptives? Give students ten minutes to write ideas. Then ask each group to share one piece of advice they would give their teenage children. Discuss. **(20–25 min., Cooperative Learning)**

Activity 3.4
Posters. After students have learned about all the different contraceptives described in this section, do this activity.

Tell students they will be doing some artwork for the health room and should think about one or two other people they would like to work with. Explain that they will be asked to design a poster that is an accurate and convincing advertisement to sell a method of birth control.

Have students bring poster board to

(continued on next page)

and blood clots that can lodge in vital organs and cause death.

Early symptoms almost always warn when serious medical conditions are developing. A woman taking oral contraceptives should call her physician if she has:

- Abdominal pain.
- Chest pain.
- Breathlessness.
- Headaches.
- Blurred vision or loss of vision.
- Leg pain.

These symptoms may warn that a serious condition is developing.

Not all side effects are negative. For example, oral contraceptives can help to regulate irregular menstrual periods and relieve excessive menstrual cramping. Oral contraceptives have also been linked with reduced risks of certain cancers.

You may read reports that link oral contraceptives to a risk of cervical cancer, but factors other than the Pill may be the cause. Pill users often have intercourse at young ages, have many sex partners, and are unlikely to use condoms. They are therefore often exposed to the sexually transmitted virus that causes a type of cervical cancer. The Pill alone provides no protection from STDs. People relying on the pill for pregnancy protection should still use condoms to prevent STDs.

A very dangerous combination is smoking and using the Pill. Together, they greatly increase the risk of heart attack or stroke. Chapter 15 presented a graph showing this effect (see Figure 15–4 on page 381).

The minipill produces fewer and less severe side effects than the combination pill, so women sometimes switch to it. Of course, the minipill has possible side effects of its own, including menstrual disorders and, less often, headaches. Also, the minipill is less effective in preventing pregnancy.

Most women who use the Pill experience no side effects at all. Others who experience minor symptoms at first may find that they disappear after about three months. Sometimes a switch from one brand to another can bring relief (the woman can ask her physician).

It is important to be aware that depression, a relatively common side effect, may take some time to develop. The user therefore may not realize that it comes from oral contraceptive use. When moodiness, sadness, or irritability is not explained by life events and does not improve after several months, Pill users should suspect the pills and ask their physicians for another type.

A woman who thinks she may be pregnant should not take the Pill, because it increases the risks of birth defects. In fact, a woman using oral contraceptives who decides to become pregnant should switch to another method of contraception for at least two months (some health care providers suggest six months to a year) before becoming pregnant.

Key Points *Oral contraceptives are highly effective in preventing pregnancy, but they must be used correctly. Side effects range from minor to severe. The most severe side effects are rare.*

Mini Glossary

oral contraceptives: pills that prevent pregnancy by stopping ovulation or by changing conditions in the uterus; often called *birth control pills* or "the Pill."

combination pill: an oral contraceptive that contains progestin and synthetic estrogen.

estrogen: a hormone that, in females, regulates the ovulatory cycle.

progesterone: a hormone secreted in females during that portion of the menstrual cycle in which the uterine lining builds up.

progestin: a synthetic version of progesterone used in contraceptives.

minipill: a progestin-only oral contraceptive.

①

✎ **Fast Facts**

500,000 teen pregnancies occur each year in the United States.

Teacher Support Notes

① **Comparing Effectiveness:** Ask students the difference between the user effectiveness of the minipill vs. the combination pill. (95% to 98%) In a group of 100 women, how many more will become pregnant using the minipill as compared to the combination pill? (3 more—5 in a 100 for the minipill as opposed to 2 in a 100 with the combination pill)

✉ **Where to Write**

Association of Voluntary Sterilization
122 E. 42nd Street
New York, New York 10168

create the advertisements. Have students bring markers, colored pencils, crayons, or any medium they choose to work with from home. The students will need to have some class planning time to get their ideas together. Pick a day that the posters will be created in class. Allow enough time at the end of the hour for students to show

and explain their posters. Display the posters on the health room walls. **(20 min. planning time, one class period for poster work; Interdisciplinary)**

Activity 3.5
Behavior Risks. Make three columns on the board. Label them *High Chance of Pregnancy Occurring, Low Chance of Pregnancy Occurring,* and *No Chance of Pregnancy Occurring.* Go

around the room and ask each student to suggest a sexual behavior that a couple might engage in. When a behavior is mentioned, ask another student to say under which heading it belongs. Keep asking for responses until students run out of ideas. Discuss why people would participate in a high-risk behavior if they did not want to begin a pregnancy. **(15–20 min.; Reteach, Reinforce)**

B10

Hormone Implants and Injections

Progestin, the synthetic hormone of the minipill, can also be delivered by slow-release capsules implanted under the skin. The product **Norplant** (shown in Figure B–4) consists of tubes of progestin. In a simple surgical procedure, a physician implants six thin capsules (each the size of a matchstick) under the skin of a woman's upper arm. Norplant works by slowly releasing progestin for up to five years. Its effectiveness is about the same as the minipill's laboratory effectiveness. As an alternative to implants, women can receive a shot of progestin (called **Depo-Provera**) that lasts for three months. Women using these methods also need to use condoms for STD prevention.

> **Key Points** *Norplant delivers progestin for up to five years from capsules implanted under the skin.*

Intrauterine Device (IUD)

Many women choose an **intrauterine device,** or **IUD,** for contraception. The IUD is a small plastic or plastic and metal object that a physician inserts into a woman's uterus. A tiny nylon thread hangs from the IUD through the cervix into the vagina (Figure B–5a). So long as the thread is there, the woman can know that the IUD is in place.

The IUD is best suited for women who have had at least one child, are in a stable, mutually monogamous relationship, and have no history of pelvic inflammatory disease (PID). Teens are usually *not* the best candidates for IUD use.

The way an IUD prevents pregnancy is not fully known. One theory is that the IUD makes the uterus hostile to sperm. Another is that it prevents implantation. One available IUD contains the hormone progesterone, which it releases into the uterus.

Pelvic inflammatory disease (PID), which can lead to sterility, has been associated

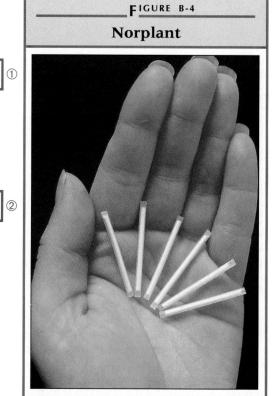

FIGURE B-4
Norplant

Norplant effectiveness:
Laboratory rating = 99.96 percent.
User effectiveness = 98 to 99 percent.

Figure B–5a IUD

FIGURE B-5b

IUD

IUD effectiveness:
Laboratory rating = 98.5 percent.
User effectiveness = 97 percent.

FIGURE B-6

Vaginal Spermicides

Spermicide (foams, creams, gels, sheets and suppositories) effectiveness:
Laboratory rating = 95 to 97 percent.
User effectiveness = 79 percent.

②

---

with IUD use. PID may occur if, during insertion of the device, bacteria are introduced into the uterus. Also, a woman with an IUD may fail to use condoms to prevent STDs, and STDs often cause PID. An IUD may prevent pregnancy (Figure B–5b), but it has no effect in preventing STDs.

> **Key Points** ▸ *IUDs are devices inserted into the uterus to prevent pregnancy. An IUD is best used by a woman who has had a child, is in a stable, monogamous relationship, and has no history of PID. They do not protect against STDs.*

Vaginal Spermicides

The spermicides are sperm-killing or sperm-immobilizing products that can be inserted into the vagina just before intercourse. They are available over the counter in the forms shown in Figure B–6—foams, creams, gels, sheets, or suppositories. These contraceptives are **barrier methods**—they place a physical and chemical barrier between sperm and ovum at the opening of the uterus. Most do not last long—only half an hour or so—and therefore must be inserted just prior to each occasion of sexual

①

MINI GLOSSARY

Norplant: a trade name for a surgical hormone delivery system that provides continuous release of progestin, thereby preventing pregnancy for up to five years.
Depo-Provera (DEE-po pro-VAIR-uh): a trade name for an injectable form of progestin.
intrauterine device (IUD): a device inserted into the uterus to prevent conception or implantation.
barrier methods: contraceptive methods that physically or chemically obstruct the travel of sperm toward the ovum. These devices do not alter body processes with drugs or devices.

Healthy or have *Permanent Problems*, like sterility. Put these two possibilities under *Curable*. If they cannot be cured, as is the case with herpes or AIDS, they may have the STD for *The Rest of Their Life* or *Die From It*. Put these risks under *Incurable*.

If a girl decides to *Have Her Baby*, she has three choices—she can *Marry the*

Father, *Raise the Baby by Herself*, or *Give the Baby Up for Adoption*. Write these three choices under *Have Her Baby* on the board.

This diagram will help students to see that when they begin sexual activity their lives can become very complicated and they will run many risks. For an example of the completed diagram see "Choices Diagram" in your supplementary material. **(15 min.; Reteach, Reinforce)**

Activity 3.7
Excuses! Excuses! Excuses! Ask the class to list excuses they have heard sexually active teens give for not using contraceptives. If answers are not forthcoming help students by naming some, such as "It is too embarrassing," or "I'll use withdrawal," or "They're too expensive," or "It is like planning sex and makes us feel cheap," or "It breaks the romance," or "I can't get pregnant at this time of

---

✍ Fast Facts
A woman has about a 2% to 4% chance of becoming pregnant during intercourse without contraception. If intercourse occurs the day after ovulation, the chance of pregnancy is 30%. If it occurs on the day of ovulation, there is a 50% chance. Over the period of a year a couple that does not use contraception has a 90% chance of pregnancy.

Teacher Support Notes

① **Overhead— Diaphragm:** Your supplementary material contains an overhead showing insertion of the diaphragm, cervical cap, and contraceptive sponge. The illustrations on the overhead are more graphic than those in the text, showing how the female puts these contraceptives in place.

✉ **Where to Write**
Parents Anonymous 22330 Hawthorne Blvd. Suite 208 Torrance, California 90505

B12 Special Unit Sexual Behavior and Pregnancy Prevention

intercourse. Spermicides are often used with other forms of contraception, such as the diaphragm or condoms.

The killing action of spermicides also kills some of the pathogens that cause STDs. Spermicides alone do not kill all viruses, however; the AIDS and herpes viruses are unaffected by them. Latex condoms used with spermicide can prevent most types of STDs.

Key Points ▶ *Spermicides can kill or stop sperm. They also kill some forms of pathogens that cause STDs.*

Diaphragm

The **diaphragm** is a circular metal spring or ring fitted with a shallow cup of thin rubber that the user fills with spermicidal cream or jelly. The device is folded into the vagina. Once inside, it springs open to cover the cervix. The diaphragm is shown in Figure B–7. The diaphragm holds spermicide snugly against the entrance of the cervix and bars sperm from entering the uterus. The diaphragm is a barrier device and provides no protection against viruses that cause STDs. It does provide some protection from bacteria that cause STDs.

To work properly, a diaphragm must be the right size for each woman, and must be custom fitted. (Some people may be tempted to borrow a diaphragm "just to try it" before going in to be fitted by a health care professional. This is a mistake, because the

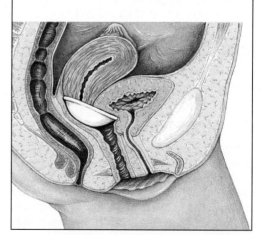

FIGURE B-7

Diaphragm with Spermicide

Diaphragm with spermicide effectiveness:
    Laboratory rating = 98 percent.
    User effectiveness = 82 to 86 percent.

month," or "I'm too embarrassed to go to the drug store," or "If my parents found contraceptives in my room, purse, car, etc., they'd blow up!"

Once these have been listed on the board, divide the class into small groups. Ask each group to discuss the validity of these excuses. Give them about ten minutes to discuss and write their feelings. At the end of that time ask each group to give one of their responses as to

how valid they felt the excuse was. Discuss whether or not teens should have unprotected sex if they are not ready for the responsibility of contraception. **(40 min., Cooperative Learning)**

Activity 3.8
Envelope Exchange. Reaffirm that no matter what contraceptive method is used, protection against STDs is a major concern. The latex condom with

nonoxynol-9 is the only protection, besides abstinence, we have against STDs. But, this condom isn't foolproof. Tell students that one in approximately seven to ten teens has an STD, usually warts, chlamydia, gonorrhea, or herpes.

Prepare enough envelopes before class so that there is one for each student. Let's assume that you have 30 students. If so, leave 27 envelopes blank.

(continued on next page)

---

likelihood that a borrowed diaphragm will fit properly is slim indeed.) A woman must be refitted if she gains or loses 10 pounds or if she has a child.

The user of a diaphragm can insert it up to six hours before intercourse. If two hours or so have passed before intercourse occurs, however, the user should apply another dose of spermicide by removing the diaphragm, applying the spermicide and reinserting the diaphragm. After intercourse, the woman should leave the diaphragm in place for at least six hours and then remove it, when convenient, within 24 hours. To repeat intercourse within the six-hour period during which the diaphragm must remain in place, the woman can simply insert an application of spermicide into the vagina. The user should store her diaphragm with care and check it often for holes or other defects by holding it up to a light. It has a limited life span.

> **Key Points** *The diaphragm is a barrier device that blocks sperm from entering the uterus. The diaphragm is ineffective in preventing many sexually transmitted infections.*

Vaginal Contraceptive Sponge

A barrier device similar to the diaphragm is the vaginal **sponge**. The sponge resembles a diaphragm in shape but is made of thick, disposable sponge rubber. It is available over the counter. With the sponge, one size fits all. The bowl shape of the sponge helps hold it in place over the cervix, and its woven handle helps in its removal (see Figure B–8). The sponge contains a spermicide that becomes active when wet. The user moistens it with water before insertion.

The user can insert the sponge any time before sexual intercourse. It protects against pregnancy for 24 hours, with nothing more to do, even for repeated intercourse. The

FIGURE B-8
Vaginal Contraceptive Sponge

Sponge effectiveness:
Laboratory rating = 95 to 98 percent.
User effectiveness = 76 to 83 percent.

MINI GLOSSARY

diaphragm: a dome that fits over the cervix and holds spermicidal cream or jelly against the uterine entrance to block the passage of sperm.
sponge: a disposable sponge-rubber dome, filled with spermicide, that works in the same way as the diaphragm.

Teacher Support Notes

① **Diaphragm vs. Sponge:** After students have read the information about vaginal sponges, ask them to compare the sponge to the diaphragm. What are some differences? (diaphragm must be fitted, one size sponge fits all; the diaphragm requires renewed applications of spermicide if sexual intercourse occurs more than once, a sponge need not be attended to even for repeated intercourse; the diaphragm is effective for a 6-hour period only, the sponge protects for 24 hours; the diaphragm has a user effectiveness of 82% to 86%, the sponge has a user effectiveness of 76% to 83%)

✎ Fast Facts

One major study found that during their first intercourse fewer than half of the couples used contraception.

Then, on the inside flap of one envelope, in small letters, write the initials *C W* (chlamydia and warts). On a second envelope write the letter *H* (herpes), and on a third *G* (gonorrhea). If you have 30 students, these three envelopes with initials representing the common STDs will

represent a one in ten risk of the students contracting an STD.

Without telling the class this is an STD exercise, tell the class each person is going to get one envelope. Without letting anyone else see, tell students to look at the inside flap of their envelopes when they receive them. If they see any initials, they are to commit them to memory. Then they are to exchange envelopes with another person in the class. If they had

initials on the first envelope, they now write them on the new envelopes they have just received. Whether they had initials on the first envelope or not, have them "pretend" to write something on their envelopes so no one else will know who has the initialed envelopes. Tell students they will exchange envelopes three times. Each time they exchange, they will add any initials they received on any exchange. (unless, of course, the enve-

---

✍ Fast Facts

In the time it takes to read this sentence, the world population will have increased by twelve.

Teacher Support Notes

① **Cervical Cap vs. Diaphragm:** After students have read the information about the cervical cap, ask them to name at least two advantages of the cap over the diaphragm. (more durable, requires less spermicide, no additional applications) There is, however, at least one disadvantage. Ask them to name it. (has a user effectiveness of 73% to 92% as compared to 82% to 86% for the diaphragm) The 92% is better than the 86%, but of more concern is the low of 73%.

✉ Where to Write

Planned Parenthood Federation of America
810 7th Avenue
New York, New York 10019

user must leave it in place for at least six hours after intercourse and then remove it as soon as is convenient. The sponge alone is useless in preventing viral STD infections such as AIDS. However, it does provide some protection against bacterial infections such as gonorrhea.

Key Points ▶ *The contraceptive sponge resembles the diaphragm in many ways. It prevents pregnancy but is not protective against most STDs.*

Cervical Cap

The **cervical cap**, shown in Figure B–9a, is a flexible, cuplike device about an inch and a half in diameter that covers the woman's cervix. Like the diaphragm, it must fit perfectly to prevent the passage of sperm into the uterus (Figure B–9b). A health care provider chooses the size to fit the user. Like the diaphragm, the cap is

Figure B–9b Cervical Cap

used with spermicide. The recommended time periods for leaving the cervical cap in before and after intercourse are approximately the same as for the diaphragm.

The cervical cap differs from the diaphragm in that it is smaller and more durable, and it requires less spermicide per use. Since the cap fits tightly and rarely leaks, no additional applications of spermicide are necessary before intercourse. Only women with healthy cervix tissue (negative Pap tests) can use the cap.

In a very few instances, the dangerous bacterial poisoning known as toxic shock syndrome (TSS) has been associated with diaphragm, sponge, and cervical cap use. Teenage girls are its most frequent victims. (More often, as discussed in Chapter 11, toxic shock syndrome has been associated with the use of superabsorbent tampons.) Because of the risk of toxic shock syndrome, it may be wise to avoid using the diaphragm, sponge, or cap during a menstrual period and always to remove it after no more than 24 hours. The early warning signs of TSS are listed on page 280 in Chapter 11.

FIGURE B-9a

Cervical Cap with Spermicide

Cervical cap with spermicide effectiveness:
   Laboratory rating = 98 percent.
   User effectiveness = 73 to 92 percent.

Key Points ▶ *The cervical cap fits tightly over the cervix to prevent passage of sperm into the uterus. Toxic shock syndrome has been associated with diaphragm, sponge, and cervical cap use during menstruation.*

lope they got already has that initial on it) Go over the directions again to make sure students understand and then hand out the envelopes and do the exchanges.

Now make the analogy that the initials stand for chlamydia, warts, herpes and gonorrhea. Passing the envelopes three times equates to having three different sexual partners. Tell the class they started with the national average of one in ten teens being infected with an STD. Ask

how many people now have initials on their envelopes. Discuss. **(15–20 min.; Reteach, Reinforce)**

EVALUATE
SECTION III

Activity 3.9
Pop Quiz.
1. What method of birth control is 100% effective? (abstinence)

2. The synthetic hormone found in the minipill is called _____. (progestin)
3. If a woman forgets to take a birth control pill, she should take it as soon as possible, resume her pill schedule, and use a back-up method of birth control the rest of the month. True or False. (True)
4. Norplant is surgically implanted progestin that prevents pregnancy up to six years. True or False. (False)

(continued on next page)

Male Condom

Up to this point, only women's methods of contraception have been discussed. Use of a **male condom** is the only method, aside from sterilization, available to men. The condom is a disposable, thin sheath of latex (a type of rubber) or processed lamb tissue. The condom is rolled onto the erect penis before intercourse.

Condoms are shown in Figure B–10. There are many varieties, shapes, and colors, but those designed to prevent pregnancy all work the same way. Semen collects in the tip of the condom and is discarded with it.

The choice of latex condoms for contraception is valid for two reasons. First, latex

① condoms offer some protection against sexually transmitted diseases, such as AIDS. This effect is so important that even women who use another form of contraception against pregnancy are urged to insist that their partners use condoms as well. The Pill, IUD, and other methods may prevent pregnancy, but they leave people open to sexually transmitted diseases. Latex condoms can often prevent them, but lambskin condoms do not provide STD protection. Lambskin has pores (small holes), as does all natural skin. The pores are too small to allow the passage of sperm, but large enough to permit bacteria and viruses to cross the membrane easily. Latex is a continuous film without holes. Thus bacteria and viruses cannot cross it.

The other reason that latex condoms are a wise choice for contraception is that they are superior at preventing pregnancy. Condoms with spermicide added, if used correctly, can provide pregnancy protection rivaling that of the Pill.

When applying a condom, the user should leave it rolled up as it comes from the wrapper and place it loosely on the tip of the erect penis. The condom is gently and slowly unrolled down to the base of the penis, while the thumb and index finger of one hand hold the condom's tip to create a reservoir for the semen. The condom should not be stretched tightly over

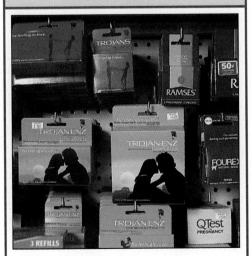

FIGURE B-10

Male Condoms

Condom effectiveness:
  Condom, laboratory rating = 98 percent.
  Condom, user effectiveness = 88 percent.
  Condom with spermicide = same as combination pill—98 to 99.5 percent.

MINI GLOSSARY

cervical cap: a rubber cap that fits over the cervix, used with spermicide to prevent conception.
male condom: a sheath worn over the penis during intercourse to contain the semen, to prevent pregnancy, and/or to reduce the risks of sexually transmitted diseases; condoms are also called *rubbers*.

Teacher Support Notes

① **Overhead—Condoms:** Your supplementary material contains an overhead that shows both the male and the female condoms in place. Be aware that these illustrations are somewhat more graphic than the illustration included in the text. You may or may not want to use the transparency, depending upon the age and maturity level of your students.

✍ Fast Facts

Oral contraception is used by approximately ten million women in the United States. Worldwide use has been estimated at 55 to 56 million.

66 Thoughts on Health 99

Contraceptives should be used on every conceivable occasion.
– **Spike Milligan**

EVALUATE
(Continued)

5. What is PID? (pelvic inflammatory disease)
6. What is one contraceptive device that must be used with a spermicide? (diaphragm)
7. What barrier device is similar to the diaphragm but disposable? (sponge)

8. Name a reusable barrier device that must be fitted by a doctor and fits snugly over the cervix. (cervical cap or diaphragm)
9. Toxic shock syndrome is an allergic reaction some women have to the use of spermicides. True or False. (False)
10. Any petroleum-based or oil lubricants should not be used with which contraceptive device? (condom)

CLOSE
SECTION III

Activity 3.10
Contraceptive Review. Although many students memorize facts for a test on contraception, they may not be able to explain how a contraceptive is used correctly or what it does to prevent pregnancy.

📖 Fast Facts

70% of condoms are purchased by women.

Teacher Support Notes

① **Drawbacks for Condoms:** You may want to discuss with students some major drawbacks to the use of condoms. One of the chief drawbacks is that the condom must be put on after the man has been aroused but before he enters the woman. This necessary interruption in the lovemaking is the major reason for users neglecting or "forgetting" to put them on. Another drawback is that some men complain that sensation is dulled by the condom. The use of condoms made from animal tissue will help remedy this problem, but as the text states, the animal tissue condoms such as the lambskin condom will not prevent STDs.

✉ Where to Write

Single Parent Resource Center
225 Park Avenue South
New York, New York 10003

B16

B16   Special Unit Sexual Behavior and Pregnancy Prevention

the tip of the penis—it could break during intercourse. A condom will slip off a penis that is not fully erect. A man who uses a condom must withdraw from the vagina immediately after ejaculation.

Some condoms are coated with lubricating jelly or powder on the outside to reduce friction in the vagina. Products that provide extra lubrication are sold especially for this purpose. A warning is in order here. Using petroleum jelly (Vaseline) or any oil-containing ("moisturizing") lotion for lubrication can weaken the condom and make it break during intercourse. Also, condoms that have been stored in wallets or places of high temperature, such as cars, will also become weak. Instructions for proper storage of condoms were presented in the Straight Talk section on page A14.

The condom must be in place before any contact occurs between the penis and the vagina, to contain the drops of sperm-containing fluid released from the penis before intercourse begins. If the condom is applied too late, its effectiveness drops dramatically. Condoms vary in quality. Cheap ones may break easily. The stronger, more expensive ones are recommended.

Key Points ▶ *Condoms are the only contraceptive method available for use by men, aside from sterilization. Latex condoms with spermicide can prevent pregnancies and often prevent transmission of many STDs.*

Female Condom

Women need to protect themselves from sexually transmitted diseases, even if their partners refuse to use condoms. To give women control of their own protection, researchers have invented the **female condom**. The device is a disposable tubular sack six and a half inches in length (shown in Figure B–11). The material from which it is made resembles the plastic of sandwich bags, but is stronger. Flexible plastic rings at each

end of the tube hold it in place in the vagina. One ring, at the closed end of the sack, fits over the cervix. The other ring remains outside the vagina to anchor the device in place and to cover parts of the female genital area (to cut down on contact with semen).

To use the device successfully, the woman must be sure that both rings are snugly in place before any contact occurs between penis and vagina. If the internal ring slipped out of place, no extra risk would result, because semen would still not escape from the pouch. Extra risk would occur if the external ring slipped into the vagina, since semen would easily spill over the edges of the condom into the vagina. The female condom is packaged with a lubricant. Using it with spermicide may boost its effectiveness in preventing pregnancy and some STDs.

FIGURE B–11
Female Condom

Female condom effectiveness:
    Laboratory rating = 88 percent.
    User effectiveness = 80 percent.
Note: These ratings are based on preliminary data and may change as new data become available.

Prepare before class slips of paper, each one having one contraceptive method on it. You will have to have two or three slips with the same method to accommodate a class of 30 students. Fold the slips and put them in a box. Have each student draw out one. Their assignment is to describe on paper how the method they picked works and how it is correctly used. You may want to put a diagram of the male and female repro-

ductive system on the board or on an overhead projector to aid students. Collect the papers and check for understanding. **(15–20 min.; Reteach, Reinforce)**

FOCUS
SECTION IV

In this section students will learn:
1. To name several contraceptive methods that aren't effective.

2. To describe why those methods don't work.

Activity 4.1
Ineffective Contraception. Ask students why someone might use one of the ineffective contraceptive methods. After students give their responses, reemphasize the importance of the responsibility a person must take with regard to

(continued on next page)

> **Key Points** ▶ *The female condom provides protection from pregnancy and gives women control of their own protection against some STDs.*

Rhythm Method ①

The **rhythm method** involves neither drugs nor devices. If used perfectly, the method could be up to 95 percent effective (actual user effectiveness in typical couples is much lower—only about 80 percent). The woman is taught to track the menstrual cycle and to observe body signs of ovulation, such as body temperature and mucous secretions. She can then refrain from having intercourse during the few days right after she has produced a fresh ovum.

The rhythm method requires no use of equipment during intercourse. It is available to anyone. However, people who wish to use it must first be trained by health professionals, because its use is complicated. Even the most technical references warn that merely reading about this method is not enough training to ensure that people can use it successfully to prevent conception. People who choose to use it, then, must go to a professional for help in getting started.

All of the methods discussed so far are effective against pregnancy to some degree. Figure B–12 on the next page sums up facts concerning each method's effectiveness.

> **Key Points** ▶ *The rhythm method is complex to use. It gives better results to those trying to conceive than to people trying not to conceive.*

SECTION III REVIEW

Answer the following questions on a sheet of paper.
Learning the Vocabulary
The vocabulary terms for this section are *oral contraceptives, combination pill, estrogen, progesterone, progestin, minipill, Norplant, Depo-Provera, intrauterine device (IUD), barrier methods, diaphragm, sponge, cervical cap, male condom, female condom,* and *rhythm method.*

1. Match each of the following phrases with the appropriate term.
   a. a progestin-only oral contraceptive.
   b. a rubber cap that fits over the cervix.
   c. a trade name for a surgical hormone delivery system that provides continuous release of progestin, thereby preventing pregnancy for up to five years.

Learning the Facts
2. List the side effects of taking the pill.
3. How does Norplant work?
4. Name the different types of spermicides available.

Making Life Choices
5. After reading this section, which contraceptive method would you use? Why would you choose that method? What method would you want your partner to use and why?

SECTION IV

Methods Not Recommended for Contraception

People have many false notions about contraception and may recommend methods other than the effective ones just described. For example, popular belief has it that a couple can prevent pregnancy by

MINI GLOSSARY

female condom: a soft, thin plastic tube with two end rings—one to fit over the cervix and one to serve as an anchor outside the entrance to the vagina; also called a *vaginal pouch.*
rhythm method: see *fertility awareness,* page 519.

Teacher Support Notes
① **Rhythm Method:** Tell students that the rhythm method is one of several *fertility awareness methods.* All of these methods require education, training, and planning. Other types of fertility awareness methods are the basal body temperature (BBT) method, the mucus (also called the Billings or ovulation) method, and the sympto-thermal method.

Section III Review
Answers
1. **a.** minipill **b.** cervical cap **c.** Norplant
2. Refer to the last paragraph on page B8 for possible answers.
3. with the surgical implantation of six tubes of progestin in the woman's upper arm that slowly release the progestin for up to five years
4. foams, creams, gels, sheets, suppositories
5. Answers will vary.

B17

Focus
(Continued)

when that person will decide to engage in sexual intercourse. **(5–10 min.; Reteach, Reinforce)**

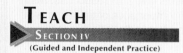

TEACH
SECTION IV
(Guided and Independent Practice)

Activity 4.2
Contraception Myths. Brainstorm with the class all of the myths they have heard about contraception. Make a list on the board. Students will respond with statements such as "You can't get pregnant the first time you have sex," "You can't get pregnant if you drink ice water after sex," "A male won't be able to get a girl pregnant if he sits in a hot or cold bath before sex," "You can't get pregnant if you

have sex standing up," "A girl can't get pregnant during her period," "A male can't get someone pregnant if he wears a rubber band around his penis during sex," etc.

Discuss with students why these myths are untrue. Why do students think the myths persist? Why do some people still believe them? **(20–25 min.; Extend, Enrich)**

Teacher Support Notes

① **Comparing Contraceptive Methods:** Use the questions below to get students involved in this figure. But first, you may want to have them do a simple evaluation of these methods. Have them number from 1 to 14 on a sheet of paper. Then, for each of the 14 methods listed, have them write yes or no to indicate whether or not that method would be acceptable to them. Some students might prefer to keep their evaluations private; others might be willing to discuss their choices. Here are the questions:
a. Of the 14 methods listed, which is the most effective if used perfectly? (abstinence) Which is the most effective in typical users? (male sterilization)
b. Excluding abstinence and sterilization, what is the most effective method in typical users? (Norplant)
c. What is the least effective method in typical users? (cervical cap with spermicide)
d. Which method provides the best protection against STDs? (abstinence)
e. Other than abstinence, which methods provide the best protection against STDs? (male condoms with spermicides and female condoms)

B18 Special Unit Sexual Behavior and Pregnancy Prevention

FIGURE B-12

Standard Contraceptive Methods Compared for Effectiveness ①

Method	Effectiveness If Used Perfectly (%)	Effectiveness in Typical Users (%)	Factors to Consider
Abstinence	100	Unknown[a]	Abstinence must be used consistently and perfectly or effectiveness drops to 0%. Only method that provides 100% protection against STDs.
Oral contraceptives combination pill and minipill	99.5 99	98 95	Users who find it easy to take pills regularly use the method most successfully. No protection against sexually transmitted diseases (STDs).
Norplant	99.96	98 to 99	Implant may be slightly visible. Long-term use is recommended. No protection against STDs.
Intrauterine device (IUD)	98.5	97	The device can be expelled without the user's wareness. Pregnancy may occur with the device in place. No protection against STDs.
Vaginal spermicides	95 to 97	79	Users who follow directions exactly use the method most successfully. Slight protection against STDs.
Diaphragm with spermicide	98	82 to 86	Successful use requires proper fit and following instructions. Slight protection against STDs.
Vaginal contraceptive sponge	95 to 98	76 to 83	Users who follow directions exactly use the method most successfully. High cost. Slight protection against STDs.
Cervical cap with spermicide	98	73 to 92	Successful use requires proper fit and following instructions exactly. Slight protection against STDs.
Male condom	98	88	High quality condoms are most protective. Some protection from STDs. Improper use makes failure likely.
Male condom with spermicide	99.5	98	Users must follow directions exactly. Good protection from some STDs. Poor-quality condoms make failure likely.
Female condom	88[b]	80[b]	High cost. Still proving effectiveness. Good protection against some STDs.
Rhythm method	80 to 95	80	Ovulation is unpredictable. A high degree of training, skill, and dedication is required.
Male sterilization	99.85	99.85	Successful, except if the user has intercourse before sperm are absent from semen or if ends of tubes grow together (very unlikely).
Female sterilization	99.7	99.7	Pregnancy is likely only if ends of tubes grow together, (very unlikely).

[a]*Unknown* for those who allow contact between penis and vagina; otherwise, provides perfect protection.
[b]Based on preliminary data.

ing. (15–20 min.; Reteach, Reinforce)

conclusions "might" be drawn about him/her? What might be some of the outcomes of the decision? Answers will vary. List them on the board and discuss. **(10–15 min., Critical Thinking)**

Activity 4.3

Not Recommended. Review with the class the forms of contraception that don't work by having them list all of them on a piece of paper. Have the students also explain why they are ineffective. Collect their papers and check for understand-

Activity 4.4

Outcomes of Decisions. Ask students the following questions: If a sexually active teen decides not to use a contraceptive device or uses a non-recommended form of birth control, what

---

using the **withdrawal method**, also known as **coitus interruptus**. It is just what it sounds like—the man withdraws his penis from the vagina before he ejaculates, taking care that his semen is not deposited in, at, or near the vagina.

Two built-in errors make withdrawal useless. First, the man finds it difficult to withdraw his penis when he is near ejaculation. Second, even if he is able to withdraw before ejaculation, live sperm in the fluid from the penis will already have entered the vagina and may fertilize an ovum. Withdrawal may be better than no method at all, but it still allows one woman out of four to become pregnant in one year of use. It is not recommended as a contraceptive method. ①

Some people have tried to save money on condoms by using other replacements. Covering the penis with plastic kitchen wrap, sandwich bags, or other items is unlikely to prevent semen from spilling into the vagina. Pregnancy and STD transmission can easily occur.

Throughout history, women have attempted to wash out or kill sperm after intercourse by using douches of such fluids as vinegar or carbonated beverages. Hazardous-chemical douches, such as turpentine, are extremely damaging to tissues and do not prevent pregnancy. Most douches available over the counter are not intended for contraception. All forms of douches are useless for preventing pregnancy. In fact, they may even help the sperm along, because a stream of fluid can wash sperm into the cervix as easily as it can wash them out.

Women have also thought, wrongly, that as long as they breastfed their babies, they could not become pregnant. It is true that during lactation (milk production), many women are less likely to ovulate. However, there is no way an individual woman can know for sure. Lactation does reduce the total number of children born in a popula-

tion, but it is not reliable as a contraceptive method for any one woman.

Key Points ► Methods not *effective for contraception* include *withdrawal, using douches, or relying on lactation.*

SECTION IV REVIEW

Answer the following questions on a sheet of paper.

Learning the Vocabulary
The vocabulary term in this section is *withdrawal method (coitus interruptus).*
1. Write a sentence using the vocabulary term.

Learning the Facts
2. Why is the withdrawal method of birth control considered worthless?
3. How can using douches help a woman to become pregnant?
4. If lactation reduces a population's fertility rate, why can't a woman use it successfully to prevent conception?

Making Life Choices
5. Look at Figure B–12, "Standard Contraceptive Methods Compared for Effectiveness." Explain why there is such a difference between effectiveness rates for typical users and effectiveness rates for people using the methods perfectly. Which methods show the largest differences in percentages? What factors contribute to the large differences?
6. Review Figure B–12 again. This time, score each method on "control"—that is, to what extent you could control the method if you and a partner chose to use it. (A man can control condom use, a woman can control pill use.) If control were important to you, which methods would you use?

MINI GLOSSARY

withdrawal method (coitus interruptus): a technique in sexual intercourse of withdrawing the penis from the vagina just prior to ejaculation. It is not useful for preventing pregnancy or STDs.

Teacher Support Notes

① **Effectiveness of Withdrawal:** Ask students what the user effectiveness rate for withdrawal would be. (75%) How does this rate compare to the typical user effectiveness rate for the methods listed in figure B–12? (not good, only one method, the cervical cap with spermicide, is potentially less effective)

Section IV Review

Answers
1. Answers will vary.
2. The man finds it difficult to withdraw from the vagina before ejaculation and live sperm in the fluid from the penis will already have entered the vagina and may fertilize an ovum.
3. A stream of fluid can help wash sperm into the cervix as easily as it can wash them out.
4. A woman cannot be sure that she hasn't ovulated.
5–6. Answers will vary.

In this section students will learn about:
1. The permanent methods of contraception—vasectomy and tubal ligation.

Activity 5.1
  Sterilization. Ask students why someone would choose sterilization as a form of contraception. Get responses

from students on the most likely age of people seeking this operation. What would a person need to consider before having the surgery done? Discuss. **(10–15 min., Critical Thinking)**

TEACH
SECTION V
(Guided and Independent Practice)

Activity 5.2
Vasectomy and Tubal Ligation.

Explain to students that a large supply of sperm is stored in the male reproductive tract. This is the reason a man can still cause a pregnancy for about six weeks after a vasectomy. A sample of the man's semen would need to be examined under a microscope to determine for sure that he could have intercourse without causing a pregnancy.

  The tubal ligation is done with a small incision below the woman's navel and

---

Teacher Support Notes

① **Choosing Sterilization:** Ask students if they think it would be wise for teenagers to choose sterilization. Do they know any who have? Students should realize that this would not be a wise choice for most of them. They have no way of knowing whether or not they will want to have families. Even though they may think they know now that they will not want to have children later in life, they should be aware of the fact that they will mature and change a great deal in the next 20 to 30 years.

② **Overhead—Vasectomy:** Your supplementary material contains an overhead of Figure B–13.

⊠ **Where to Write**

National Alliance for Optional Parenthood
2010 Massachusetts Avenue NW
Washington, D.C. 20036

B20

B20   Special Unit Sexual Behavior and Pregnancy Prevention

SECTION V

Sterilization

Surgical **sterilization** is a highly effective contraceptive method—in most cases, close to 100 percent effective. It is also almost always irreversible. Each year, millions of people choose sterilization, and the number is increasing. In fact, sterilization is the leading contraceptive method in the world.

People choosing sterilization should be sure they will want to bear no children in the future. No one can count on being able to reverse the procedure later. Reversal works only very occasionally to restore fertility. Most often, though, attempts at reversal fail. (In rare cases, fertility is restored without efforts to reverse the sterilization. The ends of the tubes that were surgically cut find each other and grow back together, restoring fertility.) The simplest and most common sterilization procedures are **vasectomy** in men and **tubal ligation** in women. ①

Vasectomy

In vasectomy, a surgeon makes one or two tiny cuts in the scrotum and severs the tubes through which the sperm travel to become part of the semen (the **vas deferens**). Figure B–13 shows how this is done. The ② procedure takes about half an hour and may be performed under local anesthesia in a physician's office. The incisions are so tiny that vasectomies are called "bandaid surgery."

The vasectomized man continues to produce sperm. However, they are reduced in number, and they are absorbed by the body rather than being released into the semen. The fluid of semen is still present in ejaculation. Only the tiny portion made up by sperm cells is missing. The difference is not noticeable. The sperm do not build up or

Vasectomy effectiveness:
Laboratory rating = 99.85%
User effectiveness = 99.85%

Figure B–13 Vasectomy

cause any unusual feelings or symptoms. A vasectomy interrupts only the delivery of sperm. It has no effect on the production of the male hormone testosterone or on sexual desire or activity.

A man is not sterile immediately after a vasectomy, because living sperm are still in storage. Usually it takes some weeks to clear them out. Once the sperm are absent from the semen, the chance of pregnancy is practically zero.

Vasectomy is a low-cost, one-time procedure. It permits the man to resume normal activity within a day or so and sexual activity within a few days. Pain is minimal, and side effects are rare.

Key Points *In vasectomy, a surgeon cuts and seals off a man's vas deferens to produce sterility.*

another off to one side slightly above the pubic hair. A lighted viewing scope is put into one opening so the doctor can view the tubes. The instrument that does the work on the tubes is put into the other opening. There are many variations to this procedure. For example, the tubes can be cut and tied, burned in half, or clipped with a device to seal them shut. **(Extend, Enrich)**

EVALUATE
SECTION V

Activity 5.3
Pop Quiz.
1. Which surgery can be done in the doctor's office, vasectomy or tubal ligation? (vasectomy)
2. Which surgery is the most effective, vasectomy or tubal ligation? (vasectomy)

3. Is the laboratory rate for effectiveness of either surgery different from the user effectiveness? Why? (No, effectiveness is not dependent upon the user but the doctor who did the surgery.)
4. Why is a vasectomy not effective immediately? (The male reproductive tract stores sperm.)
5. Does a woman's tubal ligation work immediately? (yes)

Tubal Ligation

For a tubal ligation a surgeon cuts and seals off the tubes that conduct ova from the ovaries to the uterus (the fallopian tubes). Sperm traveling up the tubes arrive at a dead end and cannot fertilize the ovum a woman might have produced. To have the surgery performed, a woman may check into a hospital or clinic in the morning and check out that afternoon. The operation can be performed with either a local or general anesthetic. Commonly referred to as "tying the tubes," the surgery involves small incisions in the woman's abdomen through which the surgeon cuts the fallopian tubes and seals their ends. Any number of surgical methods accomplish the same objective: permanent blockage of the tubes to prevent ova and sperm from meeting.

The procedure is slightly more involved than a vasectomy, because the surgeon must cut through abdominal muscle. Still, it leaves only a tiny scar on the abdomen; in the navel; or in cases of surgery through the upper vaginal wall, in the vagina. Figure B–14 shows the abdominal operation. The woman's hormones and her sex drive remain normal. After the surgery, the woman continues to menstruate and ovulate as before. The ripe ovum is released, but the body reabsorbs it.

Although tubal ligation is more costly than vasectomy, it is still less expensive than the costs of years of many other contraceptive methods. Most women tolerate the surgery well and recover quickly with little discomfort.

Tubal ligation effectiveness:
Laboratory rating = 99.7%
User effectiveness = 99.7%

Figure B–14 Tubal Ligation

SECTION V   REVIEW

① *Answer the following questions on a sheet of paper.*
Learning the Vocabulary
The vocabulary terms in this section are *sterilization, vasectomy, tubal ligation,* and *vas deferens.*

MINI GLOSSARY

sterilization: the process of permanently interrupting a person's ability to bear children, usually by surgically severing and sealing the vas deferens or the fallopian tubes.
vasectomy: surgical cutting and sealing off of the vas deferens to sterilize men.
tubal ligation (lye-GAY-shun): surgical cutting and sealing off of the fallopian tubes to sterilize women.
vas deferens: tubes that conduct sperm from the testicles toward the penis.

Key Points *In tubal ligation, a surgeon cuts and seals off a woman's fallopian tubes, making her sterile.*

Teacher Support Notes

① **Overhead—Tubal Ligation:** Your supplementary material contains an overhead of Figure B–14.

✐ Fast Facts

As many as 46% of American women have had an unintended pregnancy between the ages of 15 and 44. Of these, 21% have had abortions.

✉ Where to Write

National Clearing House for Family Planning Information P.O. Box 2225 Rockfield, Maryland 20852

CLOSE
SECTION V

Activity 5.4
World Solutions? Ask students why they think these methods of permanent contraception aren't used around the world more, given the problems of over-population, pollution, and starvation. Discuss the impact of overpopulation on

future generations. You may want to refer students to the discussion of this topic in Chapter 25. **(15 min., Multicultural)**

FOCUS
SECTION VI

In this section students will learn:
1. The difficult choices that must be made when contraception fails.
2. To describe the problems that may

accompany adoption and abortion.

Activity 6.1
Pregnancy Scenarios. Before class, make up five or six scenarios involving teen couples in which the girl is pregnant. Use different ages, financial and educational backgrounds, parents' beliefs, and life plans the couple had before becoming pregnant. Type each story to give as handouts to the students

---

66 Thoughts on Health 99

I have noticed that all the people who favor abortion have already been born.
— *Ronald Reagan*

Teacher Support Notes

① **The Exception:** Read the second sentence. Ask what the one exception is. (abstinence)
② **Teacher Information Sheet—Abortion:** Your supplementary material has background information on abortion.

Section V Review

Answers

1. **a.** vasectomy **b.** sterilization **c.** tubal ligation
2. millions
3. the route that sperm takes to become part of the semen
4. it is absorbed by the body
5. Answers will vary.

✍ Fast Facts

Almost 75% of the world's population live in countries that permit abortions, at least for health reasons. Almost 40% of the world's people live in countries where abortion is available upon request.

B22

B22   Special Unit Sexual Behavior and Pregnancy Prevention

1. Use the clues given to help you unscramble the terms.
   a. **aeocmstvy** _____
      surgical cutting and sealing off of the tubes in a man through which sperm travel
   b. **aeiiiolnrsttz** _____ the process of permanently interrupting a person's ability to bear children
   c. **aublt aiioglnt** _____ _____
      surgical cutting and sealing off of the tubes in a woman in which sperm and ova meet

Learning the Facts
2. How many people choose sterilization each year?
3. What does a vasectomy interrupt?
4. What happens to the ovum after a tubal ligation?

Making Life Choices
5. Brent and Denise have three children and they have decided not to have any more. They have decided that one of them should become sterile. What arguments do you have for Brent to get a vasectomy? What arguments do you have for Denise to get a tubal ligation?

SECTION VI

Contraceptive Failure

Unwanted pregnancies are not unusual, even when couples are using contraception. All contraceptive methods, with one exception, can fail. A method's failure rate is expressed as an impersonal statistic. In human terms, however, it means that a number of couples are facing unwanted pregnancies despite efforts to prevent them. The one fail-proof exception is, of course, abstinence.

As an illustration of the human reality of contraceptive failure, let's say that a certain method is 97 percent effective. Also assume that the whole adult, fertile female population of the United States—close to 100 mil-

lion women—were all using this method and using it correctly. Every single year of their reproductive lives, 3 million of these women would still become pregnant.

Actually, over 4 million women in the United States alone face unwanted pregnancies each year. Considering that each woman's fertility lasts 30 years or more, it is clear that nearly every woman may face an unwanted pregnancy sometime during her life. She and her partner may have failed to use contraception or may have used it incorrectly. She may have used contraception, but it may have failed to work. She may be the victim of rape, incest, or other sexual abuse. She may be young or old, poor or rich, a student, a professional, a blue-collar worker, or a homemaker.

Deciding about Abortion

Each woman facing an unwanted pregnancy also faces the decision of whether or not to continue her pregnancy. For some, the choice is really no choice. They have decided a course of action in advance. It may be that a woman's religious beliefs forbid **abortion**, or that she has decided to continue every pregnancy to birth for any number of reasons. She may have decided never to carry to birth any but a wanted pregnancy, and so chooses abortion.

Young people who are risking pregnancy are wise to do some thinking in advance. A woman who has done little thinking about the subject and becomes pregnant unexpectedly has to think fast and answer the question on the spot. With the help of counselors, parents, or religious teachers, each person can make a right decision.

Abortion is not a method of contraception. *Contraception* means "to prevent conception." Abortion interrupts a pregnancy that is already under way.

A woman who suspects that she is pregnant should obtain a pregnancy test. She for group discussion or use the handout in your supplementary material.

Put students into groups of four. Distribute the scenarios, one to each group. More than one group can have the same scenario. Tell each group to decide what would be the best decision for each couple regarding their pregnancy. Should the couple marry, give the baby up for adoption, have an abortion, or should the mother or father raise the baby alone?

Ask each group to report back to the class by reading their teen pregnancy story and telling the class why they made the decision they did. **(50 min., Cooperative Learning)**

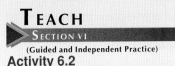

TEACH

SECTION VI
(Guided and Independent Practice)

Activity 6.2
Pros and Cons. Put *Abortion* on one

side of the board and *Adoption* on the other. Divide each side of the board into two parts. Label one section *Pros* and one *Cons* for each of the two sides.

Have the class brainstorm the pro and con aspects of each choice and write their responses in the appropriate place. Discuss. **(25–30 min., Critical Thinking)**

(continued on next page)

must choose carefully where to go for the test. Heated battles rage between groups that support legal abortion and groups that oppose it. Both groups include extremists who may worsen a pregnant woman's stress and make the situation harder. A woman may encounter unwelcome pressure if she is tested for pregnancy by the wrong agency. Some possible choices are: a physician's office; the local health department, which will offer free or low-cost tests without accompanying advice; an abortion clinic, which will assist and support a woman in obtaining an abortion if she is pregnant; and a religious organization, which will help support a woman in carrying her pregnancy to term and assist with adoption if she chooses it. A choice to continue the pregnancy brings other choices: whether to keep the baby or give it up for adoption, and whether to marry the partner.

Chapter 2 said that in making decisions, a person must weigh feelings, judgments, and values. In the case of an unwanted pregnancy, all of these may well conflict with one another. Objective counseling can be a great help in deciding how to handle an unplanned pregnancy. A teenager who faces an unwanted pregnancy may have a strong support system in her family, and so may benefit from seeking their help early on.

Whatever choice is made, the woman must act promptly. Delays increase a woman's risks, whether she ultimately has an abortion or continues the pregnancy. If she chooses abortion, the longer she waits, the riskier the procedures become. If she continues the pregnancy, the longer prenatal care is delayed, the greater the danger to her health and to that of her fetus.

Abortion Procedures

Abortion methods vary according to the length of the pregnancy. Surgical abortions performed early in pregnancy require little anesthesia and carry minimal risk to the woman's health. They are routine for the medical staff. In vacuum aspiration, suction is applied to empty the uterus of the early tissues of pregnancy, including the embryo and the tissues that would form a placenta. (These structures were described in Chapter 21.) In other countries, early pregnancies can also be ended nonsurgically by taking a pill—RU 486. Normally, the hormone progesterone maintains pregnancy. The RU 486 drug interferes with the action of progesterone and brings on menstruation and loss of the pregnancy. RU 486 has not been approved for use in the United States at the time of this writing.

Between 13 and about 16 weeks of pregnancy, more direct methods must be used to scrape or vacuum the uterus. These involve anesthesia, and so increase the risk to the woman. The scraping, but not vacuuming, of the uterus is also used for medical purposes other than abortion.

① For abortions after 13 weeks' gestation, some medical methods can be used. Hormones can be administered, the woman goes into labor, and abortion results.

② The physical risks of abortion are much lower today than in the past. The procedures still carry some risk, however, and the risks increase as the pregnancy goes on. Generally, abortion during the first three months is only slightly riskier than contraception. Early abortions have no effect on the woman's ability to carry future preg-

Key Points▶ *When unplanned pregnancy occurs, the choice of where to go for help should be made carefully. Action to obtain abortion or prenatal care must be swift.*

MINI **G**LOSSARY

abortion: a procedure to end a pregnancy before the fetus can live outside the uterus.

Teacher Support Notes

① **Handout—Conflicting Views on Abortion:** Your supplementary material contains a handout that provides "pro-life" and "pro-choice" views on abortion side by side. If you intend to discuss abortion, use the handout to stimulate students' thinking and to encourage their participation in a discussion. You could, for example, ask them to pick the viewpoints that they most identify with and to explain why.

② **Increased Risk:** Refer students back to Figure B–2 earlier in the chapter. Have them compare the chances of death for the different time periods in which abortions are performed. What are the chances if the abortion is performed before nine weeks? (1 in 500,000) If it is performed after 15 weeks? (1 in 8,700)

B23

Teach (Continued)

Activity 6.3

Changes in Attitude. Discuss how society shapes people's attitudes about out-of-wedlock pregnancy. Ask: What has changed over the last 100 years? What would have been the outcome of an 18-year-old single woman becoming pregnant in 1893? 1918? 1943? 1968? 1993? What would have been expected of the man who made her pregnant? Why did "shotgun weddings" last thirty years ago and before, but not today? Why have attitudes changed? Do students think attitudes about unwed pregnancies will change back? Why or why not? **(15–20 min., Critical Thinking)**

Activity 6.4

Adoption as an Alternative. A recently released study of thousands of infants born out of wedlock indicated that the babies did better when adopted. The children were more confident and better adjusted socially than those babies who remained with their natural mothers. Ask students why they think this would be true. Ask why so many teens keep their babies, instead of putting them up for

---

Teacher Support Notes

① **Handout—Public Health Service Objectives:** Your supplementary material contains a handout listing family planning objectives as stated by the U.S. Department of Health and Human Services.

Section VI Review

Answers

1. Answers will vary.
2. four million in the U.S.
3. local health department, abortion clinic, a religious organization, physician's office
4. Early abortions are believed not to affect later fertility and carry little risk to the health of the woman, while late abortions are a higher risk to the woman's health and future fertility.
5. religious teaching; group counseling; medical care before, during, and after the birth; housing; adoption services; maternity and infant clothing; day care
6. Answers will vary.

✍ Fast Facts

The Center for Disease Control reports that a majority of U.S. high school students have sex. One out of four sexually active teens does not use an effective birth control method.

---

nancies. Some question remains about whether late abortions have long-term effects on fertility and on the outcomes of future pregnancies.

> **Key Points** *Early abortions carry little risk and can be performed through vacuum aspiration. Later abortions are riskier and can be accomplished through the administration of hormones or by surgical means.*

Adoption

Women who choose to carry their unwanted pregnancies to term often need help. Agencies are available to provide for them. Women may need to find sources of help for problems such as abandonment by family or the father of the child, lack of medical treatment, low income, lack of emotional support, and many other problems.

Agencies that provide resources for such women are often associated with organizations calling themselves *pro-life* or *right-to-life*. They hold strong moral convictions against abortion, and they support women in unwanted pregnancies. They usually include religious teaching in their counseling. Such groups can be especially helpful when a woman wants to continue a pregnancy but needs support in doing so. Services vary from place to place. They can include free pregnancy testing; group counseling; medical care before, during, and after the birth; housing; adoption services; maternity and infant clothing; and day care.

Whether a woman chooses abortion or continues with her pregnancy, she urgently needs to use a means of contraception afterward. Otherwise, she may be faced with the same hard choices all over again—a common occurrence.

> **Key Points** *Several kinds of organizations provide for the needs of women who carry unplanned pregnancies to term.* ①

SECTION VI   REVIEW

Answer the following questions on a sheet of paper.

Learning the Vocabulary
The vocabulary term in this section is *abortion*.
1. Write a sentence using the vocabulary term.

Learning the Facts
2. How many unwanted pregnancies occur each year?
3. Name possible places a woman can get a pregnancy test or help with her decision about an unwanted pregnancy.
4. What is said about abortions that occur early in pregnancy and abortions that occur later in pregnancy?
5. How do agencies help support a woman who is having a baby that she will give up for adoption?

Making Life Choices
6. Kerri became pregnant in the ninth grade. Kerri didn't know what to do. Kerri and her parents decided that she would have an abortion before the first nine weeks. Should Kerri have had an abortion? What are your views on abortion? Are abortions ever needed? In what circumstances do you think abortions are necessary?

Answers to Fact or Fiction

Here are the answers to the questions at the start of the chapter.

1. False. For healthy, sexually active heterosexual couples, pregnancy occurs easily. **2.** True. **3.** False. No contraceptive method is perfect. To obtain the advantages of one method, a person must be willing to put up with its disadvantages. **4.** True. **5.** False. Withdrawal fails to prevent pregnancy in most users. **6.** True.

---

adoption, when the odds are against them. Approximately 80% of teen moms are on welfare and don't finish high school. **(15 min., Critical Thinking)**

E VALUATE

▶ SECTION VI

Activity 6.5
Advantages of Abstinence. Have the class write their feelings about the fol-

lowing statement: "Why might abstinence be a better choice than risking pregnancy while still in high school?" Collect papers and check for understanding. **(15 min.)**

C LOSE

▶ SECTION VI

Activity 6.6
Looking Ahead. Bring a regular broom to school. Ask for a student volun-

teer to balance the broom on one finger. Ask the student first to try balancing the broom looking just at the bottom of it, where it rests on the finger. The class will observe that the student has quite a bit of difficulty doing it this way. Now have the student try again, looking at the top of the broom. The student should be able to balance it with much less difficulty. Now make the analogy that a person who makes their

(continued on next page)

STRAIGHT

TALK _____ **Why People Don't Use Contraception**

Many people consciously choose not to use contraception. They may have moral, religious, or personal reasons for this choice. Their culture may discourage contraception, or they may want to become pregnant. However, enormous numbers of teenage girls face unwanted pregnancies each year that end in unwanted births or abortions. It is estimated that 40 percent of teen girls who are 14 years old today will become pregnant before age 20—more than a million per year. Most of these unplanned pregnancies are not the result of a conscious choice, but of simple failure to use contraception.

Why do people take such chances? ①]

Fear and emotional immaturity are two powerful reasons. People in their teen years, especially, may fear disapproval of their parents. They may be too embarrassed to purchase condoms or other contraceptives. Some may lack information about contraception, or even fail to realize that sexual intercourse leads to pregnancy. A teen who is afraid to seek information or help may rely on friends' or partners' advice rather than on advice from reliable sources such as parents or health professionals.

Emotional immaturity can also prevent people from dealing with contraception. An immature mind often rejects sexuality as part of the person's self-image. The assumption seems to be that sex is great, but nice people don't plan for it—it "just happens." If they plan for

intercourse and obtain contraceptives, this illusion is destroyed.

People who think this way pretend to lead a lifestyle in keeping with traditional values, while still having sexual intercourse on impulse, now and then. Using contraception makes a statement—that the person is sexually active. So does pregnancy, but an immature mind is unable to think far enough ahead to make this connection. Psychologists would call this a failure to "own" one's sexual identity— that is, a failure to accept, and take responsibility for, being sexual.

Aren't the mass-communication media also partly responsible for many teenagers' unwanted pregnancies?

Partly, yes. The media push sex in every form but do not educate. The media often

depict bedroom scenes and other sexual images, but seldom do couples on TV or in movies pause in their passion to use contraception. When such scenes do occur, they are usually humorous ones that make using contraception seem foolish and unromantic.

Television presents its audience with practically nonstop sexual suggestions. Yet networks do not advertise contraception. Magazines use sexy images to sell everything from automobiles to zebra-striped underclothes— everything, that is, except contraception. In fact, romance novels and many movies and television programs do much to reinforce the attitude already mentioned: an unwillingness to own one's sexual identity.

The media provide poor role models. The couples

(Continued on next page)

Teacher Support Notes

① **Teen Views:** The student responses to the question "Who's at fault when an unmarried teenager becomes pregnant?" on page 545 include several of the students' ideas about why people take such chances. You may want to have students read this special Teen Views feature before they read the response to this question. It should spark their interest. Ask students to compare the response here to the student responses in the Teen Views feature. How many are the same? What reasons did the text give that the students didn't? What reasons did the students give that the text didn't?

decisions looking only at today may experience problems because of disregard for future consequences of their actions. A person who looks ahead and projects into the future the actions they take today will usually avoid making mistakes about major life decisions.

You could also stress that a person who has sex today may be thinking only of his or her desires at that moment, and not thinking that nine months later a baby will drastically and permanently change his or her life. A person who thinks about the possibility of pregnancy resulting from sex may decide not to engage in it at all until after he/she marries. **(10–15 min.; Reteach, Reinforce)**

RETEACH/BONUS

Estimating Expenses.
Part 1
Inquire at the Welfare Department in your state, how much money a woman will get per month if she is unmarried, on welfare, and has one child. Two children? Once you have this information, do the

Teacher Support Notes

① **Choosing Contraception:** Four reasons for using contraception are given in this paragraph. Have students read the paragraph, close their books, and write the four reasons in their own words. Do students agree that all of these reasons would make it more likely that a couple would use contraception? Which reason do they think would be most likely to cause teenagers to use contraception?

 Fast Facts

For centuries people have known that a foreign object placed in the uterus would prevent pregnancy. For hundreds of years, Arab camel drivers would place a round stone in the uteri of their camels. This would keep the camels from getting pregnant during long caravans across the desert. Although the camel drivers did not know why it worked, this tactic was the beginning of the use of the contraceptive we know today as the IUD.

B26

STRAIGHT TALK *(Continued)*

shown are not in control of their sexuality. They also are not responsible for it. Furthermore, their lives are unrealistic. Even though they often are swept off their feet by overwhelming passion, they never get pregnant. They never catch sexually transmitted diseases. They never, in other words, pay a price.

Has anyone asked teenagers how they feel about contraception?

The attitudes of sexually active teenagers, when studied, seem sensible enough. They often say that they should postpone sex or use contraception. However, many teens' behaviors are like those of their poor media role models—out of line with their own knowledge and values.

Many sexually active teenagers who say they should use contraception also say they did not use it the last time they had intercourse. It is as if contraception was for other people—as if the rules did not apply to themselves. It seems that they think getting pregnant is as likely as the sky's falling, and that they are equally helpless to prevent both.

Does anyone know what makes people decide to use contraception?

Four things have been observed. The more a woman owns her own normal sexuality, the more likely she is to use contraception. The more a couple cares about each other, the more likely they are to protect each other with contraception. The older and more sexually experienced they are, the more likely they are to use it. And the more they see pregnancy prevention as a shared responsibility, the more they will use it.

That sounds like the kind of relationship everyone would like. Do only older partners have such supportive relationships?

Not always, but the four attributes mentioned often come along with maturity. A mature woman has had time to get to know herself and so may be able to accept her own sexuality as part of her life. Also, people in a committed, mature love relationship didn't get there overnight. They gave their love plenty of time to grow naturally without complicating its development with early sexual intimacy.

Genuine concern for the partner is also a mark of maturity. Also, as couples make decisions about when or whether to have a child together, each partner *wants* to share responsibility for

achieving that family goal. ① Without the shared psychological intimacy of a mature love, sexuality is more likely to be self-centered, and contraception is more likely to be ignored.

Some people I know just don't seem to think about the price they'll pay should pregnancy occur, and so they don't use contraception.

That's a common attitude. They may think, "If I have a baby, I'm sure someone will take care of it. The father will marry me; or the mother will take care of it; or my parents will help; or I'll be an adult, then, so somehow it'll be OK." In fact, teenagers may believe that pregnancy must be all right or else it wouldn't happen. Some think pregnancy is a ticket away from an unhappy home life. They have no idea of the enormous burden they'll carry when they alone have responsibility for a child during all its years of dependency. Some even have to carry the responsibility for the child's children—early childbearing runs in families.

I've also heard some people say they think contraception lowers the

(Continued on next page)

following activity. Inform students that 80% of teenage mothers are on welfare. Ask students how much they think the weekly allotment is. After having them guess, tell them the amount for one child. Ask if they think this amount doubles when they have a second child. (Many people are led to believe that a good living can be made on welfare.) They may be shocked to hear how low the dollar amount is for a second child. However, the total amount of money may seem like a lot to a high school student. Ask them if they think they could support themselves and a baby on that amount for a month.

Part 2

Have students imagine they are all 16 years old, female, unmarried, getting no help from parents, on welfare, and have just brought their newborn home from the hospital. What expenses would they have? List them on the board. If students forget any important budget items, add them. See handout, "Sample Welfare Expenses" in your supplementary material.

Help the students estimate how much each item would cost. Will the welfare money cover the expenses? Remind students that if the mother works, she must pay a babysitter and the money from her job will be deducted from her welfare check. Discuss. **(50 min., Interdisciplinary)**

STRAIGHT TALK   *(Continued)*

sex drive or hinders performance. It that true?

No, contraception does not reduce the sex drive or performance in people of either gender. In reality, the opposite is often true. With fear of pregnancy removed, people often feel more free to enjoy sexual intercourse.

Some people who seem to know everything there is to know about contraception still don't use it. Why?

That's the most puzzling question of all. People can read and hear the facts so often that they can recite them. They can take classroom tests on the material and pass them with high marks. Yet, when the moment of decision arrives in real life, they choose to ignore everything they know. Impulse, indecision, inconvenience, insecurity with the partner—only individuals can pinpoint the reasons for their own failure to use contraception.

Also, part of the reason may be that people haven't ① yet learned to accept that they, too, can be affected by pregnancy. People can develop a false sense of security. When one time of unprotected sexual intercourse does not produce pregnancy, they "learn" that they do not need to worry. They may fantasize that they cannot become pregnant or impregnate someone.

Unfortunately, the odds stack up. As mentioned earlier, 90 percent of normal, sexually active couples who do not use contraception do become pregnant within one year. It is a sign of maturity to understand that what happens to "other people" also can happen to "me."

Does sex education help? And if so, who should be responsible for it?

Yes, it can help. Ideally, parents should be the primary sex educators. However, they sometimes fail to provide the needed information.

To make sure that all children have the information they need, society tries to provide these facts through the schools. In places where meaningful sex education is provided along with wholehearted community support, the numbers of teenage pregnancies drop. Most places in the United States, though, fail to provide such education and support, and so are seeing increased numbers of teenage pregnancies.

Sex education is only part of the solution, though. Research shows that when parents have discussed sex with their teens, those teens are least likely among peers to engage in sexual intercourse early in life and are most likely to use contraceptives later on. Individual families and society as a whole must take responsibility.

Right now, our society promotes the sex act itself without promoting a responsible attitude toward it. If children today are receiving the same mixed messages as their parents did in the past, we should not be surprised to see teen pregnancies become an even greater problem in the future.

Teacher Support Notes

① **Accepting Reality:** Ask students if they can think of acts they've engaged in knowing the behavior was dangerous or had potential negative outcomes. Running a stop sign or speeding would be two obvious examples. Ask them what effect going ahead with these actions and not suffering the consequences has on future decisions. How do the potentially negative consequences of these activities compare to the negative consequences of having unprotected sex? Do they see that the "I can probably get away with it one more time" philosophy may be common for minor consequences, but is very dangerous in situations that can change their entire life (unwanted pregnancy), or even causes death (AIDS)?

PART B REVIEW
Answers

Vocabulary

1. Effectiveness is how well a contraceptive prevents pregnancy, expressed as a percentage. The laboratory effectiveness is the percentage of women protected from pregnancy in a year's time under ideal laboratory conditions. The user effectiveness is the percentage of typical women users who are protected.
2. **a.** abortion **b.** vas deferens **c.** intrauterine device (IUD) **d.** male condom
3. **a.** female condom **b.** vasectomy **c.** Oral contraceptives **d.** tubal ligation **e.** barrier methods
4. **a.** progestin **b.** diaphragm **c.** rhythm method **d.** progesterone
5. Answers will vary.

Recall
Section I
1. abstinence

2. both members of a sexually active couple—a shared responsibility
Section II
3. effectiveness
Section III
4. to avoid pregnancy and the threats of AIDS, herpes, and other sexually transmitted diseases
5. one month

6. the Pill (oral contraceptives)
7. The minipill contains no estrogen, only progestin, and affects the uterus itself. The progestin thickens the mucus surrounding the uterine opening so that sperm cannot penetrate. Progestin can also deactivate sperm cells and interrupt the normal preparation of the uterine lining.

8. abdominal pain, chest pain, breathlessness, headaches, blurred vision or loss of vision, leg pain
9. condoms
10. It increases the risks of birth defects. It is suggested that a woman switch to another method of contraception for at least two months prior to becoming pregnant.

PART REVIEW

LEARNING THE VOCABULARY

contraception	minipill	female condom
effectiveness	Norplant	rhythm method
laboratory effectiveness	Depo-Provera	withdrawal method
user effectiveness	intrauterine device (IUD)	(coitus interruptus)
oral contraceptives	barrier methods	sterilization
combination pill	diaphragm	vasectomy
estrogen	sponge	tubal ligation
progesterone	cervical cap	vas deferens
progestin	male condom	abortion

Answer the following questions on a separate sheet of paper.

1. Explain the differences between effectiveness, laboratory effectiveness, and user effectiveness.
2. *Matching—Match each of the following phrases with the appropriate vocabulary term from the list above:*
   a. procedure to end a pregnancy before the fetus can live outside the uterus
   b. tubes that conduct sperm toward the penis
   c. a device inserted into the uterus to prevent conception
   d. a sheath worn over the penis during intercourse to contain the semen
3. a. A _____ is a soft, thin plastic tube with two end rings—one to fit over the cervix and one to serve as an anchor outside the entrance to the vagina.
   b. A surgical procedure that cuts the tubes that conduct sperm from the testicles toward the penis is called a _____.
   c. _____ are pills taken by mouth which contain synthetic hormones that prevent pregnancy by stopping ovulation.
   d. A surgical procedure that cuts the tubes that conduct the ova from the ovaries towards the uterus is called a _____.
   e. Contraceptive methods that physically or chemically obstruct the travel of sperm towards the ovum are called _____.
4. *Word Scramble—Use the clues from the phrases below to help you unscramble the words:*
   a. **sepignotr** _____ a synthetic version of progesterone
   b. **aaidghmpr** _____ a dome that fits over the cervix and holds spermicidal cream or jelly against the uterine entrance.
   c. **yhmthr hedotm** _____ _____ a method of contraception that involves tracking the menstrual cycle and observing signs of ovulation
   d. **eeeoognprrst** _____ a female hormone secreted during that portion of the menstrual cycle in which the uterine lining builds up.
5. Write a paragraph using at least ten of the vocabulary terms. Underline each vocabulary term that you use.

RECALLING IMPORTANT FACTS AND IDEAS

1. What is the only 100% effective method to avoid pregnancy?
2. Who is responsible for contraception?
3. What is one of the most important facts to consider about a contraceptive method?
4. Why are teens all over the United States choosing abstinence more often than before?
5. When a woman begins using the Pill, for how long should she use a backup method of birth control?
6. What is the most popular nonsurgical method of birth control?
7. Explain the differences between the minipill and the combination pill.

11. women who have had at least one child, those in a monogamous relationship, have no history of pelvic inflammatory disease (PID)
12. have a custom-fitted diaphragm, apply spermicide no more than two hours before intercourse, leave the diaphragm in place for at least six hours after sexual intercourse, apply new spermicide between repeated intercourse
13. at least six hours
14. The cap is smaller, more durable, requires less spermicide, and needs no additional applications of spermicide to stay effective.
15. The dangerous bacterial poisoning known as toxic shock syndrome can occur.
16. Latex condoms offer some protection against sexually transmitted diseases and they are superior over lambskin condoms in preventing pregnancy.
17. They can break down the latex in condoms, increasing the risk for pregnancy and STDs.
18. The female condom. It gives women control of their own protection. When used with spermicide it is highly effective for preventing pregnancy and some STDs.
19. be trained by a health professional to track the menstrual cycle and to observe body signs of ovulation

Section IV

20. the withdrawal method, using other replacement materials for condoms, douching after intercourse, relying on breastfeeding to prevent ovulation

Section V

21. several weeks
22. Nearly every woman may face an unwanted pregnancy for many reasons including failure of contraceptives, incorrect use of contraceptives, or becoming a victim of rape, incest, or other sexual abuse.

8. What symptoms should prompt a woman to call her physician if she is on the Pill?
9. What should be used to prevent STDs when the Pill is being used for contraception?
10. Why should a woman who may be pregnant stop taking the Pill?
11. Who are the best candidates for an intrauterine device?
12. What must a woman do for a diaphragm to work properly?
13. The sponge and diaphragm must be left in place for how long after intercourse?
14. What are the differences between the cervical cap and the diaphragm?
15. What is one danger of using a diaphragm, sponge, or cervical cap during menstruation?
16. Why should a person choose latex condoms over other condoms?
17. Why shouldn't Vaseline or moisturizing lotion be used on condoms?
18. What is one of the newer forms of contraception and why is it effective?
19. What should a woman do before using the rhythm method of birth control?
20. Describe several ineffective methods of birth control.
21. How long after a vasectomy does it take a man to become free of sperm?
22. What sort of women are especially likely to experience unwanted pregnancies?

C RITICAL THINKING

1. Reread the Straight Talk on page B25, "Why People Don't Use Contraceptives". What is said about maturity and those who don't use contraceptives? How do the media push sex? Which couples are likely to use contraceptives? Does sex education help? How?
2. Maria and Joe have been dating steadily for one year. They plan to be married after graduating high school in six months. They have not been sexually active thus far and talk about remaining virgins until marriage. Joe was severely burned in the genital region as an infant, and his doctor told him he was probably sterile. Maria has concerns about premarital sex based on her family and her religious values. What is your opinion of the way Joe is handling the situation? What do you think the outcome of this situation might eventually be? Why?
3. Suppose you had the ability and resources to invent the ideal method of birth control. What would it be? How would it differ from what is already available? Would men or women be responsible for using it? What would be the advantages of this new method?

A CTIVITIES

1. Visit a local Health Department that deals with contraceptives. Write a report on the services they offer teenagers with and without a parent's consent.
2. Interview your parents or guardians about the type of birth control they use. Talk to them about the different methods available to you, and decide on the method that is best for you.
3. Make a pamphlet that describes all the methods of contraception. Give advantages and disadvantages, and effectiveness rates for each method.
4. Write an editorial in your school newspaper about abortion. Next, plan a school debate on this issue and invite all those who are interested to attend.

Be aware that this is a sensitive issue. Many people feel very strongly about abortion. When you write your editorial and when you debate the issue, be sure to observe the common rules of personal courtesy at all times. Your arguments should not be personal in any way and there should definitely not be any personal attacks or name-calling. Your side in the debate will win or lose the debate based on the evidence you present and the logical, organized way in which you present your evidence. Therefore, it would be wise to do some research in your school and local libraries to accumulate information that supports your view.

5. Make a chart showing the Risks of Contraception in Perspective. Post this in your classroom.
6. Take a survey and ask at least 50 friends and relatives about their use of contraceptives. What type of contraceptive do they use? Have they ever had unprotected sexual intercourse? If so, how many times? Have they ever had an unplanned pregnancy? If so, what did they do about it? Tabulate all the results. Report your findings to the rest of the class.
8. Make a video for the rest of the class explaining how to use each method of contraception discussed in this unit. Give at least one advantage and disadvantage of each method.

MAKING DECISIONS ABOUT HEALTH

1. Kelly tried the Pill, but it gave her headaches. The IUD she tried gave her cramps. Gels and diaphragms or condoms were too inconvenient. The sponge made her itch. Her monthly cycle is erratic, so natural family planning is out. Now what? a. What other choices do you think Kelly has in this situation? b. If you were Kelly, what would you do? Why?

2. Jody has never taken time to learn much about birth control. Now when his partner assures him that she'll take care of it, he feels a bit uneasy—will she really take care of it? She's so forgetful. The last thing he needs right now is for his partner to become pregnant. a. What options do you think Jody has in this situation? b. If you were in Jody's situation, what would you do? Why?

TEEN VIEWS

Who's at fault when unmarried teenagers become pregnant?

①

Responsibility cannot and should not lie on one person, and we have to learn to pay for our mistakes. That doesn't include walking out on each other. **Brianna Fitzgerald, 14, South Carroll High School, MD**

If a young teenage girl becomes pregnant, it's no one's fault but her own. A man doesn't have to worry about pregnancy and can leave the relationship if his girlfriend gets pregnant. The females are the ones who take the responsibility of being pregnant, so they should take the responsibility of making their partner wear a condom, taking birth control pills, or practicing abstinence. **Tricia Reeves, 15, Robert E. Lee High School, TX**

Both the guy and girl are at fault. It does take two to tango. The girl has more things to worry about, though. **Jeff Mathews, 15, Pine Bluff High School, AR**

She is mostly at fault because there is too much protection they could have used. Society also has something to do with it because they're always projecting the image that girls are supposed to be good. It makes it hard for a girl to talk to an adult about birth control methods because she doesn't want people to think of her as "easy." Adults need to understand and educate more. **Shirley Greenawalt, 15, Sharon High School, PA**

Parents are partly responsible. Parents are so scared to discuss sexual activity with their children that they end up never talking about it at all; or if they do talk about it, they impose guilt. Parents should start talking to their children about sex at a very young age. **Sascha Von Tiergarten, 17, Wilson High School, CA**

Today's standards have changed from when our parents were our age. Back then it was fine to date someone steady for months at a time and not have sex. Now, though, you can almost bet that if two people are dating, they're having sex. That's just how it is. Society is to blame. **Tara Mills, 15, Carter High School, TN**

When an unmarried teen becomes pregnant, there usually is a lack of communication in the family situation. If communication was an open line and you could truly talk about sex, you wouldn't have as many teenage girls becoming pregnant. **Patricia Boodell, 16, Robert E. Lee High School, TX**

I'm an unmarried teen parent. I had my son at the age of 14 and he's 2 years old now. I feel that both the boy and girl are at fault because both of them thought that they were mature enough to make a decision to have sex at an early age. They should have been mature enough to use some kind of contraception. On the other hand, the girl is more at fault than the boy. When I first found out that I was pregnant, I felt more at fault than my baby's daddy. There are some boys out there that get a girl pregnant and say it's not theirs. The girl is left all by herself to raise the baby. **Paulette Singleton, 17, Sharon High School, PA**

Teacher Support Notes

① **Teen Views— Follow-Up Questions:** Following are some questions you can use to encourage discussion of the ideas expressed by the students in the Teen Views feature:

a. Does responsibility for the unwanted pregnancy lie with the female, the male, or equally with both?

b. Do fathers sometimes "walk out" on the mothers of their children? Should there be a penalty? If so, what?

c. Several students place major blame on the female, but no one places the major blame on the father. Why is this? Is it justified?

d. Do people think a girl is "easy" if she asks about obtaining one of the devices for birth control?

e. Should young people learn about sex from their parents, in school, or on their own?

f. Do students agree with Tara Mills when she says that "you can almost bet that if two people are dating, they're having sex?"

g. Do students think that Paulette Singleton's opinion should carry more weight than the other opinions since she is an unwed mother? Do they agree with her that the mother is really more at fault?

CHAPTER 22 PLANNER

OVERVIEW

Chapter 22 is 22 pages long and divided into the three sections listed to the right. Major learning outcomes are also listed to the right. This chapter discusses aging and dying. Students are introduced to the concept of successful aging and the idea of planning to age successfully. The different aspects of dying and death are also discussed. Students are informed about the different ways to prepare for death. The *Straight Talk* in this chapter deals with grief.

MAKING LIFE CHOICES RESOURCES

A variety of activities, handouts, quizzes, and tests to accompany this chapter are available in the *Making Life Choices* supplementary material. You may pick and choose from those materials as appropriate for your amount of class time and the ability levels of your students. Some of the resources you might want to consider using are:

Overhead
• The Effects of Bone Loss

Handouts
• Anti-Aging Products
• Questionnaire on Death
• Why Worry About Death
• Living Will

Teacher Information Sheets
• Anti-Aging Strategies
• Nutrition, Aging, and Disease
• Malnutrition
• Food Assistance
• Institutional Care
• Stages of Grief
• Death Topic Statements

Answers to "Fact or Fiction"

1. False. The happiest people are those who have lived through at least one major life tragedy.
2. False. The human life span has not changed, but the average life expectancy has increased steadily over the past 100 years. **3.** False. People remain sexual beings throughout life. **4.** True. **5.** False. Only a fraction of older people live in nursing homes.

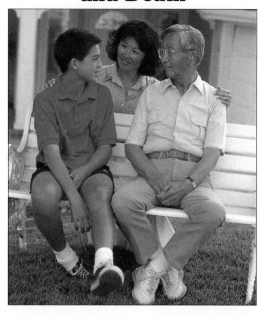

CHAPTER 22

Mature Life, Aging, and Death

Activity To Introduce Chapter

The following activities can help you and your students get an idea what it's like to experience some of the physical limitations that can accompany aging.
1. *Stroke/Paralysis Exercise:* Try to write your name, using the opposite hand from the one you normally use. Try to write a short note to someone, or attempt to fill out a form. Put a ping-pong ball in your mouth, and try to talk with someone.
2. *Loss of Hearing Exercise:* Stuff an earplug into the outer part of each ear. On top of that, put on a pair of earmuffs or a stereo headset, or tie a heavy scarf around your ears. Have someone go into another room and try to carry on a conversation.
Using the same equipment, try to listen to the television, radio, or stereo with the sound turned low.
3. *Impaired Vision Exercise:* Put on goggles or scratched eyeglasses.
Try to read, watch television, walk outdoors, or ride in a car (with someone else driving) for a few minutes.

OUTCOMES

After reading and studying this chapter, you will be able to:

✓ List characteristics of people who age successfully.
✓ Discuss some healthful behaviors to follow in planning for good health in old age.
✓ Describe the physical changes that occur during the aging process.
✓ Describe the mental changes that may occur as people age.
✓ List ways that people can prepare for death.
✓ Describe the stages a person goes through in accepting death.
✓ Discuss some ways to help a grieving person.

FACT OR FICTION

What do you think? *Are the following statements true or false? If you think they are false, then say what is true.*

1. The happiest people are those who have experienced the fewest tragedies.
2. The human life span has increased steadily over the past 100 years.
3. People should expect to lose their sexuality at around 50 years of age.
4. Most people's incomes are reduced at retirement.
5. Most people can expect to spend their later years in nursing homes.

(Answers on page 563)

■ **Reminder:** Knowing how to study can increase your knowledge, improve your grades, *and* cut down on your study time. See the *Studying Health* section at the front of your text for some suggestions to help you study this chapter.

CONTENTS

I. Expectations and Successful Aging
II. The Aging Process
III. Dying

    Straight Talk: *Helping Others Deal with Death and Grief*

NOT ENOUGH TIME?*

You could easily spend four or five days teaching this chapter if students read the entire chapter, do a fair number of the suggested activities in the teacher's edition, and complete a sampling of the handouts from the resource material accompanying this text. It is likely, however, that you will have only two or three days to devote to this chapter. Following are some suggestions to help you make sure that you cover the key topics if you have limited time.

TIME	SUGGESTIONS
1 Day	Assign Section I prior to class. During class have students complete Activities 1.1 and 1.2.
2 Days	On day 2, assign Section II prior to class. During class have students complete Activities 2.2, 2.3, and 2.13.
3 Days	On day 3, assign Section III prior to class. During class have students complete Activities 3.2 and 3.3.

*Please refer to the 18-week daily lesson plans in the supplementary material for additional suggestions.

SUGGESTED RESOURCES

Student Readings
1. Kart, Cary S., Metress, Eileen K. and Metress, Seamus P. *Aging, Health and Society*. Boston: Jones and Bartlett Publishers, 1988.
2. Dychtwald, Ken and Flower, Joe. *Age Wave*. Los Angeles: Jeremy P. Tarcher, Inc., 1989.

Teacher Readings
1. "Wrinkles." *Health Gazette*. October 1990, p. 3.

2. Grollman, Earl. *Living When a Loved One Has Died*. Boston: Beacon Press, 1989.
3. Viorst, Judith. *Necessary Losses*. New York: Ballantine Books, Inc., 1986.

Videos
1. *Adjusting to Aging*. Good Samaritan Hospital and Medical Center, Audio Visual/Video Services, 1015 Northwest 22nd Ave., Portland, OR 97210.

CHAPTER PROJECT

Assign students to interview five people over the age of 40. At least two of the interviewees must be 60 or older. As a class, prepare a questionnaire for the students to use in the interview. The students should be seeking information on lifestyle—is the person doing anything to prevent or slow down the aging process? Is he or she looking forward to the retirement years or currently enjoying the retirement years, and why? What do they like the most and the least about their present ages? On the day the interviews are completed and turned in, use the students' findings to develop an open discussion. Ask how the students felt doing the interviews. What did they learn? Allow the students to respond to specific answers their subjects gave during the interviews. As the discussion draws to a close, ask the students if their views on aging changed. If so, how and why? Stress that people of all ages are great resources for a variety of information, and that we can learn about ourselves and our own views, by listening to others.

In this section students will learn the:
1. Correlation between one's views of "old age," and how one actually lives out these views.
2. Similarities and differences in classmates' views of aging.

Activity 1.1

Old Age Begins At . . . Give each student two index cards and a marker. On one card ask the students to answer the following question: "At what age does old age begin?" The students should be instructed to write the answer on the card and include enough reasons to fill the whole card.

On the other card, ask the students to answer the next question with the words "positive" or "negative." Question: "When you think of growing old and passing the age you put down on the first card, do you think of it in a positive or negative way?" Give each student two pieces of double-sided tape. They are to put the tape on the backs of the cards and then put them on one of the following, which you have prepared beforehand:

A. Two poster boards—one with the words "Old age begins at . . ." and the

---

Teacher Support Notes

① **Perceptions of Older People:** Ask students, before they begin to read this chapter, to express their opinions of older people. Do they enjoy being with older people? Do they think that older people tend to have different views than their own on most issues? If so, can they provide some examples?

② **Free Association:** Have students write down the first five words or phrases that come to mind when you say the word *aging*. Then ask them to do the same when you say *death* and *dying*. Count the positive responses and the negative responses. Are their ideas about these topics primarily negative or positive? If they're negative, ask them what they can do to change these feelings.

---

548 UNIT 6 The Life Cycle

Why study aging when you are still under 20? Because you are setting your course now for the kind of older person you will become—that's why. An old expression says it this way: "As the twig is bent, so grows the tree." As the master of your "twig" (your young life), how will you bend it to grow into your "tree" (your later life)? And while you are still young, how well can you develop your understanding of older people?

SECTION I

Expectations and Successful Aging

The quality of life in the future tends to become what people expect it to become. Physical health makes a difference, and so does financial security. However, people's expectations also contribute more to their futures than most people realize.

Expectations

Are you aware of how you expect your later life to be? Most people, without realizing it, believe in a stereotype—largely negative—of what it is like to be old. Then, later, they become that way. To see what your life might be like as you age, answer the questions in this chapter's Life Choice Inventory.

Most people want their later lives to be successful. Some say they want to be like those who have made great intellectual and artistic achievements in their 70s and 80s. They claim they want to model themselves after older people they admire. Such older people are vibrant and happy. They can offer unique wisdom and perspective, having experienced more life than anyone else.

Key Points ▶ *The views people hold on aging can affect the way they live in their later years.*

Successful Aging

A 90-year-old man visited his physician, seeking relief from the pain in his left knee. Unable to find a cause for the ache, the physician said, "For heaven's sake, at your age, you have to expect such problems." The mature man replied, "Look here, Doc, my right knee is also 90, and it doesn't hurt."

The physician's attitude reflects how most people view growing old. They think disability and disease are inevitable consequences of aging. In contrast, the older man's remark suggests that elderly people may have a different view of old age. They

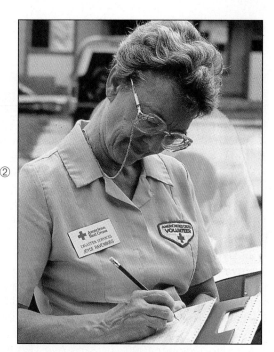

A mature life can be one of continued productive activity.

548

other "Old age is a _____ thought."

B. A bulletin board or wall section prepared with those two statements.

C. The chalkboard prepared with those statements.

Once the students have put both cards under the appropriate statements, discuss the results using the following questions and statements as guidelines:

1. What is the range of ages at which old age begins? Why do you think our views are so varied?

2. Count the number of positives and negatives in answer to the second question. What could these answers possibly tell us? Why did some of you say "negative?" Why "positive?" Is it possible that those of us who said "positive" may not fear getting older and those of us who said "negative" do fear old age? What is there to fear? What is there to look forward to?

(15–20 min.; Critical Thinking)

TEACH
SECTION I
(Guided and Independent Practice)
Activity 1.2
Life Choice Inventory Discussion. Use the Life Choice Inventory as a class activity. After students have scored their answers, have a discussion using

(continued on next page)

LIFE CHOICE INVENTORY

What Will the Aging Process Be Like for You?

For each of the following questions, choose the answer that more nearly describes what you expect the aging process to be like for you.

1. In what ways do you expect your appearance to change as you grow older?
   a. I expect to grow less and less attractive.
   b. I expect to grow more and more radiant, confident, and attractive.
2. How fit do you expect to be at 70?
   a. I expect to be less fit than I am now.
   b. I expect to be very fit for my age.
3. What will be your financial status at 70?
   a. I expect to be financially dependent on my family or the state.
   b. I expect to be financially independent. ①
4. How much sexual activity will you engage in when you are 70? Will others see you as sexy?
   a. I expect my sexual activity to decline; other people will not see me as sexy.
   b. I expect to continue to be interested in sexual activity; other people will see me as sexy.
5. Will you have many friends, only a few, or none?
   a. I will have only a few or no friends.
   b. I will have many friends.
6. What sorts of things will you do with your friends?
   a. I won't do much of anything with my friends.
   b. I expect to enjoy many, varied activities with my friends.
7. Will you be happy? Cheerful? Curious? Or will you be set in your ways?
   a. I will be set in my ways.
   b. I will be happy, cheerful, and curious.

SCORING

Your answers reveal not only what will probably become of you, but also what you think of older people. Count only your *b* answers:

7 *b* answers: Your attitudes are consistent with a rewarding and fulfilling later life.

5 or 6 *b* answers: You will be a happy older person, for the most part. However, you could be preparing better for old age in the areas in which you answered *a*.

4 or fewer *b* answers: Unfortunately, you hold some views of older people that may impair the quality of your own later life.

Teacher Support Notes

① **Old-Age Predictions:** Many students may be skeptical that their answers to this inventory will predict the type of life they will have in their later years. Explain to students that their current ideas can become self-fulfilling prophecies. Their own attitudes more than any other factor can determine their behavior. Unless their attitudes change, the corresponding behavior is likely to occur. Do those who scored low on the inventory think that they could change their attitudes? How? When?

> 66 **Thoughts on Health** 99
>
> *I remember my youth and the feeling that will never come back any more—the feeling that I could last forever, outlast the sea, the earth, and all men.*
> **– Joseph Conrad**

often think that the advanced years can still be lively.

Most people in their later years are self-sufficient, physically active, socially involved, and clear thinking. Most are fully participating members of society, and report themselves to be happy and healthy. Such people tend to think positively throughout their lives. They do not believe in a rigid definition of success. Rather, they define success by their own values and live accordingly. They work not to-

Teach
(Continued)

A. Do you agree with what the score indicates about your views and lifestyle? Why or why not?
B. What changes can we make to assure a fulfilling later life? Is this important? Why?

EVALUATE
SECTION I

Activity 1.3
Pop Quiz.
1. There is nothing you can do to make the aging process less painful. (F)
2. Education is often a factor in happiness. (T)
3. It is necessary to be rich in order to be

happy in old age. (F)
4. Those who age successfully have meaning and direction in their lives. (T)
5. Those who age successfully live like hermits. (F)

CLOSE
SECTION I

Activity 1.4
Setting Goals. Tell students to

Section I Review
Answers
1. physical health, financial security, expectations
2. those making great intellectual and artistic achievements in their 70s and 80s; vibrant, happy, and offer unique wisdom and perspective
3. disability and disease are inevitable
4. Answers will vary. Refer to the list on this page.
5. practice happiness, and preserve your health
6. Answers will vary.

Fast Facts

More and more research is being done in trying to unlock the secrets of aging. It is estimated that approximately 2,000 molecular biologists, geneticists, immunologists, and other researchers across the United States are studying aging. The federal government's National Institute of Aging is among the fastest-growing branches of the National Institute of Health. Its budget nearly doubled in the three years from 1989 to 1992.

ward power and wealth but toward meaningful goals. They feel their lives have purpose. Those who age successfully display these characteristics:

- Their lives have meaning and direction.
- They handle life's events in their own, sometimes unusual, ways.
- They rarely feel cheated by life.
- They have attained several long-term goals.
- They are pleased with their own growth and development.
- They love and are loved by others.
- They have many friends.
- They are cheerful.
- They can take criticism.
- They have no major fears.

What is more, the people who are enjoying life the most are likely to be beyond their 20s, and to have lived through the fears and anxieties of youth. Many of the happiest people have lived through at least one major life tragedy. Being well educated is a factor in their happiness, as is having enough money to cover life's basic needs. They also know how to balance spontaneity with planning so that their lives are neither rigid nor aimless. They strike a balance between helping others and a healthy commitment to meeting their own needs. All of these traits, taken together, define successful aging.

In short, if you want to be happy when you are old, begin practicing happiness now. If you want to strive for a long life, preserve your health to support it. It can be done. More people than ever before are living full, healthy lives in their advanced years. This chapter describes the aging process and offers insight into how to grow old gracefully.

Key Points   *Many people in their later years live interesting and fulfilling lives. They practiced by living well in their earlier years.*

SECTION I   REVIEW

Answer the following questions on a sheet of paper.
Learning the Facts
1. What are three factors that will contribute to the quality of your future, perhaps more than you realize?
2. Identify characteristics of older people whom you might want to use as models for yourself.
3. How do most people view growing old?
4. List five of the ten characteristics that people who age successfully display.
5. If you want to be happy when you are old, what must you begin doing now?

Making Life Choices
6. Aging is a process that starts early in life. What are some things you can do at your age to make the aging process easier? What attitudes have you picked up, up to now, about the aging process? How can you change your attitudes about aging?

SECTION II

The Aging Process

Although many people believe that aging starts around 40 or 45, aging really begins at birth. Until about age 20, aging takes the form of growth and maturing. After growth is completed, aging brings about the gradual loss of youthful appearance and condition. Inside the body, the organs and cells age, too.

Within the different body organs, cells have different aging patterns and life spans. Some blood cells live only three days or so. Most nerve cells last for the person's lifetime. In a healthy older person, each cell lives on to the end of its normal life span in much the same fashion as in the person's younger years. As the person ages, though, the cells lose some of their funcchoose one topic from the Life Choice Inventory, then develop and write a goal for yourself based on that topic. This goal should include either a change in view or lifestyle, or maintenance of a positive attitude. **(15–20 min.; Reteach, Reinforce)**

FOCUS
SECTION II

In this section students will learn the:
1. Strategies necessary for successful aging.
2. Terminology associated with old age.
3. Differences between senility that is preventable and senility that is not preventable.

Activity 2.1
Successful Aging. With books closed, ask the students to list the names

of people over the age of 50 who have aged successfully. These people can be famous or not. Ask for some examples from their lists and write these on the board. Now ask the students to list the characteristics these people have that led to their successful aging. Again, ask for examples and write these on the board. Ask the students to open their books to page 555 and compare their list to the list,

(continued on next page)

Older and younger people have much to offer each other.

tion, they collect products not found in younger people's cells, and their cells lose some of their ability to reproduce.

> **Key Points** *Each cell in the body has its own aging pattern. Aging of the whole body begins at maturity, about age 20.*

Life Span and Life Expectancy

The human **life span** is the *maximum* possible length of life that people can reach, conditions being ideal. A person's **life expectancy** is the *average* length of life predicted by statistics. The human life span is in the neighborhood of 100 years or more. Many people, however, do not live this long, owing to disease or accidents. Today, the life expectancy for men in the United States is about 72 years; for women, about 78 years. Another term referring to length of life is **longevity**—the actual length of life observed in an individual. Some people are blessed with extraordinary longevity, perhaps thanks to their genetic inheritance combined with the events of their lives.

People are living longer today than ever before, but the human life span (maximum)

has not changed. What has changed is the life expectancy (average), mainly for two reasons. First, the rate of deaths from diseases and accidents among the very young has declined. Thus there are fewer young deaths to bring the average down. Second, medical advances are prolonging adults' lives so that they more nearly reach their maximum.

Many strategies have been proposed to extend the lengths of human lives, and many do not work. A scientific review of some 200 research studies concluded that none of the proposed strategies had any life-extending effect. This chapter's Consumer Awareness section helps to explain why people are fooled into buying products that promise to delay or

MINI GLOSSARY

life span: the maximum years of life a human being can live.
life expectancy: the number of years an individual can expect to live based on hereditary and other factors.
longevity: an individual's length of life.

Teacher Support Notes

① **Human Life Span:** You may want to point out to students the possibility of the human life span increasing in the years to come. People who are 100 years old today were born in the 1890s. Have students think about the difficulties those people had to deal with in terms of living conditions, lack of medicine, and lack of knowledge regarding such things as nutrition and disease. Then have students think about the conditions in which today's newborn will grow up and mature with regard to these same areas. It could be that the life span will increase simply due to these changes and conditions.
② **Handout—Anti-Aging Products:** Your supplementary material contains a handout listing several different products that supposedly retard or halt the aging process.

Focus

"Growing Old Gracefully" in the book. Choose a few items to discuss, such as numbers 1, 2, and 4. Ask the students to give examples and explanations. Ask if they agree with this list. In closing, stress that these 22 characteristics might tell us something about our own lifestyles and

goals in life. **(15–20 min.; Reteach, Reinforce)**

Activity 2.2
Term Discussion. Put these three terms on the board: *life span*, *life expectancy*, *longevity*. Ask the students to define them, and to explain the differences. Discuss which of the three has changed and which remains the same. **(10 min.; Reteach, Reinforce)**

Activity 2.3
Advertising Vulnerability. Have the students read "Longevity Frauds." Bring to class magazine advertisements for products that promise to slow down or reverse the aging process. Show these ads to the students. Ask if they believe any of them, and if so, why. Ask if they would do any of the following if they were older:

a. Dye their hair to hide the gray?

> **66 Thoughts on Health 99**
>
> *The old believe everything; the middle-aged suspect everything; the young know everything.*
> – **Oscar Wilde**

Teacher Support Notes

① **Answers to Critical Thinking:**
1. They often become desperate. They want nothing more than a way of prolonging life. **2.** They become targets because of their strong desire to avoid old age and death, because of their frustration with their failing bodies, because they may not be critical of advertisements, and in some cases, because of their surplus incomes. **3.** First and foremost, it would be to realize that there is no known way to stop the aging process. As students have learned throughout the text, there are no easy solutions; no "quick fixes."
② **Teacher Information Sheet—Anti-Aging Strategies:** In your supplementary material you will find background information about various strategies to combat aging.

---

552 UNIT 6 The Life Cycle

CONSUMER **A**WARENESS

Longevity Frauds

People have tried everything imaginable to delay or reverse aging. Years ago, the Spaniards sailed to the New World in search of the legendary Fountain of Youth. Today, people rush to buy products, based on "new scientific breakthroughs," that promise to restore youth.

The motivation behind these efforts is always the same: people want miracles. Whenever many people desire something that is impossible to have, someone steps in with empty promises and useless products and wins a growing bank account for the effort.

Frauds that plague the elderly are not limited to longevity hypes. Older people are targets of many other schemes. Why are the elderly the targets for such deception? First, many of them have ready access to money—retirement funds, pensions, insurance policies, paid-up mortgages. Second, as people age, they

experience more symptoms and may be frustrated by the medical profession's inability to help or unwillingness to take them seriously. They seek help where it is offered, proven or not. And as people get older, they may develop a "what have I got to lose" attitude about trying products that claim to prolong life or improve health. Money seems less important than even the slightest chance of better health or longer life. Even brilliant, sophisticated people let themselves be bamboozled by longevity frauds.

① **C**RITICAL **T**HINKING

1. *Why are people so open to promises of miracles concerning aging?*
2. *Why are older people so often the targets of scams?*
3. *Based on what you've learned in other Consumer Awareness sections, how can you detect a longevity fraud when one is offered?*

reverse aging. Strategies that do help slow aging have more to do with lifestyle and less to do with pills and shots.

②

Key Points ▶ *The human life span has not changed, but life expectancy has increased. Longevity frauds are numerous.*

How to Age Gracefully

No magic can keep a person young forever. No matter what you do to prevent it, your body will age. You can, however, do quite a bit to slow the process of aging and maximize your wellness and enjoyment of

life. One of the most important things to do is to maintain appropriate body weight. Obesity shortens life. Aside from that, other keys to health maintenance in the later years involve all of the principles of this book's chapters: sound nutrition, including an ample water intake; adequate sleep; regular physical activity; and avoidance of alcohol, tobacco, and other drug abuse.

Much of the quality of the later years depends on the daily choices a person makes in youth and on the habits that become fixed as a result of those choices. Figure 22–1 shows a sampling of changes that

b. Have hair replacement surgery if balding?

c. Get a facelift?

d. Buy products to hide or "wash away" wrinkles?

e. Drink a product to look younger?

f. Take an experimental drug to cure arthritis?

Ask how great a risk they would take, or how much money they would spend to prevent aging. Use this as an introduction to a discussion on the vulnerability of the elderly to scams on youthfulness. **(10–15 min.; Extend, Enrich)**

Activity 2.4

The Aging Process. As a homework assignment have students find a current magazine article on the process of aging, or some aspect of this topic. (Example: the effects of alcohol and/or tobacco on the aging process, advance-ments on slowing down the aging process, etc.) The students are to bring in a copy of the article after reading it and underline five to ten major points. Combine a list of facts versus fiction on the topic of aging. Compare the factual list to the facts mentioned under the heading, "How to Age Gracefully," and to the 22 items in the Health Strategies box on page 555. Discuss why it is important for

(continued on next page)

FIGURE 22-1

Changes with Age: Preventable versus Unavoidable ①

Change with Aging	You Probably Can Slow or Prevent These Changes by Exercising, Maintaining Other Good Health Habits, and Planning Ahead:	You Probably Cannot Prevent These:
Appearance		
Greying of hair		✓
Balding		✓
Drying and wrinkling of skin	✓	
Nervous System		
Impairment of near vision		✓
Some loss of hearing		✓
Reduced taste and smell		✓
Reduced touch sensitivity		✓
Slowed reactions (reflexes)		✓
Slowed mental function		✓
Mental confusion	✓	
Cardiovascular System		
Increased blood pressure	✓	
Increased resting heart rate	✓	
Decreased oxygen consumption	✓	
Body Composition/Metabolism		
Increased body fatness	✓	
Raised blood cholesterol	✓	
Slowed energy metabolism	✓	
Other Physical Characteristics		
Menopause (women)		✓
Loss of fertility (men)		✓
Loss of elasticity in joints		✓
Loss of flexibility in joints	✓	
Loss of teeth; gum disease	✓	
Bone loss	✓	
Accident/Disease Proneness		
Accidents	✓	
Inherited diseases		✓
Lifestyle diseases	✓	
Psychological/Other		
Reduced self-esteem	✓	
Loss of sex drive	✓	
Loss of interest in work	✓	
Depression, loneliness	✓	
Reduced financial status	✓	

Teacher Support Notes

① **Preventable vs. Unavoidable Changes:** Tell students that there are 30 changes listed in this figure. Ask them how many of those changes they can help slow down or prevent. (17) How many can they not prevent? (13) Ask them if they disagree with any of these. As a more extensive follow-up activity, you may want to ask students to list behaviors that they could practice or avoid in order to slow or prevent the changes that have check marks in the middle column. For example, smoking, excessive alcohol consumption, and other drug abuse ages the skin.

✎ Fast Facts

There are more people over the age of 65 in the United States than there are teenagers.

teenagers to know these facts and to know what is fiction. **(40 min.; Extend, Enrich)**

TEACH
SECTION II
(Guided and Independent Practice)

Activity 2.5

Essay on Changes. Ask the students to study Figure 22–1 on the preceding page. Ask them to write an essay, choosing five items listed in the Preventable column, and explaining how they personally will prevent these from happening. Give them one day for the assignment. Use this the next day for discussion. **(5 min. to explain assignment, Critical Thinking)**

Activity 2.6

Attitudes. Take a class poll on the following statements. Have students indicate whether they agree or disagree with the statements. Allow volunteers to share their opinions.
1. Television accurately portrays how elderly people behave and look.
2. People over the age of 65 should not be allowed to drive.
3. Older people are boring.

Teacher Support Notes

① **Overhead—The Effects of Bone Loss:** Your supplementary material contains an overhead that shows the effects of osteoporosis on a woman's height.

② **Estrogen Replacement:** Estrogen replacement therapy has been associated with possible cancer risks, but researchers agree that the benefits outweigh the risks. Estrogen not only retards bone loss but improves the serum lipid profile and reduces cardiovascular disease risk.

③ **Preventing Osteoporosis:** For enrichment you may want to give students some additional behaviors that will help fend off the onset of osteoporosis in later years. These are adequate fluoride and vitamin D intakes, abstinence from alcohol and other drugs, moderation in caffeine use, minimal prescription drug use, and control of stress.

☎ Where to Call

National Council on Aging
1-800-424-9046
Call for information and referrals about aging.

554

To be young at heart is to be young where it counts.

happen with age. The figure shows that some of these changes can be prevented by continued exercise and other health-supporting habits, and that some changes will occur no matter how hard you try to prevent them. The Health Strategies box on the next page, "Growing Old Gracefully," provides further suggestions.

Key Points *Some changes of aging are preventable by choosing wise lifestyle habits throughout life.*

Dealing with Physical Changes

Knowledge helps people deal with the changes that come with age. It is comforting to realize that some negative changes of aging are accompanied by positive ones that help compensate for lost abilities. For example, although older people are less able than younger people to recover from

stress physically, older people are more able psychologically. Older people have learned how to "bounce back" from setbacks. Perhaps this is because they have seen more of life and have learned to adjust to unexpected turns of events. Another example: the immune system becomes less efficient at fighting off disease once it takes hold, but older people get infections less often than younger people do. Perhaps this is because they have developed immunity against many diseases.

In women, the later years bring **menopause,** in which monthly ovulation becomes irregular and finally ceases. As the supply of the hormone estrogen dwindles, menstruation also stops. Reduced estrogen also causes the periodic feelings of warmth some women call **hot flashes.** Hot flashes are related to the dilation of the blood vessels in the skin.

A major surge of bone loss (osteoporosis) takes place at the beginning of menopause. ① Women whose calcium intakes and physical activity levels have been insufficient to build up the bones before menopause may lose bone material rapidly and become crippled with osteoporosis within a few years (see Chapter 8). To prevent further bone loss, as well as to prevent some of the other effects ② of menopause, physicians often prescribe estrogen replacement therapy. In the younger years, though, the best prevention is an ③ abundant calcium intake from food, together with plenty of physical activity to cement the calcium into place in the bones.

Menopause sets in early in women who smoke. So does osteoporosis. This may be because smoking suppresses production of the hormone estrogen or because the ingredients of tobacco are directly toxic to the ovaries. Chapter 15 gave abundant reasons for abstaining from smoking; add these to them.

The **male menopause** is experienced as

4. Elderly people are unable to make important decisions.

5. It's stimulating to talk with elderly people.

6. Most elderly people are forgetful.

7. Elderly people should be able to work until they no longer want to.

8. Most elderly people should be in nursing homes.

9. Younger people can benefit from the experience of the elderly.

10. Elderly people are no longer productive members of society.

After discussing the students' feelings, ask them why they think they feel the way they do about the elderly. Ask if they have any suggestions for getting to know an elderly person better and finding out what he or she is really like. **(20 min., Critical Thinking)**

Activity 2.7

Preventable Causes of Confusion. Write the word "senility" on the board. Ask the students to define it and give examples. Clarify the definition, and ask the students if they think it can be prevented. Tell the students to turn to page 557 (Figure 22–2). Discuss the eight preventable causes of mental confusion in older people. Ask the students which ones surprise them. Stress that we

(continued on next page)

HEALTH **S**TRATEGIES

Growing Old Gracefully ①

1. Maintain appropriate body weight.
2. Obtain regular and adequate sleep throughout life.
3. Consciously practice your stress-management skills.
4. Limit your time in the sun, or use sunscreen protection.
5. For women, see your physician about estrogen replacement against osteoporosis.
6. Do not smoke. If you do smoke, quit.
7. Expect to enjoy sexual activity with your husband or wife, and learn new ways of enhancing it.
8. Maintain physical fitness. Change activities to suit changing abilities and tastes.
9. Protect your eyes against excessive sunlight.
10. Be aware that your brain's and nerves' reactions are slowing down. Plan to compensate by being more careful.
11. Use alcohol only moderately, if at all. Use drugs only as prescribed. Ask your physician about potential interactions of prescribed medicines with other drugs.
12. Take care to prevent accidents. Seek medical attention if impairment from a fall seems to last too long.
13. Expect good vision and hearing throughout life. Obtain glasses and hearing aids, if necessary.
② 14. Maintain adequate nutrition.
15. Be alert to confusion as a disease symptom, and seek diagnosis. Do not live with an unidentified disease.
16. Stay interested in life, make new friends, adopt new activities—control depression.
17. Drink eight glasses a day of water or other liquids, even if you aren't thirsty.
18. Practice your mental skills. Keep on solving math problems, reading, following directions, writing, imagining, and creating.
19. For adult children of aging parents: provide or obtain the needed care and stimulation.
20. Make financial plans early to ensure your security.
21. Accept change. Work at recovering from losses; practice making new friends.
22. Cultivate spiritual health. Consult your values, and make your life meaningful.

M**INI** G**LOSSARY**

menopause: the years of stopping ovulation and menstruation in a woman.

hot flashes: sudden waves of feeling hot all over, a symptom related to dilation of blood vessels in the skin, which is common during the transition into menopause.

male menopause: the gradual decline in male fertility due to advancing age.

a gradual decline of fertility rather than as the abrupt end experienced by women. In fact, some men still have the ability to make sperm into their 80s. Testosterone production gradually decreases, as does sperm production. Hormones and testicular functioning may decrease, as may the desire for sexual activity.

Physical ability does change. Older mus-

Teacher Support Notes

① **Growing Old Gracefully:** One way of getting students involved with this list of strategies would be to have them go through the list with at least one older person. This activity can serve two purposes: **1.** It could help an older person change some negative behaviors and thereby grow old more gracefully; and **2.** make a stronger impression on students of the importance of these strategies. For each strategy, they could ask the older person whether or not he or she has practiced the strategy and then record the answers. They could also ask whether or not the person thinks that he or she could change the negative behaviors, and if so, how?

② **Teacher Information Sheet—Nutrition, Aging, and Disease:** There is extensive information in your supplementary material regarding the relationships among nutrition, aging, and disease. You may or may not want to give this additional information to students for enrichment.

555

so often think of senility as permanent brain deterioration from "old age" that we really don't stop to think it might be preventable. **(15 min.; Reteach, Reinforce)**

Activity 2.8
Speaker on Aging. Check with your local speakers' bureau to see if there is an elderly person who speaks to youth about aging. Invite this person to discuss what life was like during his or her teen years and how it has felt aging over the years. This might be combined with a social studies class to discuss the depression era, wars, etc. Help students prepare questions. **(Extend, Enrich, Interdisciplinary)**

Activity 2.9
Gerontology. Have a guest speaker come in to discuss gerontology. Check your local hospitals or social service agencies for the name of a reputable gerontologist. Be sure the speaker is knowledgeable about both preventable senility and Alzheimer's disease. Guidelines should be given to the students concerning talking to and helping the elderly. **(Extend, Enrich)**

---

66 Thoughts on Health 99

The reason grandparents and grandchildren get along so well is that they have a common enemy.
    – Sam Levenson

Teacher Support Notes

① **Teacher Information Sheets—Malnutrition and Food Assistance:** Many experts believe that malnutrition among the elderly is most often due to the deep, pervasive feelings of isolation and loneliness that overwhelm them as changes in the quality of their lives take place. You will find more information on this topic and on food assistance programs for older people in the supplementary material.

☎ **Where to Call**

The Alzheimer's Disease Association
1-800-272-3900

✏ **Fast Facts**

42% of American parents over the age of 65 talk to their children on the telephone every day.

556

---

556   UNIT 6   The Life Cycle

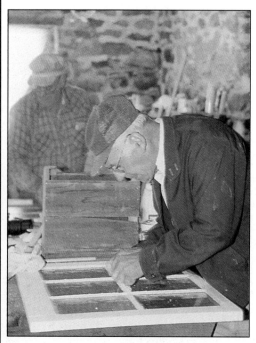

People who stay involved tend to stay happy.

cles do not build up as quickly as younger ones do, so it takes longer and harder work to gain condition. Balanced against that, older muscles lose condition at a slower rate than young muscles do. Once fit, an older person who has to take a break from physical activity will maintain condition longer, although he or she still should resume exercising as soon as possible.

The more people exercise, the less likely they are to die of heart and lung diseases. This does not mean for sure that exercise prolongs life. However, it does enhance the quality of life and helps keep you from dying before your time.

An older person's reflexes are slowed. The joints may be less flexible than a younger person's. Arthritis, a painful condition affecting the joints, is to some extent unavoidable in older people. Weight control and moderate activity, however, help people to withstand its worst effects. Aspirin helps quell the pain of arthritis. Fad diets do not help.

The fact that continued physical activity helps fend off arthritis is another reminder that people should stay active all their lives. Sometimes a pain that an older person believes to be arthritis may instead be a normal ache caused by joint stiffness from years of inactivity. Older people need not exercise the same way younger people do, though. Activities should be adjusted to fit the body's changing abilities. A former Olympic gold medal acrobat may hike and bike in later years. A once-bone-bruising football player may jog and play a little golf. Wise advice to the older person: "Regular exercise is important, but go easy on yourself."

Key Points *Knowing in advance what physical changes are unpreventable can help people to cope as the changes take place. Compensations accompany these changes. The knowledge that this is so eases acceptance of aging.*

① **Dealing with Mental Changes**

Some changes take place in the brain and nervous system as people age. Research has discovered declines in five areas: reasoning skill, recall (memory), spatial sense, speed, and senses. These declines, however, are offset by increased wisdom and judgment. People can also adopt strategies to compensate for these declines, such as learning to write things down so that they will not forget or allowing more time for certain tasks.

The mental confusion called **senility** is many times avoidable. Mental confusion in older people comes from many different causes—and most are preventable. Only one, brain disease itself, is not. The preventable causes of mental confusion are listed in Figure 22–2. If an older person be-

Activity 2.10

Practice Happiness. Write the following ingredients for successful aging on sheets of paper before class (one sentence on each sheet): **1.** Many of the happiest people have lived through at least one major life tragedy. **2.** Being well educated is a factor in happiness. **3.** Having enough money for life's basic needs is essential. Write the following sentence on poster board: "If you want to be happy when you are old, begin practicing happiness now."

Divide the class into three groups. Give each group a piece of paper with one of the ingredients on it. Ask the students to take five minutes to brainstorm why this is such an important ingredient. Have them write their ideas on the paper. As a class, discuss the importance of each ingredient, based on students' brainstorming. Ask if everyone agrees with them. Would they add others? Then hold up the poster board and read the statement aloud. Have the students think about it and ask themselves if they practice the ingredients. Do they practice happiness? **(20 min.; Reteach, Reinforce)**

Activity 2.11
Preparing for Retirement Years.
Write the following question on the board:

(continued on next page)

FIGURE 22-2

Preventable Causes of Mental Confusion in Older People

Abuse of drugs. This includes alcohol abuse and the misuse or incompatibility of prescription drugs. The effects of alcohol and drugs can sometimes resemble those of strokes and seizures.

Accidents. Falls can cause skull fractures (concussions) or bleeding that puts pressure on the brain, which surgery can relieve.

Dehydration. The thirst signal may become faint. As a result, an older person may not drink enough to meet fluid needs. One of the major symptoms of dehydration is confusion.

Depression. Depression can slow down the mind in old people, as in the young.

Disease states. Diseases present different symptoms in older people than in younger ones. Tuberculosis, diabetes, and even heart attacks can all begin with confusion, rather than with fever or pain.

Disuse of mental skills. People do lose what they don't use. Practicing mental skills brings them back.

Malnutrition. Taste enjoyment, digestive secretions, and appetite diminish. Older people eat less, yet nutrient needs remain the same.

Poor vision and hearing. Both can cause confusion. Both can be corrected or compensated for.

comes confused, try correcting these possible causes before jumping to the conclusion that senility has set in.

Depression, especially, often causes the symptoms of senility. The story is told of a woman who invited her mother to live with her while the older woman waited for a place in a nursing home. The mother had all the classic signs of senility—mental confusion, inability to make decisions, forgetting simple tasks—so the family decided she needed institutional care. However, after several weeks in her daughter's home—eating meals with the family and enjoying social stimulation—she became her old self again and was able to return to her home. This story has been repeated with many variations and serves to remind us that factors other than senility cause confusion. What harm could there be in first trying home life, regular meals, and plenty of tender, loving care?

One unpreventable cause of confusion is **Alzheimer's disease.** The condition appears most often in people over 65 and is a major cause of death in that age group. It afflicts an average of 30 percent of all those over 85. It starts as the loss of memory, then becomes an inability to perform everyday functions, and then leads to the total inability to care for oneself. In the brain, the nerve pathways become tangled and blocked, cutting off the memory functions. Once it sets in, Alzheimer's disease is irreversible and progresses from mild confusion to disability and death in a period of months or years. The person suffering from it usually requires a level of care beyond what family members can provide. The causes are still unknown, and no cure is in sight.

Key Points *Losses of mental sharpness in aging are offset by gains in wisdom and judgment. Brain disease such as Alzheimer's disease is an unavoidable cause of senility, but most other causes are preventable.*

MINI GLOSSARY

senility: a general term meaning weakness of mind and body occurring in old age.
Alzheimer's disease: a brain disease of some older people that brings mental confusion; inability to function; and in the final stage, death.

Teacher Support Notes

① **Overmedication:** Mental confusion among older patients is often caused by overmedication. Many older people take several types of long-term medications, and some use more than a dozen different drugs. Interactions among drugs, as well as overdoses of some drugs, can cause a host of complications, including mental confusion. People in their advanced years should request that their health care providers monitor their use of mixtures of prescription drugs.

Fast Facts

The Alliance for Aging Research estimates that it costs the nation 90 billion dollars to treat people with Alzheimer's, which affects at least two million and possibly four million Americans.

"Will you be prepared for your retirement years?" Ask the students what they hope to be doing during the retirement years. You may need to stress that whether they hate the thought or not, or avoid it or not, these advanced years will happen to them, provided they survive the risky teen years. Then, ask them what they'll need to do to prepare for these years. Cover both financial and mental preparedness. Stress again that how we live our lives now will largely determine how we live out our later years. **(30 min.; Reteach, Reinforce)**

Activity 2.12
Financial Planning. Invite a financial planner who specializes in retirement planning to speak to the class. Ask the planner to have a list of questions the students can take home for their parents to look over. Or, make your own list of questions for the students to ask their parents about future planning. **(Reteach, Reinforce)**

EVALUATE
Section II

Teacher Support Notes

① **Teacher Information tion Sheet—Institutional Care:** In your supplementary material you will find background information on the topic of selecting institutional care for older people.

② **Practice Happiness:** Be sure students reread this sentence. Not only does it restate a reason for young students studying old age and maturity, it emphasizes the point that has been made throughout this text—that each person is responsible for his or her own health and happiness and that each person can take action to achieve the desired health and happiness.

66 Thoughts on Health 99

All would live long, but none would be old.
– Benjamin Franklin

558 UNIT 6 The Life Cycle

Physical activity promotes mental alertness.

Preparing for Social and Other Changes

Other changes faced by people who are aging are financial and social losses. Being ② aware of this and preparing for it will enable people to weather losses successfully.

Financial planning is essential. Nearly everyone suffers a loss of income, made worse by inflation, in the retirement years. It is important to have set aside enough money for retirement—to have the home paid for or adequate income to pay the rent—and to have insurance to cover unexpected medical and other expenses.

Financial preparation will not, however, prevent emotional and social losses, which may be many. Old friends may die or move away. Children may move away also and may be too busy to write or call. Status in the community is lost upon retiring.

Another way to prepare is to plan for alternative living arrangements, should it become too difficult to care for the present home. A nursing home is not the only choice and usually not the best one. Fewer than a third of older adults spend any time in a nursing home. Of those, most spend only about a year there. Rather than leave it to their children to decide for them where they will live, older adults usually decide for themselves.

Loss of control of the environment—such as finding that the home that was to be a haven in retirement now sits in the middle of a high-crime area, or that the familiar shops and fruit stands have closed—also occurs. A person can develop a feeling of deep loneliness as the familiar environment shifts. A loss of identity may accompany retirement or the death of a spouse. A working person can say, "I'm a farmer, a nurse, a manager," but what can a retired person say? A part of the person's identity is gone.

You may think it's unnecessary for a person of 15 or 18 to confront the problems of loneliness and loss in later life, but such is ① not the case. Emotional and social health in the later years is affected by what happens during youth. To be happy when you are old, you need to practice happiness when you are young. Losses occur when you are young, too. Learn to grieve over them and move on. Practice refilling your life with new loves, new activities, new enthusiasms. Maintain a strong social support system. Keep reaching out; create a web of support so that as relationships are lost, others are gained.

Continue your education forever. New information exercises the mind.

Cultivate spiritual health, too. Think about the meaning of life—both yours and that of others. Find ways to contribute your gifts, to leave something of value to those you care for. Keep working at projects that are meaningful to you. Growing is not for children only. It is a lifelong engagement.

"I've spent my whole life becoming who I am. Was it worth it?" A message of this chapter is that what a person becomes later in life is, to a large extent, whatever that person chooses to become today. The way a person deals with life's final challenge—death—is often also a matter of choice.

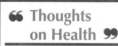

Activity 2.13

Essay. Give the following assignment: Using all the terms found in the Mini Glossaries in Sections I and II, develop an essay stating your opinion on "Growing Old in the 21st Century." Use all terms properly. State your opinion thoroughly and clearly. This essay should be 500 to 750 words in length.

CLOSE
SECTION II

Activity 2.14

Service Project. Have the students develop a service project for a local nursing home or for local senior citizens. They may want to join the local Humane Society for their "adopt a pet" days at the nursing homes, develop a pen pal system for those elderly with no relatives or visitors, plan a Christmas party for the elderly, or hold a spring clean-up day for the senior citizens who need help with their yards and windows. These activity days should prove to be very successful and give the students a wonderful sense of worth and accomplishment. **(Extend, Enrich)**

TEEN VIEWS

What makes your favorite senior citizen your favorite? ①

My grandfather is a retired navy shipman with the energy of a teenager. The jokes he tells with a devilish grin on his face always make us laugh until we cry, and he has the best war stories. You learn a lot about life by listening to him talk. But above all else, he cares so much about me. **Erin Tanaka, 16, Wilson High School, CA**

I love older people; they are so interesting. Some teens take senior citizens for granted, and others don't have any respect for them. I could sit and listen to them telling stories of their childhood and teen years for hours. **Gretchen Brougher, 17, Connellsville High School, PA**

The stories of things she remembers about her youth and the memories she shares with me are things that I like about Betty. Her eyes light up when I visit her. We talk, play games, and have fun. She is important to me and we have a lot of fun together. **Lisa Glaesemann, 14, Fargo South High School, ND**

Despite having multiple heart surgeries, my grandfather makes every effort to accomplish tasks on his own and doesn't ask to be catered to. He is always willing to learn about today's trends. I teach him to use the computer and VCR, and he explains the early years of technology in America (cars and radios). Everyone should make it a part of their lives to spend some time with a senior citizen. **Jeremy Mineweaser, 16, Orange Park High School, FL**

My grandmother is my favorite citizen because of her community involvement. Once a month she writes an article for the local newspaper. On her own time she organizes sewing circles and baking days for the less fortunate in nursing homes. **Brooklynn Holt, 17, Orange Park High School, FL**

Key Points ▶ *A person must plan for changes in living arrangements, financial support, and social support in the later years. You are becoming now what you will be in old age.*

SECTION II REVIEW

Answer the following questions on a sheet of paper.

Learning the Vocabulary
The vocabulary terms in this section are *life span, life expectancy, longevity, menopause, hot flashes, male menopause, senility,* and *Alzheimer's disease.*

1. Write a sentence using each of the vocabulary terms above.

Learning the Facts
2. List key principles to maintain health in the later years.
3. What might teenage women do to avoid osteoporosis later in life?

Making Life Choices
4. Describe any experiences you've had with people who are senile. What strategies can you recommend to make these situations as comfortable as possible for everyone involved?

Teacher Support Notes

① **Teen Views Follow-Up Questions:** Here are some questions that will help promote classroom discussion of the issues raised in the Teen Views comments: **a.** Do the students have grandparents who tell lots of stories about the "good old days?" Are there any favorites that students could relate to the class? **b.** Do students agree with Gretchen Brougher that older people are interesting? Do teens often take senior citizens for granted? Do some teens fail to give older people the proper respect?

Section II Review

Answers
1. Answers will vary.
2. Answers will vary; see the Health Strategies on page 555.
3. have an abundant calcium intake from food, together with plenty of physical activity
4. Answers will vary.

In this section the students will learn:
1. The lessons death can teach us about life.
2. Important steps that should be taken in preparation for death.
3. Classmates' views on death issues.
4. The definition of euthanasia and the legal implications surrounding this term.
5. The stages of grief work often found in people coping with a major loss.
6. Some guidelines for dealing with a friend who is dying.

Activity 3.1
Questionnaire on Death Topics.
Develop a ten-item, multiple choice questionnaire on various death topics or use the one provided in the supplementary materials. Give the students five–seven minutes to answer the questions. Be sure to stress that there are no right or wrong answers; this is purely based on opinion. When they are finished, ask them to circle two or three questions they would like to hear discussed in class. Discuss each question. Ask for student responses and rationale. Feel free to give your opinion. This helps the students realize it's OK to talk about these topics. Allow the conver-

---

66 Thoughts on Health 99

What's a man's age?
He must hurry more
that's all;
Cram in a day what his
youth took a year to
hold.
– Robert Browning

Teacher Support Notes

① **Handout—Why Worry About Death?** In your supplementary material you will find a handout that in a clever way expresses one person's opinion about how it is pointless to worry about death. You may want to distribute this and ask students to compare the opinions expressed in this handout with those expressed in Figure 22–3. Did one or the other make more of an impression on them? Why?

✍ Fast Facts

In the fall of 1992, according to *Longevity Magazine*, Eddie Mae Green of Lindside, West Virginia, was the oldest living person in the United States. She was 114 years old, born on September 8, 1877.

560

SECTION III

Dying

Imagine you were told today that you had only a few weeks to live. What would you do? Would you change the way you live? Would you take any practical or financial steps? Are there emotional issues you'd wish to work out with parents, brothers or sisters, or friends? What ideas would you pass on to others who will follow you?

Now imagine that someone close to you has only weeks to live. How will you spend your time with that person? What will you say? The value of asking these questions is that they help you realize that time in life is limited—not only for you but for every other person. Knowing this can help people to spend their time today wisely.

Fear of Death

Many people cannot stand to think of death. It is natural to fear death. All creatures strive to live. To express your fear and think about death is healthy. To flee and hide from reality is unhealthy.

Consider this view: death gives meaning to life! If you knew that you had only a few weeks left to live, wouldn't that knowledge give you a keen sense of how precious life is? Many people, on learning they are soon to die, report that they have started enjoying their days as never before. Sunsets are more beautiful. Jokes are funnier. Friends are dearer. Especially, the way they spend their time becomes more important. They try to make the most of every moment.

A narrow brush with death gives people this same sense of life's values. Many people, on having near-death experiences, say

their lives are totally changed afterward. One man reports that he was planning a career in law until he almost died in an accident. "I realized I wanted more than anything to work with disadvantaged children," he says, "so I gave up the law, and now I'm doing what I really love." A woman who had a similar experience decided the opposite. She quit teaching as a career and worked her way through law school for the very same reason. Given only one life to live, practicing law was what she chose to do. Others have chosen not careers but changed attitudes toward life. Figure 22–3 reports one person's reaction to the idea of death.

Death gives you a task—to make something worthwhile of your life. Like everyone alive on earth today, you have a deadline to meet. Whatever you want to accomplish in life, you must accomplish it before you die. Death has inspired towering works of art. People who face death pass on ideas and traditions to those who follow, for it encourages them to make a heritage for their children. Death acts as a reminder to not wait until tomorrow to do what you wish to do today.

This doesn't mean people must rush through life being busy. One of life's great pleasures is to savor each present moment. Even simple things, when you stop taking them for granted, bring great rewards. An orange sunset, the twinkle of a friend's smile, a breath of scented spring breeze, or the surprise of discovery in a child's eyes can be experienced fully only when we know that our experiences of them are numbered. Acknowledging death helps people cherish their lives rather than simply pass through them.

To get over the fear of death completely may be impossible. However, people fear most the things they are unprepared to face. If you prepare for death, you will fear it less.

sation to flow as different ideas are offered. Add factual information on each topic. Once a topic is discussed thoroughly, go to another question. Explain that it is healthy and normal to be curious about these topics. We just don't often have the chance to talk about them. **(one class period, Critical Thinking)**

TEACH
SECTION III
(Guided and Independent Practice)

Activity 3.2
Stages of Grief. Put the stages of grief on the board. (see page 564, first column) Ask the students to take ten minutes to write what they remember doing and saying after experiencing a major loss. Stress that this loss could be a

death, a divorce, a major breakup, the loss of a best friend, etc. Explain how the survivors of a loss go through these stages. Give specific examples of each stage. (An information sheet entitled "Stages of Grief" is provided in the supplementary material.) As you explain each stage, ask the students if they wrote anything that seems to fit the stage. Offer some of your own examples. Once you

(continued on next page)

FIGURE 22-3

One Person's Reaction to the Thought of Death: I'd Pick More Daisies

If I had my life to live over, I'd try to make more mistakes next time.
I would relax.
I would limber up.
I would be sillier than I have been this trip.
I know of very few things I would take seriously.
I would be crazier.
I would be less hygienic.
I would take more chances.
I would take more trips.
I would climb more mountains, swim more rivers, and watch more sunsets.
I would eat more ice cream and less beans.
I would have more actual troubles and fewer imaginary ones.
You see, I am one of those people who lives prophylactically and sensibly and sanely, hour after hour, day after day.
Oh, I've had my moments and, if I had it to do over, I'd have more of them.
In fact, I'd try to have nothing else.
Just moments, one after the other, instead of living so many years ahead each day.
I have been one of those people who never goes anywhere without a thermometer, a hot water bottle, a gargle, a raincoat, and a parachute.
If I had it to do over again, I would go places and do things and travel lighter than I have.
If I had my life to live over, I would start bare-footed earlier in the spring and stay that way later in the fall.
I would play hookey more.
I wouldn't make such good grades except by accident.
I would ride on more merry-go-rounds.
I'd pick more daisies.

Source: Nadine Stair, 87, Louisville, Kentucky.

Key Points *Fear of death is natural, but it need not be destructive. It can be channeled to give more meaning to life.*

Preparation for Death

Even young people should prepare for death in a few ways. For one thing, each young person should make a will, and start thinking about life insurance. When someone dies without having done so, the state divides up the person's property according to its laws, and often the family loses much of it.

You may not think you have any property worth mentioning, but still, don't postpone this step for too long. Your belongings may consist of nothing more than a bicycle and a backpack, but they are your estate. Make an informal will, to be sure that the people you care about receive what you

Teacher Support Notes

① **Fear of Death:** You may want to discuss further with students their fears of death. If you think such a discussion would have a positive effect with your students, ask them to examine their fears. What are they afraid of, exactly? Tell them that some people are afraid of the uncertainty of the afterlife—they fear what may await them. Some people fear that everything will end. Others fear the particular process of death; for example, a person with a painful, terminal illness fears the manner in which death will occur rather than death itself. Can they put their fears into words? You may want to have them write about this rather than discuss it in class.

✉ Where to Write

Concern for Dying
250 West 57th Street
New York, NY 10107

Teach
(Continued)

are finished with the stages, stress the importance of knowing these behaviors so we can accept ourselves as normal when we go through a major loss. Also, we can have a more accurate perception of what our friends are going through when they experience a loss. **(40–60**

EVALUATE
SECTION III

Activity 3.3
Pop Quiz. Develop a quiz that lists the stages of grief. Ask the students to give an example of a behavior that might be found in each stage. Ask the students to write two guidelines for helping a friend

CLOSE
SECTION III

Activity 3.4
Valuable Letters. Give each student an envelope and two pieces of paper. Ask each student to think about the following scenario: "You have just gone to see the doctor and have been told you only have

---

Teacher Support Notes

① Without a Will: As enrichment you may want to tell students something about what happens when a person dies without a will. The state distributes that person's property according to its laws and often the family loses much of the property. Typically, much more of the estate goes toward taxes than is necessary. Without a will, the assets go, not to the people the person would have chosen, but to the people the state chooses.

② Handout—Living Will: Your supplementary material contains an example of a living will. You may want to check to see if these documents are legal and recognized in your state before you distribute this to students. Also, make sure that they understand the distinction between a living will and a more traditional will. Make sure that they understand that the living will deals exclusively with situations that result from a person being alive but unable to make decisions for himself or herself.

Fast Facts

Fifty percent of the people in the United States die without a will.

---

562 UNIT 6 The Life Cycle

want them to have. This can be a simple letter, carried in your wallet or given to your parent or guardian to keep for you. A good time to make a formal will is when you first marry or become a parent.

Another preparation worth the effort is to decide what you want done if you lose consciousness. In that case, other people will have to decide what will happen to you. You can make your wishes known ahead of time in a **living will.** Such a document states exactly how you want to be treated, should you become unable to decide for yourself. Some people wish to instruct their families to use no **life-support systems** after **brain death** has occurred. They may even instruct their families to "pull the plug" if such measures have been started. Other people who fear that relatives won't have their best interests at heart may request the opposite—that *every* measure be taken to save their lives, regardless of chances for recovery. If you have feelings one way or the other, put them in a living will. Not all states recognize the living will as a legal document. In such places a person must name a proxy who then can make decisions concerning medical treatments to prolong life.

You may not have complete control over what happens in all cases. Questions about **euthanasia,** for example, are still being debated by medical and legal professionals. If you want to die, should you be allowed to? If someone you love wants to die, should you let him or her? Should you help a person stay alive as long as possible? Decisions of all these kinds are faced daily.

A familiar case is that of the person who has a fatal illness, is unconscious, has no hope of recovery, and requires machines to stay alive. One argument is to do everything possible to prolong that person's life, on the theory that where there is life there is hope. Another opinion holds that to sup-

port life with no hope of recovery is to prolong the suffering of the dying. Clearly, it helps if the person has earlier made a living will. Most states now honor such wills, although each state places some restrictions on them.

Another choice you may make someday is whether to die in a hospital. Given the choice, many people prefer not to go to the hospital. They would rather die at home, using a **hospice** for support. A hospice is an agency that assists people with **terminal illnesses** and their families. The purpose is to allow a dying person to choose to stay at home—and, if appropriate, to die there—while staff people from the hospice help the family to care for the person and to deal with their own grief.

Hospice services are provided by a team of physicians, nurses, and a psychiatrist or psychologist; often social workers, members of the clergy, and trained volunteers assist as well. The hospice has a twofold mission: to control the dying person's pain and distressing symptoms, and to support the client and family psychologically and socially. Care for the family continues beyond the person's death into the grieving period.

Key Points *Preparation for death includes making a will, taking out insurance, making a living will, and learning about hospice services in your area.*

SECTION III REVIEW

Answer the following questions on a sheet of paper.
Learning the Vocabulary
The vocabulary terms in this section are *living will, life-support systems, brain death, euthanasia, hospice,* and *terminal illnesses.*
1. Match the following phrases with the appropriate terms:
   a. a support system for dying people and their families

562

a short time to live. After your initial shock, you decide what you want to do with the 24–48 hours you have left. You begin to think about the people in your life, the good relationships, the bad ones, and those relationships that have unfinished business (things left unsaid). You decide there are one or two people you must speak to before you die. There are things you must say before it is too late." Once you have described this situation,

have the students write a letter to one of those people as if there were only a short amount of time left. Assure them that no one else will see the letters. When they are finished with the letters, ask the following questions:
1. How many of you wrote something that you have never said to that person before? Why have you never chosen to say it? (fear of his/her reaction; fear of rejection)

2. Imagine that instead of you dying, the person you wrote to died before you got to say the things in that letter. Would you regret never having said these things?
3. If your answer is yes, you would regret it, ask yourself why you don't take the risk now and say the things you want to say.

On the other sheet of paper, ask them to write a letter to themselves, telling what they hope to accomplish over the next

(continued on next page)

---

   b. illnesses that are expected to end in death
   c. a term used to refer to mechanical means of supporting life
   d. allowing a person to die

Learning the Facts
2. Why is it natural to fear death?
3. How do near-death experiences change people's lives?
4. Describe ways in which people should prepare for their death.

Making Life Choices
5. Your parents are in their mid-50's. You want to talk to them about their will but death is a subject that is seldom discussed. How can you help your parents understand the importance of a living will? What can you say to them without hurting their feelings? How can you help make it easier for your family to talk about death?

MINI GLOSSARY

living will: a will that declares a person's wishes regarding treatment, should the person become unable to make decisions (for example, in the event of brain death).

life-support systems: a term used to refer to mechanical means of supporting life, such as feedings given into a central vein or machines that force air into the lungs.

brain death: irreversible, total loss of higher brain functions, reflected in a flat line brainwave pattern, as opposed to the wavy pattern made by an active brain.

① **euthanasia** (you-than-AY-zee-uh): allowing a person to die by choosing not to employ life-support equipment such as artificial respirators; or the removal of life-support equipment from a patient with no hope of recovery; both may be legal in some cases.

hospice (HOS-pis): a support system for dying people and their families, which helps the family let the person die at home with dignity and in comfort.

terminal illnesses: illnesses that are expected to end in death.

Answers to Fact or Fiction

Here are the answers to the questions at the start of the chapter.

1. False. The happiest people are those who have lived through at least one major life tragedy. **2.** False. The human life span has not changed, but the average life expectancy has increased steadily over the past 100 years. **3.** False. People remain sexual beings throughout life. **4.** True. **5.** False. Only a fraction of older people live in nursing homes.

---

year. They are to put both letters in the envelope, self-address, and stamp the envelope. Tell them they will receive this in one year to see if they made the most of the year or wasted it. (You'll have to remember to mail the letters in a year.) **(40–60 min., Critical Thinking)**

Opinions on Death Topics. Write the word "Agree" on one end of the board and "Disagree" on the other end. Explain to the students that you will be reading a statement to them. (A Teacher Information Sheet entitled "Death Topic Statements" can be found in the supple-

mentary materials.) If students agree with the statement, they are to go to the side of the room where "Agree" is written. If they disagree, they are to go to the other side of the room. Once they have chosen sides, each side will have a turn to defend its choice. If, once an opinion has been stated, someone changes his or her mind, that person can switch sides. Make sure the students understand that everyone is entitled to their own opinions, and

Teacher Support Notes

① **Teacher Information Sheet:** Your supplementary material contains an information sheet that provides you with additional descriptions of what people typically go through during each of these stages of grief.

✎ Fast Facts

Widows achieve a level of satisfaction with their lives equal to married women their ages according to a study by Ohio State University researchers. The sample included 61 widows and 96 married women ranging in age from 50 to 91. The widows were just as satisfied with their lives even though in the sample group the widows tended to have less income and education. Long-time widows tended to be more optimistic than recent widows.

S TRAIGHT T ALK — Helping Others Deal with Death and Grief

Grief is hard to deal with, especially for young people. Still, grief cannot be avoided. Those who know something about it are best prepared to deal with it and to help others do the same.

Grief is just awful pain, isn't it? What more is there to know about it?

Grief is painful at first, but it moves through several stages and ends with acceptance. Knowing what these stages are can help you manage grief. You can say to yourself, "What I am feeling is natural. This anger (or depression) is part of my grief." It still hurts, but understanding what you are going through can give you some feeling of control. That helps make it bearable.

The stages of grief are:

- Denial—"No, it can't be!"
- Anger—"It's not fair! It's too soon!"
- Bargaining—"I'll do anything; just don't let this happen."
- Depression—"There is no hope; I just want to be alone."
- Acceptance—"I am ready, now. It's all right."

It helps to know that you will feel these emotions, sometimes over and over again, in the process of accepting death—your own or someone else's. Not

everyone goes through all the stages, however, and they don't always come in the order shown here.

I have a friend who is dying, and I think I must be feeling grief already.

Of course you are grieving. Your friend is, too. People grieve not only at death but at all kinds of losses, and at the news that losses are to come.

Grief may make it seem as if joy will never come again.

The news that my friend is going to die is a shock to me. I find myself avoiding my friend.

Yes, that is not an uncommon reaction. We can be so shocked at the news that a death is coming that we feel we can't deal with it at all. It is natural to feel like avoiding your friend. This may help you postpone your feelings of pain, but it won't take the pain away. Furthermore, it certainly won't help your friend. Nothing you say can embarrass you, or hurt your friendship, or damage your self-esteem as badly as avoiding your friend until it is too late to help.

But I don't know what to say, and it frightens me how bad my friend is hurting.

You don't have to say smart things. Just be there. Even saying nothing is all right. This can show your friend you care, even though you can't take away the pain.

Don't say, "I know how you feel," though—that is, unless you really do. If you have never been in the same situation that your friend is

(Continued on next page)

that it is OK to disagree, as long as we don't attack the person. Once everyone has had a chance to speak, go to the next statement. If some students are not sure, they may stand in the middle, but must move one way or the other once both sides have spoken.

This activity can initiate such intense conversations that you may cover only three or four items. The format allows for the dissemination of information and opin-ions. Closure to the activity can include complimenting the students for their par-ticipation and asking them to highlight major points that were brought out during the discussions. **(one class period, Critical Thinking)**

STRAIGHT TALK (Continued)

in, a better answer is, "Yes, it must be hard," or "I can't imagine how you must be feeling." Don't look for positive things to say, either. Bad news is bad news. Don't refuse to listen to your friend's real feelings.

One of the most helpful things you can do is to give your friend a chance to talk. Anyone who is facing death has many thoughts and feelings that need expression. Listen. Let your friend share feelings of anger, frustration, or guilt. Let your friend tell you what to do to help.

Sometimes I forget the situation, and start to have fun. Then I remember, and I feel guilty.

One of the most important things for you to do is to take care of your own needs, and one of your needs is to be happy. Don't feel that you have to show grief all the time. In the strictest sense, much as you love your friend, the problem that someone is dying is not your problem. You are alive. You have the right to experience joy and happiness even at such a time.

How can I help the family of a friend who is dying? ①

Each person has different needs. It is especially important to pay attention to children in a grieving family, because they often feel lost and left out. Often, too, they don't understand what's happening, and they have irrational fears. Your attention can help them feel better.

One member of the family seems to be grieving forever. How can I make him stop?

Grief has no time limit. Many think that it takes about a year to get over someone's death. There is some truth to that, because a year permits every occasion (religious holidays, birthdays, anniversaries) to pass, once, without the person. Still, grief can spring to the heart years after a loss and be felt as keenly as if the person had died just yesterday.

Don't set limits on anyone's recovery time and don't feel you must grieve longer than your feelings say to. Everyone has a personal timetable for recovery. If you are ready to move on, do so.

A person who doesn't seem able to pull out of grief at all, for a very long time, may need help. Perhaps you can suggest that the person see a grief counselor—a professional who helps people to say their goodbyes and go on.

Even the most painful grief passes with time.

Once the family has adjusted to the loss, should we all try to forget the person who has died?

No, not at all. The very opposite is usually true. After someone close has died, the memory is still very much alive. It helps a family member to know that others are thinking of the person, too. Bring back and share memories: "Sis would have enjoyed this," or "I thought of your mom today." Remarks like these let the grieving person know that you, too, remember and miss the one who is gone.

When you arrive at the point of accepting a death, you may find you have gained a deeper serenity than you knew before, and a deeper joy in life.

Vocabulary
1. **a.** brain death **b.** life span **c.** senility
2. **a.** Menopause **b.** life expectancy
c. Alzheimer's disease
d. living will
3. Answers will vary.
4. **a.** hospice **b.** longevity
c. hot flashes **d.** terminal illnesses

Recall
Section I
1. Answers will vary; could include: self-sufficient, physically active, socially involved, clear thinking, fully participating members of society, happy, and healthy.
Section II
2. gradual loss of youthful appearance and condition, aging of cells and organs
3. genetic inheritance and events in life
4. maintain appropriate weight; sound nutrition, including ample water intake; adequate sleep; regular physical activity; avoidance of alcohol, tobacco, and other drug

abuse
5. Smoking causes early onset of menopause because it suppresses production of the hormone estrogen or because the ingredients of tobacco are directly toxic to the ovaries.
6. diminish in size and function
7. The more people exercise, the less likely they are to die of heart and lung diseases and more likely to fend off arthritis.
8. reasoning skill, recall (memory), spatial sense, speed, and senses
9. Preventable causes of mental confusion include abuse of drugs (including alcohol abuse, as well as misuse or incompatibility of prescription drugs); accidents (surgery can often relieve skull fractures or bleeding that puts pressure on the brain, caused by accidents); dehydration (older people do not sense thirst as easily, and a major symptom of dehydration is confusion); depression (slowing of the mind is caused); disease states (tuberculosis, diabetes, and even heart attacks can all

---

CHAPTER REVIEW

LEARNING THE VOCABULARY

life span
life expectancy
longevity
menopause
hot flashes

male menopause
senility
Alzheimer's disease
living will
life-support systems

brain death
euthanasia
hospice
terminal illnesses

Answer the following questions on a separate sheet of paper.

1. **Matching**—*Match each of the following phrases with the appropriate vocabulary term or phrase from the list above:*
   a. irreversible, total loss of higher brain functions
   b. maximum years of life a human being can live
   c. general term meaning weakness of mind and body occurring in old age
2. a. _____ is the time in a woman's life when ovulation and menstruation cease.
   b. The number of years an individual can expect to live, based on hereditary and other factors, is called _____.
   c. _____ is a brain disease of some older people that brings mental confusion, inability to function, and in the final state, death.

   d. A _____ is a will that declares a person's wishes regarding treatment in case the person becomes unable to decide for himself or herself.
3. Write a paragraph using as many of the vocabulary terms as you can. Underline each term that you use.
4. **Word Scramble**—*Use the clues from the phrases below to help you unscramble the vocabulary terms from the list above:*
   a. **eiochps** _____ a support system for dying people and their families
   b. **eoiyglntv** _____ an individual's length of life
   c. **oht aefhlss** _____ _____ sudden waves of feeling hot all over
   d. **aeilmnrt einslsesl** _____ _____ illnesses that are expected to end in death

RECALLING IMPORTANT FACTS AND IDEAS

1. List some characteristics that describe most people who are in their later years.
2. After growth is completed, what does aging bring about?
3. What two things could increase your longevity?
4. Describe strategies to help slow the aging process.
5. What effect does smoking have on menopause in women?
6. Explain what physically happens to the sex organs with age.
7. How can exercise enhance the quality of your life?

8. List the five areas in the brain and nervous system that are affected by aging.
9. Discuss the preventable causes of mental confusion in older people.
10. Describe how Alzheimer's disease progresses in an older person's brain.
11. Why is financial planning so essential for people who are aging?
12. Describe why it is important to maintain a strong support system.
13. Discuss why it is important to continue your education forever.
14. How can we view death in a healthy way?
15. What changes occur in many people who learn that they will die soon?

begin with confusion); disuse of mental skills (people lose what they don't use); malnutrition (older people eat less because taste enjoyment, digestive secretions, and appetite diminish as nutrition needs stay the same); and poor vision and hearing (both cause confusion).

10. In the brain, the nerve pathways become tangled and blocked, cutting off the memory functions.

11. Nearly everyone suffers a loss of income, made worse by inflation, in the retirement years. There must be enough money set aside to pay for rent and have insurance to cover medical and other expenses.

12. to create a web of support so that as relationships are lost, others are gained

13. New information stimulates new thinking and exercises the mind. A sharp mind is less likely to become confused in old age.

Section III

14. by thinking about death and expressing our fears

15. they start enjoying life as they never have before; the way they spend their time becomes more important, trying to make the most of every moment

16. Death reminds us to not wait until tomorrow to do what we wish to do today.

Straight Talk

17. Denial—"No, it can't be."
Anger—"It's not fair! It's too soon!"
Bargaining—"I'll do anything; just don't let this happen."
Depression—"There is no hope; I just want to be alone."
Acceptance—"I am ready, now. It's all right."

18. at least a year, but the grief could remain in the heart forever

19. It helps a family member know that others are thinking of the person. It lets the grieving person know that you, too, remember and miss the one who is gone.

---

16. How does death act as a reminder to us?

17. List and identify the stages of grief.

18. How long should a person grieve?

19. Why is it important to talk about someone who has died?

CRITICAL THINKING

1. Figure 22–1 on page 553 gives you a list of preventable vs. unavoidable changes with age. You cannot do anything about the unavoidable changes of aging, but you can do something about the preventable changes. What can you do to prevent all these changes? Are you practicing these behaviors now? Are your parents and grandparents doing things to prevent or delay some of the changes that come with aging?

2. At what age do you think it is appropriate to make out a will? When are you going to make out a will? Are you going to make a living will? What are some of the problems relatives face when a living will has not been written?

3. After reading the Straight Talk, "Helping Others Deal with Death and Grief" on page 564, do you feel you are better prepared to face the loss of a friend? How about a family member? What have you learned about dealing with death? Do you have a grief therapist in your area? What will you do to help others deal with grief?

ACTIVITIES

1. Visit a nursing home in your area and adopt a grandparent. Visit this person for at least five weeks and talk with the person at least once each week for an hour. Write a report about your experience.

2. Create a pamphlet about grief and the stages one goes through when dealing with grief. Make sure you have addresses and phone numbers of professionals in your area who deal with grief.

3. Have a class debate on euthanasia. Do you think terminally ill patients should have the right to die? What would you want your family to do if you were terminally ill?

4. Make a list of things you need to do to prepare for your funeral.

5. Watch television for an hour and write down all the commercials that deal with aging and the elderly. What are the products' claims? Do you think their claims are fraudulent?

MAKING DECISIONS ABOUT HEALTH

1. Gladys and Sylvia are seniors in high school and are best friends. They had talked about everything together for as long as they could remember. On her way home from school one day, Gladys was in a terrible car accident. She was in a coma and put on a respirator. The girls had talked about death several times and agreed that they never wanted to be kept alive by a machine. Sylvia went to the hospital every day and talked to Gladys with no change ever taking place. Sylvia told Gladys' parents of their discussion about life-support systems. Sylvia suggested letting Gladys die peacefully. Gladys' parents didn't agree. They felt that as long as Gladys' heart was beating they had a chance for a miracle. They have been keeping Gladys alive for the past six months.

How would you feel if you were Sylvia knowing your best friend didn't want to live like this? What action would you take if you were Sylvia? Why would you take that action? What could Gladys have done to avoid this situation completely?

CHAPTER 23 PLANNER

OVERVIEW

Chapter 23 is 24 pages long and divided into the seven sections listed to the right. Major learning outcomes are also listed to the right. Briefly, this chapter introduces students to the concept of accident and injury prevention in various aspects of daily living. The chapter also introduces students to some key concepts and skills necessary to take care of themselves in some life-threatening situations.

MAKING LIFE CHOICES RESOURCES

A variety of activities, handouts, quizzes, and tests to accompany this chapter are available in the *Making Life Choices* supplementary material. You may pick and choose from those materials as appropriate for your amount of class time and the ability levels of your students. One of the resources you might want to consider using is:

Handouts
• Fire Safety Checklist
• Guest Speaker Follow-Up Worksheet

SUGGESTED RESOURCES

Student Readings
1. Bever, David L. *Safety: A Personal Focus.* St. Louis: The C. V. Mosby Co., 1987.
Teacher Readings
1. Waller, Julian. *Injury*

Control: A Guide to the Causes and Prevention of Trauma. Lexington, Mass: Lexington Books, 1985.

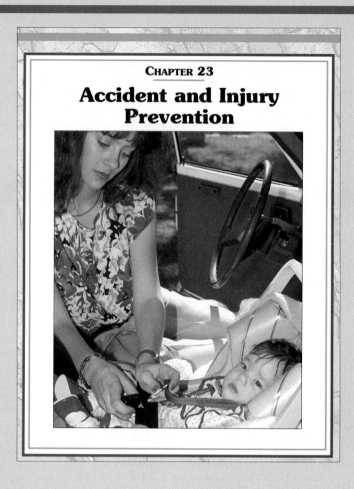

CHAPTER 23
Accident and Injury Prevention

CHAPTER PROJECT

Have the students choose, or you can assign students to either visit or call one of the following agencies to find out what educational safety programs are available in the community. Match as closely as possible each section in this chapter with an agency. Some possibilities are:
1. safety commission; 2. American Heart Association;
3. American Red Cross; 4. fire marshal; 5. hospital;
6. sheriff's department; 7. U.S. Coast Guard; 8. forest rangers; 9. wildlife and game commission; 10. State Division of Parks and Recreation

Activity To Introduce Chapter

Borrow or purchase from your local chapter of the American Red Cross, the video entitled "The American Red Cross Emergency Test" hosted by John Ritter. This video comes with official video test score cards to use for student responses as they watch the video. A score analysis is discussed at the close of the video. The video addresses all the topics discussed in this chapter plus others. Discuss the statement, "Accidents are almost always a result of human error." Before

OUTCOMES

After reading and studying this chapter, you will be able to:

✓ Describe how being a defensive driver can reduce your risk of accidents.
✓ List specific guidelines for preventing fires and burns.
✓ Explain how to reduce the risk of accidents at home, during swimming, boating, biking, and during play.
✓ Describe how to prepare for natural disasters.
✓ Describe how to defend against aggression.
✓ List the safety precautions for child care.

CONTENTS

I. Highway Accidents
II. Home Safety
III. Burns
IV. Safety During Swimming, Boating, Biking, and Other Play
V. Preparedness for Natural Disasters
VI. Defenses against Aggression
VII. Care of Others: Child Care

Straight Talk: Fire Prevention and Escape

FACT OR FICTION

What do you think? *Are the following statements true or false? If you think they are false, then say what is true.*

1. One out of every ten people suffers an injury every year.
2. Injuries claim more young lives each year in the United States than do any diseases, even AIDS.
3. The primary characteristic you need to prevent accidents on the road is driving skill.
4. Of all parts of the body, the head affects balance the most.
5. The emergency telephone number in most parts of the United States is 911.
6. You can injure your back picking up a feather.
7. Everyone knows how to take care of children; it's just a matter of plain, common sense.

(Answers on page 587)

■ **Reminder:** Knowing how to study can increase your knowledge, improve your grades, *and* cut down on your study time. See the *Studying Health* section at the front of your text for some suggestions to help you study this chapter.

After students are assigned an agency, suggest that they gather the following information:

1. Type of educational information available: life-saving courses offered, literature, guest speaking, TV spots, advertisements, brochures
2. When the information is available
3. How you obtain the information
4. How much it costs
5. Where the agency is located

Have the students compile a report on the information.

---

you show the video, tell students that after it's finished you will be asking for examples from the video that suppport this statement.

As an additional activity to kick off the chapter, have the students respond to the Life Choice Inventory on page 572. They should score themselves. Ask them to identify four things they could do to improve their scores.

NOT ENOUGH TIME?*

You could easily spend four or five days teaching this chapter. If the students read the entire chapter, do a fair number of the suggested activities in the teacher's edition, and complete a sampling of the handouts from the resource material accompanying this text. It is likely, however, that you will have only two or three days to devote to this chapter. The following are some suggestions to help you make sure that you cover the key topics if you have limited time.

TIME	SUGGESTIONS
1 Day	Do Activity 1.1 to introduce the chapter, to promote awareness, and to stimulate thought about safety in their own activities. For homework before beginning this chapter, assign students to read the chapter.
2 Days	On day 2, because this chapter is so diverse, select one or two sections to emphasize depending on the most prominent needs of your students. For example, if most of your students drive and accidents are high, select one or two activities from Section I. Conclude the class with the quiz given under the Evaluate for this section.
3 Days	On day 3, divide the class into the same number of groups as remaining sections you want to teach. Assign each group one of these sections along with your choice of an activity for that section. Allow student groups one half of the class time to prepare a five-minute class presentation to be given during the remainder of class. This should highlight the key points of the chapter for the benefit of the entire class.

*Please refer to the 18-week daily lesson plans in the supplementary material for additional suggestions.

Answers to "Fact or Fiction"

1. False. One out of every three, not ten, people suffers an injury each year. **2.** True. **3.** False. Skill is important, but attitude is equally important in preventing accidents on the road. **4.** True. **5.** True. **6.** True. **7.** False. To deliver competent child care, you have to do some formal learning.

In this section students will learn that:
1. With car accidents causing nearly one half of all accidents, defensive driving is the key to saving lives.
2. Driving skills, knowledge, and judgment are dependent on driver attitude for preventing automobile accidents.

3. Responsible driving precautions are necessary for preventing automobile accidents.

Activity 1.1
Accident Statistics. Invite a guest speaker from the local AAA Safety Division or city/state Motor Vehicle Safety Commission to present statistics on auto accidents, injuries, and fatalities in your area. An alternative would be to ask

these agencies to supply you with current local statistics to present yourself. Ask students to write down the statistic most surprising to them and explain why. Discuss the statistics and student reactions to the statistics in class . **(30 min.; Extend, Enrich)**

Activity 1.2
Bumper Stickers. Have students design a bumper sticker to promote safe

Teacher Support Notes

① **Spontaneity vs. Caution:** Some students may need to be told that spontaneity means to do something on the spur of the moment without thinking about it; to react instantly. Ask them if they can think of situations where they, or friends of theirs, have acted spontaneously while others have been more cautious. In general, do students tend to be more spontaneous or more cautious?

② **Accidents:** Ask students what injuries and accidents they have experienced in the last year or so. Have them give details of what happened. Could the accidents have been prevented? Had they done anything to prevent what could have been a worse injury?

📖 Fast Facts

Injuries that could have been avoided claim the lives of 8,000 children 14 and under each year, and permanently disfigure 50,000 more. According to the National Safe Kids Campaign chaired by former U.S. Surgeon General C. Everett Koop, M.D., 90% of all permanent childhood injuries could be avoided.

570

Whatever age you are, you probably know things you wish you had known sooner. But have you ever noticed that when you try to tell others of what you have learned, they seem uninterested in your advice? Being careful is boring, and until accidents happen, they seem unlikely. If only people could learn to be careful enough to avoid getting hurt without losing spontaneity and joy in life!

We should note right away that not all accidents and injuries are preventable, of course. Some just happen. But many accidents and injuries are preventable.

This year, chances are that one out of every three people you know will suffer an injury. Among injuries nationwide are tens of thousands of brain and spinal cord injuries leading to permanent disability. Injuries claim more young lives than any disease does.

Relatively little attention has been paid to this major public health problem. Older adults usually die of heart disease or cancer, so those diseases get most of the public's attention. Young people more often die of accidents and injuries. When you consider that a young person who dies loses more years of life than an older person, and then count the years of life lost, accidents and injuries suddenly take first place. Figure 23–1 shows the toll they take, not in terms of lives lost, but in terms of *years* of life lost. Because accidents and injuries rob the young of their useful lives, this whole chapter is devoted to accident and injury prevention.

Answering the questions in this chapter's Life Choice Inventory can help you find out whether you are now skilled in accident prevention or whether you have more to learn. Young people, once they realize that accidents are likely to affect them, are often willing to learn how to prevent accidents.

Key Points *Injuries from preventable accidents claim more young lives than do any diseases. It's left to individuals to prevent accidents.*

SECTION I

① # Highway Accidents

Nearly half of the accidents that take place are car accidents. Good drivers do not usually cause them, but they do have them—because some accidents are unpreventable. Until you have had an accident, it is hard to believe that such a thing is possible. Remember, though, that accidents are not deliberate. You do not see them coming; you do not expect them; you do not have time to avoid them. Just think about the last time you cut yourself even slightly. You did not mean to. The trouble was, you did not see that it was about to happen. The control was not all in your hands.

The Likelihood of a Collision

A lot of people buried in cemeteries had only one car accident in their lives. Knowledge and skill are not enough to prevent car accidents. An equally important aspect of the driver is attitude. Consider the attitudes of two different drivers. Attitude 1 is, "I never have accidents. I'm in control." A person with attitude 1 simply goes out and drives, unaware of potential hazards. Attitude 2 is, "The control is not all in my hands. I need to be aware of other drivers and watch for possible accidents about to happen." A person with attitude 2 drives defensively.

For a person to move from attitude 1 to attitude 2, no more is required than to translate statistics into real-life events. Is that car you see coming from the right going to run through that intersection in driving. (You could assign Activity #11 on page 591 of the student text.). Choose the best ones. Have other teachers judge first place and get your graphic arts or other appropriate department to print the sticker for sale within your school and community. This project can be a great fund-raiser for your school, clubs, or class. **(30 min.; Extend, Enrich)**

Activity 1.3

Accident-Prone? Write the term "accident-prone" on the board. Ask students to define the term. Ask them to identify behaviors of an accident-prone person and list them on the board. Students should then identify which behaviors could be changed and what cautious behaviors could be substituted for the accident-prone behaviors. Have students draw a conclusion from this activity. For example: "All behaviors can be changed

to reflect safety consciousness." **(15 min., Critical Thinking)**

TEACH
SECTION 1
(Guided and Independent Practice)

Activity 1.4
Accident Prevention. Collect newspaper articles detailing all types of vehicle accidents (auto, bicycle, motorcy-

(continued on next page)

Percentage of Total Years of Life Lost to Various Causes[a]

Accidents and Violence[b]	31%
Cancer	15%
Heart and Disease	11%
Birth Defects	5%
AIDS[c]	5%
Premature Birth	3%
SIDS[d]	3%
Stroke	2%
Liver Disease	2%

This top bar shows the causes of death that most often strike the young.

0%   5%   10%   15%   20%   25%   30%   35%

[a] This graph shows percentage of total years of life lost to various causes in the United States, 1991. The causes shown add up to 77% of total years of life lost. Other, lesser causes account for the remaining 23%, in increments smaller than 2% each.

[b] These causes account for 31 percent of all years prematurely lost. Of the 31 percent, 18 percent are lost to accidents and 15 percent to aggression (murder) and self-inflicted violence (suicide).

[c] AIDS is acquired immune deficiency syndrome, a disease transmitted by exchange of body fluids, usually via sexual activity or the use of infected needles used to administer drugs.

[d] SIDS is sudden infant death syndrome, death of infants due to unknown causes.

Figure 23–1 Years of Life Lost to Accidents and Injuries, United States, 1991   ①

front of you? No, it's not. And the next car? No, it's not, either. In fact, the chances are only 1 in 10,000 that you will be going through an intersection just as a car drives out in front of you.

So how long will it be before a car does

run in front of you just as you are driving through an intersection? If you pass through enough intersections (say, ten a day), then it will take 1,000 days, on the average, for you to encounter this event 10,000 times. A thousand days is three

Teacher Support Notes

① **Years of Life Lost:** Point out to students that each of these bars represents *years*. For example, more people might have died of cancer than died of accidents, but most of those dying of cancer did so later in life. Therefore, not as many years were lost. Or, if a five-year-old were killed in an auto accident, 69 years of life would be lost (74 − 5 = 69); but, if a person died of cancer at the age of 74, no years would be lost. If this is the first time that students have looked at the seriousness of different death-causing events, ask them if they think this is worthwhile, or misleading. If they were in a position of power and had to decide how federal money was to be spent to promote health, would they use a chart such as this one, looking at years of life lost, or would they look at numbers—how many people died of particular causes—to determine the most serious problem?

cle, etc.) and ask students to choose one, read it, and write an analysis as to cause(s). They should also suggest possible ways the accidents could have been prevented. An alternative would be to obtain some copies of old accident reports from police or insurance compa-

nies and do the same activity. Develop a folder of articles for these types of accidents, which can be shared with classes in the future. **(20 min.; Reteach, Reinforce)**

Activity 1.5
Insurance Speaker. Ask a representative of a local auto insurance company to speak to the class about statistics on driver's education courses reducing

the number of accidents and how driver's education courses affect the insurance rates. Ask students to comment on this and whether or not they plan on taking a driver's education course. Have the students examine the findings with their parents, since many students get their first car insurance on their parents' policies. **(30 min., Critical Thinking)**

Activity 1.6

Teacher Support Notes

① **Safety Assessment:** Encourage the students to take the questions in this Life Choice Inventory seriously. They should stop and think about the ways in which they typically confront the type of situations mentioned before they answer. If they do this, their scores should be a fairly good indication of whether or not they are conscious of safety and acting in a cautious manner. Discuss the scores in class. What is the range from high to low? What is the average? Would anyone like to change his or her level of safety consciousness?

LIFE **C**HOICE **I**NVENTORY

How Safety-Conscious Are You? ①

Answer these questions to find out whether you are now doing all you reasonably should do to prevent accidents, or whether you have room for improvement in this respect.

1. I have taken a first aid course (or I have made plans to take one).
2. I have taken a driver education course (or I plan to take one before I begin to drive).
3. When driving, I always slow down when approaching an intersection (or I am sure I will do this when I begin to drive).
4. I always buckle my safety belt when driving or riding in a car.
5. I never drink or use drugs and then drive (or I am sure I would never do this).
6. I cross the street at crosswalks only; I do not jaywalk.
7. I keep my home (room) in order, with no objects or cords on the floor that might trip people.
8. I use a stepladder for climbing and reaching.
9. I keep a fire extinguisher where I can get to it in case of fire and I know how to use it.
10. I know how I would escape from my bedroom in case of fire.
11. I never smoke in bed (or I do not smoke).
12. I dispose of my trash regularly.
13. I have my community's emergency phone numbers right by the phone.
14. I can swim (or I have made plans to learn to swim).
15. I obey all safety rules around water and boats.
16. I read and heed all label directions on containers of chemicals and drugs.
17. Children are not likely to hurt themselves in my home (room).
18. I maintain all electrical equipment as instructed; I replace old cords and plugs or have them replaced by a qualified person.
19. I know how to avoid back injury when lifting an object, and I practice what I know.
20. I keep containers of drinkable water available where I live.
21. I am on guard against the risks of aggression by strangers and people I know.
22. I know and abide by the rules for safe care of children.
23. I know how to perform the Heimlich maneuver.

SCORING

Give yourself 1 point for each yes answer.
20–23: You are a safety-conscious person.
16–19: You have a few more refinements to make on your choices.
11–15: You have a lot of room for improvement.
10 or below: You need to make major efforts to improve your safety awareness and behavior.

Air Bags. For extra credit, have students call a local car dealership and ask about the current status of air bags in their new cars and the future plans for air bags. Have the students report the information to the class. To further promote the idea of air bags in cars, have a panel discussion with students pretending to be executives of leading car companies in the United States. Discuss the necessity vs. the cost of safety precautions available in cars. **(30 min., Advanced)**

Activity 1.7
Inspection Information. For extra credit, students may take their cars to the highway safety inspection center and gather the following information for reporting to the class: **1.** What is inspected? **2.** What are the criteria for passing inspection? **3.** How long does a driver have to make repairs? **4.** Is inspection required? If not, why not? **(5 min. for explanation, Advanced)**

Activity 1.8
Safety Belts. Ask students to respond in writing on a 5 × 7 index card to one of the following statements:
a. I always wear a safety belt. I have been most influenced to do this because . . .

(continued on next page)

Accidents will happen.

Knowledge and skill are not enough to prevent accidents.

years. Thus if you accumulate a total of 30 years' driving experience in your life, it is almost inevitable that ten times in your life a car will unexpectedly pull out in front of you as you pass through an intersection. That it will happen once is virtually certain. You cannot know when, but it will occur.

② You can probably avoid collisions if you approach every intersection, all your driving life, with the thought that a car may suddenly pull out in front of you. With that in mind, you will slow down, you will be ready to turn or hit the brake, and you will be planning ahead to avoid colliding with the cars next to you and behind you. That is the spirit of defensive driving as it applies to one of hundreds of driving situations. Defensive driving saves thousands of lives each year; it can save yours.

Key Points *It is a certainty that every driver will encounter other drivers who are careless. Defensive driving saves lives.*

The Defensive Driving Attitude

The instructor of a defensive driving course warns the pupils: "At the end of this course, you'll have an exam. It's a long exam. It's a tough exam. If you miss any one question, you'll fail it." Then, on the last day, the instructor doesn't give an exam on paper. Instead, he or she explains, "The exam is outside this room. You will start taking it when you get back in your car to drive home. It will go on for the rest of your life. Every time you get on the road, you'll be taking this exam. And if you miss one question, you fail it."

① Driver's education courses reduce accidents. As a result, automobile insurance rates are lower for drivers who have had driver's education courses.

③ Judgment is also essential to driving safety; in fact it is just as important as skill. Driving skill is the person's ability to control the vehicle under all road conditions. Driving judgment is the driver's ability to recognize a potential accident and to know how to avoid it. The use of both skill and judgment, the Red Cross points out, depends on the driver's *attitude*.

Part of the defensive driving attitude is self-defense against injury. Defensive drivers buckle their lap belts (not just their shoulder belts) whenever driving and insist that passengers do the same. Some people claim that safety belts injure people in accidents. They sometimes do, but far more often,

b. I do not always, or I do not ever wear a safety belt because . . .

Students should begin their responses with the words from **a** or **b**.

Place the index cards on the board in two columns titled "YES to Safety Belts" and "NO to Safety Belts." Discuss the choices and reasonings. Help students dispel any myths they've heard. (i.e., It is better to be thrown from the vehicle, than to be stuck in a safety belt.) **(15 min., Critical Thinking)**

Activity 1.9
Risky Thoughts. Ask students to write a paragraph or two expressing their feelings about the common thought or belief that we all experience when we are engaging in an activity that has a certain amount of risk involved. ("It will never happen to me") Included in their reports can be any personal experiences that show they didn't think they would get hurt, but did. **(15 min., Critical Thinking)**

EVALUATE
SECTION I

Activity 1.10

Teacher Support Notes

① **Teen Views Follow-Up Questions:** Following are some questions to help promote classroom discussion of the ideas expressed by the students in this feature:

a. Several of the students mention situations involving trains and railroad tracks; ask if these sorts of activities are common in your area.

b. Have students ever been scared in a car driven by someone else, but were afraid to ask the person to slow down or stop because of possible embarrassment?

c. Have students noticed any distracting behaviors such as those mentioned by Keith Peterson? How dangerous are these practices?

d. Ask students how prevalent drinking and driving is in their community among teenagers. Among adults? Do they think penalties are stiff enough? Too stiff?

e. Amanda Schell believes stress can have a negative impact upon a person's driving actions. Have they ever witnessed examples of how stress has negatively affected a driver?

TEEN **V**IEWS *What unsafe driving behaviors have you noticed?* ①

People get hurt or killed trying to beat a train or by jumping railroad tracks. I have experienced this and it isn't fun, especially if you're in someone else's car, or you have to answer to your parents. **Terry Hicks, 16, Carter High School, TN**

I am amazed at the risks people take while they drive. I have seen women putting on makeup, people eating, and a few even reading the paper. **Keith Peterson, 16, Duluth East High School, MN**

Many people drink and drive. Most of them think they can never be hurt. After my cousin was killed driving drunk, reality set in—it can happen to anyone. I will never drink and drive. **Tricia Reeves, 15, Robert E. Lee High School, TX**

I've seen a group of kids playing "chicken" with their cars on the railroad tracks near my house. Playing games with a train isn't high on my priority list. I don't like games where if you lose you never get a chance to play again. **Christy Hart, 16, Orange Park High School, FL**

Stress is hard to deal with and when you're disturbed you should not get behind the wheel. **Amanda Schell, 15, Sharon High School, PA**

they save lives. The safest people are as motivated as the person (call her Susan) who says she cannot even repark her car without first buckling her safety belt. Buckling up becomes an effortless, unconscious action.

Susan explains that a driving instructor told her, "Think of your unprotected body flying through the air at 50 miles an hour and suddenly hitting a stationary car dashboard. When you are driving at 50 miles an hour, both your car and your body are moving *independently* at that speed. If the car hits something and stops, you'll keep flying at 50 miles an hour until *you* hit something." A safety belt slows a person's momentum as the car's momentum decreases. It distributes the force of the impact across the body's strongest parts. Also, it keeps the driver behind the wheel and in control, able to prevent further collisions.

Being thrown from the vehicle is not an advantage in a collision. Rather, it increases

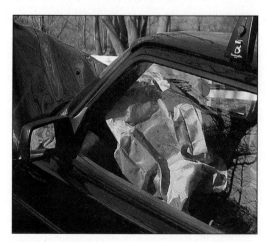

Airbags save lives.

Pop Quiz.

1. Driving _____ is the driver's ability to recognize a potential accident and know how to avoid it. (judgment)

2. The use of skill and judgment, when driving, depends on the driver's _____. (attitude)

3. Half of all fatal driving accidents involve _____. (alcohol)

4. _____ sometimes cause injuries in auto accidents, but more often they save lives. (Safety belts)

5. In addition to themselves, drivers should be responsible for protecting their _____. (passengers)

6. _____ _____ courses reduce accidents. (Driver's education)

7. Half of all the accidents that take place are _____ accidents. (auto)

8. One sign of an impaired driver is _____. (See "How to Avoid Alcohol-Related Driving Accidents." Answers will vary.)

CLOSE
SECTION 1

Activity 1.11
Review Questions. Before going on to the next lesson, students should be able to answer these questions:

(continued on next page)

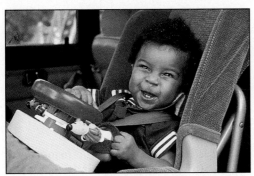

Until infants are three months old, they should face the rear of the car.

Infants and children over three months should be protected as shown.

the chances of death 25 times. Safety belts keep you inside and safe.

Two other pieces of safety equipment are important: **head restraints** to prevent whiplash injury, and **airbags** to cushion the body's impact with the dashboard. Head restraints are provided on all cars sold in this country, while airbags may still be optional equipment.

Drivers need to learn to protect their babies, children, and passengers, too. Strap the baby into a certified child passenger carrier every time you ride in the car. Safety belts alone do not protect young children well enough. Make sure children in the back seat are always buckled in. And if you have automatic self-closing shoulder belts, make sure that you and your passengers buckle their lap belts. Shoulder belts without lap belts can injure people badly.

The responsible driver also:

- Keeps the vehicle in good condition—tires, windshield wipers, horn, lights, brakes, wheel alignment, and steering mechanism.
- Wipes or washes all windows clean before starting the car.
- Wears glasses, if needed.
- Adjusts driving to different driving conditions.
- Obeys traffic signs and all regulations.

- Watches for pedestrians and bicyclists.
- Does not drive after drinking alcohol or after taking drugs that cause drowsiness, or when emotional, anxious, distracted, irritated, or tired.

This last item is especially important. Half of all fatal driving accidents involve alcohol. Many others involve other mind-altering drugs. The most important steps you can take to protect yourself against car accidents are never to ride with a driver who has been drinking, and never to get behind the wheel if you have been drinking yourself.

Keep in mind that being tired or upset can impair your driving, too. The more urgently you want to get where you are going, the more important it is for you to resist pushing yourself. If you are tired, admit it. Stop and rest. Beyond this, the

MINI GLOSSARY

head restraints: high seatbacks or other devices attached to seats in cars at head level. A head restraint prevents the person's head from snapping back too far when the body is thrown backward. This prevents neck and spinal cord injuries.

airbags: inflatable pillows, designed to inflate upon impact, stored in the center of the steering wheel of a car or in the dashboard.

Teacher Support Notes

① **Safe Automobiles:** Ask students if any of the automobiles owned by members of their families are in need of repair. Are any of the items mentioned here faulty? Ask students to imagine a situation in which this faulty part could cause an accident that might otherwise be prevented. If they are not sure of the condition of their family automobiles, have them check out these parts and report back to class. You might also want to have the students do some research to determine the cost of fixing various problems and have them compare the costs to the potential damage should an accident occur.

Fast Facts

According to former Surgeon General C. Everett Koop, 1,700 young people every year are killed in automobile crashes. Five hundred of those lives could be saved if all children were wearing seat belts.

CLOSE
(Continued)

1. Name the four necessary aspects of defensive driving.
2. List four responsibilities of a driver in preventing accidents.
3. Identify four guidelines for recognizing driving under the influence of alcohol or drugs.

4. Name two safety precautions taken in the manufacture of an automobile to ensure driver protection.
5. Name four things that affect insurance rates for teenagers.
   Discuss the answers to these questions in class.

Activity 1.12
Essay. Have students write a short essay about a situation (either made up

or real) that exemplifies "The Spirit of Defensive Driving." They should include the safe habit(s), the safe act(s), and the accident avoided.

FOCUS
SECTION II

In this section students will learn:
1. Several ways to prevent slips, trips, and falls when reaching and climbing.

---

66 Thoughts on Health 99

Danger for danger's sake is senseless.
— Leigh Hunt

Teacher Support Notes

① **Reporting Dangerous Drivers:** Ask students if they have ever seen any of the driving behaviors described above. Ask them to recount the situation, then ask if they reported that driver to the police. Why or why not?

Section I Review

Answers

1. Head restraints
2. Airbags
3. Answers will vary.
4. accidents and injuries
5. *Driving skill* is the person's ability to control the vehicle under all road conditions, and *driving judgment* is the driver's ability to recognize a potential accident and to know how to avoid it.
6. Shoulder belts used without lap belts can injure people. Shoulder belts used in conjunction with lap belts distribute the force of an accident across the body's strongest parts. They also keep the driver behind the wheel.
7. Answers will vary.

HEALTH
STRATEGIES

How to Avoid Alcohol-related Driving Accidents

Alcohol and drugs are involved in the great majority of serious accidents each year. To protect yourself:

1. Don't get into a car with anyone who has been drinking.
2. If driving yourself, watch out for any other driver who:

   • Drives very slowly or fast.
   • Stops without an apparent reason.
   • Swerves, weaves, or straddles the center line.
   • Just misses hitting other vehicles or objects.
   • Drives into oncoming traffic.
   • Turns abruptly or illegally.
   • Fails to obey traffic signs and signals or is slow to obey.
   • Drives with a window down in cold weather.
   • Drives with headlights off after dark.

3. If such a driver is in front of you, stay a safe distance behind.
4. If you are in front, get off the road as soon as possible.
5. To help protect others, note the license number if you can. Report it to the police as soon as possible. ①

suggestions made in the Health Strategies section on this page, "How to Avoid Alcohol-related Driving Accidents," can help you avoid becoming a victim of someone else's drunk driving.

In a letter to columnist Ann Landers (January 3, 1992), a professional driver

offers three changes in driving habits that he believes would save lives:

1. Look over your shoulder when changing lanes. Don't rely on mirrors.
2. Keep a safe distance from the car in front of you. If you can read the license plate, you are too close.
3. After a red light turns green, pause for a good five seconds before proceeding. "I have seen too many cars zip right through those lights at 60 miles an hour," he says.

All of these statements about attitude apply equally to motorcyclists. In addition, motorcyclists must use safety techniques specific to them (the highway patrol offers courses in these). They should wear helmets, whether or not they are required by law to do so.

Key Points *Driver attitude is important in preventing collisions. Defensive drivers take precautions against injuries by wearing safety belts. They take precautions against accidents by attending to the condition of the vehicle, and of the driver.*

SECTION I   REVIEW

Answer the following questions on a sheet of paper.
Learning the Vocabulary
The vocabulary terms in this section are *head restraints* and *airbags*.
1. _____ prevent a person's head from snapping back too far when the body is thrown backward in a car.
2. _____ are stored in the center of the car's steering wheel and inflate on impact.
3. Write a sentence using each vocabulary term.

Learning the Facts
4. What is the number-one killer of young people?
5. Why are driving skill and driving judgment essential?

2. Several ways to prevent work and leisure-time accidents.

Activity 2.1

Injury Articles. Have students find articles that indicate situations where precautions were not taken at home and a preventable injury in the form of a fall or careless use of tools, toys, guns, or other items occurred. Have students pair up and discuss the articles. They should decide what could have prevented the accidents. Keep a file of these articles for future classes. **(15 min.; Reteach, Reinforce)**

TEACH

> **SECTION II**
> (Guided and Independent Practice)

Activity 2.2

Home Safety. Discuss the safety tips suggested in this section to prevent slips and trips at home. Have students decide if slips and trips are regularly occurring in their own homes and what they could do to correct the situation. Ask the students to discuss their findings with their families and suggest changes. If a student and his or her family have made changes, have them report on these changes once they have been implemented. **(10 min.; Reteach, Reinforce)**

6. Why should lap belts always be used when shoulder belts are used?

Making Life Choices

7. Answer the following questions that apply to driving regulations:
   a) Do you think that every licensed driver should be required to take a driving test every few years? Why, or why not?
   b) Do you think that people convicted of drunk driving should lose their licenses permanently on the first offense? Why, or why not?
   c) What do you think are the most common reasons why people do not wear safety belts? Should every state in our nation have a mandatory seat belt law for all drivers and passengers? Why, or why not?

SECTION II

Home Safety

Second to highway accidents, falls cause the most accidental deaths. Statistics demonstrate that for each person, sooner or later, one accidental fall will likely be a devastating one. The same attitude that prevents driving accidents works for falls. Anticipation and defensive action against falls can prevent them. Most falls happen at home. To prevent slips and trips:

- Wipe up spills.
- Use nonslip floor wax.
- Secure small rugs. Do not use them at tops and bottoms of staircases.
- Clean up snow in walking areas. Use sand or salt on icy spots.
- Keep a safety mat in the bathtub, and install handholds on the wall.
- Be careful in wet grass, especially with a power mower.
- Repair torn and frayed carpet promptly.

- Keep walking areas clear and the yard picked up.
- Keep stairs and hallways well lighted—install handrails.

① To prevent falls that occur when climbing or reaching:

- Use a sturdy ladder. Do not use makeshift piles of furniture or boxes.
- Inspect the ladder before you use it.
- Never paint a ladder. Paint hides structural defects.
- Move the ladder instead of reaching to the side from the top of it. Climb down, move the ladder, and climb up again.
- Lean a straight ladder at an angle to the wall, not straight up. The bottom should be placed away from the wall one-quarter of the distance from the base of the ladder to its contact point.
- Place both feet of the ladder firmly on level, non-slippery ground and have someone steady the ladder as you climb.
- Keep your hands free to grip the ladder as you climb. Wear your tools in a tool belt.
- Keep your body weight centered.
- Face the ladder when climbing down.
- Hire an expert for high jobs, especially roof jobs or those where power wires are nearby.

Plan climbs sensibly.

Teacher Support Notes

① **Ladder Safety:** Have students inspect the ladders in their homes. First, ask if they have ladders. If not, should they have one? Have they ever seen anyone around their homes using something other than a ladder to climb on? If they do have a ladder, what potential problems do they see with it? Have they ever observed a family member breaking one of the rules listed here? Has anyone fallen? Do they think someone will fall if they continue to use these practices?

✎ **Fast Facts**

From the years 1982 to 1991, 44 children were crushed to death by automatic garage doors according to the U.S. Consumer Product Safety Commission.

Activity 2.3
Pop Quiz.
1. List three precautions to be taken at home to prevent slips and/or trips. (See page 577 for answers.)
2. List three precautions to be taken at home to prevent climbing or reaching accidents. (See page 577 for answers.)
3. List three precautions to be taken at work or during leisure-time activities to prevent injuries and/or death. (See page 578 for answers.)
4. Most accidents can be prevented through _____ and a few precautions. (awareness)

Activity 2.4
Prevention Posters.
Ask the students to add items to the list of work and leisure-time precautions found in this section that would further help to reduce accidents, injuries, and possible death. For extra credit, have students make posters

Teacher Support Notes

① **Other Causes of Home Accidents:** Ask students to think for a few minutes about accidents, other than the falls (discussed previously), that have occurred in their homes. What were the causes of these accidents? Could they have been prevented? What will family members do to prevent a recurrence of this type of accident?

② **List of Precautions:** Ask students if they think that posting a list of precautions, such as the one here in the book, somewhere in their home, would help to prevent accidents? Where would they post the list? Would they be willing to spend some time making a small safety poster for their homes? You might want to spend some time on such an activity if students are interested.

Section II Review

Answers
1. Answers will vary; could include at least three from the list on page 577.
2. Answers will vary; could include at least four from the list on page 577.
3. falls
4. Answers will vary; could include at least three from the list on this page.
5. Answers will vary.
6. Answers will vary.

Special notes for special age groups: falls are the leading cause of accidental death and injury to older people, so be aware that balance declines with age. Sudden motions affect balance the most—especially motions involving the head, which is heavy and can pull the whole body off center. Slow down, and move with grace. For the other special age group, infants, falls from tables and bassinets are a frequent cause of injury and falls into buckets of water, swimming pools, or other bodies of water can cause death by drowning. Do not look away from an infant in such a place, even for a moment.

Other accidents can arise from the careless use of tools, toys, guns, and other devices. Again, most such accidents occur in the home. Work and leisure-time accidents add significantly to the number of deaths and injuries. To prevent them:

- Use sharp objects only for their intended purpose, handle them with care, and keep them out of the reach of children.
- Mark large glass windows and doors so that everyone can see that they are not walk-through spaces.
- Follow the manufacturer's instructions carefully when using equipment.
- Unplug electric cords when equipment is not in use.
- Do not use electric appliances, such as hair dryers, around water, including full bathroom basins, tubs, and other sinks.
- Clean up spills promptly to prevent slipping.
- Sweep up broken glass promptly. Discard cracked china and glassware. Use nonbreakable dishes and containers around tile and cement surfaces.
- Remove nails from boards in storage.
- Learn and obey all firearm safety rules.
- Keep guns and ammunition in separate places, each protected by lock and key.
- Never load a gun until you are ready to shoot it. Assume that all guns you handle are loaded, even when you know they are not. Do not misuse blank cartridges. They can cause serious injury and even death.

Key Points ► *Falls and other accidents at home claim many lives each year. Most of these accidents can be prevented through awareness and a few precautions.*

SECTION II   REVIEW

Answer the following questions on a sheet of paper.

Learning the Facts
1. Give three recommendations for preventing slips and trips.
2. List four ways to prevent falls that occur when climbing or reaching.
3. What is the leading cause of accidental death for older people?
4. Name three recommendations for avoiding work and leisure-time accidents.

Making Life Choices
5. Look over the lists in this section which specify how to prevent slips, trips, and falls. Which safety precautions do you most often ignore? Discuss why you do not follow these safety tips.
6. Falls are the leading cause of accidental death and injury to elderly people. If your grandmother was going to move into your home, what changes would you make to ensure her safety?

SECTION III

Burns

Fires and burns are the fifth leading cause of accidental death. Many of those to illustrate these ideas and display them in your room or hallway. **(10 min.; Extend, Enrich)**

FOCUS
SECTION III

In this section students will learn:
1. Prevention is the key to reducing deaths and injuries due to fires.
2. What to do in case of fire or burns.

Activity 3.1
Preventive Measures. Bring to class a number of newspaper articles about fires: brush fires, house fires, and business fires. Divide the class into groups. Give one article to each group. Have the groups read the articles to determine whether authorities found a cause for the fire. Then have groups brainstorm ways the fires could have been prevented. **(15 min., Critical Thinking)**

TEACH
SECTION III
(Guided and Independent Practice)

Activity 3.2
Home Inspections. Have students make a home inspection and formulate the following lists:

(continued on next page)

Ch. 23 Accident and Injury Prevention   **579**

who die are children. The majority of the deaths occur in fires at home. Fire prevention is the topic of this chapter's Straight Talk. The next chapter offers basic tips for assisting burn victims. A course in first aid can give you more.

A special class of burns—chemical burns—damages eyes, skin, and lungs without fire. Read the labels of sprays, products that contain gases, and compounds that can burn your skin or hurt your eyes. Follow directions.

Other specifics to prevent fires and burns:

① • Install fire extinguishers near danger spots.
• Keep a garden hose near a faucet.
• Use chemical fire extinguishers—never water—on electrical fires. Baking soda will safely smother a grease fire, so keep a box handy in the kitchen. (See Figure 23–2)
• Change heat-and-air filters on schedule, and maintain heating systems.
• Dispose of trash immediately.
• Hang clothes well away from stoves or fireplaces.
• Store matches in a metal container and out of the reach of children.

ORDINARY

COMBUSTIBLES

FLAMMABLE
B
LIQUIDS

ELECTRICAL

EQUIPMENT

or   or   or

If you see these symbols on a fire extinguisher...

Class A
(paper, wood, cloth)

Class B
(flammable liquids, greases)

Class C
(electrical fires)

follow these instructions:
Do use the extinguisher on an ordinary combustible fire.

Do use the extinguisher on a flammable liquid or grease fire.

Do use the extinguisher on an electrical fire.

If you see these symbols on a fire extinguisher...

follow these instructions:
Do NOT use the extinguisher on an ordinary combustible fire.

Do NOT use the extinguisher on a flammable liquid or grease fire.

Do NOT use the extinguisher on an electrical fire.

Figure 23–2 Types of Fire Extinguishers and Fires ②

1. Existing fire hazards—for example, paper, chemicals, storage, faulty wiring, unsafe habits.
2. Existing fire prevention measures—for example, fire extinguishers, safe storage, safe habits, smoke alarms, fire alarms.

Ask students to score a +1 for each preventive measure and –1 for each

hazard that exists in their homes. In addition, students should make suggestions to correct hazards. Ideally the final objective would be for the student and family to implement these changes at home. Ask students to share any changes that have been made in their homes after they discussed this activity with their families. **(15 min.; Extend, Enrich)**

EVALUATE
SECTION III

Activity 3.3
Pop Quiz.
Tell students to list three fire prevention guidelines in each of the following categories: **a.** personal habits, **b.** cooking and heating, **c.** electrical equipment, **d.** other areas of your choosing.

Teacher Support Notes

① **This is a Fire:** Several causes of fires have been listed here. Ask students if they can think of others. Some examples would be playing with matches, letting a camp fire burn out of control, and bringing flammable materials such as paints, lighter fluids, and insecticides near fires.

② **Fire Victims:** To impress upon students the importance of learning about fire safety, discuss some of the tragic results of fires. Ask a fire victim to visit the class and talk about the pain, the scars, and any psychological fears.

③ **Learning How to Swim:** Ask students if they know how to swim. If any do not, recommend a place where they can get swimming instruction. Ask students who do know how to swim to talk about how long it took them to learn and how difficult it was. Also, ask them to talk about the fun that they have swimming.

Section III Review

Answers

1. fires and burns
2. Answers will vary; could include at least four from the bulleted list on pages 579 and 580.
3. 120 degrees F
4. 911
5. Answers will vary.

580

- Be careful with hot tap water; it can cause scalds that require hospitalization. Turn down the temperature setting of the water heater to 120 degrees Fahrenheit, if possible. This will help save energy, too.
- Do not allow anyone to smoke in bed. Provide adequate ashtrays to smokers, or ask them to smoke outside.
- Install home fire detectors. The local fire department can help you choose the right types and decide on their placement. ①

Finally, if a fire starts, what will you do? Think now, because you need to know ahead of time what moves to make. The Straight Talk section tells you how to plan your way out of burning buildings. One thing to carry in your head at all times is the emergency telephone number for most parts of the United States: 911. You'd be smart to memorize the fire department number if it's not 911. ② ③

Key Points *Many lives are lost to fires each year. Home fires are preventable through cautious handling of equipment and chemicals.*

SECTION III   REVIEW

Answer the following questions on a sheet of paper.

Learning the Facts
1. What is the fifth leading cause of accidental death?
2. Give four recommendations on how to prevent fires and burns.
3. The water heater in your home should not exceed what temperature?
4. What is the emergency help number for most parts of the United States?

Making Life Choices
5. Develop a fire escape plan for your home. Figure out two ways to get outside from every room. Designate a place outside where you will all meet, so that you can be sure everyone is out. Advance planning is your only effective weapon.

SECTION IV

Safety during Swimming, Boating, Biking, and Other Play

Drowning is the fourth leading cause of accidental death. For teens, it is second only to highway accidents as a cause of accidental death. Most drownings occur when someone who can't swim falls into the water—often from a boat. Surprisingly, people who can't swim often put themselves in situations in which they may drown. Then they do drown.

To reduce the risk of drowning:
- Learn to swim.
- Never swim alone or let others do so.
- Choose swimming places with care.
- Protect pools with fences.
- Use extra caution around moving water (rivers, canals, creeks, etc.). It is much more powerful than it looks.
- Supply boats with personal flotation devices (PFDs). Nonswimmers should always wear PFDs the proper size to fit them, when on a boat.
- Ease into the water when it is cold.
- Never play rough in or near the water.
- Swim only when you feel well.
- Do not swim if you have been drinking alcohol or using other drugs.

When diving, never dive where obstructions might lurk or where you don't know the depth. Ease in feet first the first time, anyway. Do not overestimate your ability. Do not dive too deep. It is also wise to have a boat accompany you on a distance swim and to get out of the water when lightning threatens. The boat should go to shore quickly. Except in emergencies, rely

Activity 3.4

Extinguisher Review. Have the students identify the three classes of fire extinguishers and either draw the symbols for each one's use(s) or name the use(s) for each one. Discuss where the

fire extinguishers are located around the school facility. **(15 min.)**

 FOCUS
SECTION IV

In this section students will learn that:
1. Training, skills, and knowledge of safety rules can prevent most accidents during swimming, boating, biking, and other play.

Activity 4.1

Recreational Safety Slogans. Ask individual students to develop an original safety slogan for a recreational activity of their choice. The slogans should be catchy and easy to remember. They must be able to support each slogan by explaining why it's important. **(30 min.; Extend, Enrich)**

Don't dive where obstructions might lurk.

on your own swimming ability, not on inner tubes or floats.

If you see someone in trouble in the water, help by using the techniques described in "Water Rescue Techniques," the Health Strategies section on this page. Only a trained lifeguard should attempt rescue by swimming out to the victim. A drowning person can easily overpower a novice and drown them both.

You may have heard that you should not swim until an hour after eating, to prevent stomach cramps. It is not necessarily dangerous to swim with a full stomach, especially if you exercise lightly. However, if you swim hard after eating, you may indeed experience cramps. They are just as likely to occur in your legs or arms as in your stomach. The reason may be that digestion requires energy and oxygen, which are taken from the hard-working muscles. You need not stay out of the lake altogether after a picnic. Just take it easy while your stomach is full.

To ensure safe boating pleasure:

- Do not operate boating equipment if using alcohol or other drugs.
- Know your boat and the rules of the waterway.
- Make sure there are enough Coast Guard–approved flotation devices for everyone. Do not rely on inner tubes or toys as flotation devices.

HEALTH
STRATEGIES

Water Rescue Techniques

Even if you cannot swim, you can assist a swimmer who is nearby and in trouble.

1. If the swimmer is near a dock or in a pool:
   - Lie flat on the dock or pool edge. Extend an arm, leg, shirt, fishing pole, oar, or other object. Pull the victim within reach of the edge. Most pools have long cleaning tools around that work well. If a lifesaving cushion or float is nearby, aim carefully, and throw it to the victim.

2. If the troubled swimmer is farther away than you can reach:
   - Wade into the water up to your waist. Extend an object, push a float or board, or throw a rope where the victim can reach it.

3. If the victim fell from a boat, or you are in a boat:
   - Allow the victim to hang onto the boat or to an object you hold out.

4. If the victim is too weak to hold on:
   - Pull the victim into the boat carefully to avoid worsening any injuries.

5. If the victim fell through ice:
   - Push a ladder or other long object, tied with a rope at the bottom rung and secured, out to the victim. Or use ropes, poles, sticks, or a human chain to reach the person.
   - If the victim is too weak to hold on, a rescuer can crawl along the ladder to help.

① Fast Facts

1,200 children in the United States drown annually. Most drown in swimming pools.

Teacher Support Notes

① **Rescuing a Drowning Person:** Ask students if they have read about would-be rescuers drowning as they have attempted to save others. When and why did this happen? If you have articles describing such events, read them to the students. What would they do if they became aware of a person drowning and there was no one else to help?

① Fast Facts

33% of Americans over the age of 14 have never learned to swim.

TEACH

SECTION IV
(Guided and Independent Practice)

Activity 4.2
Recreation Posters. As a class, have students identify recreational and outdoor activities in which they participate. Divide the class into groups and assign one of the activities to each group. Students should join a group for which

they have a high interest. Give each group a large (3' × 4') piece of chart paper on which to list the following about its activity: **1.** hazards **2.** precautions **3.** regulations or rules (established or understood) that promote safety within the activity **4.** prevention education available. Encourage them to illustrate the information. Display the posters. **(25 min.; Extend, Enrich)**

EVALUATE
SECTION IV

Activity 4.3
Pop Quiz.
1. For land activities, the most important single guideline for accident prevention is wearing _____. (good shoes)
2. _____ is the second leading cause of accidental death for teens. (Drowning)

Teacher Support Notes

① **Safe Shoes and Gear:** Ask students to evaluate their shoes and the equipment they use when participating in various activities. Have they ever invited injury by wearing the "wrong" shoes or defective shoes? Have they ever gone bicycling, skateboarding, etc. when their equipment was in need of repair?

✎ Fast Facts

400 young people a year die in bicycle crashes—primarily because of preventable head injuries.

Section IV Review
Answers

1. Answers will vary; could include at least five from the list on page 580.
2. Cramps occur when digestion takes the oxygen and energy from hard-working muscles.
3. Push a ladder or other long object out to the victim; use ropes, poles, sticks, or a human chain to reach the person; if victim is too weak to hold on, a rescuer can crawl along the ladder to help.
4. puts entire weight of the upper body on lower back muscles
5. Answers will vary.

582

582 UNIT 7 First Aid and Safety

- Load the boat reasonably.
- Keep your weight low in the boat. Sit, don't stand.
- Tell people on shore where you are going and when to expect you back.
- If the boat upsets or fills with water, hang onto it (it will probably still float).
- If the weather threatens, skip the trip.

Of course, accidents also happen when people are moving fast on land—biking, skateboarding, running, and the like. Probably the most important guideline for prevention is to wear good shoes. Not only do they protect the feet; they also give stability to the whole body. A second guideline is to use proper gear: the right-size bike, a skateboard in good condition, and so on. Helmets are also recommended for biking and skateboarding. Keep in mind that no one ever has an accident on purpose. It is the unlikely, unexpected event—the one you can't control—against which you are safeguarding yourself.

Your upper body is itself a heavy object.

Finally, protect your back. Lift *nothing* by bending over, not even a feather. Your own upper body is heavy, and whenever you bend over, your lower back muscles must hoist its weight. To avoid back injury while lifting something, the Red Cross says:

- Plant the feet firmly and slightly apart. Keep your head up.

- Squat—do not lean—forward, keeping the back as straight as possible, and get a firm grip on the object.
- Lift slowly, pushing up with the strong thigh and leg muscles.
- Do not jerk the object upward or twist your body as you lift.
- To lower an object, reverse this procedure.

Key Points *The first rule for water safety is "learn to swim." The next is "never swim alone." When active on land, wear shoes, use proper gear, and use your body with care.* ①

SECTION IV REVIEW

Answer the following questions on a sheet of paper.
Learning the Facts
1. List five ways to reduce the risks of drowning.
2. Why might cramps develop if a person swims hard after eating?
3. How might a victim who has fallen through ice be rescued?
4. Why shouldn't you lift anything by bending over?

Making Life Choices
5. Describe three instances in which you or someone you know have had accidents on bicycles. Describe the causes of the accidents. What factors were common to these accidents? Develop some guidelines for cyclists which would help prevent or lessen injuries from accidents.

SECTION V

Preparedness for Natural Disasters

Natural disasters such as hurricanes, floods, earthquakes, tornadoes, and the like

3. The most important safety rule to prevent drowning is _____. (learn to swim)

CLOSE
SECTION IV

Activity 4.4
Article Analysis. Collect newspaper articles about various accidents. (recreational) Ask students to pick one and identify the following:
1. the hazard; **2.** the unsafe act, habit, or behavior; **3.** the attitude; **4.** the prevention. **(10 min., Critical Thinking)**

FOCUS
SECTION V

In this section students will learn:
1. How to prepare for natural disasters.

Activity 5.1
Disaster Precautions. List the following disasters on the board and have students name precautions for each:
1. lightning; **2.** flood; **3.** hurricane; **4.** tornado; **5.** blizzard; **6.** earthquake **(15 min.)**

---

are, for the most part, beyond people's ability to avoid. However, there is much people can do to prepare for them. Imagine yourself stuck in your house or in a car, unable to leave the area, having to cope for several days without outside help. What would you wish you had done beforehand? What would you wish you had with you?

Water is the first thing that should come to mind. Store some fresh, drinkable water in clean, closed containers now, in the building where you live. Store water in the car, too, if you have one. Store enough to sustain you for at least a day or so. Then, think of shoes. Suppose you had to walk a long distance to get help. Sandals or high-heeled shoes would get old fast. Store good shoes where you may need them.

Other equipment you should have ready:

- Extra fuses, in case some are blown in your fuse panel.
- A portable radio, in case the power goes down.
- Extra batteries, in case the radio goes dead. (Alkaline batteries last the longest.)
- A working flashlight and batteries; also candles and matches, in case the lights go out.
- An adjustable wrench to turn off the electrical main switch and the gas line. (Learn how to do this in advance.)
- A first aid kit, in case someone gets hurt.
- Canned food and a can opener, in case you can't cook.

You can get by in good shape under many emergency situations with just these few simple supplies. On the other hand, you can be miserable, and your life can even be threatened, without the needed items. Remember, the time to stock up on them is now, ahead of time.

Different geographic areas are prone to different events. Learn the preparedness routines for those that are likely to strike your area. A few additional rules:

①

Have on hand water to drink and good shoes to walk in.

- Obey instructions. If told to leave an area, do so.
- In an earthquake, get under a sturdy desk, table, or other furniture, if you can. Do not run outside, where objects may fall on you.
- In storms, stay indoors. When lightning is nearby, keep away from water, plumbing, other metal objects, and all electrical outlets. Do not use the telephone.
- If rising water is a problem or if your home has structural damage from an earthquake, turn off the main power switch. Let an electrician check your home before turning on the power again.
- Afterwards, be aware that electrical power lines may be damaged or down. Keep well away from them.

Key Points ▶ *The person who has stored water, good shoes, a radio, candles, a first aid kit, and food is best prepared for a natural disaster.*

SECTION V   REVIEW

Answer the following questions on a sheet of paper.
Learning the Facts
1. Give three examples of natural disasters.
2. List six types of equipment you should have available in the event of a natural disaster.

Teacher Support Notes

① Water and Shoes:
Ask students if they would have thought first of these two basic items—water and shoes— if they were told to prepare for a disaster. Do they have water stored in their home? In their cars? Do they have a good pair of walking shoes handy?

Section V Review
Answers
1. Answers will vary; could include: hurricanes, floods, earthquakes, and tornadoes.
2. Answers will vary; could include: water, sturdy walking shoes, extra fuses, portable radio, extra batteries, working flashlight and batteries, candles and matches, an adjustable wrench, first aid kit, canned food, and a can opener.
3. under sturdy furniture
4. stay indoors, away from water and all electrical and metal objects
5. Answers will vary.

Activity 5.2

World Disaster Map. Before beginning this chapter, collect periodical articles and identify library resources on each of the natural disasters addressed in this section. Have the periodical articles available in the classroom and request the library resources be loaned to you to be used in the classroom. Make a copy of a world map for each student. Using your resources, have students place symbols on their maps (in at least 20 locations) for natural disasters common to different parts of the world. **(30 min.; Extend, Enrich)**

Activity 5.3

Pop Quiz.
1. Water is the most important item to have on hand in a natural disaster. (T)
2. If there is structural damage to your home, turn off the main power. (T)
3. Radios are not necessary during

Teacher Support Notes

① **Assaults:** Ask students if they are often afraid of being assaulted. Tell them that they should not be embarrassed to admit fear; it is normal. Have they ever been assaulted? Could they have done anything to prevent the assault? Do they feel capable of defending themselves in such a situation? Do they have any ideas about what they may be able to do to increase their abilities to defend themselves?

Section VI Review

Answers

1. street rape or stranger rape
2. Assault
3. acquaintance rape or date rape
4. Answers will vary. Refer to the Health Strategies, "Rape Prevention Tips," on the next page.
5. Answers will vary. Refer to the Health Strategies on the next page.
6. Answers will vary.

✉ Where to Write

The National Safety Council
444 W. Michigan Ave.
Chicago, IL 60611

3. In the event of an earthquake, where should you seek safety?
4. What are some precautions you should take during a lightning storm?

Making Life Choices

5. Develop a fictitious situation in which you have to prepare for a natural disaster. Describe the situation you are facing and exactly how you will prepare for it in order to ensure your safety. Discuss the damage that the disaster may cause and how you plan to survive its aftermath.

SECTION VI

Defenses against Aggression

Aggression takes many forms—**assault** and beatings, robbery, and rape are among them. No one leads a life so charmed that these things are impossible. Everyone needs to know ways to defend against them: walking with friends, staying away from places known to be unsafe, staying out of dark places, and the like.

People may fail to realize, though, that crimes of violence can be committed not only by strangers but by people you know—even friends or family members, and even in your own home or room. An important crime in this category is rape.

When people think of rape, they usually picture a woman walking down a dark street at night and being sexually assaulted by an unknown attacker. This kind of rape, sometimes called **street rape,** does occur. The Health Strategies section on the next page, "Rape Prevention Tips," sums up the precautions people should take to avoid it. Street rape, though, is not the most common kind of rape. The most common kind is **acquaintance rape**, also called *date rape*.

In acquaintance rape, the victim knows the attacker and may even be a friend, but does not want to be physically intimate with the person. When one person forces sex against another person's will, no matter what the aggressor may say, it is a crime of violence. It can do major damage to the victim—not only physically but also emotionally. Everyone (males included) should take precautions against acquaintance rape. Don't get into a situation where it can happen. Don't let people who might harm you get you alone.

Key Points *Take precautions against street rape, but keep in mind that the most common kind of rape is acquaintance rape. Don't get into a situation where it can happen.*

SECTION VI REVIEW

Answer the following questions on a sheet of paper.

Learning the Vocabulary

The vocabulary terms in this section are *assault, street rape,* and *acquaintance rape.*
Fill in the blank with the correct answer.
1. Sexual assault by a stranger is called _____.
2. _____ is one person's attack on another, with intent to do harm.
3. Sexual assault by someone you know is called _____.

Learning the Facts

4. List four recommendations to avoid becoming a victim of street rape.
5. Name some techniques that may help if you are being approached by an attacker.

Making Life Choices

6. The most common type of rape is acquaintance rape. Develop a list of strategies you can follow, to keep from becoming a victim of acquaintance rape.

disasters. (F)

CLOSE
SECTION V

Activity 5.4
Community Evacuation Maps.
Have students find out from a variety of local resources (civil defense, fire department, etc.) how different areas of their community would be evacuated if the

necessity arose. To receive extra credit, students should obtain a street map of their community and clearly mark the evacuation routes. Display one in your classroom and post the others throughout your school. **(1 week out-of-school time; Extend, Enrich)**

FOCUS
SECTION VI

In this section students will learn:
1. Ways to defend themselves against an attack.

Activity 6.1
Speaker. Invite a guest speaker from your local Rape Crisis Center to give a presentation on street rape. Provide your students with the Guest Speaker Follow-Up Worksheet in your supplementary material. **(45 min.; Extend, Enrich)**

HEALTH STRATEGIES

Rape Prevention Tips

To avoid becoming a victim of rape:

Do not go anywhere alone after dark; use an escort service.

Always run with a partner, and even then, never run in the dark.

Always ask who is at your door before opening it. Do not open your door to strangers.

Leave word with family or friends of where you plan to go and when you will return.

Stay alert to suspicious-looking people.

Keep your arms free for defense. Use backpacks, shoulder bags, and the like.

Stay on busy, well-lit streets.

Have your keys in your hand before you get to your front door or car door.

Lock the car door as soon as you are inside.

Keep your car full of gas and well-maintained.

Carry a hatpin or stickpin in your hand. You will not have time to fumble for it.

Carry a whistle.

If efforts fail, and you are followed:

Ring the nearest doorbell.

Move away from shadowy areas into open, crowded, well-lit areas.

If you are approached:

Try to stall for time. Someone may come along.

Scream "fire" (not "police," since others are then likely to avoid becoming involved).

Pull a fire alarm, if possible.

Break a window. Someone is likely to respond to the noise.

Use your key or a stickpin to aim forcefully for the attacker's eyes, temples, Adam's apple, or ears. Stab hard, without warning.

Try to disgust your attacker by urinating or by gagging yourself to induce vomiting.

Tell the attacker you have a sexually transmitted disease.

These precautions are not guaranteed, but are worth trying. They may save your life.

① ②

SECTION VII

Care of Others: Child Care

"Taking care of children is a matter of plain common sense. Everyone knows how to do it." Many people think this is so, but it is not. Love and enjoyment of children may come naturally. However, to deliver competent child care, you also have to do some formal learning. Safety precautions are a part of child care.

Keeping a safe home is a major part of the responsible care of children. Whether you care for younger sisters and brothers, or baby-sit, or have children of your own,

MINI GLOSSARY

assault: one person's attack on another, with intent to do harm.

street rape: sexual assault by a stranger; also called *stranger rape.*

acquaintance rape: sexual assault by a known person. If such a rape takes place on a date, it is called *date rape.*

Teacher Support Notes

① **Rape:** The Straight Talk on page 507 also discusses rapes, focusing on date rape. If you did not cover that section earlier in the course, you may want to refer students to it now.

② **Preventing Rape:** Have students go through the list of items below evaluating their own activities to determine whether or not they use these strategies. After they have finished, discuss their responses. Which strategies are not being used? Why? How can students implement these strategies?

Fast Facts

Experts say that one child a week drowns in a bucket. Large industrial buckets often found around the home are the culprits because they are deep and don't tip over. The average age of victims is eight months to a year.

TEACH
SECTION VI
(Guided and Independent Practice)

Activity 6.2
Precaution Discussion Groups.
Discuss the strategies listed in this section to avoid becoming a rape victim. Divide the class into small groups of four or five and have the students tell why each of these precautions would help to discourage a potential attacker. Ask students in the group to think of more ideas to ward off a possible assault. Share these ideas together as a class, having each group present their additions. **(20 min., Cooperative Learning)**

EVALUATE
SECTION VI

Activity 6.3

Pop Quiz.
1. _____ is one person's attack on another with intent to do harm. (Assault)
2. Street rape is sexual assault by a _____. (stranger)
3. Acquaintance rape is sexual assault by a _____ person. (known)

CLOSE
SECTION VI

Teacher Support Notes

① **Caring for Children:**
Ask students how many are responsible for younger children from time to time, either in paid baby-sitting situations or in taking care of younger siblings. In these situations do they feel that they are as protective as they should be of the safety of the children? How often do they check on the children? Have any accidents or injuries ever occurred while they were responsible for the children? How did they react?

✎ Fast Facts

A study by the Centers for Disease Control suggests that children are safer in a day-care center than they are at home. When researchers studied children from six weeks to five years of age, they found that youngsters in out-of-the-home child care settings had lower rates of injury and poisonings than those who stayed at home.

586 UNIT 7 First Aid and Safety

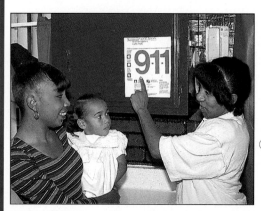

Keep a safe home and know what to do in emergencies.

you should check the home, yard, garage, storage areas, basement, and play areas for hazards to the children's safety. Ask yourself these questions:

1. Are all areas free of hazards that could cause falls, as described in Section II of this chapter?
2. Are all areas well defended against fire, as described in Section III?
3. If there is a pool or other body of water nearby, is it fenced off, so that the children cannot play there unsupervised or accidentally fall in?
4. Are all areas neat and free of trash and bottles?

Fix any areas that are not safe.

Pay special attention to children's toys:

- Make sure that children do not play with sticks, or with toys or other objects that may break if the children fall. This warning applies to bottles, glasses, and even some plastic toys.
- Do not allow children to play with fireworks.
- Make sure children do not play with or around television sets, electrical devices in the kitchen and bathroom, fans, power

tools, household cleaning equipment, sewing machines, lawn tools, and other dangerous objects.
- Do not allow children to play with any guns, including pellet guns, BB guns, and toy guns that look real.

① Even if the home and toys are safe, children should not be left to play without your watchful attention. Their own judgment cannot keep them from harm. You must do so.

When feeding children, be aware that they can easily choke on food. (So can you, actually, so consider taking these precautions for yourself as well.) To prevent choking, cut meat into small pieces. Let children take only small forkfuls of any food. Don't let them speak or laugh with food in their mouths. Make sure they chew each bite thoroughly before attempting to swallow. Take particular care with round pieces of food such as grapes or cherry tomatoes. Teach children to bite them with their front teeth to crush them. For small children, cut food (even grapes and hot dogs) into tiny pieces. Peanuts should be split open. Popcorn should not be served to small children at all, because it is light enough to be carried by the breath and round enough to lodge in the throat.

Competent childcare involves both love and learning.

586

Activity 6.4

Avoiding Assault. Read aloud to the class the key points in this section and emphasize the importance of their behavior in avoiding an assault. **(5 min.; Reteach, Reinforce)**

FOCUS

SECTION VII

In this section students will learn:

1. Safety precautions for the home and play areas of children.
2. Safety tips when accepting responsibility for someone else's children.

Activity 7.1

Home Safety Evaluation. Have the students visit the home of a neighbor who has small children (the age range from six months to three years is preferable). Have the students interview the parent(s) to find out what precautions they have taken in the home and play areas to ensure the safety and well-being of the child. Ask the students to share their findings in groups of four and make some suggestions to help improve the safety of the home and play areas they have observed. If possible, have the students take the suggestions they have made for the home and play area back to the family involved. **(20 min.; Extend, Enrich)**

Learn the Heimlich maneuver. If a child does choke, use the Heimlich maneuver to dislodge the particle from the throat. The next chapter gives a basic description of the maneuver, but you can best learn it in a first aid course.

When you are baby-sitting, some additional precautions are in order. See the Health Strategies section, "Pointers for Baby-Sitters," below.

Key Points ▶ *Competent care of children includes attention to their safety. The home and toys must be safe. The person who is responsible must keep a watchful eye on children.*

SECTION VII REVIEW

Answer the following questions on a sheet of paper.

Learning the Facts

1. List four precautions you should follow when caring for children in your home.
2. How can children be kept from choking?
3. Name five precautions baby-sitters should take.

Making Life Choices

4. In your mind, make a safety inspection of your home. Picture yourself walking from room to room. Evaluate each specific area in terms of potential safety hazards that may exist for infants and small children. List all the safety hazards you discovered and describe how each can best be remedied.

HEALTH STRATEGIES

Pointers for Baby-Sitters ⌐①

Before accepting responsibility for someone else's children:

1. Find out where the parents will be and how you can reach them if you need them. Write down the phone number(s) or address(es).
2. Write down one or more neighbors' names and numbers.
3. Write down the telephone numbers of:

   - The family doctor or pediatrician.
   - The police department or sheriff.
   - The fire department.

   or have the parents show you where they keep them.
4. Ask if it's safe to go outside.
5. Know how to lock the door(s). Chain them, if you can. Secure all windows.
6. Let no one in unless told in advance that they're coming. Politely tell visitors to return a little later when the parents are home.
7. Keep an awake child in view at all times. Check a sleeping child frequently (every 15 minutes).

Answers to Fact or Fiction

Here are the answers to the questions at the start of the chapter.

1. False. One out of every three, not ten, people suffers an injury each year. **2.** True. **3.** False. Skill is important, but attitude is equally important in preventing accidents on the road. **4.** True. **5.** True. **6.** True. **7.** False. To deliver competent child care, you have to do some formal learning.

Teacher Support Notes

① **Baby-Sitting Pointers:** Ask students to evaluate their baby-sitting with regard to these strategies. Do they practice these strategies all of the time, most of the time, occasionally, or never? Are any of these unreasonable? If so, why?

Section VII Review

Answers

1. Answers will vary; could include: check the home, yard, garage, storage areas, basement, and play areas for hazards.
2. cut meat into small pieces, insist children take only small forkfuls of any food, do not allow speaking or laughing with food in their mouths, make sure children chew each bite thoroughly before swallowing, and teach children to bite round pieces of food (grapes & cherry tomatoes) with their front teeth to crush them
3. Answers will vary. Refer to the Health Strategies on this page.
4. Answers will vary.

Activity 7.2
Preventing Childhood Injuries.
Obtain a copy of the American Red Cross CPR workbook *Infant and Child*. Read Chapter 1 to your students. Do the review questions orally at the end of the chapter to ensure the students made note of the important information. Encourage students who baby-sit or have small children at home to take a skills class in caring for small children. **(20 min.; Special Needs, Extend, Enrich)**

Activity 7.3
Child Safety Slogans. Have students develop safety slogans to put around various places in the home and/or play area to help remind parents and child care providers of safety precautions. If time permits, make up signs and distribute them to young families in your community. **(30 min.; Extend, Enrich)**

EVALUATE
SECTION VII

Activity 7.4
Pop Quiz.
1. Safety precautions are a part of child

Teacher Support Notes

① **Handout—Fire Safety Checklist:** Your supplementary material contains an extensive checklist that requires students to evaluate their households in terms of fire safety. You may want to distribute and have students complete the checklist before they read the following material.

② **Fire Stories:** Ask students if any of them have been involved in or witnessed up close a major fire. Do they know how the fire started? Could it have been prevented? How? Was anyone hurt or killed? Could the injuries or deaths have been prevented? Did they help put out the fire? What did they learn from this experience?

STRAIGHT **T**ALK — **Fire Prevention and Escape**

Fires and burns are the fifth leading cause of accidental death in the United States. It is worth studying the guidelines offered here on fire prevention, before a time comes when you need them. ①

That's fine with me. It never hurts to review precautions.

Good. That attitude may save your life.

Many fires are caused by childrens' and adults' careless use of fire. Many fires are also caused by smoking in bed. To prevent these fires: ②

- Don't smoke. If you do, quit. *Or. . .*
- Dispose of cigarettes and matches safely. Never assume they are out when they might not be.
- Keep matches and lighters out of the reach of children.
- Do not smoke in bed. If you make a habit of smoking in bed, sooner or later (by the laws of chance) it is virtually certain that you will fall asleep while doing so.

Drinking alcohol and taking other drugs that make people drowsy is particularly hazardous in combination with smoking.

Other fires are caused by cooking and heating equipment:

- Keep cooking and heating equipment clean and in good repair.
- If a gas pilot light or a burner on the stove or oven goes out, ventilate the area before lighting a burner. Do not turn electric switches on or off before the area is ventilated, as switches make a tiny spark when used.
- Turn pots on the stove so that you won't knock them when you walk by. Make sure that children cannot reach the handles.
- Keep the cords of electric cookware on the counter, not dangling.
- Keep portable space heaters out of indoor traffic lanes. Turn them off before going to bed. Keep flammable materials away from space heaters.
- Keep cloth (curtains, pot holders, your own loose clothing) and other

flammable materials away from cooking surfaces and fires.

Still other fires are caused by liquids:

- Use flammable liquids only as directed.
- Store them in safety containers that will not leak fumes into the air.
- Store surplus quantities outside.

Also, buy fire-retardant clothes for children. Be especially careful to buy fire-retardant pajamas, nightgowns, and robes.

Parents should try to buy fire-retardant clothes for children.

(Continued on next page)

care. (T)

2. It is important to know the telephone numbers of police and fire departments when baby-sitting. (T)

3. Caretakers should be careful of round foods like grapes and hot dogs when feeding them to small children. (T)

4. It is okay to leave a child alone to play if the area is safe. (F)

5. Popcorn is a safe food for children. (F)

CLOSE
SECTION VII

Activity 7.5
Classroom Safety Evaluation.
Have the students take a visual trip around the classroom. Have the students look for the various safety problems discussed in the chapter. If a young child were to enter the classroom, what would

be some hazards that could endanger the child's safety? Discuss this as a class and point out ways the classroom could be made safe. **(15 min.; Extend, Enrich)**

Ch. 23 Accident and Injury Prevention 589

STRAIGHT TALK   *(Continued)*

What if a fire starts? What should I do?

First of all, whenever you go into an unfamiliar building, imagine it going up in flames while you are in it, and plan your escape. Locate the exits, fire escapes, extinguishers, and stairways (never use an elevator in a fire).

Most importantly, make an escape plan for your home. Figure out two ways to get outside from every room. Involve everyone. Make plans to ensure that handicapped people can get out. Rehearse. Have a fire drill or two. Designate a place to meet outside, so that you can be sure everyone is out.

Picture the fire actually burning in your home. By thinking through how a fire would spread from one place to another and how you would fight it, you can prepare the area ahead of time. Put a fire extinguisher here and another here. Remove the trash from this area, so fire will not spread across it. Install an outdoor faucet here and keep a hose nearby. Advance planning is the only effective weapon. Wishes are of no use in emergencies.

① How about installing fire alarms in homes?

By all means do. Maintain them, too. Often, by the time people feel the heat or smell the smoke of a fire, it is too late to get out. Most people die in fires because they are unable to breathe, not because they are burned. Fire alarms warn people early to make their escape. The fire alarms most recommended for homes are smoke detectors. They should first be placed in sleeping areas. Additional detectors can be placed in other areas.

Install fire extinguishers, too, but do not put them where the fire is most likely to be. Put them where you can most likely get to them in case of fire. Learn how to use them. Using water on an electrical or chemical fire can do more harm than good (see Figure 23–2 on page 579).

OK, let's say a fire has started. Now what?

Because most fatal home fires happen when the occupants are asleep, it is best to sleep with the bedroom door closed. Smoke can be deadly.

If you are alerted to a fire:

1. Roll out of bed, staying low.
2. Crawl to the door.
3. Feel the door for heat. If it's cool, open it carefully, but stand behind it. Be ready to slam it shut if smoke or heat rush in. If the door is hot, don't open it. Go some other way.
4. Crawl out quickly. Close doors behind you.
5. Don't use elevators during fires, use stairs. If trapped on an upper floor, wrap yourself in a blanket, cover your head, hang out a window, and yell. Don't jump unless you absolutely must.
6. Meet as prearranged.
7. Don't go back inside.
8. Call the fire department from a neighbor's phone.

If your clothes catch fire, *do not run*. Stop, drop, and roll. To help someone else whose clothes have caught on fire, force the same motion if you can. Then smother the person's flaming clothes with a coat or blanket.

🔖 Fast Facts

Safety experts say that accidents due to human error are most likely to occur between 2:00–7:00 a.m. and 2:00–5:00 p.m.

Teacher Support Notes

① Planning for Home Fires: In addition to the information in the text you may want to give students a few more guidelines for anticipating and preparing for a house fire:

• Everyone in the family should have a responsibility.

• Older children should look out for younger ones.

• Rehearsals should be conducted in the dark.

• Make sure the plan is realistic and doable. Don't assume anything (that a small child can climb out of a window, for example). Practice it to make sure.

• Adults can be hard to wake up. Children should try to wake the adults but then leave by themselves if they can't arouse the adults.

Vocabulary

1. Street rape is sexual assault by an attacker with whom the victim is unfamiliar. Acquaintance rape is sexual assault by someone the victim knows.

2. Head restraints

3. airbags

4. assault

5. Answers will vary.

Recall

Section I

1. 1 out of 3

2. A defensive driver knows accidents are likely and takes precautions against them.

3. It slows the person's

momentum and distributes the force of the impact across the body's strongest parts. It also keeps the driver behind the wheel.

4. Answers will vary. Refer to the Health Strategies on "How to Avoid Alcohol-Related Driving Accidents" on page 576.

5. a. Look over your shoulder when changing lanes. Don't rely on mirrors. **b.** Keep a safe distance from the car in front of you. **c.** Pause five seconds after a red light turns green before proceeding to ensure that no cars are still going through.

Section II

6. balance declines with age

7. falls from tables and bassinets

8. Answers will vary; could include: learn and obey all firearm safety rules; keep guns and ammunition in separate places; and never load a gun until you are ready to shoot it.

Section III

9. baking soda

Section IV

10. Class A, ordinary combustibles (paper, wood, cloth);

CHAPTER REVIEW

LEARNING THE VOCABULARY

head restraints   assault   acquaintance rape
airbags   street rape

Answer the following questions on a separate sheet of paper.

1. What is the difference between street rape and acquaintance rape?
2. _____ are high seat backs or devices attached to seats in cars, intended to prevent neck and spinal cord injury.
3. Inflatable pillows known as _____ are stored in the steering wheels of cars and are designed to inflate on impact.
4. An _____ is known as a harmful attack.
5. Write a paragraph using the vocabulary terms from the list above. Underline each term.

RECALLING IMPORTANT FACTS AND IDEAS

1. What are the chances that someone you know will suffer an injury this year?
2. Describe the attitude of a defensive driver.
3. Explain why safety belts should be worn by all occupants in a car.
4. What are some ways to avoid alcohol-related accidents?
5. Name three changes in driving habits that could save lives.
6. Why are falls the leading cause of accidental death and injury for older people?
7. What are the most common types of falls experienced by infants?
8. Give two firearm safety precautions.
9. What product should be used to smother a grease fire?
10. List the various classes of fire extinguishers. For what type of fire is each used?
11. List three safety precautions for diving.
12. If you cannot swim, how can you assist a swimmer who is in trouble?
13. List three tips for safe boating.
14. What can you do if you believe you are being followed by someone?
15. When baby-sitting, what phone numbers should you be sure to have in your possession before the parents leave?
16. How can house fires be prevented?
17. Why shouldn't water be used on electrical or chemical fires?
18. What should you do if your clothes catch on fire?

CRITICAL THINKING

1. Imagine the governor of your state has just signed a law stating that all cars must have a device installed that will prevent cars from going over 55 mph. Do you agree with this law? Why, or why not? Do you believe it will lower the accident rate? What are the advantages and disadvantages of this law? If you had the power to do so, and money were not a factor, what would be your choices of ideal safety features for automobiles?
2. Describe an emergency situation that you personally experienced or witnessed. Comment on how it felt to be at the scene. Do you ever worry about what to do or whether you would panic in an emergency? Why, or why not? Injuries and deaths during emergencies frequently occur because people panic. How can feelings of panic be reduced? Give some ideas about what would help people feel calm in an emergency.
3. Why do people take unnecessary risks? Discuss why people behave in unsafe ways when they *know* better. Why do you think most of us think, "It won't happen to me"?
4. Discuss an unnecessary risk you took with your own safety. Describe what you could have done to lessen the risk.

Class B, flammable liquids (gases); Class C, electrical equipment (see Figure 23–2 on page 579)

11. Answers will vary; could include: never dive where obstructions might lurk or where you don't know the depth; don't overestimate your ability; and do not dive too deep.

12. Answers may vary. Refer to the Health Strategies on "Water Rescue Techniques" on page 581 for possible answers.

13. Answers will vary; could include: do not operate boating equipment if using alcohol or other drugs; know your boat and the rules of the waterway; make sure there are enough Coast Guard-approved flotation devices for everyone; load the boat reasonably; keep your weight low in the boat; tell someone on shore where you are going and when to expect you back; if the boat upsets or fills with water, hang onto it; and if the weather threatens, skip the trip.

Section VI

14. ring the nearest doorbell, move away from shadowy areas into open, crowded, well-lit areas

Section VII

15. phone numbers of where the parents will be, one or more neighbors, family doctor or pediatrician, police department or sheriff, and the fire department

Straight Talk

16. Answers will vary. Refer to Straight Talk on "Fire Prevention and Escape" starting on page 588.

17. Using water on an electrical or chemical fire can do more harm than good.

18. stop, drop, and roll

ACTIVITIES

1. Investigate the different first aid and lifesaving courses that are available in your community this year. Make a poster and list the dates, locations, and any fees for these courses.

2. Using library resources, research what disasters have occurred in your state. Write a brief summary of your findings.

3. Develop a bicycle safety pamphlet. Include illustrations of specific bicycle parts that should be checked periodically, illustrations of hand signals, and information on safety gear. Describe safety precautions to be taken in various traffic and weather conditions.

4. Obtain and read a new car brochure from an automobile dealer in your community. Describe the safety features built into the car. Rate the automobile strictly from a safety viewpoint. Discuss any features you feel need to be added to make the car safer. Write a one-page report on your investigation and include the brochure.

5. Interview the fire marshal in your area and discuss the most serious problems the Fire Department faces and what students can do to help promote fire safety. Hand in an audio tape of your interview.

6. Hand in a list of seven sources of medical help that could be called in the event of an accident. Identify the name and phone number of each source.

7. Imagine you are a state legislator who is responsible for establishing laws to curtail drinking and driving. Discuss the laws you would propose regarding: suspending and revoking drivers' licenses, plea bargaining, jail sentences, community service, and fines.

8. Investigate the safety belt laws in your state. What do these laws state about securing small children? What is the weight or age a small child must reach before being allowed to use the same safety belt as an adult? Are the laws different for front-seat and back-seat passengers? Are there any fines for not wearing a safety belt or for not securing a small child in a car seat? If so, what are they? Write a brief report on your findings.

9. Create a photo essay on accident prevention tips. Use your photographs to portray five basic safety rules that are general enough to apply to most types of accidents and emergencies covered in the chapter.

10. Interview a counselor from a rape crisis prevention center about the lasting effects a sexual assault has on the victim. Ask the counselor to discuss some of the feelings rape victims share and how they can overcome them. Write a one-page report on your findings and include the name of the person interviewed and the center where the person works.

11. Develop eight original safety slogans for bumper stickers. Design each bumper sticker. Include illustrations on the stickers if you choose.

12. Investigate the new safety features that have been introduced into automobile designs in the last 20 years. Make a poster that illustrates these features.

13. Meet with the school nurse to find out what the most common accidents and injuries are at school. List them and identify ways these accidents could be prevented.

MAKING DECISIONS ABOUT HEALTH

Describe how each of the following situations could best be handled:

1. Your car breaks down on a deserted road at night and you are alone.

2. One of the children you are baby-sitting for has just fallen and received a cut that may require stitches.

3. You are in your home when an earthquake hits.

4. Your friend who is drunk offers you a ride home.

5. You are walking home alone at night and believe you are being followed.

6. The smoke detector in your home has just gone off and awakened you from a sound sleep.

CHAPTER 24 PLANNER

OVERVIEW

Chapter 24 is 32 pages long and divided into the six sections listed to the right. Major learning outcomes are also listed to the right. This chapter introduces students to first aid skills and techniques to be used in emergencies. The chapter emphasizes the importance of knowing what emergency measures to use to help protect and possibly save lives. It is recommended that before you begin this chapter, you become a certified instructor in CPR and first aid through the American Red Cross or the American Heart Association.

MAKING LIFE CHOICES RESOURCES

A variety of activities, handouts, quizzes, and tests to accompany this chapter are available in the *Making Life Choices* supplementary material. You may pick and choose from those materials as appropriate for your amount of class time and the ability levels of your students. Some of the resources you might want to consider using are:

Handouts
• Treatment of Minor and Serious Wounds
• Snakebite Kits: No Substitute for Knowledge

SUGGESTED RESOURCES

Student Readings
1. Carter, S., Monnig, J., and Lee, D. *Coping with Medical Emergencies.* New York: Rosen, 1988.
2. *American Red Cross Standard First Aid* (workbook). Washington, DC: The American Red Cross, 1991.
Teacher Readings
1. American Medical Association. *Handbook of First Aid and Emergency Care.* New York: Random House, 1990.

Videos
1. *American Red Cross Emergency Test.* Cambridge Educational, 800-468-4227.
2. *First Aid for the Home.* Cambridge Educational, 800-468-4227.
Software
1. *Basic First Aid and Illness.* Opportunities for Learning, Inc., 800-243-7116.
2. *First Aid Basics* (for the Apple computer). Cambridge Educational, 800-468-4227.

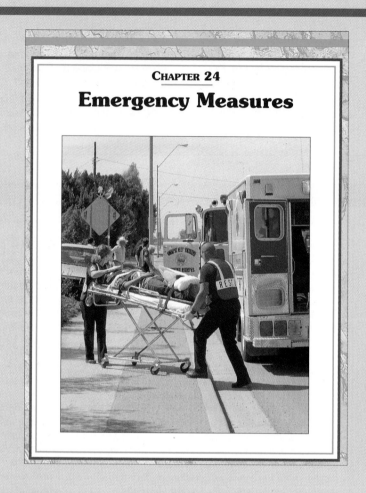

CHAPTER 24
Emergency Measures

CHAPTER PROJECT

Use either this chapter's Life Choice Inventory, the Fact or Fiction questions, or a combination of the two to develop a questionnaire. Then have your students use the questionnaire to survey ten students each in your school to assess the students' individual and the overall student body preparedness for dealing with medical emergencies.

Give students one week to complete their surveys. Instruct them to bring the results to class. You will then need to com-

Activity To Introduce Chapter

Call your community's department responsible for fire and rescue. Ask to have a rescue truck and its personnel come to your class to show students the equipment available on the truck for CPR and first aid emergencies. Ask the emergency medical technicians to share with students the nature of their work, the most frequent type of call they respond to, what their response time is, how citizens contact their local fire and rescue, and how well the community deals with emergency situations before rescue arrives.

NOT ENOUGH TIME?*

You could easily spend three weeks teaching this chapter. If the students read the entire chapter, do a fair number of the suggested activities in the teacher's edition, and complete a sampling of the handouts from the resource material accompanying this text they would have a good understanding of emergency procedures. It is likely, however, that you will have only two or three days to devote to this chapter. The following are some suggestions to help you make sure that you cover the key topics if you have limited time.

TIME	SUGGESTIONS
2 Days	On day 1 read aloud Chapter 24 as a class. Pick several students to read the various sections. At the end of each section, discuss the key points. On day 2 after reading and discussing this chapter, do the Activity to Introduce Chapter, bringing a rescue truck and its personnel to your class to share with the students what they do when responding to emergency cases.
3 Days	On day 3 have students score themselves using the Life Choice Inventory—"How Well Prepared for Emergencies Are You?" found on page 595. Students may then determine how well prepared they would be in responding to a medical emergency.

*Please refer to the 18-week daily lesson plans in the supplementary material for additional suggestions.

Answers to "Fact or Fiction"

Answers to "Fact or Fiction" can be found on page 618.

bine the results from all the surveys. Enlist help from your best students to compile the statistics question by question. Instruct all students to write an analysis of the final results and for overall preparedness, identifying strengths and weaknesses, and making suggestions for ways to improve student preparedness. Involve your school newspaper to use this project to develop total school and community awareness.

To promote discussion, have students write on a piece of paper one question that they would like to have answered by the rescue personnel. Give these questions to the EMTs when they come so that all students' questions can be answered.

After the rescue personnel have finished their presentation, have students do a summary of the presentation listing five new ideas they learned and writing one paragraph on their feelings about the importance of learning CPR and first aid.

FOCUS
SECTION 1

In this section students will learn:

1. What standard supplies should be stocked in the home medicine chest and portable first aid kit.

2. That rubber gloves and a face shield are useful devices for self-protection against the risk of contracting AIDS and other communicable diseases.

Activity 1.1

Supplies and Substitutions. Divide your class into four groups and assign each group one of the four categories of supplies found in Figure 24–1. (Most Important, Bandages and Dressings, Medicines, and Miscellaneous) Tell students to brainstorm possible substitutes for each item in their group's category. (Some items may not have substitutes.) One person should record the ideas or suggestions. Another person should write the list of substitutes on the board. A third member of the group should present the list to the class, indicating what each item is a substitute for. Remaining student groups should offer agreement or disagreement with the list. You should give the final confirmation on each one. **(30 min.; Cooperative Learning, Critical Thinking)**

Teacher Support Notes

① **Emergency:** Students may wonder what is considered an emergency. Give them the following guidelines:

• An oral temperature above 104° F.

• Any serious accident or injury including animal bites, puncture wounds, wounds with much blood loss, severe burns, suspected breaks or fractures, or possible poisoning.

• Falls with possible injury to head or spine followed by headache; vision abnormality; vomiting; bleeding from the ears, nose or mouth; unusual behavior or drowsiness; paralysis; or convulsions.

• Sudden, severe pain or cramps in the abdomen.

• Breathing difficulty.

• Loss of consciousness.

• Persistent, severe headache.

• Possible cardiovascular abnormality.

• Any adverse drug reaction.

• Continuous diarrhea or vomiting.

② **Calling for Help:** Ask students if 911 is the number to call in their community. What other emergency numbers do they know? You may want to make overheads of pages providing local emergency numbers from your local phone books.

594

594   UNIT 7 First Aid and Safety

In an emergency, fast, effective action can save a life, perhaps your own. Many people die needlessly after accidents each year because no one nearby knows how to help effectively. This chapter presents some basic emergency treatment measures. However, understand that reading alone cannot adequately prepare you to be of real help in an emergency. Also, attempts to help without the right knowledge can many times do more harm than good.

Get some training from a qualified instructor who teaches **first aid** in a school, hospital, fire department, or emergency service center. The information here will re-① mind you that emergencies can and do arise and can help you become aware of ways to deal with them. The Life Choice Inventory will show you the basics you need in order to be really helpful in emergencies.

First and most important is to know how to call for help in emergencies. A single call to the number 911 will, in most communities, connect you right away with a **dispatcher**. No money is needed for calls to 911, even from pay phones: they are free.

The dispatcher can, with one call, send out a team of people who can help. These people, plus poison control centers and hospital emergency room personnel, are all

In an emergency call 911.

TEACH
SECTION 1
(Guided and Independent Practice)

Activity 1.2

Item Inventory. Over a period of time collect several of each of the items (or appropriate substitutes) from the list of "Standard Supplies for the Medicine Chest." (Figure 24–1) In many cases, you won't need the item itself. Instead, just obtain the container for it or make a substitute item by labeling a different container. You could also enlist the help of students and colleagues to collect appropriate empty containers or substitute items. Students could receive extra credit for this work. Place a variety of the containers in several cardboard boxes. Each box should be numbered and include different inventories. Divide students into teams. Give each team a box of these supplies. The team is to make an inventory of the items in its box, listing information such as whether or not the item is listed in Figure 24-1, if it's an appropriate substitute, what it's a substitute for, if it's needed for first aid kit, etc. Students should turn their completed papers in to you with the box number they worked from. **(15 min.; Cooperative Learning, Critical Thinking)**

LIFE CHOICE INVENTORY

How Well Prepared for Emergencies Are You? ①

Answer each question true or false to see how well prepared you are for emergencies.

1. I have a well-stocked medicine chest (or my family does).
2. I carry a first aid kit in my car (or my family does).
3. My (my family's) emergency supplies include face masks and gloves to protect us from exposure to blood.
4. I own an up-to-date first aid manual, and I can put my hands on it when I need it.
5. I have taken a first aid course.
6. I know how to give CPR (cardiopulmonary resuscitation).
7. I know how to perform the Heimlich maneuver.
8. On the scene of an accident, I know what to do first, second, third, and fourth.
9. I know the emergency telephone number for my area.
10. I know how to determine whether I should attempt a rescue or whether the attempt might threaten my own life.

SCORING

Give yourself 1 point for each true answer.

8–10: Excellent. You are well prepared for emergencies.

6–7: Good. You are better prepared than average, but you may want to fill in the gaps in your knowledge.

4–5: Fair. You are on your way to becoming a competent manager of emergencies. Learn more.

Below 4: Poor. You have much to learn. A good way to begin is to read this chapter.

---

known as the **emergency medical service (EMS)**. ②

Other communities may rely on other forms of emergency help. If you don't know how to contact the services available to you, find out today by looking in the front section of your phone book, or by dialing the telephone operator to ask.

If you know how to give first aid, you may be able to save a life. Give help if you know what to do. At home, this means setting things up ahead of time so as to have the needed supplies on hand. On a trip, it means carrying such supplies with you.

MINI GLOSSARY

first aid: literally, "help given first"—medical help given immediately in an emergency, before the victim is transported to a hospital or treatment center.

dispatcher: a person who answers calls and relays messages to the proper helping service.

emergency medical service (EMS): a team of people who are trained to respond in emergencies, and who can be contacted through a single dispatcher.

Teacher Support Notes

① **Are They Prepared?**
Have students number from 1 to 10 on a sheet of paper and answer true or false to each of the ten items in the inventory. Some of the questions will need to be answered at home or after students have had an opportunity to talk to their parents about a few of the items. Discuss the results of the inventory in class. What actions do the students plan to take? An alternative approach is to have students exchange their papers after doing the inventory, and then have the student grading each paper make recommendations for improvement. Ask more advanced students also to supply a rationale for their recommendations.

② **Emergency Personnel:** Ask students if they know anyone who works in the emergency medical service. Has the person told stories of his or her experiences? What sorts of emergencies has the person had to deal with?

EVALUATE
SECTION 1

Activity 1.3
  Pop Quiz.
1. Training is as important as proper supplies when dealing with medical emergencies. (T)
2. First aid travel kits should contain all standard medical supplies. (F)

3. There is a risk of contracting AIDS when administering first aid. (T)
4. A face shield will help protect you from exposure to body fluids when giving mouth-to-mouth breathing assistance. (T)
5. Rubber gloves will help protect you from exposure to blood and body fluids when giving first aid. (T)
6. Face shields can be used over and over again. (F)
7. You may not substitute items for the

standard first aid supplies. (F)
8. The Red Cross publication *Standard First Aid* should be available for use when giving first aid in a medical emergency. (T)
9. Tweezers should be included in a first aid kit kept in the car. (F)
10. Large safety pins should be a part of your car first aid kit. (T)

Teacher Support Notes

① **Medicine Chest:** Ask students if there is one place in their homes where medical and first aid supplies are stored. Have they ever used any of the first aid equipment in the medicine chest? Without inspecting the chest, which of the items listed on this page do they think are contained in their medicine chests at home? Do they have any items in their medicine chests that are not listed on this page? After discussing this in class, have students inspect the medicine chest at home and make an inventory (complete list) of every item, excluding prescription medicines. Have them compare their lists to the items listed in Figure 24–1. Students should then write a statement regarding their families' preparedness for emergencies. They should state strengths and weaknesses.

② **Most Important Items:** Ask students if they know why these first two items are included. Tell them a similar list would not have included these items several years ago. If they don't guess, tell them that the AIDS epidemic has made items such as these essential.

FIGURE 24-1

Standard Supplies for the Medicine Chest   ①

Items marked with an asterisk (*) should be included in a first aid kit kept in the car.

Item	Purpose
Most Important	
*Disposable rubber gloves ②	To protect you from disease when you assist a bleeding person
*Pocket mask	To protect your airways when you give breathing assistance
Bandages and Dressings	
*Ace bandages, 3-inch	To wrap and hold sterile dressings or splints in place
*Rolled white gauze bandages, 2- and 3-inch widths	To wrap and hold sterile dressings or splints in place
*Ready-to-apply sterile first aid dressings, individually packaged, various sizes	To apply directly to open wounds or burns
*Triangular bandages, 36 x 36 inches	To fold diagonally, as slings for fractured or broken arms or shoulders; to hold dressings in place; to make into folded compresses
*Rolls of sticky tape, 2- and 3-inch widths	To be cut to size for simple wounds
*Bandaids, various widths and shapes	To cover minor cuts and scrapes
Medicines	
Aspirin or aspirin substitute[a]	To relieve pain
*Antiseptic cream or petroleum jelly	To prevent bandages sticking to minor wounds; to keep wounds sterile
*Liquid antiseptic	To cleanse skin surfaces in cases of minor wounds
Calamine lotion	To relieve itching from insect bites or exposure to skin irritants
*Table salt packets[b]	To treat shock with salted fluids if told to do so
Syrup of ipecac[b]	To induce vomiting in certain cases of poisoning if told to do so
Activated charcoal[b]	To treat certain cases of poisoning if told to do so
Epsom salts[b]	To use as a laxative, to treat certain cases of poisoning if told to do so
Miscellaneous	
*Adhesive tape	To fasten bandages or dressings
*Large safety pins	To fasten bandages or slings
Tweezers	To remove splinters or insect stingers
*Blunt-tipped scissors	To cut lengths of bandages, adhesive tape, and the like
Thermometer(s)	To take rectal or oral temperature
Hypoallergenic soap	To cleanse wounds
*Absorbent cotton, paper tissues	To wipe and cleanse wounds

[a]Reye's syndrome is a rare and potentially life threatening condition linked to aspirin use associated with chicken pox or flu. Children and teenagers should never take aspirin. They should be treated with an aspirin substitute such as acetaminophen.
[b]You should have these supplies on hand so that when you call for help in an emergency, you can use them as directed.

Review Questions. Before going on to the next lesson, students should be able to answer these questions:
1. What two self-protective items should always be available to minimize the risk of AIDS and other communicable diseases

when administering first aid?
2. Explain the application or use of these two self-protective items when administering first aid. How are they used and for what purpose?

FOCUS
SECTION II

In this section students will learn:
1. The necessity for making assess-

ments when an emergency strikes.
2. The three action steps to take in sequence when dealing with an emergency situation.

Activity 2.1
Emergency Scene Actions. To get students thinking critically and to raise the student interest level, open class with a dramatic scene planned ahead of time

(continued on next page)

SECTION I

The Medicine Chest and the First Aid Kit

To best offer emergency treatment, you need the right supplies and the right training. Stock your home medicine chest with the equipment listed in Figure 24–1 and take a first aid course to learn how to use it. On trips, take along a first aid kit, so that the supplies will go wherever you go. The items marked with an asterisk (*) in Figure 24–1 are all a traveling first aid kit need contain.

The risk of contracting AIDS and other diseases makes it important to have self-protective items in your first aid kit. The two most useful devices are shown in Figure 24–2. Rubber gloves will protect you from exposure to the blood or body fluids of anyone who might have a disease. A face shield will permit you to give breathing assistance without direct mouth-to-mouth contact. Face shields come in rolls and are disposable. You can drop one over the face of the person, breathe through the rectangle of gauzy material in the middle,

and throw it away when you are through.

If you don't have the supplies named here, find substitutes. For example, if you have no gauze to cover wounds or burns, substitute freshly laundered clothing. A standard reference, such as the American Red Cross publication *Standard First Aid*, will help remind you of what to do in emergencies. Keep it close at hand.

Key Points ▶ *To help in emergencies, a person must have access to basic first aid supplies or make substitutes from materials at hand.*

SECTION I REVIEW

Learning the Vocabulary
The vocabulary terms in this section are *first aid, dispatcher,* and *emergency medical services (EMS).*
1. Write a sentence using each vocabulary term.

Learning the Facts
2. What is the first and most important thing to do in an emergency?
3. What do you need to have to best offer emergency treatment?
4. What are two items needed in your first aid kits that will help protect you from contracting AIDS?

Making Life Choices
5. Look at Figure 24–1. Do you have a first aid kit at home? If not, why not? If so, does it have all the items listed in Figure 24–1? Do you have first aid kits in all your cars?

Use rubber gloves to avoid contact with blood or body fluids.

Use a face shield to give breathing assistance.

Figure 24–2 Self-Protective Devices for Giving First Aid Safely

SECTION II

First Actions

When emergency strikes, what should you do? Take a moment to think clearly and take these three actions:

with the cooperation of student volunteers. Example: A student is passed out on the floor, broken plastic is scattered around to represent broken glass, water is on the floor, an electric cord is lying across the victim (student), who is cut and bleeding. Ask students, not involved in the scene, to list on a piece of paper all

the observations they can make of the actions *you* take as you enter and deal with this emergency situation. You should display both correct and incorrect actions as you proceed through the three action steps identified in this section of the chapter. (Give them about five minutes to observe this scene.) Ask students to look over their lists and mark each action observed with either a Y (yes) for

those actions they view as being correct or an N (no) for those actions they view as being incorrect. Initiate a discussion in which students share what they observed about your actions. Ask, "What should I have done that you did not see me do?" Next, ask students to read in their textbooks "First Actions" and "Step 1: Survey The Scene and Victims." Allow about five minutes for reading. Now, ask them again what was right or wrong with your actions. Repeat

Teacher Support Notes

① **Surveying the Scene:** A great deal of information is provided on this page. After students have read the explanations in step 1, have them close their books and, as a group, see how many of the procedures they can remember. The key points are:
• Get someone to call for help
• Assess the danger—don't put yourself in jeopardy
• Determine if someone else can help
• Avoid moving the injured party or move the person as little as possible
• Help the person who needs it most, first
• Get information from the patient if possible
• Look for clues to what happened

66 Thoughts on Health 99

A timid person is frightened before a danger, a coward during the time, and a courageous person afterwards.
– John Paul Richter

• Survey the scene for safety and information and inspect the victim swiftly (2 to 4 minutes). Help only if there are immediate threats to life.
• Phone for help (2 to 3 minutes).
• Inspect the victim more closely (2 to 5 minutes).

The sections that follow describe each of these three actions.

Step 1: Survey the Scene and Victims (2 to 4 Minutes)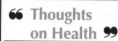

In surveying the scene quickly, you should ask yourself:

• Is it safe?
• What has happened?
• Are there victims? How many?

Get someone to call for help right away if you can.

As for yourself, first and foremost, don't rush in. Look around. Is it safe? Are hazards present, such as fire, fumes, fast traffic, live electrical wires, or fast-moving water? If the hazards are extreme, do not attempt rescue. Placing yourself in harm's way serves no one. Don't let haste or a false sense of bravery make you a victim.

As you survey the scene, survey the people around you. Might there be other victims nearby? Who can help by controlling crowds, or by directing traffic? Ask them to do whatever is needed.

Do not move anyone. Assume that every accident victim has an injured neck or spine. Further injury to the spinal cord can cause permanent paralysis or death.

The only exception to this rule is if you must move someone to save a life *and* if you can do so safely.

If you must move someone, and can do so safely, keep on assuming that the spine may be injured. Move the shortest possible

distance. Keep the head and body in line. If possible, pull from the head end, with your hands under the shoulders and the head resting on your arms. Pull the person in a straight line.

If the person is floating in water face down, you must move the person a little. (Remember, don't risk your own life.) If you can walk in and stand while you do it, roll the person face up as a unit and pull the person out of the water just enough to permit you to start giving breathing help.

If several people are injured, help first the one who seems to need your help most, and can benefit from it. Most urgent is to help those with the life-threatening A, B, C, and S conditions described on the next page.

First, speak to the person, Reassure: "I am here to help you." Get information: "What happened?" Caution: "Please don't try to move until help arrives."

The responses to these questions will tell you things you must report when you call for help. A victim who can answer you is conscious; an inappropriate answer may suggest injury to the head. When you know what happened, you can guess how the injury occurred and how serious it is. You can guess if the spine is injured.

If the victim cannot speak, look around quickly for clues. For example, should you find an unconscious person lying near a tipped canoe in shallow water you might suspect that the person had inhaled water or sustained a blow to the head. On finding a crying child lying near a bicycle you might suspect broken bones, and so on.

Say who you are. If the victim can talk, ask for permission to help. If you have been trained by a professional instructor, say so, but you cannot make the claim of being trained in first aid after simply reading a chapter such as this one.

TEACH
SECTION **II**
(Guided and Independent Practice)

Activity 2.2
The Good Samaritan Law. Have students investigate the Good Samaritan law in your state using the following questions as guidelines. (A Good Samaritan law is one that protects people who help others in emergencies from being sued for accidentally doing the wrong thing or not doing the right thing.)
1. What is the degree of legal protection a rescuer has when helping a victim?
2. What does your state law say are the guidelines for deciding if a person is protected against or open for lawsuit? OR:
Get a copy of your state's Good Samaritan law, read it to your students, and discuss the degree of protection afforded the rescuer. Ask students for examples of what might constitute gross negligence or willful misconduct. **(10 min., Advanced)**

(continued on next page)

In inspecting each victim, you are looking for four life-threatening conditions, and for three other conditions that you must report when you call for help. The four life-threatening conditions you must look for are:

A Airway—is it blocked?
B Breathing—has it stopped?
C Circulation—has the heartbeat stopped?
S Severe bleeding—is blood pulsing or welling up from a wound?

The other three things to notice are:

- Is the person conscious?
- Does the person have a neck or spinal injury?
- Is the person in shock?

For A, B, C, and S, you must give help right away. Courses that teach **CPR** or **cardiopulmonary resuscitation** explain how to correct these conditions. Often you can rule them out, but if you can't, proceed as follows.

Figure 24–3 shows how to find these immediate threats to life. Concentrate and do not let anyone interrupt you. Inspect the victims, allowing just a minute or two for each. Follow these steps.

Airway and Breathing: To check for a blocked airway and for breathing, place your ear and cheek close to the victim's mouth and nose. Look, listen, and use the sensitive skin of your cheek to feel for breathing, as shown in Figure 24–4 on the next page. Chest movements alone don't mean breathing is occurring; they may just be muscle spasms that mimic breathing.

Circulation: At the same time, determine if the person's heart is beating. Take the **carotid pulse,** also depicted in Figure 24–4. To be sure you'll be able to find it in an emergency, practice on yourself right now.

Severe Bleeding: The spurting of blood from a large artery can reduce the body's

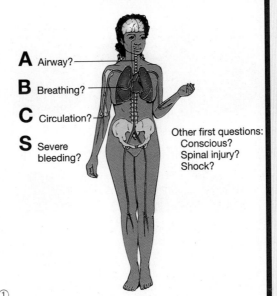

A Airway?
B Breathing?
C Circulation?
S Severe bleeding?

Other first questions:
Conscious?
Spinal injury?
Shock?

Figure 24–3 The Primary Survey: A, B, C, S

supply of blood dangerously in just seconds. Respond quickly to stop it as instructed on page 610.

While providing care, keep shouting for help if no one has called yet. If no one responds, then wait to call until after you have controlled airway, breathing, circulation, and severe bleeding the best you can.

MINI **G**LOSSARY

CPR (cardiopulmonary resuscitation): a technique of maintaining blood and oxygen flow through the body of a person whose heart and breathing have stopped.
carotid (ca-ROT-id) **pulse:** the pulse in either of the carotid arteries, the main arteries next to the airway (and "Adam's apple") in the front of the neck.

When the vital four conditions are controlled, check or review three other things and then go make your call. Here are the three:

Teacher Support Notes

① **CPR:** At this point, you may want to refer students back to Chapter 18 for a quick review of the cardiovascular system. Then tell them that cardiopulmonary resuscitation is a lifesaving technical procedure that requires exactness and good physical coordination. Simple textbook knowledge on how to administer CPR is not enough. Correct practice at frequent intervals is required. A manikin—not a healthy person—should be used during CPR practice sessions. Training in a formal course of instruction is offered and certified by either the American Heart Association or the American National Red Cross.

✉ **Where to Write**

American Red Cross
17th and D St., NW
Washington, DC
20006

Activity 2.3

Guest Speaker. Invite a Red Cross or American Heart Association volunteer/instructor to visit your class to talk to your students about taking a CPR course. Ask them to address at least the following information:
1. Locations where classes are offered

2. Times when classes meet
3. Which courses are offered
4. Which certifications can be earned
5. Number of hours of training required for certifications
6. Age requirements
7. Validity periods for certifications
8. Cost for taking a course
9. Which courses are needed for jobs in day care and lifeguarding
(25–45 min.; Extend, Enrich)

Activity 2.4
Pop Quiz.
1. To determine if a person's heart is beating you should check the carotid pulse. (T)
2. Moving a victim is okay if you think no spinal or neck injury is involved. (F)

Teacher Support Notes

① **Shock:** You may want to give students some additional information at this point about shock. Tell them that the state of shock may develop rapidly or may be delayed until hours after the event. Shock occurs to some degree after every injury; it may be so slight as not to be noticed or so serious that it results in death even though the injuries received ordinarily would not prove fatal. Some of the major causes of shock are the severe loss of blood, intense pain, severe injury, burns, anxiety, poisonous gases, surgical operations, extremes of heat or cold, electrical shock, allergic reactions, bites and stings of poisonous snakes or insects, poisons taken internally, certain illnesses, emotional stress, and intense emotion.

② **Calling for Help:** Have students close their books after studying the bulleted list of items they need to remember before calling. Have them practice writing each of the six items from memory until they can list all six quickly and easily.

600   UNIT 7 First Aid and Safety

Touch the Adam's apple lightly, using two fingers.

Slide your fingers into the groove next to the Adam's apple. You should feel a pulse.

In an infant, look for a pulse in the arm.

Figure 24–4 Airway, Breathing, and Circulation. Look, listen, and feel: *Look* at the person's chest for the rise and fall of breathing. *Listen* for breathing. *Feel* with your cheek for moving air. *Feel* for the carotid pulse.

- Is the victim conscious?
- Are neck and other spinal injuries a possibility?
- Is the victim in shock?

You have checked to see if the person is conscious. You have surveyed the scene and determined what has happened, so you have some idea whether neck or other spinal injuries have occurred. Also check for **shock**.

In shock, the circulation is disrupted. Shock has many causes, but presents one danger: it can cause death. It is very common in accident victims. It can come on fast, or in stages. At first, blood flow to the brain may diminish, causing loss of consciousness. Blood supply to other vital organs may also fail, and the heart itself may fail.

The signs and symptoms of shock are shown in Figure 24–5. It demands professional emergency treatment. Notice if the victim seems to be in shock, and call for help. Other injuries, such as broken bones, can wait.

Key Points ▸ The first action in an emergency is to survey the scene to determine whether or not it is safe, what may have happened, and who is available to help. The first inspection of a victim serves to identify and treat for the four life-threatening conditions—(A) blocked airway, (B) failure to breathe, (C) no circulation, and (S) severe bleeding. Give help for these. Inspect for consciousness, spinal injuries, and shock, and call for help.

Step 2: Calling for Help

When you call for help, you must report:

- Your name.
- Where you are.
- The telephone number you are calling from.
- What has happened.
- How many victims there are.
- How each is hurt.

In a serious emergency, it is urgent that someone call for help at the earliest possible moment. If you are the only one avail-

3. If you must move someone, do not touch his/her head, neck, or back; pull gently by his/her feet. (F)
4. In a primary survey, the A of the ABCs means "Assume" that every accident victim has an injured neck. (F)
5. If an injured person is conscious, you should ask the victim for permission to help. (T)
6. When several people are injured, help the person with the most life-threatening

condition first. (T)
7. When you call for help, time is best saved by reporting the place of the accident only. (F)
8. When you conduct a secondary survey, it is best not to touch the person. Instead, ask the victim questions to gain information. (T)
9. Never endanger yourself to save someone else's life. Get help first. (T)
10. Always protect yourself against exposure to infectious disease by using a face shield or another type of barrier when performing rescue breathing. (T)
(10 min.; Reteach, Reinforce)

CLOSE
▶ **SECTION II**

Activity 2.5
Review Questions. Before going on

(continued on next page)

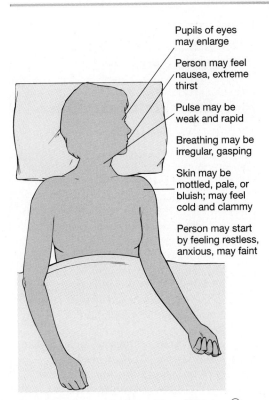

- Pupils of eyes may enlarge
- Person may feel nausea, extreme thirst
- Pulse may be weak and rapid
- Breathing may be irregular, gasping
- Skin may be mottled, pale, or bluish; may feel cold and clammy
- Person may start by feeling restless, anxious, may faint

Figure 24–5 Signs and Symptoms of Shock ①

able and you have been trained in first aid techniques, give first aid first, then call.

The key to making an effective call is to be prepared to give the needed information. If you send someone else to make the call, be sure that person knows all the needed information.

Here is an example of a poor accident report: "I'm somewhere downtown and I've just seen an accident. It's awful. Please come quickly." (Click.)

Here is an example of a useful report: "This is Kevin White. I'm at the intersection of Adams and Congress streets, at the pay phone. The number here is 625-4949. A truck has hit a car head on, and two people were thrown out of the car. One is bleeding, not badly, but I think he's going

into shock. He's very pale, his hands are cold, and he seems confused. The other one is trapped under the car, he's unconscious but breathing OK. Before losing consciousness, he said he had no feeling in his legs. The truck driver is OK. I have a first aid kit with me, but I haven't been trained in first aid. What do you want me to do?"

From the second report, the dispatcher knows how many ambulances and what personnel and equipment to send. The caller kept a level head and gathered all the necessary information before calling.

Key Points ▶ *Call emergency services. Provide accurate information.*

Step 3: Secondary Survey of Victims (2 to 5 Minutes)

The secondary survey is a head-to-toe survey, and should be swift. You have checked for life-threatening conditions, have controlled the ones you can, and have called for help, so now you are inspecting the victim for less severe, but still serious, injuries. Such injuries may require first aid to prevent their getting worse.

The best way to start is to ask the victim about pain. Injured areas usually hurt (although spinal injuries may not). Don't touch or move the painful part, except to provide the needed aid. Pain in breathing indicates a problem in the chest or abdomen.

Conduct a rapid inspection, not more than five minutes in duration. Start with the head and work downward. Look for bumps, bruises, blood, or any odd formations or positions of body parts. Repeat: if

Mɪɴɪ **G**ʟᴏssᴀʀʏ

shock: failure or disruption of the blood circulation, a life-threatening reaction to accidents and injuries.

Teacher Support Notes

① **Signs of Shock:** You may want to comment on the precise use of language here. *Sign* means something the first-aider sees, hears, or feels—for example, a pale face, no respiration, or cold skin. A *symptom* is something the victim tells about himself, such as, feels nauseous, his back hurts, or he has no sensation in the extremities. The first-aider, of course, wants all the information he or she can gather—both signs and symptoms, and any information that bystanders might have in evaluating the nature of a given illness or injury. Signs are important in shock because frequently the victim is unable to speak. Some signs the first-aider might notice in addition to those shown in the illustration are anxious or dull expressions, mental confusion and disorientation, and weakness or dizziness.

to the next lesson, students should be able to answer these questions:

1. List three emergency action steps, in proper sequence, when dealing with an emergency situation.

2. For each of the three emergency action steps, explain why you take the step, and how you carry it out.

3. List three possible risk categories for the rescuer when giving aid in an emergency situation.

4. State the rule regarding moving a victim.

5. State the only exception to the rule regarding moving a victim.

6. How do you check the person for a clear airway, breathing, and circulation? Discuss the answers to these questions

in class. **(10 min.; Reteach, Reinforce)**

Activity 2.6

Rescue Scenario. Tell students, "Pretend you are a rescuer in an accident. Create a scenario and write a report you would give on the phone to rescue personnel when calling in the accident." **(5 min., Advanced)**

Section II Review

Answers

1. carotid pulse

2. CPR (cardiopulmonary resuscitation)

3. shock

4. that every accident victim has an injured neck or spine

5. blocked airway, no breathing, no circulation, severe bleeding

6. your name, where you are, the telephone number you are calling from, what has happened, how many victims there are, how each is hurt

7. Answers will vary.

✍ Fast Facts

Approximately 3,200 Americans die each year as a result of choking.

---

you suspect head, neck, or back injuries, do not move the person at all except to get out of immediate danger.

Healthy limbs move freely. If you do not suspect neck or back injuries, ask the person to *slowly* move each joint. For example, a person with a broken collar bone would not be able to shrug the shoulders. Do not lift or try to move the joints for the victim. You may dislocate the ends of a broken bone or worsen other injuries in doing so.

During this close inspection of the victim, keep the person lying quietly until you are certain no serious injury exists. Meanwhile, help defend the person's body temperature. Provide blankets if necessary. Help the victim rest comfortably. Treat all conditions according to the instructions in the following sections. Always stay aware of the person's breathing and heartbeat.

The Health Strategies section on this page reviews the first actions in emergencies as described so far. The next sections return to the A, B, C, and S life-threatening conditions to give details of treatment.

Key Points *A close inspection of the victim can reveal injuries that require treatment to prevent further damage.*

SECTION II REVIEW

Learning the Vocabulary

The vocabulary terms in this section are *CPR (cardiopulmonary resuscitation), carotid pulse,* and *shock.*

Match each of the following phrases with the vocabulary term from above.

1. the heartbeat in the main arteries in the front of the neck
2. techniques of maintaining blood and oxygen flow through the body of a person whose heart has stopped
3. life-threatening reaction to injuries

Learning the Facts

4. What should you always assume about an accident victim?

5. What are the four life-threatening conditions to look for when calling for help?
6. What information should you report when you call for help?

Making Life Choices

7. Reread the Health Strategies box above. Why is it important to follow these steps in order? How can you encourage other people to learn these steps?

HEALTH STRATEGIES

Emergency Actions

A helper should first take these actions in an emergency:

- Survey the scene for any danger, such as traffic or toxic gases. Take action to evade danger.
- Don't help if you are likely to lose your life or be severely injured yourself.
- Assume each victim's neck is broken. Do not move anyone at all, except to escape immediate danger.
- Check quickly for life-threatening conditions: (A) blocked airway, (B) no breathing, (C) no circulation, (S) severe bleeding.
- If any of these are present, quickly take appropriate steps to correct them.
- Check or recheck for consciousness, spinal injuries, and shock.
- Call or have someone else call emergency services for help.
- Inspect the victim again to identify other injuries.
- Do nothing to worsen injuries and do not rush recovery.
- Provide first aid for each condition.
- Maintain the victim's temperature and comfort.

In this section students will learn:
1. How to clear a blocked airway when a person is choking by using the Heimlich maneuver.
2. What to do to deliver air to a person who has stopped breathing.

Activity 3.1
Universal Gesture for Choking.
At the beginning of class, inform students they will be studying the Heimlich maneuver. Tell them you are going to make five different distress gestures, which they are to observe. With each gesture they should try to guess what message you are trying to convey. Let them guess after each gesture. (The purpose here is to give four general distress gestures that

could easily be interpreted in numerous ways. Examples: throwing your hands in the air and waving them around; a coughing or vomiting type of noise; just pointing to your face or head area.) One of the gestures that you give should be the universal sign for choking, placing your hands at your throat. Discuss why this gesture is the best. **(5–10 min., Critical Thinking)**

SECTION III

A and B: Airway and Breathing Assistance

If breathing stops, restoring it is urgent. Within five minutes after breathing stops, death occurs in over 50 percent of people. Almost all others die within ten minutes. Many emergencies can stop a person's breathing: allergic reactions, burns, drug overdoses, poisoning, and others. To help someone who has stopped breathing, though, you need not know the cause, except in one instance—choking (a blocked airway). Everyone should learn to give and to recognize the universal distress signal for choking shown in Figure 24–6.

The Heimlich Maneuver

When someone is choking, you must perform the **Heimlich maneuver** immediately. Take these steps:

1. First, ask, "Can you make any sound at all?"

If the victim makes a sound, air is moving over the vocal cords, which means that some air can get into the lungs. In this case, the person can try bending over, coughing, and other self-help maneuvers before you intervene. Whatever you do, don't hit the victim on the back, or the particle caught in the throat may lodge deeper in the air passage.

If the victim cannot make a sound, this means the airway is blocked. Your next moves are to:

2. Shout for help.
3. Perform the Heimlich maneuver as shown in Figure 24–7 on the next page.

Position the person, place your fist above the navel (belly button) as shown, grasp

Figure 24–6 Universal Distress Signal for Choking. A person giving this signal has a blocked airway and needs help right away.

your fist with your other hand, and thrust inward and upward four or five times in rapid succession to propel the obstacle out of the throat.

① If the person is large or unconscious, you can perform the maneuver while the victim remains lying on his or her back. Kneel astride the thighs, and place your fist below the rib cage. Press on your fist with your other hand, quickly and firmly, upward, four times. Be sure to make contact with
② your fist before the thrust—don't punch, but press suddenly.

MINI GLOSSARY

Heimlich (HIME-lick) **maneuver:** a technique of dislodging a particle that is blocking a person's airway, named for the physician who invented it.

Teacher Support Notes

① **When *Not* to Act:** Make sure students realize that while they must act quickly when someone is choking, they should not overreact and try to use the Heimlich maneuver when it is not necessary. Tell them that if the victim is able to speak or cough effectively, they should *not* interfere with the victim's attempts to expel the foreign particle.

② **Abdomen:** Emphasize with students that they are not to punch the victim. They should place their fists firmly against the victim's abdomen before thrusting. Also make sure that all students know the location of the abdomen. They must start the movement below the rib cage.

TEACH
SECTION III
(Guided and Independent Practice)

Activity 3.2
Role-Playing. Have students read the first paragraph under "The Heimlich Maneuver." Ask a student to volunteer as your victim. Then ask that student to stand with hands at throat. (Use this opportunity to have classmates identify the universal

sign for choking again.) Do the following:
1. Say, "Are you choking? Can you speak? I can help you."
2. The student makes a high-pitched wheezing sound.
3. Say, "Keep trying to clear your throat. I will stay with you."
4. You might even place your hand on his/her arm or shoulder to help him/her remain calm or not panic.

Have pairs of students role-play simi-

lar situations. **(3–5 min.; Extend, Enrich)**

Activity 3.3
Demonstrating the Heimlich Maneuver. Explain and demonstrate the three steps to be taken when performing the Heimlich maneuver on a completely obstructed airway. Using a student volunteer (he/she should have his/her hands at his/her throat) go through the steps:
1. Say, "Can you speak? I can help you."

Teacher Support Notes

① **Chest Thrust:** In some cases a victim may be overweight or pregnant so that it is impossible for the rescuer to get his or her arms around the victim's abdomen. Tell students that in such a case they should use a chest thrust. Hands are positioned in the same way as the abdominal thrust but the arms are wrapped around the person's chest so that the fist is on the middle of the victim's breastbone. The rescuer then pushes with quick, *backward* thrusts.

② **Breathing Assistance:** You may want to tell students that breathing assistance is often needed with drowning victims. The rescuer's first priority is to get the victim to shore. As the rescuer moves the victim to shore, two full breaths should be given and the pulse checked. The rescuer should continue giving a slow breath every five seconds and checking the pulse every minute. Breathing assistance should continue on shore. It is normal for the victim to vomit water from the stomach in the recovery from drowning; the first-aider should turn the victim's head to the side to prevent choking.

604

604 UNIT 7 First Aid and Safety

For a person who can stand:

Stand behind the person. Ball up your fist. Rotate your thumb toward the person's stomach. Grasp your fist with your other hand and position it against the abdomen just below the rib cage. Squeeze rapidly, inward and upward—one, two, three, four times in rapid succession. The object is to propel air upwards out of the lungs and eject the article from the throat. Repeat, if necessary. ①

For yourself:

Use the back of a chair or the edge of a table to push against, and perform the same maneuver.

Figure 24–7 Unblocking the Airway with the Heimlich Maneuver

If it is you who is choking, you can act as your own rescuer by thrusting your fist into your own abdomen, or thrusting your body forward forcefully against a firmly placed object—the back of a chair, side of a table, or edge of a sink or stove.

Often, the Heimlich maneuver is all it takes to save a life. One student who rescued his mother this way reports that her first words, as soon as she could speak, were: "Teach this to everyone else in the family, right now." He did.

> **Key Points** *If a person is choking, use the Heimlich maneuver. This technique can dislodge a particle that is caught in the throat and is blocking breathing.*

Breathing Assistance

What if the person is unconscious and you don't know if something is lodged in the throat? Don't use the Heimlich maneuver. Assume the airway is clear, because it nearly always is.

Do check the mouth, though, because something in the mouth could fall into the throat and block the airway. Don't move the person unless you have to, for access. If you move the person, keep the spine straight. Position the person and clear the mouth as shown in Figure 24–8. ②

Even now, the airway may be collapsed shut. Open it without disturbing the neck bones, as shown in Figure 24–9.

2. Your volunteer should shake his/her head no and should not make a sound.

3. Say, "Help!"

4. Perform the Heimlich maneuver. (Simulate abdominal thrusts with hands in the correct position.)

(3–5 min.; Extend, Enrich)

Activity 3.4

Student Simulations. Pair up students in your class and have each pair practice (perform by simulation only) in unison as you call out each of the steps for the Heimlich maneuver. Step 1—They should say in unison after you, "Can you speak? I can help you." Step 2—They should say in unison after you, "Help!" Step 3—All should move into the correct hand position for abdominal thrusts and you should check each one before letting them go on. Make suggestions and corrections wherever necessary. Be sure to caution them again that when demonstrating abdominal thrusts they are to simulate only. **(5–7 min.; Extend, Enrich)**

Activity 3.5
Pop Quiz.

1. The universal distress signal for chok-

(continued on next page)

---

1. If you must roll the person over, keep the spine straight as shown.

2. Use a finger. Be careful. Don't push anything down the throat. Sweep out anything you find in the mouth.

Figure 24–8 Preparing to Give Breathing Assistance

Tongue is out of the way and airway is open.

Tongue is blocking airway.

If head and neck are flat on the ground, the tongue can block the airway.

Hold the forehead, lift the chin, and the tongue will move out of the way.

Alternative: Open the jaw without moving the neck, as shown.

Infant: Don't tilt the head back. The force of your breath will open the airway.

Figure 24–9 Opening the Airway ①

Teacher Support Notes

① **Opening the Airway:** As students study these illustrations, you may want to reinforce the point made earlier about minimal movement, as stated in the caption beneath the lower left-hand drawing. The rescuer should try to open the jaw without moving the neck in case there is a neck injury. Further injury to the spinal cord can cause permanent paralysis or death.

> **Fast Facts**
>
> Some people have been saved after as many as eight hours of artificial respiration.

EVALUATE
(Continued)

ing is to put the hands at the throat. (T)
2. Never hit a choking victim on the back. (T)
3. The first step of the Heimlich maneuver is to shout for help. (F)
4. A partially obstructed airway means some air is getting through. (T)

5. If a victim has a completely obstructed airway, he/she will be unconscious. (F)
6. When breathing stops, it must be restored within four to six minutes before death or brain damage may occur. (T)
7. To clear your own airway when it is blocked, use the back of a chair for abdominal thrusts. (T)
8. The Heimlich maneuver may not be performed on an unconscious person. (F)
9. The techniques for performing the

Heimlich maneuver on others and yourself are the same. (F)
10. A person should receive special training to give breathing assistance to a person who has stopped breathing. (T)
(5 min.; Reteach, Reinforce)

CLOSE
SECTION III

Teacher Support Notes

① Rescue Breathing— Common Mistakes:

Tell students to guard against the following common mistakes made while administering rescue breathing:
• Failure to give two full breaths initially
• Failure to allow the victim to exhale between breaths; the lungs must deflate fully
• Giving too many or too few breaths
• Not keeping an adult's head tilted back far enough or tilting an infant's or child's head too far back
• Failure to form an adequate seal around the victim's mouth and/or nose
• Failure to pinch the nostrils tightly closed

The rescuer should continue resuscitation efforts until one of the following occurs:
• effective, spontaneous circulation and respiration have been restored
• resuscitation efforts have been transferred to another responsible person
• the rescuer is exhausted and unable to continue

To learn to properly perform the breathing assistance method described here, a person should obtain first aid training and practice on a model of a victim. Several hazards make the procedure risky for untrained people to try:

• If you blow air into the stomach, it may cause vomiting. This can block the airway and make breathing impossible.
• If you try to move the head of someone with a neck injury, it may cause permanent paralysis.
• You have to know when to stop giving assistance. When a victim begins to breathe spontaneously but weakly, continued efforts on your part using a different rhythm may shut the victim's spontaneous breathing down.
• If you force air into a drowning person's lungs when the person is struggling to cough up water, you may push water into the lungs.

• The procedures for helping adults can harm infants.

The details are too numerous to cover adequately in this chapter, but too important to skip. For these reasons, the next two figures show how to give breathing assistance to an adult (Figure 24–10), or a child or infant (Figure 24–11). You are urged to take a first aid course, though, to master the techniques. You will be better prepared to save a life if you do.

Key Points ► *For a person who has stopped breathing, deliver air to the lungs by using the standard breathing assistance method.*

SECTION III REVIEW

Learning the Vocabulary
The vocabulary term in this section is *Heimlich maneuver.*
1. Write a sentence using the vocabulary term.

Keep holding the airway open. Drop a face shield over the victim's mouth if you have one. Pinch the victim's nose closed. Cover the mouth with your mouth. Blow air into the lungs. You can feel it go down. Let it come out. Blow again. Your normal breathing rate (about 12 breaths per minute) is fine for an adult. Make each breath long and strong, about 1½ seconds.

After two breaths, back off. Has breathing started? Look, listen, and feel for about 5 seconds. If no breathing, check for a pulse: Use two fingers. Feel for the carotid artery in the groove of the neck, next to the Adam's apple. If there's a pulse, give another full breath, wait 5 seconds, give another, and listen for breathing. Repeat this sequence until breathing starts. If there's NO pulse, try to restart the heart: go to "Six Steps to Chest Compression" in Figure 24-12 on page 609.

Figure 24–10 Rescue Breathing for an Adult

Activity 3.6
Family Class on the Heimlich Maneuver. For extra credit, ask students to teach the members of their families the Heimlich maneuver. To verify the student has done this ask them to bring a note from home stating that this activity has been completed. You may wish to create a printed verification statement for this purpose. **(allow one week out of school time; Extend, Enrich)**

Focus
SECTION IV

In this section students will learn that:
1. CPR is a life-sustaining technique when a victim is not breathing and has no pulse.
2. Everyone can and should be trained by a certified instructor before attempting to perform CPR.

Activity 4.1
Review of a Heart Attack or Stroke. Review the warning signs of a heart attack and stroke from Chapter 18 (page 455). **1.** Ask students to name as many symptoms as they can remember. **2.** List the symptoms on the board as they are identified. End this activity by having a student find the heart attack and stroke symptoms in Chapter 18 for the

(continued on next page)

C: Circulation and CPR

When a victim's heart stops beating, breathing also ceases. During the first critical few minutes, the chest compression and breathing technique called cardiopulmonary resuscitation (CPR) can do much to prolong life until help arrives. However, it takes professional trainers to properly teach the method. Practice on medical models is part of the training. An untrained person who attempts CPR may even stop a heart that is already beating, thus placing the victim in severe danger.

Heart attack and stroke victims need emergency help, because their hearts may be about to stop. Their pain may be slight, and they may deny that a life-threatening event is occurring, yet most heart attack victims die within an hour or two after the first symptoms appear. They die before professional help is delivered. The symptoms of heart attacks and strokes were listed in Chapter 18, page 455. If you notice any of these symptoms, you should:

- Lay the victim down with the head elevated.
- Loosen clothing. Keep the victim quiet and still.
- Call an emergency rescue service, and describe the person's symptoms. Alternative: if you can, transport the victim to an emergency treatment facility.
- Administer breathing assistance if necessary.
- Treat for shock if necessary (next section).

When the heart has stopped, CPR can provide the person's only chance of survival. CPR keeps oxygen flowing into the lungs and keeps the blood circulating to the brain and heart. This allows these critical

Keep your finger under the chin, lifting slightly. This will help to keep a seal between your lips and the child's face. Use a face shield if necessary. Put your mouth over the child's mouth and nose. Give small, slow, gentle breaths. Blow just enough air to make the chest rise. Release, and let the breath be exhaled. Each breath should take 1½ seconds.

After two breaths, back off. Has breathing started? Good. If no breathing, check for a pulse. If there's a pulse, give one slow breath every 3 seconds. Keep repeating this sequence. If there's no pulse, try to restart the heart. Go on to Figure 24-13.

Figure 24–11 Rescue Breathing for a Child or Infant

Learning the Facts
2. What happens to people who have stopped breathing after five minutes? What happens after ten minutes?
3. List the emergencies that may stop a person's breathing.
4. Describe the action you would take if you were choking, and by yourself.

Making Life Choices
5. Identify the hazards in giving breathing assistance without being trained. Are you trained in breathing assistance? What would you do at this time if you had to perform breathing assistance on a family member?

Section III Review
Answers
1. Answers will vary.
2. death to 50 percent, death to all others
3. allergic reactions, burns, drug overdoses, poisoning, choking
4. thrusting your fist into your abdomen, or thrusting your body forward forcefully against a firmly placed object—the back of a chair, side of a table, or edge of a sink or stove
5. Answers will vary. If you blow air into the stomach, it may cause vomiting, possibly blocking the airway; moving the head of someone with a neck injury may cause permanent paralysis; know when to stop giving assistance—continued efforts on your part using a different rhythm may shut down the victim's spontaneous breathing; forcing air into a drowning person's lungs may push water down into them; the procedures for helping adults can harm infants.

purpose of checking to see that none have been overlooked. **(10–15 min.; Reteach, Reinforce)**

TEACH
▶SECTION IV
(Guided and Independent Practice)

Activity 4.2

CPR Demonstration. If you are trained in CPR, you should give a demonstration and explanation of CPR. You should use a CPR manikin. If you are not trained in CPR, ask a rescue worker in your community to visit your classes and demonstrate CPR on a manikin. **(15–45 min.; Extend, Enrich)**

EVALUATE
▶SECTION IV

Activity 4.3
Pop Quiz.
1. You have seven to ten minutes to restore breathing before death or brain damage will occur. (F)
2. A person could be breathing with no pulse. (F)

Teacher Support Notes

① **Bloated Stomach:**
Occasionally, and especially among children, CPR can result in an accumulation of air in the victim's stomach, causing the abdomen to become bloated, almost like an inflated balloon. This is usually the result of breathing that is too rapid and too forceful. Remember that infants require much less force than older children or adults. Two problems can result. First, if the bloating becomes severe, it can restrict the movement of air into the lungs. Second, it can cause vomiting, which can lead to possible aspiration and choking. The American Heart Association recommends that a person not try to correct this bloating unless the abdomen has become so rigid that the first-aider is no longer able to force air into the lungs. If the abdomen does become so rigid that air can no longer be forced into the victim's lungs, the first-aider should turn the victim on his or her side, with the face pointing slightly downward, and then press gently on the victim's abdomen with the heel of the hand to force air out of the stomach.

608

---

608 UNIT 7 First Aid and Safety

organs to live until professional help arrives. The brain begins to die within just a few minutes after circulation ceases, so start CPR quickly—don't wait:

- Check pulse and breathing.
- If no pulse, shout for help.
- Ask helper to phone for emergency service.

Begin CPR:

- Lay the person face up on the floor or ground.
- Clear the airway (see previous section).
- Give 2 full breaths (see previous section).
- Check the pulse.

If the heart is beating, check the breathing. If breathing resumes, monitor both heartbeat and breathing until help arrives.

Warning: a beating but weakened heart can be stopped by chest compression. Be sure no heartbeat is present before administering chest compressions. When you are sure, follow the steps outlined in Figure 24–12 on the opposite page. Give 15 chest compressions and two breaths per cycle. Repeat the cycle three more times (four in all) before stopping once again to check for breathing and pulse.

For infants and children, you must be much gentler, and the pace must be faster. Figure 24–13 below shows the key differences.

To learn the proper timing of chest compressions it helps to know that, for an adult, 15 compressions should take about 10 seconds. Practice this: try counting aloud: "one-up-two-up . . . ," while pushing down on the count, and letting up on the "up." Use a stopwatch to time yourself, or have a partner time you. You should reach the count of 15 as the time reaches 10 seconds.

> **Key Points** ▶ For a victim of heart attack or other heart-stopping event, CPR may be the only means of keeping someone alive. To learn to perform it correctly and safely requires training by professionals.

Figure 24–13 CPR for Infants and Children ①

INFANT

Position 2 fingers as shown, on the child's breastbone, about a finger's width below the nipples. Do compressions and give breaths at a rapid pace: 1, 2, 3, 4, 5 compressions, 1 breath, 5 and 1, 5 and 1, 20 times a minute. At each compression push the chest down ½ to 1 inch. Keep repeating until heartbeat and breathing resume.

CHILD

Move two fingers' breadth above the notch of the ribs and place the heel of the hand on the breastbone as shown. Keep fingers up (don't touch ribs). Do 5 compressions and give 1 breath 12 times a minute. Make each compression 1 to 1½ inches deep. Keep repeating until heartbeat and breathing resumes.

3. CPR should not be attempted unless you have been trained by a certified instructor. (T)
4. Nausea and vomiting may be symptoms of a heart attack. (T)
5. A rescuer should administer two full breaths after every ten compressions when performing CPR. (F)

CLOSE
SECTION IV

Activity 4.4
Review Questions. Before going on to the next lesson, students should be able to answer these questions.
1. List five measures you should take when you suspect you are dealing with a victim of a heart attack.

2. Who should administer lifesaving CPR techniques?
3. When should CPR be started?
4. How long does a victim have before brain damage or death may occur if breathing and pulse have ceased?
(5 min.; Reteach, Reinforce)

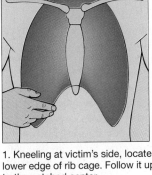
1. Kneeling at victim's side, locate lower edge of rib cage. Follow it up to the notched center.

2. Place your middle finger in the notch, index finger above on breastbone.

3. Press heel of other hand above index finger on breastbone.

Avoid pressing on this part of the breastbone (the xiphoid process)—it breaks easily
4. Place heel of hand used to find notch on top of other hand. Hold fingers slightly upward, off the victim's chest.

5. Align your shoulder over heel of bottom hand, elbow straight.

6. Press down to compress victim's chest, and release compression in a smooth series of motions. Do not lift your hand away from chest. Repeat 15 compressions and 2 breaths 4 times per minute.

Figure 24–12 CPR for Adults: Six Steps to Chest Compression ①

SECTION IV REVIEW

Learning the Facts
1. What steps should you follow if you think someone may be having a stroke or heart attack?
2. What does CPR actually do for the victim?
3. What should you be sure of before giving chest compressions?

Making Life Choices
4. Why is it important to have a current CPR certificate? If you have current CPR certification, encourage other friends and family members to get theirs. If you don't have current CPR certification, go to the local American Red Cross or American Heart Association to obtain it.

Teacher Support Notes

① **Proper Positioning of Hands:** Emphasize that when pressure is properly applied just above the xiphoid process, the sternum is flexible enough to be compressed. However, improper positioning can cause fractures and/or internal damage.

Section IV Review

Answers
1. **a.** Lay the victim down with the head elevated.
b. Loosen clothing. Keep the victim quiet and still.
c. Call an emergency rescue service, and describe the person's symptoms. Alternative: if you can, transport the victim to an emergency treatment facility. **d.** Administer breathing assistance if necessary. **e.** Treat for shock if necessary.
2. keeps oxygen flowing into the lungs and keeps the blood circulating to the brain and heart
3. no heartbeat is present
4. Answers will vary.

FOCUS
SECTION V

In this section students will learn that:
1. Direct pressure to the wound and elevating the limb controls severe bleeding.
2. Every injury victim should be treated for shock.

Activity 5.1

Bleeding Victim Scenario. Ask a student to lie down on the floor. Say, "My victim has cut his/her lower arm very seriously. Please observe my actions." Then demonstrate how to stop the bleeding using the directions in Section V. Then ask students to list all the actions you took. Ask students to share their lists until all actions have been identified. Have students correct their own lists. **(10–15 min.)**

TEACH
SECTION V
(Guided and Independent Practice)

Activity 5.2
Purpose Discussion. Using the list from Activity 5.1, ask students to give a purpose for each of the actions. They are to write these next to each action on the list. Discuss these and again have students correct their own lists. **(10 min.,**

Teacher Support Notes

① **Severe Bleeding:** Impress upon students the importance of controlling external bleeding. This is second in importance only to the maintenance of air passages and the restoration of breathing. Survival can be threatened by loss of a quart or more of blood. Bleeding from a combination of internal and external injuries can be so rapid and extensive that death may result almost immediately.

② **Tourniquet:** Ask students if they have seen a movie in which someone has wrapped a piece of cloth tightly around someone's arm or leg to stop excessive bleeding. The wrap used in these situations is called a *tourniquet.* While tourniquets used to be used, they are no longer recommended. Tell students that, if the bleeding is over a bony area, as in the case of a ruptured varicose vein of the leg, a coin held firmly against the vein will provide immediate control of the blood loss. The patient should then be seen by a physician as soon as possible. A tourniquet should only be used when the bleeding is so severe that the victim's life is endangered and when no other methods of control are effective.

610

---

610 UNIT 7 First Aid and Safety

SECTION V

S: Severe Bleeding and Shock

Bleeding can be life-threatening when arteries or veins have been severed in an injury. If you can't see a wound because of clothing, cut or tear away the clothing. In severe bleeding, the blood will be welling or pulsing out of the wound, and the amount of blood will seem dramatically great.

In almost all cases, bleeding can be controlled by continuous, direct pressure. Figure 24–14 shows an example of how to apply pressure on a bleeding wound. *Don't use a tourniquet (a tight band around a limb) to control bleeding. A tourniquet almost always kills the limb to which it is applied and should be used rarely, if ever. And don't try to apply pressure at "pressure*

Use sterile gauze or a clean folded cloth to cover the wound. Wear gloves. Use your hand to apply pressure. Bleeding should stop or slow to oozing in under 30 minutes.

Figure 24–14 Using Direct Pressure to Control Bleeding

points," unless you have been trained in the technique. Constricting an artery can damage the healthy tissue normally fed by that artery, and should be used only in cases of severe hemorrhage where direct pressure will not stop the flow.

Elevate the injured part to encourage blood to drain back into the body and to slow the blood flow from it. After bleeding stops, prompt treatment of wounds will be necessary to prevent infection.

Shock follows all major injuries, including drownings. Its symptoms were shown on page 601. The severity of shock depends partly on the extent of physical injury and on the amount of blood lost, and partly on the victim's nervous system characteristics. Rough treatment, delayed treatment, emotional reactions, and pain worsen it. After first treating for blocked airway, breathing, a stopped heart, and severe bleeding, a rescuer should treat every injury victim for shock.

Shock due to injury is not related to electric shock or the shock of an impact, but those conditions can certainly bring it on. Shock caused by injury is a last-resort attempt by the body to protect its blood supply by routing it away from outer tissues to the vital organs deep inside the body. In shock, the brain may become starved for blood and for the oxygen that it carries, and this may stop the heart. Shock is a condition as dangerous as breathing obstruction. People whose injuries would not have killed them have died of shock.

The treatment for shock is relatively simple. The Health Strategies section on the next page, "Treating Shock," gives you the step-by-step details for handling shock.

Key Points ▶ *To stop severe bleeding, use direct pressure. Shock follows injuries and can cause death. First aid for shock is simple and should be offered to all accident victims.*

EVALUATE
SECTION V

Activity 5.3
Pop Quiz.
1. After any serious injury always treat for shock. (T)
2. Shock left untreated can result in death. (T)

3. Elevating an injured limb helps to slow the blood flowing from it. (T)
4. A tourniquet can be used in place of direct pressure. (F)
5. High temperature means shock. (F)

CLOSE
SECTION V

Activity 5.4
Review Questions. Ask students to

describe: **1.** The best way to stop severe bleeding. **2.** The four steps in treating shock.
(10 min.; Reteach, Reinforce)

HEALTH STRATEGIES

Treating Shock

When you have determined that a person is in shock:

- Lay the person flat to ease circulation. Elevate only those body parts that have been treated for bleeding. The feet may be raised slightly by resting them on a folded blanket or other object if there is no chest bleeding.
- Loosen any tight clothing, particularly collars, belts, and waistbands.
- Help the person maintain normal body temperature. For example, if the person appears overly cool or chilled, try to cover the person with blankets. You may also want to insert padding such as spare clothing between the victim's body and the surface beneath.
- Normally it is best to give *no* food or liquids to people in shock. However, if the victim is conscious and has no abdominal or head injuries, and if help is not likely to arrive within an hour, you may want to give very small amounts of room-temperature fluids every 15 minutes. If salt is available, add ⅛ tsp. or less to each half glass of fluid.

SECTION V REVIEW

Learning the Facts
1. When is bleeding life threatening?
2. What should you do after you control bleeding?
3. Explain why the body goes into shock after an injury.

Making Life Choices
4. Look at the Health Strategies box above, entitled "Treating Shock." Why is it

important to treat all serious injuries for shock? Why is it important to follow the steps in this section to treat shock?

SECTION VI

Other First Aid Procedures

The first aid measures described so far are basic to many emergencies, but there is much more to know about treating injuries and burns, normalizing temperature, dealing with poisonings, and other specifics. The sections that follow provide a few more basic techniques.

Classifying and Treating Wounds

① Wounds are of four types: scrapes, tears, cuts, and punctures. Each can be mild or serious. If they are mild, the most important step is to wash them well with soap and water, then keep them clean.

If a wound is deeper than the outer layers of the skin, it is serious. Serious wounds should be evaluated by a health care professional after the first aid treatments are provided. Medical treatment is a must for any wound that has spurted blood, even if first aid has controlled it. Medical treatment is also necessary for any wound that may have involved muscles, tendons, ligaments, or nerves; any bite wound (animal or human); any heavily contaminated wound; or any wound that contains soil or object fragments. Objects sticking into the flesh should be left in place when possible.

A concern in providing first aid to bleeding victims is your own safety. Some serious diseases can be transmitted to you through contact with an infected person's body fluids—blood, vomit, feces, or urine. This doesn't mean you should not help a

Teacher Support Notes

① **Handout—Treatment of Minor and Serious Wounds:** Your supplementary material contains a handout that lists the four types of wounds and treatment for both minor and serious wounds for each type. You may want to distribute the handout at this time.

Section V Review

Answers
1. when arteries or veins have been severed
2. promptly treat wounds to prevent infections
3. The body tries to protect its blood supply by rerouting blood from the outer tissues to the vital organs deep inside the body.
4. Answers will vary.

In this section students will learn:
1. How to classify first-, second-, and third-degree burns.
2. The signs, symptoms, and first aid for victims of temperature extremes—hypothermia and hyperthermia.
3. The signs, symptoms, and treatments

of poisoning.
4. What a fracture consists of and the two types of fractures that can occur.

Activity 6.1

Rescue Barriers. Read aloud or have a student read the Health Strategies, "Reducing Disease Risks." Have on display in the classroom rubber gloves and other items such as plastic bags, plastic wrap, etc., that could be used by the res-

cuer while treating a victim's wound. Stress the importance of minimizing the risk of disease being spread by placing a barrier between the rescuer and the victim when body fluids are involved in treatment. **(10 min.; Reteach, Reinforce)**

TEACH
SECTION VI
(Guided and Independent Practice)

Activity 6.2

Teacher Support Notes

① **Teen Views Follow-up Questions:** Following are some questions you may want to use to encourage discussion of the ideas expressed by the students in the Teen Views feature:
a. Have students been in emergency situations? Did they panic? Why do they think some people panic, but others don't?
b. Vickie Reed's emergency involved her best friend. Is it more difficult to react in an emergency situation if the victim is a close friend or relative? Or, do they think that their feelings for that person would help them to perform at peak efficiency?
c. Have students used fireworks? Have any injuries resulted?
d. Krista Redpath was helped in her emergency situation by knowing that a neighbor was a registered nurse. Do students know most of their neighbors? Are they aware of any of those neighbors being health care providers of some sort? Do they think that a worthwhile neighborhood project would be identifying the presence of any health care providers?
e. Which of the situations described sound the most serious to students? Which would present them with the most problems?

TEEN VIEWS

How have you reacted in an emergency situation? ①

I've only had one emergency situation and I panicked. I should have stayed calm, but when you see your best friend fall to the floor and start convulsing, you get pretty shaken up. I screamed for my mom and she came to help me. I calmed down and called 911. We now know my friend is epileptic. **Vickie Reed, 16, Pine Bluff High School, AR**

It was July 4th and I was lighting fireworks. It didn't get out of hand until my

neighbor's backyard caught fire from a smoke bomb I threw over the fence. I have never been so scared in my life. Finally I got the hose and jumped over the fence to put it out. **Melissa Miller, 16, Orange Park High School, FL**

I was babysitting for my brother and his friends. One of the kids flew off a big inner tube and landed on her arm. I

took one look at her bone sticking out of her arm and just about got sick. I immediately called our neighbor who is a registered nurse. She told me what to do. **Krista Redpath, 15, Great Falls High School, MT**

Once my neighbor overdosed on drugs. Her son came out and said his mom was asleep on the bathroom floor. I told my parents and they called 911. She lived. **Brad Ker, 15, South Carroll High School, MD**

---

wounded person, but it does mean that you should take measures to protect yourself from contact with the victim's body fluids. See the Health Strategies at the right.

 Key Points *Treat minor wounds to prevent infection. Major wounds need professional care. Protect yourself from contact with the victim's blood and other body fluids.*

Burns

Burns are classified by the depth of tissue injury. Proper help for a burn victim depends on whether the burn is of the first, second, or third degree. First-degree burns injure just the top layers of skin and appear as redness, with mild swelling and pain;

HEALTH STRATEGIES

Reducing Disease Risks

To minimize your contact with someone else's blood or other body fluids:

• Place a barrier between you and the fluid, such as rubber gloves, plastic wrap, or plastic bags.
• Keep your hands away from your own face or any other opening on your body during and after giving treatments.
• Wash your hands with soap and water after providing treatment. Wash under nails gently with a soft brush.

(continued on next page)

they heal rapidly. A light sunburn and a mild scald are examples.

Second-degree burns involve deeper tissue damage and appear red or mottled, develop blisters, swell considerably, and are wet at the surface. A deep sunburn, a flash burn from burning fluid, or a burn from contact with very hot liquid is likely to be a second-degree burn.

Third-degree burns involve deep tissue destruction and have a white or charred appearance. Sometimes third-degree burns will appear to be second degree at first. Flames, ignited clothing, prolonged contact with hot fluids or objects, or electricity can all cause third-degree burns.

One key thing to remember about burns is that the skin regulates the body's temperature. When skin is burned, the body can grow very hot or very cold, very fast. That's why covering a burn victim can be important—but don't cover a person whose clothing is still smoldering. Remove the clothing and any jewelry first, let the surface reach a neutral temperature, then cover.

Another key: burns on the face may mean that the airway is burned. Look for singed facial hair (eyebrows, mustache). A facial burn may lead to swelling and a blocked airway. Monitor breathing closely in a person who is burned. Figure 24–15 on the next page shows the standard treatments for first-, second-, and third-degree burns.

Never put water on a burn that is caused by a dry powder. Just brush the powder off. A powder may react with water and burn the victim further.

> **Key Points** *Burns require first aid according to their severity. Defend the victim's body temperature.*

Temperature Extremes

For the body tissues to function normally, they must be kept at normal temperature—close to 98.6° Fahrenheit. A person whose internal body parts lose heat is at serious risk and needs help fast. Similarly, internal body parts must not be overheated; this too poses a serious threat. While **hypothermia** and **hyperthermia** can threaten life when allowed to advance unchecked, some simple first-aid measures can, when administered quickly, be life saving. In cases of temperature extremes, call the emergency services immediately. Then proceed as described here.

Hypothermia, or abnormally low internal body temperature, develops when the body loses heat to the environment faster than it can generate heat. Exposure to low temperatures, high winds, and high humidity makes anyone likely to develop hypothermia, but people who are ill or elderly can grow cold internally even in a room as warm as 65 degrees Fahrenheit. The temperature of the surroundings does not have to be anywhere near freezing for the condition to occur. Thousands of older people probably die of hypothermia each year.

A person with hypothermia may have stiff muscles, with some shivering or trembling; dizziness; weakness; cold skin; problems with coordination; and slowed breathing and heart rate. As hypothermia progresses, the person may become confused and drowsy, may lose muscle coordination, and may stop shivering.

M<small>INI</small> G<small>LOSSARY</small>

hypothermia (*hypo* means "too low"; *thermia* means "temperature"): a condition of too little body heat with abnormally low internal body temperature.
hyperthermia (*hyper* means "too high"; *thermia* means "temperature"): a condition of too much body heat with abnormally high internal body temperature.

Activity 6.4

Burn Precautions. As a class, discuss precautions that can be taken around the home to prevent burns from happening to family members. Students may relate any specific incidents that occurred to them or their family members, describing what happened and what, if anything, could have been done to prevent the burns from occurring. **(10 min., Critical Thinking)**

Activity 6.5

Hypothermia Prevention. On the board, list as many activities as possible that could cause hypothermia. Once the activities have been listed, have the students pick five activities and write down five precautions that could be taken while involved in each activity to prevent hypothermia from occurring. **(15 min.; Extend, Enrich)**

Activity 6.6

Treating Frostbite. Write the word "Frostbite" on the board. Under frostbite make two columns, DO'S and DON'TS. Fill each column with the do's and don'ts of treating a victim of frostbite. **(10 min.;**

Teacher Support Notes

① **Dealing with Hypothermia:** For enrichment, tell students that a hypothermia victim may deny being in trouble. A first-aider should believe the signs, not the victim. Even mild signs demand an immediate, drastic treatment, especially in camping or hiking situations when shelter, heat, and help are not readily available. If the victim is still conscious, try to keep the victim awake—warm drinks might help. Some people erroneously believe that alcohol will help warm the hypothermia victim. Alcohol should never be given to a person with hypothermia. Alcohol causes a dilation of the blood vessels in the skin and can cause a too sudden release of cold blood from the surface vessels to the body's core, further reducing core temperature. Although a feeling of warmth may occur, there is actually a loss of body heat.

FIGURE 24-15

Standard Treatments for Burns

To treat first-degree burns:
- Dip the burned part in cool water, or apply gauze soaked in cool water.
- Then, if exposure to anything unclean is likely, layer dry gauze over the wet gauze to create a barrier to bacteria.
- Never apply grease of any kind to any burn.

To treat second-degree burns:
- Treat as described above for first-degree burns, and seek medical treatment. Do not break blisters; remove tissue; or use antiseptic spray, cream, or any other product.
- Elevate burned part.

To treat third-degree burns:
- Elevate the burned part, especially the limbs.
- Cover the burn with many layers of dry, sterile gauze.
- Do not apply water unless the area is still burning.
- An ice pack wrapped in a dry towel may be applied on top of the gauze for pain relief.
- Treat for shock, and arrange transportation to an emergency medical facility.
- Do not attempt to remove clothing or debris from the burn.

If you suspect hypothermia, call for help immediately. While waiting for help, move the person to a warm place, taking care to prevent injury. Do not handle the person roughly (the heart is weak when the body is cold). Do not attempt to rewarm the person with hot baths, electric blankets, or hot-water bottles. Do, though, offer warm food ① or drink to victims who are conscious. If the person is unconscious, don't force anything—fluids or food. Do not raise the feet or legs, for the blood there is cooler than in other parts of the body and can further chill the body's core. Do wrap the person in available covering such as blankets, towels, pillows, scarves, or newspapers.

Another risk of exposure to cold is **frost-bite.** A child busily making a snowman or a teen skiing down a powdered slope may not be aware of frostbite's dangers as they set in. Yet the later effects of frostbite—painful injury to the fingers, toes, ears, cheeks, or nose, and possible loss of function—are severe. Some frostbite injuries are so severe as to require surgical removal of the injured part.

Frostbite sets in when ice crystals form in body tissues. The crystals freeze the body part and cut off its circulation. Also, ice crystals form as sharp jagged daggers that easily puncture delicate cell membranes as they grow larger. Once their membranes are punctured, cells spill out their internal contents, collapse, and die.

Frostbite's symptoms include color changes in the skin, usually to white, gray, or blue. The part may feel numb, so the person may have no warning that injury is setting in. Pain can be severe, however, when warmth restores feeling to the previously numb parts.

One of the worst things to do when frostbite sets in is to rub the affected body part. Rubbing saws the ice crystals back and forth, jabbing the membranes of neighboring cells and killing them, too. To prevent this unnecessary destruction of tissue, always handle frostbitten parts gently. Remove wet or tight clothing. Cover the affected parts with dry, sterile dressing. Don't pack the area in snow or cold water. The affected tissues need to be gently warmed, so that the ice crystals will slowly melt.

Transport the victim to a hospital. If that is impossible, treat the frostbite as best you can. Move the victim in from the cold. Soak the injured part in warm (100 degrees Fahrenheit), not hot, water. (If the water is too hot, or if the part thaws and refreezes, it will die.) Loosely bandage the part by wrapping it lightly with gauze, and seek medical help.

①

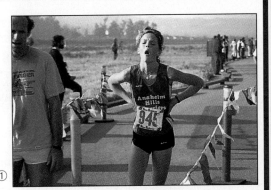

If overheated, drink water, seek shade, and rest.

Hyperthermia is likely whenever people are exposed to high temperatures with high humidity. You need not be active to experience it—you need only be hot. Athletes and exercisers aren't the only ones prone to hyperthermia. Babies, old people, those taking certain medications, and the overweight are especially likely to tolerate heat poorly. Figure 24–16 on the next page describes the symptoms of the two dangerous stages of hyperthermia—heat exhaustion, and heat stroke. (You learned in Chapter 10 about heat cramps, heat exhaustion, and heat stroke, but a review is given here.)

An overheated person who receives no help may sicken as the body tries to defend itself against the high temperature. In the early stages, the body struggles to cool itself through heavy sweating. Should exposure to the hot conditions continue, though, the body may sweat so much that it begins to run out of fluid with which to make more sweat. As the body loses fluid, it stops sweating, and thereby loses its only defense against overheating further. Then, like an overheating car radiator, the body tempera-

MINI GLOSSARY

frostbite: the formation of ice crystals in body parts exposed to temperatures below freezing; freezing of body parts, especially toes and fingers, and nose and other face parts.

Extend, Enrich)

Activity 6.7
Symptoms of Heat Exhaustion and Heat Stroke. Choose a student to read aloud the symptoms of heat exhaustion found in Figure 24–16. Another student should read aloud the symptoms of heat stroke. Once the symptoms have been read, discuss the following questions:

1. What is first aid for heat exhaustion? What is the first aid for heat stroke?
2. Who is most susceptible to hyperthermia?
3. Which is the most severe—heat exhaustion or heat stroke? Why?
(15 min.; Reteach, Reinforce)

Activity 6.8
Poisoning Collages. Bring in magazines or have students bring in magazines from home. Have students go through the magazines and make collages with pictures of items that can cause poisoning. Display these collages in the room. As the posters are displayed, point out any unusual or noteworthy sources that students found. **(25 min.; Extend, Enrich)**

(continued on next page)

Teacher Support Notes

① **Severity of Frostbite:** Frostbite, like burns, is classified into categories. There are three categories, measured by the extent of tissue damage: 1. *Incipient first-degree frostbite.* This is injury to surface skin. Somewhat like a sunburn, the affected part will show redness, swelling, burning, and tingling without formation of blisters. There is usually no tissue loss. 2. *Superficial second-degree frostbite.* This is similar in appearance to first-degree frostbite. Blisters occur minutes to hours after the cold injury. Undue redness of skin on rewarming, and swelling may occur. 3. *Deep third-degree frostbite.* This involves damage to deep tissues. Much of the frozen part is lost, possibly all of it. Usually no blisters or swelling occur.

📖 Fast Facts

In an average year about 175 Americans die from summer heat and too much sun.

Activity 6.9
Poisoning Sources. After students have read this section, have each student take a piece of paper and divide it into four columns. Head each column with one of the four ways a poison can enter the body system—eaten or drunk,

inhaled, injected, or absorbed through the skin. Under each column, students should list as many examples as they can of specific ways that poisoning can occur by that route. Example: injected (bee sting), inhaled (car exhaust), absorbed (insecticides), eaten (spoiled food). Once each student has completed a list, divide the class into groups of five to share and combine lists. **(20 min., Cooperative Learning)**

Activity 6.10
Strain, Sprain, or Break? Put the words *break*, *sprain*, and *strain* on the board. Make a column under each word. Under each word, write clues that would indicate each condition existed in a victim. The students can volunteer these clues from past experiences, scenarios they have seen on television, looking up the words in the dictionary, etc. The students then should draw a conclusion from

Teacher Support Notes

① **Treatment for Hyperthermia:** Students may try sponging the victim's bare skin with cool water, applying cold packs, placing the victim in a tub of cold water, or vigorously rubbing the victim's skin with ice until the temperature is sufficiently lowered. They also could try using fans or an air conditioner to create a draft and promote cooling. They can improvise with whatever is available to help cool patients.

② **What is Poison:** Students probably have some preconceived ideas of what a poison is. Have them reread this sentence to emphasize the point that any substance can be poisonous, even a substance such as aspirin that students think of as a "good" substance. Poisonings from such obvious sources as arsenic, cyanide, or strychnine are rare compared with those from ordinary household substances or drugs.

✍ Fast Facts

The mortality rate of heat stroke is from 25% to 50%. It is seen most commonly in men over 40, especially alcoholics.

616 UNIT 7 First Aid and Safety

FIGURE 24-16 Symptoms of Hyperthermia		
	Hyperthermia (heat exhaustion)	**Severe Hyperthermia (heat stroke)**
Skin	Cool, moist, pale or red	Dry, hot, red
Sweating	Heavy sweating	No sweating
Body Temperature	Normal or below normal	Very high, possibly to 106 degrees Fahrenheit
Pulse	Faster than normal	Fast and weak
Breathing	Possible deep breathing	Fast, shallow breathing
Other	Dizziness and weakness, headache, nausea	Loss of consciousness, brain damage, death

ture climbs to the point of damaging all systems, especially the brain.

To prevent damage or death from heat injuries, first call for emergency help. Then cool the person's body by fanning. Apply cold, wet wraps such as wet towels or clothing. Offer the conscious victim a small amount, about half a cup, of plain cool water to drink every 15 minutes or so. Between drinks, lay the person down and treat for shock.

> **Key Points** *First aid for hypothermia consists of allowing the person's body to slowly regain its proper temperature. First aid for frostbite consists of slowly warming the parts and seeking help. First aid for hyperthermia consists of calling for help, cooling the person, offering fluids, and treating for shock.*

Poisonings, Bites, and Stings

Any adverse effect on the body from a chemical substance is considered poisoning, from an overdose of drugs to the inhalation of fumes from household products. Poisonings pose difficult problems for those ad-

ministering first aid, because they vary in symptoms and treatments according to the substance involved. Poisons can enter the body by being eaten or drunk, breathed in, absorbed through the skin, or injected.

The most common household poisonings involve overdoses of aspirin or other over-the-counter pain relievers, eaten by children or taken by mistake by adults. A person who has eaten poison may display any of the symptoms shown in Figure 24–17. In such a case, give nothing by mouth. Quickly call the emergency services.

FIGURE 24-17
Symptoms of Poisoning

- Burns or injury to tongue or lip area (if the poison was taken by mouth)
- Difficulty breathing
- Pain in the chest or abdomen; diarrhea, nausea, vomiting
- Sweating
- The person may have seizures or lose consciousness.

the list presented on the board that many of the signs and symptoms for a break, sprain, and strain are the same. Therefore, tell the students that when in doubt, treat a sprain or a strain like a break as far as the first aid procedure is concerned. **(15 min., Critical Thinking)**

EVALUATE

SECTION VI

**Activity 6.11
Pop Quiz.**

1. It is important to place a barrier between you and the victim when body fluids are involved. (T)
2. Wounds deeper than the outer layers of the skin need professional help. (T)
3. Burns are classified by the depth of tissue injury. (T)
4. A first-degree burn involves many layers of skin being involved. (F)

5. Hypothermia is caused when the body temperature gets too high. (F)
6. Heat stroke and heat exhaustion can be life threatening. (T)
7. Poison can enter the body through injection, absorption, inhalation, or by being eaten. (T)
8. First aid for bee stings is to pinch out the stinger. (F)
9. An open break is a break on the arms

(continued on next page)

Then call the poison control center (the number is on the front page of your telephone book). Describe the poisoning.

If the poison involved is an illegal drug, do *not* try to protect the victim by concealing information. Legal penalties are small when compared with loss of life. Don't hesitate—call. If possible, read aloud over the phone, from the poison container, the information on its label. Follow the instructions given by the poison control experts.

If a poison has been taken by injection, the person may need breathing assistance. It may also be necessary to treat for shock.

Bites and stings present a special case of poisoning. Insect bites and stings are especially common. These can be extremely threatening to those who are allergic to them.

The primary threat from most insect bites and stings is allergic reaction to the **venom**, which can set in within seconds of the bite. Call emergency services immediately if the person has a red, flushed, or swelling face or trouble breathing. Be ready to administer breathing assistance until help arrives. For ordinary stings in nonallergic people, remove the stinger by scraping, not by pinching, the stinger with tweezers. Pinching may squeeze more venom into the sting.

Few people are bitten by snakes in the United States each year and only a handful of those suffer lasting effects or are killed by such bites. Most people receive help promptly. The majority of snakebites occur near home. Most snakebites need no first aid treatment. However, the victim should receive medical help within 30 minutes, just to be sure. Never cut or suck on a snakebite. Never use a snakebite kit to treat a bite.

> **Key Points** ▷ *Poisonings demand immediate help. Call a poison control center and follow directions. Allergic reactions to stings may lead to*

breathing failure; obtain help quickly. Snakebites require medical attention.

Broken Bones

① A person with a **fracture** (a break in a bone) needs medical treatment. A break in a bone that does not penetrate the skin is called a "closed" break. Open breaks, where the bone end has punctured the skin, may bleed. In the case of an open break, control the bleeding, remembering to use rubber gloves or materials to protect your hands from the blood.

Neither you nor the injured person may be able to tell whether an injury is a broken bone, a sprain, or a strain. For this reason, the Red Cross suggests, "When in doubt, splint." In other words, if you suspect a fracture, tie a **splint** to the injured part while waiting for emergency help. The Health Strategies box on the next page, "Splinting a Broken Bone," tells how to do this. Also, if any part of the bone is exposed to the air, keep it moist. Don't try to put it back in place, just cover it with moist, sterile, or clean dressing.

Splinting techniques vary with injury location, and a first aid course teaches many splinting techniques. No matter the location, though, the main task remains to keep the injured bone still to prevent fur-
② ther damage.

MINI GLOSSARY

venom: poison from a living creature such as a snake or scorpion.
fracture: a break in a bone. An *open fracture* is a break with a wound in the overlying tissues; a *closed fracture* is a break or crack with no visible wound.
splint: a stick or board used to support a broken bone to keep its separated parts from moving until it can be set.

Teacher Support Notes

① Drug and Alcohol Emergencies: Here are some basic strategies for helping a person suffering from a drug overdose or excessive alcohol intake:
• Induce vomiting if the victim is conscious and if the overdose was taken in the preceding 30 minutes.
• Protect hyperactive victims from hurting themselves and others.
• Maintain consciousness.
• Monitor respiration.
• Instill confidence—the victim should be reassured that he or she will be okay.
• Preserve evidence.

② Handout—Snakebite Kits: In your supplementary material you will find a handout entitled "Snakebite Kits: No Substitute for Knowledge," which you may want to distribute at this point.

617

or legs. (F)
10. Treat a broken limb in the position in which you found it. (T)

CLOSE
SECTION VI

Activity 6.12
Television Victims and Treatments. Divide the class into groups of five. As a group, have the members describe a scene from a television show in which someone was injured. Each group should produce a two-paragraph report describing the incident and what rescue personnel did to treat the victim. Groups can then share their findings with the class. **(15 min., Cooperative Learning)**

RETEACH/ BONUS

Here are some additional activities for the various sections of this chapter. You may want to use these activities to reteach certain concepts, or you may choose them as alternatives to earlier activities.

Unconscious Victim Simulation.

Section VI Review
Answers

1. hypothermia
2. Venom
3. fracture
4. when a wound has spurted blood; involves muscles, tendons, ligaments, or nerves; any bite wound; any heavily contaminated wound, or any wound that contains soil or object fragments
5. deep tissue destruction, white or charred appearance
6. changes in the skin's color (to white, gray, or blue), numbness in the affected area
7. eaten or drunk, breathed in, absorbed through the skin, or injected
8. Answers will vary; could include: all but third-degree burns should involve putting water on the burn; third-degree burns must be treated more seriously and the victim must be taken to a medical facility. Incorrect treatment of burns could cause tissue damage or in the case of third-degree burns, result in death. Remaining answers will vary.

HEALTH
STRATEGIES

Splinting a Broken Bone

When a bone is broken:

- Treat the limb in the position in which you found it—don't move it.
- Place a stick, board, or other such unbendable object (a splint) against the limb. Usually, support an arm from below, a leg from the side.
- If possible, place the splint so that it holds the joints still, too, both above and below the break.
- Tie the splint snugly to the limb in several places, leaving the broken area untied. Don't tie it too tightly. A tight splint may cut off circulation.
- Elevate the part, if possible.
- Cover exposed bone with moist, sterile dressing.

Key Points *If you suspect that a bone may be broken, apply a splint to keep the part still and prevent further damage.*

SECTION VI REVIEW

Learning the Vocabulary
The vocabulary terms in this section are *hypothermia, hyperthermia, frostbite, venom, fracture,* and *splint.*
Fill in the blank with the correct answer.
1. If a person has too little body heat it is called _____.
2. _____ is a poison from a living creature.
3. A break in a bone is called a _____.

Learning the Facts
4. When is medical treatment necessary for wounds?
5. Describe characteristics of a third degree burn.

6. What are the symptoms of frostbite?
7. How can poisons enter the body?

Making Life Choices
8. Look at Figure 24–15 on page 614, "Standard Treatment for Burns." Describe the differences in treatments for the different degrees of burns. Why is it important to know the treatments? What could happen to a person who is treated incorrectly?

Answers to Fact or Fiction

Here are the answers to the questions at the start of the chapter.

1. False. To be of real help and not make things worse, the helper needs to apply training gained through a class in first aid from a qualified instructor.
2. True. **3.** False. The first thing to do in an emergency is to inspect the scene to determine what happened. Move the victim only if the scene presents immediate danger. **4.** False. The best way to determine if a victim has broken any bones is to ask the person to move each joint. Forcing limbs with broken bones to move can worsen a break.
5. True. **6.** False. A person in a state of shock is experiencing a *physical* reaction to injury. Shock is a dangerous condition, and first aid treatment is recommended. **7.** False. You should not use a tourniquet to control bleeding. A tourniquet almost always kills the limb to which it is applied.
8. True. **9.** False. Frostbitten parts should be handled gently to prevent tissue destruction.

Demonstrate the use of the Heimlich maneuver on an unconscious victim. Following the same type of format as outlined in Activity 3.4, have your students practice this technique in pairs. Again, caution them only to simulate the steps that involve any body contact, doing the steps in unison and saying the steps out loud under your direct supervision. **(10 min., Cooperative Learning)**

Obstructed Airway Techniques. Demonstrate the techniques of the Heimlich maneuver for clearing an obstructed airway on yourself. Simulate the use of the back of a chair and administering abdominal thrusts to yourself. **(3–5 min.)**

Categorizing Actions and Purposes. Using the list from Activities 5.1 and 5.2, ask students to place each of the

actions on the list in one of the following two categories: 1. Bleeding control, or 2. Shock. They may do this by listing each action under one of those appropriate headings or by marking each action either BC (for bleeding control) or S (for shock). Have students share their decisions, discuss their choices, and have them add, delete, or correct their responses until all are complete and cor-

(continued on next page)

Straight Talk

Folk Medicine

[20,000 years ago] **"The camp was quiet, settling down for the night. By the dim glow of hot coals, Iza checked the contents of several small pouches spread out in orderly rows on her cloak. . . . She always carried certain things with her in the otter-skin bag, but to her, the small pouches of dried leaves, flowers, roots, seeds, and barks in her medicine bag were only first aid. In the new cave she would have room for greater quantity and variety."**

—J.M. Auel,
The Clan of the Cave Bear (Crown Publishers, Inc., 1980)

From earliest times, people have treated their coughs, aches, infections, sleeplessness, wounds, burns, and other ills with tissues from the plants and animals that surrounded them. Even today there is no question that many wild plants and animals contain compounds that act as drugs. ①

*Today, many of these same **herbs** and other "remedies" are for sale on store shelves. People may wonder if "folk medicine" might offer safer, or more "natural remedies" for curing human ills than drugs made in the chemist's laboratory. The vast majority of such potions do not work. People may be fooled into thinking that they do, though, because the treatment may produce a sensation the taker can feel. For example, a leaf said to have powers to cure a sore joint may not cure, but may irritate the skin. Even if they do work, the products may not be safe. For this reason, some warnings are in order: See Figure 24–18.*

Figure 24-18

Warnings About Herbal Medicines ②

Warning #1: Even if an herb is known to contain an effective drug, people cannot be sure that the products they buy contain the drug they hope to receive. All plants, including herbs, vary from batch to batch, from strain to strain, and from season to season. Also, people make mistakes in using herbs. A man confused **foxglove** (from which the potent heart medicine digoxin is extracted) with **comfrey** (an herb popular for making tea). Upon drinking about a quart of foxglove tea over several days, the man was poisoned with digoxin. Comfrey itself is poisonous when used regularly, but foxglove is even more so.

Warning #2: Different people react differently to the drugs in herbs, just as they do to other drugs. Children and people with certain medical conditions are most sensitive and should not be given any folk medicines.

Warning #3: False claims are common. Many products claim to promote health, but few do in truth. Products may also bear the wrong labels. The label may say that the package contains one substance, but the item in the container may be something else entirely.

(Continued on next page)

Teacher Support Notes

① **Family Remedies:** Ask students if they have any special medicines or treatments in their families. Does someone in the family prepare home remedies? Ask them to describe any of these special medicines or treatments. Ask other students if they would try these remedies.

② **Warnings:** Ask students to close their books and write the four warnings given in this figure. Have students explain why children, especially, should not take folk medicines. (Their smaller bodies will be more severely affected by any harmful chemicals in the "medicines.")

RETEACH/BONUS (Continued)

rect. **(5–10 min.; Cooperative Learning, Critical Thinking)**

Shock. Explain that emotional shock is not related to shock due to injury but that an emotional shock can certainly bring on the condition of shock to the body. Ask students to recall when they or someone they know has experienced emotional shock or shock due to injury. Ask them to write down how that person looked and behaved. Ask them to try to recall at least four or five symptoms the person displayed at that time. Next, ask them to look at the symptoms of shock in Figure 24–5 and compare what they have written to the symptoms listed in the text. Discuss. **(10 min., Critical Thinking)**

Label Analysis. Ask students to look on containers at home that have a potentially poisonous material in them. The students need to find what is poisonous in the container and write a one-page report on what symbol is used to represent poisonous materials, whether any antidotes are listed on the container, and any other warning information stated on the label. Report the findings to the class. **(20 min.; Extend, Enrich)**

Teacher Support Notes

① **Natural:** Ask students to free-associate with the word *natural*. Write the words that come to mind on the board. Are most of the terms positive rather than negative? Ask students if they generally assume that anything natural is "better for you" than a synthetic, man-made product. Point out to students that it is okay to favor natural over synthetic products, but it is not okay to assume that because something is natural it is safe and good for you, as the examples in the text show.

② **Ginseng and the Sex Drive:** Students may have heard people talk about ginseng increasing a person's sex drive. If they ask about this, you can tell them that no substance has ever been proved to increase the sex drive. You may want to use this opportunity to remind students that they should not believe rumors without proof.

③ **Risks vs. Benefits:** Students learned about the *risk/benefit ratios* of drugs in Chapter 17. You may want to refer them back to that discussion at this point.

620

---

620   UNIT 7 First Aid and Safety

STRAIGHT TALK   *(Continued)*

> **Warning #4:** Harmful side effects are common. A product that contains useful compounds is likely to contain some harmful ones as well. Some 700 plants have caused serious illnesses or deaths in this part of the world.

All those warnings make me afraid to think about trying folk medicines. Why do people bother with them?

There are probably as many reasons as there are users. Some people want to return to the olden days. Other people grew up in families that used herbs as medicines and feel comfortable in using them. Still others claim to believe that herbs are safer than refined drugs because they're "natural."

Aren't natural things safe?

The word *natural* doesn't mean harmless—far from it. ① The natural herbs **hemlock** and **belladonna** are two infamous and deadly poisons. The herb **sassafras** contains a cancer-causing chemical. Other herbs, such as **witch hazel,** are harmless but also useless.

What about the herb ginseng? How does it rate as a medicine?

The herb **ginseng** is the root of a wild, slow-growing plant. It is so highly prized for its proved and imaginary drug effects that it has been hunted and gathered almost to extinction. In a scientific study, ginseng worked against inflammation (the swelling, heat, and redness of injuries) more effectively than the medical drug hydrocortisone. In another study, ginseng changed people's blood chemistries in a way that reduced their risks of heart disease. Ginseng has a wake-up effect like that of caffeine, too.

Even if ginseng itself is useful in some cases, the products called ginseng for sale on store shelves are rarely effective. Unfortunately, ginseng products vary so widely in contents that there's no guessing at their effects. Also, real ginseng may cause negative side effects. Insomnia, nervousness, confusion, and depression make up a group of symptoms called the **ginseng abuse syndrome.** Ginseng ③ makes a poor drug, because its negative effects occur at about the same dose levels as its drug effects.

Do any herbs work, that aren't too dangerous to try?

You know of one already—caffeine, described in the Straight Talk section of Chapter 12. Two other herbs that may be useful and seem safe are **aloe** and **chamomile.** People have used aloe plants for thousands of years to treat burns and skin injuries. Experienced cooks may keep potted aloe plants on kitchen windowsills. For minor kitchen ② burns and cuts, they pluck a leaf and apply the gel that oozes out. It relieves pain, and some scientists think it makes minor wounds heal faster.

Other researchers, however, think aloe may delay or complicate the healing of severely damaged skin. A wise course might be to rub aloe on minor scratches and burns, but let a physician treat any major burns, deep cuts, or rashes.

As for chamomile, it contains a drug that relieves digestive and menstrual cramping. Whether tea brewed from chamomile flowers has these effects is unknown. This is because the drug doesn't dissolve in water, and only a little of it ends up in a cup of tea. Perhaps the

(Continued on next page)

Splint Demonstration. Demonstrate the proper techniques according to the American Red Cross or the American Heart Association for splinting a broken forearm, leg, and ankle. Stress that the splint should be done to prevent further damage to the victim. Remind the students that if there is an open break and blood is present, to protect themselves before dealing with the wound. **(20 min.)**

Temperature Extremes. Show a film on temperature extremes from the American Red Cross or the American Heart Association. Students should be able to recognize signs and symptoms of hyperthermia and hypothermia and the proper first aid for treating victims of temperature extremes. **(15 min.; Reteach, Reinforce)**

STRAIGHT TALK   *(Continued)*

effects of drinking the tea may build up over time.

After thousands of years' use, reports of negative side effects from chamomile tea are almost unknown, except for one: the flowers can cause allergy in people who are sensitive to pollen. If you have hay fever, stay away from chamomile and other herbs as well.

What about other folk remedies?

Among the thousands of claims made for herbs and potions, a few more folk remedies are worth mentioning. One is a kitchen product, meat tenderizer (the kind without seasoning). This product contains papain, a chemical that breaks down proteins. The stinging venoms of bees and jellyfish are made of protein. Some people find that meat tenderizer kills the pain and reduces the swelling of these stings. To treat a sting, remove the stinger, if any, and apply ice. Then spread a paste of tenderizer to destroy the painful protein in the venom.

Some other accurate folksy tips include these: ①

- Sugar, if allowed to dissolve and trickle down the throat, can interfere with the nerve signals that cause hiccups.

- A gargle of warm salt water can soothe a sore throat and may kill more germs than commercial mouthwashes can.
- A mixture of lemon and honey can soothe a sore throat and may quiet a minor cough.

While these treatments are safe to try, stay away from most other folk remedies. They often are more harmful than helpful. At the very least, they are a waste of money. ②

Mini Glossary

herbs: nonwoody plants or plant parts valued for their flavor, aroma, or medicinal qualities.
folk medicine: the use of herbs and other natural substances in the treatment of disease as practiced among people of various regions.
foxglove: a plant that contains a substance used in the heart medicine digoxin.
ginseng (JIN-seng): a plant containing chemicals that have drug effects.
comfrey: leaves and roots of the comfrey plant; believed, but not proved, to have drug effects. Comfrey

contains cancer-causing chemicals.
hemlock: any part of the hemlock plant, which causes severe pain, convulsions, and death within 15 minutes.
belladonna: any part of the deadly nightshade plant; a deadly poison.
sassafras: root bark from the sassafras tree, once used in beverages but now banned as an ingredient in foods or beverages because it contains cancer-causing chemicals.
witch hazel: leaves or bark of a witch hazel tree; not proved to have healing powers.
ginseng abuse syndrome: a group of symptoms associated with the overuse of ginseng, including high blood pressure, insomnia, nervousness, confusion, and depression.
aloe: a tropical plant with widely claimed, but mostly unproved, medical value.
chamomile: a plant with flowers that may provide some limited medical value in soothing intestinal and stomach discomforts.

Teacher Support Notes

① **Do They Work?:** Ask students if they have ever tried any of these remedies. Did they work? If they haven't tried them, would they be willing to try them the next time they have one of these problems? Have volunteers report to class periodically on the effectiveness of these folk remedies.
② **Folk Medicines vs. Commercial Medicines:** Ask students to write a brief essay expressing their opinions of folk medicines as they compare to commercial medicines. In their papers they should state whether or not they would ever use folk remedies and give reasons for their opinions. If they would use folk medicines, they should describe personal experiences of successful use of the medicines or experiences of people they know who have had success with these remedies. Have students read their papers in class.

Vocabulary

1. **a.** dispatcher **b.** frost-bite **c.** splint
2. **a.** shock **b.** Venom **c.** fracture **d.** emergency medical service
3. **a.** carotid pulse **b.** Heimlich maneuver
c. first aid **d.** hypothermia
4. Answers will vary.

Recall
Section II
1. Answers may vary; could include fire, fumes, fast traffic, live electrical wires, fast-moving water.
2. by checking each victim for blocked airways, no breathing, no circulation, and severe bleeding, and helping the person who needs immediate help
3. Place your ear and cheek close to the victim's mouth and nose. Look, listen, and use the sensitive skin of your cheek to feel for breathing.
4. death
5. Blood flow to the brain and other vital organs is diminished, causing loss of consciousness. Blood supply to other vital organs may fail as well as the heart itself.
6. less severe, but serious injuries
Section III
7. clutch the throat area with both hands while the mouth is open
8. intervene only after the vic-

CHAPTER REVIEW

LEARNING THE VOCABULARY

first aid	Heimlich maneuver	herbs	witch hazel
dispatcher	hypothermia	folk medicines	ginseng
emergency medical service (EMS)	hyperthermia	foxglove	ginseng abuse syndrome
CPR (cardiopulmonary resuscitation)	frostbite	comfrey	aloe
carotid pulse	venom	hemlock	chamomile
shock	fracture	belladonna	
	splint	sassafras	

Answer the following questions on a separate sheet of paper.

1. **Matching**—*Match each of the following phrases with the appropriate vocabulary term from the list above:*
   a. person who answers calls and relays messages to the proper helping service
   b. formation of ice crystals in body parts exposed to temperatures below freezing
   c. a stick or board to support a broken bone
2. a. A life-threatening reaction to accidents and injuries is called _____.
   b. _____ is a poison from a living creature such as a snake or scorpion.
   c. A break in a bone is called a _____.
   d. The _____ is a team of people who are trained to respond in emergencies, and who can be contacted through a single dispatcher.

3. **Word Scramble**—*Use the clues from the phrases below to help you unscramble the terms:*
   a. **aiocdrt eulps** _____ _____ the heartbeat in main arteries next to the airway in the front of the neck
   b. **eiichhlm aeeumnrv** _____ _____ a technique of dislodging a particle that is blocking a person's airway
   c. **ifstr ida** _____ _____ medical help given immediately in an emergency
   d. **aeiohhmprty** _____ a condition of too little body heat with abnormally low internal body temperature
4. Write a paragraph using at least ten of the vocabulary terms. Underline each vocabulary term that you use.

RECALLING IMPORTANT FACTS AND IDEAS

1. What are common hazards present when you survey an accident scene?
2. How do you decide who needs treatment first when there are several victims?
3. Describe how you should check a victim's airway.
4. What is the worst thing that can happen if a person goes into shock?
5. What happens to the blood and other vital organs of a person who goes into shock?
6. When you do a secondary survey of a victim, what are you looking for?
7. Explain the universal distress signal for choking.
8. If a person is choking but can make a sound, what should a rescuer do?
9. If a person is choking but cannot make a sound, what should a rescuer do?
10. When should a rescuer stop giving breathing assistance?
11. What is one problem with an untrained person who attempts CPR?
12. How long does it take for the brain to begin to die when oxygen is cut off?
13. Why shouldn't a tourniquet be used to control bleeding?
14. How are burns classified?
15. Describe what a second degree burn looks like.

tim has tried self-help maneuvers without success

9. shout for help and perform the Heimlich maneuver

10. when a victim begins to breathe spontaneously, even if weakly

Section IV

11. They may stop a heart that is already beating, placing the victim in severe danger.

12. a few minutes

Section V

13. A tourniquet almost always kills the limb to which it is applied.

Section VI

14. by the depth of tissue injury

15. red and mottled, with blisters, considerable swelling, wet at the surface

16. that the airway is burned

17. 98.6 degrees F.

18. stiff muscles, with some shivering or trembling; dizziness; weakness; cold skin; problems with coordination; slowed breathing and heart rate; confusion and drowsiness

19. warm food or drinks; not raising the feet; wrapping the person in blankets, towels,

pillows, scarves, or newspapers

20. do not handle the person roughly; do not attempt to rewarm with hot baths, electric blankets, or hot water bottles; do not raise feet or legs

21. overdoses of aspirin or other over-the-counter pain relievers, eaten by children or taken by mistake by adults

---

16. What should you be concerned about when a person has a facial burn?

17. What temperature should the body be for tissues to function normally?

18. What are symptoms of hypothermia?

19. What is the treatment for hypothermia?

20. What shouldn't you do when treating for frostbite?

21. What is the most common cause of poisoning?

CRITICAL THINKING

1. After taking the Life Choice Inventory on page 595, how do you feel about your results? What can and will you do to improve your score? If you are already in the excellent range, what will you do to stay in the excellent range?

ACTIVITIES

1. Make a video of how to perform the Heimlich maneuver and show it to the rest of the school.

2. Visit a local hospital. Ask the emergency room personnel how many people have died in the last month. Out of that number how many have died because no CPR was performed on them? Give an oral report to your class.

3. Make posters on the ABC's of first aid. Put them up around your school.

4. Make a pamphlet that explains other types of wounds, burns, and broken bones. Explain the first aid procedures necessary for treating these problems.

5. Question your family members on the procedures to follow in first aid situations. Explain to them the importance of knowing how to perform first aid. Encourage them to take a class in first aid and emergency procedures.

6. Interview your principal and see how prepared the school is in case of an emergency. How many teachers are certified in first aid? How many in CPR? Write a report on your findings.

7. Make up a play that explains what to have in a first aid kit, and what the items are for. Show this play to the local elementary schools.

8. Check to see if you have a first aid kit at home. Bring it to class and describe the items that are in the kit and what they are needed for. Also describe the items that are missing and why they are needed. If you don't have a kit at home describe the items you would put in one and what their purposes are.

MAKING DECISIONS ABOUT HEALTH

1. You are at your neighbor's house baby-sitting. About halfway through the evening one of the kids, Katherine, feels very sick. You feel her forehead and she is burning up. The other two kids, Webster and Jimmy are fine. What would you do in this situation? How will you take care of Katherine and keep the other two kids supervised?

2. You are backpacking on your family vacation, and your mother has slipped off the trail and stumbled down a large embankment. When you go to help her, all her vital signs are good. You think she may be going into shock, though. What action will you take? Why will you take such action?

CHAPTER 25 PLANNER

OVERVIEW

Chapter 25 is 28 pages long and divided into the five sections listed to the right. The major learning outcomes are also listed to the right. Chapter 25 focuses on developing student empathy regarding global environmental issues and student involvement in implementing environmentally sound practices into daily life. Students become informed about local environmental issues, realize that one person or a small group can make a difference, and create and carry out action plans. Activities encourage students to lead simpler lives and persuade others to do the same, thereby consuming less energy and fewer resources.

MAKING LIFE CHOICES RESOURCES

A variety of activities, handouts, quizzes, and tests to accompany this chapter are available in the *Making Life Choices* supplementary material. You may pick and choose from those materials as appropriate for your amount of class time and the ability levels of your students. Some of the resources you might want to consider using are:

Handouts
• Lifestyle Choices Affect the Environment and Health
• Sound Intensities and Their Effects
• Some Ways to Reduce, Reuse, and Recycle
• Home Appliances and Global Warming
• Energy Used by Appliances
• Using Nontoxic Products in the Home
• U.S. Public Health Service Objectives
• Living a Simpler Lifestyle

Overheads
• Human Impact (All Things Connected)
• Accumulation of Toxic Compounds at the Top of the Food Chain
• Hazardous Wastes in the United States
• Radiation Levels After the Chernobyl Nuclear Accident, 1986
• The Rate of Loss of the World's Rain Forests
• Population Growth

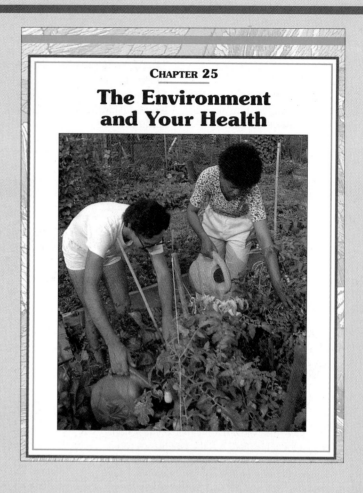

CHAPTER 25

The Environment and Your Health

CHAPTER PROJECT

Have students bring in a variety of waste products and packaging that can be recycled, as well as some that cannot. Have students help you sort through the items and place each in its proper pile for recycling. Have students find locations of places that will accept each type of item to be recycled. Then have students highlight these places on a map of your community, using different colors of highlighter for each type of recyclable material. Make a key below the map that shows the colors on the map and which materials correspond. Display the map where it can be seen by all students.

OUTCOMES

After reading and studying this chapter, you will be able to:

✓ Describe how the environment affects your body's health.
✓ List and identify the global environmental problems in the 1990s.
✓ Explain how our lifestyle choices affect the environment and our health.
✓ Discuss how we can help our environment while shopping.
✓ Describe how we can conserve energy and water in our homes.
✓ Describe the environmental problems associated with waste disposal.
✓ Discuss the impact of hunger on the environment.

CONTENTS

I. Human Impacts on the Earth
II. Shopping
III. Energy Use in the Home
IV. Water Use, Trash, and Garbage
V. Hunger and the Environment

Straight Talk: Personal Strategy—Voluntary Simplicity

FACT OR FICTION

What do you think? Are the following statements true or false? If you think they are false, then say what is true.

1. Small groups of people can change the world.
2. All products that people buy are harmful to the environment.
3. Local products cost less than the same products shipped in from far away.
4. The average electric range uses more energy than the average refrigerator.
5. All-electric homes pollute the environment less than homes that use gas or oil for heating and appliances.
6. If U.S. consumers used less energy, this would help solve the world's hunger problem.
(Answers on page 647)

■ **Reminder:** Knowing how to study can increase your knowledge, improve your grades, *and* cut down on your study time. See the *Studying Health* section at the front of your text for some suggestions to help you study this chapter.

NOT ENOUGH TIME?*

You could easily spend a week or more teaching this chapter if students read the entire chapter, do a fair number of the suggested activities in the teacher's edition, and complete a sampling of the handouts from the resource material accompanying this text. It is likely, however, that you will have only a few days to devote to this chapter. Following are some suggestions to help you make sure that you cover the key topics if you have limited time.

TIME	SUGGESTIONS
1 Day	Complete Activity 1.2 and 1.6. Have students take the Life Choice Inventory, and close with 1.14. Assign students to read Sections I and II for homework.
2 Days	On day 2 begin class with Activity 2.2. Assign Activity 2.6 for homework and give the students a few days to complete the assignment. Assign students to read Sections III and IV for homework.
3 Days	On day 3 begin class with Activity 3.1 to promote interest. Complete Activity 3.6 in class.
4 Days	On day 4 begin class with Activity 4.1. For homework assign Activity 4.2.

Please refer to the 18-week daily lesson plans in the supplementary material for additional suggestions.

Activity To Introduce Chapter

Recycling. Ask students to list all of the products that they used this morning to get ready for school. Ask if they created any waste. If so, could this waste be recycled? Did they save it for recycling? Tell students that not only do people need to be aware of the items they purchase that cause waste, they also need to recognize that some wastes can be recycled.

Answers to "Fact or Fiction"

1. True. 2. False. Products are beneficial to the environment if they help *relieve* pollution or displace other products that pollute. 3. False. Local produce may cost more, but it may be a good choice for environmental reasons.
4. False. The refrigerator uses more energy, because it is on all the time. 5. False. Fossil fuels are burned to produce electricity. 6. True.

SUGGESTED RESOURCES

Student Readings
1. Berry, Thomas. *The Dream of Earth.* San Francisco: Sierra Club Books, 1988.
2. Causey, Ann S. *Environmental Action Guide Action for a Sustainable Future.* Redwood City, CA: The Benjamin/Cummings Publishing Company, Inc., 1991.

Teacher Readings
1. Seymour, John and Girardet, Herbert. *Blue-print for a Green Planet.* Englewood Cliffs, NJ: Prentice Hall, 1987.

Videos
1. *Survival of Spaceship Earth.* Cambridge Educational, 800-468-4227.
2. *America's Rainforest.* Cambridge Educational, 800-468-4227.

Software
1. *Water Pollution.* Opportunities for Learning, Inc., 800-243-7116.

In this section students will learn:
1. How the environment affects their health.
2. To describe the major global environmental problems of the 1990s.

Activity 1.1

Identifying Environmental Problems. Have students name as many environmental problems as possible. They should name global problems, not just local ones. Discuss these problems and what is being done about them. **(5–10 min.)**

Activity 1.2
Environmental Effects on Our Health. Have students brainstorm ways

the environment can affect our health. Discuss student answers and use their responses to introduce topics that will be covered in this chapter. **(5 min.)**

TEACH
▶ SECTION 1
(Guided and Independent Practice)

Activity 1.3
Future Issues. After discussing environmental issues in earlier activities, tell

Teacher Support Notes

① **Your Environment:** Ask students how close their environment comes to matching the ideal environment described here. Which elements in this description match the students' own environment?

② **A Single System:** Make sure students understand the meaning of this sentence. First ask them to define *environment* in a way that suggests that they are separate from the environment. Then ask them to explain how a person and his or her environment are part of a single system. (environment supplies material making up the body; environment provides energy; materials and energy flow through our bodies from the environment and back to the environment)

66 Thoughts on Health 99

The twentieth century will be remembered chiefly, not as an age of political conflicts and technical inventions, but as an age in which human society dared to think of the health of the whole human race as a practical objective.
– Arnold Toynbee

626 UNIT 8 Global Issues

A healthy **environment** supports personal health; a damaged environment erodes it. Consider your needs. Ideally, wherever you lived and worked—inner city, farm, or wilderness—the air would be clean; the water, pure; the food, nourishing and safe; the scenery and sounds, enjoyable; the space, open for play; and all other elements, both seen and unseen, in harmony together. It is unrealistic, of course, to think that everyone in today's world can enjoy such a life. It is also untrue that such perfect conditions are necessary to health. It is true, however, that people will survive only so long as we maintain our environment so that it can sustain us.

We and our environment are really part of a single system. Our environment supplies the materials our bodies are made of. It also provides forms of energy (especially light and heat energy) that make our lives possible. Materials and energy constantly flow into and through us, and we alter the environment just by being here.

Just as your environment affects your body's health each day, you also affect the environment each day. Each day of your life, you breathe its air, eat its food, and leave your wastes in it. To make your choices consciously, you have to think about the effects you are having on the earth each day. In this chapter, you can learn which of your choices leave the earth better or worse off each day.

It is in your interest to learn this, partly because of the environment's impact on you.

- If the air is clean, your lungs can be healthy. If the air is polluted, you and your family may suffer chronic lung diseases.
- If the water is pure, you can drink it without fear. If the water is polluted, it can bring with it all manner of harmful chemicals, including many that cause cancer.

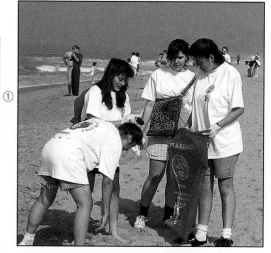

①

② For your health's sake, take care of your environment.

- If the soil is free of poisons, it will grow food that will sustain you. If it is contaminated, the food may be unwholesome. Some contaminated soil cannot even support plant life, or any kind of living things.

Because you are a biological creature, you depend on the environment for the elements that support your life—air, water, soil, climate, and living plants and animals.

Vast changes are taking place in your environment today. You may not recognize these changes. Once your eyes are open, however, you will see them all around you. When you have become conscious of how your own choices affect the environment, you will also see the effects of the choices of others—and not only of individuals but of groups, including industry, agriculture, and government.

You have the right to a healthy environment—the right to clean air, pure water, and safe food. Together with your neighbors, you can demand that other people respect that right. As large as the world's environmental problems may be, they are

626

students to use their imaginations and descriptive language to write about what the world might be like in 50 years if we continue all our destructive activities. **(30 min. to create, 30 min. to present; Interdisciplinary)**

Activity 1.4
Effects of Polluted Water. Plant three ivies in the room in similar containers. Water one with plain water. Water the other two with water mixed with two common substances that pollute our water and that are put into our waterways through human use. To decide which substances to use as pollutants, have students brainstorm a list of all products we use that eventually end up in our waterways. Then have the students vote for two. Use the two products with the most votes.

At times throughout the semester, check the ivies with the class to see if there are any noticeable changes in the appearance or growth of the ivy that may be due to the pollution in the water. Have students develop a list of ways that water pollution affects living things. **(5–10 min. to setup, Critical Thinking)**

Activity 1.5
Consumer Choices. Ask students

(continued on next page)

---

all caused by people's choices. They can also only be solved by people's choices.

The sections that follow show you, first, how human behaviors are affecting the earth. They then explain how you can shape your behaviors for the better in several areas—in your shopping choices, your home energy use, and others. The Life Choice Inventory gives you a starting point. It allows you to see how aware you already are of your responsibilities toward the earth.

> **Key Points** *All things are connected. Human behaviors affect the world's air, water, and living things; and the air, water, and all life on earth affect human health.*

SECTION I

Human Impacts on the Earth

① ②

Most people buy and use goods and services without thinking about the effects these products have on our environment. Seldom do they ask such questions as "What is the cost of this product or service in electricity, gasoline, water, and **pollution**?" or "How does my choice of this product or service affect the global environment?" Yet the ways our clothes, foods, and toys are produced do affect the global environment. They are even linked to poverty, hunger, and disease of populations on the other side of the world. If we realized the impacts of our choices, we might choose differently—yet still enjoy our lives just as much as we do now.

Impacts of U.S. Consumption

The production of goods for U.S. consumers is one of the globe's biggest businesses. It involves huge manufacturing efforts involving water and fuel; huge tracts of land to produce raw materials; huge amounts of packaging materials and fuel to make goods ready for market; a huge transportation network—in short, enormous consumption of resources and production of pollution. Today's consumers, becoming aware of the environmental impacts of their choices and eager to become conscious choosers, are fascinated by facts like the following:

- The average molecule of food eaten in this country travels 1,300 miles before the consumer swallows it.
- To drive a semi-trailer 1,300 miles requires some 250 gallons of gas.
- 250 gallons of gas burned as fuel release 2½ tons of carbon dioxide. Carbon dioxide accumulation in the atmosphere is warming up the globe.
- The consumer who drinks a typical can of diet soda obtains from it 1 calorie of food energy. But to manufacture the can costs 800 calories in fuel, pollutes the soil at the mining site with toxic materials, and uses more water than the soda that ends up in the can.

Other choices, far less harmful to the environment, are possible. For example, Floridians need not eat carrots that have been shipped in from California. They can eat carrots grown in Florida (and Californians can eat carrots grown in California). In

M INI G LOSSARY

environment: everything "outside" the living organism—air, water, soil, other organisms, and forms of radiation.
pollution: contamination of the environment with anything that impairs its ability to support life.

Teacher Support Notes

① **Overheads— Human Impact:** Your supplementary material contains two overheads, both of which show how the different parts of our environment are all connected. When used together the overheads make it possible to see how humans have impacted the earth. One transparency shows the environment before humans; the other transparency shows the environment with humans.
② **Impact of Goods and Services:** Have students make a list of five to ten items they have purchased recently. Then next to each item have them write *yes* or *no* to indicate whether or not they thought about the impact the *manufacturing* of that item had on our environment. Finally, have them indicate what impacts they think the product itself has on our environment.

to answer the question, "In what ways might your choice of food or clothing as a consumer affect the environment?" Discuss their answers. **(3 min., Critical Thinking)**

Activity 1.6

Local Environmental Problems. Have students brainstorm a list of environmental problems found in local cities and communities. Were students aware of most of these problems? How do the students feel about these problems? Have any of the problems inspired students to become more involved in the fight to solve one or more of these problems?

If none of the environmental problems listed in the text or discussed earlier by students have affected your local communities, ask students which problems are most likely to have an impact in the years to come. What would students' reactions be? Would they become more involved? **(10 min.; Extend, Enrich)**

Activity 1.7
Legal Limitations. Have students research existing laws that attempt to

---

Teacher Support Notes

① **Caring for the Environment:** Before students begin the inventory, have them read the scoring directions. They need to go through the list of suggestions in the inventory twice. It might help to have them make two columns on a sheet of paper, one entitled "I am aware of this," and another entitled "I practice this habit." They should then put check marks in the appropriate columns for each number. When they're finished, check marks in the first column count one point and check marks in the second column count two points. Compare scores in class.

❝ **Thoughts on Health** ❞

The human race will be the cancer of the planet.
– Julian Huxley

LIFE **C**HOICE **I**NVENTORY

How Well Do You Care for The Environment? ①

The following questions are selected and adapted from a conservation action checklist subtitled "65 Things You Can Do to Help Save Tropical Forests and Other Natural Resources."

Keep a copy of these suggestions in a place where you will be sure to see them once every month. Every time you read the list, try to adopt another conservation habit. If everyone does these things, it will significantly help our planet's health, and in turn, your own health.

In your home, do you:

1. Recycle everything you can: newspapers, cans, glass bottles and jars, scrap metal, used oil, etc?
2. Use cold water in the washer whenever possible?
3. Avoid using appliances (such as electric can openers) to do things you can do by hand?
4. Reuse brown paper bags to line your trash? Reuse bread bags, butter tubs, etc?
5. Store food in reusable containers rather than plastic wrap or aluminum foil?

In your yard, do you:

6. Pull weeds instead of using herbicides?
7. Fertilize with manure and compost, rather than with chemical fertilizers?
8. Compost your leaves and yard debris, rather than burning them?
9. Take extra plastic and rubber pots back to the nursery?

On vacation, do you:

10. Turn down the heat and turn off the water heater before you leave?
11. Carry reusable cups, dishes, and flatware (and use them)?
12. Dispose of trash in trash containers (never litter)?
13. Buy no souvenirs made from wild or endangered animals?
14. Stay on roads and trails, and not trample dunes and fragile undergrowth?

About your car, do you:

15. Keep your car tuned up for maximum fuel efficiency?
16. Use public transit whenever possible?
17. Ride your bike or walk whenever possible?
18. Plan to replace your car with a more fuel-efficient model when you can?
19. Recycle your engine oil?

At school or work, do you:

20. Recycle paper whenever possible?
21. Use scrap paper for notes to yourself and others?
22. Print or copy on both sides of the paper?
23. Reuse large envelopes and file folders?
24. Use the stairs instead of the elevator whenever you can?

When you're buying, do you:

25. Buy as little plastic and foam packaging as possible?
26. Buy permanent, rather than disposable, products?
27. Buy paper rather than plastic, if you must buy disposable products?
28. Buy fresh produce grown locally?
29. Buy in bulk to avoid unnecessary packaging?

In other areas, do you:

30. Volunteer your time to conservation projects?

(Continued on next page)

help provide us with a clean and natural environment. How are these laws supposed to work, to what populations are they directed, and what environmental issues do they address? Have students share their findings in class. **(1 hr.; Extend, Enrich)**

Activity 1.8
Interviews. Have students brainstorm strategies for protecting the environment. List their ideas on the board. Have each student copy the list and then use the list to interview ten friends or family members. The students will ask which strategies each person uses, what other strategies they might use, and how involved that person is in the various strategies.

Have the students share their findings, and compile a master list of most used tips. Discuss why some are more used than others. **(30 min., Critical Thinking)**

Activity 1.9
Making Waves. Ask students, "What needs to be done before the majority of people will start to be environmentally conscious? How can these people be reached?" Discuss why students often "make waves" first and make them the biggest. (because today's adults did not

(continued on next page)

How Well Do You Care for The Environment? (continued)

31. Encourage your family, friends, and neighbors to save resources, too?
32. Write letters to support conservation issues?

Scoring   ①

First, give yourself 4 points for answering this quiz:_____
Then, give yourself 1 point each for all the habits you know people should adopt. This is to give you credit for your awareness, even if you haven't acted on it, yet (total possible points = 32): _____

Finally, give yourself 2 more points for each habit you have adopted—or honestly would if you could (total possible points = 64): _____
Total score:
1 to 25: You are a beginner in stewardship of the earth. Try to improve.
26 to 50: You are well on your way. Few consumers do even as well as this, yet.
51 to 75: Excellent. Pat yourself on the back, and keep on improving.
76 to 100: Outstanding. You are a shining example for others to follow.

Source: Adapted from *Conservation Action Checklist,* produced by the Washington Park Zoo, Portland, Oregon, and available from Conservation International, 1015 18th St. NW, Suite 1000, Washington, D.C. 20036; 1-202-429-5660. Call or write for copies of the original or for more information.

---

place of five or six diet sodas in aluminum cans, the consumer might take repeated drinks of soda from one large plastic bottle. Both cans and plastic bottles are recyclable, but producing and recycling the large bottles costs less environmentally.

Many other examples of environmental impacts will appear in this chapter. In every case, the purpose is to make you aware of your alternatives. A choice one person makes, one time, of local carrots or a plastic bottle may be insignificant in the scheme of things. However, several benefits come out of such choices. For one, a single person's awareness and example, shared with others, is shared again, and so it multiplies. For another, an action taken one time is likely to happen a second and third time, so that a habit is formed. For still another, a person making choices with awareness has a sense of control over environmental impacts.

> **Key Points** The United States consumes vast amounts of the world's resources. Choices of U.S. consumers powerfully influence the environment.

Global Environmental Problems

② A sense of individual control is needed for people to take action. Today's global environmental problems can easily seem so overwhelming to single individuals as to make them feel passive and hopeless. During the 1990s all of the following trends are taking place at once:

* *Hunger, poverty, and population growth.* Millions of people are starving. Fifteen children die of malnutrition every 30 seconds, but 75 children are born in that same 30 seconds.
* *Losses of land to produce food.* Land to produce food is becoming more salty, eroding, and being paved over.

Teacher Support Notes

① **Stewardship:** Ask students if they know the meaning of *stewardship.* Have them look it up. (responsibility to manage life and property with proper regard to the rights of others) Emphasize that we must all be "stewards of the earth."

② **Choices:** Emphasize that each person's choices make a difference in our environment. Tell the students that some of the choices are small. For example, a motorist who sits for ten minutes in a traffic jam could keep the car running or could turn it off so that it would pollute the air a little less. Then there are big choices. For example, a hospital administrator might choose for the sake of profit to have disease-carrying refuse dumped into the nearest river rather than disposing of it properly. All these choices make a difference.

have as many environmental problems to deal with when they were younger, they are not as educated about environmental problems as are today's teens, and today's adults will not be impacted as much as today's youth by the results of current attempts to solve the environmen-

tal problems) **(10 min., Critical Thinking)**

Activity 1.10
Guest Speaker. Ask someone from a recycling business to talk to the class about current uses of recycled materials, which local neighborhoods have the most effective recycling programs, and the biggest problems associated with recycling. **(1 hr.)**

EVALUATE
SECTION 1

Activity 1.11
Environmental Awareness Unit. Divide students into groups. Have each group create a way to teach environmental awareness to elementary school children. Give students different topics, such as energy use, reducing solid wastes,

Teacher Support Notes

① **Environmental Problems:** Beginning on the preceding page, the text identifies ten trends that are having a negative effect on our environment. Have students study the list, close their books, and practice writing the problems until they can list all ten. For extra credit they should be able to write a sentence explaining or describing something about that problem to indicate that they understand its meaning.

② **Taking Action:** Have students reread Margaret Mead's quote and ask them to come up with examples of how small groups of committed people have changed the world. One example would be the colonists who started the Revolutionary War.

 Fast Facts

In 1989 only 40% of Americans lived in cities that did not violate EPA Clean Air Standards set in 1970.

630

630   UNIT 8 Global Issues

- *Accelerating* **fossil fuel** use. Fuel use is accelerating, along with pollution of air, soil, and water; ozone depletion; and global warming.
- *Increasing* **air pollution**. Air quality is diminishing all over the globe. Acids in the air are causing **acid rain.**
- **Global warming**, *droughts and floods*. Atmospheric levels of heat-trapping carbon dioxide are now 26 percent higher than before the age of industry, and they are continuing to climb. As a result, a massive warming trend, known as the **greenhouse effect**, is taking place. This is changing the climate, causing both droughts and floods, destroying crops, and forcing people from their homes.
- *Ozone loss from the outer atmosphere*. The outer atmosphere's protective **ozone layer** is growing thinner, permitting harmful radiation from the sun to damage crops and ecosystems and to cause cancers in people.
- *Water shortages*. The world's supplies of fresh water are dwindling and becoming polluted.
- *Deforestation and desertification*. Forests are shrinking. Deserts are growing. By the year 2000, *new* deserts worldwide will cover an area 1½ times the size of the United States.
- *Ocean and lake pollution*. Ocean and lake pollution is killing fish. Overfishing is depleting the numbers of those that remain. Pollution is making them unsafe to eat.
- *Extinctions of species*. Vast extinctions of animals and plants are taking place—a minimum of 140 species *a day*. Some 20 percent more of those species remaining are expected to die out in the next ten years. Extinction is forever. Many kinds of whales, birds, giant mammals, colorful butterflies, and thousands of others will never again be seen in the universe.

Despite the magnitude of these disasters, there is much that people can do to help slow, stop, and even reverse these processes and restore a livable world. On some fronts people can act as individuals. Each of us can choose what products to buy, what foods to eat, and the like. On other fronts people can act in groups. Groups can lobby legislators to write laws that protect the environment, demand that the laws be enforced, and insist that corporations and governments honor their principles. According to a famous activist (Margaret Mead), you should "never doubt that a small group of thoughtful, committed people can change the world. Indeed," she says, "it is the only thing that ever has."

This chapter describes global problems as briefly as possible, so as to devote most of its space to "What we can do." The object is to help readers gain awareness of the ways in which their own personal choices affect global environmental health, for people's rising awareness is the hope of the future.

Once aware of their impacts, if people choose to change them, two kinds of **ripple effect** can follow. One is the ripple effect that takes place in each person's own mind, as one level of awareness leads to another. First, a person learns how to improve the immediate surroundings, but soon, the person learns how to reach much farther than seemed possible at first. The other is the effect that extends to other people who hear and see what the person is doing. A word of awareness dropped into another's ear may start a ripple that grows into a wave. Students often start such waves as they learn of current events and start trying to change them.

The global problems that need to be solved are all related. Their causes overlap, and so do their solutions. That means that any action a person takes to help solve one problem will help solve many others. Figure 25–1 on page 632 shows a few of the keeping air and water clean, recycling, and using toxic chemicals. Have the groups develop an educational program around their topics to teach to small children. Assess student knowledge by watching them present their educational programs to the class. Pick the best programs and take those students on a field trip to a neighboring elementary school to present the programs to the children. **(1–2 hrs., Cooperative Learning)**

Activity 1.12
Service Projects. Have the students think of and carry out community service projects aimed at protecting or cleaning up the local environment. Some examples of projects might include cleaning up around a lake or pond, picking up and recycling aluminum cans, educating consumers about how their choices affect the environment, or becoming involved in a demonstration or movement surrounding

a local environmental issue. **(30 min., Cooperative Learning)**

CLOSE
SECTION I

Activity 1.13
Production Process. Bring in an item from the grocery store. Have students write the steps involved in getting

(continued on next page)

---

many links among today's global environmental problems, to which U.S. consumers unknowingly contribute.

The task for consumers is to become aware of their impacts, and to find **sustainable** ways of doing things. These are ways of living that use up resources at a rate that nature, forestry, or agriculture can replace. They are ways of living that pollute the earth at a rate that nature or human cleanup efforts can keep up with.

One of the nicest things about sustainable ways of living is that the choices most beneficial to the environment also benefit the health of the human body. People's health greatly depends on the health of their surroundings, for the two are closely connected.

Key Points ▶ *Human impacts are damaging the earth's land, air, water, oceans, climate, and outer atmosphere. This endangers people's health. Alternatives are possible and require that people find sustainable ways of doing things.*

SECTION I   REVIEW

Answer the following questions on a sheet of paper.
Learning the Vocabulary
The vocabulary terms in this section are *environment, pollution, fossil fuel, air pollution, acid rain, global warming, greenhouse effect, ozone layer, ripple effect,* and *sustainable.*
Fill in the blanks with the correct answer.
1. _____ is the contamination of the air with gases or particles not normally found there.
2. The outer atmosphere that protects living things on earth from harmful ultraviolet radiation from the sun is called the _____.
3. _____ is any resource such as coal, oil, or natural gas, burned to provide energy.

Learning the Facts
4. What does your environment do to your personal health?
5. Contrast the environmental impacts of different choices to buy foods.

6. Why is it better to buy plastic bottles of soda instead of cans?
7. Describe how the ripple effect works.

Making Life Choices
8. Study Figure 25–1 on the next page. Choose one environmental problem and describe how it contributes to others and how others contribute to it. Explain how, if you helped solve one problem, you would be helping solve all the others.

— MINI GLOSSARY —

① **fossil fuel:** coal, oil, and natural gas, which all come from the fossilized remains of plant life of earlier times.
air pollution: contamination of the air with gases or particles not normally found there.
acid rain: rain that carries acid air pollutants, which harms the plants and damages the soil on which it falls.
global warming: warming of the planet, a trend that threatens life on earth.
greenhouse effect: the heat-trapping effect of the glass in a greenhouse. The same effect is caused by gases that are accumulating in the earth's outer atmosphere, which are trapping the sun's heat and warming the planet.
ozone layer: a layer of ozone in the earth's outer atmosphere that protects living things on earth from harmful ultraviolet radiation from the sun.
ripple effect: the effect seen when a pebble is thrown into a pond and waves radiate out from it. The term is used to describe how one person's actions may affect many other people, and how their actions will affect still other people.
sustainable: a term used to describe the use of resources at such a rate that the earth can keep on replacing them—for example, a rate of cutting trees no faster than new ones grow. Also, *sustainable* describes the production of pollutants at a rate that the environment or human cleanup efforts can handle, so that there is no net accumulation of pollution.

Teacher Support Notes

① **Handout—Lifestyle Choices and the Environment:** Your supplementary material contains a handout about sustainable choices.

Section I Review
Answers
1. Air pollution
2. ozone layer
3. Fossil fuel
4. See page 626 for possible answers.
5. It involves manufacturing efforts involving water and fuel; huge tracts of land to produce raw materials; huge amounts of packaging materials and fuels; a huge transportation network; and production of pollution.
6. Producing and recycling the large bottles costs less environmentally.
7. For a complete description, see the next-to-last paragraph on page 630.
8. Answers will vary.

CLOSE
(Continued)

this item to the shelf of the store for purchase. Have them tell how these steps affected our environment. **(5 min., Critical Thinking)**

Activity 1.14
Identifying Human Impact. Ask

students to tell you ways humans have had a negative effect on their environment. What could be done in a sustainable way to change each of these negative effects? **(5 min.; Extend, Enrich)**

FOCUS
SECTION II

In this section students will learn the:
1. Ways we can help our environment

while shopping.
2. Tips for selecting products that are environmentally safe.
3. Impact of environmental problems on living things and the food chain.

Activity 2.1
Effects of Consumer Choices. Have students name ways in which our choices of what to buy can have an effect on our environment. Write all their ideas

Teacher Support Notes

① **Hub of Global Problems:** The purpose of this illustration is to help students see that all the major environmental problems are interconnected. The problems identified in the ten circles are roughly equivalent to the list of ten environmental problems that students studied on preceding pages in this chapter. Each numbered arrow is explained in a key on the opposite page. You can make many different kinds of assignments using this illustration, but first make sure that students appreciate the main point—that each problem contributes to the worsening of the other problems. Students should then begin to realize, as the text stated earlier, that if one problem is solved it will help solve all of the others. Among the different activities you could have students do are the following:
a. Have them pick a number, any number, follow that arrow, and then guess without looking at the key how the one problem affects the other. After writing down one or two guesses, students could look at the key.
b. The class could read through the entire list of impacts from 1 to 43 in

(continued on next page)

632

632 UNIT 8 Global Issues

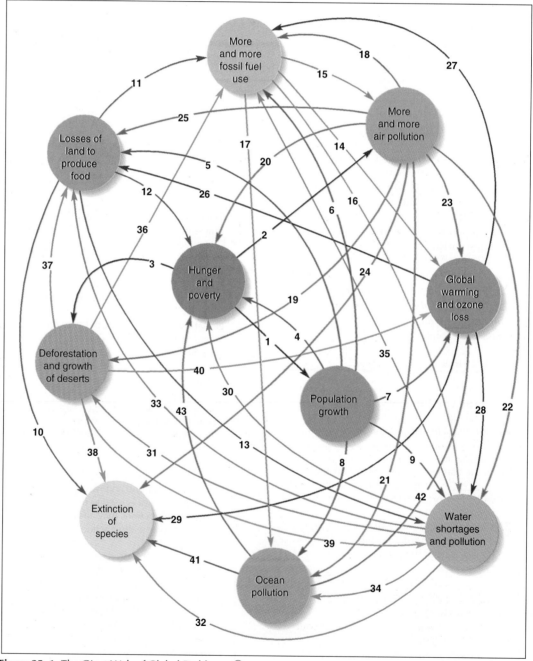

Figure 25–1 The Giant Web of Global Problems ①

on the board. Discuss which decisions have the greatest impact. **(3 min.)**

Activity 2.2
Foot Traffic. Have students think of places they have been that encourage foot traffic. (You may need to explain that this means places where people must walk rather than use another form of transportation.) Have them describe the place and answer, "Do you like it? Why,

or why not? Would you go there again? Do the stores or businesses benefit as a result of the foot traffic?" Discuss the benefits of places that encourage foot traffic. **(20 min.)**

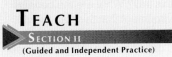

TEACH
SECTION II
(Guided and Independent Practice)

Activity 2.3
Grocery Analysis. Have students

create a list of items that their parents routinely buy at the grocery store. Next to each item, have them write what feature of the item to check for or substitute for in order to make that choice more environmentally sound. In doing their analysis, students should consider, among other things, packaging, energy used in transporting or manufacturing the item, and energy used to store the item. **(30 min.,**

(continued on next page)

Figure 25-1 (continued)

1. Hunger and poverty make people fear their children will die, so they bear as many children as they can.
2. Poor people burn wood for fuel.
3. Landless people cut and burn trees to establish farmland.
4. The more mouths to feed, the worse the poverty becomes.
5. Growing cities eat up former farms.
6. Growing populations use more and more gas, coal, and oil for homes, cars, and factories.
7. The more people, the more cattle, which release methane that contributes to both global warming and ozone loss. Also, the more people, the more air conditioners and refrigerators, which leak ozone-destroying refrigerants.
8. Growing populations pollute waterways and the ocean with sewage, garbage, fertilizers, and pesticides.
9. Growing populations need more water to drink, to grow their food, and to support their mining and manufacturing. The more people, the more human waste and agricultural and industrial pollution.
10. Land losses lead to losses of habitats; then species die out.
11. As farmland is paved over, new farms try to use land with poorer soil, requiring more tractors (which use fossil fuels) and more fertilizer (which is made from fossil fuels).
12. As land suitable to produce food diminishes, food shortages intensify.
13. New farmland on poor soil demands irrigation, which uses up water, salts the land, and pollutes waterways.
14. The more gas, coal, and oil are burned, the more they release global-warming gases and pollutants that destroy outer-atmosphere ozone.
15. The more gas, coal, and oil are burned, the more air pollutants they release.
16. Fuels (and fertilizers made from them) pollute rivers and groundwater.
17. The transportation of fossil fuels in ocean-going tankers leads to oil spills.
18. As outdoor air becomes impossible to breathe, people use more air conditioners and purifiers, demanding more fuel to run them.
19. Air pollution deprives plants of needed sunlight.
20. Air pollution worsens living and working conditions and destroys health.
21. Rain falling through polluted air washes the pollutants into the ocean.
22. Air pollution pollutes the rain and this pollutes both surface water and groundwater.
23. Many air pollutants rise to the outer atmosphere, trapping heat and destroying ozone.
24. Air pollution degrades the conditions for life.
25. Air pollution falls in rain and ruins land.
26. As the ocean warms, it expands, and land masses shrink.
27. The warmer the climate, the more people use air conditioning and refrigeration.
28. Droughts cause water shortages and floods wash pollution into water supplies.
29. A warmer climate threatens plant and animal life; ozone loss means harmful radiation from the sun will damage living things.
30. Water shortages and pollution force people from their homes.
31. Water shortages cause fields and forests to dry up and die.
32. Water shortages and pollution wipe out plants and animals.
33. Water shortages dry up land and polluted water ruins soil.
34. Polluted rivers pollute the ocean.
35. To transport water over long distances, to desalt ocean water, and to purify polluted water for reuse requires more and more energy.
36. With less wood to rely on, people turn to fossil fuels to burn for energy and to make plastics.
37. As deserts grow, land areas suitable for farming shrink.
38. Losses of once-forested or fertile lands rob species of needed habitat.
39. Deforested lands and dried-up wetlands cannot absorb and hold pollutants. Instead, pollutants run into rivers and lakes.
40. The more tropical forests are burned, the more global-warming gases trap earth's heat and the fewer trees remain to remove these gases from the air.
41. Even though the ocean is very large and its species very numerous, pollution can destroy the conditions necessary for life.
42. Ocean pollution is beginning to kill ocean algae, which help control the planet's temperature.
43. Ocean pollution kills ocean life, leading to losses of fisheries.

order, with each student reading a different number.
c. Students could be divided into ten groups, one for each type of problem. Each group would be assigned to develop a poster of its problem. They would also then create an original way of presenting each of the impacts originating from their circle.
d. Another possibility would be to have each student in the class represent one of the 43 factors. Designate ten areas in the classroom, one for each of the ten major problems. Have each student begin in the area from which his arrow originates. Students would state the sentence of their numbers and then walk to the area affected. Number 1 would be followed by number 2 and so on.

✎ Fast Facts

The EPA estimates that from 1980 to 1990 the average yearly increase in the amount of garbage an American discarded was 69 pounds.

Critical Thinking)

Activity 2.4

Creating Bike Trails. Ask students to consider a place in their neighborhoods where a bike trail would be useful, especially for transportation to and from schools and local stores. Find a route for the bike trail and draw it accurately on a map. Have students answer these questions: "Is there enough room to put in the trail? What steps would have to be taken to put in this trail? What are the benefits to the environment that this trail might provide?" Have students present their ideas and drawings at a community meeting or civic club, then answer: "What type of feedback did you receive? Did they support your idea? Why, or why not? Were their reasons valid and environmentally conscious?" **(1–2 hrs., Critical Thinking)**

Activity 2.5

Car Posters. Have students create posters with pictures of their favorite cars in the middle. Have them draw arrows coming away from the car. Beside each of the arrows, have students write physical, emotional, or financial reasons to buy a

Teacher Support Notes

① **Air Pollution:** You may want to give students some additional information about air pollution. People-generated air pollutants come from four main sources: oil and gasoline burned to run cars and other forms of transportation; oil, coal and natural gas burned to generate electricity for homes, businesses, and industry; waste products from manufacturing; and in cities, solid waste being burned for disposal. Normal clean air consists of about 1/5 oxygen and 4/5 nitrogen, with trace amounts of other gases mixed in.

② **City Planning:** Ask students how practical and desirable it is for their families to work, live, and shop in the same area. What aspects of their neighborhoods or their shopping areas make them desirable from an environmental standpoint? Many cities are trying to do a better job of planning to make the cities attractive and efficient. The city of Charleston, South Carolina, for example, is famous for intelligent planning that makes each city block inviting to pedestrian traffic. Are there any such cities in your area?

634 UNIT 8 Global Issues

SECTION II

Shopping

Shopping involves trips to stores, choices of goods once you are at the store, package choices, and choices of bags in which to carry things home. Let's consider the shopping trips first.

Shopping Trips

In late 1990, 400 million cars were in use around the world. Every year, 19 million more cars are being added. Even without that increase, motor vehicles were the world's single largest source of air pollution. ① They harmed people with lung problems, children, and the elderly; reduced crop yields; caused acid rain; damaged forests; and produced major amounts of the global-warming gas carbon dioxide. Transporting oil to provide gasoline for cars is a major cause of oil spills that harm ocean life.

Alternatives to the use of private cars are carpools, mass transit, walking, bicycling, and even skateboarding or roller skating, where practical. It will help if cities combine homes, workplaces, and retail stores in neighborhoods and provide sidewalks and bike paths to make walking and biking feasible.

While awaiting the changes needed to help people wean themselves from dependence on their cars, shoppers can make the following choices. Get organized, make a list, and limit shopping trips to once each week. Share rides to the mall, or take turns shopping for one another. Shop at neighborhood stores, and walk or bicycle to get there. When choosing a car, look for the most fuel-efficient model you can find.†

Shopping without a car can be a pleasure.

If the choices suggested seem insignificant, consider this example. Suppose, for the next 30 years, you visit a shopping mall 5 miles away, in a 25-mile-per-gallon car, every day. You will drive over 100,000 miles round-trip just shopping, and use ② over 4,000 gallons of gas. (You'll use up one or two cars, too.) On the other hand, if you shop once a week at stores 1 mile away in a 50-mile-per-gallon car, you'll drive only some 3,000 miles round-trip and use only about 63 gallons of gas over the whole 30 years. Even if gas cost only $1 per gallon, then by using about 63 gallons instead of over 4,000, you would save about $4,000. Every dollar saved on gas is a unit of pollution saved, since each gallon of gas burned in a car releases some 16 pounds of carbon dioxide. By choosing positively, you would account for nearly 70,000 pounds (over 30 tons) of carbon dioxide saved, just in your shopping trips.

†By 1993, the U.S. market offered several cars with fuel efficiency rated at 40 to 50 miles to the gallon.

car. Beside some of the arrows write the negative impacts that a car can have on the environment. Have students come up with titles for their posters that portray the real dilemmas of car ownership. **(30 min., Special Needs)**

Activity 2.6
Shopping Bags. Have students design and sew reusable bags for shopping. Have them create environmental slogans to write, glue, or embroider on the sides of the bags. **(2 hrs., Interdisciplinary)**

Activity 2.7
Green Products. Bring labels of products to class and have students help you decide which of the products could be labeled as "green" products. Then have students go to the store and find at least ten products that are "green" products. "Green" products must meet all of the eight requirements listed below. **(30 min.; Extend, Enrich)**

Activity 2.8
Student Impact. Have students make a list of products they know are bad for the environment. Beside each product have students list the way in which the product negatively impacts the environ-

(continued on next page)

On each trip, by the way, take along your own shopping bags—either retail bags you received with other purchases or canvas or net bags you can reuse indefinitely. They save pollution in another way, as shown later.

> **Key Points** *Automobiles are the world's single largest cause of air pollution. Future societies need to find ways of reducing or eliminating car use.*

Products to Choose: Green Products

From the point of view of the environment, the ideal product is a truly "green" product. A product is "green"—that is, most environmentally harmless—if it earns a yes answer to each of these questions:

1. Is it designed to meet reasonable human needs without being frivolous? ①
2. Is it durable and reusable (best)? If not, then is it **recyclable** or **biodegradable** (second best)? If it is **disposable**, avoid it. ②
3. Does it release only safe substances—no **persistent** toxins—into the environment during production? During use? When it is thrown away?
4. Does it consume minimal energy and resources during production, use, and disposal?
5. Is it made from recycled materials or renewable resources?
6. If processed, is it processed in a way that preserves the environment?
7. Is it minimally packaged?
8. Is it responsibly packaged (does the packaging material fit the same criteria as the product)?

On Question 2, you may wonder why recyclable is second best. The reason is that at even a 50 percent recycling rate, after just five cycles only 3 percent of the original material is still being recycled. (Fifty percent of 50 percent of 50 percent of 50 percent of 50 percent is about 3 percent.) We need to do much better than that.

Unfortunately, many products are labeled "green" that really are not. Beware of misleading "green" labels on products. Figure 25–2 lists products that truly benefit the earth.

> **Key Points** *To benefit the environment, buy only products that you need; that have not been, and will not be, responsible for any pollution; and that are responsibly packaged. Refuse nonrecyclables and disposables.*

Cleaning Supplies and Other Home Products

Many of the products we use in our homes contain or release toxins. If used as directed, these products may not harm us. However, their manufacture may pollute the environment. Furthermore, when we dispose of them or their containers, they may again cause harm.

A prime example is chlorine bleach. It works well as a disinfectant, because it kills living cells. That same quality, however, makes it deadly when it goes down the drain. Where strong chlorine concentrations run into waterways, they kill all life—from

---

MINI GLOSSARY

recyclable: made of material that can be used over again.

biodegradable: able to decompose; able to be converted by living organisms into harmless waste products that can be used over again to build or grow new things.

disposable: a description of any product that is intended to be used once and then thrown away.

persistent: the opposite of biodegradable—unable to decompose or to be converted by living organisms into harmless wastes.

Teacher Support Notes

① **Frivolous Products:** Ask students to define *frivolous.* (of little weight or importance; lacking in seriousness) What are two or three of the most frivolous products available? You may want them to limit their choices to products that are intended to serve a purpose. (electric can openers, electric knives, and remote controls)

② **Is It Recyclable?** Point out to students that many products labeled "green" or "recyclable" are actually neither. Many plastic items fall in this category. Plastic containers of all sorts are now printed with recycle symbols. Recycling centers, however, may be able to handle only beverage containers. The other plastics, even if they bear the symbol, are actually throwaway types. Another scam is the recycle label on paper products that actually contain no paper that has been through human hands. Real recycled paper is *postconsumer* paper.

ment. Have each student interview ten friends to see how many people use each of these products and whether or not these students know how the product is bad for the environment. If they don't, students should explain. Discuss student responses to interviews. Discuss the positive impact that your students can have on the environment by educating those people with whom they have just made contact. Count the number of students in your classes and multiply that number by ten to show what kind of an impact student activities can generate. **(40 min.; Extend, Enrich)**

Activity 2.9
    Letters to Manufacturers. Have students list five products they use on a regular basis that could be changed to become "green." Have students write to the manufacturer of one of the products with suggestions on how to make that product more environmentally sound. Suggest that students with good ideas mail their letters after you have proofread them. **(30 min.; Interdisciplinary, Critical Thinking)**

Teacher Support Notes

① **Beneficial Products:** Have each student evaluate his or her family's use of the products listed in this figure. Have them use a grading system, such as 1 to 10 with 10 being very good. Have students write a sentence or two summarizing the family's use of the product.

② **Overhead—Food Chain:** Your supplementary material contains an overhead illustrating how toxic compounds accumulate at the top of the food chain. The overhead is similar to the illustration in Figure 25–3.

③ **Handout—Nontoxic Products:** Your supplementary material contains a handout that gives students suggestions for using nontoxic products rather than toxic products in the home. You may want to distribute the handout at this time.

④ **Meats:** To expand on this information you may want to tell students that not all meats are equally harmful environmentally. Range-fed beef, for example, is a relatively neutral choice. Cattle on the range eat grass that people cannot eat. Grain-fed beef, on the other hand, eat grain that people could eat.

636

FIGURE 25-2

Products to Benefit the Earth

Each of the products recommended benefits the environment:

- Compact fluorescent light bulbs (because they replace many incandescent bulbs and use much less electricity). Remember, electricity is usually made by burning fuels, such as oil and coal, which pollute the environment.

- Cloth or net shopping bags (because they eliminate the need for both paper and plastic bags at the grocery store and other stores).

- Cloth diapers, dishrags, napkins, and towels to replace the throwaway types.

- Dishes, cups, glasses, and tableware to replace the disposable versions. (Yes, it costs fuel and hot water to wash them, but not as much as the fuel and water it costs to keep manufacturing and shipping disposables to you.)

- Flow-reducing shower heads and other devices that help you save water and the fuel to heat it.

- Energy-efficient appliances (if you must have them at all).

- Haircuts, rather than permanent waves and coloring (since cutting hair means a pollution-free job for somebody, while perms and colorings involve chemicals, containers, fuel, and pollution).

- A bicycle (to use in place of a car).

- Recycled paper products with a high post-consumer waste content (rather than paper made from new trees).

- Secondhand items (garage-sale items, used clothing, and the like).

---

tiny creatures at the bottom of the **food chain** on up to fish and fish-eating birds. (Figure 25–3 shows the workings of a food chain.) Also, chlorine combines with naturally occurring ammonia to produce deadly **dioxins.**

People can learn to do without chlorine. Norway has banned its production and use altogether. Other nations are following suit. People can also do without aerosol cans (the propellants destroy ozone and pollute the air), strong cleansers, polishes, insecticides, and many other products.

> **Key Points** ▶ *Many cleansers are unnecessarily toxic. Nontoxic alternatives are available and cost less.*

Foods

Like nutritionists, environmentalists urge you to eat low on the meat-producing food chain. That is, center the diet on plant foods rather than on meats and other products from animals, especially grain-eating animals.

The health benefits of a diet high in grains and vegetables, and low in meats and fats, are well known and were presented in earlier chapters. Eating less meat makes sense environmentally, too. Growing meat animals by feeding them grain uses more land than does growing grain to feed directly to people. Meat animals also use more water; pollute waterways worse; and in general, destroy more native vegetation and wildlife than most plants (there are significant exceptions, however). Furthermore, more fossil fuels are needed just to grow the feed for animals—to run tractors, harvest grain, and transport it. The growing of feed pollutes the environment with fertilizers and pesticides. Wastes from the animals themselves pollute it further.

It also makes sense, as far as possible, to avoid buying canned beef products of any

Activity 2.10

Effects on the Food Chain. Hand students a representation of the food chain. Through science classes, students should learn about the different parts of the food chain and how they are related to each other. In health, expand the relationship to include pollution and poisoning. Help students realize that the ways people live or affect the earth have an effect on all other living things. Chemicals used by humans can accumulate in the food chain and become concentrated by the time they reach the carnivores. Have students draw a diagram that shows how the toxins at the first level (producers–plants) can affect humans at the top. **(40 min.; Extend, Enrich)**

Activity 2.11

Pop Quiz. Have students list at least three activities or products whose use requires money and energy that is not necessary. The papers should point out that simple ways are more cost effective and more environmentally sound. **(20 min.)**

EVALUATE
SECTION II

Level 4
A 150-pound person

Level 3
100 pounds of fish

Level 2
A few tons of plant-eating fish

Level 1
Several tons of tiny organisms

Figure 25–3 How a Food Chain Works. A person who eats many fish may consume about 100 pounds of fish in a year. These fish will, in turn, have consumed a few tons of plant-eating fish in the course of their lifetimes. The plant eaters, in their lifetimes, will have consumed several tons of the tiniest organisms. If these bottom-level organisms have become contaminated with toxic chemicals, these chemicals become more concentrated in the bodies of the fish that consume them. *One person* may ingest the same amount of the contaminant as was present in the original *several tons* of bottom-level organisms.

If strong chemical agents, such as chlorine kill off the bottom-level population, organisms at all other levels either starve or move to a healthier environment.

① kind—soups, stews, chili, corned beef, even pet food. Some of it comes from land that was part of the tropical rain forest only a few years ago. The rain forests are the earth's most threatened **ecosystems.** They are home to many tribes of native people and many species of plants and animals that are in danger of being wiped out. To cut the forest and convert it to beef ranches is an unsustainable practice. Rain forest soil wears out within only a few years when used this way. To keep growing beef, ranchers exploiting such land have to keep clearing more land, and the forest can't grow back on the ruined soil. Each pound of beef produced this way costs the loss of 200 square feet of rain forest—permanently.

You can't tell which products contain rain forest beef, because as yet, labels do not include this information. The only way to be sure not to buy rain forest beef is to buy no canned beef at all.

② Buy products that support the sustaining of the rain forest—products produced low on the forest's food chain. These foods can be produced sustainably. When consumers buy Brazil nuts, cashews, or fruits harvested from the rain forest, they are helping to preserve the rain forest for its long-range economic value. As long as the people who

MINI GLOSSARY

food chain: the sequence in which living things depend on other living things for food. Algae are near the bottom and human beings at the top of the food chain.

dioxins: deadly pollutants formed when chlorine bleach reacts with other compounds.

ecosystems: systems of land, plants, and animals that have existed together for thousands or millions of years and that are interdependent.

Teacher Support Notes

① **Environment vs. Economy:** If you live in an agricultural area in which many jobs are based on meat production, you may want to discuss with students the conflicts that often arise between actions that improve our environment and those that eliminate or reduce jobs. Will a trend towards eating less meat affect the jobs of any family members of your students? If so, do students see any solutions to the problem of maintaining a healthy economy as well as a healthy environment?

② **Surviving Rain Forests:** You may want to expand upon the information in the text by telling students that rain forest soil wears out within a few years when used in this way. To keep growing beef, ranchers have to keep clearing more land and the forest can't grow back. Each pound of beef produced this way costs the loss of 200 square feet of rain forests *permanently*.

Activity 2.12
Philosophical Chairs. Have students research current arguments between environmentalists and those attempting to save jobs in the timber industry. Emphasize that students should know the arguments on both sides. Have students present this information to the class. Divide the class into three groups, facing one another. One side is *pro*, one side *con*, and the section in the middle is *undecided*. Have students play philosophical chairs to debate this issue. Only the pros and cons can make statements. Whenever someone in undecided makes up his/her mind, he/she can move to the appropriate side only after the current speaker has finished speaking. The sides will take turns with comments. Everyone should have an opportunity to comment before others are allowed to speak for a second time. Start the discussion with a statement such as: "People are more important than the environment or a bunch of trees. If we save trees, then people will die of starvation." **(1 hr.; Extend, Enrich)**

Teacher Support Notes

① **Degradable Plastics:** As a class experiment you may want to have students bring in plastic bags. Place some in the open air where they will be exposed to the sun; others can be buried. After a period of time check the bags to see what has happened. Were the bags degradable?

live in the forest can sell its renewable products, they will preserve the forest along with their own ways of life.

In general, though, buy foods grown as close to home as possible. Locally grown foods have traveled the shortest distance to the market, and so have required little fossil fuel for packaging, labeling, refrigeration, transportation, and marketing.

> **Key Points** *Eat more plant foods and fewer meats. Buy locally grown foods when possible.*

Packages

The products we buy come in a multitude of packages—cans, shrink-wrap, foam trays, waxed cardboard, clay-coated cardboard, plastic bottles, glass jars, and dozens of others. Shoppers are becoming more and more aware that these packages are related to environmental concerns. It costs energy and resources to make them, and it may cost land or pollution to dispose of them, too. In general, the packages that are best for the environment are *no* packages. Next best are minimal, reusable, or recyclable ones. Look for labels that boast of environmentally sound products and packaging. Such labels are not 100 percent reliable, but they do show an awareness on the part of the company.

Carry everything home in a nonpolluting, nonwasteful way. This applies not only to food but also to clothing, books, household items, cosmetics, and everything else you shop for. Reject one-time-use paper or plastic bags that have to be thrown away. Every 700 paper bags not used represent one 15- to 20-year-old tree that need not be cut down.

Paper is made from a renewable resource—trees. However, trees are being cut in this country faster than they are being grown. Environmentalists fear that the nation's forests are not being managed sustainably. Furthermore, in the making of

Permanent bags are infinitely reusable and leave the earth less burdened with litter.

paper, pulp mills use chemicals such as chlorine bleach. This results in contamination of waterways by dioxins in quantities so large and so destructive that they have destroyed whole bays and fisheries. Paper mills even kill all life along long stretches of ocean at the mouths of rivers where such mills are located.

① Plastic bags, like most plastics, are a petroleum product. This means in most cases that the oil used to make the plastic bags has had to be transported here from the Middle East at a great cost in fuel, oil spills, and military readiness. Furthermore, when thrown away, plastics last for years or decades, creating masses of refuse that clog landfills. Some plastics are labeled "degradable," but few really do degrade fully to pure, simple compounds that nature can recycle. Some degrade only if exposed to sun and air—not when buried under other trash, and they almost always end up buried. Some plastics are recyclable. This makes them highly preferable to other plas-

In this section students will learn the:
1. Ways to conserve energy in the home.
2. Alternatives to traditional energy sources and energy-using appliances.

Activity 3.1
Appliance Cutback. Ask students to brainstorm a list of appliances they use in the morning when getting ready for school. Go through this list and have students decide if any of these items could be taken away without much change in their preparation. **(10 min.)**

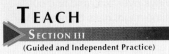

TEACH
SECTION III
(Guided and Independent Practice)

Activity 3.2

Lights Out. Have students think of a time that the electricity went out in their homes. Ask students what they had to go without during that time and what they did for entertainment. Tell them that before electricity was discovered, people did everything they needed to do in other ways. Find out whether students think they could live with fewer appliances. Ask them how they would prepare for another

(continued on next page)

tics, but still not perfect, since recycling is only partially efficient.

The best choice, then, is to carry reusable shopping bags to the store and refuse all others. Failing in this, ask for plastic bags if they are recyclable—and then be sure to recycle them. The third choice is paper bags, and last is nonrecyclable plastic.

> **Key Points** ▶ *Reject unnecessary packaging, including paper and plastic bags. Carry your own reusable shopping bags.*

SECTION II REVIEW

Answer the following questions on a sheet of paper.

Learning the Vocabulary
The vocabulary terms in this section are *recyclable, biodegradable, disposable, persistent, food chain, dioxins,* and *ecosystems.*
1. Match each of the following phrases with the appropriate term from above.
   a. a product intended to be used once and then thrown away
   b. deadly pollutants formed when chlorine bleach reacts with other compounds
   c. made of material that can be used over again

Learning the Facts
2. How does pollution from automobiles harm people's health and their environment?
3. What are the effects of chlorine bleach on our environment?
4. How does eating less meat make sense environmentally?

Making Life Choices
5. Figure 25–2 on page 636 presents a list of products to benefit the earth. What can you do to replace products that you use at home with these products?

SECTION III

Energy Use in the Home

Home energy use has many environmental implications. A naive consumer might respond to such a statement by saying, "I don't use any fossil fuels in my home. My home is all electric." However, electricity, of course, is most often generated by burning fossil fuels, too—only at the power plant, rather than at the site of use. An all-electric home produces air pollutants and global-warming gases just as if the homeowner were burning fossil fuels at home.

Cooking Methods

An example of an environmentally sound way to prepare foods is the Asian way. Asian cooks cut foods into bite-sized pieces, and then stir-fry them fast in small amounts of oil. This uses little fuel, so it pollutes only a little.

Other than stir-frying, two ways to cook foods quickly are to use the pressure cooker or the microwave oven. The pressure cooker can tenderize pounds of meat in half the normal cooking time, or cook a potful of potatoes in 5 minutes. The microwave can cook small portions quickly or warm whole plates of leftovers (which saves using several burners on the stove and washing up the pots afterward).

The conventional oven, in contrast, is a fuel waster, especially when the entire oven must be heated just to bake a potato, a small chicken, or a single sheet of cookies. To be an energy-conscious cook, when using the oven, cook on both racks, using all the heated space. Don't peek often. Each door opening drops the oven temperature by 25 to 50 degrees Fahrenheit.

The stove top, too, can be an energy waster. It makes sense to use flat-bottomed pots on the stove, with close-fitting lids, so that each burner will donate all its heat to cooking something, not just to heating the kitchen (and the planet). Turn burners and ovens off before food is fully cooked. Let the cooking finish as the stove cools.

Section II Review
Answers
1. **a.** disposable
   b. dioxins **c.** recyclable
2. Answers may vary; could include: lung problems, harm to children and the elderly, reduced crop yields, acid rain, damage to forests, and producing global-warming carbon dioxide.
3. Concentrated amounts in waterways kill tiny creatures on up to large fish and fish-eating birds.
4. Since meat production uses so much more land and natural resources than production of grain, it is smart to eat less of it. Meat production also causes the depletion of rain forests, because the trees are cut down to provide grazing areas for cattle.
5. Answers will vary.

Teach
(Continued)

"lights out" if they knew in advance that it would happen. Have them imagine what life might be like if energy were rationed and people had to use less energy. **(20 min., Critical Thinking)**

Activity 3.3

Photovoltaic Savings. Call a local distributor and find out the cost of installing photovoltaic panels and how much money would be saved on the monthly electric bill. Set up an activity for students to complete in which they calculate the savings over time and find out how much time might pass before the cost of the panels would be reimbursed in the form of energy savings. **(30 min., Interdisciplinary)**

Activity 3.4
Guest Speaker. Invite someone from an energy company to speak to the class about how students can make their homes energy efficient. Ask about alternative sources of energy, how well they work, and the cost of installation and regular usage. **(1 hr.)**

Teacher Support Notes

① **Teen Views Follow-Up Questions:** Following are some questions you may want to use to encourage discussion of the ideas expressed by the students in the Teen Views feature:

a. Where are your local landfills? How are they maintained and managed?

b. How many students recycle? Do they do it faithfully or sporadically?

c. Are students concerned, as Dan Richardson is, about the rain forests? Why should people in this country be worried about rain forests in other countries?

d. Do students think Howard Manuel's fear of space uniforms being required to protect people on earth is reasonable?

e. Do students agree with Toni Malkovich that we should be worried about our children and grandchildren; or, should each generation take care of itself?

f. Do students know the air quality in their area? If the quality is poor, what are the major causes of this and what can they do about it?

g. Do students agree with Michelle Porter that most people are not as concerned as they should be about the environment? What can be done?

TEEN VIEWS ①

What concerns you most about our environment?

So much garbage is being thrown away when many landfills are already full. How can we say that all this litter is bad for the earth and then go and bury it in the earth? We should all be recycling every day, as much as we can, no matter how much it costs. If we don't recycle, it's going to cost us this planet and then we'll have no future to look forward to. It worries me every time I take out the garbage. I think, should I be doing this? How bad are the effects of one bag of trash going to be ten years from now? Twenty years? **Angela Becker, 16, Great Falls High School, MT**

If we don't stop cutting down our rain forests, our planet will be doomed. We also need to stop using styrofoam cups and plates. The CFC's in these products are destroying the ozone layer. **Dan Richardson, 14, South Carroll High School, MD**

The ozone really worries me. Soon we'll be using space uniforms to protect ourselves from the harmful ultraviolet rays. In Hawaii, it's more dangerous because we are more exposed to the sun and we're in a climate that is sunny almost every day. **Howard Manuel, Farrington High School, HI**

I am afraid that my children and grandchildren won't know what it is like to live in a pollution-free environment. We only have one world, and once it is gone, we have no backup waiting to be used. It's up to us to save the earth before it's too late. **Toni Malkovich, 15, East High School, MN**

The environment is in serious danger because of all the pollutants we expel daily. I am most concerned with air pollution because air is our most important resource. Chemicals from our automobiles and factories affect the changes in the earth's climate causing the greenhouse effect. We must all help by car pooling, recycling, and conserving water. Remember—Earth is the only planet we have. **Zeenat Shah, 15, Robert E. Lee High School, TX**

Lack of concern bothers me most. Unless other people start worrying about and trying to help our environment, the problems facing us will multiply. Too many people don't believe that one person can make a difference. Other people take the environment for granted. Mother Nature has a lot to take care of; it's time we learned to clean up the messes we have made. **Michelle Porter, 15, Orange Park High School, FL**

Key Points ▸ *Cutting foods up and cooking fast are energy-efficient ways to cook foods. Pressure-cooking and microwaving also save energy.*

Power Tools and Appliances

A tour around the home reveals many appliances, large and small, that people use

EVALUATE
SECTION III

Activity 3.5
Energy-Saving Appliances. Have students go to an appliance store for information on energy-saving appliances and fixtures. Have students do a cost evaluation, explaining the cost of installing the newer model as compared to the cost of installing a traditional model. Emphasize the importance of finding out how much energy will be saved monthly and how soon a person can expect to see those savings above and beyond the difference in the installation costs. Have students ask how popular these energy-saving appliances are, if they are growing in popularity, and why or why not. **(Interdisciplinary)**

CLOSE
SECTION III

Activity 3.6
Energy Sources. Ask students to list the different types of energy and tell why each is important in our attempts to conserve energy sources. **(3 min.)**

---

to cook, to clean, to heat and cool their homes, and to entertain themselves. All of these appliances run on energy from fossil fuels, with pollution and global warming as by-products.

Because of fossil fuels' polluting nature, the fewer appliances you use and the shorter the times you use them, the better for the environment. Realizing this, many consumers today are returning to "old-fashioned" ways of doing things. They dry clothes on a clothesline in the sun; trim yard greenery with hand tools; and rake the refuse with rakes rather than using electric dryers, weed whackers, hedge trimmers, and leaf blowers.

These practices save only small amounts of energy, but it is more than just the energy the power tools and appliances would consume during use. Refraining from buying power tools and appliances also saves the energy it would have cost to manufacture, transport, package, advertise, and market them.

What is true of small tools and appliances is more true of large ones—but with exceptions. Many people believe, falsely, that the appliances that use the most energy *per minute* are the biggest energy guzzlers. Many believe, for example, that the electric range uses more energy than the refrigerator. It does, while it's on. However, most ranges are turned on for only an hour or so a day at most, whereas most refrigerators run most of the time. Refrigerators are by far the greater energy users. In fact, they use more energy than any other appliances in most people's homes. ①

Besides the refrigerator, a big energy user is the hot-water heater. The less hot water you can use, the less fuel must be burned to heat that water.

About 20,000 U.S. families are now using solar energy to meet most of their homes' electricity needs. In an **active solar** home, the sun's light strikes **photovoltaic (PV)** ② panels on the roof. These convert the light energy to electrical energy, which is stored in a battery. Having a battery permits the use of a DC (direct current) refrigerator, rather than an AC (alternating current) refrigerator.† No fossil fuel is used to run a

A refrigerator that uses DC electricity from a battery requires only ¹⁄₂₀ the energy of an AC refrigerator. The motor is small, releases little heat, and is on top. In contrast, a "regular" refrigerator's large motor, which is below the unit, heats the very unit it is trying to cool—an inefficient design.

†This book was written in an office that the authors converted to run on solar PV panels. They keep their lunches in a DC refrigerator there.

MINI GLOSSARY

active solar: using photovoltaic panels to generate electricity from sunlight. (A passive solar home is one that is built to take advantage of the available sun and shade so as to minimize heating and cooling costs.)
photovoltaic (PV) panels: panels that convert light (photons) into electricity (volts).

Teacher Support Notes

① **Handout—Home Appliances and Global Warming:** Your supplementary material contains an interesting handout showing a typical home and how the various appliances produce carbon dioxide, thereby contributing to global warming.

② **Solar Energy:** As enrichment you may want to tell students that as of 1992 there were over 15,000 active solar installations in California and over 1,000 in Florida. Some 15,000 solar devices were also in use in Florida, and solar technologies were in much wider use elsewhere—for example, in Japan, Germany, and Greece.

✍ **Fast Facts**

A Rutgers University researcher estimates that Americans open their refrigerators an average of 22 times a day.

In this section students will learn the:
1. Environmental problems associated with waste disposal.

Activity 4.1
Water Saving Tips. Have students list ways to cut down on water usage in

their homes. Suggest that students keep these tips in mind and perhaps make water saving notes to be placed by each faucet in their homes. **(5–20 min., Critical Thinking)**

TEACH
SECTION IV
(Guided and Independent Practice)

Activity 4.2
Water Sources. Have students

research sources of ground water and find out what water source supplies their homes. Have students share their findings in class. **(20 min.; Extend, Enrich)**

Activity 4.3
Lunch Containers. Have students tell you what type of containers they carry their lunches in. Multiply the percentages of the types of containers in your class by the entire student body to represent how

Teacher
Support Notes

① **Hot-Water Heaters:**
For enrichment you may want to give students another example of how they can conserve energy use in the home. For example, there are several measures they can use to save water-heating energy. They can set the heater at 130 degrees Fahrenheit, no hotter; they can put it on a timer; they can wrap it in a blanket, and wrap the pipes carrying the hot water. They can also install heat-trapping devices at the inlets and outlets to the tank to keep heat from creeping along the lines when the water is standing. When buying a hot-water heater people can choose smaller, instant-type heaters, gas rather then electric, and solar heaters.

✉ **Where to Write**

Consumer Information Center
Dept. 572Y
Pueblo, CO 81009
For guide to saving energy in the use of household appliances.

642 UNIT 8 Global Issues

DC refrigerator operated this way. Sunlight is free, reliable, and pollution-free.

The high initial cost of PV panels, the battery, and the DC refrigerator prevents most people from considering them. For those who can afford to get started, it becomes possible to meet most of a home's electrical needs with solar energy, thus reducing utility bills to only a few dollars a month. The savings in utilities pay back the initial investment within 5 to 15 years. From that point on, energy is virtually free—compliments of the sun. ①

If this discussion of solar energy seems to have strayed far from the subject of the environment, remember that U.S. energy use is contributing to air pollution, global warming, and ozone depletion. According to the Worldwatch Institute's *State of the World, 1992*, the highest priorities for the human race to save the planet are to convert to solar energy, get off automobiles, use land and wealth so as to relieve poverty, and stop multiplying. To take these steps demands "reduced consumption of resources by the rich to make room for higher living standards for the poor."

> **Key Points** *Use appliances efficiently, replace them when possible with energy-efficient models, and start converting to solar energy.*

Lights

An ordinary 75-watt incandescent light bulb burns for about 2,500 hours, gives off considerable heat, and demands fuel whose carbon dioxide output amounts to 200 pounds or so over the lifetime of the bulb. Energy- and pollution-conscious people are replacing these light bulbs with 22-watt, high-efficiency compact fluorescent (CF) bulbs such as those shown in Figure 25–4. One CF bulb can match the light output of the incandescent bulb it replaces, but it

Figure 25–4 Energy Efficient Light Bulbs Can Replace Incandescent Bulbs. A typical compact fluorescent bulb costs $17, but replaces some ten or so incandescent bulbs (10 x $.75, or $7.50). Then, because it uses one-quarter the electricity, it saves about $32 on your bill. Net savings: $22.50.

uses one-fourth the energy to do so. The CF bulbs also last ten or more times as long. Each CF bulb used in place of a succession of "regular" light bulbs keeps a ton of carbon dioxide out of the air.

> **Key Points** *Replace incandescent light bulbs with compact fluorescent bulbs to save energy.*

SECTION III REVIEW

Answer the following questions on a sheet of paper.
Learning the Vocabulary
The vocabulary terms in this section are *active solar* and *photovoltaic (PV) panels.*
1. Write a sentence using each of the vocabulary terms.

much energy might be wasted each day in one school in the form of containers. Discuss how habits could be changed to save energy. **(15 min.; Extend, Enrich)**

EVALUATE

Activity 4.4
Test Waste Packages. Test students one at a time by having them sort various waste packages into piles for recycling. If time doesn't allow for individual, oral testing, have a written test prepared with the waste packages listed and columns labeled for sorting. Have them locate on a map where they would take each pile of material to have it recycled. **(5 min. each)**

CLOSE
SECTION IV

Activity 4.5
Creating Slogans. Have students brainstorm environmental slogans and create new slogans of their own. You might want to buy T-shirt paints and tell students to bring a T-shirt to class to decorate with their environmental slogans. **(1 hr.)**

Learning the Facts
2. List three ways to save energy while cooking.
3. Name three "old-fashioned" ways of doing things that are better for the environment.
4. What household appliance uses the most energy?

Making Life Choices
5. This section deals with conserving energy at home. Do your parents follow these procedures? If not, how can you persuade your parents to conserve energy at home? What arguments can you make for energy conservation?

SECTION IV

Water Use, Trash, and Garbage

Where water is abundant and inexpensive, people use it freely. It is really not free, though. Major expenses may not be visible on water bills, but are paid for by people's tax money—expenses such as those of water purification, monitoring, and cleanup.

Conscious of water's true worth, people become more inclined to conserve it. There are many ways to do so. A running faucet uses up to 3 to 5 gallons of water a minute. Just at the bathroom sink, then, you can save many gallons by turning the faucet off while brushing your teeth. You can run the faucet only when actually filling a glass or rinsing your toothbrush, and turn it off between times. You can install a water-saving washer on the faucet to deliver a pleasant stream of water with a reduced flow per minute. For dishes, a dishwasher uses less water than does washing dishes by hand (just load it full, for maximum efficiency). You can also reuse

clean water. After boiling an egg, for example, let the water cool, and then water the houseplants with it.

As for trash, an average American household of four people produces about 100 pounds a week. National concern has focused on this issue, for the nation is running out of landfill space in which to dispose of all this trash. However, landfill space is not the only problem associated with trash. Every item thrown away is a resource lost—an aluminum can that could be used to make a new aluminum can; a cereal box that, but for its clay coating, could become recycled paper; a plastic bottle that could become part of a beautiful carpet.*

Trash need not become the undesirable mess that used materials make when they are treated without respect. Recycled trash is a national treasure. Yet as it is now, about 70 percent of all the metal mined in the United States is used only once and then discarded. The aluminum thrown away every three months could rebuild the entire U.S. air fleet.

The ideal community recycles everything—paper, cardboard, glass, cans, plastic—and permits no materials to be sold that cannot be recycled. A person fortunate enough to live in such a community needs only to set up the "waste" baskets accordingly—one for each type of material. People who are not adequately served by community recycling programs face a challenge. They must solve the disposal problem for themselves, by studying their own trash to see what they are forced to throw away, recycling what they can, and then refusing to buy more nonrecyclable items.

As for garbage—that is, vegetable scraps, fruit peelings, and leftover plant-based foods—it is a special material. It is biodegrad-

---

* The authors' office floor is covered with a luxurious wall-to-wall carpet made of recycled plastic soda and ketchup bottles—45 bottles per square yard.

In this section students will learn the:
1. Impact of hunger on the environment.

Activity 5.1

How? Ask students to answer this question: "How might a person who is living comfortably come to be one of the homeless or suffer from hunger? Are the hungry people to blame for their situation? Why or why not?" **(10 min., Critical Thinking)**

Activity 5.2

What Can I Do? Ask students: "What can you do to decrease the number of hungry people in your neighborhood? What would your first step be?" **(5 min., Critical Thinking)**

Activity 5.3

Food Pantry. Have students set up and run a food pantry at school. If this is not possible, have students lead a food drive to collect for a local community pantry. Have competition between classes to see which class can donate the most

---

✐ Fast Facts

Twenty percent of the children in the United States grow up in poverty. One hundred thousand are homeless.

✉ Where to Write

Cultural Survival
53-A Church Street
Cambridge, MA 02138
A tax-exempt organization that recommends the purchase of products that promote survival of native peoples.

Section IV Review

Answers

1. Answers will vary.
2. 3 to 5 gallons of water per minute
3. 100 pounds
4. 70% of it is used only once
5. paper, cardboard, glass, cans, plastic, and vegetable scraps, fruit peelings, and leftover plant-based foods as compost
6. Answers will vary.

---

able, like the leaves and grass cuttings people rake up in their yards. All of these materials can be piled up together with some soil and allowed to decompose naturally. They will form **compost,** a rich, crumbly material that can be used, as it is in nature, to fertilize growing things. Natural fertilizers such as compost and manure are preferable, environmentally, to synthetic fertilizers on both a large and small scale. They require no mining; they recycle natural materials rather than wasting them; and they add needed texture, as well as nutrients, to the soil. Some communities, recognizing this, conduct composting programs to recycle people's yard debris. Some homeowners maintain their own composting piles.

Key Points *Save water by using water-conserving habits and devices. To the greatest extent possible, recycle trash and compost plant scraps.*

SECTION IV REVIEW

Answer the following questions on a sheet of paper.
Learning the Vocabulary
The vocabulary term in this section is *compost.*
1. Write a sentence using the vocabulary term.

Learning the Facts
2. How much water can you save by turning the water off while brushing your teeth?
3. How much trash is produced per week by an average American household of four?
4. What is said about all metal mined in the United States?
5. Describe what the ideal community recycles.

Making Life Choices
6. Landfills are a national concern. People are producing more trash each year, and our nation is running out of landfill space. What do you think should be done about this problem?

SECTION V

Hunger and the Environment

In the early 1990s, one person in every ten was experiencing hunger, both worldwide and in the United States. Due to droughts and wars, the world was consuming more food than it could produce. Twenty-four nations were experiencing food shortages, and some were facing famine. At the same time, the population was continuing to grow, and the world's reserves of stored food had dropped to lower levels than ever.

Hunger is terrible. A Boston writer describes it this way:*

I've had no income and I've paid no rent for many months. My landlord let me stay. He felt sorry for me because I had no money. The Friday before Christmas he gave me ten dollars. For days I had nothing but water. I knew I needed food; I tried to go out but I was too weak to walk to the store. I felt as if I were dying. I saw the mailman and told him I thought I was starving. He brought me food and then made some phone calls and that's when they began delivering these lunches. But I had already lost so much weight that five meals a week are not enough to keep me going.

I just pray to God I can survive. I keep praying I can have the will to save some of my food so I can divide it up and make it last. It's hard to save because I am so hungry that I want to eat it right away. On Friday, I held over two peas from the lunch. I ate one pea on Saturday morning. Then I got into bed with the taste of food in my mouth and I waited as long as I could. Later on in the day I ate the other pea.

*L. Schwartz-Nobel, *Starving in the Shadow of Plenty* (New York: Putnam, 1981), pp. 35–36.

food or run a campus-wide food campaign. Have students make posters advertising the food drive to hang in the halls.

Activity 5.4
Group Research. In groups, have
the students research countries that have
the biggest problems with hunger and
starvation. Assign a different country to
each group. Have each group share its
report orally in class. Require that they

begin their presentations with the
answers to the following questions: "What
event or series of events caused this
problem? What is being done, if anything,
in these countries to solve this problem?"
(1 hr.; Extend, Enrich)

Activity 5.5
Things We Take for Granted.
Have students write a short paragraph
describing things in their lives that

improve the quality of life and are taken
for granted. Pick something that a person
who is poor, homeless, or hungry would
probably not have access to. **(30 min.,
Interdisciplinary)**

Activity 5.6
Philosophical Chairs. Have stu-
dents set up the chairs in the room for a
Philosophical Chairs activity as described

(continued on next page)

---

*Today I saved the container that the mashed
potatoes were in and tonight, before bed, I'll
lick the sides of the container.*

*When there are bones I keep them. I know
this is going to be hard for you to believe and
I am almost ashamed to tell you, but these
days I boil the bones till they're soft and then
I eat them. Today there were no bones.*

Some 20 million people in the United
States—12 million children and 8 million
adults—are chronically hungry. U.S. hunger
reaches into all segments of society. Not
only the poor (migrant workers, unemployed minorities, and some elderly) are
hungry. Also the new poor—displaced farm
families and former blue-collar and white-
collar workers forced out of their trades and
professions into minimum-wage jobs—suffer from hunger. A minority of the poor in
America are on welfare. Most are working
people. The most compelling single reason
for their hunger is poverty.

Hundreds of millions of people around
the globe are also suffering from hunger.
About 250 million are children of preschool
age, and 10 million of these are drastically
underweight. Half a million children go
blind every year because of vitamin deficiencies. Tens of thousands of people die
each day as a result of undernutrition. Millions of children die each year from the disease of poverty. Death takes one child every
2 seconds—15 have died in the 30 seconds
it may take you to read this paragraph.
Poverty, infection, and malnutrition are the
killers that cut life short in dozens of developing countries.

Of the world's 5 billion population, 1 billion people have no land and no possessions at all. They survive on less than $1 a
day each, they lack water that is safe to
drink, and they cannot read or write. The
average U.S. housecat eats twice as much
protein every day as one of these people,
and the yearly cost of keeping that cat is
greater than these people's annual income.

Families in developing countries depend on their
children to help provide for daily needs.

① **Key Points** *Poverty is extreme for 1 billion of the
world's 5 billion people. It is a major
cause of disease, starvation, and death.*

The Environment and Poverty

The giant web of Figure 25–1 on pages
632 and 633 showed that many environmental causes contribute to poverty and
hunger. Population growth contributes, for
the more mouths there are to feed, the
worse poverty and hunger become. As more
people need homes, the land best suited for
producing food may be taken to build houses. Pollution caused by more and more fossil
fuel use worsens the health problems and
misery of the poor. Water shortages force the
poor from their homes, too, and create further hardship. The world's poorest people
live in the world's most damaged and harmful environments.

Key Points *Environmental degradation not only
causes hunger directly but contributes
indirectly by worsening the effect of poverty.*

MINI GLOSSARY

compost: rotted vegetable matter, used as
fertilizer.

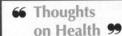

*There is no finer
investment for any
community than
putting milk into
babies. Healthy citi-
zens are the greatest
asset any country can
have.*
– Winston Churchill

Teacher
Support Notes

① **Hunger and Pover-
ty:** Paragraphs from the
beginning of Section V to
this key point contain
numerous facts and exam-
ples about the terrible
worldwide problems resulting from hunger and
poverty. Have students
reread this information and
pick the one fact or example that makes the great-
est impression on them.
Have each student state
which piece of information
he/she picked and why.

earlier for Activity 2.12. Start the conversation by making a controversial statement such as: "Due to all the hunger, overpopulation, and starvation in some countries, women in those countries should be injected with some sort of contraceptive material so that fewer children will be born." Or: "With all of the starvation in the world, it is inhumane to own, feed, and care for pets with money that could support families in other countries." Or: "Laws should be passed that ban the production of all unnecessary products." **(1 hr., Critical Thinking)**

EVALUATE
SECTION V

Activity 5.7
Energy Tips Posters. Refer to the handout "Living a Simpler Lifestyle" in the supplementary material. Have students use tips from this chart to make a poster complete with pictures, either drawn or from magazines, that illustrate these tips. Tell them to hang the posters in their houses so that their families will have a constant reminder of how to live simpler lives that require less energy consump-

Teacher Support Notes

① **Poverty and Family Size:** Before students read the following information, ask them if they think couples in poverty would be more likely or less likely to have large families. Ask for reasons for their opinions. They will probably be surprised that poverty and hunger actually encourage larger families.

② **World Population:** For enrichment, you might want to tell your students that in the mid-1800s the world population was a billion, in 1880 it was two billion, in 1930 it was four billion. Now it is over five billion. If growth remains steady, in less than 50 years it will be ten billion—the maximum the world can support.

③ **Overhead—Population Growth:** Your supplementary material contains an overhead showing the growth of the world's population from 1950 to 1990 and projected growth up to the year 2150.

✎ Fast Facts

In 1950 the world produced 44 tons of grain for every 1 ton of fertilizer. In 1990 only 13 tons of grain were produced for each ton of fertilizer.

Feeding the hungry—in the United States.

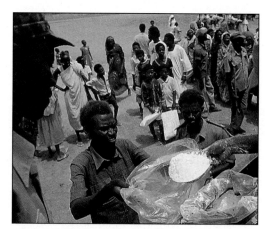

Feeding the hungry—in a developing country.

Poverty, Hunger, and Overpopulation

Strange as it may seem, poverty and hunger encourage people to bear more children. A family in poverty depends on its children to farm the land for food, to haul water, and to make the adults secure in their old age. To complicate things, poverty costs many young lives, so parents must bear many children to ensure that a few will survive to adulthood. Children represent the "social security of the poor."

To help reduce population growth, it is first necessary to help relieve poverty and hunger. When people have better access to health care and education, the death rate falls. As more family members survive, families become willing to risk having smaller numbers of children. Then the birth rate falls.

At present, however, the world's population is continuing to grow. This is threatening the world's capacity to produce adequate food in the future. The activities of billions of human beings on the earth's limited surface are seriously and adversely affecting the planet. We are wiping out many varieties of plant life, heating up the climate, using up freshwater supplies, and

① destroying the protective ozone layer that shields life from the sun's damaging rays. In short, human beings are overstraining the earth's ability to support life.

Population control is one of the most pressing needs of this time in history. Until the nations of the world solve the population problem, they can neither succeed in supporting the lives of people already born, nor remedy the planet's galloping destruction. And to resolve the population problem, they must remedy the poverty problems. Of the 92 million people being added to the population each year, 88 million are being added in the poorest areas of the world.

U.S. consumers could help substantially to slow and reverse the downward trends described here by altering their choices. If we were willing to use fewer goods, devour fewer resources, create less pollution, and consume less energy, this would go a long way toward remedying global environmental problems. It would also help solve the hunger problem—indirectly, but it would help a lot.

Many other steps to resolve these problems are needed at many levels. To find out how you can fight against hunger and tion. Have each student outline a plan for his/her family to follow that meets these guidelines. The plan should include how the students will educate family members about the need to live simple lives. **(1 hr., Critical Thinking)**

CLOSE
SECTION V
Activity 5.8

Ways to Help. Have students brainstorm a list of ways they can help alleviate local problems of hunger. Discuss with students ways that they would go about accomplishing these tasks. **(10 min.)**

Activity 5.9
Illustrations. Have students draw an illustration showing poverty and starvation as they imagine it. Tell them that their art-

work should represent some of the feelings the people living in that situation might be experiencing. **(1 hr., interdisciplinary)**

---

poverty, write to some of the organizations listed in Figure 25–5.

To many people, the preservation of the health of the earth matters not just for people's sake, but for the sake of wildlife as well. Its preservation is a moral responsibility. It concerns us at a deep, spiritual level. Native Americans have traditionally known:

This we know. The Earth does not belong to man; man belongs to the Earth. This we know. All things are connected like the blood which unites one family. All things are connected. Whatever befalls the Earth befalls the sons of the Earth. Man did not weave the web of life, he is merely a strand in it. Whatever he does to the web, he does to himself.

—Chief Seattle, 1854

Key Points *Population growth worsens environmental damage, poverty, and hunger. Economics and population increases are interdependent. All things are connected.*

SECTION V REVIEW

Answer the following questions on a sheet of paper.

Learning the Facts
1. How many people in the United States are chronically hungry?
2. List at least four environmental causes that contribute to poverty and hunger.
3. Why do parents bear so many children when they are poor?

Making Life Choices
4. This section described how we as U.S. consumers could slow and reverse the downward trends of global environmental problems. What are the steps to resolve these problems? Would the steps also help solve the hunger problems? Explain your answer.

FIGURE 25-5

Hunger Relief Organizations You Can Join

Bread for the World
802 Rhode Island Ave. NE
Washington, DC 20018

Food Research and Action Center
1319 F Street NW, Suite 500
Washington, DC 20004

Institute for Food and Development Policy
145 Ninth St.
San Francisco, CA 94103

Interfaith Impact for Justice and Peace
110 Maryland Ave. NE, Box 63
Washington, DC 20002

Oxfam America
115 Broadway
Boston, MA 02116

Seeds
P.O. Box 6170
Waco, TX 76706

Answers to Fact or Fiction

Here are the answers to the questions at the start of the chapter.

1. True **2.** False. Products are beneficial to the environment if they help *relieve* pollution or displace other products that pollute. **3.** False. Local products may cost more, but they may be good choices for environmental reasons. **4.** False. The refrigerator uses more energy, because it is on all the time. **5.** False. Fossil fuels are burned to produce electricity. **6.** True.

Teacher Support Notes

① **Handout—Public Health Service Objectives:** Your supplementary material contains a handout listing the public health service objectives for environmental health as established by the U.S. Department of Human Services. You may want to distribute this handout as students conclude the chapter.

Section V Review
Answers
1. 20 million
2. Answers will vary; could include: population growth, pollution, water shortages, used-up land, heating up the climate, and wiping out many varieties of plant life.
3. to have more workers to help support the family; children are "social security for the poor"
4. Answers will vary.

RETEACH/BONUS

Here are some additional activities for the various sections of this chapter. You may want to use these activities to reteach certain concepts, or you may choose them as alternatives to earlier activities.

Energy-Efficient Homes. Have students design an energy-efficient way of living, from the layout of their homes to the appliances and tools used within. Have them create a plan on graph paper of the house structure they would build, showing energy-saving features. Have them write about the energy uses in the home and the internal features and appliances that save energy. **(40 min.)**

Energy Alternatives Posters. Have students find energy-saving alternatives for commonly used electric tools. Have them create posters showing the substitution of an energy-saving tool for the other. Have students title their posters in such a way that you can see from a distance the point that the poster is making. Hang the finished posters in the hall. **(40 min.)**

✍ Fast Facts

Increasing the average fuel economy in American automobiles from 28 miles per gallon to 40 miles per gallon could save 2.4 million barrels of oil a day and prevent 440 million tons of carbon dioxide from entering the atmosphere each year.

Teacher Support Notes

① **Ripple Effect:** Ask students if they can think of any examples in their own lives that demonstrate how the ripple effect works. Perhaps one or two students at school began wearing a certain type of gym shoe or other article of clothing, leading to a majority of students in this school eventually wearing the same clothing. What examples can they think of?

✍ Fast Facts

Nearly 60% of Americans say they frequently recycle cans, bottles, or papers. Fewer than 20%, however, save energy by frequently cutting back on their driving.

STRAIGHT TALK ⊗

Personal Strategy— Voluntary Simplicity

The problems of the environment and the world's growing population may appear so great that they seem solvable only by political leaders. But consider this: you can change the world. Perhaps most fitting for a book about personal choices is to describe some of the things one person can do. After all, a society is the sum of its people. As we go, so goes our world.

I'm just a kid. I can't have any effect on the way the world goes. In fact, when I think about it, I feel overwhelmed, depressed, and pessimistic.

Thoughtful people of all ages feel just as you do at times and are tempted to give up. Optimism is important, though, and many people are working to develop it. They know that optimism gives them energy and makes their efforts to shape the world's future more effective.

How do I go about developing optimism?

By living your own life. Don't try to solve all the world's problems. Mentally draw a small circle around yourself. Work to better yourself through education, spiritual growth, and physical health. Work, too, to better the small world within the circle around yourself.

That sounds simple enough, but I don't see

how it will help anything. In fact, it almost sounds selfish.

It will help, though. Every move you make leaves the world a better or worse place. Your actions have a ripple effect, often far beyond what you may think. Tending to the lives nearest you, including your own, is your first responsibility. Many great religious teachings express that value.

Your second responsibility is to make sure you can answer yes to the following question: If everyone lived as I do, would the young children of today grow up in a better world?

Those who study the future are convinced that the hope of the world lies in everyone's adopting a simple lifestyle. Many experts agree that the simplification of our lives can benefit all of the world's people.

Are you saying that everybody needs to live in poverty? I can't see how

my being poor would help anyone. Besides, wealthy people would never agree.

No, the suggestion is not that everyone become poor. It is said that poverty is repressive, and simplicity is liberating. Poverty gives people a sense of helplessness, but simplicity gives them creativity. In other words, to become poor would solve nothing. Poverty hinders personal growth, but simplicity opens the way to it. You are also right that few people would willingly give up their wealth, even if it would help. What *is* suggested has nothing to do with wealth. It is a lifestyle— a commitment to live more simply in view of the world's limited resources.

Think in terms of *elegance*, not poverty. Streamlined things, that have no unnecessary frills, are elegant. Life is, too. Don't carry extra baggage around. It only burdens you.

(Continued on next page)

Water Treatment. Ask students if they know what happens to the water that goes down the drain and is flushed down the toilet. Discuss students' answers and correct their misunderstandings. Tell them how a sewage treatment plant ends up with everything that comes from their houses and has the job of cleaning that water and releasing it into a natural waterway so that it can be recollected and used again. Explain the difference in what happens in homes with septic systems. **(10 min.)**

Ground Water Pollution. Have students research ground water pollution. In what ways can ground water become polluted and how does this affect humans? Have students use this information to create a class bulletin board illustrating their findings. **(20 min.)**

Compost Posters. Make posters advocating composting as a way of handling organic trash. Have students draw a picture of a compost bin and the materials for building it as well as a representation of the types of things that go in it. **(30–50 min.)**

STRAIGHT TALK   *(Continued)*

What does living a life of voluntary simplicity involve?

Such a life involves a thousand small decisions, like the ones that were presented in the chapter. The chapter described ways to reduce consumption of goods, energy and water use, and the throwing away of trash and garbage. Everything you do, you can do simply, with little cost or even a benefit to the earth, or complexly, with a high cost and no benefit. Together, all the things you do add up to your personal style.

   To live simply, it isn't necessary to make every choice the chapter suggested. Some choices may not be right for you. Some choices may be your own original ones, and they may be better ideas than anyone else has yet dreamed up.

   Voluntary is a key word, just as *simplicity* is. Each individual must look within to discover a personal sense of what actions are appropriate. Each person needs to find a balance—a path, suitable for that individual, that leads between the extremes of poverty and self-indulgence.

I'm not ready to apply the ideas in the chapter, yet. I still have to gain my education and prepare for life. I'll wait and begin to live simply when I'm ready.

Some of the chapter ideas may have to wait, but you have already begun your life, and in some ways it is already beneficial to the earth. Improving yourself is the first step toward improving the world—remember the ripple effect. Learn all you can. Work on your education, and on your emotional and spiritual growth. You will then be better equipped to participate in the world community.

Do you really think that if everyone made choices like these, it would help the state of the world?

Yes. Every agency that has studied the future has reached the same conclusion: voluntary simplicity can work. It does not mean living primitively. Most people prefer beauty and ease to ugliness and discomfort. Voluntary simplicity does mean seeking a life free of distractions, clutter, and self-importance—a life that includes self-discipline. The words of an old poem speak to this idea, and they are fitting here:

Beyond a wholesome discipline, be gentle with yourself. You are a child of the universe, no less than the trees and the stars; you have a right to be here. And whether or not it is clear to you, no doubt the universe is unfolding as it should. Therefore be at peace with God, whatever you conceive him to be, and whatever your labors and aspirations . . . keep peace with your soul—
Desiderata, *found in Old St. Paul's Church, Baltimore, dated 1692, author unknown. Although it has not been proven, some authorities believe that Max Ehrmann wrote the* Desiderata *in 1948.*

Vocabulary

1. **a.** pollution **b.** global warming **c.** compost **d.** food chain
2. **a.** Photovoltaic (PV) panels **b.** ripple effect **c.** greenhouse effect **d.** acid rain **e.** Active solar
3. **a.** ecosystems **b.** persistent **c.** sustainable **d.** biodegradable **e.** environment
4. Answers will vary.

Recall

Section I

1. You can get sick, and possibly get cancer.
2. hunger, poverty, and population growth; losses of land to produce food; accelerating fossil fuel use; increasing air pollution; global warming, droughts, and floods; ozone loss from the outer atmosphere; water shortages; deforestation and desertification; ocean and lake pollution; extinctions of species
3. Individually choose what products to buy and what foods to eat. Groups can lobby legislators to write laws that protect the environment, demand that the laws be enforced, and insist that corporations and governments honor their principles.
4. Sustainable choices help to keep the level of pollution down so that the environment can recover from its effects and replace natural resources. The

CHAPTER REVIEW

LEARNING THE VOCABULARY

environment	ozone layer	food chain
pollution	ripple effect	dioxins
fossil fuel	sustainable	ecosystems
air pollution	recyclable	active solar
acid rain	biodegradable	photovoltaic (PV) panels
global warming	disposable	compost
greenhouse effect	persistent	

Answer the following questions on a separate sheet of paper.

1. **Matching**—*Match each of the following phrases with the appropriate vocabulary term from the list above:*
   a. contamination of the environment with anything that impairs its ability to support life.
   b. warming of the planet, which threatens life on earth.
   c. rotted vegetable matter, used as fertilizer
   d. the sequence in which living things depend on other living things for food
2. a. _____ are panels that convert light into electricity.
   b. The term used to describe how one person's actions may affect many other people is the _____.
   c. The _____ is the heat-trapping effect of the glass in a greenhouse.
   d. Rain that carries acid air pollutants, which harms plant life and endangers the soil is called _____.
   e. _____ is the use of photovoltaic panels to generate electricity from sunlight.

3. **Word Scramble**—*Use the clues from the phrases below to help you unscramble the vocabulary terms from the list above:*
   a. **eeocmsssty** _____ systems of land, plants, and animals that have existed together for thousands or millions of years and that are interdependent
   b. **eeipnssttr** _____ the opposite of biodegradable—unable to decompose
   c. **aaeiublnsst** _____ the use of resources at such a rate that the earth can keep on replacing them
   d. **aaeeiobbdddglr** _____ able to be converted by living organisms into harmless waste products that can be used over again to build or grow new things
   e. **eeiomnnnnrtv** _____ everything "outside" the living organism—air, water, soil, other organisms
4. Write a paragraph using at least ten of the vocabulary terms listed. Underline each vocabulary term that you use.

RECALLING IMPORTANT FACTS AND IDEAS

1. What can happen to your body when the water you drink is polluted?
2. List and briefly describe ten global environmental problems.
3. How can you help slow, stop, or even reverse the global environmental problems?
4. Describe how sustainable choices you make are beneficial to the environment and also to your health.
5. What is the single largest source of air pollution?
6. How often should you shop? What other tips are given about shopping?
7. How long do plastics last?
8. How many families are now using solar energy?
9. What keeps most people from using PV panels, a battery, and a DC refrigerator?

choices most beneficial to the environment also benefit health. People's health greatly depends on the health of their surroundings.

Section II

5. motor vehicles
6. once each week. Answers may vary; could include: share rides to the mall, take turns shopping for one another, shop at neighborhood stores, walk or use a bicycle, choose the most fuel-efficient model of car.
7. for years or decades, creating masses of refuse that clog landfills

Section III

8. 20,000 families
9. the high initial cost
10. refrigerator
11. use high-efficiency compact fluorescent bulbs

Section IV

12. part of a beautiful carpet
13. vegetable scraps, fruit peelings, and leftover plant-based foods
14. They require no mining; they recycle natural materials; and they add needed texture and nutrients to the soil.

Section V

15. 500,000; vitamin deficiencies
16. Answers may vary; could include: wiping out many varieties of plant life, heating up the climate, using up freshwater supplies, and destroying the protective ozone layer that shields life from the sun's damaging rays.

10. Among kitchen appliances, which is the biggest energy user?
11. What can you do to save energy while using light bulbs?
12. What can a recycled plastic water bottle become?
13. What materials can be piled up together with some soil and decompose naturally?
14. Describe why natural fertilizers are better for the environment than synthetic fertilizers.
15. How many children go blind each year? What causes this blindness?
16. In what ways are we overstraining the earth's ability to support life?

CRITICAL THINKING

1. Take the Life Choice Inventory on page 628. Which sustainable choices do you make every day? Which habits do you need to change? Which will be hard to change? Explain your answers.
2. Look back to the Straight Talk on page 648, "Personal Strategy—Voluntary Simplicity." What suggestions are given about our lives? How can you change your life to be more simple? What will happen to our environment if nobody changes?

ACTIVITIES

1. Visit a local health care clinic. Find out how many people have come in due to hunger. What health problems do they have, due to hunger? Report your findings to the rest of the class in an oral report.
2. Contact a Hunger Relief Organization in your area. What will your donations actually do for hungry people? How much money goes directly to the people who need it for food? How much money goes to the organization that is helping?
3. Make posters on ways we can recycle products in our homes. Post these around school.
4. Write an editorial in your school newspaper about how our lifestyle choices affect our environment and our health. Challenge students in your editorial to change habits to help the environment and their health.
5. Design a pamphlet that explains how to use non-toxic products to clean our homes. Make copies available to all students.
6. Interview your parents on how they are helping the environment by recycling. Ask them how they are recycling their trash and garbage. What else are they doing to help the environment?
7. Visit the local waste water treatment plant. How are your waste products being disposed of? Write a one-page report about your trip and the process the plant goes through each day.
8. Make a video about the ten different global environmental problems described in this chapter. For each problem listed, come up with a solution. Show these to the rest of the class.
9. Make up a play on ways to help our environment. Show this play to a local elementary school.
10. Watch television for an hour and write down all the products that are being advertised. Which of these products are most concerned about the environment? How? Rank the products from best to worst for the environment.

MAKING DECISIONS ABOUT HEALTH

1. Hunger is a major problem in the world. If you could do something about the hunger problem, what would you do? Would you concentrate your efforts on the United States or on other countries? Why?
2. Garbage is a major problem for our environment. Recycling can help control this problem. How could you make everyone in the world recycle? What laws would you pass? How would you enforce these laws?

CHAPTER 26 PLANNER

OVERVIEW

Chapter 26 is 20 pages long and divided into the three sections listed to the right. Major learning outcomes are also listed to the right. This chapter introduces the concept of the individual as a consumer within the health care system. The importance of understanding methods of paying for health care is explained. Medicare, Medicaid, HMOs, and different kinds of insurance are compared. The costs of health care are affected by the increasing number of lawsuits, the expense of malpractice insurance, and problems in the health care system. There are many health care resources available in our communities and it is important to learn how to access and choose them appropriately. Students will learn about career options in the field of health care as well as how to detect and report fraudulent advertising practices.

MAKING LIFE CHOICES RESOURCES

A variety of activities, handouts, quizzes, and tests to accompany this chapter are available in the *Making Life Choices* supplementary material. You may pick and choose from those materials as appropriate for your amount of class time and the ability levels of your students. Some of the resources you might want to consider using are:

Handouts
- Health Care Delivery Past, Present, and Future
- Health Care Reforms
- Guidelines for Chapter Project

Teacher Information Sheet
- Advertising of Drugs

Activity To Introduce Chapter

Have students look in the yellow and business pages of the local phone book for listings of various medical services and health care providers. Have students make a list of the categories as represented by the headings in the local phone book under which medical information/services can be found. Then have them place check marks by the services their families have used.

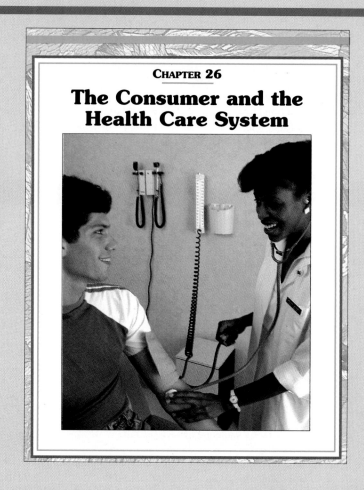

CHAPTER 26

The Consumer and the Health Care System

CHAPTER PROJECT

Provide students with the project guidelines from your supplementary material. Students, working in small groups of two–four, will choose one topic, gather information on it, prepare a class presentation, and orally give the report to the class. Groups can report on one of the following topics or an additional topic approved by you:
1. Private vs. Group Practice; 2. Health Maintenance Organizations. 3. Walk-in, Free, or Sliding Fee Clinics. 4. Medical Specialists. 5. Second and Third Opinions. 6. Health Insurance. 7. Health Products. 8. Quackery & Fraud. 9. Careers in Health Care. 10. Inpatient/Outpatient Facilities. 11. Choosing a Health Care Professional. 12. Self-Care. 13. Care for the Elderly. 14. Other Topics of Interest to Students.

OUTCOMES

After reading and studying this chapter, you will be able to:

✓ Describe three broad areas of health insurance.

✓ Discuss the benefits of health maintenance organizations (HMO).

✓ Identify reasons why health care insurance costs are on the rise.

✓ Identify ways to select a medical care facility.

✓ Discuss the problems associated with our health care system.

✓ Describe the services of health care providers.

✓ Discuss how to choose a health care provider.

CONTENTS

I. Paying for Health Care
II. Our Health Care System
III. Health Care Providers: Physicians and Others

Straight Talk: *Health Claims and Quackery*

FACT OR FICTION

What do you think? Are the following statements true or false? If you think they are false, then say what is true.

1. HMO stands for *home medical operation*—minor surgery that people can perform for themselves.
2. If you have medical and surgical insurance, you are probably covered for the costs of most medical treatments you might need.
3. Some operations are often recommended when they are not necessary, so it pays to get a

second opinion before having surgery.

4. If a person arrives at the hospital bleeding to death, the hospital has to provide emergency treatment.
5. Anyone can adopt the title "doctor," but there are penalties for falsely claiming to be a medical doctor (M.D.).

(Answers on page 665)

■ **Reminder:** Knowing how to study can increase your knowledge, improve your grades, *and* cut down on your study time. See the *Studying Health* section at the front of your text for some suggestions to help you study this chapter.

Answers to "Fact or Fiction"

1. False. HMO stands for *health maintenance organization.* People should not perform surgery on themselves.
2. False. You may need as many as five different kinds of insurance. Even then, specific medical needs might not be covered. **3.** True. **4.** False. Hospitals can turn away people who can't afford to pay, even if they need emergency treatment. **5.** True.

NOT ENOUGH TIME?*

You could easily spend three or four days teaching this chapter if students read the entire chapter, do a fair number of the suggested activities in the teacher's edition, and complete a sampling of the handouts from the resource material accompanying this text. It is likely, however, that you will have only one or two days to devote to this chapter. Following are some suggestions to help you make sure that you cover the key topics if you have limited time.

TIME	SUGGESTIONS
1 Day	On the day prior to beginning Chapter 26, ask students to read the chapter so they will be ready to discuss it in class. On day 1, start with the Activity to Introduce Chapter. Review payment options and availability of resources in your community. Evaluate with Activity 2.8 in Section II.
2 Days	On day 1 begin with the Activity to Introduce Chapter. Then have the students read Sections I and II. Discuss as time allows. Evaluate with Activity 1.8 in Section I and Activity 2.8 in Section II.
	On day 2 begin with Activity 3.1 in Section III. Then read Section III. Discuss health resources in your community. Close the class with Activity 3.14 in Section III.

Please refer to the 18-week daily lesson plans in the supplementary material for additional suggestions.

SUGGESTED RESOURCES

Student Readings
1. Vickery, Donald M. and Fries, James F. *Taking Care of Yourself: A Consumer's Guide to Medical Care*, 3d ed. Reading, MA: Addison-Wesley, 1986.

Teacher Readings
1. *FDA Consumer.* Washington, D.C.: U.S. Department of Health and Human Services, current issues.

In this section students will learn:
1. Three different approaches to paying for health care: no insurance, insurance, and health care provider.
2. How services are paid for under each option.
3. Some advantages and disadvantages of each option.

Activity 1.1
Best Care? Write on the board: "True or False—the best way to get help for medical services is to just go to the hospital emergency room."

Discuss why students chose True or False. (convenience, don't have a regular doctor, costs more than office visit, etc.) **(5 min.)**

Activity 1.2
Reasons for Having Insurance. Write on the board: "Everyone needs health insurance because it is cheaper than 'paying as you go' health care. Be prepared to defend your position." Have students write True or False and then give reasons for their responses in a class discussion.

654

---

654 UNIT 8 Global Issues

No doubt you have been a consumer of the **health care system.** Virtually everyone who attends public school must be immunized, and many teens have been treated for bouts of flu or broken bones. When you need the health care system, nothing else can take its place. At present, your parents, your guardians, or other adults probably attempt to get you the treatment you need at a cost your family can afford. By the time you leave home, though, you will need to know how to find your own way around in the system.

This chapter invites you to learn to use the health care system to best support your health. The Life Choice Inventory can help you see how much you already know about the system and how skilled you are in using it.

SECTION I

Paying for Health Care ①

Let us suppose you are going to have three problems this year. For one thing, you are going to get a severe sore throat that, unless promptly treated, will develop into a major, whole-body infection. Second, you are going to break your arm. And third, you are developing a heart condition (even though you may be young), but you will not have any symptoms for 15 years.

How these events will affect your health and your wallet depends on the choices you have already made. Consider three possibilities.

First, suppose you have chosen the defenseless approach: you have no insurance, you have no personal health care provider, and you have no health care plan. When your sore throat strikes, you try to live with it. Then it becomes so painful that

Suppose you are going to have three things happen to you this year.

you have to go to the hospital emergency room. There, you have to pay $100 in advance, are given some medicine, and are dismissed. You are still so sick that you lose a week of classes or work. When you break your arm, you again rush to the hospital and find that they will not even set your arm in a cast until you have again paid in advance—this time, $500. Total cost of treatment for the year: $600, a week of missed classes or work, and failure to detect your advancing heart condition.

The second approach is the insurance approach. Having insurance makes the story different. You are paying, say, $50 a month for insurance. Now you get your sore throat; let it get really painful, as before; and go to the hospital. With insurance, you are admitted and treated without question. The same thing happens when you break your arm: you are admitted and treated without question. After both events, you may find that the bills are simply paid for you. (If you have to pay the bills at first, you will soon receive your money back—or most of it.) Total cost to you: still $600 for the year. However, this time you have 12 equal payments, called **premiums,** of $50 rather than two surprise lump sums to pay. You still miss a week of classes or work, and still, no one detects your heart condition.

TEACH

SECTION 1
(Guided and Independent Practice)

Activity 1.3
Handling Emergencies. Ask students to give examples of how they have handled illnesses and/or medical emergencies in their families. Emphasize that different people choose different methods based on availability of services and/or

insurance. There is no one best way. **(5–10 min.; Reteach, Reinforce)**

Activity 1.4
Analyzing A Medical Bill. Have students bring in examples (bills) of charges for medical services. Examine how much was paid by the insurance and how much by the individual. Discuss or write an explanation of whether or not the health problem could have been handled

in a different way that might have cost more or less. (walk-in clinics, emergency room, private doctor) **(10–15 min.; Extend, Enrich)**

Activity 1.5
Employer-Provided Insurance. Ask students who have jobs whether or not their employers provide health insurance. Have them explain what it covers;

(continued on next page)

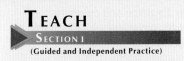

LIFE CHOICE INVENTORY

How Well Do You Know and Use the Health Care System? ①

For each yes answer, give yourself 1 point.

1. Do you understand your own health insurance? (Someone else may pay for it, but do you know what your policies cover?)
2. Are you familiar with the five types of health insurance you may need? (Can you name them?)
3. Do you know what breaks you can get on health/medical insurance, based on your lifestyle choices?
4. Do you know several different ways in which people can pay for their health care? (Could you explain to someone else the differences between a prepayment plan and a fee-for-service system?)
5. When you need treatment, do you try to go to a clinic or health care practitioner's office rather than to the hospital emergency room?
6. When you receive a bill for medical care, do you read it to make sure that you received all the services it lists?
7. Can you name several kinds of health care providers and say who is trained to perform which services?
8. If you meet a "doctor," do you keep in mind that the person may not be an M.D.? (Can you name several other possibilities?)
9. Can you spot a quack?
10. Have you ever reported quackery to a watchdog agency?

SCORING

8 to 10: You are a skilled consumer of health care services.

6 or 7: You know the system fairly well, but have a little more to learn.

4 or 5: Your skill at using the health care system needs improvement.

3 or less: You don't use the health care system well. In fact, you may be losing out in many ways.

The third approach is the health care provider approach. You have insurance and you have your own personal health care provider, who not only treats, but also tries to prevent, illness. When your sore throat develops, you telephone this person's office and are seen immediately. Prompt treatment spares you the pain of a bad sore throat, as well as the loss of a week's classes or workdays. When you break your arm,

MINI GLOSSARY

health care system: the total of all health care providers and medical treatment facilities that work together to provide medical care to the population.

premiums: regular payments made to an insurance company to cover the costs of unforeseen events such as medical emergencies.

Teacher Support Notes

① **Assessing Health Care Knowledge:** It is likely that many of your students will score low on this inventory. A low score may, however, motivate them to learn more. As a follow-up to the inventory, ask the following questions:

a. Do you have health insurance?

b. Is it provided by one of your parents' employers?

c. How much is the deductible for your expenses?

d. Does your parent's employer pay the entire cost of the insurance?

e. How many claims against that policy have your parents made on your behalf in the past year?

f. If you have no insurance, how much have your actual medical bills been during the past year? How does this cost compare to insurance for the same period of time?

did they have an option or specific time in which to enroll in the group plan; do they have to do anything special in order to keep the insurance; have they ever used it? **(5–10 min.; Reteach, Reinforce)**

Activity 1.6

Student Insurance Policy. Obtain a copy of your school's group insurance policy for students, if your school has one. (It is usually offered to all students, but especially athletes.) Examine what it costs, covers, excludes, etc. **(5–15 min., Interdisciplinary)**

Activity 1.7
School Employee Health Plan. Obtain a copy of the school's employee

health plan. Examine and compare options, costs, coverage, etc. **(5–15 min., Interdisciplinary)**

EVALUATE
SECTION 1

Activity 1.8
Pop Quiz.
1. A health maintenance organization (HMO) is a type of prepayment health

---

Teacher Support Notes

① **HMOs vs. Insurance:** Ask students to compare an HMO plan to insurance. What are the similarities? What are the differences? Basically students should see that belonging to an HMO is much the same as buying insurance. You pay premiums for your insurance policy whether you receive any benefits or not. You pay a monthly fee to the HMO whether you use it or not. The basic difference is that most insurance policies do not cover well-care, whereas the HMO plan usually does. Another difference is that the insurance policy probably provides for hospital expenses that can be substantial, whereas the HMO plan probably will not.

✎ Fast Facts

Over a typical two-year period, at least 25% of the U.S. population goes without health insurance for at least one month, according to the U.S. Census Bureau. Young adults between the ages of 18 and 21 were the age group most likely to lack insurance.

you still go to the hospital emergency room, and you pay $500, as before (you get this back later). One other thing happens, to your benefit. Your health care provider gives you a routine physical examination this year, detects the heart trouble, and starts treating you for it. This may add years to your life.

In the health care provider approach, your insurance does not cover your general physical examination, so you are out $100 for that. However, the future benefits of freedom from heart disease outweigh the price by far. Insurance does pay for the sore throat treatment and for the broken arm, so your costs are $600 for insurance, $100 for the general physical exam, and no loss of a productive week.

You may have another health care provider option if you live in a community with a walk-in medical clinic. Here a staff physician can treat your sore throat, possibly at lower cost than the cost of private treatment. Another less expensive option for the sore throat is the community public health center.

Still another option in the health care provider approach is to join a **health maintenance organization (HMO).** The HMO charges you a fee each month. You then receive many services without paying extra for them. The routine physical examination may be included under the basic monthly fee. The HMO might well assign you to a physician who would catch your heart problem early, explain the risk factors for heart disease, and offer effective actions to correct them.

As a member of an HMO, you do not hesitate to go in when you have a sore throat, because it does not cost anything extra. Therefore, you receive prompt treatment, and you do not lose a week to illness. And when you break your arm, although you still go to the hospital for

treatment, the HMO pays most of the fees. You might end up paying more—maybe $75 a month—to belong to an HMO. However, the benefits might be greater, too. One important benefit is knowing in advance almost exactly what your health care will cost you, so that you encounter no nasty surprises. Another benefit is that you're likely to take advantage of more services, because they don't cost extra. Some of those services, such as a physical exam, can help you prevent future illnesses.

The key difference between an HMO and other health care providers is in how they are paid. An HMO offers a **prepayment plan.** Other health care providers charge for each service as you receive them. Their method of payment is described as a **fee-for-service system.**

In summary, of the three approaches to health care, the defenseless approach is most risky. The insurance approach is safer but doesn't offer the benefits of preventive care. It also doesn't tell you where to go or whom to see in emergencies. You have to figure that out for yourself. The health care provider approach provides a map to ① the health care system. It guides you along its paths as your needs arise.

The rest of this chapter offers insights into your choices related to these options:

1. What insurance do I need, if any?
2. What hospitals will be best for me?
3. Should I consider joining an HMO? Are other alternatives available?
4. Should I have a personal health care provider? Should this person be a physician (M.D.)? What are the alternatives?

Key Points ▶ *People who have no medical insurance must pay at each illness. Those with insurance pay in advance, and only a limited amount. Members of health maintenance organizations (HMOs) also pay in advance, and then receive treatment at little or no extra cost through the HMO providers.*

2. Premiums are the payments you make directly to the doctor or service provider. (F)

3. Hospital emergency rooms may require you to pay for a service before they do anything if you do not have insurance. (T)

4. Health insurance covers all costs of medical services. (F)

5. Having no insurance is usually a safe way to go because you don't have monthly payments for insurance premiums. (F) **(5 min.)**

CLOSE
SECTION I

Activity 1.9
Guest Speaker. Invite guest speakers, such as a health insurance agent, an HMO representative, or someone who does not believe it wise to buy health coverage of any kind. Have the speakers explain the different types of coverage, costs, exemptions, etc. Then have students compare the different options and give reasons for the choices they would make.

TEEN VIEWS

Are medical expenses higher than they should be?

Yes. Definitely much higher than they should be. Medical care is now more of a luxury than a necessity. The people that need the help the most are the least likely to receive it. **Elana Krueger, 17, Wilson High School, CA**

Medical expenses are higher than they should be. The United States is one of the only countries that does not put the health of the people as a priority. **Heather Amerson, 17, Orange Park High School, FL**

No! Medical expenses are not too high. Medical technology is expensive and expands quickly. Part of high prices goes to improve future care by raising extra money for new technology. Doctors go through many years of school and work hard to get where they are. **Brian Doyle, 14, Westside High School, NE**

Yes. You have to have a good job or be on welfare to have health coverage. If someone gets sick or has an accident and has to go to the emergency room, they will be making payments for years. It's ridiculous how much is charged to spend one night in the hospital. A national health coverage plan should be established that will give coverage to everyone—rich or poor. **Mike Gorzo, 15, Sharon High School, PA**

SECTION I REVIEW

Answer the following questions on a sheet of paper.

Learning the Vocabulary
The vocabulary terms in this section are *health care system, premiums, health maintenance organization (HMO), prepayment plan,* and *fee-for-service system.*
1. Use each of the vocabulary terms above in a sentence.

Learning the Facts
2. What are the three health care approaches listed in this section?
3. Describe three other health care provider options listed in this section.
4. List three benefits of an HMO.

Making Life Choices
5. Your family has just moved to a little town from a big city. Your family used to belong to an HMO, but the little town does not have one. How are you going to provide for your medical care? How will you choose the best care?

MINI GLOSSARY

health maintenance organization (HMO): a group of physicians who practice together and who treat people's health problems under a prepayment plan.

prepayment plan: a system of paying for health care in which the clients pay a fixed fee every month, regardless of how many services they receive.

fee-for-service system: a system of paying for health care in which clients pay individual fees for the services they receive.

Teacher Support Notes

① **Teen Views Follow-Up Questions: a.** Is medical care a "luxury" in the U.S.? **b.** Do other countries put a higher priority on health care? If so, why? **c.** Are doctors overpaid? **d.** Should the federal government try to solve our health care problem with a national plan?

Section I Review
Answers
1. Answers will vary.
2. defenseless, insurance, health care provider
3. health maintenance organization, prepayment plan, fee-for-service
4. knowing the cost of health care in advance, a person is more likely to take advantage of more services, you might be assigned to a physician who would catch a health problem early
5. Answers will vary.

657

In this section students will learn:
1. About various types of insurance coverage.
2. Ways to reduce health care costs by carefully selecting the appropriate care provider or service.
3. That there are many problems with the health care system in this country.

Activity 2.1

Type of Insurance. Write on the board: "List as many types of health insurance or coverage as you can think of." (medicine/pharmacy, pregnancy, surgical, disability, Medicare, Medicaid, etc.) Compile their lists and discuss. **(5 min.)**

Activity 2.2

Help with Health Care Costs.
Write on the board: "Think of the times when your family has used health insurance to help with health care costs. Be ready to share with the class." Have students volunteer their stories. **(5–15 min.)**

TEACH
SECTION II
(Guided and Independent Practice)

Teacher Support Notes

① **Picking Policies:**
You may want to give students additional information about how to evaluate an insurance policy for health care. First they should ask how much the deductible is, and whether or not the policy covers the following: in-hospital and outpatient costs, diagnostic tests, second opinions, medicines, prevention, education, ambulance service, and psychological counseling.

② **Life Spans and Health Costs:** Ask students if they think the fact that people live longer would increase or decrease the cost of health insurance. Students might think that people are living longer and are healthier, therefore, insurance rates would go down. Just the opposite is the case, however, because people live longer and need more care for a longer period of time later in life.

✎ Fast Facts

American industry pays about 25% of all medical costs. Businesses now spend more on employee health care than they distribute in profits. About $500 of the price of a new automobile goes toward paying workers' medical bills.

SECTION II

Our Health Care System

Medical care isn't cheap. A serious illness may easily require treatments costing more than the average family makes in a year. One part of the health care system devised to help people avoid being wiped out financially by serious illness is the system of insurance.

Health Insurance

"I'm sorry, but your insurance policy doesn't cover this. Pay in advance please." People can avoid the pain of this situation only if they use some know-how in shopping for health insurance. The five types of insurance related to people's personal health care are:

1. **Hospitalization insurance.**
2. **Surgical insurance.**
3. **Medical insurance.**
4. **Major medical insurance.**
5. **Disability insurance.**

The different kinds of insurance cover each of these: accidents, hospitalization, surgery, physician services, medicines, pregnancy, and disabilities that might prevent your working. Policies differ. Read them, and think about your particular needs. For example, if you are planning to start a family soon, be sure your insurance covers the cost of prenatal care, delivery, and newborn care.

If you have a healthy lifestyle, you may be given the privilege of paying lower insurance rates than others. Some companies offer reduced rates for nonsmokers, people of normal weight, nonusers of alcohol, or regular exercisers. Insurance companies know that they are more likely to have to pay large medical bills for people who smoke, who are obese, who use alcohol, who fail to exercise, who don't wear safety belts, and whose blood cholesterol and blood pressure are high.

② Special groups of people may be covered by **Medicare** and **Medicaid.** Medicare pays hospital expenses for senior citizens who also receive Social Security benefits. Medicaid is medical insurance provided for those who receive public assistance (welfare).

Health insurance has saved the financial skins of millions of individuals who have faced high medical costs. However, no matter how much insurance you have, you cannot be sure of covering every circumstance. Clients of insurance companies and their families pay all costs not covered by insurance, so insurance is not a substitute for careful financial planning.

Key Points *Insurance can pay for the costs of accidents, hospitalization, surgery, health care provider services, medicines, and disabilities. It does not cover everything, and it is no substitute for careful financial planning.*

Malpractice Insurance

Insurance is imperfect in another way: it can be abused. The chief insurance abuse driving the cost of medical care higher is the abuse of **malpractice insurance.** Malpractice insurance is not for you. It is for your physician or other health care provider. If a physician is sued for providing improper care, and loses the case, the insurance will pay the cost.

Only a few physicians hurt clients on purpose or by foolish errors. However, almost all feel they must protect themselves with malpractice insurance. And unfortunately, some greedy people and their attorneys abuse malpractice insurance, sometimes winning huge awards for false claims. As a result, the premiums are high.

(continued on next page)

They amount to up to a third of a physician's yearly income. This forces physicians to raise their fees. You, the physician's client, end up paying extra because of the greed of a few people who unjustly sue physicians to gain huge rewards.

> **Key Points** *Insurance abuse, such as excessive suing of physicians to cash in on malpractice insurance, helps drive up the costs of health care.*

Medical Resources in the Community

A goal of the health care system is to meet the needs of people within their own communities. Many agencies—both government-run and private, voluntary types—work together to achieve this goal. The federal government runs programs to provide many functions that everyone needs, such as the law-enforcing functions of the Food and Drug Administration (FDA). The FDA is a watchdog agency that checks up on the manufacturers of foods and drugs.

Some aspects of health care are better provided at the local level. That is because some communities' needs differ from other communities' needs. For example, a large city may need to provide more services for urban low-income groups, while a farming community may have entirely different needs. This is why local agencies—such as health departments and school-run clinics—are free to make decisions on how to best serve individuals in a community. Figure 26–1 on the next page gives a view of some of the many resources that focus on meeting the health needs of the nation's communities.

Among the private providers of health services, medical facilities have different strengths and weaknesses. When you need the services provided by such facilities, you must decide which to use. The better you know what is available ahead of time, the

Regular checkups support good health.

MINI **G**LOSSARY

hospitalization insurance: insurance to pay the cost of a hospital stay.

surgical insurance: insurance to pay the surgeon's fees; see also *Medicaid.*

medical insurance: insurance to pay physicians' fees, lab fees, and fees for prescription medications.

major medical insurance: insurance to pay high bills not covered by other insurance.

disability insurance: insurance to replace lost income if a person should be unable to work due to a long illness.

Medicare: hospitalization insurance for people who are receiving Social Security.

Medicaid: hospitalization and surgical insurance available for people who qualify as needy.

malpractice insurance: insurance that protects providers of health care against lawsuits by people claiming to have been harmed by a health care provider.

plan that would be good for them as young single adults going to postsecondary school or working with no insurance coverage. Let them choose from options and plans reviewed in class. **(10–15 min., Critical Thinking)**

Activity 2.5
Health Resources. Write on the board: "List as many health resources in our community (or nearby community if yours is small/rural) as you can think of." (private/public hospitals, walk-in clinic, state H&W clinic, local health department classes, paramedics, ambulance, school clinic, school nurse, support groups for various ailments or families of sick individuals, Veterans Administration, Elks

Rehabilitation, sports medicine clinics, physical therapists, chiropractors, state commission for the blind or deaf, Ronald McDonald House, local pharmacy, Red Cross, poison control center, Planned Parenthood, drug detox centers, hospice services, nursing homes, medical supply and equipment outlets, buses for handicapped persons, etc.) See how many students can name. Add any they omitted to a group list. Have students make a list in

Teacher Support Notes

① **Other Agencies:**
Eight different groups of health agencies are represented in the illustration. Only minimal descriptions are provided. To have a better understanding of what each of these agencies or types of agencies do, you may want to divide students into eight groups and have them research the agencies. Students should concentrate on reporting back to the class examples of the specific kinds of actions engaged in by health care providers in that particular type of agency.

660   UNIT 8   Global Issues

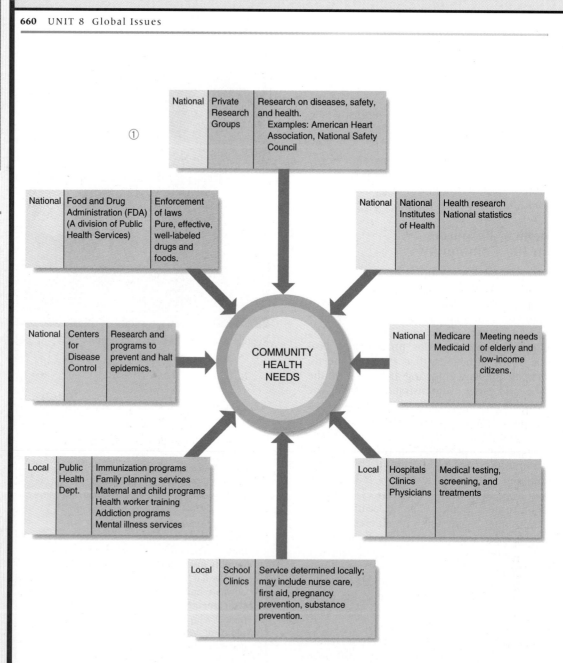

Figure 26–1 Sample Agencies That Focus on Meeting Community Health Needs. Nationwide organizations, local agencies, and other groups all ultimately meet community needs. These and many other organizations work to protect and promote the health of individuals.

their notebooks. Ask students to find out which ones they and their families have used. **(10–20 min.)**

Activity 2.6

Resource Brochures. Divide students into groups and have them design a brochure describing various community medical resources. This could be done using the headings in Activity 2.5, or others as appropriate. The brochure should include information such as: names of places, locations, phone numbers, types of services, types of medical persons employed, hours of operation, methods of payment accepted, or other information that seems important. They may need to call or visit some of the options to get this information. **(30–50 min., Cooperative Learning)**

Activity 2.7

Cultural Beliefs. Have students research beliefs, practices, and resources used to take care of medical situations in various ethnic and/or religious groups. (Native American, Hispanic-American, Jews, Latter-Day Saints, Seventh-Day Adventists, Christian Scientists, Amish, or others in your community) Have students report their findings. Students should take notes, then identify differences between

(continued on next page)

better you can choose one that will serve you in time of need. The Health Strategies section on this page can help you make that choice.

Smart strategies can also help you save money and needless struggles. For example, if possible, try to see a health care professional during office hours—do not go to a hospital emergency room. Emergency rooms always cost extra. In case you must go to the emergency room, the Health Strategies section on the next page entitled "Hints for Emergency Room Visits" offers a few suggestions to make your visit easier.

Another suggestion is to seek a **second opinion** before allowing any test or surgery. Some operations, especially **tonsillectomy** and **hysterectomy,** are overperformed. That is, they are often recommended when they are not medically necessary. Insurance may cover the cost of a second opinion. If the two opinions differ, consider getting a third.

For long-term recovery from an injury, or for training in dealing with a disability such as blindness or loss of a limb, you may need to visit a special **rehabilitation** center. Alternatively, you may use a regular hospital, if it has rehabilitation facilities. Ask what types of help are available at each. Pick the one best suited to your needs.

If you need special tests or surgery, you have choices to make, too. For simple surgery, you can choose a walk-in center rather than a hospital. In such a center you will not have to pay for an overnight stay. For complex procedures that require hospital facilities, plan to check into the hospital on a weekday and check out before the weekend, if possible. The weekdays are when the work gets done.

About payment: as many as 90 percent of most hospital bills contain errors. Read through your bills to check that you have not been overcharged. If you question any charge, ask for an itemized list of services you received, and send it to your insurance

① (circled, in margin)

HEALTH STRATEGIES

Selecting and Using Medical Care Facilities

When selecting and using medical care facilities:

1. Know what facilities are available and what their specialties are.
2. Avoid emergency room visits.
3. Get a second opinion.
4. Consider alternatives to hospital tests and surgery.
5. Use the hospital on weekdays; avoid weekends.
6. Ask about each facility's policy on payment.
7. Find out the physician's and hospital's ways of handling insurance claims. They may file, or you may have to.
8. Protest if the bill is in error.
9. Be willing to go out of state, if necessary, for specialized medical care.

MINI GLOSSARY

second opinion: a second assessment of a diagnosis and treatment plan by another health care provider usually on the request of a client, to double-check the validity of the original plan.

tonsillectomy: removal of the tonsils (in the throat), an operation sometimes performed needlessly.

hysterectomy: removal of the uterus, an operation performed more often than necessary.

rehabilitation: learning how to live with the effects of an injury, such as blindness or loss of a limb; assistance in recovering function after such injuries.

Teacher Support Notes

① **Paying the Bill:** You may want to give students some additional information about paying for a hospital stay. For example, tell them that many hospitals must give some care to people who cannot afford to pay. Hospitals that serve as teaching facilities often are required to take all clients. Tell students that the time when they receive the bill is not the time to discover that they do not have adequate insurance coverage. They should check insurance policies *before* the need arises. If they are scheduling an operation or other treatment, they should ask in the physician's office whether their insurance will cover it and what help will be available in filing the claim. Many hospitals expect the bill to be paid immediately, with the patient being reimbursed later by the insurance company. Some will help the patient file the claim; others will not.

661

the groups. **(Multicultural, Extend, Enrich)**

EVALUATE
SECTION II

Activity 2.8
Pop Quiz.

1. There are many different types of medical insurance available. (T)
2. Everyone is covered by Medicare or Medicaid. (F)
3. Insurance abuse helps drive up the costs of health care. (T)
4. The Food and Drug Administration is a watchdog agency that checks up on the manufacturers of foods and drugs sold on

the market. (T)
5. You should go to the emergency room first for any medical problem. (F)
6. Hospital bills are usually accurate. (F)
7. It is wise to get a second opinion before allowing medical tests or surgery to be performed. (T)
8. The United States has more than enough health care providers. (F)
9. People have died after being turned away from hospital emergency rooms

---

Teacher Support Notes

① **Teacher Information Sheets and Handouts—Health Care Reform:** As this text was being written, many different plans for reforming the U.S. health care system were being proposed and debated. Because of the enormous complexity of the issues involved, understanding even a single plan (much less comparing the various alternatives) can be difficult for most adults, not to mention the difficulty for less experienced and less knowledgeable high school students. Because of the timing and the complexity of this issue, the text does not make an attempt to provide students with the information they would need to evaluate the various health care plans.

Your supplementary material does, however, contain background information to help you understand the types of reform being proposed and some simplified handouts to give students enough basic information to initiate classroom discussion.

Hints for Emergency Room Visits

When you must go to an emergency room:

1. Call your regular health care provider first. Leave a message with the answering service stating who you are, what the problem is, and where you are going.
2. Have only one person go with you, not the whole family.
3. Take some identification and your insurance card with you.
4. Tell the person at the admissions desk if you have been there before. If you have, the personnel can find your file and skip some paperwork.
5. Know your own medical history and what medicines you are taking.

company. The insurance company may be able to get the charges reduced.

The hospital system can be highly successful in treating injuries and illnesses. No drama is greater than the swift actions of health care providers in a medical emergency—beginning with a speedy ambulance ride and ending with cure and dismissal. Such dramas are played out daily in the world's great medical centers. Health care needs are not always of an emergency nature, though. For routine health care, using your own intelligence can serve you better than calling an ambulance, and will cost you much less.

Key Points ▶ *To use health care facilities to your advantage, compare those available, choose the ones that will serve you best, and assert your rights as to choices in treatments and reasonable costs.*

The cost of medical care can be high.

① ## Problems of our Health Care System

Not all nations' health care systems operate as the U.S. system does, funded by a massive, complex, and competitive insurance industry. For example, Canada has a national program of hospital and medical care insurance that offers basic health care to more than 99 percent of its citizens. A problem of the Canadian system, however, is a lack of advanced technology. Canadian physicians often find they must send clients with special needs to U.S. medical centers.

In our highly specialized system, basic health care may not be available to all who need it. There are not enough care facilities or professionals to serve everyone. Especially in rural areas, people may find themselves far away from needed services. Sometimes it is hard to find the exact services needed. Furthermore, it is possible to be turned away for lack of funds, even in an emergency. People have died after being turned away from hospital emergency rooms because they could not pay for their care. Another problem is quality control. Although the medical profession attempts to police itself, mistakes, incompetence, and even dishonesty are not unknown.

Cost may be the worst problem. Costs are high and rapidly growing higher. Malpractice insurance was already mentioned as a driving force behind the spiraling cost of

because they could not pay for care. (T)
10. Malpractice insurance and modern technology have caused the cost of medical care to go down. (F)

CLOSE
SECTION II

Activity 2.9
Oral Reports. Have students report orally on their research from Activity 2.7.

Compare the beliefs, practices, etc., of the different ethnic groups. **(20–40 min., Multicultural)**

FOCUS
SECTION III

In this section students will learn:
1. Factors to consider when choosing a health care provider.
2. The training and education require-

ments to receive a medical degree (M.D.).
3. Who to ask and where to look for information when choosing a new health care provider.
4. What to watch for in fraudulent products, advertising, services, and care providers.

Activity 3.1
Health Care Careers. Write on the

(continued on next page)

---

health care. Another is the extreme high costs of modern hospital technology. Former surgeon general C. Everett Koop has suggested that simpler equipment in many locations would better serve the needs of the population. That way, most people would have access to everyday care, while those with needs for the latest technology could travel to large medical centers to obtain it.

The problem of shortages of health care professionals and services is partly solved by medical personnel other than high-cost physicians. For example, a community clinic may provide the services of nurse practitioners trained to deliver women's health care or nurse midwives trained to attend normal births.

The backbone of any health care system is the people who provide health care. The next section discusses the educational qualifications of some health care providers.

> **Key Points** Problems in the health care system include high costs and limited supply. Solutions to these problems include systems such as community clinics that offer basic care at a low cost by nurse practitioners.

SECTION II REVIEW

Answer the following questions on a sheet of paper.
Learning the Vocabulary
The vocabulary terms introduced in the section are *hospitalization insurance, surgical insurance, medical insurance, major medical insurance, disability insurance, Medicare, Medicaid, malpractice insurance, second opinion, tonsillectomy, hysterectomy,* and *rehabilitation.*
1. Match each of the following phrases with the appropriate term.
   a. insurance to pay the surgeon's fee
   b. hospitalization insurance for people who are receiving Social Security
   c. learning how to live with the effects of an injury
2. Write a paragraph using at least five of the vocabulary terms.

Learning the Facts
3. List the five types of insurance related to your personal health.
4. Who is eligible for Medicare?
5. Describe the role of the Food and Drug Administration in helping to meet people's health needs.
6. List and describe what to do when selecting and using medical care facilities.
7. Describe the problems with Canada's health care system.
8. What is the backbone of the health care system?

Making Life Choices
9. Matt was out on a bike trip when he came across a woman lying in the street. He stopped to see if there was anything he could do. The woman was breathing and had a faint heartbeat. He waved down a motorist and together they took her to the local hospital. She was refused treatment because she did not have any medical insurance. How would you feel if you were Matt? How would you feel if you were the injured woman? What can we do to change the problems of medical treatment and insurance?

SECTION III

Health Care Providers: Physicians and Others

Many types of health care professionals provide many distinct services. A person who gets sick usually will think in terms of "going to the doctor"—but what is a doctor? Anyone can be called "doctor," but not all are trained the same way, and some are even dishonest. The next two sections attempt to sort out who's who in the health care world. Appendix A, at the end of this book, lists these and many more health care providers for the person who wants to sort them all out—or become one.

✉ **Where to Write**
Consumer Reports Health Letter
P.O. Box 52148
Boulder, CO 80322

board: "List as many health care jobs as you can think of in one minute." Ask volunteers to read their lists aloud and compile a list with as many different jobs as time allows. Discuss the careers that students think they would enjoy. **(5 min.)**

Activity 3.2
Specialists Chart. Divide students into groups and give each group a phone book. Ask each group to find how many doctors are listed under each specialty. The list could include, but is not limited to Community/Environmental Health (aller-

gist), Drugs (pharmacist), Substance Abuse Counselor, Nutrition (dietitian), Diseases (family doctor, internist), Safety and First Aid (EMT), Growth and Development, (pediatrician), Mental Health (psychiatrist, counselor), Fitness and Exercise (athletic trainer), Rehabilitation (physical therapist). The specialties will vary from community to community. Ask if there are obvious missing specialties that a person would have to go to another community to access.

✏ Fast Facts

In the United States there are about 20 practicing physicians per every 10,000 people. The ratio is slightly higher than in England, Canada, and Australia but considerably lower than in Italy, Germany, France, and Scandinavia.

✏ Fast Facts

The United States has more than its share of specialists. In developed countries other than the United States, generalists make up 50% to 75% of the medical professionals. In the United States only 30% of physicians are generalists.

✏ Fast Facts

Evidence suggests that anywhere from 20% to 50% of the commonly performed specialty procedures in this country could be avoided without harming the health of the public.

The Health Care Provider

The health care provider most people think of is the medical doctor, or M.D. This is as it should be, for medical school training equips the M.D. to handle many kinds of medical problems. This book refers to such a person as the *doctor* or *physician*.

A long course of education leads to the M.D. degree and to the license to practice medicine. Another type of doctor, the osteopath (D.O.), takes the same course of training as an M.D., but in a school of osteopathy, which specializes in the muscles and skeleton. In many ways, people with D.O. degrees are equal to those with M.D.'s.

Following four years of college, the person seeking to become a physician attends three years of medical school to learn to treat diseases. This is followed by a two-year **internship** and a one-year **residency.** Then the person must pass a state examination to receive a license to practice. Even more schooling is necessary to become a **specialist,** such as a **gynecologist** or **pediatrician**.

A physician is licensed to provide medical care under his or her own authority. Other professionals who can provide care independently are the nurse practitioner (N.P. or R.N.P.) and the physician's assistant (P.A.). These people have quite a bit of medical school training and can handle all routine medical problems—but they consult physicians when necessary. Appendix A lists these and other legitimate health care providers and describes what they are qualified to do.

One specialist many people use as a health care provider is the chiropractor (doctor of chiropractic, or D.C.). Not everyone realizes that this person, although called "doctor," has not been through the same course of medical training that the M.D. has. A chiropractor's office may resemble a physician's office, but the services are not the same. Chiropractors can relieve pain (especially from pressure on nerves).

A nurse practitioner can provide some basic medical care.

However, other medical services, such as diagnosing illness and prescribing treatments for them, are the exclusive domain of the M.D.

Some dishonest people, hoping to make money on people's illnesses, may claim to have medical training that they don't have. Anyone can claim the title "doctor." There are penalties only for falsely claiming to have an M.D. degree from a particular medical school. Wherever local governments fail to license health care providers, citizens have no guarantee that health care providers will give them useful, or even safe, services. This chapter's Consumer Awareness explores the fake **credentials** of corrupt people who only claim to be trained to provide health care.

Besides those already mentioned, many other people practice as health professionals alone or in **group practice,** in private offices or clinics. Some of these people may be well qualified to help you. Some have skills within limited realms that are useful. Some may be out-and-out frauds waiting to ambush anyone with full pockets and a trusting nature.

Key Points ▶ *Health care providers other than physicians, physician's assistants, and nurse practitioners come in many stripes. None are as well trained as those specialists, and some are untrustworthy.*

Make a chart with the names of each specialty and the number of specialists for each. Post in the room. **(20–30 min., Cooperative Learning)**

Activity 3.3
Health Career Research. Have students research different kinds of health care careers and report to the class. They should include information such as: training or schooling, job outlook, employment practices, working conditions, earnings, advantages, disadvantages. **(Extend, Enrich)**

Activity 3.4
Group and Private Practices. Have students identify group and private practices in your community. Then have them phone or make visits to find: hours of operation, typical costs for services, types and number of employees, payment policies, insurance policies, services available, credentials of care providers, or other information that seems appropriate for your community. **(Extend, Enrich)**

Activity 3.5
Panel Discussion. Invite various health care providers to participate on a panel discussion about health careers, services offered, benefits, advantages, disadvantages, wages, training, education, etc.

(continued on next page)

How to Choose a Health Care Provider

How do you go about choosing a health care provider? Earlier, we mentioned a personal health care provider as a person who gives routine examinations and tries to prevent illnesses. This person will learn your medical history, and will be able to refer you to specialists as needed. Choosing a personal health care provider is worth some time and effort, for the relationship between client and provider should be one of trust.

You might choose a physician, a nurse practitioner, or a physician's assistant as your health care provider. Using the physician as an example, a reasonable first step in selecting a health care provider is to call the local American Medical Association office or county medical society. They can give you lists of physicians in a given area. Alternatively, simply ask friends whom they recommend. Then, check the credentials of each of the recommended providers. Look in Appendix A for the degrees listed by their titles. After you have some names, make sure the physician is a member of the American College of Physicians (or, if a surgeon, of the American College of Surgeons). Also, ask the local hospital to provide you with a list of staff physicians and their ranks and privileges. This will give you some sense of how respected each person is by fellow physicians.

Once you have found a qualified health care provider, call the person's office. Ask the questions listed in the Health Strategies section on page 667, "Choosing a Health Care Provider." Most people want someone they can talk to. It is a good idea—especially if you may forget—to write down questions before your appointment. Also, jot down answers as you talk to the professional.

A good health care provider will take a thorough **history**—that is, a question-and-answer session about your past medical experiences. The history provides about 70

Answers to Fact or Fiction

Here are the answers to the questions at the start of the chapter.

1. False. HMO stands for *health maintenance organization*. People should not perform surgery on themselves.
2. False. You may need as many as five different kinds of insurance. Even then, specific medical needs might not be covered. **3.** True **4.** False. Hospitals can turn away people who can't afford to pay, even if they need emergency treatment. **5.** True.

MINI GLOSSARY

internship: a length of time spent in a medical facility as part of the training of health care providers.
residency: a length of time spent in a medical facility as part of the M.D.'s training after the internship.
specialist: a physician with training in a specialty area beyond the medical degree requirements.
gynecologist: a specialist in the care of the female reproductive system.
pediatrician: a specialist concerned with the health care of infants and children.
credentials: (kre-DEN-shulls): official evidence of education or other qualifications of an authority; diplomas, licenses, and the like.
group practice: an organization of physicians who practice medicine together. An example is the HMO (see page 656).
history (medical): an interview in which a health care professional asks about past medical experience.

①

 Fast Facts

According to a *Wall Street Journal* poll, 69% of Americans believe that the health care system in the U.S. should be run mainly by the government.

Teacher Support Notes

① **Communication with the Physician:** You may want to tell students that many people are intimidated by doctors; they believe that doctors are much smarter and better educated and, therefore, when they don't understand a doctor's answer, they assume they lack sufficient knowledge. Tell students competent, concerned health care providers want their patients to know and understand any conditions or illnesses being discussed, but that they can't clarify their explanations unless the patient asks questions. As patients, students should not be embarrassed if they don't understand. It's important that they ask questions.

665

Activity 3.6

Interviews. Have each student interview and/or shadow a health care worker and write a report on his/her findings. As a class, prepare the questions to use during the interview. **(Extend, Enrich)**

Activity 3.7

Role-Play. Divide students into pairs to role-play visiting a health care provider. Have them brainstorm questions to ask when they get to their appointments. Think of questions for different types of problems. Use different health situations, such as headaches, shortness of breath, blurry vision, ringing in the ears, routine or sports physical. **(10–30 min.; Reteach, Reinforce)**

Activity 3.8

Choosing A Health Care Provider. Have students interview parents or other adults to find out how they chose their health care providers. What criteria did they use? What helped them make their decisions? Have they ever changed providers? Why? **(Extend, Enrich)**

Activity 3.9

Design a Product. Have each stu-

Teacher Support Notes

① **Answers to Critical Thinking:**

1. Their health and possibly their lives are at stake. Few things are more important than choosing an appropriate health care provider.

2. The person wouldn't be accepted into a professional group. In checking out their credentials they would discover that the person was a fraud and would not admit the person into the group.

3. Contact a state licensing agency or a local government. Print and broadcast journalists are also often on the lookout for frauds who can be exposed.

② **Diagnosis:** Don't assume that students know this fairly common word. Ask them to define it. *Diagnosis* means the use of scientific and skillful methods to establish the nature of a person's illness. This is done by evaluating the history of the disease process; the signs and symptoms present; and laboratory data. The value of establishing a diagnosis is to provide a logical basis for treatment and prognosis (prediction of the course and end of the disease, and an estimate of the chances for recovery).

666

CONSUMER AWARENESS — Genuine and Fake Credentials

Most degrees listed next to health care providers' names are strong degrees that equip people to truly provide help to those who need it. However, **bogus** degrees complicate the picture. Not everyone who posts a doctor's diploma on the office wall has spent all those years studying and has passed all those examinations. Some organizations that call themselves colleges or universities simply sell official-looking diplomas for $50 or $75 by mail.

To find out whether a college or university is for real, a person must do some research at the library. The institution should have an address, some buildings, and a faculty consisting of people with valid degrees and credentials of their own. If you telephone and ask to speak to the dean of undergraduate studies, that person should exist. A post office box number without a street address is almost a guarantee that the degree-granting institution is a fraud. The university should also be **accredited** by a professional group (for example, the American Medical Association, for physicians).

Watch out, though. There are also bogus professional groups and bogus licenses to practice. The rule seems to be that for every true symbol of legal right to practice, there is a counterfeit that copies it.

A famous quack buster, Victor Herbert, M.D., took action to show how little knowledge some fake "institutions" require of the "graduate." He applied for diplomas from two official-sounding groups, and sent in the required fees on behalf of Charlie Herbert and Sassafras Herbert. Both are fully accredited now. If you can apply to an institution for a degree, a diploma, or a license to practice in the name of your pet poodle—and get it—then you have uncovered a fraud.

CRITICAL THINKING

1. *Why is it important for clients to be certain of their health care providers' credentials?*
2. *If a person with a bogus degree applied for membership in a real professional group, what do you think would happen? Why?*
3. *If you were suspicious of someone's credentials, how would you check on them?*

---

percent of the information needed for an accurate diagnosis. Time spent on providing an accurate history can save both illness and money later on.

Also expect a thorough **physical examination,** head to toe. The person who gives you a once-over-lightly is not starting by getting to know your physical condition

very well. Expect certain tests—for example, a blood and urine analysis or a chest x ray.

Expect to be told the diagnosis and the treatment options. By the time you leave the office, you should feel satisfied that you have been well examined, understood, and instructed. If this is not the case, you may want to find another health care provider.

dent write an advertisement for a fictional health product. They should also design a logo, label, and packaging for their products. Have students share their products with the class. **(10–20 min.; Extend, Enrich)**

Activity 3.10
Collages. Have half of the students make collages of legitimate, useful health products found in magazine and newspaper advertisements. Have the other half make collages of questionable products, such as weight loss products/gadgets, hair growth tonics, exercise gimmicks, and muscle developers. Discuss and compare the collages. **(10–20 min.; Review, Reteach)**

Activity 3.11
Product Cost Comparisons. Have students visit a drug store to compare

costs and ingredients of name brand vs. generic or store brand health products. Have students share their findings in class. **(Interdisciplinary)**

EVALUATE
▶ SECTION III

Activity 3.12
Role-Play Interviews. Have stu-

(continued on next page)

Key Points ▶ *The match between you and your health care provider should be a satisfying one. Select this person with care. Don't accept second best.*

HEALTH **S**TRATEGIES

Choosing a Health Care Provider

When choosing a health care provider:

1. Ask for recommendations.
2. Check the provider's credentials.
3. Ask these questions:

   - What are the fees for office visits? Other visits?
   - Will you accept my insurance as complete payment for the care you provide?
   - What are your office hours?
   - Can I obtain advice by phone? At what times?
   - Do you recommend that I have periodic checkups? How often?
   - Who handles the calls when you are not around?

4. Try a first appointment, and notice how it goes.
5. Expect to be listened to.
6. Expect a thorough history.
7. Expect a thorough physical examination.

SECTION III **R**EVIEW

Answer the following questions on a sheet of paper.

Learning the Vocabulary
The vocabulary terms for this section are *internship, residency, specialist, gynecologist, pediatrician, credentials, group practice, history (medical), bogus, accredited,* and *physical examination.*

1. What is the difference between a gynecologist and a pediatrician?
2. What does it mean when an institution is accredited?
3. What are credentials?

Learning the Facts
4. Counting the years of college, internship, and residency, how long does a doctor stay in school altogether?
5. What services can chiropractors offer?
6. Describe how a hospital can help you pick a physician from the staff.
7. List six questions you should ask a physician before your visit.

Making Life Choices
8. After rereading the Consumer Awareness in this section, "Genuine and Fake Credentials" (on the opposite page), how would you feel about being treated by a fraud? What can you do to help control this problem? What could your school do to help in this area? How about your community?

MINI **G**LOSSARY

bogus: fake. There are bogus doctors, bogus professional groups, bogus licenses to practice, bogus certifications, and bogus registrations.

accredited: approved; in the case of a college or university, approved by a professional group qualified to judge the program offered.

physical examination: an examination of the body to gather information about its general condition or to make a diagnosis. It normally includes observations by looking, listening, or feeling body parts and by medical test results.

Section III Review
Answers
1. A gynecologist is a specialist of the female reproductive system, while the pediatrician specializes in the care of infants and children.
2. That institution is approved by a professional group qualified to judge the programs offered.
3. written evidence of education or other qualifications of an authority
4. A general practitioner has ten years. A specialist has more.
5. They can relieve pain, but not diagnose illnesses or prescribe treatments.
6. A hospital will provide a list of staff physicians and their respective ranks and privileges.
7. Refer to the Health Strategies on this page for possible answers.
8. Answers will vary.

dents role-play an interview with a doctor or other health care provider using the guidelines in the Health Strategies feature for choosing a health care provider. **(10 min.)**

Activity 3.13

Fraudulent Ads. Have students write an ad for a fraudulent product or service using the key phrases/words described in the Straight Talk. Ask students to share their "products" with the class. **(10–15 min.)**

CLOSE
SECTION III

Activity 3.14

Being A Good Health Consumer. Remind students that there are many kinds of health care providers, and that it is their responsibility as consumers to evaluate and select the ones who are qualified to meet their health needs. There are many ways to be a good health consumer. Ask students to summarize ideas for being smart consumers of health care. **(10 min.)**

Teacher Support Notes

① **Reading about Health:** Ask students if they regularly read articles in newspapers and in magazines about health topics. Why or why not? Have they become more interested as they've taken this course? Do they tend to believe what they read?

② **Verifying Claims:** Have students find an article about a health product or issue and read that article with their parents. Have them ask their parents for their opinions of the information. How did they evaluate the article's claims? Students should make a list, similar to this one in the text, of the questions their parents used to evaluate the article. Have the students report their findings in class and compare the compiled list of questions and strategies to those in the text. Can they, as a class, develop a more comprehensive list of evaluation questions, or would this brief list be adequate?

668

---

668 UNIT 8 Global Issues

STRAIGHT
TALK ___ Health Claims and Quackery

In all the previous chapters, your responsibility for your own health took the spotlight. The chapters showed how to take charge of your lifestyle habits. They urged you to make choices that support your well-being. Once you leave the classroom, you will continue learning and applying new knowledge about health. But how can you be sure that the information you hear on television or read in magazines, books, or other sources is valid? How can you know what to believe and what to apply to your own life?

I like reading about health in magazines and in the newspaper, but should I trust that the information printed there is true?

You are wise to question your sources. Not all sources are equally valid, although all may claim that their statements are facts. Take, for example, advertisements in which actors, dressed as scientists or physicians, appear on the television screen or on the magazine page and make solemn statements about "research." When you look closely, you often find little or no evidence to back their claims. Everyone needs to develop skill in sifting the valid health information from the rubbish.

How can I tell the difference between valid and invalid claims?

When you first see a claim for a product or service, find

answers to the following five questions:

① • *Question 1.* Who is making the claim?
• *Question 2.* What are that person's qualifications for making such statements?
• *Question 3.* On what evidence is the claim based?
• *Question 4.* Where is that evidence published?
• *Question 5.* In what language style is it stated?

That sounds complicated. How would I know how to judge a person making claims?

It can be complicated and time-consuming to check a person out completely. For most purposes, however, just viewing the claim and its maker through some "skeptical spectacles" may be enough. For example, a simple rule can help you make a judgment. If the person or organization

making the claim stands to profit (make money, gain power) by selling you something you would not otherwise buy, the claim is probably false. It is as simple as that.

When assessing health claims, put on your skeptical spectacles.

Is that all there is to it? Just trust people who have nothing to gain?

No, you should also check the

(Continued on next page)

RETEACH/BONUS

Health Care in Other Countries.
Have students research health care in other countries and report findings to the class. Check with your school and town librarians to see what information is available. Perhaps a day of research in the school library is possible. **(Multicultural)**

Resource Charts. Divide students into groups and make charts on construction or butcher paper of all the community listings under specific headings or categories such as those listed in Activity 2.5. Post around the room for all students to see. **(10 min., Cooperative Learning)**

Resource Choices. After discussing various health resources in the community, create possible health situations or scenarios that require use of some of the resources. Have students make a chart, graph, or list to indicate which ones they would use. Compare choices. Have students explain or defend their choices. **(10–30 min.)**

STRAIGHT TALK (Continued)

assets of the person, for a person may not be qualified to make a health claim. Fame alone is not enough to certify a person's knowledge. A famous poet's words on physical fitness may sound beautiful, but the trainer of Olympic athletes has more accurate information. A famed heart surgeon knows hearts, but the family therapist is more qualified to give advice about love. When someone makes pronouncements, ask yourself whether the person is qualified to speak on that particular topic.

In sizing up an expert, focus on the person's assets. Education is most important. There is no substitute for the hundreds of hours of book learning that prepare a person to become an authority. Training is another asset, for book learning must be applied in real-life situations. Skill is a third. It normally develops as the result of practice and time—experience. Fourth comes reputation. A person earns that by developing the first three assets. Finally, consider the person's credentials—such as

membership in professional societies and license to practice in the profession.

Where can I find information I can trust? ①

One believable source of scientific information is the scientific journal. When researchers perform experiments that reveal new information, reports of the studies are first published in journals. These provide strong evidence, especially when the writer describes many studies on the same topic, all pointing to the same conclusions. Most people don't read the scientific journals, but they should know that they are there. Scientific findings, accurately reported, are the ultimate authority on what is true.

Can't I judge health information more easily?

Yes, but if you take shortcuts, you do so at your own risk. One way is to try to pick up clues from the language used by quacks. Many buzzwords and phrases can alert you to false or misleading information. Among them are the following:

- *Health, herbal, natural.* These terms have no legal meaning. Those who use them may try to imply, falsely, that a product they are selling has unusual powers to promote health.
- *Scientific breakthrough, medical miracle.* Seldom do popular reports prove true when they make statements that oppose accepted facts—a new cure for cancer, a way to lose weight without cutting calories, a tiny pill that will give you enormous powers. Such claims almost *never* prove true.
- *Doctors agree, authorities agree.* When the identity of the doctors is not stated, or when no evidence is provided, these statements are meaningless. They may mean only that the advertiser persuaded three "doctor" friends to agree.

This brings us back to the first guideline offered: be suspicious of claims made by people who have something to gain from your believing their claims.

Teacher Support Notes

① **Newspapers and Magazines:** Students will probably ask whether or not the newspapers and magazines they read are trustworthy sources of health information. Tell them that even the most well-known national publications should not be trusted blindly. They are in the business of selling a product and the newest, latest findings, whether tested or not help sell newspapers and magazines. Point out that in most cases these publications are not printing fictitious information—their reports are true; it's just that there may be conflicting reports or the reports may not yet be substantiated by the scientific community.

✉ **Where to Write**

American Medical Association
535 Dearborn Street
Chicago, IL 60610

Vocabulary

1. **a.** bogus **b.** group practice **c.** medical insurance **d.** Medicaid **e.** health care system
2. **a.** residency **b.** health maintenance organization (HMO) **c.** specialist
   d. Malpractice insurance
3. **a.** disability insurance **b.** internship **c.** pediatrician **d.** gynecologist

Recall

Section I

1. prevents illness, gives routine exams
2. The defenseless plan is most risky because you have no insurance, no health care provider, and no health care plan.

Section II

3. people on welfare
4. the client
5. abuse of malpractice insurance as greedy people unjustly sue physicians to win huge rewards
6. — Call your regular health care provider—this allows that person's office to know who you are, what the problem is, and where you are.
   — Have only one person go with you—this cuts down on overcrowding and high noise level in the emergency room.
   — Take some identification and your insurance card—this cuts down on time deciding on payment methods.

CHAPTER REVIEW

LEARNING THE VOCABULARY

health care system	disability insurance	specialist
premiums	Medicare	gynecologist
health maintenance organization (HMO)	Medicaid	pediatrician
prepayment plan	malpractice insurance	credentials
fee-for-service system	second opinion	group practice
hospitalization insurance	tonsillectomy	history (medical)
surgical insurance	hysterectomy	bogus
medical insurance	rehabilitation	accredited
major medical insurance	internship	physical examination
	residency	

Answer the following questions on a separate sheet of paper.

1. **Matching**—*Match each of the following phrases with the appropriate term:*
   a. fake
   b. an organization of physicians who practice medicine together
   c. insurance to pay physicians' fees, lab fees, and fees for prescription medications
   d. hospitalization and surgical insurance available for people who qualify as needy
   e. the total of all health care providers and medical treatment facilities that work together to provide medical care to the population
2. a. A _____ is a length of time spent in a medical facility as part of the M.D.'s training after an internship.
   b. The _____ is a system of paying for health care in which the clients pay a fixed fee every month regardless of how many services they receive.
   c. A physician with training in a specialty area beyond the medical degree requirements is called a _____.
   d. _____ protects providers of health care against lawsuits by people claiming to have been harmed by their treatments.
3. **Word Scramble**—*Use the clues from the phrases below to help you unscramble the terms:*
   a. **aiibidlsty aeiucnnrs** _____ _____ insurance to replace lost income if a person should be unable to work due to a long illness
   b. **eiihnnpstr** _____ a length of time spent in training in a medical facility as part of the curriculum of a health care provider
   c. **eitcpairdnai** _____ a medical specialist concerned with the care of infants and children
   d. **eioocgglnsty** _____ a medical specialist in the care of the female reproductive system

RECALLING IMPORTANT FACTS AND IDEAS

1. Describe what a health care provider does beyond treatment.
2. Which of the three approaches to health care is the most risky and why?
3. What people can receive Medicaid insurance?
4. Who must pay costs not covered by insurance?
5. What drives our insurance premiums up higher than they should be?
6. List five hints for emergency room visits and explain the value of each one.
7. What should you do before an operation, especially a tonsillectomy or hysterectomy, and why?
8. If you have questions about your hospital bill, what should you do?

— Tell the person at the admissions desk if you have been there before—this will cut down on paper work.
— Know your own medical history and what medicines you are taking—this will avoid adverse reactions to certain medications being administered.
7. Get a second opinion because these surgeries are often overperformed.
8. Ask for an itemized list of services you received and send it to your insurance company.
Section III
9. $50–$75 by mail
10. call the local American Medical Association office or county medical society for a list of physicians in the area
11. blood and urine analysis, chest X-ray
12. The medical history provides about 70 percent of the information needed for an accurate diagnosis.

9. How much would it cost to purchase an official-looking physician's diploma?
10. What is the first step in selecting a health care provider?
11. Describe what tests you should expect during a physical examination.
12. Why is it important to give the physician your medical history?

CRITICAL THINKING

1. After taking the Life Choice Inventory (on page 655), how do you feel about your results? Can you spot quackery? What can you do to improve your results? What can you teach others about the health care system?
2. Marie has been looking for medical insurance. She has discovered that most insurance companies require that you have a physical examination before they sell you a policy. She is a smoker, uses alcohol, and is obese. She cannot find an insurance company that will cover her. Most premiums are too expensive for her. What can Marie do? Why is it necessary for her to have insurance? What will happen to her family if she gets sick without insurance? What can her family do? What would you do? Why would you take that action if you were in this situation?

ACTIVITIES

1. Divide into groups and interview local insurance agents. Compare prices and coverage from two companies on:
   a. Medical insurance
   b. Hospitalization insurance
   c. Surgical insurance
   d. Major medical insurance
   e. Disability insurance
   Report your findings to the other groups.
2. Write a report on your family's hospital and surgical insurance policies, or, if you have no policies, on a friend's family's policies. Include costs and coverages. Include how long you or your friend will be covered on your parents' policies and when you need your own policies.
3. Make a video about the different kinds of disability insurance policies you can get and the benefits of long-term coverage as opposed to term coverage. How do insurance companies encourage you to purchase a policy? What are some of the advertising quirks they use? Put these in your video.
4. Have a class debate on the health and medical care system of the United States vs. Canada's health care system. What are some positive and negative aspects of each? Combine the good qualities of both and make up your own health care system.
5. Describe a physician you know. Would you choose to go to this physician? What are your personal impressions of this doctor? What do you like and dislike about him or her?
6. Look in several magazines for articles on quackery. Cut them out and make a collage on quackery for your class. What do these articles have in common?
7. Write or call the American College of Physicians and the American College of Surgeons. Have them send you a list of all the physicians in your area who are members of their associations. Report your findings in your school newspaper.

MAKING DECISIONS ABOUT HEALTH

1. You have had a medical emergency and had to spend a few days in the hospital. On admitting you, the desk clerk asks for your insurance and you present your card. Now you are checking out, and you have to stop by the cashier's office. The cashier tells you that your insurance does not cover the expenses you have just incurred. You are expected to pay $1,000 in fees yourself within the next 90 days. Describe how you would handle this situation based on this chapter.

Appendix A

Careers in Health

Do you think you might be interested in a health-related career? If so, you can use this glossary to discover some possible careers and to find out what schooling is necessary to prepare for them.

audiologist: a specialist in hearing disorders. Credentials usually include college, completion of a master's degree, and a license from the state.

cardiologist: a physician who specializes in diagnosing and treating heart conditions. See *medical doctor (M.D.)* for training requirements.

certified surgical technologist: a member of a surgical team who prepares clients and equipment for surgery and who may assist during surgery. Certification follows completion of an accredited program and passing an examination.

counselor: a term for a helping person. A person who is qualified to be a counselor has a graduate degree in counseling (M.S. or Ph.D.) from an accredited university, accompanied by training in alcohol and other addictions, families, workplaces, adolescents, and other counseling specialty areas. Many states require licensing for counselors to practice.

dentist (D.D.S. or D.M.D.): a person trained and licensed to deal with care of the teeth and associated structures of the mouth. Dentists can prescribe medication and perform oral surgery. Training includes 2 to 4 years of college, completion of the Dental Admission Test, and four years of dental school.

dermatologist: a physician who is specially trained to diagnose and treat diseases of the skin. See *medical doctor (M.D.)* for training requirements.

dietitian: a person trained in diet planning. A registered dietitian (R.D.) is a dietitian who has graduated from a state-approved program of dietetics, has passed the professional American Dietetic Association registration examination, and has served in an internship program to practice the necessary skills. Some states require licensing for dietitians; others do not.

emergency medical technician (E.M.T.): a medical team member specially trained to participate in rescue operations or assist a physician, permitted to make medical decisions in emergencies but charged with consulting a physician whenever possible. Training includes CPR certification, first aid certification, plus a one or two-year college program, depending on the type of certification sought.

exercise physiologist: a person with a university degree in exercise physiology—the study of the changes that occur in the body in response to exercise.

home health aide: a helper who provides basic household help and hygiene care to people who cannot perform the tasks for themselves—for example, those who are ill, recovering from surgery, or in need of supervision.

medical doctor (M.D.): a physician; a person trained to provide medical care and licensed by the state to practice. Training includes 4 years of college, 3 years of medical school, a two-year internship and a one-year residency. Physicians who want to become specialists such as pediatricians and neurologists must receive further training.

medical technologist (M.T.): a person with three years of college training and a year of additional training, and who has passed an examination administered by the Board of Registry of Medical Technologists. One of the M.T.'s career choices is to be a blood bank technologist, who withdraws and oversees handling of human blood for medical uses.

microbiologist: a person with a university degree in microbiology—the study of microorganisms. Many microbiologists work as specialists in sanitation, food safety, and epidemiology (the study of diseases and how they spread), and as research scientists in industry and agriculture.

nurse: a general term for any person who provides health care. A licensed practical nurse (L.P.N.) or licensed vocational nurse (L.V.N.) has graduated from a technical or vocational nursing program that lasts about one year and has passed the professional nursing state board exam. The registered nurse (R.N.) is a nurse who receives either a 2-year Associate of Science (A.S.) degree in nursing, a 4-year Bachelor of Science (B.S.) degree in nursing, or a 3-year nursing degree from a hospital-based nursing school, depending on the program available and the state in which the nurse is training. The R.N. must then pass the professional nursing state board exam. Training programs for nurses include both classroom hours and patient-care hours in hospital settings.

nurse midwife: a registered nurse (R.N.) who has had additional training in obstetrics and gynecology and is licensed as a certified nurse midwife (C.N.M.) after completing a program accredited by the American College of Nurse Midwives and passing the association's board examinations. The nurse midwife is trained to perform episiotomies, deliver breech babies, and handle most routine complications. Most are also trained to deliver normal prenatal and postnatal care and well-woman care.

nurse practitioner (N.P.): a registered nurse (R.N.) who has received additional medical training to assess the physical and psychosocial status of individuals and families. When working in cooperation with a physician, a nurse practitioner can manage some common illnesses. Some are registered as nurse practitioners (R.N.P.)'s.

obstetrician: a physician who specializes in providing medical care to pregnant women and oversees childbirth. See *medical doctor (M.D.)* for training requirements.

occupational therapist (O.T.): a person who assists people with handicaps to learn skills needed to function independently and find employment. Training includes four years of college and six months of specialized study.

optometrist (O.D.): a person specifically trained through four years of graduate study beyond college and licensed to examine the eyes in order to determine the presence of vision problems and to prescribe and adapt lenses to preserve or restore maximum efficiency of vision. (In contrast, an optician can fit glasses and lenses but may not examine, test, or prescribe. The optician's training is usually on-the-job training.)

orthodontist: a dentist with further training to straighten teeth and correct jaw alignment problems.

osteopath (D.O.): a health care provider who takes the same course of training as a physician, but in a school of osteopathy, which specializes in disorders of the musculoskeletal system.

paramedic: a health care professional trained to administer first aid in advanced life support to critically ill and injured people and to use medical procedures as directed by supervising physicians.

pathologist: a physician who diagnoses the changes caused by disease in tissues removed during operations and postmortem examinations.

periodontist: a dentist with further training to provide care for the gums and to deal with gum diseases.

physical therapist (P.T.): a person who assists people in regaining strength, mobility, or sensation after injury or accident. Training includes four years of college and further study.

physician: see *medical doctor (M.D.)* and *osteopath (D.O.).*

physician's assistant (P.A.): a person with medical training, authorized to perform medical services under the supervision of a physician. Training includes two to four years of college and two years of specialized training. In some states, physician supervision can be by telephone. In some, P.A.s can prescribe certain drugs.

psychiatrist: a physician (M.D.) who, after completing medical school, received additional special training to treat emotional problems and is licensed to prescribe drugs.

psychoanalyst: a psychiatrist who specializes in analysis (seeking the root psychological causes of emotional problems).

psychologist: a person with a graduate degree (M.S. or Ph.D.) in psychology from a university. A desirable credential for a psychologist is certification by the American Psychology Association (APA). Many states require licensing for psychologists to practice.

social worker: a person with a graduate degree in social work (M.S.W.), a respected degree that includes training in counseling.

speech-language pathologist: a person who assists people with speech and language problems. Most must have completed college, obtained a master's degree, and received a state license to practice.

sports medicine practitioner: a physician who diagnoses and treats injuries and conditions of amateur and professional athletes. Many are specialists trained in other, related fields.

surgeon: a physician who diagnoses and treats conditions by performing operations.

Obviously the list above includes just a few of the many occupations in health care and the information provided for the occupations listed is limited. Unfortunately, space does not permit thorough descriptions of the hundreds of occupations that could be included here. The purpose of this list, therefore, is to give you a sampling of the types of occupations that you might want to explore further. A few additional occupations that you might want to read about are ambulance driver, anesthesiologist, dental assistant, hospital administrator, medical laboratory technician, optician, orderly, pharmacist, radiologic technologist, and school nurse.

The duties, responsibilities, educational requirements, and working conditions for people in the health care industry are extremely varied. If you think you might enjoy a career in this industry, the first step would be to determine your personal interests and aptitudes so as to narrow the range of choices to those that most closely fit your needs and abilities. As was mentioned in Chapter 3 of the text, two good ways of doing this are to volunteer for different jobs and to do career assessments such as the "Self-Directed Search," "Strong Campbell Interest Inventory," and the "Armed Services Vocational Aptitude Battery." Your school guidance counselor can give you one of these assessments or one of many others that will help you determine your strongest interests and aptitudes, and will enable you to identify the careers that are most appropriate for you.

You can then go to your school or local library to find out more about the health careers that interest you the most. Perhaps the best reference to begin with is the *Occupational Outlook Handbook*, which is updated every two years by the Department of Labor and contains the most up-to-date and accurate occupational information available. Much of the career information you will find in other sources is adapted from this reference book. In your library you will probably also find books on individual health related occupations and computer programs with a wealth of information.

After you have done some reading and identified two or three occupations that appeal to you, try to find a part-time or volunteer job as closely related to the occupation you are interested in as possible. You should realize that because the occupation you are interested in may require several years of education and training, it is very likely that you will not be able to work at that particular job right away. Instead, you will need to work as a support person or helper. Still, this will give you an opportunity to observe firsthand the duties of and the working conditions of the occupation, as well as give you an opportunity to associate with the people who work in that career field. These experiences will help you decide whether or not you might enjoy that particular area of health care.

Nutrition Standards

Many countries have developed nutrient standards. Those of the United States (the Recommended Dietary Allowances, or RDA) are presented here. The main RDA table is presented in Figure B–1. The energy RDA are presented in Figure B–2. The estimated safe and adequate daily dietary intakes of selected vitamins and minerals appear in Figure B–3. Figure B–4 presents the estimated minimum requirements of electrolytes. Figure B–5 offers standards for triceps fatfold measures.

Figure B-1

Recommended Dietary Allowances (RDA), 1989[a]

Age (Years)	Weight (Kilograms)	Weight (Pounds)	Height (Centimeters)	Height (Inches)	Protein (g)	Vitamin A (µg RE)	Vitamin D (µg)	Vitamin E (mg α-TE)	Vitamin K (µg)	Vitamin C (mg)	Thiamin (mg)	Riboflavin (mg)	Niacin (mg NE)	Vitamin B_6 (mg)	Folate (µg)	Vitamin B_{12} (µg)	Calcium (mg)	Phosphorus (mg)	Magnesium (mg)	Iron (mg)	Zinc (mg)	Iodine (µg)	Selenium (µg)
Males																							
11–14	45	99	157	62	45	1,000	10	10	45	50	1.3	1.5	17	1.7	150	2.0	1,200	1,200	270	12	15	150	40
15–18	66	145	176	69	59	1,000	10	10	65	60	1.5	1.8	20	2.0	200	2.0	1,200	1,200	400	12	15	150	50
19–24	72	160	177	70	58	1,000	10	10	70	60	1.5	1.7	19	2.0	200	2.0	1,200	1,200	350	10	15	150	70
25–50	79	174	176	70	63	1,000	5	10	80	60	1.5	1.7	19	2.0	200	2.0	800	800	350	10	15	150	70
51+	77	170	173	68	63	1,000	5	10	80	60	1.2	1.4	15	2.0	200	2.0	800	800	350	10	15	150	70
Females																							
11–14	46	101	157	62	46	800	10	8	45	50	1.1	1.3	15	1.4	150	2.0	1,200	1,200	280	15	12	150	45
15–18	55	120	163	64	44	800	10	8	55	60	1.1	1.3	15	1.5	180	2.0	1,200	1,200	300	15	12	150	50
19–24	58	128	164	65	46	800	10	8	60	60	1.1	1.3	15	1.6	180	2.0	1,200	1,200	280	15	12	150	55
25–50	63	138	163	64	50	800	5	8	65	60	1.1	1.3	15	1.6	180	2.0	800	800	280	15	12	150	55
51+	65	143	160	63	50	800	5	8	65	60	1.0	1.2	13	1.6	180	2.0	800	800	280	10	12	150	55
Pregnant					60	800	10	10	65	70	1.5	1.6	17	2.2	400	2.2	1,200	1,200	300	30	15	175	65
Lactating																							
1st 6 months					65	1,300	10	12	65	95	1.6	1.8	20	2.1	280	2.6	1,200	1,200	355	15	19	200	75
2nd 6 months					62	1,200	10	11	65	90	1.6	1.7	20	2.1	260	2.6	1,200	1,200	340	15	16	200	75

[a]The allowances are intended to provide for individual variations among most normal, healthy people in the United States under usual environmental stresses. They were designed for the maintenance of good nutrition. Diets should be based on a variety of common foods in order to provide other nutrients for which human requirements have been less well defined.

Source: Adapted with permission from *Recommended Dietary Allowances*, 10th ed., © 1989 by the National Academy of Sciences. Published by the National Academy Press, Washington, D.C.

FIGURE B-2
Median Heights and Weights and Recommended Energy Intakes (United States)

Age	Weight		Height		Average Energy Allowance			
(Years)	(Kg)	(Lb)	(Cm)	(Inches)	REE[a] (Cal/Day)	Multiples of REE[b]	Cal/Kg	Cal/Day[c]
Males								
11–14	45	99	157	62	1,440	1.70	55	2,500
15–18	66	145	176	69	1,760	1.67	45	3,000
19–24	72	160	177	70	1,780	1.67	40	2,900
25–50	79	174	176	70	1,800	1.60	37	2,900
51+	77	170	173	68	1,530	1.50	30	2,300
Females								
11–14	46	101	157	62	1,310	1.67	47	2,200
15–18	55	120	163	64	1,370	1.60	40	2,200
19–24	58	128	164	65	1,350	1.60	38	2,200
25–50	63	138	163	64	1,380	1.55	36	2,200
51+	65	143	160	63	1,280	1.50	30	1,900
Pregnant (2nd and 3rd trimesters)								+300
Lactating								+500

[a]REE (resting energy expenditure) represents the energy expended by a person at rest under normal conditions.
[b]Recommended energy allowances assume light to moderate activity and were calculated by multiplying the REE by an activity factor.
[c]Average energy allowances have been rounded.
Source: Adapted with permission from *Recommended Dietary Allowances,* 10th ed., © 1989 by the National Academy of Sciences. Published by the National Academy Press, Washington, D.C.

FIGURE B-3

Estimated Safe and Adequate Daily Dietary Intakes of Selected Vitamins and Minerals[a]

	Vitamins	
Age (Years)	Biotin (μg)	Pantothenic Acid (mg)
Children and Teens		
7–10	30	4–5
11+	30–100	4–7
Adults	30–100	4–7

	Trace Elements[b]				
Age (Years)	Chromium (μg)	Molybdenum (μg)	Copper (mg)	Manganese (mg)	Fluoride (mg)
Children and Teens					
7–10	50–200	50–150	1.0–2.0	2.0–3.0	1.5–2.5
11+	50–200	75–250	1.5–2.5	2.0–5.0	1.5–2.5
Adults	50–200	75–250	1.5–3.0	2.0–5.0	1.5–4.0

[a]Because there is less information on which to base allowances, these figures are not given in the main table of the RDA but are provided here in the form of ranges of recommended intakes.

[b]Because the toxic levels for many trace elements may be only several times usual intakes, the upper levels for the trace elements given in this table should not be habitually exceeded.

Source: Adapted with permission from *Recommended Dietary Allowances,* 10th ed., © 1989 by the National Academy of Sciences. Published by the National Academy Press, Washington, D.C.

FIGURE B-4

Estimated Sodium, Chloride, and Potassium Minimum Requirements of Healthy Persons

Age (Years)	Sodium (mg)[a]	Chloride (mg)	Potassium (mg)[b]
Adolescents	500	750	2,000
Adults	500	750	2,000

[a]Sodium requirements are based on estimates of needs for growth and for replacement of obligatory losses. They cover a wide variation of physical activity patterns and climatic exposure but do not provide for large, prolonged losses from the skin through sweat.

[b]Dietary potassium may aid in the prevention and treatment of hypertension. Including in the diet many servings of fruits and vegetables a day can raise potassium intakes to about 3,500 milligrams per day.

Source: Adapted with permission from *Recommended Dietary Allowances,* 10th ed., © 1989 by the National Academy of Sciences. Published by the National Academy Press, Washington, D.C.

FIGURE B-5
Triceps Fatfold Standards (Millimeters) for Teenaged Males and Females (Percentiles)

Age	Male					Female				
	5th	25th	50th	75th	95th	5th	25th	50th	75th	95th
12–12.9	6	8	11	14	28	8	11	14	18	27
13–13.9	5	7	10	14	26	8	12	15	21	30
14–14.9	4	7	9	14	24	9	13	16	21	28
15–15.9	4	6	8	11	24	8	12	17	21	32
16–16.9	4	6	8	12	22	10	15	18	22	31
17–17.9	5	6	8	12	19	10	13	19	24	37
18–18.9	4	6	9	13	24	10	15	18	22	30

Source: Adapted from A. R. Frisancho, New norms of upper limb fat and muscle areas for assessment of nutritional status, *American Journal of Clinical Nutrition* 34 (1981): 2540–2545. © American Society of Clinical Nutrition.

Figure B–5 presents standards for fatfold measures taken at the back of the arm (over the triceps muscle). Triceps fatfold measurements should be taken on the person's right arm while the person is standing (see Figure 9–1 on page 210). Here's how to take the measurement:

1. Place your fingers on the back of the person's upper arm, midway between the shoulder and the elbow.
2. Grasp, between your thumb and your forefinger, a fold of skin and fat that lies just under the skin. To be sure that you are holding only skin and fat—no muscle— have the person contract and relax the triceps muscle.
3. Place the "pinchers" of the fatfold calipers just above where your finger and thumb are holding the fatfold (they don't hurt). Let the pressure of the caliper alone close the pinchers and establish the measurement; read the measurement and remove the caliper. Repeat this entire procedure three times and average the two closest measures to establish the final value.
4. Compare the final value with the percentile values listed for a person of the same age and gender in Figure B–5. A value that falls at the 75th percentile means that the person's fatfold is thicker than the triceps fatfolds of 75 percent of the rest of the population. A fatfold measure that falls at the 50th percentile is in the middle—half of the population have thicker fatfolds and half have thinner fatfolds.

A fatfold value close to the middle of the range of percentiles is considered to reflect an appropriate amount of body fat. Values much above the 75th percentile or below the 25th percentile may also be appropriate but a person with an extra-high or extra-low value would probably be wise to consult a physician for further evaluation.

Glossary

A

abdominals the long, flat "stomach" muscles that run from the chest to the pelvis and hold the abdominal contents; called the *rectus abdominus* (REK-tus ab-DOM-ih-nus).

abortion a procedure to end a pregnancy before the fetus can live outside the uterus.

abstinence refraining completely from a behavior. Refraining from sexual relations with other people is also called *celibacy* (SELL-ih-ba-see).

abuse see *active abuse, passive abuse*.

accredited approved; in the case of a college or university, approved by a professional group qualified to judge the program offered.

acetaminophen (ah-SEET-ah-MIN-o-fen) a drug that relieves fever, pain, and inflammation.

acid rain rain that carries acid air pollutants, which harms the plants and damages the soil on which it falls.

acne a continuing condition of inflamed skin ducts and glands, with a buildup of oils under the skin forming pimples.

acquaintance rape sexual assault by a known person. If such a rape takes place on a date, it is called *date rape*.

acquired immune deficiency syndrome (AIDS) a fatal, transmissible viral disease of the immune system that creates a severe immune deficiency, and that leaves people defenseless against infections and cancer.

acromegaly (ack-ro-MEG-a-lee) a disease caused by above-normal levels of human growth hormone, characterized in adults by thickening of the bones, hands, feet, cheeks, and jaw; thickening of the soft tissue of the eyelids, lips, tongue, and nose; and thickening and rumpling of the skin on the forehead and soles of the feet. Internally, the heart, liver, and other organs become abnormal. A child with the condition is said to have *gigantism*, because the bones grow abnormally long.

active abuse abuse involving one person's aggression against another, such as hitting or sexually abusing the victim.

active ingredients ingredients in a medicine that produce physical effects on the body.

active solar the use of photovoltaic panels to generate electricity from sunlight.

acute stress a temporary bout of stress that calls forth alertness or alarm to prompt the person to deal with an event.

adapt change or adjust to accommodate new conditions.

addiction dependence on a substance, habit, or behavior; a physical or psychological craving for higher and higher doses of a drug that leads to bodily harm, social maladjustment, or economic hardship. See also *physical addiction; psychological addiction*.

adolescence the period of growth from the beginning of puberty to full maturity. Timing of adolescence varies from person to person.

adrenal (add-REE-nal) **glands** a pair of glands located above each kidney that make many hormones for the body.

aerobic (air-ROE-bic) refers to energy-producing processes that use oxygen (*aero* means *air*).

afterbirth the placenta and membranes expelled after the birth of the child.

aggressive possessing the characteristic of being insulting to others or otherwise invading their territory; an inappropriate expression of feelings.

AIDS see *acquired immune deficiency syndrome*.

air pockets sacs at the ends of airways in the lungs; the lungs contain thousands of these, known as *alveoli* (al-VEE-oh-lie).

air pollution contamination of the air with gases or particles not normally found there.

airbags inflatable pillows, designed to inflate upon impact, stored in the center of the steering wheel of a car or in the dashboard.

alarm the first phase of the stress response, in which the person faces a challenge and starts paying attention to it.

alcohol a class of chemical compounds. The alcohol of alcoholic beverages, *ethanol* or *ethyl alcohol*, is one member of this class.

alcoholism the disease characterized by dependence on alcohol, which harms health, family relations, and social and work functioning.

alienation withdrawing from others because of differences that cannot be resolved.

aloe a tropical plant with widely claimed, but mostly unproved, medical value.

alveoli (al-VEE-oh-lie) the air sacs at the ends of the airways in the lungs (singular, *alveolus*, al-VEE-oh-lus).

Alzheimer's disease a brain disease of some older people that brings mental confusion; inability to function; and in the final stage, death.

amino acids simple forms of protein normally used to build tissues or, under some conditions, burned for energy. See also *essential amino acids*.

amnesia loss of memory of a period of time.

amniocentesis (am-nee-oh-cen-TEE-sis) a test of fetal cells drawn by needle through the woman's abdomen.

amniotic (am-nee-OTT-ic) **sac** the "bag of waters" in the uterus, in which the fetus floats.

amotivational syndrome loss of ambition and drive; a characteristic of long-term users of marijuana.

amphetamines powerful, addictive central nervous system stimulant drugs. They suppress appetite, but they can also hook the taker. Thus they are reserved for use in cases where overfatness threatens health. Also called *speed*.

anaerobic (AN-air-ROE-bic) refers to energy-producing processes that do not use oxygen (*an* means *without*).

anemia reduced number or size of the red blood cells; a symptom of any of a number of different diseases, including several nutrient deficiencies.

anesthetics (an-us-THET-icks) drugs that kill pain, with or without producing loss of consciousness.

aneurysm (AN-your-ism) the ballooning out of an artery wall at a point where it has grown weak.

angina (an-JYE-nuh or ANN-juh-nuh) pain in the heart region caused by lack of oxygen.

anorexia (an-or-EX-ee-uh) **nervosa** an eating disorder of self-starvation to the extreme.

antagonist (an-TAG-uh-nist) a drug that opposes the action of another drug.

antibiotics drugs used to fight bacterial infection.

antibodies large protein molecules produced by the body to fight infective or foreign tissue.

antigens foreign substances in the body, such as viruses or bacteria, that stimulate the immune system to produce antibodies.

antihistamines drugs that counteract inflammation caused by histamine, one of the chemicals involved in allergic reactions.

antiseptics agents that prevent the growth of microorganisms on body surfaces and on wounds.

anus a circular muscle that holds the rectum closed; it opens to allow elimination.

anxiety an emotional state of high energy; the stress response is the body's reaction to it.

anxiety attack a sudden, unexpected episode of severe anxiety with symptoms such as rapid heartbeat, sweating, dizziness, and nausea.

aorta (ay-OR-ta) the largest artery in the body; it conducts freshly oxygenated blood from the heart to the tissues.

aphrodisiac (af-roh-DIZ-ee-ack) a substance reputed to excite sexual desire. Actually, no known substance does this, but many claim to do so.

appendix a small sac that opens into the large intestine.

appetite the psychological desire to eat that normally accompanies hunger.

arousal heightened activity of the brain with excitement or anxiety.

arteries blood vessels that carry blood from the heart to the tissues.

artificial heart a pump designed to fit into the human chest cavity and perform the heart's function of pumping blood around the body.

asexual having no sexual inclinations.

aspirin a drug that relieves fever, pain, and inflammation.

assault one person's attack on another, with intent to do harm.

assertive possessing the characteristic of appropriately expressing feelings, wants, and needs. Assertiveness is the key to obtaining cooperation.

asthma difficulty breathing, with wheezing sounds from the chest caused by air rushing through narrowed air passages.

atherosclerosis (ATH-uh-roh-scler-OH-sis) the most common form of CVD; a disease characterized by plaques along the inner walls of the arteries.

athlete's foot a fungal infection of the feet, usually transmitted through floors. Wearing rubber shower shoes will prevent its transmission.

atria (singular, *atrium*) the two upper chambers of the heart, the receiving areas that pool incoming blood. The *right atrium* receives used blood from the superior and inferior vena cava. The *left atrium* receives freshly oxygenated blood from the lungs.

B

B cells lymphocytes that make antibodies.

back muscles the large muscles of the middle and lower back; called the *latissimus dorsi* (lat-ISS-ih-mus DOOR-sy).

bacteria (singular, *bacterium*) microscopic, single-celled organisms of varying shapes and sizes, some capable of causing disease.

balanced meal a meal with foods to provide the right amounts of carbohydrate, fat, and protein.

barbiturates depressant drugs that slow the activity of the central nervous system.

barrier methods contraceptive methods that physically or chemically obstruct the travel of sperm toward the ovum.

basal energy the sum total of energy needed to support all the chemical activities of the cells and to sustain life, exclusive of voluntary activities; the largest component of a person's daily energy expenditure.

belladonna any part of the nightshade plant; a deadly poison.

benign (be-NINE) noncancerous; not harmful; a description of a tumor that is not able to spread from one area to another.

beta-carotene an orange pigment in plants that can be changed to vitamin A in the body.

biceps (BY-seps) the muscles of the fronts of the upper arms.

binges (BIN-jez) episodes of vast overeating.

biodegradable able to decompose; able to be converted by living organisms into harmless waste products that can be used over again to build or grow new things.

biofeedback a clinical technique used to help a person learn to relax by reflecting back muscle tension, heart rate, brain wave activity, or other body activities.

birth control any method of preventing conception or birth.

birth control pills see *oral contraceptives*.

birth defects physical abnormalities present from birth.

bisexual being sexually oriented to members of both sexes.

blackhead an open acne pimple with dark skin pigments (not dirt) in it.

blackouts episodes of temporary amnesia regarding previous events. Blackouts are likely to occur during periods of drinking in the life of a person with alcoholism.

bladder a sac; in the urinary system, the sac-like organ that collects and holds urine until it is released from the body.

blood the thick, red fluid that flows through the body's blood vessels and transports gases, nutrients, wastes, and other important substances around the body. Blood also plays roles in body temperature regulation.

body image the way a person thinks his or her body looks, which may or may not be the way it actually does look.

body systems groups of related organs that work together to perform major body functions.

bogus fake.

bone marrow the soft gelatin-like material inside bones; the marrow in some bones produces red blood cells; the marrow in other bones produces white blood cells.

botulin toxin a potent poison produced by bacteria in sealed cans, plastic packs, or jars of food causing the often fatal condition **botulism** when eaten.

botulism an often fatal condition of food poisoning caused by the botulin toxin.

brain the part of the nervous system that receives information from the nerves and issues instructions to the body.

brain death irreversible, total loss of higher brain functions, reflected in a flat line brainwave pattern, as opposed to the wavy pattern made by an active brain.

brain stem the section of the brain that connects the spinal cord to the cerebellum.

brand names the names companies give to drugs; the names by which they are sold.

breastbone the narrow, flat bone located in the middle of the chest; also called the *sternum*.

breathalyzer test a test of the alcohol level in a person's breath, which reflects the blood level of alcohol.

breech birth a birth in which the infant is born in a position other than the normal head-first position.

bronchi (BRONK-eye) see *bronchus*.

bronchiole (BRONK-ee-ole) a small airway branching from a bronchus.

bronchitis (bron-KITE-us) a respiratory disorder with irritation of the bronchi; thickened mucus; and deep, harsh coughing.

bronchus (BRONK-us) a large airway branching from the windpipe toward the lung (plural, *bronchi*, BRONK-eye).

bubonic plague a bacterial infection causing swollen lymph glands and pneumonia, frequently fatal. Also called *black plague* or *black death*, it caused the near extinction of the human race in the Middle Ages and is still common in India. It is transmitted to people by bites from fleas, which in turn live on rats.

bulimia (byoo-LEEM-ee-uh) a disorder of repeated binge eating, sometimes followed by vomiting (also spelled *bulemia*).

buttocks muscles the rear and side muscles of the buttocks; the *gluteus* (GLOO-tee-us) *maximus* and the *gluteus medius*.

C

caffeine a mild stimulant of the central nervous system (brain and spinal cord) found in common foods, beverages, and medicines.

calf muscles the large muscles in the back of the calf; known as the *gastrocnemius* (gas-tro-K'NEE-mee-us) muscles.

calisthenics exercise routines for strength conditioning that use the parts of the body as weights.

calories units used to measure energy. Calories indicate how much energy in a food can be used by the body or stored in body fat.

cancer a disease in which abnormal cells multiply out of control, spread into surrounding tissues and other body parts, and disrupt normal functioning of one or more organs.

candidiasis (can-did-EYE-a-sis) an infection caused by a yeast that multiplies out of control in the vagina; also called *yeast infection moniliasis*.

capillaries the smallest blood vessels, which connect the smallest arteries with the smallest veins.

carbohydrate a class of nutrients made of sugars, that include sugar, starch, and fiber. All but fiber provide energy. Often referred to in the plural, *carbohydrates*.

carbon monoxide a gas formed (among other things) during the burning of tobacco.

carcinogens (car-SIN-oh-gens) cancer-causing agents.

carcinomas (car-sin-OH-mahs) cancers that arise in the skin, body chamber linings, or glands.

cardiovascular disease (CVD) a general term for all diseases of the heart and blood vessels.

cardiovascular endurance a component of fitness; the ability of the heart and lungs to sustain effort over a long time.

cardiovascular system the system of structures that circulate blood and lymph throughout the body, also called the *circulatory system*.

carotid (ca-ROT-id) **pulse** the pulse in either of the carotid arteries, the main arteries next to the airway (and "Adam's apple") in the front of the neck.

carpals (CAR-pals) the bones of the wrist.

cartilage connective tissue that resembles bone but is not hardened by minerals; in joints, cartilage reduces friction and cushions the ends of bones.

cavity a hole in a tooth caused by decay. (Tooth decay is also called dental *caries*.)

celibacy see *abstinence*.

cells the smallest units in which independent life can exist. All living things are single cells or organisms made of cells.

centenarians people who have reached the age of 100 years or older.

cerebellum (sare-eh-BELL-um) the section of the brain that coordinates muscle movements.

cerebral cortex the layer of gray matter that covers the cerebrum; the outermost layer of the brain.

cerebral thrombosis the closing off of a vessel that feeds the brain by a stationary clot, or *thrombus*.

cerebrum (seh-REE-brum) the two hemispheres of the upper brain.

cervical cap a rubber cap that fits over the cervix, used with spermicide to prevent conception.

cervix (SER-viks) the neck of the uterus, where it joins the vagina.

cesarean (si-ZAIR-ee-un) **section** surgical childbirth, in which the infant is taken through a cut in the woman's abdomen.

chambers rooms; in the heart, large, hollow areas that receive incoming blood from the lungs and tissues and ship it out again.

chamomile a plant with flowers that may provide some limited medical value in soothing intestinal and stomach discomforts.

chancre (SHANG-ker) a hard, painless sore; on the genitals, it may be a sign of syphilis infection.

chemotherapy the administration of drugs that harm cancer cells, but that do not harm the client, or at least usually do not harm the client as much as the disease does.

chest muscles the large muscles that permit flexing of the chest; called the *pectoralis* (pek-tore-AL-is) muscles, often nicknamed "pecs."

chicken pox a usually mild, easily transmitted viral disease causing fever, weakness, and itchy blisters that, if scratched, may leave permanent scars on the skin. The virus stays in the body for life and may later cause shingles. Once a person has been infected, immunity to chicken pox is lifelong.

child abuse verbal, psychological, physical, or sexual assault on a child.

chlamydia (cla-MID-ee-uh) an infection of the reproductive tract, with or without symptoms; a frequent cause of ectopic pregnancy or failure to become pregnant.

cholera (KAH-ler-uh) a dangerous bacterial infection causing violent muscle cramps, severe vomiting and diarrhea, and severe water loss. Without treatment, death is likely. People contract cholera by consuming infected water, milk, or foods (especially seafoods harvested from contaminated water).

cholesterol a type of fat made by the body from saturated fat; a minor part of fat in foods.

chromosomes slender bodies inside the cell's nucleus, which carry the genes.

chronic in relation to illness, this term refers to a disease or condition that develops slowly, shows little change, and lasts a long time.

chronic fatigue syndrome unexplained repeated bouts of extreme fatigue that bed rest does not cure and that last at least six months; may be accompanied by fever, chills, sore throat, swollen glands, muscle weakness and pain, reduced ability to exercise, severe or frequent headache, joint pain without swelling, emotional irritability, forgetfulness, confusion, lack of concentration, or depression.

chronic obstructive lung disease (COLD) a term for several diseases that interfere with breathing. Asthma, bronchitis, and emphysema are examples of COLD.

chronic stress unrelieved stress that continues to tax a person's resources to the point of exhaustion; stress that is damaging to health.

chronological age age as measured in years from date of birth.

cilia hairlike structures extending from the surface of cells that line body passageways, such as the trachea and upper lungs. The cilia wave, propelling mucus along to sweep away debris.

circulatory system see *cardiovascular system*.

clavicle (CLA-vik-ul) the collarbone.

cliques peer groups that reject newcomers and that judge their members harshly.

clitoris (KLIH-toh-ris) the primary female organ of sexual response that arises from the same fetal structure as the penis of males.

codependency a pattern of helping others in unhealthy ways; a group of behaviors, beliefs, and feelings that direct all energies toward people and things outside the self, along with neglect of one's own needs.

codependent an enabler who is a member of the family of, or has a close relationship with, a person addicted to a drug.

codeine a narcotic drug that is commonly used for suppressing coughs.

coitus see *sexual intercourse*.

coitus interruptus see *withdrawal method*.

cold an infection of the upper respiratory tract, usually caused by a virus, characterized by sore throat or watery eyes; hoarseness; and thick, greenish yellow nasal discharge.

collarbone a curved bone in the upper chest area; also called the *clavicle* (KLA-vik-ul).

colon the large intestine.

colostrum (co-LAHS-trum) a milklike substance rich in antibodies; the breast milk made during the first few days after birth.

combination pill an oral contraceptive that contains progestin and synthetic estrogen.

comedogenic causing acne.

comfrey a plant whose leaves and roots are believed, but not proved, to have drug effects. Comfrey contains cancer-causing chemicals.

commitment a decision adhered to for the long term; a promise kept. In relationships, a decision to embark on a long-term monogamous relationship with another person, without a guaranteed outcome.

compost rotted vegetable matter, used as fertilizer.

conception the union of an ovum and a sperm that starts a new individual.

condom see *female condom*, *male condom*.

condyloma see *genital warts*.

confrontation a showdown, an interaction in which one person expresses feelings to another. Managed aggressively, a confrontation may be a destructive fight. Managed assertively, a confrontation may be a constructive conversation in which one person makes his or her wishes known to another.

congeners (CON-jen-ers) ingredients in alcoholic beverages, other than the alcohol itself, that may irritate the nervous system.

congenital (con-JEN-ih-tal) present from birth.

constipation hard stools that are difficult to eliminate; often a result of too little fiber in the diet.

contraception any method of preventing conception. The term *birth control* is often used to mean the same thing, but technically, birth control includes abortion.

coping devices nonharmful ways of dealing with stress, such as displacement, sublimation, or ventilation.

copulation see *sexual intercourse.*

coronary arteries the two arteries that supply blood to the heart muscle.

coronary artery bypass surgery surgery to provide an alternate route for blood to reach heart tissue, bypassing a blocked coronary artery.

coronary thrombosis the closing off of a vessel that feeds the heart muscle by a stationary clot, or *thrombus.*

cortex the outer layer of an organ; in the brain, the outer, thinking portion—the gray matter.

Cowper's glands a pair of pea-shaped glands that empty a slippery, neutralizing fluid into the male urethra.

CPR (cardiopulmonary resuscitation) a technique of maintaining blood and oxygen flow through the body of a person whose heart has stopped.

crack a form of cocaine that is smoked.

credentials (kre-DEN-shulls) official evidence of education or other qualifications of an authority; diplomas, licenses, and the like.

crib death see *sudden infant death syndrome.*

critical periods periods during development when a body organ is especially sensitive to harmful factors. A critical period is usually a period of rapid cell division.

critical phase in atherosclerosis, the stage when plaques cover more than half of the inner surfaces of the arteries.

crowning the moment during childbirth in which the top (crown) of the baby's head is first seen.

cruciferous vegetables vegetables of the cabbage family.

cults groups of people who share intense admiration or adoration of a particular person or principle.

cuticles the borders of hardened skin at the bases of the fingernails.

CVD see *cardiovascular disease.*

cyst (SIST) an enlarged, deep pimple.

D

date a social event designed to allow people to get to know one another.

date rape see *acquaintance rape.*

defense mechanisms self-destructive ways of dealing with stress; automatic subconscious reactions to emotional injury, such as denial, fantasy, projection, rationalization, regression, selective forgetting, or withdrawal.

deficiency (dee-FISH-en-see) too little of a nutrient in the body. Severe deficiencies cause diseases.

dehydration loss of water. The symptoms progress rapidly from thirst to weakness to exhaustion, confusion, and even death.

delirium a state of mental confusion, usually with hallucinations and continual movement.

deltoids the triangular muscles of the upper arms at the shoulders, which permit sideways arm motion.

denial (dee-NIGH-al) refusal to believe the facts of a circumstance—for example, refusal to admit that a person is a problem drinker in the face of clear evidence that it is so.

dental plaque (PLAK) a buildup of sticky material on the surfaces of the teeth, a forerunner of tooth damage.

dentin a tooth's softer, middle layer.

dependence see *addiction.*

Depo Provera (DEE-po pro-VAIR-uh) a trade name for an injectable form of progestin, a contraceptive agent.

depression the condition of feeling apathetic, hopeless, and withdrawn from others. A *major depression* is an emotionally crippling depressed state linked to physical causes; it may be, at the extreme, a suicidal state.

dermatologist a physician (M.D.) who specializes in treating conditions of the skin.

designer drugs laboratory-made drugs that closely resemble illegal drugs in chemical structure, but that are different enough to be legal for a while.

deviant outside the normal system.

diabetes a disease that causes a dangerous buildup of the blood sugar glucose in the body; if left untreated, diabetes damages many tissues and organs including the heart and eyes and can lead to heart disease and blindness.

diaphragm (DYE-uh-fram) in the respiratory system, the sheet of muscle below the lungs that pulls them open, forcing them to draw in air, and then relaxes, allowing them to expel air. Also a contraceptive device; a dome that fits over the cervix and holds spermicidal cream or jelly against the uterine entrance to block the passage of sperm.

diastolic (DYE-as-tol-ic) **pressure** the blood pressure during that part of the heartbeat when the heart's ventricles are relaxing. Diastolic pressure is the lowest pressure in the arteries and is represented by the second number in a blood pressure reading.

diet pills medications that reduce the appetite or otherwise promote weight loss. Pills available over the counter usually contain caffeine and other drugs that cause more nervousness than weight loss. Prescription pills include *amphetamines.*

digestion the breaking down of food into nutrients the body can use.

dilation stage the stage of childbirth during which the cervix is opening, before expulsion of the infant begins.

dioxins deadly pollutants formed when chlorine reacts with other compounds.

disability insurance insurance to replace lost income if a person should be unable to work due to a long illness.

discipline the shaping of behavior by way of rewards and/or punishments.

disinfectants chemicals that kill microbes on surfaces. Bleach is a disinfectant.

dispatcher a person who answers calls and relays messages to the proper helping service.

displacement channeling the energy of suffering into something else—for example, using the emotional energy churned up by problems for tasks or recreation.

disposable a description of any product that is intended to be used once and then thrown away.

diuretic (die-yoo-RETT-ick) a drug that causes the body to lose fluids; not effective for loss of body fat.

douches (DOOSH-es) preparations sold to cleanse the vagina. Actually, vaginas clean themselves constantly with no help, and douches can wash dangerous bacteria into the reproductive tract.

Down's syndrome an inherited condition of physical deformities and mental retardation.

drink with respect to alcoholic beverages, the amount of a beverage that delivers 1/2 ounce of pure ethanol—12 ounces of beer, 3 to 4 ounces of wine, 1 (10 ounce) wine cooler, or 1 ounce of 100 proof liquor.

drives motivations that are born, not learned, such as hunger, thirst, fear, and needs for sleep and sex. Also known as *instincts*.

dropouts students who were enrolled in school, but who no longer attend and are not seeking a diploma or equivalent, and who have not left because of illness or other school-approved reasons.

drug abuse the deliberate taking of a drug for other than a medical purpose and in a manner that can result in damage to a person's health or ability to function.

drug addiction (dependence) a physical or psychological craving for higher and higher doses of a drug that leads to bodily harm, social maladjustment, or economic hardship.

drug misuse the taking of a drug for its medically intended purpose, but not in the appropriate amount, frequency, strength, or manner.

drug use the taking of a medical drug for its medically intended purpose, and in the appropriate amount, frequency, strength, and manner.

drugs substances taken into the body that change one or more of the body's functions.

DUI driving under the influence (of alcohol or other mind-altering substances). See *DWI*.

duration in terms of exercise, the length of time spent in each exercise session.

DWI driving while intoxicated with alcohol or any abusable substance—a crime by law. Intoxication is defined by blood alcohol level (a level of 0.10 percent in most states).

dysfunctional family a family with abnormal or impaired ways of coping that injures the self-esteem and emotional health of family members.

dysphoria (dis-FORE-ee-uh) unpleasant feelings that often follow drug-induced euphoria.

E

eating disorder abnormal food intake stemming from emotional causes and related to addiction. In *anorexia nervosa*, young people starve themselves to lose weight. In *bulimia*, they binge on food, then starve or vomit.

ecosystems systems of land, plants, and animals that have existed together for thousands or millions of years and that are interdependent.

ectopic pregnancy a pregnancy that develops in one of the fallopian tubes or elsewhere outside the uterus; a dangerous condition.

effective as used to describe medical drugs, having the medically intended effect; part of the legal requirement for a drug.

effectiveness in contraceptive technology, a description of how well a contraceptive method or device prevents pregnancy, expressed as a percentage. The *laboratory effectiveness* is the percentage of women protected from pregnancy in a year's time under *ideal* laboratory conditions. The *user effectiveness* is the percentage of *typical* women users who are protected.

ejaculation the expelling of semen from the penis, brought about by the involuntary muscular contractions of orgasm.

elasticity (for example, of muscles or joint tissues) the characteristic of being easily stretched or bent and able to return to the original size and shape.

electrocardiogram a record of the electrical activity of the heart that, if abnormal, may indicate heart disease.

electrolytes (ee-LECK-tro-lites) minerals that carry electrical charges that help maintain the body's fluid balance.

embolism the sudden closure of a blood vessel by a traveling blood clot, or *embolus*.

embolus (EM-bow-luss) a clot that breaks loose and travels through the bloodstream. When it causes sudden closure of a blood vessel, this dangerous event is an *embolism*.

embryo (EM-bree-oh) the developing infant during the third through eighth week after conception.

emergency medical service (EMS) a team of people who are trained to respond in emergencies, and who can be contacted through a single dispatcher.

emetics (em-ETT-ics) drugs that cause vomiting.

emotion a feeling of being attracted to or repelled by something. Examples are love, anger, and fear.

emotional health health in relationship to self, others, and society.

emotional problems patterns of behavior or thinking that cause a person to feel significant emotional pain or to be unable to function in one of three important areas—social or family relations, occupation (including school performance), or use of leisure time.

emphysema (em-fih-ZEE-muh) a disease of the lungs in which many small, flexible air sacs burst and form a few large, rigid air pockets.

empty calories a popular term referring to foods that contribute much energy (calories) and few nutrients.

enable make possible. In addiction, enabling means "helping" by trying to "save" the addicted person from the consequences of the behavior. This makes possible continued alcohol or other drug abuse.

enamel a tooth's tough outer layer.

endorphins chemicals in the brain that produce feelings of pleasure in response to a variety of activities.

energy the capacity to do work or produce heat.

engorgement swelling; with reference to the sexual response, the sex organs' filling with blood preparatory to orgasm.

environment everything "outside" the living organism—air, water, soil, other organisms, and forms of radiation.

epidemic (EP-ih-DEM-ick) an infection that spreads rapidly through a population, affecting many people at the same time.

epiglottis (ep-ee-GLOT-is) the flap over the windpipe, which keeps food from falling into the airway during swallowing.

epinephrine (EP-ih-NEFF-rin) one of the stress hormones, also called *adrenaline*.

episiotomy (eh-PEEZ-ee-OT-oh-me) a surgical cut made in the vagina during childbirth to allow the baby to pass when the vagina cannot stretch enough without tearing.

erection the state of a normally soft tissue when it fills with blood and becomes firm. Both penis and clitoris can become erect.

ergogenic (ER-go-JEN-ick) a term applied to foods and drinks that claims to mean "work-enhancing." In fact, no products do this.

esophagus (e-SOF-a-gus) the long tube that passes food from the mouth to the stomach.

essential amino acids amino acids that are needed, but cannot be made by the body; they must be eaten in foods.

estrogen a hormone that, in females, regulates the ovulatory cycle.

ethanol (ethyl alcohol) see *alcohol*.

ethics moral principles or values.

euphoria (you-FORE-ee-uh) a sense of great well-being and pleasure brought on by some drugs; popularly called a *high*.

euthanasia (you-than-AY-zee-uh) allowing a person to die by choosing not to employ life-support equipment such as artificial respirators; or the removal of life-support equipment from a patient with no hope of recovery; both may be legal in some cases.

excitement as used to describe a stage of sexual intercourse, the early stage.

exercise physiology the study of how the body works and changes in response to exercise. An exercise physiology laboratory has equipment to measure the components of fitness and to take other measures.

exhaustion a harmful third phase of the stress response, in which stress exceeds the body's ability to recover; breakdown follows.

expulsion stage the stage of childbirth during which the uter-ine contractions actively push the infant through the birth canal.

eye field the area of the brain that controls the eyes.

F

fallopian (fah-LO-pee-an) **tube** the tube through which the egg travels from the ovary to the uterus.

false labor warm-up contractions that many women experience before the birth process.

FAS see *fetal alcohol syndrome*.

fat-soluble (SOL-you-bul) a chemist's term meaning able to dissolve in fat.

fatfold caliper a pinching device that measures body fat under the skin.

fatfold test a test of body fatness done with a *fatfold caliper*.

fat a class of nutrients that does not mix with water. Fat is made mostly of fatty acids, which provide energy to the body. Commonly referred to as *fats*.

fatty acids simple forms of fat that supply energy fuel for most of the body's cells.

fee-for-service system a system of paying for health care in which clients pay individual fees for the services they receive.

female condom a contraceptive device; a soft, thin plastic tube with two end rings—one to fit over the cervix and one to serve as an anchor outside the entrance to the vagina; also called a *vaginal pouch*.

femininity traits, including biological and social traits, associated with being female.

femur (FEEM-ur) the thigh bone, which extends from the hip to the knee, the longest and strongest bone in the entire skeleton.

fertility awareness method a method of charting ovulation. It involves tracking menstrual periods, body temperature, and types of cervical mucus.

fertilization the joining of an ovum and a sperm, which starts a new individual.

fetal alcohol syndrome (FAS) a cluster of birth defects, including permanent mental and physical retardation and facial abnormalities, seen in children born to mothers who abuse alcohol during pregnancy.

fetus (FEET-us) the developing infant from the ninth week after conception until birth.

fiber indigestible substances in foods, made mostly of carbohydrate.

fibula (FIB-u-la) the smaller, outer bone of the shin, one of the longest and thinnest bones in the body.

fight-or-flight reaction the body's response to immediate physical danger; the stress response. Energy is mobilized, either to mount an aggressive response against the danger, or to run away.

first aid literally, "help given first"—medical help given immediately in an emergency, before the victim is transported to a hospital or treatment center.

fitness the characteristics of a body that enable it to perform physical activity, to meet routine physical demands with enough reserve energy to rise to sudden challenges, and to withstand stresses of all kinds.

flap over windpipe see *epiglottis*.

flexibility a component of fitness; the ability to bend the joints without injury.

flu short for **influenza** (in-flew-EN-za), a highly contagious respiratory infection caused by any of a variety of viruses. Symptoms often include dry cough, fever, chills, aches and pains, weakness, and headache.

folk medicine the use of herbs and other natural substances in the treatment of disease as traditionally practiced among the people of various regions.

follicles vessel-like structures that contain the oil glands, the muscles that control hair movement (and also goose bumps), and the roots of hairs.

food chain the sequence in which living things depend on other living things for food.

foreplay activity in which each partner gives pleasure to the other prior to intercourse.

foreskin in the female, the loose skin that covers the end of the clitoris like a hood; in the male, the skin that covers the end (glans) of the penis.

formaldehyde a substance related to alcohol. Formaldehyde is made by the body from alcohol and contributes to hangovers.

fossil fuel coal, oil, and natural gas, which all come from the fossilized remains of plant life of earlier times.

foxglove a plant that contains a substance used in the heart medicine digoxin.

fracture a break in a bone. An *open fracture* is a break with a wound in the overlying tissues; *a closed fracture* is a break or crack with no visible wound.

fraternal twins twins formed by the fertilization of two different ova by two different sperm.

frequency in terms of exercise, the number of activity units per unit of time (for example, the number of exercise sessions per week).

frigidity see *sexual dysfunction*.

fringe the beating finger-like structure that surrounds the opening of the fallopian tube; technically, the *fimbriae*.

frostbite the formation of ice crystals in body parts exposed to temperatures below freezing; freezing of body parts, especially toes and fingers, and nose and other face parts.

fungi living things that absorb and use nutrients of organisms they invade. Fungi that cause illnesses include *yeasts* and *molds*.

G

gall bladder a sac that stores bile until it is needed in the small intestine.

gangs peer groups that exist largely to express aggression against other groups.

gastrocnemius (gas-tro-K'NEE-mee-us) **muscles** the large muscles in the back of the calf of the leg.

gender the classification of being male or female.

gender identity that part of a person's self-image that is determined by the person's gender.

gender roles roles assigned by society to people of each gender.

generic (jeh-NEHR-ick) **names** the chemical names for drugs, as opposed to the brand names; the names everyone can use.

genes (JEENZ) the units of a cell's inheritance, which direct the making of equipment to do the cell's work.

genetic counselor an advisor who is qualified to predict and advise on the likelihood that congenital defects will occur in a family.

genital herpes (HER-peez) a common, incurable STD caused by a virus that produces blisters. The symptoms clear up on their own, but the virus remains to cause future outbreaks.

genital warts a viral STD that causes wartlike growths on the infected areas, sometimes called *condyloma* (condi-LOW-ma).

gestation (jes-TAY-shun) the period from conception to birth. For human beings, gestation lasts from 38 to 42 weeks. The term of pregnancy itself is often divided into thirds, called *trimesters*.

gigantism see *acromegaly*.

ginseng (JIN-seng) a plant containing chemicals that have drug effects.

ginseng abuse syndrome a group of symptoms associated with the overuse of ginseng, including high blood pressure, insomnia, nervousness, confusion, and depression.

gland an organ of the body that secretes one or more hormones.

glans the bulb-shaped end of the penis.

global warming warming of the planet, a trend that threatens life on earth.

glucose the body's blood sugar; a simple form of carbohydrate.

gluteus (GLOO-tee-us) **maximus** the large, rear muscles of the buttocks.

gluteus (GLOO-tee-us) **minimus** the side muscles of the buttocks.

glycogen the form in which the liver and muscles store glucose.

gonorrhea (gon-oh-REE-uh) a bacterial STD that often advances without symptoms to spread though the body, causing problems in many organs.

grams (abbreviated *g*) units of weight in which many nutrients are measured; 28 grams equal one ounce.

greenhouse effect the heat-trapping effect of the glass in a greenhouse. The same effect is caused by gases that are accumulating in the earth's outer atmosphere, which are trapping the sun's heat and warming the planet.

grieve to feel keen emotional pain and suffering over a loss.

group practice an organization of physicians who practice medicine together.

growth hormone see *human growth hormone*.

guided imaging see *positive imaging*.

guilt the normal feeling that arises from the conscience when a person acts against internal values ("I did a bad thing").

gynecologist a specialist in the care of the female reproductive system.

H

hallucinations false perceptions; imagined sights, sounds, smells, or other feelings, sometimes brought on by drug abuse, sometimes by mental or physical illness.

hallucinogens (hal-LOO-sin-oh-jens) drugs that cause hallucinations.

hamstrings the muscles of the back of the thigh.

head lice tiny, but visible, white parasitic insects that burrow into the skin or hairy body areas and obtain nourishment from blood. Lice eggs often look like tiny rice grains that cling to strands of hair.

head restraints high seatbacks or other devices attached to seats in cars at head level to prevent neck and spinal cord injuries.

health a range of states with physical, mental, emotional, spiritual, and social components. At a minimum, *health* means freedom from physical disease, poor physical condition, social maladjustment, and other negative states. At a maximum, *health* means "*wellness.*"

health care system the total of all health care providers and medical treatment facilities that work together to provide medical care to the population.

health maintenance organization (HMO) a group of physicians who practice together and who treat people's health problems under a prepayment plan.

hearing center the area of the brain that controls hearing.

heart the circulatory system's pump, a large muscle with hollow chambers; its contractions push blood into the large arteries.

heart attack the event in which vessels that feed the heart muscle become blocked, causing tissue death.

heart disease any disease of the heart muscle or other working parts of the heart.

heart murmur a heart sound that reflects damaged or abnormal heart valves.

heart transplant the surgical replacement of a diseased heart with a healthy one.

heat exhaustion a serious stage of overheating, which can lead to heat stroke.

heat stroke a life-threatening condition that results from a buildup of body heat; can be fatal.

Heimlich (HIME-lick) **maneuver** a technique of dislodging a particle that is blocking a person's airway, named for the man who invented it.

hemlock any part of the hemlock plant, which if taken internally causes severe pain, convulsions, and death within 15 minutes.

hemorrhoids swollen, painful rectal veins; often a result of constipation.

hepatitis inflammation of the liver caused by one of several types of viruses that are transmitted by infected needles (drug use, tattoos, blood transfusions), by eating raw seafood harvested from contaminated water, and by any contact (including sexual contact) with body secretions from infected people.

herbs nonwoody plants or plant parts valued for their flavor, aroma, or medicinal qualities.

heroin a narcotic drug derived from morphine.

heterosexual feeling sexual desire for persons of the other gender.

hierarchy a ranking system in which each thing is placed above or below others.

high-density lipoproteins (HDL) lipoproteins that carry fat and cholesterol away from the tissues (and from plaques) back to the liver for breakdown and removal from the body.

high-risk pregnancy a pregnancy more likely than others to have problems, such as premature delivery or a low birthweight.

histamine (HIST-uh-meen) a chemical of the immune response that produces inflammation (swelling and irritation) of tissue.

history (medical) an interview in which a health care professional asks about past medical experience.

HIV an abbreviation for *human immunodeficiency virus,* the virus that causes AIDS.

Hodgkin's disease a lymphoma that attacks people in early life and is treatable with radiation therapy.

homeostasis (HOH-me-oh-STAY-sis) the maintenance of a stable body environment, achieved as body systems adapt to changing conditions.

homophobia an irrational fear and hatred of homosexuals, usually based on the fear of becoming a homosexual.

homosexual feeling sexual desire for persons of the same sex, popularly called *gay* or, in women, *lesbian.*

hormonal system the system of glands—organs that send and receive blood-borne chemical messages—that control body functions in cooperation with the nervous system.

hormone a chemical that serves as a messenger. Each hormone is secreted by a gland and travels to one or more target organs, where it brings about responses.

hospice (HOS-pis) a support system for dying people and their families, which helps the family to let the person die at home with dignity and in comfort.

hospital infections infectious illnesses acquired during hospitalization—carried by health care staff, other patients, or visitors—that greatly extend the length and cost of a hospital stay and that can threaten the lives of already sick and weakened patients.

hospitalization insurance insurance to pay the cost of a hospital stay.

hot flashes sudden waves of feeling hot all over; a symptom, related to dilation of blood vessels in the skin, which is common during the transition into menopause.

human growth hormone a hormone produced in the body that promotes growth; taken as a drug by athletes to enhance muscle growth; also called *somatotropin.*

humerus (HYOO-mer-us) the bone of the upper part of the arm, between the elbow and the shoulder joint.

hunger the physical need to eat; a negative, unpleasant sensation.

hyperactivity a condition in children that makes them overly active, unable to pay attention, aggressive, and easily distracted.

hypertension high blood pressure.

hyperthermia a condition of too much body heat with abnormally high internal body temperature.

hypothalamus (high-po-THALL-uh-mus) the part of the brain that is the main coordinator between the nervous system and the hormonal system; it monitors information about the state of the body, and controls the release of hormones from the pituitary gland.

hypothermia a condition of too little body heat with abnormally low internal body temperature.

hysterectomy removal of the uterus, an operation performed more often than necessary.

I

ibuprofen (EYE-byoo-PRO-fen) a drug that relieves fever, pain, and inflammation.

identical twins twins produced from a single fertilized ovum; the two cells produced by the first cell division separate and develop into two individuals.

immune system the cells, tissues, and organs that protect the body from disease; composed of the white blood cells, bone marrow, thymus gland, spleen, and other organs.

immunity the body's capacity for identifying, destroying, and disposing of disease-causing agents.

immunizations injected or oral doses of medicine that stimulate the immune system to develop the long-term ability to quickly fight off infectious diseases; also called *vaccinations*.

implantation the lodging of a fertilized ovum in the wall of the uterus.

impotence see *sexual dysfunction*.

inactive ingredients ingredients that give a medicine qualities other than medical effects. For example, oils and waxes may be mixed with a medication to be used on the skin; water, colorants, and flavors may be added to liquid medicines taken by mouth.

inert not active.

infatuation the state of being completely carried away by unreasoning passion or attraction; addictive love.

infectious diseases diseases caused, and transmitted from person to person, by microorganisms or their toxins; also called *communicable* or *contagious diseases*, or simply *infections*.

infectious mononucleosis see *mononucleosis*.

inferior vena cava (VEE-na CAVE-a) the large vein that returns used blood from the lower body to the heart.

inflammation pain and swelling caused by irritation.

initiator a carcinogen, an agent required to start the formation of cancer.

inner thigh muscles the long thigh muscles, the longest muscles in the body; known as the *sartorius muscles*.

insomnia (in-SOM-nee-uh) sleep abnormalities including difficulty in falling asleep and wakefulness through the night.

intensity in terms of exercise, the degree of exertion while exercising (for example, jogging takes more exertion than walking and so is more intense).

intercourse see *sexual intercourse*.

internship a length of time spent in training in a medical facility as part of the curriculum of health care providers.

intimacy being very close and familiar, as in relationships involving private and personal sharing.

intoxication literally, a state of being poisoned, including being poisoned by alcohol; drunkenness.

intrauterine device (IUD) a device inserted into the uterus to prevent conception or implantation.

intravenous (IV) drug abuse the practice of using needles to inject drugs of abuse into the veins. (The word *intravenous* means "into a vein.")

J

jock itch a fungal infection of the groin and inner thigh.

joints places where two or more bones meet, allowing for body movement.

juvenile delinquent a youth under age 18 who has committed illegal acts.

K

Kaposi's (cap-OH-zeez) **sarcoma** a normally rare skin cancer causing a purplish discoloration of the skin, seen commonly among people with AIDS.

keratin the normal protein of hair and nails.

kidneys the main working organs of the urinary system; they cleanse the blood and maintains its composition.

kneecap the lens-shaped bone located in front of the knee; also called the *patella*.

L

laboratory effectiveness (of a contraceptive device or technique) see *effectiveness*.

lactation the production of milk by the mammary glands of the breasts for the purpose of feeding babies.

lapse a falling back into former habits. Lapses are a normal part of both weight change and weight maintenance.

large intestine (colon) the portion of the digestive tract that absorbs water and minerals; it passes undigested waste (fiber, bacteria, and some water) to the rectum.

larynx (LARE-inx) the voice box, the part of the throat that contains the vocal cords.

latent temporarily unseen or inactive.

latissimus dorsi (lat-ISS-ih-mus DOOR-sy) the large muscles of the middle and lower back.

leukemias (loo-KEE-me-ahs) cancers that arise in the blood cell-making tissues.

leukoplakia (loo-koh-PLAKE-ee-uh) whitish or greyish patches that develop in the mouths of tobacco users and that may lead to cancer.

life expectancy the number of years an individual can expect to live based on hereditary and other factors.

life management skills the skills that help a person to realize his or her potential to be well and enjoy life; the subject of this book.

life span the maximum years of life a human being can live.

life-support systems a term used to refer to mechanical means of supporting life, such as feedings given into a central vein or machines that force air into the lungs.

lifestyle choices choices, made daily, of how to treat the body and mind. Examples are what to eat and how often, when to exercise and how much, whether to use alcohol or other drugs, and how to deal with mental challenges and emotional stresses.

lifestyle diseases diseases that are made likely by neglect of the body. They cannot be passed from person to person. Examples are heart disease, cancer, and diabetes. Lifestyle choices that promote health can help prevent lifestyle diseases.

ligaments flexible straps of connective tissue that connect bones to one another and that support joints.

lightening the sensation a pregnant woman experiences when the fetus settles into the birth position.

lipoproteins (LIP-oh-PRO-teens) protein and fat clusters that transport fats in the blood.

liver an organ that, among many things, makes bile to help digest fats.

living will a will that declares a person's wishes regarding treatment, should the person become unable to make decisions (for example, in the event of brain death).

lockjaw see *tetanus*.

longevity an individual's length of life.

look-alikes combinations of OTC drugs and other chemicals packaged to look like prescription medications or illegal drugs.

love affection, attachment, devotion. See also *mature love*.

low birthweight a birthweight of 51/2 pounds (2,500 grams) or less, used as a predictor of poor health in the newborn infant. Normal birthweight for a full-term baby is 61/2 pounds or more.

low-density lipoproteins (LDL) lipoproteins that carry fat and cholesterol from the liver, where they are made, to the tissues where they are used. LDL also deposit cholesterol in arteries, forming plaques.

low-impact aerobic dance aerobic dance in which one foot remains on the floor to prevent shock to the lower body.

low-risk pregnancy a normal, healthy pregnancy supported by medical and social advantages.

LSD (lysergic acid diethylamide) a powerful hallucinogenic drug; also called *acid*.

lungs the pair of large, spongy, capillary-rich organs in the chest that expand to draw air in and collapse to expel air; the site of gas exchange between the outside air and the blood.

Lyme disease a bacterial infection spread by tiny deer ticks.

lymph (LIMF) the clear fluid that bathes each cell and transfers needed substances and wastes back and forth between the blood and the cells. Lymph also plays a role in immunity.

lymph capillaries small vessels that transport lymph throughout the body.

lymph duct any of several ducts that connect lymph vessels to the large veins of the blood circulatory system.

lymph node a small bead of tissue in a lymph vessel that contains white blood cells and filters out bacteria to prevent their entering the bloodstream.

lymph vessels vessels that contain and transport lymph.

lymphocytes (LIM-fo-sites) white blood cells, active in immunity.

lymphomas (limf-OH-mahs) cancers that arise in organs of the immune system.

M

mainstream smoke the smoke that flows through the cigarette and into the lungs when a smoker inhales.

major medical insurance insurance to pay high bills not covered by other insurance.

male condom a sheath worn over the penis during intercourse to contain the semen, to prevent pregnancy, and/or to reduce the risks of sexually transmitted diseases; condoms are also called *rubbers*.

male menopause the gradual decline in male fertility that takes place due to advancing age.

malignancy a dangerous cancerous growth that sheds cells into body fluids and spreads to new locations to start new cancer colonies.

malnutrition the result in the body of poor nutrition: undernutrition, overnutrition, or any nutrient deficiency.

malpractice insurance insurance that protects providers of health care against lawsuits by people claiming to have been harmed by health care providers.

mammogram x-ray examination of the breast, a screening test for cancer.

marriage the institution that joins a man and a woman by contract for the purpose of creating and maintaining a family.

masculinity traits, including biological and social traits, associated with being male.

masturbation stimulation of one's own genitals, usually until orgasm occurs.

mature love a strong affection for, and an enduring, deep attachment to, a person whose character the partner knows well.

measles a highly contagious viral disease characterized by rash, high fever, sensitivity to light, and cough and cold symptoms; preventable by immunization.

Medicaid hospitalization and surgical insurance available for people who qualify as needy.

medical insurance insurance to pay physicians' fees, lab fees, and fees for prescription medications.

Medicare hospitalization insurance for people who are receiving Social Security.

medicines drugs used to help cure disease, lessen disease severity, relieve symptoms, prevent disease, help with diagnosis, or produce other desired effects.

meditation a method of relaxing that involves closing the eyes, breathing deeply, and relaxing the muscles.

melanin (MELL-eh-nin) the protective skin pigment responsible for the tan, brown, or black color of human skin; produced in abundance upon exposure to ultraviolet radiation.

melanoma an especially dangerous cancer of the pigmented cells of the skin, related to sun exposure in people with light-colored skin.

menopause the years of stopping ovulation and menstruation in a woman.

menstrual cramps contractions of the uterus, during and a few days before menstruation, that may cause pain.

menstrual cycle the cyclic ripening of an ovum and the preparation of the uterus for pregnancy; also called the *ovulatory cycle*.

menstruation the monthly shedding of the uterine lining in nonpregnant females.

mentor a wise person who gives advice and assistance.

mercy killing see *euthanasia*.

mescaline the hallucinogen produced by the peyote cactus.

metacarpals the bones in the hands.

metastasized (meh-TASS-tuh-sized) when speaking of cancer cells, a term that means the cancer cells have migrated from one part of the body to another, and started new growths just like the original tumor.

metatarsals the bones of the feet.

methadone a drug used to treat heroin addiction that holds off withdrawal and helps people recover socially.

microbes (microorganisms) tiny organisms, such as bacteria, yeasts, and viruses, that are too small to be seen with the naked eye.

midbrain the upper part of the brainstem, which controls emotions.

minerals elements of the earth. Some, the *essential minerals*, are needed in the diet, and perform many functions in body tissues.

minipill a progestin-only oral contraceptive.

miscarriage see *spontaneous abortion*.

moderation with respect to alcohol consumption, an amount of alcohol that causes no harm to health: not more than one to two drinks a day for healthy adults.

molds many-celled fungi, some of which cause diseases.

monogamous (mon-AH-ga-mus) a term describing relationships, especially marriage, in which the partners are sexually intimate with each other, but with no one else. These relationships are usually long-term relationships.

mononucleosis (MON-oh-new-klee-OH-sis) a viral infection involving mononucleocytes, a type of white blood cell. The symptoms vary from mild, coldlike symptoms to high fevers, swollen glands, and spleen and liver involvement; also called *mono*.

morning sickness the nausea (upset stomach) a pregnant woman may suffer at any time of the day; thought to be related to the hormones that maintain pregnancy.

morphine a narcotic drug that doctors prescribe as a painkiller.

motivation the force that moves people to act. Motivation may be either instinctive (drives) or learned.

motor cortex the area of the brain that controls voluntary muscles.

mouth the first portion of the digestive system; it chews and mixes food with saliva.

mucus (MYOO-cuss) a slippery secretion produced by cells of the body's linings that protects the surfaces of the linings.

mumps a highly contagious viral disease that causes swelling of the salivary glands and, occasionally, of the testicles; preventable by immunization.

muscle endurance a component of fitness; the ability of muscles to sustain an effort for a long time.

muscle strength a component of fitness; the ability of muscles to work against resistance.

mutation (myoo-TAY-shun) a change in a cell's genetic material. Once the genetic material has changed, the change is inherited by the offspring of that cell.

myeloma a cancer originating in the cells of the bone marrow.

N

narcotic antagonists drugs that oppose the action of other drugs. The word *antagonist* means something or someone who struggles with, or opposes, another.

narcotics drugs that relieve pain and produce sleep when taken in moderate doses; also called *opiates*, because most are derived from the opium poppy. These drugs are habit forming.

Narcotics Anonymous (NA) a free, self-help program of addiction recovery. It uses a 12-step program, promotes personal growth, and leads to the person's helping others to recover.

neck muscles the muscles that control head movements.

needs urgent wants for necessary things.

nephrons (NEF-rons) the basic working units of the kidneys.

nerves the long, thin cells of the nervous system that transport messages between the central nervous system and the tissues.

nervous system the system of nerves—organized into the brain, spinal cord, and nerves—that send and receive messages and integrate the body's activities.

nicotine (NICK-oh-teen) an addictive drug present in tobacco.

night blindness slow recovery of vision after flashes of bright light at night; an early symptom of vitamin A deficiency.

nonconformist a person who does not share society's values and therefore behaves in unconventional ways.

norepinephrine one of the stress hormones, also called *noradrenaline*.

Norplant a trade name for a surgical hormone delivery system that provides continuous release of progestin, thereby preventing pregnancy for up to five years.

nucleus inside a cell, the structure that contains the genes.

nutrient deficiencies (dee-FISH-en-sees) too little of one or more nutrients in the diet; a form of malnutrition.

nutrients compounds in food that the body requires for proper growth, maintenance, and functioning.

O

obesity overfatness to the point of injuring health. Obesity is often defined as 20 percent or more above the appropriate weight for height.

obliques the slanting muscles that form a natural girdle around the abdomen and permit side-to-side bending.

opiates a group of drugs that are derived from the opium poppy, that relieve pain and induce sleep; also known as *narcotics*.

opium a narcotic drug that relieves pain and induces sleep, made from the opium poppy.

oral contraceptives pills that prevent pregnancy by stopping ovulation or by changing conditions in the uterus; often called *birth control pills* or "the Pill."

organs whole units, made of tissues, that perform specific jobs.

orgasm a series of muscular contractions of the sex organs that typically occur after a period of sexual stimulation, release tension, and end in relaxation.

osteoporosis (OS-tee-oh-por-OH-sis) a disease of gradual bone loss, which can cripple people in later life.

ostracism exclusion from, and rejection by, society.

ova (singular, *ovum*) the female cells of reproduction. Ova are also called *eggs*.

ovaries (OH-vah-rees) the glands that produce the female hormones estrogen and progesterone; the ovaries also produce the female reproductive cells, *ova*.

over-the-counter (OTC) drugs drugs legally available without a prescription.

overload in terms of fitness, an extra physical demand placed on the body.

overnutrition too much food energy or excess nutrients to the degree of causing disease or increasing risk of disease; a form of malnutrition.

ovulation the ripening and release of an ovum.

ovulatory cycle see *menstrual cycle*.

ovum (O-vum) the female reproductive cell; the egg; plural, *ova*.

ozone a form of oxygen; an air pollutant in the lower atmosphere; a protective shield in the upper atmosphere (see *ozone layer*).

ozone layer a layer of ozone in the earth's outer atmosphere that protects living things on earth from harmful ultraviolet radiation from the sun.

P

pacemaker a device that delivers electrical impulses to the heart to regulate the heartbeat.

pancreas (PAN-kree-as) a gland near the stomach that functions in both the digestive system and the hormonal system. In the digestive system, the pancreas makes and secretes digestive enzymes. In the hormonal system, the pancreas makes and secretes the hormones insulin and glucagon, which regulate glucose and other fuels in the blood.

Pap test a test for cancer of the cervix (the lower part of the uterus). A few cells are removed painlessly and examined in a laboratory.

parasites living things that obtain nourishment from the bodies of others that they inhabit; worms, lice, and others usually large enough to be visible through part of their life cycles.

parathyroid glands four glands mounted on the thyroid gland, which produce a hormone that regulates the minerals of the blood.

passive possessing the characteristic of not expressing feelings appropriately, of remaining silent.

passive abuse abuse involving not taking needed actions, such as neglecting to provide food or shelter to a dependent victim.

patella the kneecap.

pathogens microbes that cause diseases.

PCP (phencyclidine hydrochloride) a drug used as an animal tranquilizer, abused by human beings as a hallucinogen.

pectoralis (pek-tore-AL-is) **muscles** the large muscles that permit flexing of the chest.

peer groups groups of people who are similar in age, stage, and style of life.

peer pressure the internal pressure one feels to behave as a peer group does, to gain its members' approval.

pelvic inflammatory disease (PID) an infection of the fallopian tubes and pelvic cavity in women, causing ectopic pregnancy and pregnancy failures.

pelvis the bowl-shaped bone that supports the spinal column, protects the lower body's organs, and contains sockets in which the legs are attached.

penis the male external genital organ.

persistent the opposite of biodegradable; unable to decompose or to be converted by living organisms into harmless wastes.

personality the characteristics of a person that are apparent to others.

peyote a cactus that produces the hallucinogen mescaline.

phalanges (fah-LAN-jeez) the bones of the fingers or toes.

phenylketonuria see *PKU*.

phobia (FOH-bee-uh) an extreme, irrational fear of an object or situation.

photovoltaic (PV) panels panels that convert light (photons) into electricity (volts).

physical addiction a change in the body's chemistry so that without the presence of increasing doses of a substance (drug), normal functioning begins to fail, and withdrawal symptoms set in; also called *physical dependence*.

physical examination an examination of the body to gather information about its general condition or to make a diagnosis.

physiological age age as estimated from the body's health and probable life expectancy.

pinch test an informal way of measuring body fatness by lifting a fold of skin on the back of one arm with the fingers and then measuring its thickness.

pinworms small, visible, white parasitic worms that commonly infect the intestines of young children.

pituitary (pi-TOO-ih-tare-ee) **gland** called "the master gland," and attached to the base of the brain, a gland that makes hormones that regulate growth, reproduction, and the making of many other hormones.

PKU (phenylketonuria) a congenital disease causing severe brain damage with mental retardation if left untreated; now detected and treated at birth by required testing of newborns.

placebo effect the healing effect that faith in medicine, even inert medicine, often has.

placenta (plah-SEN-tah) an organ that develops during pregnancy; it permits exchange of materials between maternal and fetal blood.

placental stage the final stage of childbirth, after the infant has been born, in which the placenta is expelled.

plaques (PLACKS) mounds of fat, mixed with minerals, that build up along artery walls in atherosclerosis. (The term *plaque* is also used to describe material that collects on teeth and promotes dental caries.)

plateau literally, a high, flat place. In sexual intercourse, the plateau phase is the period of intense physical pleasure preceding orgasm.

platelets tiny, disk-shaped bodies in the blood, important in blood clot formation.

PMS see *premenstrual syndrome*.

pneumonia a disease caused by a virus or bacterium that infects the lungs, with high fever, severe cough, and pain in the chest; especially dangerous to the very old or young.

polio (poliomyelitis) a viral infection that produces mild respiratory or digestive symptoms in most cases but that may produce permanent paralysis or death; preventable by immunization.

pollution contamination of the environment with anything that impairs its ability to support life.

polyps tumors that grow on a stem, resembling mushrooms. Polyps bleed easily, and some have the tendency to become malignant.

polyunsaturated a type of unsaturated fat especially useful as a replacement for saturated fat in a heart-healthy diet.

positive imaging (guided imaging) a technique used to help achieve the relaxation response. The person imagines achieving positive outcomes to present challenges.

positive self-talk the practice of making affirming statements about oneself to oneself, helpful in building self-esteem.

post-traumatic stress disorder a reaction to stress such as wartime suffering or rape, arising after the event is over.

postpartum depression the emotional depression a new mother or father may experience after the birth of an infant.

prefrontal cortex the part of the brain responsible for intellectual activities.

premature born before the end of the normal nine-month term of pregnancy.

premenstrual syndrome (PMS) symptoms such as physical discomfort, moodiness, and nervousness that occur in some women each month before menstruation.

premiums payments made to an insurance company to cover the price of insurance.

prenatal care medical and health care provided during pregnancy.

prepayment plan a system of paying for health care in which the clients pay a fixed fee every month, regardless of how many services they receive.

prescription drugs drugs legally available only with a physician's order.

prodrome the onset of general symptoms common to many diseases, such as fever, sneezing, and coughing.

progesterone a hormone secreted in females during that portion of the menstrual cycle in which the uterine lining builds up.

progestin a synthetic version of progesterone used in contraceptives.

progressive muscle relaxation a technique of learning to relax by focusing on relaxing each of the body's muscle groups in turn.

progressive overload principle the training principle that a body system, in order to improve, must be worked at frequencies, durations, or intensities that increase over time.

promoter a substance that assists in the development of malignant tumors, but does not initiate them on its own.

proof a term that describes the percentage of alcohol in alcoholic beverages. *100 proof* means 50 percent alcohol, *90 proof* means 45 percent, and so forth.

prostate gland a gland that produces a fluid that forms part of the semen.

protein a class of nutrients that builds body tissues and supplies energy. Protein is made of amino acids. Referred to only in the singular, *protein*.

protozoa (PRO-toh-ZOH-ah) tiny, animal-like cells, some of which can cause illnesses.

psilocybin, psilocin two hallucinogens produced by a type of wild mushroom.

psychological addiction a craving for something; mental dependence on a drug, habit, or behavior; also called *psychological dependence*.

puberty (PYOO-ber-tee) the period of life in which a person becomes physically capable of reproduction.

pubic lice an STD caused by tiny parasites that breed in pubic hair and cause intense itching.

pulmonary (PUL-mo-nair-ee) **artery** the large artery that carries oxygen-starved blood from the heart to the lungs to pick up fresh oxygen.

pulmonary veins the large veins that return freshly oxygenated blood to the heart from the lungs.

pulp cavity a tooth's deepest chamber that houses its blood vessels and nerves.

pulse the number of heartbeats per minute.

pus a mixture of fluids and white blood cells that collects around infected areas.

Q

quacks people pretending to have medical skills, and usually having products for sale.

quadriceps (KWOD-rih-seps) the large muscles of the front of the thigh.

quid a small portion of any form of smokeless tobacco.

R

rabies a viral disease of the central nervous system that causes paralysis and death. Mammals transmit it by biting. Before symptoms show up, treatment with vaccine halts the disease. Once symptoms start, there is no cure.

radiation therapy the application of cell-destroying radiation to kill cancerous tissues.

radius the outer bone of the forearm, between the wrist and the elbow.

radon a gas that arises from the earth where radioactive materials are present.

rape sexual assault. See also *acquaintance rape, street rape.*

recovery a healthy third phase of the stress response, in which the body returns to normal.

recreational drug use a term made up, to describe their drug use, by people who claim their drug-taking produces no harmful social or health effects; a term not defined by the FDA.

rectum the last portion of the digestive system; it stores waste prior to elimination.

rectus abdominus (REK-tus ab-DOM-ih-nus) the stomach muscles.

recyclable made of material that can be used over again.

rehabilitation learning how to live with the effects of an injury, such as blindness or loss of a limb; assistance in recovering function after such injuries.

relapses illnesses that return after being treated and almost cured. Relapses are often more severe than the original illnesses.

relaxation response the opposite of the stress response; the normal state of the body.

REM (rapid-eye-movement) sleep the periods of sleep in which a person is dreaming.

resentment anger that has built up due to failure to express it.

residency a length of time spent in training in a medical facility as part of the medical doctor's education.

resistance a force that opposes another; in fitness, the weight or other opposing force against which muscles must work; in the stress response, the second phase in which the body mobilizes its resources to withstand the effects of a stressor.

resolution in sexual intercourse, the stage of relaxation that follows orgasm.

rhythm method see *fertility awareness method.*

ribs twelve narrow, curved bones attached to the spine and surrounding the upper body, that protect the upper body's vital organs.

ripple effect the effect seen when a pebble is thrown into a pond and waves radiate out from it. The term is used to describe how one person's actions may affect many other people, and how their actions will affect still other people.

risk factors factors linked with a disease by association but not yet proved to be causes.

rubber see *male condom.*

rubella a viral disease that resembles measles but that lasts only a few days and does not cause serious complications for the sufferer; preventable by immunization; dangerous to pregnant women because it can cause malformations in fetuses.

runaway a youth who voluntarily leaves and lives away from home to escape an adverse environment, real or imagined.

S

safe causing no undue harm; part of the legal requirement for a drug.

safer-sex strategies behavior guidelines to reduce STD risk, but that do not reduce the risk to zero.

salivary glands glands that make the digestive juice saliva, which starts digesting starch in the mouth.

Salmonella a common foodborne pathogenic bacterium that causes digestive system infections in many people each year.

salt a compound made of minerals that, in water, dissolve and form electrolytes.

sarcomas (sar-KOH-mahs) cancers that arise in the connective tissue cells, including bones, ligaments, and muscles.

sartorius muscles the long thigh muscles that permit crossing of the legs.

sassafras a tree whose root bark was once used in beverages but is now banned as an ingredient in foods or beverages because it contains cancer-causing chemicals.

saturated concerning fats and health, those fats associated strongly with heart and artery disease; mainly fats from animal sources.

scapula the shoulder blade.

schizophrenia (SKITZ-oh-FREN-ee-uh) a mental illness, a condition of losing touch with reality accompanied by reduced ability to function.

scrotum (SKRO-tum) the double pouch that contains the testicles.

sebum (SEE-bum) the skin's natural oil—actually a mixture of oils and waxes—that helps keep the skin and hair moist.

second opinion a second assessment of a diagnosis and treatment plan by another health care provider usually on the request of a client, to double-check the validity of the original plan.

sedatives drugs that have a soothing or tranquilizing effect.

sedentary physically inactive (literally, "sitting down a lot").

self-actualization the reaching of one's full potential; the highest attainable state in Maslow's hierarchy of needs.

self-esteem the value a person attaches to his or her self-image. Self-esteem is high in those who value themselves. It is a vitally important part of emotional health.

self-image the characteristics that a person sees in himself or herself.

semen (SEE-men) the mixture of fluids (made by the glands) that carries the sperm (made by the testicles) out of the penis.

seminal (SEM-in-al) **vesicle** (VESS-ih-cul) a sac that lies behind the bladder, that produces a thick fluid that forms part of semen.

seminiferous (sem-in-IFF-er-us) **tubules** (TUBE-yules) tiny tubes in the testicles that produce sperm cells.

senility a general term meaning weakness of mind and body occurring in old age.

septum (SEP-tum) a divider; in the heart, the wall that separates its two sides.

set in terms of exercise, a specific number of times to repeat a weight-training exercise.

sex a general term used to mean both gender and sexual intercourse.

sexual dysfunction impaired responses of sexual excitement or orgasm due to psychological, interpersonal, physical, environmental, or cultural causes; formerly called *impotence* in men and *frigidity* in women.

sexual intercourse the reproductive act between the sexes. The term *intercourse* means communication of any kind—talking, for example. Sexual intercourse between human beings is termed *coitus* (CO-ih-tus). Between animals it is termed *copulation* (cop-you-LAY-shun).

sexuality the quality of being sexual, a part of each person's identity.

sexually transmitted diseases (STDs) diseases that are transmitted by way of direct sexual contact. An older name was *venereal diseases.*

shame the extreme feeling of guilt that arises when a person internalizes mistakes ("I am a bad person because I did a bad thing").

shin splints damage to the muscles and connective tissues of the lower front leg from stress.

shingles a painful skin condition caused by the reemergence of the chicken pox virus in later life.

shock failure or disruption of the blood circulation, a life-threatening reaction to accidents and injuries.

shoulder blade the large, flat, triangular bone of the shoulder; also called the *scapula.*

shoulder muscles the triangular muscles of the upper arms at the shoulders; called the *deltoids.*

side effects effects of drugs other than the desired medical effects.

side muscles the slanting muscles of the middle body, which form a natural girdle and permit side-to-side bending, called the *obliques* (oh-BLEEKS).

sidestream smoke the smoke that escapes into the air from the burning tip of a cigarette (and may then be inhaled by the smoker or by someone else).

SIDS see *sudden infant death syndrome.*

sinuses (SIGN-us-es) eight spaces in the bones of the skull.

skull the bone of the head that protects the brain from injury.

small for date a term used to describe an infant underdeveloped for its age, often because of malnutrition of the mother.

small intestine the major digestive organ, which digests all food to small nutrients.

smallpox a severe viral infection with skin eruptions similar to those of chicken pox.

smokeless tobacco tobacco used for snuff or chewing rather than for smoking.

sober free of alcohol's effects and of addiction; not drunk and not craving alcohol.

specialist a physician with training in a specialty area beyond the medical degree requirements.

sperm the male reproductive cells.

spermicide the compound nonoxynol-9, intended for birth control, that also kills or weakens some STD organisms.

spinal column the column made of vertebrae (bony segments) that house and protect the spinal column.

spinal cord the trunk of the nervous system from which nerves branch out. Messages between tissues and brain travel along its length.

spine the stack of 33 vertebrae that form the backbone and hold the spinal cord; nerves enter and exit through spaces between these bones.

spleen an organ lying behind the stomach that filters blood to remove old blood cells from circulation. It also stores blood. If the bone marrow is damaged, the spleen can produce red blood cells.

splint a stick or board used to support a broken bone to keep its separated parts from moving until it can be set.

sponge a contraceptive device; a disposable sponge-rubber dome, filled with spermicide, that fits over the cervix and holds spermicidal cream or jelly against the uterine entrance to block the passage of sperm.

spontaneous abortion or **miscarriage** the expelling of a zygote, embryo, or fetus from the uterus, not induced by medical means.

starch a carbohydrate, the main food energy source for human beings.

status a person's standing or rank in relation to others, many times falsely based on wealth, power, or influence. While desirable to many, these characteristics do not define human worth.

STDs see *sexually transmitted diseases.*

stepparents people who marry into a family after a biological parent's death or departure through divorce.

stereotypes fixed pictures of how everyone in a group is thought to be, ideas that do not recognize anyone's individuality.

sterilization permanent interruption of a person's ability to bear children, usually by surgically severing and sealing the vas deferens or the fallopian tubes.

sternum the breastbone.

steroids hormones of a certain chemical type that occur naturally in the body, some of which promote muscle growth. Available as drugs, they are abused by athletes seeking a shortcut to large muscles.

stimulant any of a wide variety of drugs, including amphetamines, caffeine, and others, that speed up the central nervous system.

stomach the part of the digestive system that first works on food from the mouth; it churns, mixes, digests, and grinds food to a liquid mass.

stranger rape see *street rape.*

street rape sexual assault by a stranger; also called *stranger rape.*

stress the effect of physical and psychological demands (stressors) on a person. Stress that provides a welcome challenge is *eustress* ("good" stress, pronounced YOU-stress); stress that is perceived as negative is *distress* ("bad" stress). See also *acute stress, chronic stress.*

stress eating inappropriate eating in response to arousal.

stress fractures bone damage from repeated physical force that strains the place where ligament is attached to bone.

stress hormones epinephrine and norepinephrine, secreted as part of the reaction of the nervous system to stress.

stress response the response to a demand or stressor. The stress response has three phases: *alarm, resistance,* and *recovery* or *exhaustion.*

stroke the shutting off of the blood flow to the brain by plaques, a clot, or hemorrhage.

subclinical FAS a subtle version of FAS, with hidden defects including learning disabilities, behavioral abnormalities, and motor impairments.

sublimation channeling the energy of suffering into creative, productive work.

sudden infant death syndrome (SIDS) the unexpected and unexplained death of an apparently well infant; the most common cause of death of infants between the second week and the end of the first year of life; also called *crib death.*

sugar a kind of carbohydrate found both in food and in the body.

superior vena cava (VEE-na CAVE-a) the large vein that returns used blood from the upper body to the heart.

supplement a pill, powder, liquid, or the like containing only nutrients; not a food.

support system a network of individuals or groups with which one identifies and exchanges emotional support.

suppress to hold back or restrain.

surgical insurance insurance to pay the surgeon's fees; see also *Medicaid.*

sustainable a term used to describe the use of resources at such a rate that the earth can keep on replacing them—for example, a rate of cutting trees no faster than new ones grow. Also, *sustainable* describes the production of pollutants at a rate that the environment or human cleanup efforts can handle, so that there is no net accumulation of pollution.

syphilis a bacterial STD that, if untreated, advances from a sore (chancre) to flu-like symptoms, then through a long symptomless period, and later to a final stage of irreversible brain and nerve damage, ending in death.

systolic (sis-TOL-ic) **pressure** the blood pressure during that part of the heartbeat when the heart's ventricles are contracted and the blood is being pushed out into the arteries. Systolic blood pressure is the maximum blood pressure in the vascular system and is represented by the first number in a blood pressure reading.

T

T cells lymphocytes that can recognize invaders that cause illness. T cells alert B cells and instruct them to produce antibodies.

target heart rate the heartbeat rate that will condition a person's cardiovascular system—fast enough to push the heart, but not so fast as to strain it.

tarsals (TAR-sals) the bones of the ankle.

tars chemicals present in (among other things) tobacco. Burning tars release many carcinogens.

tendons elastic, flexible straps of connective tissue that anchor the ends of muscles to bones.

tennis elbow a painful condition of the arm and joint, usually caused by strain, as from poor form in playing tennis.

terminal illnesses illnesses that are expected to end in death.

testicles (TES-ti-culs) the glands that produce the male hormone testosterone; testicles also produce the male reproductive cells sperm.

tetanus a disease caused by a toxin produced by bacteria deep within a wound, which causes sustained contractions of body muscles and results in rigidity of the body and death from lack of oxygen or from exhaustion; preventable by immunization; also called *lockjaw.*

therapy treatment that heals.

thoughts those mental processes of which a person is always conscious.

thrill seekers people who are especially likely to take chances in exchange for momentary excitement. Psychologists believe thrill-seeking behavior to be at the root of some people's needs for dangerous sports such as sky diving, or the taking up of dangerous habits such as smoking, drug abuse, or indiscriminate sexual activity.

thrombus a stationary clot. When it has grown enough to close off a blood vessel, this dangerous event is a *thrombosis.*

throwaway a youth who leaves home at the demand of his or her parent. Throwaways often seek help from shelters and social agencies.

thymus (THIGH-mus) **gland** a small gland at the base of the throat; important in the development of the immune system in newborns and in the maturation of certain immune system cells (T cells) throughout life.

thyroid (THIGH-royd) **gland** a gland located in the neck that releases thyroxine, a hormone that controls the ways the body uses energy.

tibia (TIB-i-a) the large bone of the lower shin.

tissues systems of cells working together to perform special tasks.

tolerance a state that develops in users of certain drugs that makes larger and larger amounts of the drugs necessary to produce the same effect.

tonsillectomy removal of the tonsils (in the throat), an operation sometimes performed needlessly.

tonsils three sets of structures surrounding the throat; made of lymph node material and active in immune defense of the area.

toxic shock syndrome (TSS) a type of poisoning that can occur when bacteria break down menstrual blood; often associated with use of super-absorbent tampons.

toxin a poison.

trace minerals minerals essential in nutrition, needed in small quantities (traces) daily. Iron and zinc are examples.

trachea (TRAY-kee-uh) the windpipe, the main airway from the mouth and nose to the lungs.

trapezius (tra-PEE-zee-us) **muscles** the flat, triangle-shaped muscles of the back of the neck and shoulders, which control neck and shoulder movements.

tremors continuous quivering or shaking.

triceps (TRY-seps) the muscles of the back of the upper arms.

trichomoniasis (trick-oh-mon-EYE-uh-sis) an STD caused by a parasite that can cause bladder and urethral infections.

trimesters see *gestation*.

tubal ligation (lye-GAY-shun) surgical cutting and sealing off of the fallopian tubes to sterilize women.

tuberculosis a bacterial infection of the lungs.

tumor an abnormal mass of tissue that can live and reproduce itself, but performs no service to the body.

U

ulcers open sores in a membrane, such as the lining of the digestive system.

ulna (UL-na) the inner bone of the forearm, between the wrist and the elbow.

umbilical (um-BIL-ih-cul) **cord** the ropelike structure through which the fetus's veins and arteries extend to and from the placenta; the route of nutrients and oxygen to the fetus and of wastes from the fetus.

undernutrition too little food energy or too few nutrients to prevent disease or to promote growth; a form of malnutrition.

underweight weight too low for health. Underweight is often defined as weight 10 percent or more below the appropriate weight for height.

unsaturated concerning fats and health, fats less associated with heart and artery disease; mainly fats from plant sources.

upper back and neck muscles the flat, triangle-shaped muscles of the back of the neck and shoulders; called the *trapezius* (tra-PEE-zee-us).

upper respiratory infection an infection of the membranes of the nasal cavities, sinuses, throat, and trachea, but not involving the lungs.

ureter (yoo-REE-ter) the tube that conducts urine from each kidney to the bladder.

urethra (yoo-REE-thra) the tube that conducts urine from the bladder to the outside of the body. In males, the urethra also conducts semen out of the body.

urinary tract infections (UTIs) bacterial infections of the urethra that can travel to the bladder and kidneys.

urine fluid wastes removed from the body by the kidneys.

user effectiveness (of a contraceptive device or technique) see *effectiveness*.

uterus (YOO-ter-us) the organ that holds and nourishes an embryo from the time the fertilized egg is implanted to the time of birth of the infant.

V

vaccinations see *immunizations*.

vaccine a drug made from altered microbes or their poisons injected or given by mouth to produce immunity.

vagina (vah-JYE-nah) a muscular tube that serves as a passageway for childbirth, menstrual flow, and semen reception.

vaginal pouch see *female condom*.

values a person's set of rules for behavior; what the person thinks of as right and wrong, or sees as important.

valve in the circulatory system, a flap of tissue that opens and closes to allow the flow of blood in one direction only.

variables changeable factors that affect outcomes.

vas deferens tubes that conduct sperm from the testicles toward the penis.

vasectomy surgical cutting and sealing off of the vas deferens to sterilize men.

vegetarians people who omit meat, fish, and poultry from their diets. Some vegetarians also omit milk products and eggs.

veins blood vessels that carry blood from the tissues back to the heart to be pumped to the lungs.

venereal diseases see *sexually transmitted diseases* (STDs).

venom poison from a living creature such as a snake or scorpion.

ventilation the act of verbally venting one's feelings; letting off steam by talking, crying, swearing, or laughing.

ventricle (VEN-trik-l) one of the two lower chambers of the heart—the shipping areas that send blood on its way to the lungs or tissues. The *right ventricle* pumps used blood through the pulmonary artery to the lungs. The *left ventricle* pumps oxygenated blood through the aorta to the tissues.

vertebrae (VERT-eh-bray; singular, **vertebra**) the delicate, hollow bones of the spine.

virgin a term applied to people before their first occasion of sexual intercourse.

viruses infective organisms that contain only genetic material and protein coats, and that are totally dependent on the cells they infect. They use the cells' reproductive equipment for their own reproduction.

visual center the back of the brain, where visual messages are received and interpreted.

vitamins essential nutrients that do not yield energy, but that are required for growth and proper functioning of the body.

voice box   see *larynx*.
voluntary activities   movements of the body under the command of the conscious mind; one component of a person's daily energy expenditure.

W
water-soluble   able to dissolve in water.
weight training   exercise routines for strength conditioning that use weights or machines to provide resistance against which the muscles can work.
wellness   maximum well-being; the top of the range of health states; the goal of the person who strives toward realizing his or her full potential physically, mentally, emotionally, spiritually, and socially. See also *health*.
wet dreams   dreams during which orgasm occurs; a normal release for the sexual drive; in boys, these are also called *nocturnal emissions*.
whitehead   a pimple filled with pus, caused by the plugging of oil-gland ducts with shed material from the duct lining.
will   a person's intent, which leads to action.
windpipe   see *trachea*.
witch hazel   a tree whose leaves or bark are popularly thought, but not proved, to have healing powers.

withdrawal   the physical symptoms that occur when a drug to which a person is addicted is cleared from the body tissues.
withdrawal method (coitus interruptus)   a technique in sexual intercourse of withdrawing the penis from the vagina just prior to ejaculation. It is not useful for preventing pregnancy or STDs.
worms   visible, long, slender, legless animals; parasites that obtain nourishment by burrowing into the blood supply of intestinal or other tissue.

Y
yeast infection   see *candidiasis*.
yeasts   one-celled fungi, some of which cause diseases.
yo-yo effect   the gain of body fat that results, in the end, from repeated rounds of dieting without exercising.

Z
zygote   the product of the union of ovum and sperm, so termed for two weeks after conception. (After that, it is called an *embryo*.)

Index

Photo Credits

Cover ©Richard Mackson/*Sports Illustrated*;   **xvi** Comstock ©Henry Georgi;   **2** Photo Researchers ©Richard Hutchings;   **9** Photo Researchers ©Renee Lynn;   **15** PhotoEdit ©Michael Newman;   **22** Stock Boston ©Ellis Herwig;   **25** PhotoEdit ©Felicia Martinez;   **32** (TL) Comstock ©Laura Elliot, (TR) PhotoEdit ©Tony Freeman, (BL) Photo Researchers ©Jeff Isaac Greenberg, (BR) Int'l Stock ©Bill Stanton;   **35** Comstock ©Mike & Carol Werner;   **40** ©FPG;   **48** FPG ©John T. Turner;   **51** Int'l Stock ©Gary Bigham;   **58** FPG ©H. Blume;   **64** ©Comstock;   **67** PhotoEdit ©Myrleen Ferguson;   **74** Stock Boston ©Frank Siteman;   **89** (T) PhotoEdit ©James Shaffer, (B) Stock Boston ©Bob Daemmrich;   **95** Stock Boston ©Donald Dietz;   **102** Sheila Terry/Science Photo Library;   **104** PhotoEdit ©Myrleen Ferguson;   **115** ©Bob Daemmrich;   **119** PhotoEdit ©Mary Kate Denney;   **121** PhotoEdit ©Michael Newman;   **122** PhotoEdit ©Michael Newman;   **123** PhotoEdit ©Myrleen Ferguson;   **124** (T) PhotoEdit ©Mary Kate Denney, (B) Photo Researchers ©James Prince;   **132** FPG ©Telegraph Colour Library;   **162** PhotoEdit ©Tony Freeman;   **165** Private Eye Photography: Karelle Scharff;   **168** Photo Researchers ©Lawrence Migdal;   **170** PhotoEdit ©Ray Stanyard;   **176** PhotoEdit ©Ray Stanyard;   **178** (L) FPG ©Evgen Gebhardt, (R) FPG ©Bill Losh;   **184** Int'l Stock Photo ©Phyllis Picardi;   **187** ©David Farr;   **192** FPG ©Michael Keller;   **196** Stock Boston ©John Maher;   **197** (TL) Courtesy United States Department of Agriculture, (BR) ©Four by Five, Remaining images Courtesy United States Department of Agriculture;   **206** FPG ©James Chen;   **208** (L) PhotoEdit ©Tony Freeman, (R) PhotoEdit ©Myrleen Ferguson;   **217** PhotoEdit ©Mary Kate Denney;   **221** Photo Researchers ©Richard Hutchings;   **223** Visuals Unlimited ©Arthur R. Hill;   **227** ©Rudy Von Briel;   **229** Comstock ©Mike & Carol Werner;   **230** PhotoEdit ©Michael Newman;   **234** Photo Researchers ©Gerard Vandystadt;   **236** Photo Researchers ©Jean Marc Barey;   **243** ©Richard Levine;   **244** FPG ©Richard Mackson;   **253** ©Alan R. Wycheck;   **256** Pacific Rim Productions ©Bob Abraham;   **258** ©Mary E. Messenger;   **265** PhotoEdit ©Felicia Martinez;   **268** PhotoEdit ©David Young-Wolff;   **292** Photo

Researchers ©Biophoto Associates;   **280** Stock Boston ©Stephen Frisch;   **290** Photo Researchers ©Will and Deni McIntyre;   **292** ©Rob Goldman;   **299** ©Comstock;   **303** PhotoEdit ©Mary Kate Denney;   **310** PhotoEdit ©Michael Newman;   **319** FPG ©Ken Reid;   **326** ©William Hopkins;   **328** ©VU/Cabisco;   **331** (L) ©Rudi Von Briel, (R) FPG ©Bill Losh;   **333** Unicorn Stock Photos ©Aneal Vohra;   **335** ©Larry Mulvehill;   **346** PhotoEdit ©Mary Kate Denney;   **348** PhotoEdit ©David Young-Wolff;   **356** ©Alan R. Wycheck;   **358** FPG ©Terry Qing;   **359** Int'l Stock Photo ©Ryan Williams;   **370** Pacific Rim ©Mary Van de Ven;   **372** Stock Boston ©Barbara Alper;   **374** PhotoEdit ©Richard Hutchings;   **380** Visuals Unlimited ©SIU;   **382** Unicorn Stock Photos ©Jeff Greenberg;   **384** PhotoEdit ©Michael Newman;   **398** Unicorn Stock Photos ©Greg Greer;   **401** PhotoEdit ©Myrleen Ferguson;   **418** ©Bob Daemmrich;   **427** Custom Medical Stock Photo;   **428** (L & M) Custom Medical Stock Photo;   **428** (R) Science VU/Visuals Unlimited;   **430** ©Ulrike Welsch;   **433** Bettmann/UPI;   **435** Unicorn Stock Photos ©Alon Reininger;   **442** Stock Boston ©Jeffrey Dunn;   **446** ©Larry Mulvehill;   **450** Comstock ©Russ Kinne;   **468** PhotoEdit ©David Young-Wolff;   **476** The Skin Cancer Foundation, Robert J. Friedman, M.D., Darrel S. Rigel, M.D., Alfred W. Kopf, M.D.;   **477** PhotoEdit ©Tony Freeman;   **479** Visuals Unlimited ©S. C. Reuman;   **488** Photo Researchers ©Art Stein;   **492** PhotoEdit ©Tony Freeman;   **496** PhotoEdit ©David Young-Wolff;   **498** Photo Researchers ©Jeff Isaac Greenberg;   **503** FPG ©Dick Luria Photography, Inc.;   **512** ©Bob Daemmrich;   **514** FPG ©Michael A. Keller;   **521** (TL) Photo Researchers ©Andy Walker, Midland Fertility Services, Science Photo Library, (TR) Photo Researchers ©Petit Format/Nestle, (BL) FPG ©J. E. Stevenson, (BR) Photo Researchers ©David Leah/Science Photo Library;   **526** Bob Daemmrich;   **527** PhotoEdit ©Amy C. Etra;   **530** ©Larry Mulvehill;   **533** PhotoEdit ©David Schaefer;   **535** (L) PhotoEdit ©Myrleen Ferguson, (R) PhotoEdit ©Tony Freeman;   **538** FPG ©Nancy Ney;   **A2** PhotoEdit ©Myrleen Ferguson;   **A4** Visuals Unlimited ©William J. Weber;   **A5** PhotoEdit ©Tony Freeman;   **A6** PhotoEdit ©Deborah Davis;   **A9** Unicorn Stock Photos ©Karen Holsinger Mullen;   **A11** Unicorn Stock Photos